Foreign & Commonwealth Office

The Diplomatic Service List 1993

TWENTY-EIGHTH EDITION

London : HMSO

First published 1992

ISBN 0 11 591744 6

Preface

Her Majesty's Diplomatic Service provides the staffs of British Diplomatic and Consular posts overseas in Commonwealth and Foreign countries, as well as in the Foreign & Commonwealth Office in London.

The organisation of the Service and the careers of its members, are described in this List which will be published each year. It is based on information available in September 1992; but includes details of some later changes.

The Diplomatic Service was established on 1 January, 1965, by the merger of the former Foreign, Commonwealth and Trade Commissioner Services. Subsequently it incorporated the staffs of the Colonial Office in London, which merged with the Commonwealth Relations Office on 1 August, 1966, to form the Commonwealth Office.

The Foreign Office and Commonwealth Office continued as separate Departments of State responsible to separate Secretaries of State until 17 October, 1968. On that day they combined into the Foreign and Commonwealth Office responsible to one Secretary of State. The Permanent Under-Secretary of the Office and the Head of the Diplomatic Service is Sir David Gillmore KCMG.

Overseas development has been the ultimate responsibility of the Secretary of State for Foreign and Commonwealth Affairs since 1970, except for the period from March, 1974 to June, 1975 when the Ministry of Overseas Development (now the Overseas Development Administration) reverted to its former independent status.

Representatives of Commonwealth countries and foreign states serving in London are shown in a separate publication, the London Diplomatic List, published by HMSO every six months.

January 1993

Table of Contents

Part I

HOME DEPARTMENTS

List of Ministers, Senior Officers and Home Departments in the Foreign and Commonwealth Office.

Part II

BRITISH REPRESENTATION OVERSEAS

Part III

CHRONOLOGICAL LISTS FROM 1972 of SECRETARIES OF STATE, MINISTERS OF STATE, PERMANENT UNDER-SECRETARIES, AMBASSADORS, HIGH COMMISSIONERS AND PERMANENT REPRESENTATIVES TO INTERNATIONAL ORGANISATIONS

Part IV

BIOGRAPHICAL NOTES AND LISTS OF STAFF

Home Departments

List of Ministers, Senior Officers and
Home Departments in the
Foreign and Commonwealth
Office

Part I: Home Departments

ACCOMMODATION

Ministers, Senior Officers and most geographical departments are accommodated in the Main Building, Downing Street, London, SW1. Departments are also accommodated in other buildings.

	Telephone No.
Foreign & Commonwealth Office, Downing Street (West), SW1A 2AL	071-270 3000
Foreign &Commonwealth Office, Downing Street (East), SW1A 2AL	071-270 3000
Foreign & Commonwealth Office, Whitehall, SW1A 2AP	071-270 3000
Foreign & Commonwealth Office, King Charles Street, SW1A 2AH	071-270 3000
Apollo House, 36 Wellesley Road, Croydon, CR9 3RR	081-686 5622
3 Carlton Gardens, SW1Y 5AA	071-270 3000
Century House, Westminster Bridge Road, SE1 7XF	071-928 5600
Clive House, Petty France, SW1H 9HD	071-270 3000
Cornwall House, Stamford Street, SE1 9NS	071-211 3000
Cromwell House, Dean Stanley Street, SW1P 3JG	071-276 7676
94 Victoria Street, SW1E 5JL	071-917 7000
Hanslope Park, Hanslope, Milton Keynes, MK19 7BH	0908-510444
2 and 3 Central Buildings, Matthew Parker Street, SW1H 9NL	071-210 3000
4 Central Buildings, Matthew Parker Street, SW1H 9NL	071-210 3000
Old Admiralty Building, Whitehall, SW1A 2AF	071-210 3000
60 Vauxhall Bridge Road, SW1V 2RR	071-270 0201

TELEPHONE ENQUIRIES
If an enquirer knows the building in which a department is housed he should ring the appropriate number: otherwise he should telephone 071-270 3000, and ask to be connected to the Central Enquiry point.

Telegraphic Address: PRODROME LONDON, SW1
Telex: 297711 (a/b PRODROME LONDON)

MINISTERS AND THEIR STAFFS

Secretary of State for Foreign and Commonwealth Affairs
The Rt Hon Douglas Hurd, CBE, MP

Private Secretary: R H T Gozney
Assistant Private Secretaries: C N R Prentice;
S L Gass, C H Eakin, Miss H Drysdale

Minister of State for Foreign and Commonwealth Affairs
The Rt. Hon. Tristan Garel-Jones, MP

Private Secretary: T M Hitchins
Assistant Private Secretaries:
Miss A J Pring, Miss A Webb

Minister of State for Foreign and Commonwealth Affairs
The Rt Hon Alastair Goodlad, MP

Private Secretary: G J Dorey
Assistant Private Secretary: I Ruff

Minister of State for Foreign and Commonwealth Affairs
The Rt. Hon Douglas Hogg, QC, MP

Private Secretary: N S Archer
Assistant Private Secretary: A Ashcroft

Minister of State for Foreign and Commonwealth Affairs and Minister for Overseas Development
The Rt Hon Baroness Chalker

Private Secretary: M Lowcock
Assistant Private Secretaries: G H Milton,
Mrs J Knowlton

Parliamentary Under-Secretary for Foreign and Commonweath Affairs
The Hon Mark Lennox-Boyd, MP

Private Secretary: P A Speller
Assistant Private Secretary: C J R Moore

Parliamentary Relations Unit
Head of Unit: R Calder
Parliamentary Clerk and Deputy Head of Unit:
J P Rodgers
Assistant Parliamentary Clerk: W L Ross
Unit Legal Adviser: H Llewellyn

SENIOR OFFICERS AND THEIR STAFFS

Permanent Under-Secretary of State and Head of HM Diplomatic Service
Sir David Gillmore, KCMG

Private Secretary: T M J Simmons
Assistant Private Secretary: Miss J A Booker

Chief Clerk: A M Wood, CMG

Deputy Under-Secretaries of State:
L V Appleyard, CMG (Political Director)

Sir John Coles, KCMG

M Elliot, CMG

B L Crowe, CMG

Sir Timothy Daunt, KCMG

Assistant Under-Secretaries of State:
J Ling, CMG *(Director of Communications and Technical Services)*;
Miss R J Spencer, CMG; P. Lever, CMG; Mrs V E Sutherland CMG *(Deputy Chief Clerk and Principal Security Officer)*;* J Q Greenstock, CMG *(Deputy Political Director)*; D B C Logan, CMG; R J S Muir *(Chief Inspector and Principal Finance Oficer)*; R B Bone; A J Beamish, CMG; The Hon David Gore-Booth, CMG; R O Miles CMG; M H Jay, CMG; A M Goodenough, CMG; J T Masefield, CMG; C O Hum.
Her Majesty's Vice-Marshal of the Diplomatic Corps (Assistant Under-Secretary of State and holds personal rank of Ambassador):
A St J H Figgis.

ADVISERS

Legal Adviser: F D Berman, CMG

Second Legal Adviser: D H Anderson, CMG

Deputy Legal Advisers: M R Eaton; K J Chamberlain, CMG.

Legal Counsellors: A I Aust; Ms E S Wilmshurst; Mrs A F Glover; C A Whomersley; Miss S Brooks

Chief Economic Adviser: S H Broadbent

Senior Economic Adviseer: N R Chrimes

International Labour Adviser: A E Smith

Overseas Police Adviser: J W Kelland, LVO, QPM

Africa Department (Equatorial)
(King Charles Street, London SW1A 2AH)
Superintending Under-Secretary:
A M Goodenough, CMG
Political and economic relations with Nigeria, Ghana, Sierra Leone, The Gambia, Kenya, Tanzania, Uganda, Ethiopia, Somalia, Djibouti, Seychelles, Mauritius, Madagascar, The Comros, Reunion, Liberia, Senegal, Guinea, Mali, Burkina Faso, Côte d'Ivoire, Togo, Benin, Niger, Chad, Cameroon, Gabon, Congo, Zaire, Burundi, Rwanda, Central Africa Republic, Equatorial Guinea, Guinea Bissau, Cape Verde, UN Economic Commission for Africa, OAU and ECOWAS, Administration of British Indian

Ocean Territory (BIOT).
Head of Department and Commissioner of BIOT:
T G Harris

Aid Policy Department
(Joint FCO/ODA Dept)
94 Victoria Street, SW1E 5JL
Superintending Under-Secretary:
B R Ireton (ODA)

Size, distribution and composition of the aid programme; aid policy and systems; aid aspects of the work of the Organisation for Economic Co-operation and Development; development policies of other donors.
Head of Department: S Chakrabarti
Assistant: A J Seaton

*Mr J Q Greenstock is also the United Kingdom Permanent Representative on the Council of Western European Union.

Arms Control and Disarmament Department
(King Charles Street, London SW1A 2AL)
Superintending Under-Secretary:
P Lever, CMG

Arms control and disarmament, at the UN and CD, including CBW; public information and research on arms control and disarmament
Head of Department, Director of ACDRU:
P W M Vereker
Assistant Head of Department and Deputy Director of ACDRU: J R Nichols

Aviation and Maritime Department
(FCO, Whitehall, SW1A 2AP)
Superintending Under-Secretary:
R B Bone

Civil Aviation: Aerospace Industry; ICAO
Law of the Sea: Maritime Delimitation; IMO; Shipping and Inland Transport; Channel Tunnel.
Head of Department: Dr E J Hughes
Assistant: P J Spiceley, MBE

Central and Southern Africa Department
(King Charles Street, London SW1A 2AH)
Superintending Under-Secretary:
A M Goodenough, CMG
Political and economic relations with Angola, Botswana, Lesotho, Malawi, Mozambique, Namibia, Sao Tomé and Principe, South Africa, Swaziland, Zambia and Zimbabwe; Southern African Development Co-ordination Conference (SADCC).
Head of Department: D R C Christopher
Assistants: P J Sullivan, D Wyatt

Central European Department
(Downing Street (West), London SW1A 2AL
Superintending Under-Secretary:
D B C Logan, CMG

Politcal and bilateral economic relations with
Bulgaria, Czechoslovakia, Hungary, Poland,
Romania.
Head of Department: N J Thorpe
Assistant: R M Publicover

Common Foreign and Security Policy Unit
(Downing Street (West), London SW1A 2AL)
Superintending Under-Secretary:
M H Jay, CMG
Political Director: L V Appleyard, CMG
European Political co-operation; (Co-ordination
of foreign policy among EC member states) and
preparation for implementation of common
Foreign and Security Policy
Head of Unit: N J Westcott
Deputy: J B King

Commonwealth Co-ordination Department
(Downing Street (East),
London SW1A 2AL)
Superintending Under-Secretary:
A M Goodenough, CMG

Commonwealth constitutional questions; policy,
procedures and practices relating to the
Commonwealth as a whole. Commonwealth
dimension in foreign policy formulation.
Commonwealth Heads of Government Meetings.
Policy towards small States. Commonwealth
Secretariat, Commonwealth Foundation,
Commonwealth Parliamentary Association,
Commonwealth Institute and other
Commonwealth organisations and meetings not
otherwise allocated. Liaison with Commonwealth
Societies. Commonwealth publicity in Britain.
Head of Department: D Broad
Assistant: K Cullen

CSCE Unit
(Downing Street (West), London SW1A 2AL)

Superintending Under-Secretary: D B C Logan,
CMG

UK policy on the Conference on Security and
Cooperation in Europe.

Head of Unit: R J Dalton
Deputy Head of Unit: A V G Tucker

Consular Department
(Clive House, Petty France, London SW1H 9DH)
Superintending Under-Secretary:
Miss R J Spencer, CMG

Supervises the activities of Consular posts
generally; advises on consular policy; deals with
the protection of and assistance to UK nationals
and their interests abroad, including relief and
repatriation; liaison with the Commonwealth War
Graves Commission; Electoral Registration
Overseas.

Head of Department: C J A Denne, CMG
Assistant: A R Nuttall

Cultural Relations Department
(FCO, Old Admiralty Building, SW1A 2AF)
Superintending Under-Secretary:
Miss R J Spencer, CMG

Cultural relations; Bilateral and Multilateral;
Cultural and educational activities of
International Organisations; British Council
Policy and Finance; the FCO's Scholarships
programme for overseas students, International
Sport; International Youth Matters.

Head of Department: J N Elam
Assistants: Ms A W Lewis

Eastern Adriatic Unit
(Downing Street (West), London SW1A 2AL)
Superintending Under-Secretary:
J Q Greenstock, CMG

Political and bilateral economic relations with
Slovenia, Croatia, Yugoslavia, Bosnia and
Hercegovina, the former Yugoslav republic of
Macedonia and Albania.
Head of Unit: J C R Gray

Eastern European Department
(Downing Street (West), London SW1A 2AL)
Superintending Under-Secretary:
D B C Logan, CMG

Relations with Armenia, Azerbaijan, Belarus,
Estonia, Georgia, Kazakhstan, Kirgkizia, Latvia,
Lithuania, Moldova, Russia, Tajikistan,
Turkmenistan, Ukraine, Uzbekistan.
Head of Department: R M J Lyne, CMG
Assistants: C G Crawford, Dr Rachel Aron

Economic Advisers
(Joint FCO/ODA Department)
(FCO, Whitehall, SW1A 2AP)
Superintending Under-Secretary:
Sir David Gillmore, KCMG

Specialist advice and assistance on economic
matters.
Chief Economic Adviser: S H Broadbent
Senior Economic Adviser: N R Chrimes

Economic Relations Department
(Joint FCO/ODA department), (FCO, Whitehall,
SW1A 2AP)
Superintending Under-Secretary:
R B Bone

International Economic relations, including
relations with FSU; OECD; IMF; Economic
Summits; International Debt; Developing
Countries Issues; UNCTAD; Regional Economic
Groupings including; Pacific Rim; UNECE;
International Commodity Policy; Export Credits;
Mutual Legal Assistance; Money Laundering and
Asset Confiscation; Extraterritoriality;

Commonwealth Finance Ministers' meetings and
other Commonwealth Economic Discussions
including CHOGM, Banking regulations and
secrecy; Financial regulations in Dependent
Territories.
Head of Department: K R Tebbit
Deputy: J C Millett
Head of FSU Unit: S R H Pease

Environment, Science and Energy Department
(FCO, Whitehall, SW1A 2AP)
Superintending Under-Secretary:
R B Bone

International Environment Policy; Climate
Change; Ozone Layer; Wildlife Protection;
Biodiversity Marine Pollution; UN; EC;
Multilateral and Bilateral Science and
Technology Collaboration; Large Scientific
Facilities; Relations with Royal Society and
Research Council; International Space,
Broadcasting, Postal and Telecommuications
Issues; International Energy Policy and
Collaboration; Nuclear, Oil, Gas, Coal and
Renewables; Nuclear Safety and Environment;
IEA, NEA, IAEA
Head of Department: A R Brenton
Assistant: M Bourke

European Community Department (External)
(Downing Street (West), London SW1A 2AL)
Superintending Under-Secretary:
M H Jay, CMG

Relations between the European Communities
and countries not members; external matters
within the responsibility of the European
Communities, notably international trade matters;
enlargement of the Community.
Head of Department: E Jones Parry, CMG
Assistant: Q M Quayle

European Community Department (Internal)
(Downing Street (East), London SW1A 2AL)
Superintending Under-Secretary:
M H Jay, CMG

The internal economic and institutional policies
of the European Communities.
Head of Department. M A Arthur, CMG
Deputy Haed of Department: N E Sheinwald

European Community Department (Presidency)
(Downing Street (West), London SW1A 2AL)
Superintending Under-Secretary: M H Jay, CMG

The preparation and running of the UK's
Presidency of the EC.
Head of Department: R J Sawers

Far Eastern Department
(FCO, Whitehall, SW1A 2AP)
Superintending Under-Secretary:
C O Hum

Political and economic relations with China,
Japan, Korea, Mongolia, Macao.

Head of Department: H Ll Davies
Assistant: W Morris

Government Hospitality Fund
(8 Cleveland Row, St James's, London, SW1A
1DH)

Organises Guest of Government visits to the
United Kingdom and arranges official Ministerial
entertainment functions.
Secretary: Brigadier Alan Cowan, CBE
Deputy Secretary: N C MacKenzie

Home Estate and Services Department
(FCO, Old Admiralty Building, SW1A 2AF)
(Century House, Westminster Bridge Road,
SE1 7XF)
Superintending Under-Secretary:
Mrs V E Sutherland, CMG

Home—The Home Estate, Office services.
Home and overseas—stationery; office machinery
and supplies; printing.
Overseas—transport.
Head of Department: D C Brown
Assistant: M T M Hannant

Hong Kong Department
(FCO, Whitehall, SW1A 2AP)
Superintending Under-Secretary:
C O Hum

Administration of Hong Kong. Relations between
the United Kingdom and Hong Kong. Hong
Kong's external relations. Policy on the future of
Hong Kong.
Head of Department: P F Rickets
Assistant: J C Morris

Honours Unit
(Old Admiralty Building, SW1A 2AF)
Superintending Under-Secretary:
A St J H Figgis

FCO aspects of honours policy.
Honours on the Diplomatic Service and Overseas
List, and the Prime Minister's List; British
honorary awards, investitures, presentation of
insignia; Foreign and Commonwealth honours for
British citizens.
Head of Unit: D E Tarling
Deputy Head of Unit: J M Eastwood

Human Rights Policy Unit
(King Charles Street, London SW1A 2AH)
Superintending Under-Secretary:
R B Bone

The FCO's centre of expertise on human rights
policy questions, including obligations and
commitments at the UN, Council of Europe and
CSCE. Responsible for: developing and
coordinating HMG's human rights policy and
ensuring consistency of application by FCO
departments; liaison with Whitehall departments
on new commitments; ensuring domestic policy
takes account of HMG's international human
rights obligations; supervision of UK and

Dependent Territory periodic reports under
international treaty obligations.
Head of Unit: G S Hand
Deputy Head of Unit: S A Foulds

Information Department
(FCO, Old Admiralty Building, SW1A 2AF)
Superintending Under-Secretary:
Miss R J Spencer, CMG

Direction and financial control of overseas
official information activities, including
sponsored visits and London Correspondents
Service; administration of Grants in aid to the
BBC External Services and prescription of their
output; funding for and liaison with the Wilton
Park Executive Agency and participation in
International exhibitions. The provision of
verbatim texts, guidance material background
briefing, press TV and radio material, and
publications on matters of concern to HMG.
Head of Department: A D Harris
Assistants: P J W Le Breton, S T Nash

Wilton Park
(Wiston House Conference Centre, Steyning,
West Sussex BN44 3DZ)
Director: G R Denton

Wilton Park conferences, usually lasting four
days, examine current international issues,
especially/ security policy, European and Atlantic
relations; the Soviet Union and Eastern Europe;
East-West relations; Third World areas of
conflict; and global economic policies.
Conference participants are experts on the
conference topic drawn from different
professions and from all over the world. Wiston
House is also available for conferences organised
by other institutions.

Information Systems Division (Operations)
(FCO Whitehall, SW1A 2AP)
(Hanslope Park, Hanslope, Milton Keynes,
MK19 7BH)
Superintending Under Secretary: J Ling, CMG

Telecommunications with Diplomatic Service
Posts and Governments of Dependent Territories,
implementation and support of all information
systems at home and abroad.
Head of Department: S I Soutar
Assistants: L Walters; P Jones

Information Systems Division (Projects)
(4 Central Buildings, Matthew Parker Street,
SW1H 9NL)
(Hanslope Park, Hanslope, Milton Keynes,
MK19 7BH)
Superintending Under Secretary: J Ling, CMG
The development of new Information Technology
products and the Management of Projects at
home and overseas.
Head of Department: K Willis
Assistant: N B Stickells
Assistant: N Clouting

Information Systems Division (Resources)
(Hanslope Park, Hanslope, Milton Keynes,
MK19 7BH)
Superintending Under Secretary: J Ling, CMG

Strategic Planning Personnel Management,
Personnel Services, Training, Finance and
Budgeting, Management Information services for
ISD.
Head of Department: M Hodge, MBE
Assistants: C J Compton; P J Monk

Information Systems Division (Services)
(King Charles Street, SW1A 2AH)
(Downing Street (West), SW1A 2AL)
(Hanslope Park, Hanslope, Milton Keynes,
MK19 7BH)
Superintending Under Secretary: J Ling, CMG

Mail services to Diplomatic Service posts and
the Governments of Dependent Territories, office
and estate services outside London, provision of
technical supplies and UK transport Services.
Head of Department: D J Briggs
Assistants: J M Brown, A Taylor

Internal Audit Unit
(Joint FCO/ODA Unit)
(FCO Wing: Old Admiralty Building, Whitehall,
SW1A 2AF. ODA Wing: 94 Victoria Street,
SW1E 5JL)
Superintending Under-Secretaries:
R J S Muir (FCO); B R Ireton (ODA)
Head of Joint Internal Audit Unit: R A Elias
Audit Manager FCO: R F Coombs
Audit Manager ODA: G I James

The Joint Directorate
(Overseas Trade Services, 9th Floor, Kingsgate
House, 66-74 Victoria Street, SW1E 6SW)
Director General: R O Miles, CMG
Directors: D Saunders; M G Dougal

A joint FCO and DTI department responsible
for:
(i) the formulation and dissemination of export
promotion policy and the effective
implementation of the policy throughout the
organisation, including DTI Regional offices,
Market Branches and Diplomatic Posts Overseas;
management and development of charged
information services;
(ii) marketing, promoting and publicising export
services; monitoring and evaluating customers'
views on the effectiveness of export services;
Providing and advising on export training;
(iii) liaison with the British Overseas Trade
Board and its Advisory Groups.
(iv) Providing and advising on training of DTI
and FCO export promotion staff.

Latin America Department
(FCO Whitehall SW1A 2AP)
Superintending Under-Secretary:
A J Beamish, CMG

Political and economic relations with all Latin American countries; Latin American regional organisations.
Head of Department: A R Murray
Assistant: W B Sinton

Library and Records Department
Downing Street (East), London SW1A 2AL, Old Admiralty Building, SW1A 2AF and Hanslope Park, Hanslope, Milton Keynes MK19 7BH
Superintending Under-Secretary: J Ling, CMG

Library services to FCO and posts overseas; registration and maintenance of FCO archives and their transfer to the Public Record Office; publication of Documents on British Policy Overseas and historical advice; interpretation and translation services; overseas information service; data protection; cartographic services.
Head of Department: R M Bone
Library Assistant: R L E Foreman
Records Branch: M A Cousins
Historical: Mrs H Yasamee
Translation/Interpreting: O G Hayward
Registrar's Branch: B Barrett

Management Review Staff
(Joint FCO/ODA Department)
(4 Central Buildings, Matthew Parker Street, SW1H 9NL)
Superintending Under Secretaries:
R J S Muir (FCO); J V Kerby (ODA)
Management review and inspection of FCO and ODA departments; management services.
Head of Management Review Staff: E C Glover, MVO
Deputy Head of Department: N E Hoult
Review Officers: B England, T F L Connor, T Millson, B M Bennett

Medical and Staff Welfare Unit
(Joint FCO/ODA Unit)
Superintending Under-Secretaries: Mrs V E Sutherland, CMG (FCO); J V Kerby (ODA)

Health care and welfare of staff at home and overseas.
Head of Unit (and Chief Welfare Officer): F J Savage, OBE, LVO
Deputy Head of Unit: J W Gibb

Middle East Department
(Downing Street (West), London SW1A 2AL)
Superintending Under-Secretary:
The Hon David Gore-Booth, CMG

Relations with Bahrain; Iran; Iraq; Kuwait; Oman; Qatar; Republic of Yemen; Saudi Arabia; United Arab Emirates.
Head of Department: P M Nixon, CMG, OBE
Assistant: W A Harrison

Migration and Visa Department
(Clive House, Petty France, London SW1H 9HD)

Superintending Under-Secretary:
Miss R J Spencer, CMG

Administration of United Kingdom immigration policy, and the application of the Immigration Rules, by FCO posts overseas. Liaison with the Home Office and other interested Ministries on matters arising from immigration legislation and individual cases. Arrangements for the issue of entry certificates and visas. Visa abolition agreements.
Head of Department: D I Lewty
Assistant (Policy): H Parkinson
Assistant (Director of Operations): S M Scaddan

Narcotics Control and AIDS Department
(King Charles Street, London SW1A 2AH)
Superintending Under-Secretary: R B Bone

Foreign policy implications of the Government's drugs and AIDS-related policies; management of drugs and AIDS-related issues bilaterally and in international fora.
Head of Department: P A B Thomson, CVO
Assistant: D R Snoxell

Nationality, Treaty and Claims Department
(Clive House, Petty France, London SW1H 9HD)
Superintending Under-Secretary:
Miss R J Spencer, CMG

Nationality matters, passport policy, birth and death registration, and marriages abroad. Practice and procedure for the conclusion of treaties; their custody, ratification, presentation to Parliament, publication and registration with the UN; depositary for some multilateral treaties; index of British treaties.
Extradition, taking of evidence (civil), service of process (civil), notarial acts, legalisation, estates of deceased persons abroad.
Claims by British citizens or companies for compensation from other Governments in respect of loss, injury or damage suffered overseas. UN Compensation Commission for claims against Iraq. Policy questions affecting the Foreign Compensation Commission.
Head of Department: M F Sullivan, MBE
Assistant: C C Hayward

Near East and North Africa Department
(King Charles Street and Downing Street (West), London SW1A 2AL)
Superintending Under-Secretary: The Hon David Gore-Booth, CMG

Political and bilateral economic relations with Algeria, Egypt, Israel, Jordan, Lebanon, Mauritania, Libya, Morocco, Sudan, Syria and Tunisia. Arab/Israel. Arab League, Euro-Arab Dialogue.
Head of Department: S W J Fuller
Assistant: D F Richmond

News Department
(Downing Street (West), London SW1A 2AL)
Superintending Under-Secretary:
Miss R J Spencer, CMG

Advises the Secretary of State and departments of the FCO on questions of publicity relating to the British Government's policy towards foreign and Commonwealth Governments.
Is the authorised contact between the FCO and the British Press, radio and television, as well as the overseas press, radio and television stationed in London.
Head of Department: R F Cornish, LVO
Deputy Head of Department and Head of News Room: P J Marshall

Non-Proliferation and Defence Department
(King Charles Street, London, SW1A 2AH)
Superintending Under Secretary: P Lever, CMG

Nuclear non-proliferation issues, including uranium enrichment, reprocessing, safeguards, nuclear exports. IAEA. Missile proliferation issues. Conventional arms transfers. Political implications of defence sales. COCOM. Foreign policy implications of British defence policy outside the NATO area in liaison with the Ministry of Defence and associated bodies. UK military training assistance abroad. Military exercises, visits and overflights, and other miscellaneous defence matters.
Head of Department: J B Donnelly
Assistants: S J Fraser, E W Callway

North America Department
(FCO, Whitehall, SW1A 2AH)
Superintending Under-Secretary: A J Beamish, CMG

Relations with Canada and the United States (including Puerto Rico and the US Virgin Islands).
Head of Department: M E Pellew
Assistant: N K Hook, MVO

Overseas Estate Department
(Apollo House, 36 Wellesley Road, Croydon, CR9 3RR)
Superintending Under-Secretary:
Mrs V E Sutherland, CMG

Accommodation arrangements for Diplomatic Service Posts overseas.
Head of Department: M H R Bertram, ARIBA
Deputy Head of Department: D L Brown
Assistant: C O Wood

Overseas Inspectorate
(4 Central Buildings, Matthew Parker Street, SW1H 9NL)
Assistant Under-Secretary of State, Chief Inspector and Principal Finance Officer:
R J S Muir

Inspection of Diplomatic Service establishments overseas; review of overseas allowances.
Overseas Inspectors: Dr C P Burdess, LVO, P G Harborne, D D Pearey, J Rawlinson, OBE

Permanent Under-Secretary's Department
(Downing Street (West), London SW1A 2AL)
(Century House, Westminster Bridge Road, London SE1 7XF)

Superintending Under-Secretary:
Sir Timothy Daunt, KCMG

General co-ordination duties and responsibility for liaison with the Cabinet Office and other Government Departments.
Head of Department: I R Callan, CMG
Deputy Head of Department: S F Howarth

Personnel Management Department
(3 Central Buildings, Matthew Parker Street, SW1H 9NL)
Superintending Under-Secretary:
Mrs V E Sutherland, CMG

Career planning, individual personnel movements, appointments, probation, promotions, performance assessment, secondments, and loans.
Head of Department: E Clay
Deputy Head of Department: S M J Lamport
Head of Performance Assessment Unit:
A J F Caie
Head of Career Development Unit: T V Fean
Head of Postings Group: Miss D Symes, OBE
Head of Personnel Management Services:
G A Bernard

Personnel Policy Department
(3 Central Buildings, Matthew Parker Street, SW1H 9NL)
(3 Carlton Gardens, London SW1Y 5AA)
Superintending Under-Secretary:
Mrs V E Sutherland, CMG

Administrative planning, policy aspects of personnel, management questions including relations with the trade union side, organisation and structure of the Service, recruitment, transfers to and from other Services, conduct and discipline, equal opportunities.
Head of Department: J Poston

Personnel Services Department
(2 Central Buildings, Matthew Parker Street, SW1H 9NL)
Superintending Under-Secretary:
Mrs V E Sutherland, CMG

Pay, allowances, conditions of service, superannuation.
Head of Department: R G Short, MVO
Assistants: J Long, OBE; W D Stump MBE

Policy Planning Staff
(Downing Street (West), London SW1A 2AL)
Superintending Under-Secretaries:
Sir David Gillmore, KCMG
L V Appleyard, CMG

Policy planning and co-ordination; Contacts with unofficial opinion on policy problems Speech writing.
Head of Planning Staff: R F Cooper, MVO
Assistant: R I Clarke

Protocol Department
(FCO, Old Admiralty Building, SW1A 2AF)
Superintending Under-Secretary:
A St J H Figgis

Visits to the United Kingdom by Heads of State and Heads of Government. Privileges, immunities, security and welfare of the Diplomatic Corps in London. Arrangements for international conferences and meetings at home and for visits abroad by Ministers and delegations to conferences, including security. Matters of ceremonial, protocol and precedence; Diplomatic Lists and formal documents required for Diplomatic and Consular appointments.
Head of Department & First Assistant Marshal of the Diplomatic Corps: D C B Beaumont
Assistant Head of Department & Assistant Marshal of the Diplomatic Corps: M L Dalton, LVO

Republic of Ireland Department
(Downing Street (West), London SW1A 2AL)
Superintending Under-Secretary:
J Q Greenstock, CMG

Political and economic relations with the Republic of Ireland. Northern Ireland questions affecting relations with the Republic and with other foreign countries.
Head of Department: G R Archer
Assistant: D F G Farr

Research and Analysis Department
(FCO, Old Admiralty Building, SW1A 2AF)
Superintending Under-Secretary:
Sir David Gillmore, KCMG

Contributes to the formulation of overseas policy through the provision of assessments and advice based on specialist experience.
Director of Research and Analysis:
B S T Eastwood
Assistant Directors: G Beel (Russia/Former Soviet Union); Mrs S F Morphet (International and Commonwealth); Mrs A M Gillon (West and Southern Europe); J A Penney (Americas); D J White (Africa); M J Fuller (Middle East); R F Wye (Far East); P Reddicliffe (South and South-East Asia); Ms J F Gunn (Central and Eastern Europe).

Resource and Finance Department
(Old Admiralty Building, SW1A 2AF)
(Hanslope Park, Hanslope, Milton Keynes, MK19 1BH)
Superintending Under-Secretary and Principal Finance Officer: R J S Muir

Planning and management of Diplomatic Wing financial and manpower resources; long term resource allocation policy; Secretariat of the Board of Management; Top Management System, including Top Management Round and objective-setting process; output measurement; PES and preparation of annual and supplementary Estimates; detailed accounting and in-year coordination of budgets, expenditure and recoveries on all Votes; Financial Management Information System; Value for Money; AUS pilot command project; AUS staff tallies and slot code control; Scrutinies; Citizens Charter and Competing for Quality market testing initiative.
Head of Department: R J Chase
Associate Head of Department: G F Griffiths
Assistants: A R Ingle, R E Brinkley
Chief Accountant: M J Brown

Royal Matters Unit
(FCO, Old Admiralty Building, SW1A 2AF)
Superintending Under-Secretary:
A St J H Figgis

Liaison between the FCO and Royal Households.
Head of Unit: J E Brook

Security Department
(Joint FCO/ODA Department)
(4 Central Buildings, Matthew Parker Street, London SW1H 9NL)
Superintending Under-Secretaries:
Mrs V E Sutherland, CMG, (FCO); J V Kerby, (ODA)

Supervision of security.
Head of Department: J W Hodge
Assistant: A C Walder

Security Policy Department
(King Charles Street, London SW1A 2AH)
Superintending Under Secretary: P J Goulden, CMG

NATO and WEU policy issues; the foreign policy implications of British defence policy. as regards Transatlantic and European defence; nuclear defence planning; nuclear and conventional arms control; defence equipment procurement including collaborative projects.
Head of Department: S J Gomersall
Assistant: S L Cowper-Coles, LVO

South Asian Department
(FCO Whitehall, London SW1A 2AL)
Superintending Under-Secretary:
J T Masefield, CMG

Political and economic relations with India, Pakistan, Bangladesh, Sri Lanka, Afghanistan, Nepal, Bhutan, the Maldives.
Head of Department: M J Williams, CVO, OBE
Assistant: T C Holmes

South Atlantic and Antarctic Department
(FCO, Whitehall, SW1A 2AP)
Superintending Under Secretary: A J Beamish, CMG

HMG's responsibilities for the Dependent Territories of the Falkland Islands, the British Antarctic Territory, St Helena, Ascension Island and Tristan da Cunha. South Atlantic matters HMG's responsibilities under the Antarctic Treaty
Head of Department: P M Newton
Assistant: P L Hunt

South East Asian Department
FCO Whitehall, London SW1A 2AL)
Superintending Under-Secretary:
J T Masefield, CMG

Political and economic relations with Brunei,
Burma, Cambodia, Indonesia, Laos, Malaysia,
Philippines, Singapore, Thailand, Vietnam,
ASEAN, ESCAP, and the problem of
Vietnamese migrants in Hong Kong.
Head of Department: G W Hewitt
Assistant: B E Stewart

Southern European Department
King Charles Street, London SW1A 2AL)
Superintending Under-Secretary:
J Q Greenstock, CMG

Political and bilateral economic relations with
Andorra, Cyprus, Greece, Malta, Portugal, Spain,
Turkey. External relations and some aspects of
internal administration of Gibraltar.
Head of Department: D C A Madden
Assistant: J S Buck

South Pacific Department
(FCO, King Charles Street, London, SW1A
2AH)
Superintending Under-Secretary:
J T Masefield, CMG

Relations with Australia, Cook Islands, Fiji,
Kiribati, Nauru, New Zealand, Niue, Papua New
Guinea, Solomon Islands, Tonga, Tuvalu,
Vanuatu, Western Samoa and French and US
territories in the South Pacific. Administration of
Pitcairn.
Head of Department: A R Thomas
Assistant: P R Holmes

Technical Security Department
(Hanslope Park, Hanslope, Milton Keynes, MK19
7BH)
Superintending Under-Secretary:
Mrs V E Sutherland, CMG

Technical Security for Overseas Missions.
Head of Department: Dr J W Gould
Assistants: R W Read; M A Corbett

Training Department
(Cromwell House, Dean Stanley Street, London
SW1P 3JG)
Superintending Under-Secretary:
Mrs V E Sutherland, CMG

Planning and provision of professional, language
and developmental training for the Diplomatic
Service.

Head of Department: T D Curran
Assistant: A J Abbott
*Assistant and Director of Diplomatic Service
Language Centre:* J D Moore

United Nations Department
(King Charles Street, London SW1A 2AH)
Superintending Under-Secretary:
R B Bone

Policy towards the United Nations, particularly
the Security Council, General Assembly and
ECOSOC; United Nations peacekeeping
operations; United Nations sanctions;
international humanitarian assistance, including
the Geneva Conventions and Red Cross;
migration/refugee policy; general aspects of
policy towards the UN specialised agencies.
Head of Department: Miss M G D Evans, CMG
Assistant: C H Salvesen

Western European Department
(Downing Street (West), London SW1A 2AL)
Superintending Under-Secretary:
J Q Greenstock, CMG

Political and economic relations with Austria,
Belgium, Denmark, Finland, France and Monaco,
Germany, Iceland, Italy, San Marino,
Luxembourg, Netherlands, Norway, Sweden,
Switzerland (with Liechtenstein), the Holy See
and the Council of Europe.
Head of Department: M L H Hope
Assistants: A Heath, T I Hay-Campbell

West Indian and Atlantic Department
(FCO, Whitehall, SW1A 2AP)
Superintending Under-Secretary:
A J Beamish, CMG

HMG's responsibilities for the Dependent
Territories of Anguilla, Bermuda, British Virgin
Islands, Cayman Islands, Montserrat, and Turks
and Caicos Islands.
Political and bilateral economic relations with
Antigua and Barbuda, Aruba, Bahamas,
Barbados, Dominica, The Dominican Republic,
Grenada, Guadeloupe, Guyana, Haiti, Jamaica,
Martinique, Netherlands Antilles, Saint Lucia, St
Kitts-Nevis, St Vincent and the Grenadines,
Suriname, Trinidad and Tobago, French Guiana,
and economic relations with Puerto Rico.
Regional political and economic matters. Co-
ordination of policy on Dependent Territories;
liaison on subjects of common interest to
Dependent Territories; interpretation of colonial
regulations.
Head of Department: G M Baker
Assistant: J Wilde

British Missions Overseas

Lists of British Representatives in
Commonwealth, Foreign Countries and
in the Republic of Ireland

with the Addresses of Missions and Consulates etc.

The letter (M) denotes that the Officer has a Marriage Warrant and may in certain circumstances solemnise marriages under the Foreign Marriage Acts.

The asterisk (*) indicates Commonwealth countries, in which the British representative is a High Commissioner.

Part II: British Representation Overseas

AFGHANISTAN

Kabul
British Embassy

Staff temporarily withdrawn from post.

ALBANIA

Tirana
British Embassy
via XX Settembre 80a
00187 Rome
(Tel: (39(6) 482 5441, 482 5551)
(Telex: 626119(a/b 626119 BREMB I)
(Facsimile: (396) 487 3324

Ambassador (resides at Rome):
Sir Patrick Fairweather, KCMG

ALGERIA

Algiers
British Embassy
Résidence Cassiopée, Bâtiment B, 7 Chemin des
Glycines
(BP 43, Alger,-Gare 16000), Algiers
(Tels: (2)60.56.01; (2)60.54.11; (2)60.50.38;
(2)60.58.31)
(Telex: (2) 66151)(a/b 66151 PRDRM DZ)
Telegraphic Address: PRODROME ALGIERS
(Facsimile: 604410)
(Consular/Visa Section Telex: 66266 Visa DZ.)

Ambassador: C C R Battiscombe, CMG
Counsellor, Consul-General and Deputy Head of
Mission: K G Bloomfield
Counsellor: G L St L Rolleston
Defence, Naval, Military and Air Attaché:
Group Captain K Gowing, RAF
Cultural Attaché (British Council Director):
D Munro
First Secretary (Commercial): D L Cotton
Second Secretary (Commercial/Information):
J S Thornton
Assistant Cultural Attaché (British Council):
J D Ewart
Second Secretary (Management) and Consul:
P A S Holmes
Second Secretary (Immigration) and Consul: Miss
J A Chiswell, MBE
Vice-Consul: T F Robins

ANDORRA

(Tel: 010 34 3 322 2151)

Consul-General (Resides in Barcelona): M Perceval

ANGOLA

Luanda
British Embassy
Rua Diogo Cão 4 (Caixa Postal 1244), Luanda
(Tel: 334582/3 and 392991)
Telex: 3130 (a/b PRODLDA AN)
Commercial Section: Tel: 392998
Telex: 3130 (a/b PRODLDA AN)
Telegraphic Address: PRODROME LUANDA

Ambassador: J G Flynn, CMG
Consul and Deputy Head of Mission: A D F
Henderson
First Secretary (Chancery): S M Noakes
First Secretary (Aid): C S M Shelton
Second Secretary (Commercial): P D Sherar
Third Secretary (Management) and Vice-Consul:
A J Marshall
Third Secretary (Aid/Chancery): M J Lownds

ANTIGUA AND BARBUDA*

St John's
British High Commission
Price Waterhouse Centre, 11 Old Parham Road,
(PO 483), St Johns, Antigua
(Tel: St Johns 462 0008/9)
(Telex: UKREP ANTIGUA AK 2113 (a/b 2113
UKREP ANT AK)) Telegraphic Address: UKREP
ST JOHNS, ANTIGUA
Facsimile: 809 462 2806 and 809 482 271

†High Commissioner: E T Davies, CMG
First Secretary and Resident Representative:
I D Marsh
†Deputy High Commissioner: J A Noakes
Defence Adviser (Resides at Kingston):
Colonel C S Faith, OBE
†First Secretary (Chancery): A ffrench Blake, ODE
†Assistant Defence Adviser:
Commander H M Humphreys, RN †
†Second Secretary (Management/Consular):
Miss S Kaye
†Second Secretary (Chancery/Information): P G
McCrudden †Second Secretary (Technical Works):
J I S McLean
Second Secretary (Resides at Kingston): G
Atkinson
†Third Secretary: R M Hardy
†Third Secretary (Immigration): D W Platt
(†Resides at Bridgetown)

ARGENTINE REPUBLIC

Buenos Aires
British Embassy
Dr Luis Agote 2412/52 (Casilla de Correo 2050),

1425 Buenos Aires
(Tels: 803-7070/1)
806-6220: Commercial Section
Facsimile: 803 1731
806-5731: Commercial Section

Ambassador: The Hon Humphrey Maud, CMG
Minister, Consul General and Deputy Head of Mission: L G Faulkner
First Secretary (Chancery): W G Sandover
First Secretary (Commercial): M H McIntosh
Defence and Military Attaché:
Colonel J E Neeve
Naval and Air Attaché: Group Captain J D Lunt, RAF
Cultural Attaché: (British Council Director):
H Fish, OBE
First Secretary (Commercial): M H McIntock
First Secretary (Economic): Miss E C Evans
Second Secretary (Works): D M Corield
Second Secretary (Chancery): Miss E M Scholes
Second Secretary: K W Green
Second Secretary (Management) *and Consul:*
Miss A Greatrix
Second Secretary (Information): J M Ingamells
Assistant Cultural Attaché: (British Council):
S Gammel
Third Secretary: (Commercial): Miss A Macintosh

ARMENIA

Yerevan
British Embassy Moscow

Ambassador: (resides at Moscow)
Sir Brian Fall, KCMG

AUSTRALIA*

Canberra
British High Commission
Commonwealth Avenue, Yarralumla, Canberra,
ACT 2600
(Tel: (6) 270-6666)
(Telex: 71 62222) (a/b UKREP 71 62222)
Facsimile: 273 3236
Facsimile (Commercial Section): 273 4360

Consular Passport/Visa Section
CBS Tower, Level 10, Canberra City ACT 2601
Tel: 257-2434 (Passports), 257-1982 (Entry Clearances)
Fax: 257-5857
Telex: 71 62690

High Commissioner: Sir Brian Barder, KCMG
Deputy High Commissioner, Counsellor and Director of Trade Promotion: I W Mackley, CMG
Defence and Naval Adviser and Head of the British Defence Liaison Staff:
Commodore B J Adams, RN
Counsellor and Director of Trade Promotion:
T N Young
Military Adviser: Col G A Morris, OBE

Air Adviser: Group Captain J G Sheldon, RAF
First Secretary (Political): P Beckingham
First Secretary (Defence Export Services):
M Maiden
First Secretary (Management): J B Midgley
First Secretary: D G Blunt, LVO
First Secretary: K Harding
First Secretary (Information): M R Eastburn
First Secretary (Commercial and Agricultural):
G L Minter, MVO
First Secretary (Defence Research) *and Head of the British Defence Research and Supply Staff:*
N Neve
Assistant Naval Adviser:
Lieutenant-Commander G E MacDonald, RN
Second Secretary (Consular): K Casey
Second Secretary (Works): J D Warrener
Second Secretary: R A Drew, MBE
Second Secretary: R O Arrowsmith
Third Secretary (Chancery): M M Caton

Adelaide
British Consulate-General
Hassell Pty Ltd., 70 Hindmarsh Square, Adelaide,
SA
(Tel: (08) 224 0033)
(08) 224 0363 (Consular Enquiries)
Honorary Consul-General: J Morphett

Brisbane
British Consulate-General
BP House, 193 North Quay, Brisbane,
Queensland 4000
(Tel: 236 2575, 236 2577, 236 2581)
(Telex: 40556) (a/b BRITN AA 40556)
(Facsimile: 236 2576)

Consul-General: B S Jones, LVO
Vice-Consul (Commercial): P D Broom
Management/Consular Officer: Mrs M M Hunt

Melbourne
British Consulate-General
17th Floor, 90 Collins Street, Melbourne
Victoria 3000
(Tel: 650 3699 (Commercial Section),
650 4155 (Consular Section))
(Telex: 30660) (a/b BRITN AA 30660)
(Facsimile: 010 613 650 2990)

Consul-General: S D R Brown
Consul (Commercial): H Dunnachie, MBE
Vice-Consul (Commercial/Management): R Webb

Perth
British Consulate-General
95 St George's Terrace,
Perth, Western Australia 6000
(Tel: (09) 322 3200 (Consular Section)
322 5952, 322 7674 (Commercial Section))
(Telex: 71 92493) (a/b BRITN AA 92493)
(Facsimile: 619 481 4755)

Consul-General: J B Noss
Consul (Commercial): J Liddell
Vice-Consul: R J Andrews

Sydney
British Consulate-General
Level 16, The Gateway, 1 MacQuarie Place,
Sydney
Cove, Sydney 2000, New South Wales
(Tel: 247-7521 (8 lines), 247-9731 (Consular
Section))
(Telex: 71 20680) (a/b BRITN AA 20680)
(Facsimile: 612 233 1826)

Consul-General: R S Reeve
Deputy Consul-General (Commercial):J Hillman
Cultural Adviser (British Council
Representative): M S Foot, OBE
Vice-Consul (Commercial): P J Hughes
Vice-Consul: Miss N J Wilson

Darwin
British Government Wireless Relay Station
PO Box 39670, Winnellie NT 0821
GPO Box 3670, Darwin NT0801
(Tel: 831055, 831039)
(Telex: 85114) (a/b BGWRS DN AA 85114)

Manager: P Hart
Deputy Manager: R S Nutt

AUSTRIA

Vienna
British Embassy
Jaurèsgasse 12, 1030 Vienna
(Tel: (1) 7131575/9)
(Facsimile: (222) 75 78 24)
(Telex: 132810(a/b) 132810 BRITEM B)

Consular Section: Jaurèsgasse 10, 1030 Vienna
(Tel: (0222) 756117/8714 61 17 and 18)
(Telex: 133410) (a/b 133410 BRITEM A)
(132810) (a/b 132810 BRITEM B) (Facsimile:
(222) 712 7316)

Ambassador: T C Wood, CMG
*Counsellor, Consul-General and Deputy Head of
Mission:* J W Forbes-Meyler, OBE
Counsellor (Chancery): N H McMillan, OBE
Counsellor (Labour) (Resides at Bonn):J Franklin
Counsellor (Hong Kong Trade Affairs) (Resides at
London): P A S Wise
Defence Attaché:
Lieutenant-Colonel P W L Hughes, MBE
First Secretary (Chancery): K J A Mackenzie
First Secretary (Chancery/Information): R E Dear
First Secretary (Commercial): S G Ratcliffe
First Secretary (Chancery): Dr R H Williams
First Secretary (Management and Consul):
M J Bennett, MBE
First Secretary (Chancery/Information): M R
Crompton
Second Secretary (Chancery): Miss S E Burns
Second Secretary: (Chancery/Information):
Mrs M K Alessandri
Third Secretary: D J Townsend
Attaché and Vice-Consul: J B Mee
Third Secretary (Management and Vice-Consul):
Mrs L Cross

Bregenz
British Consulate
Bundesstrasse 110,
A-6923 Lauterach/Bregenz
(Tel: (43)5574/38 586 or 611)
Telex: (43)57 733 (a/b GW BBA)
Facsimile: 5574/30 928

Honorary Consul: Dipl.-Ing. P. Senger-Weiss

Graz
British Consulate
Schmiedgasse 8-12, A-8010 Graz
(Tel: (43)(316) 826105)
(Telex: 03-1718) (a/b Bruehla)
Facsimile: (43)316/82161645

Honorary Consul: K D Brühl, OBE

Innsbruck
British Consulate
Matthias-Schmid Strasse 12, A-6021 Innsbruck
(Tel: (43)(5222) 588320)
Telex: 05-3402 (a/b WUBIB A)
Facsimile: (43)5222/586151

Honorary Consul: Ing.-Vw. Hellmut Buchroithner
Honorary Pro-Consul: Ing. H. Reinisch

Salzburg
British Consulate
Alter Markt 4, A-5020 Salzburg
(Tel: (43)(662) 84 81 33)
(Telex: c/o 063-3811 (a/b KRON A))
Facsimile: 0662/85 04 98

Honorary Consul: M M Kaindl
Honorary Pro-Consul: Mrs H Danmayr

AZERBAIJHAN

Baku
British Embassy Moscow

Ambassador (resides at Moscow):
Sir Brian Fall, KCMG

BAHAMAS*

Nassau
British High Commission
Bitco Building (3rd Floor), East Street,
PO Box N7516, Nassau
(Tel: Area Code (809) 32-57471/2/3)
(Telegraphic address: UKREP NASSAU)
(Facsimile: (809) 323-3871)

High Commissioner: B Attewell
Deputy High Commissioner: R G Church
Defence Adviser: Captain A J S Taylor, RN
Second Secretary (Chancery) (Resides at Miami):
G J Honey
Commercial/Information Officer: Mrs M A Ansell

BAHRAIN

Bahrain
British Embassy
21 Government Avenue, Manama, 306

(PO Box 114) Bahrain
(Tel: 534404, 534865/6)
(Telex: 8213) (a/b 8213 PRODRO BN)
(Telegrams: PRODROME BAHRAIN)
Facsimile: 531273

Ambassador and Consul-General: H J O R Tunnell
First Secretary (Commercial), *Consul and Deputy Head of Mission:* (M) E Jenkinson
First Secretary: J C A Rundall
Second Secretary (Commercial): D J Holden
Third Secretary: Miss F Luff
Vice-Consul: C Glass

BANGLADESH*

Dhaka
British High Commission
United Nations Road, Baridhara, Dhaka
Postal Address: P O Box 6079, Dhaka 12
(Tel: 882705 (5 lines)
(Facsimile: (880 2) 883437, 883474 (Aid) 883666
(Immigration)

High Commissioner: Sir Colin Imray, KBE, CMG
Deputy High Commissioner: G Finlayson
Defence Adviser: Colonel G M Longdon, OBE
Counsellor (Aid): S Chard
First Secretary (Political): G P R Boon
First Secretary (Aid): E C N Taylor ˋ
First Secretary (Medical Officer):
Dr S M C Michelson
First Secretary (Commercial): D E Donald
First Secretary: (Health and Population): (vacant)
First Secretary (Consular and Immigration):
(vacant)
First Secretary (Management): B D Adams, OBE
First Secretary (Natural Resources): H Potter
First Secretary (Fisheries): N Macpherson
Second Secretary (Immigration): K Knight
Second Secretary (Aid): W Evans
Second Secretary (Immigration): Mrs R P Clarke, MBE
Second Secretary (Resides at Bombay): R Affleck
Second Secretary (Management): B E Doane
Third Secretary (Consular): Mrs L Taylor
Third Secretary (Aid): Miss C A F Brown
Third Secretary (Political/Information): Mrs J Evans

BARBADOS*

Bridgetown
British High Commission
Lower Collymore Rock (PO Box 676),
Bridgetown C
(Tel: 436 6694)
(Telex: WB 2219) (a/b UKREP BRI, WB 2219)
(Telegraphic Address: UKREP BARBADOS)
Facsimile: 436 5398/7916

High Commissioner: E T Davies, CMG
Deputy High Commissioner: J A Noakes
Defence Adviser (Resides at Kingston):
Colonel C S Faith, OBE
First Secretary (Chancery): A ffrench Blake, OBE
First Secretary (Chancery): S R Morley
Assistant Defence Adviser:
Commander H M Humphreys, RN

Second Secretary: T V D Manhire
(Resides at Kingston)
Second Secretary (Chancery): P Mullee
Second Secretary (Management/Consular):
Miss S Kaye
Second Secretary (Technical Works): I Agnew
Third Secretary: J Harland
Third Secretary (Immigration): Mrs A A Howard

British Development Division in the Caribbean,
Lower Collymore Rock (PO Box 167),
Bridgetown
(Tel: 436 9873)
(Telex: WB 2236) (a/b DEV DIV BAR WB 2236)
(Facsimile: (010 1809) 436 2194)

Head of Division: M Bawden
Senior Economic Assistant: Miss F Lappin
Senior Engineering Adviser: M F Sergeant
Economic Adviser: P J Dearden
Senior Natural Resources Adviser: J B Warren
Programme Manager: G H Malley
Programme Manager: I Stuart
Programme Officer: M Rapley
Management Officer: J Leary
Programme Officer: K Miller

BELARUS

Minsk
British Embassy Moscow

Ambassador (resides at Moscow):
Sir Brian Fall, KCMG

BELGIUM

Brussels
British Embassy
Rue d'Arlon 85, 1040 Brussels
(Tel: (02) 287 6211)
(Facsimile: Chancery 287 6355; Commercial 287 6240; Information 287 6360; Consulate 287 6270)

Ambassador: J W D Gray, CMG
Counsellor, Consul-General and Deputy Head of Mission: N M McCarthy, OBE
Counsellor (Commercial): N R Jarrold
Counsellor: J W B Richards
Defence and Military Attaché:
Colonel J M Craster
Naval and Air Attaché: Wing Commander B A Horton, RAF
Cultural Counsellor (British Council Director):
K McGuinness
First Secretary (Labour): A Tyson
First Secretary (EC/External): C P D Harvey
First Secretary (Commercial): W A Kelly
First Secretary (Chancery): A J Stafford
First Secretary and Consul: (M) Miss E A Rose
Second Secretary (Chancery/Information):
Mrs R L Bryant
Second Secretary (European Community Affairs):
M T Stollery
Second Secretary: A J Perry
Second Secretary (Accommodation Manager)/
Consul: A P Smith
Third Secretary: Miss C M Elliot

Joint Management Office
Rue Marie-Thérèse 1, 1040 Brussels
(Tel: (02) 217 90 00)
(Facsimile: 219 89 24)
Counsellor (Management): G Fedrick
First Secretary (Management): M W Growcott
Second Secretary (Management): F J Marshall
Second Secretary (Management and Accountant):
A P Smith

Antwerp
British Consulate-General
Körte Klarenstraat 7
2000 Antwerp
(Tel: (03) 232.69.40)
(Telex: 34981 (a/b 34981 (KNIGHT B))
(Facsimile: (03) 231 69 75)

Honorary Consul-*General:* P A Knight

Liège
British Consulate
rue Beeckmann 45, 4000 Liège
(Tel: (041) 23.58.32)

Honorary Consul: Maître J M Delfosse, LVO

BELIZE*

Belmopan
British High Commission, PO Box 91, Belmopan,
Belize or B.F.P.O. 12
(Tel: Belmopan (8) 22146/7)
(Telex: 284 (a/b 284 UKREP BZE))
(Facsimile: 501 (8) 22761)
Telegraphic Address: UKREP BZE

High Commissioner: D P R Mackilligin
Deputy High Commissioner: G H W Morgan
Defence Liaison Officer: (Vacant)
First Secretary: S M Boldt
(Resides at Kingston)
First Secretary: Mr A Baxendine (resides at
Washington)
Third Secretary (Management/Consular): T J Hines
Third Secretary (Aid): Miss D F Partridge

BENIN

Cotonou
British Embassy (All staff reside at Lagos)

Ambassador: A C D S Macrae, CMG
*Counsellor, Consul-General and Deputy Head of
Mission:* R S Gorham
Counsellor (Commercial): E A Burner
First Secretary (Economic and Political):
C J B White
First Secretary and Consul: D B McAdam
Second Secretary (Political): F Cochrane-Dyet
Second Secretary (Consular): Miss H C Brown

British Consulate
SOBEPAT, BP147, Cotonou
(Telephone: 313342, 312058)
(Telex: 972 5047 (a/b 5047 STIN CTNOU))

Honorary Consul: D Inchelin

BOLIVIA

La Paz
British Embassy
Avenida Arce 2732-2754, (Casilla 694) La Paz
(Tel: 329401/2/3. 351400)
(Telex: 355-2341 (a/b PDRMELP BV))
(Facsimile: 391063)

Ambassador: R M Jackson, CVO
*First Secretary, Consul and Deputy Head of
Mission:* D A C Hallett
Defence Attaché (Resides at Lima): Col C H Van
der Noot, MBE
Second Secretary (Aid/Information): J McGhee
Second Secretary: R Gray
*Administration Officer, Vice Consul and
Accountant:* R J Shackell

Santa Cruz
British Consulate
PO Box 3181, Calle Parapeti 28-2 Piso, Santa Cruz
(Tel: 36415 and 45682)
(Telex: CAPUBSC BV)
(Facsimile 3329154)

Honorary Consul: F R Taendler

BOTSWANA*

Gaborone
British High Commission
Private Bag 0023, Gaborone
(Tel: 352841/2/3)
(Telex: 2370 (a/b 2370 UKREP BD))
(Telegraphic Address: UK REP GABORONE)
(Facsimile: 356105)

High Commissioner: J C Edwards, CMG
*Deputy High Commissioner and Head of
Chancery:* P Fluck
Defence Adviser (Resides at Harare):
Colonel A McNeil
Second Secretary (Commercial): K Clark
Third Secretary (Aid and Information):
Miss J M Cairns
Third Secretary (Consular and Management):
C J R Moore

BRAZIL

Brasilia
British Embassy
Setor de Embaixadas Sul, Quadra 801,
Conjunto K, 70.408 Brasilia, D.F., or Avenida das
Naçoes Caixa Postal 07-0586, 70.359 Brasilia DF
(Tel: (061) 225-2710)
(Telex: 2370 1360) (a/b 611360 EING BR)
(Telegraphic Address: PRODROME
BRASILIA)
(Facsimile: 225 1777)

Ambassador: P W Heap, CMG
*Minister/Counsellor, Consul-General and Deputy
Head of Mission:* P R Jenkins
Counsellor: A W Crooke
Defence, Military and Air Attaché:
Colonel D K W Farrant
Naval Attaché: Captain J R Luard, RN
First Secretary (Political): J D F Holt

First Secretary (Commercial): M D Aron
First Secretary (Management) *and Consul:*
G M Johnson
Second Secretary (Economic): N D Sutcliffe
Second Secretary (Works): Vacant
Third Secretary: F J Chapman
Third Secretary (Management) *and Vice-Consul:*
A Woodcock

Belém
British Consulate
Agencias Mundiais
Rua Gaspar Viana 490, Caixa Postal 98, 66.000,
Belém, Pará (Tel: (091) 224-4822)
(Telex: (091) 1184) (a/b AMUNBR)
(Facsimile: (091) 225 3607

Honorary Consul: R J Burnett, OBE

Manáus
British Consulate
Wilson and Sons Ltd, Avenida Eduardo Ribeiro,
520, 12 Andar S/1202 Caixa Postal 1091, 69.000
Manáus, Amazonas
(Tel: (092) 234-1018 and 1424)
(Telex: c/o (092) 1046 (a/b WSON BR))
(Facsimile: (092) 622 2713

Honorary Consul: G R Clarke, MBE

Recife
British Consulate
Av. Domingos Frerreira, 222 Sala 203
Recife, CEP 51.020, Pernambuco
(Tel: (081) 326 3733)
(Telex: (081) 4014 (c/o Britco))
(Facsimile: (081) 325 0247)

Honorary Consul: A E Fiore
Vice-Consul: R J M Guedes

Salvador
British Consulate
Av Estados Unidos 4, Salas 1109/1113 Edifício
Visconde de Cayru, Caixa Postal 38, CEP 40010,
Salvador, Bahia (Tel: (071) 243-9222)
(Telex: 1050)
(Facsimile: (071) 242 7848)

Honorary Consul: W N Lee

Rio de Janeiro
British Consulate-General
Praia do Flamengo 284-2nd Floor, Rio de Janeiro
Postal address: Caixa Postal 669-CEP 20010
(Tel: 552-1422 (all Departments))
(Telex: (021)-2121577) (a/b 2121577 EING BR)
(Facsimile: 552 5796)

Consul-General: Miss P M Kelly, MBE
Consul (Commercial): Mrs V B M O'Hara
Consul (Political/Economic): S P Garner-Winship
Vice-Consul: N G Whatley

Belo Horizonte
British Consulate
Edifício Guimarães, 5th Floor, Avenida Alfonso
Pena 952 (Caixa Postal 576), CEP 30.000, Belo
Horizonte, Minas Gerais (Tel: (031) 222-6318)

(Facsimile: (031) 224 1589)

Honorary Consul: R A Gough, MBE
Vice-Consul: R Pacheco

São Paulo
British Consulate-General
Avenida Paulista, 1938 (17th Floor) 01310-200,
São Paulo, (SP) Brazil
(Tel: 287-7722)
(Telex: 11-21384) (a/b 1121 384 BRIT BR)
(Facsimile: 287 7637)

Consul-General: R H Brown
Deputy Consul-General: G S Cowling
Vice-Consul (Management): D B Arkley
Vice-Consul (Commercial): P A Sinkinson

Pôrto Alegre (RS)
British Consulate
Rua Itapeva 110, sala 505, Edificio Montreal,
Bairro Passo D'Areia Pôrto Alegre RS CEP 91350
(Tel: (55) (512) 41-0720)
(Facsimile: (051) 341 0720
Honorary Consul: G J Powell

Rio Grande (RS)
British Consulate
Rua Francisco Marques 163 (Caixa Postal 455)
Centro-96.200, Rio Grande RS
(Tel: (0532) 32-7788)
(Telex: (532) 191 SIASBR) and 531014
(Facsimile: (55) (532) 32-3151)

Honorary Consul: R V Wigg, MBE

Santos (SP)
British Consulate
Rua Tuiuti No 58 (2nd Floor) (Caixa Postal 204,
11010 Santos-SP) (Tel: (0132) 33-6111 or (0132)
34-6656)
(Telex: (13) 1013)
(Facsimile: (55) (132) 35-5262)

Honorary Consul: C M Marote

Curitiba
British Consulate
Rua: Marechal Deodoro, 421 80020 - Curitiba - PR
(Tel: (041) 232-5067 or (041) 232-7715)
(Telex: (41) 5166)
(Facsimile: (041) 232-5935)

Honorary Consul: P R ter Poorten

BRUNEI*

Bandar Seri Begawan
British High Commission
3rd Floor, Hong Kong Bank Chambers, Jalan
Pemancha, PO Box 2197, Bandar Seri Begawan
(Tel: Chancery/Commercial 222231/223121,
Consular/Management 226001)
(Telex: 2211) (a/b UKREP BU 2211)
(Facsimile 226002)

High Commissioner: A J Sindall

Deputy High Commissioner: G S Dixon
Second Secretary (Chancery): J C A Clephane
Third Secretary (Management and Consular):
Mrs J Fong

BULGARIA

Sofia
British Embassy
Boulevard Vassil Levski 65-67 Sofia 1000
(Tel: 885361/2 and 879575)
(Telex: 22363 (a/b 22363 PRODROME), 24212
(a/b BRITCO BG) (British Council))
(Facsimile: (359 2) 46 20 65)

Ambassador: R Thomas, CMG
*First Secretary, Consul and Deputy Head of
Mission:* J L Buchanan
Defence, Naval, Military and Air Attaché:
Colonel N A King, MBE
First Secretary (Political/Economic):
K I Malin
First Secretary (Commercial): J C Northover
First Secretary (Embassy Medical Adviser):
Dr H M Carpenter (Resides at Moscow)
Cultural Attaché (British Council Director):
D G Stokes
Second Secretary (Political/Information):
Miss S J Lampert
First Secretary (Management) *and Consul:*
A J Lloyd
Second Secretary: P J W Hardman
Second Secretary (resides at Ankara): D Sykes
Assistant Cultural Attaché (British Council
Assistant Director): C W Rennie
Third Secretary and Vice-Consul: N R Martin
Third Secretary: K A Cody
Third Secretary: P Coggles

BURKINA FASO

Ouagadougou
British Embassy (All staff reside at Abidjan)

Ambassador and Consul-General:
Miss M I Rothwell, CMG
First Secretary (Commercial), *Head of Chancery
and Consul:* D R F Flanagan
First Secretary (Education): C Stevenson
Second Secretary and Information Officer:
P J Whitchcad
Second Secretary (Commercial) *and Vice-Consul:*
W G D Johnson, MBE
Third Secretary and Vice-Consul:
Miss W P Freeman

British Consulate
BP 1918
Ouagadougou,
Burkina
(Tel: 33 63 63)

Honorary Consul: A C Bessey

BURMA

Rangoon
British Embassy
80 Strand Road (PO Box 638), Rangoon

(Tel: (95)(1) 81700, 81138, 81703, 81708, 81702,
81812)
(Telex: 21216 (a/b 21216 PRODRM BM))
(Facsimile: 89566)

Ambassador: J D N Hartland-Swann, CMG
*First Secretary, Consul and Deputy Head of
Mission:* P R Hagart
Defence Attaché: Colonel W H Clements
Cultural Attaché: R H Isaacs
Third Secretary: Miss V J Robinson
Third Secretary (Management and Vice-Consul):
(Vacant)

BURUNDI

Bujumbura
British Embassy (All staff reside at Kinshasa)

Charge d'Affaires and Consul: Ms K W Oliver
Deputy Head of Mission and Vice-Consul:
Miss H M Horn
British Consulate
43 Avenue Bubanza, BP 1344, Bujumbura
(Tel: 23711)
(Telex: 5126 (a/b INTAC BDI))
Honorary Consul: Vacant

CAMBODIA - see under British Missions and
Delegations

CAMEROON

Yaoundé
British Embassy
Avenue Winston Churchill, BP 547 Yaoundé
(Tel: 22 05   45 and 22 07 96)
(Telex: 8200) (a/b PRODROM 8200 KN)
(Facsimile: 220148)

Ambassador and Consul-General: W E Quantrill
*First Secretary Consul and Deputy Head of
Mission:* C A Hamilton
Second Secretary (Commercial/Aid) *and
Vice-Consul:* R W Hyde, MBE

Douala
British Consulate
Boite Postale 1016, Rue de l'Hotel de Ville, Douala
(Tel: 42.21.77 and 42.81.45)
(Telex: 5353) (a/b BRITAIN 5353KN)
(Facsimile: 42 88 96)

Consul: D A Pearce

CANADA*

Ottawa
British High Commission
80 Elgin Street, Ottawa KIP 5K7
(Tel: (613) 237-1530) (Telex: 0533318)
(a/b UKREP OTT)
(Telegraphic Address: UKREP OTTAWA)
(Facsimile: 613 237 7980)

High Commissioner: Sir Nicholas Bayne, KCMG
Deputy High Commissioner: B H Dinwiddy
Minister (Hong Kong Commercial Affairs) (resides
at Washington): P Lo
Counsellor (Economic and Commercial): R J Fell

Counsellor (Cultural Affairs British Council Director): M A Evans
Counsellor: A E Lewis
Defence and Military Adviser:
Brigadier T D V Bevan
Naval Adviser: Capt R Baller, RN
Air Adviser: Group Captain J R Legh-Smith RAF
First Secretary: P Holdich
First Secretary: J Welsh
First Secretary (Management/Consular): R V Welborn
First Secretary: C Annetts
First Secretary (Economic and Commercial):
R J Northern
Second Secretary (Political/Information):
A R Penrith
Assistant Military Adviser (Technical):
Lieutenant Colonel C E E Sloan
Assistant Defence Adviser: Major B R Lawson
Head of Secretariat BDLS:
Squadron Leader A McPhee, RAF
Third Secretary (Political/Information):
Miss P A Hadley
Third Secretary (Consular): A C Perks
Third Secretary (Commercial): M D Doig

Halifax
British Consulate
PO Box 310, Station M
Halifax, Nova Scotia, B3J 3N2
(Tel: (902) 429-4230)
(Telex: 019-21587 (a/b Chandler))
Facsimile: 902 423 8548

Honorary Consul: L Straughan

St John's
British Consulate
113 Topsail Road
St John's, Newfoundland A1E 2A9
(Tel: (1) (709) 579-2002
(Facsimile: (1) (709) 579-0475

Honorary Consul: F D Smith

Winnipeg
British Consulate
111 Aldershot Boulevard, Winnipeg,
Manitoba R3P OE2
(Tel: (204) 896 1380)
(Facsimile: (204) 896-1239

Honorary Consul: J R Hignell

Montreal
British Consulate General
Suite 901, 1155 University Street, Montreal,
Quebec, H3B 3A7
(Tel: (514) 866-5863)
(Telex: 055-61224) (a/b BRITAIN MTL)
(Telegraphic Address: BRITCON MTL)
(Facsimile: (1) (514) 866 0202)

Consul-General: A R Clark
Consul (Commercial): D Herbert
Vice-Consul (Commercial): M Clark

Toronto
British Consulate-General
Suite 1910, College Park, 77 Bay Street, Toronto,
Ontario, M5G 2G2
(Tel: (416) 593-1290)
(Telex: 06524486) (a/b BRITAIN TOR)
(Telegraphic Address: BRITCON TORONTO)
(Facsimile: 416 593 1229)

Consul-General and Director-General of Trade Promotion in Canada: P D R Davies
Deputy Consul-General: T N Guina
Vice-Consul (Commercial): M J Dwyer
Vice-Consul (Commercial/Consular/Management):
R Whitehead

Vancouver
British Consulate-General
Suite 800, 1111 Melville Street, Vancouver,
British Columbia, V6E 3V6
(Tel: (604) 683-4421)
(Telex: 04 51287) (a/b BRITAIN VCR)
Telegraphic Address: BRITCON
VANCOUVER
(Facsimile: (604) 681 0693)

Consul-General: A A Joy
Consul (Commercial): C R Boardman

CAPE VERDE

Praia (All staff reside at Dakar)

Ambassador: R C Beetham LVO
First Secretary and Deputy Head of Mission:
M J Hentley
Cultural Attaché (British Council Director):
Ms A Malamah-Thomas
Assistant British Council Director:
J M McCullough
Third Secretary (Chancery): Miss S H Jump
Third Secretary (Management) *and Vice-Consul:*
K J Lynch

CENTRAL AFRICAN REPUBLIC

Bangui (All staff reside at Yaoundé)

Ambassador and Consul-General: W E Quantrill
First Secretary (Commercial), *Deputy Head of Mission and Consul:* C A Hamilton
Second Secretary/Vice-Consul: R W Hyde, MBE
Cultural Attaché (British Council Director):
H Brookes

British Consulate
c/o SOCACIG, BP 728, Bangui
(Tel: 61 03 00, 61 10 45)
(Telex: 5258 RC)

Honorary Consul: X Lambert

CHAD

Ndjamena (Fort Lamy)
British Embassy (All staff reside at Yaoundé)

Ambassador and Consul-General: W E Quantrill
First Secretary, Consul and Deputy Head of Mission: C A Hamilton
Second Secretary and Vice-Consul: R Hyde

Cultural Attaché and British Council Director:
H Brookes

Ndjamena
British Consulate
Boite Postale 877, Ndjamena
(Tel: 51 30 64)
(Telex: ACT 5235 KD)

Honorary Consul: Mrs E Abtour

CHILE

Santiago
British Embassy
La Concepción 177 (Casilla 72-D or Casilla 16552), Santiago 9
(Tel: (010562) 22 39 166)
(Telex: 340483 (a/b 340483 BRITEMB CK))
(Facsimile: 460005 (British Council) 2231917 (Embassy))

Ambassador: R A Neilson, CMG, LVO
Counsellor, Consul-General and Deputy Head of Mission: R D Lavers
Defence, Naval and Military Attaché:
Captain R A Rowley, RN
Air Attaché: Group Captain B R Hoskins, RAF
First Secretary (Commercial): J V Everard
First Secretary (Chancery): (Vacant)
First Secretary: P H C Harris
Cultural Attaché (British Council Director):
W Campbell
Second Secretary (Information): J M O'Callaghan
Second Secretary (Commercial): M D Morley
Second Secretary (Management) *and Consul:*
N P Dickerson
Third Secretary (Chancery): K D Lyne

Arica
British Consulate
Baquedano 351 (Casilla 653), Arica
(Tel: (080) 31960)

Honorary Consul: Mrs G H Hulse

Concepción
British Consulate
Ongolmo 443 Depto 3, Casilla 452, Concepción.
(Tel: 222981)

Honorary Consul: Dr J F B Pomeroy

Punta Arenas
British Consul - Punta Arenas
Roca 924
Casilla 327
Punta Arenas
(Tel: (56)(061) 247020)
(Telex: 280004 ORVIL CL for Brit Consul)
(Facsimile: (56)(061) 228177)

Honorary Consul: J C Rees

Valparaíso
British Consulate
Errázuriz 730 (Casilla 82-V) Valparaíso
(Tel: 256117)
(Facsimile: 56-32 255365)

Honorary Consul: Mrs E A Kenrick, OBE
Acting Vice-Consul: Mrs M MaCauliffe, MBE

CHINA

Peking
11 Guang Hua Lu, Jian Guo Men Wai, Peking, 100600
(Tel: Peking 5321961/5, 5321930, 5321938/9, 5322011, Ansaphone 5322011) (Telex: 22191 (a/b PRDRM CN)
Facsimile: (86)(1) 532 1939

Ambassador: Sir Robin McLaren, KCMG
Minister Consul General and Deputy Head of Mission: P A McLean
Counsellor (Political): D Coates
Counsellor (Commercial): A Kerfoot
Counsellor (Cultural): A D Johnson, CBE
Counsellor (Head of China Trade Unit) (resides at Hong Kong): J Smith-Laittan
Defence, Military and Air Attaché:
Colonel M T P M Hyland, OBE
Naval Attaché: Commander A B P Armstrong, RN
First Secretary (Management) E Loader, MVO
First Secretary and Consul: M M M Henderson
First Secretary (Chancery): Miss S E Morton
First Secretary (Cultural ELO): J D Stoddart
First Secretary (Energy): J M Candlish
First Secretary (Cultural South China) (Resides in Hong Kong): M S Davidson
First Secretary (Cultural/Science):Dr G Alexander
First Secretary (Commercial/Development): Ms C Y Haworth
First Secretary (Commercial) (Resides at Hong Kong): R M J O Graham
First Secretary (Commercial) (Resides at Hong Kong): D J Currie
First Secretary (Chancery): P Clark
First Secretary (Cultural-Books): C C Edwards
First Secretary (Chancery): Miss J E Rogan
Second Secretary (Commercial): P E Rose
Second Secretary (Commercial): Miss S Eldred
Second Secretary: T M Collard
Second Secretary: Mrs F J Weaver
Second Secretary: S Lea
Second Secretary (Cultural-Exchanges):
Dr P W C Hart
Second Secretary (Cultural/Scholarships):
A Hadley
Second Secretary (Cultural-Assistant ELO):
G Slaven
Second Secretary (Cultural-Management/Arts):
Ms C McVeigh
Second Secretary (Chancery/Information):
B J Davidson
Second Secretary (Chancery): Miss J S Hannah
Second Secretary (Consular): R A Coleman
Third Secretary (Management): K R Carter
Third Secretary (Commercial): Miss S J Cockel
Third Secretary: A E Madisons

Shanghai
British Consulate-General
244 Yong Fu Lu

Shanghai 20031
(Tel: 4330508 (4 lines) and 4374569 (1 line))
(Telex: 33476 (a/b BRIT CN))
Cable Address: Britain Shanghai
(Facsimile: (021) 4330498)

Consul-General: J W MacDonald
Consul (Commercial): I B Wellfare
Consul (Cultural): P N Grout, OBE
Vice-Consul: J W Short

COLOMBIA

Bogotá
British Embassy
Torre Propaganda Sancho,
Calle 98 No 9-03 Piso 4,
Bogotá
(Tel: 218 51 11)
Air Mail Box 4508
(Telex: 044503) (a/b 44503 BRIT CO)
(Facsimile: 218 2460)

Ambassador: K E H Morris, CMG
First Secretary, Consul and Deputy Head of Mission: P W Chandley, MVO
Defence Attaché: Colonel J D Griffiths-Eyton, MBE
First Secretary (Commercial): (Vacant)
First Secretary (Resident in Lima): D Logan
Second Secretary, (Chancery/Technical Cooperation): A F Bedford
Management Officer and Vice-Consul: . Miss D E Gordon
Third Secretary and Vice-Consul: Miss M Lawler

Barranquilla
British Consulate
Carrera 44, No. 45-57 (Air Mail Box 706)
(Tel: 326936)
(Telex: 33559) (a/b 33559 HUTCH CO)

Honorary Consul: (vacant)
Vice-Consul: Miss M Hutchinson

Cali
British Consulate
Edificio Garcés Calle 11 No 1-07, Office No. 409, (Air Mail Box 1326)
(Tel: 83 2752/53, 86 1872)

Honorary Consul: A E B Laurence, CBE
Honorary Vice-Consul: M H Laurence

Medellin
British Consulate:
Calle 9 No 43B-93, Medellin
(Tel: 246-3114 or 6835)
(Telex: 65375 (a/b UNICO CO))
(Facsimile: 2667318)

Honorary Consul: Mr F Osorio

COMOROS

Moroni
British Embassy (Staff resident in Madagascar)

Ambassador: (vacant)
Second Secretary: C G R Poole

CONGO

Brazzaville
The Embassy closed on 26 July 1991

Pointe Noire
British Consulate
British Petroleum Development Ltd
ave Marien Ngouabi, Boite Postale, 1181 Pointe Noire
(Tel: (242) 94 39 88)
(Telex: 8443 KG)
Facsimile (242) 94 39 90

Honorary Consul: J Perry

COSTA RICA

San José
British Embassy
Apartado 815, Edificio Centro Colón, 1007 (11th Floor) San José 1007 (Tel: 21.55.66, 21.57.16, 21.58.16)
(Telex: 2169) (a/b 2169 PRODROM CR)
Facsimile (506) 339938

Ambassador and Consul-General: Miss M L Croll
First Secretary, Consul and Deputy Head of Mission: R J Hutchings
First Secretary (Commercial) *and Director of Trade Promotion for Central America:* A S Green, OBE, MVO
Defence Attaché (Resides at Panama City): Lieutenant Colonel T A Glen
Third Secretary (Technical Assistance/Management Offieer) *and Vice-Consul:* Mrs E A Kehoe

COTE D'IVOIRE (see IVORY COAST)

CROATIA

Zagreb
British Embassy
Ilica 12/II, PO Box 454 4100 Zagreb
(Tel: (38) (41) 424 888, 426 200)
(Telex: 21309 (a/b 21309 BRZAG CRO)
(Facsimile: (38) (41) 420 100

Ambassador: B Sparrow, CMG
Second Secretary (Commercial):˙ F J McGinley
Second Secretary (Management/Consular): Miss G E A Agnew
Honorary Consul: B Jenkins

Split
British Consulate
Titova Obala 10/III, 58000 Split
(Tel: (058) 41-464)
(Telex: 26497 (a/b 26497 BRSPL YU))
Honorary Consul: Captain A Mekjavić

Dubrovnik
British Consulate
Atlas, Pile 1, 50000 Dubrovnik
(Tel: 050/27333)
(Telex: 27515 (a/b 27515 ATLAS YU))

Honorary Consul: (vacant)

CUBA

Havana
British Embassy
Edificio Bolivar, Carcel 101-103, e Morro y
Prado, Apartado 1069, Havana
(Tel: (010 537) 62-3071. 3072, 3073, 3074, 3075)
(Telex: 511656) (a/b 511656 UKEMB CU)
(Telegrams: PRODROME HAVANA)

Ambassador: A L S Coltman
Deputy Head of Mission: The MacLaren of MacLaren
Defence, Naval, Military and Air Attaché (Resides
at Mexico City): Colonel A J Dobson
Second Secretary (Management): G W Brown
Second Secretary (Chancery): G J Knott

CYPRUS*

Nicosia
British High Commission
Alexander Pallis Street (PO Box 1978), Nicosia
or BFPO 567
(Tel: 2-473131/7)
(Telex: 2208) (a/b UKREPNIC CY)
(Facsimile: 357-2-367198)

High Commissioner: D J M Dain, CMG
Counsellor and *Deputy High Commissioner:* C B
Jennings
Counsellor: J S S Beels
Defence Adviser: Colonel J A Anderson
First Secretary (Chancery): N P Westgarth
First Secretary (Commercial): P J Newman
First Secretary (Consular/Management):
Miss J M Taylor
First Secretary (Information): R W Potter
First Secretary (Management) BEMRS: J A
Reeves
Second Secretary (Chancery): D H Craig
Second Secretary (Commercial): G A Mackay
Second Secretary (Chancery): P McGee
Third Secretary (Chancery): A S Patrick
Attaché (Consular): Mrs J M C Banks
Attaché (Management): J P Banks

CZECHOSLOVAKIA

Prague
British Embassy
Thunovská 14, 125 50 Prague
(Tel: 533347/8/9, 533340, 533370)
Direct line to Consular/Visa Section: 536737
(Telex: 121011) (a/b 121011 PRDM C)
(Facsimile: (422) 539927)
Commercial Section: Jungmannova 30, 11000
Prague
(Tel: 224550/1, 226453/4)
(Telex: 122097 (a/b BCOM C))
(Facsimile: 220635)
Cultural Section: Narodni 10, 11000 Prague
(Tel: 203751/5)
(Telex: 294448 (a/b BCCZ C))
(Facsimile: 205863)

Ambassador: A D Brighty, CMG, CVO
Deputy Head of Mission: Miss C T Elmes
Counsellor (Economic): J G Dearlove

Defence and Military Attaché:
Lt Colonel W J Chesshyre
Air Attaché: Wing Commander R Foster, RAF
Cultural Attaché (British Council Director): W H
Jefferson, OBE
First Secretary (Commercial): J Cummins, MBE
First Secretary: W J C Meath-Baker
First Secretary (Medical) (resides in Warsaw):
Dr A C E Stacey
First Secretary (Management) *and Consul:*
D J Jackson
Assistant Cultural Attaché (British Council Deputy
Director): P de Quincey
Assistant Cultural Attaché: N Rawden Smith
Assistant Cultural Attaché (Bratislava): Mrs R
Hilhorst
Assistant Cultural Attaché: K Dharmasingham
Second Secretary (Commercial):
Miss H R Nellthorp
Second Secretary: M J Gunnett
Second Secretary: Ms C F M Blair
Second Secretary (Chancery): M H Tatham
Third Secretary (Political/Economic): N M Baker
Third Secretary (Management): Miss E M
Hancock

DENMARK

Copenhagen
British Embassy
Kastelsvej 36/38/40 DK-2100 Copenhagen, Ø
(Tel: 31 26 46 00)
(Telex: 19908 (a/b 19908 BRIEMB DK))
(Telex: (Commercial Dept) 19908 (a/b 19908
BRIEMB DK))
(Facsimile: 31 381012; Commercial Dept 35
431400)
Cultural Section (British Council)
Møntergade 1, DK-1116 Copenhagen, K
(Tel: 33 11 20 44)
(Facsimile: 33 32 15 01)

Ambassador: N C R Williams, CMG
Counsellor and Head of Chancery: P S Astley
Counsellor (Commercial/Economic):
A M Layden
Defence Attaché: Commander R Kirkwood, RN
Cultural Attaché (British Council Director):
M H Holcroft
First Secretary (Political/EC): W Whitton
First Secretary (Political/Information):
P B West
First Secretary (Political): R P Hamilton
First Secretary (Management) *and Consul:*
B Robertson
First Secretary (Commercial):
Mr C P de L Haslam
First Secretary (Economic): S C Parris
Second Secretary (Political): Miss J M Crosland
Third Secretary: P S Stevenson
Third Secretary (Political): Miss D E McKelvey
Attaché (Vice-Consul): Miss R Cooper

Aabenraa
British Consulate
Søndergade 24, DK 6200 Aabenraa
(Tel: (74) 62 30 85)

(Telex: 52115) (a/b UNION DK)
(Facsimile: (74) 62 92 87)

Honorary Consul: C Daus-Petersen (Danish)

Aalborg
British Consulate
Stationsmestervej 85, DK-9200 Aalborg SV
(Tel: 98 18 16 00)
(Telex: 69888 (a/b BLADT DK))
(Facsimile: 98 18 18 55)

Honorary Consul: J Bladt (Danish)

Aarhus
British Consulate
Havnegade 8, DK-8100, Aarhus
(Tel: 86 12 88 88)
(Facsimile: 86 13 50 98)

Honorary Consul: C R Herluf (Danish)

Esbjerg
British Consulate
Kanalen 1, DK-6700 Esbjerg
(Tel: 75 13 05 11)
(Telex: 54391) (a/b DBS DK)
(Facsimile: 75 13 03 19)

Honorary Consul: G Kragelund (Danish)

Fredericia
British Consulate
Vesthavnen, PO Box 235, DK-7000, Fredericia
(Tel: (75) 92 20 00)
(Telex: 51126) (a/b RAHFI DK)
(Facsimile: (75) 91 02 13)

Honorary Consul: M Rahbek Hansen (Danish)

Herning
British Consulate
Orebygaardvej 3-7 7400 Herning
(Tel: 97 26 88 01)
(Telex: 62188 (a/b Jensen dk))
(Facsimile: 97 26 88 26)

Honorary Consul: N C Jensen (Danish)

Nuuk/Godthaab (Greenland)
British Consulate
Royal Greenland, Vestervig 45, Postbox 1073,
3900 Nuuk, Greenland (Tel: 2 44 22)
(Telex: 90437 proghb gd)
(Facsimile: 2 24 09)

Honorary Consul: Mr O Ramlau-Hansen (Danish)

Odehse
British Consulate
Albanitorv 4, DK 5000 Odense, C
(Tel: (66) 14 47 14)
(Facsimile: 66 14 61 30)

Honorary Consul: F Niegel (Danish)

Rønne (Bornholm)
British Consulate
Fiskerivej 1, DK-3700 Rønne
(Tel: 56 95 21 11)
(Telex: 48137) (a/b 48137 ESPROE)
(Facsimile: 56 95 25 67)

Honorary Consul: H Espersen (Danish)
Tórshavn (Faroe Islands)
British Consulate
Yviri vid Strond 19, FR-110 Tórshavn
(PO Box 49)
(Tel: 13510)
(Telex: 81259) (a/b MARRCO DK)
(Facsimile: 11318)

Honorary Consul: J Mortensen (Faroese)

DJIBOUTI

British Embassy
Ambassador (Resident at Sana'a): M A Marshall

Djibouti
British Consulate
Gellatly Hankey et Cie,
Post Box 81, Djibouti
(Tel: 355718)
(Telex: 5843 (a/b GELLATLY 5843 DJ))
(Facsimile: 353294)

Honorary Consul: P Lieven
Honorary Vice Consul: P Miller

DOMINICA*

Roseau
British High Commission
Lower Collymore Rock (PO Box 676),
Bridgetown, Barbados
(Tel: (0101 809) 436 6694)
(Telex: WB 2219 (a/b 2219 UKREP BRI WB))
(Telegraphic Address: UKREP BARBADOS)
(Facsimile: 426 7916)

High Commissioner (Resides at Bridgetown):
E T Davies, CMG
Deputy High Commissioner (Resides at
Bridgetown): J A Noakes
Defence Adviser (Resides at Kingston):
Colonel C S Faith, OBE
Assistant Defence Adviser (Resides at
Bridgetown): Commander H M Humphreys, RN
First Secretary (Resides at Bridgetown):
A ffrench-Blake, OBE
Second Secretary (Management/Consular) (Resides
at Bridgetown): Miss S Kaye
Second Secretary (Chancery) (Resides at
Bridgetown): P G McCrudden
Second Secretary (Resides at Kingston):
G Atkinson
Third Secretary (Immigration) (Resides at
Bridgetown): Mrs A A Howard

Roseau
British Consulate
PO Box 6
Roseau

(Tel: 448 1000)
(Facsimile: 448 1110)
(Telex: 8610)

Hon Consul: D J Calvert

DOMINICAN REPUBLIC

Santo Domingo
British Embassy (all staff resident in Caracas)

Ambassador: G E Fitzherbert, CMG
Counsellor and Deputy Head of Mission:
M Hickson, OBE
Defence Attaché: Captain R L Perrett, RN
First Secretary (Commercial): C Dresser
Second Secretary: A R Heyn
Second Secretary (Consul): A R J Attryde

British Consulate
Saint George School,
Abraham Lincoln 552,
Santo Domingo DR
(Tel: 5015 or 5010)
(Telex: 3460781)
(Facsimile: (531) 562 5015)

Honorary Consul: Mrs M Tejeda, MBE

Santo Domingo
British Consulate
Apartado Postal 30341, Av Rómulo Betancourt
1302 Apto 202
(Tel: (809) 532 4216)
(Facsimile: 541 1100)

Honorary Vice-Consul (Commercial):
Mr F G Nicolás

Puerto Plata
British Consulate
Beller 51, No 2
(PO Box 312)
Puerto Plata
(Office Tels: (531) 586 4244)
(Facsimile: (531) 586 3096)

Honorary Vice-Consul: D M Salem

ECUADOR

Quito
British Embassy
Calle Gonzalez Suarez, 111 (Casilla 314), Quito
(Tel: 560669, 560670, 560671, 560 309, 560 755,
236867) (Telex: 308-02-2138) (a/b 2138 PRODQT
ED)
(Facsimile: (593) (2) 560730 560729
Administration and Consular Sections: Calle
Gonzalez Suarez 197 (Tel: 237 363 (direct line))

Ambassador: F B Wheeler, CMG
Head of Chancery and Consul: G J C Pirnie
Defence, Naval, Military and Air Attaché:
Group Captain J V Ball, CBE, RAF
First Secretary (Commercial): M J McLoughlin

Second Secretary (Commercial/Aid): *M G Dun*
Cultural Attaché (British Council Director):
D F M Lauder
Third Secretary (Economic/Technical
Cooperation): Mrs C R Blake
Third Secretary (Management) *and Vice-Consul:*
J C Chick

Guayaquil
British Consulate
General Córdova 623 y Urdaneta
(Casilla 8598), Guayaquil
(Telephone: 300-400)
(Telex: 3379)

Honorary Consul: C R Armstrong
Honorary Vice-Consul: X N Velasquez
Cuenca
British Consulate
Plazoleta Pedro Toulop
Pasaje San Alfonso (between Borrero and Hermano
Miguel), Planto Baja Cuenca
(Tel: (07) 831 996)
(Telex: 48565 (TEOJER ED))
(Facsimile: 832 430)

Honorary Consul: T Jerves Núñez

Galápagos
British Consulate
c/o Etica Office, Barrio Estrado, Puerto Ayora,
Isla Santo Cruz, Galápagos
(Tel: Telephone messages to Galápagos have to be
passed over a radio link via Etica office in
Guayaquil, Tel: (04) 284 666)

Honorary Consul: D E Balfour

EGYPT

Cairo
British Embassy
Ahmed Ragheb Street, Garden City, Cairo
(Tel: 354-0850, 354-0852/9)
(Telex: 94188 (a/b UKEMB UN))
(Facsimile: 354 0859)

Ambassador: C W Long, CMG
Deputy Head of Mission: A F Goulty
Counsellor (Chancery): D T Handley
Defence and Military Attaché:
Colonel E A J Gardener
Naval Attaché: Commander P G Blanchford, RN
Air Attaché: Wing Commander B C Hunt, RAF
Cultural Attaché (British Council Director):
J J Barnett
First Secretary (Political): Mrs A Aitken
First Secretary: S A Bassnett, MBE
First Secretary (Arab League): A A S Lines
First Secretary and Consul (M):
Miss A M M Sheldon
First Secretary (Commercial): I S Lockhart, MBE
First Secretary (Management): S N Lee, MBE
First Secretary (Cultural): Dr D J F Burton
Second Secretary (Commercial):
H Lattin-Rawstone
Second Secretary (Chancery): M C Day

Second Secretary (Cultural): Miss S McCreadie
Second Secretary (Political/External): M P Sedwill
Deputy Management Officer and Claims Attaché:
A T Holmes
Second Secretary (Works): J Ritchie, MBE
Attaché and Vice-Consul: D G Atkinson
Attaché and Vice-Consul: C Blanks
Attaché and Vice-Consul: H Holmes
Attaché and Vice-Consul: S B Smart

Alexandria
British Consulate-General
3 Mina Street, Kafra Abdou, Roushdi, Alexandria,
21529 (Tel: 5467001, 5467002)
(Telex: 54578 (a/b 54578 BRITN UN))
(Facsimile: 5467177)

Consul-General (M): D L Brett
Consul (Cultural Affairs): D K E Scott

Luxor
Office of the British Honorary Consular Agent
1, Nile Street, Luxor
(Tel: 382360, 382262, 383262 Office, 382374,
386244, 383155 Consulate)
(Telex: 23604 PBLXR UN)

Honorary Consul Agent: M H Y El Haggagy

Port Said
British Consulate
Hilton Compound Complex, 6 Room 623,
Port Said
(Tel: 231155 Consulate, 226963 Office)
(Telex: 63400 ATOUT UN)

Honorary Consul: Fathi Atout

Suez
British Consulate
HS Supply Co. 9 El-Galaa Street, Suez
(Tel: Suez 220145, 225382 Consulate and Office)
(Telex: 66112 DAHSS UK)

Honorary Consul: Dr Hussein Samir

EL SALVADOR

San Salvador
British Embassy, Paeso Gral. Escalón,
San Salvador (PO Box 1591)
(Tel: 24 04 73, 23 96 39, 23 90 47)
(Telex: 20033 (a/b 20033 PRODROME))
(Facsimile: 503 235817)

Ambassador and Consul-General: M H Connor
First Secretary (Commercial) *and Director of*
Trade Promotion for Central America (Resides at
San José): A S Green, OBE, MVO
Defence Attaché (Resides at Panama City):
Lieutenant Colonel T A Glen
Third Secretary and Vice-Consul: D J B Torrance

EQUATORIAL GUINEA

Malabo
Ambassador and Consul-General (Resident at
Yaoundé): W E Quantrill
Second Secretary (Commercial) *and Consul*
(Resident at Douala): D A Pearce

British Consulate
World Bank Compound, Apartado 801, Malabo
(Tel: 2400)
(Telex: 5403)
(a/b AFRIBK 5403 EG)

Honorary Consul: (Vacant)

ESTONIA

Talinn
British Embassy
Kentmanni 20
Talinn EE0001
(Tel: (7)(0142) 455328/9 353/4)
(Telex: 17394 (A/B PRODO))
(Facsimile: 010 358 298 107)

Ambassador: B B Low

ETHIOPIA

Addis Ababa
British Embassy
Fikre Mariam Abatechan Street
(Tel: 61 2354, 2305, 2307, 2309)
Postal Address (all Departments) PO Box 858
(Telex 21299 (a/b PROAD ET))

Ambassador: M J C Glaze, CMG
Deputy Head of Mission: J C W Kidd
Cultural Attaché (British Council Director):
M B L Nightingale, OBE
First Secretary: A J Barber
Assistant Cultural Attaché (British Council):
Ms R Arnott
Second Secretary (Management) *and Consul:*
R Field
Second Secretary (Aid/Commercial): D S Carter
Second Secretary (Chancery/Information):
Mrs C J Barber
Attaché: P B Holmes
Attaché and Vice-Consul: Mrs C F Unutulmaz

FIJI

Suva
British Embassy *(From 1st March 1988, the British
High Commission became the British Embassy)*
Victoria House, 47 Gladstone Road, Suva
(PO Box 1355)
(Tel: 311033)
(Telex: FJ 2129) (a/b 2129 PRODROME FJ)
(Telegrams: PRODROME SUVA)
(Facsimile: 679 301406)

*Ambassador also UK Alternate Representative for
the South Pacific Commission:* T J David
(Also non-resident High Commissioner to Nauru
and to Tuvalu).
*First Secretary, Deputy Head of Mission and
Consul:* D J Noble
Defence Attaché (Resides at Wellington):
Group Captain D W F Angela, RAF
Second Secretary (Aid): Mrs A C Hamilton-Walker
Vice Consul (Consular/Management): R Hunter

British Development Division in the Pacific
Vanua House Victoria Parade
(Private Mail Bag) Suva
(Tel: 301744)
(Telex: FJ 2289 (a/b BDDP SUVA))
(Facsimile: (679) 301 218)

Head of Division: Mrs P Wilkinson
Senior Programme Officer: Mrs G B Wright
Senior Natural Resources Adviser: D Salmon
Economic Adviser: J Clarke
Education and Training Adviser (British Council
Director): G P Thompson
Regional Fisheries Adviser: Dr N Willoughby
Finance and Management Adviser: L Wright
Architectural Adviser: D Collins
Higher Executive Officer: G J Saggers
Executive Officer: Mrs M Morrison

FINLAND

Helsinki
British Embassy
Itainen Puistotie 17, 00140 Helsinki
(Tel: 90-661293)
(Telefax: 90-661342 661943, 630 825)
(Telex: 121122)

Ambassador: G N Smith, CMG
Counsellor (Commercial) *and Deputy Head of
Mission:* N A Thorne
Defence Attaché: Lieutenant-Colonel F A B
Clement, RA
Counsellor (Hong Kong Trade Affairs) (resident in
London): P A S Wise
First Secretary (Commercial): V J Henderson
First Secretary: R P Campbell
First Secretary: R M F Kelly
Assistant Naval Attaché (Resides at Moscow):
Lieutenant Commander S E Airey, RN
Assistant Air Attaché (Resides at Moscow):
Squadron Leader A W Kerr, RAF
First Secretary, Management Officer *and Consul:*
N J Kelly
First Secretary (Commercial): R Norton
Second Secretary (Information/Political): W G Clare
Second Secretary (Commercial): J Taylor
Third Secretary, (Management) *and Vice-Consul:*
R Thain

Jyväskylä
British Consulate
Valmet Paper Machinery Inc.,
PO Box 587, SF 40101
Jyväskylä
(Tel: 295 211)
(Telex: 28213 (a/b VALRP SF))

Honorary Consul: E A Leivo (Finnish)

Kotka
British Consulate
Port Authority of Kotka, Laivurinkatu 7, 48100
Kotka
(Tel: 274 280)
(Telex: 53144)

Honorary Consul: E I Elo (Finnish)

Kuopio
British Consulate
Kuopio Chamber of Commerce, Kasarmikatu 2,
70100 Kuopio
(Tel: 220 291)
(Telex: 223 304)

Honorary Consul: O Jääskeläinen (Finnish)

Mariehamn
British Consulate
Södragatan 16 B4
22100 Mariehamn Aland Islands
(Tel: 16620, 28439)
(Facsimile: 16901)

Honorary Consul: Dr P Darby

Oulu
British Consulate
Rautaruukki Oy, PO Box 217,
Kiilakiventie 1, SF 90101 Oulu.
(Tel: 327711)
(Telex: 32109)

Honorary Consul: A V A Saarinen (Finnish)

Pori
British Consulate
Repola Oy, PL51, Antinkatu 2, PO Box 69, 28101
Pori
(Tel: 823007)
(Telex: 66155 RLEWO)

Honorary Consul: T J Hiillos (Finnish)

Tampere
British Consulate
Oy Finlayson AB, PL 407, 33101 Tampere
(Tel: 35222)
(Telex: 22170 FINTA SF)

Honorary Consul: H C Sucksdorff (Finnish)

Turku
British Consulate
Turun Kauppakamari, Puolalankatu 1, Turku
(Tel: 501 440)
(Telex: 62114)

Honorary Consul: S-O Hansen (Finnish)

Vaasa (Vasa)
British Consulate
Royal Waasa Hotel, Hovioikeudenpuistikko 18,
65100 Vaasa
(Tel: 278 111)
(Telex: 74193)

Honorary Consul: R Grönblom (Finnish)

FRANCE

Paris
British Embassy
35 rue du Faubourg St Honoré, 75383 Paris
Cedex 08
(Tel: (1) 42 66 91 42)
(Telex: 650264) (a/b INFORM 650264F)
(Commercial and Information Departments),
650287 (a/b VISA PARIS) (Facsimile: (1) 42 66
95 90)

Ambassador: Sir Ewen Fergusson, GCVO, KCMG
Minister: J R Young, CMG
Defence and Air Attaché:
Air Commodore C Adams, AFC, RAF
Military Attaché: Brigadier J F Rickett, OBE
Naval Attaché: Captain M A Johnson
Counsellor and Head of Chancery:
J M Macgregor
Counsellor (Cultural) (British Council Director): D
T Ricks, OBE
Counsellor: B P Noble
Counsellor (Management): P A McDermott
Counsellor (Technology): Dr R A Pullen
Counsellor (Information): R D Wilkinson
Counsellor (Financial and European Community):
C D Crabbie
Counsellor (Director of Trade Promotion and
Investment): R A Kealy, CMG
First Secretary and Consul-General:
Miss M E Hunt
First Secretary (Labour): Miss A R I Wilkins
First Secretary: N Marden
First Secretary (Technology): Dr J Hodges
First Secretary (Commercial): N J Paget
First Secretary (Aviation and Defence Supply):
Miss S T Lindsay
First Secretary: Miss C A Macqueen
First Secretary (Chancery): Dr V Caton
First Secretary: M J Lyall Grant
First Secretary: N E Trape
First Secretary: M A Runacres
First Secretary (Economic): Dr N M Brewer
First Secretary (Technology): Dr J Hodges
First Secretary and Consul: J H L Lacey
First Secretary (Economic/Financial): D G Roberts
First Secretary (Technology): K T Walker
First Secretary: Miss F Paterson
First Secretary (Management): A J Smith
First Secretary (Works): J I S Maclean
First Secretary (Agriculture): N F G Strang
First Secretary (British Council Deputy Director):
P D R Ellwood
Assistant Naval Attaché (Technical):
Commander P A C Lockwood, RN
Assistant Military Attaché (Technical):
Lieutenant-Colonel M G Felton
Assistant Air Attaché (Technical):
Wing Commander G W Cunningham, RAF
Second Secretary (Labour): Miss L Bridson
Second Secretary (Commercial): B W West
Second Secretary (Management): P F Wilkie
Second Secretary (Private Secretary to
Ambassador): Miss S Tiffin
Second Secretary (Science and Technology):
M J Ward
Second Secretary: D J Cockshott
Second Secretary (Economic): Miss S Gillett

Bordeaux
British Consulate General
353 Boulevard du President Wilson, 33073
Bordeaux Cedex
(Tel: 56 42 34 13)
(Telex: 570440) (a/b BRITAIN 570440F)
(Facsimile: 56 08 33 12)

Consul-General: T C Almond, OBE
Vice-Consul (Commercial): A Roberts, MBE
Vice-Consul: P M Dixon

Biarritz
British Consulate
Barclays Bank SA
7 Avenue Edward VII, BP98
64202 Biarritz Cedex
(Tel: 59 24 04 60)
(Telex: 570004)
(Facsimile: 59 24 46 34)

Honorary Consul: R F M Hope

Toulouse
British Consulate
c/o Lucas Aerospace Victoria Centre, Bâtiment
Didier Daurat, 20 Chemin de Laporte, 31300
Toulouse
(Tel: 61 15 02 02 (Consulate))
(Facsimile: 61 15 08 92 (Lucas Aerospace))

Honorary Consul: R H Virnuls

Lille
British Consulate-General
11 Square Dutilleul, 59800 Lille
(Tel: 20 57.87.90)
(Telex: 120169) (a/b BRITAIN 120169F)
(Facsimile: 20 54 88 16)

Consul-General: D M Bell
Vice-Consul (Commercial): J Gleave
Vice-Consul (Commercial): D A Hinchliffe
Vice-Consul: Mrs C Vorobieff

Calais
British Consulate
c/o P&O European Ferries
41, Place d'Armes
62100 Calais Cédex
(Tel: 21 96 33 76)
(Telex: 810750 (a/b POEFCAT))

Honorary Consul: J M Inglis

Boulogne-sur-Mer
British Consulate
c/o Cotrama, Tour Administrative, Hoverport,
62201 Boulogne-sur-Mer Cedex
(Tel: 21 87.16.80)
(Telex: 135585)

Honorary Consul: S G Ellis

Dunkirk
British Consulate
c/o L Dewulf Cailleret & Fils (1st Floor), 11 Rue
des Arbres, BP 1502, 59383 Dunkerque
(Tel: 28 66.11.98)
(Telex: 820911 LDCF)

Honorary Consul: C R Baker

Lyon
British Consulate-General
24 rue Childebert, 69002 Lyon
(Tel: 78.37.59.67 (4 lines))
(Telex: 330254 F (a/b BRITLYO 330254 F))
(Facsimile: 72 40 25 24)

Consul-General: G P Lockton
Vice-Consul (Commercial): G B Romaine
Vice-Consul: B R Bubb
Pro-Consul: Mrs N M S Contreras

Marseille
British Consulate-General
24 Avenue du Prado, 13006 Marseille
(Tel: 91 53.43.32)
(Telex: 420307) (a/b BRITAIN MARSL)
(Facsimile: 91 37 47 06)

Consul-General: J Illman, (also Consul-General
for Principality of Monaco)
Vice-Consul: Miss A L Lupo, MBE
Vice-Consul (Commercial): J J Patanchon

Nice
British Consulate
2 rue du Congres, 06000 Nice
(Tel: 93 82.32.04)

Honorary Consul (for Nice and the Principality of
Monaco): Vacant

Paris
British Consulate-General
9 Avenue Hoche, 75008 Paris (All mail should be
addressed to the British Embassy
(Tel: (1) 42.66.38.10)
(Telex: 281715) (a/b VISA 281715 F) 651018 (a/b
Consul)
(Facsimile: 40760287

Consul-General: Miss M E Hunt
Consul: J H L Lacey
Vice-Consul: F Jones
Vice-Consul: Mrs J H Gillespie
Vice-Consul: S Rebecchi
Vice-Consul: N R Heath

Cherbourg
British Consulate
P & O European Ferries, Gare Maritime Sud,
50104, Cherbourg
(Tel: 33.44.20.13)
(Telex: 170765 (a/b TTCF 170765 F))

Honorary Consul: G R Caron

French Guiana
British Consulate
16 Avenue Président Monnerville, Cayenne
(Tel: Office (594) 311034 or 31-0511, Home
(594) 311303) (Telex: NCH 910365 FG)
(Facsimile: (594) 304094)

Honorary Consul: G Nouh-Chaia, MBE

French Polynesia (Papeete)
British Consulate
Propriété Boubée, Route Tuterai Tane,
Pirae, Tahiti BP1064 Papeete Tahiti
(Tel: 428457 or 424355)
(Telex: 537 FP PTE Att. Withers)
(Facsimile: 689 41 08 47 Att. Withers)

Honorary Consul: R J Withers

Le Havre
British Consulate
Lloyds Register of Shipping, 7 rue Pierre
Brossolette, 76600 Le Havre
(Tel: 35 42 42 15 & 35 42 27 47)
(Telex: 771303 a/b LLOYREG F)
(Fax: 35 21 47 56)

Honorary Consul: K R Dagnall

Nantes
British Consulate
L'Aumarière, 44220 Couëron
(Tel: 40 63 16 02)
(Telex: 700147 (a/b Westbank Nantes))

Honorary Consul: M C V Chevalier, MBE
Honorary Vice-Consul: Mrs E Chevalier

St Malo-Dinard
British Consulate
"La Hulotte'', 8 Avenue de la Libération,
35800 Dinard
(Tel: 99 46 26 64)
(Telex: 950311 (JERSAIR 950311F))

Honorary Consul: R Frankel, MBE

Martinique (Fort de France)
British Consulate
Habitation Morne l'Etoile, Le Parnasse,
97250 St Pierre
Route du Phare 97200 Fort de France
Martinique
(Tel: 59 6 615630)
(Telex: SERGIO 912729 MR)
(Facsimile: 596 613389)

Honorary Consul: Mrs A J Ernoult

Guadeloupe (Pointe à Pitre)
British Consulate
BP 2041, Zone Industrielle de Jarry,
97192 Pointe à Pitre Cedex, Guadeloupe
(Tel: 26.64.29)
(Telex: OUVRE 019779 GL)
(Telegraphic Address: William Boyd, Pointe à
Pitre, Guadeloupe)

Honorary Consul: W G A Boyd, OBE

Réunion
British Consulate
136 Chemin Neuf,
97417 La Montagne,
Réunion
(Tel: 210619)
(Telex: MARYL 916104 RE)

Honorary Consul: L M P Gaud

GABON

Libreville
The Embassy closed on 26 July 1991

THE GAMBIA*

Banjul
British High Commission
48 Atlantic Road, Fajara (PO Box 507), Banjul
(Tel: 95133, 95134, 95578)
(Telex: 2211) (a/b UKREP GV2211)
(Facsimile: 96134)

High Commissioner: A J Pover, CMG
Deputy High Commissioner: R W Saunders
Defence Adviser (resides at Rabat):
Lieutenant Colonel C A Le Hardy
Third Secretary (Management/Consular):
P Cartwright
Aid Attaché: Miss P McKeown

GEORGIA

Tbilisi
British Embassy, Moscow 72,
Sosiiskaya Naberezhnaya
(Tel: (010)(70095) 231 8511 (8 lines)
(Facsimile: (010(70095) 233 3563

Ambassador (resides at Moscow): Sir Brian Fall,
KCMG

GERMANY

Bonn
British Embassy
Friedrich-Ebert-Allée 77, 5300 Bonn 1
(Tel: 23-40-61)
(Telex: 886 887) (a/b BRINF-D)
(Facsimile: (228) 234070, 237058)

Ambassador: Sir Christopher Mallaby, KCMG
Minister: J A Shepherd, CMG
Defence and Military Attaché:
Colonel P P Rawlens, MBE
Air Attaché: Air Commodore W M Craghill, RAF
Naval Attaché: Captain R St J S Bishop, RN
Military Attaché: Colonel N S Hunter
Counsellor (Economic): D S Broucher
Counsellor and Head of Chancery: C R Budd, CMG
Counsellor (Bilateral Relations): J R Bruce-Lockhart
Counsellor (Science and Technology): DE Lyscom
Counsellor (Political/Military): G G Wetherell
Counsellor (Management and Consular): PV Rollitt
Counsellor (Labour): J Franklin
Counsellor (Defence Supply): Miss A Walker
First Secretary: (Information): Mrs J I Link
First Secretary (Legal Adviser): P A Waterworth
First Secretary: (Economic): R Kershaw
First Secretary (Defence Supply): Miss V J Evans
First Secretary (Science and Technology):
T H Carter
First Secretary (Agriculture): D J Greig
First Secretary (Economic): Ms J Darby
First Secretary (Management): R Milburn
First Secretary: S T Wordsworth
First Secretary (Economic): D R Todd
First Secretary (Political): J E T Lewis

First Secretary (Bilateral Relations): B A Collings
Assistant Naval Attaché (Technical):
Lieutenant-Commander J G Apps, RN
Second Secretary (Press and Information):
H Haig-Thomas
Second Secretary (Management):
Mrs S D Ingram
Second Secretary (Political): C W Ross
Second Secretary: I P Gibbins
Second Secretary (Political): Miss J Thompson
Second Secretary (Chancery): A Leví.
Second Secretary (Economic): S G McDonald
Second Secretary (Political): Miss S K Simon
Second Secretary (Political/Information):
W J Shapcott
Third Secretary: G C Peers
Third Secretary (Private Secretary): A M Bates

Berlin
British Embassy Berlin Office
Mail, from United Kingdom only, should be addressed:
British Embassy, Berlin Office, BFPO 45

British Embassy Berlin Office (Political)
Hanns-Braun-Str., W-1000 Berlin 19
(Tel: (49) (30) 3091)
(Telex: 185745) (a/b BER D)
(Facsimile: (49) (30) 305 0197) (Information Section)
305 0177 (Political Section)
304 4117 (Management Section)

Georgenstrasse, 35, 0-1080 Berlin
(Commercial and Economic Sections)
(Tel: (49) (30) 2643 1681 / (37) (2) 2096 1681
(Telex: —)
(Facsimile: (49) (30) 2643 1686 / (37) (2) 2096 1686)

Uhlandstrasse 7/8, W-1000 Berlin 12
(Consular Section)
(Tel: (49 30) 309 5292)
(Telex: 184268 (a/b UKBLN D))
(Facsimile: (49) (30) 312 3892

Unter den Linden 32/34 0-1080 BERLIN
(temporarily vacant)
(Tel: (49) (30) 391 9607

Minister: M St E Burton, CMG, CVO
Counsellor and Deputy Head of Mission:
Sir John Ramsden, Bt
Counsellor: M J Reynolds
First Secretary: H R Mortimer
First Secretary (Information): Miss B Brett-Rooks
First Secretary (Management): S G Attwood
First Secretary: Miss R Sharpe
First Secretary (Economic): D J Peate, OBE
First Secretary: P J Laing
First Secretary: O J Traylor
Second Secretary: R Healy
Second Secretary: I T Maynard
Second Secretary: Miss V Ewan
Second Secretary (Management): Miss J MacLeod
Second Secretary (Consular): A Sutton
Third Secretary (Commercial): Miss J M Wigzell
Third Secretary (Consular): R S Voyce

Stuttgart
British Consulate-General
Breite Strasse 2, 7000 Stuttgart 1
(Tel: (0711) 16 26 9-0)
(Telex: 722397 (a/b 722397 UKST D))
(Facsimile: (0711)16 26 9-30)

Consul General: D R Thomas
Senior Marketing Officer: W R Seidler
Vice-Consul: Miss E Crombie

Freiburg
British Consulate
Buchenstrasse 4, 7803 Gundelfingen
(Tel: 583117)

Honorary Consul: A C McCarthy

Düsseldorf
British Consulate-General
Yorck Strasse 19; 4000 Düsseldorf 30 (Mail from
United Kingdom only can be sent to BFPO 34)
(Tel: (49) (211) 94481)

Direct lines:
Passport Section: 9448 238
Visa Section: 9448 271
Commercial Section: 9448 292
Information Section: 9448 224

Telex:
Commercial & Information Section 8584855
(brlnd) Visa, Passport, Consular and Management
Sectios: 8587737

Facsimile:
Commercial Section: 48 63 59
Passport, Consular and Management
Sections: 48 81 90
Visa Section 48 86 03

Consul-General: (Director General for Trade
and Investment Promotion) A C Hunt, CMG
Consul (Commercial): W D Townend
Consul (Consular/Management): A A Windham
Consul (Commercial): R Embleton
Vice-Consul (Commercial): I C Sergeant
Vice-Consul (Management): R K Dixon
Vice-Consul (Consular): Miss H J Arthur
Vice-Consul (Consular): E J M Brown
Vice-Consul (Consular): Miss S J Clark
Vice-Consul (Commercial): H C von Massenbach
Vice-Consul (Commercial): G M Rogers
Vice-Consul (Visas): M J Carbine

Frankfurt
British Consulate-General
Triton Haus Bockenheimer Landstrasse 42, 6000
Frankfurt 1
(Tel: (069) 17 00 02 0)
(Telex: 414932) (a/b 414932 UKFFT D)
(Facsimile: 69 72 95 53)

Consul-General: C A Munro
Consul (Commercial): M M Hall
Vice-Consul (Consular/Management):
Ms M C Cross

Vice-Consul (Consular): F Ross
Vice-Consul (Commercial):Mrs R S Holmes, MBE
Vice-Consul (Investment): Dr S P Steiner
Information Officer: Dr W Dobler
Pro-Consul (Commercial): H Holman, MBE

Hamburg
British Consulate-General
Harvestehuder Weg 8a, 2000 Hamburg 13
(Tel: 446071)
(Telex: 213562) (a/b BRHBG D)
(Facsimile: 40 410 7259)

Consul-General: P Yarnold
Consul (Commercial): L Banks, OBE
Vice-Consul (Consular/Management):
R J Beeson
Vice-Consul (Consular): Mrs M Sanderson

Bremen
British Consulate
Herrlichkeiten 6, Postfach 10 38 60,
2800 Bremen 1
(Tel: 59090)
(Telex: 244 868 (a/b LS D))

Honorary Consul: Dr H-J Enge

Hanover
British Consulate
Berliner Allee 5, Hanover 1
(Tel: 0511 9919 100)
(Facsimile: 0511 9919 303)

Honorary Consul: Dr A Erdland

Kiel
British Consulate
United Baltic Corporation GmbH, Schleuse, PO
Box 8080, 2300 Kiel 17
(Tel: 0431 30632)
(Telex: 299829 (a/b UBCKD))
(Facsimile: 0431 35895)

Honorary Consul: I B Gibson

Munich
British Consulate-General
8000 Munich 22, Bürkleinstrasse 10
(Mail from the United Kingdom only should be
addressed: British Consulate-General, PO Box
2010, BFPO 105)
(Tel: (49 89) 211090
(Telex: No 529959) (a/b UKMUN D)
(Facsimile: Consul-General and Information
Section (49 89) 2110966
Commercial Section (49 89) 2110955
Management and Consular Section (49 89)
2110944

Consul-General: A P Ceurvorst, MBE
Consul (Commercial): C V Thompson
Consul: J Betts, OBE
Vice-Consul (Consular/Management):
Miss F M Murray
Information Officer: Mrs B I Dammert
Vice-Consul (Consular): Ms M I Blacklock, MBE

Vice-Consul (Commercial): N U Rothnie
Vice-Consul (Commercial): C Pattinson
Vice-Consul (Investment): Dr S P Steiner
Vice-Consul: H I Anderson

Nuremberg
British Consulate
c/o Schwan-Stabilo Schwanhausser GmbH & Co.,
PO Box 4553, 8500 Nuremberg, Maxfeld Str. 3
(Tel: 3609-522/521/520)
(Telex: 623162 (a/b SWAN D))

Honorary Consul: G Schwanhäusser

GHANA*

Accra
British High Commission
Osu Link, Off Gamel Abdul Nasser Avenue,
(PO Box 296), Accra
(Tel: (101 233 21) 221665, 221715, 221738,
221745, 669585)
(Telex: 2323 (a/b 2323 UKREP GH))
(Facsimile: 010 233 21 22 4572)

High Commissioner: D C Walker, CVO
Deputy High Commissioner: M J Greenstreet
Defence Adviser:
Lieutenant-Colonel T E A Hawkins, MBE
First Secretary (Political): S C E Holt
First Secretary (Management): Miss D J Walker
First Secretary (Commercial): S S Strong
First Secretary (Aid): Ms R B Stevenson
Second Secretary (Aid): A W Wilson
Second Secretary (Chancery/Information):
D J G Barton
Second Secretary (Consular): S M Pakes
Third Secretary: J M Lawrie
Third Secretary (Comm.): D P Goodall

GREECE

Athens
British Embassy
1, Ploutarchou Street, 106 75 Athens
(Tel: 7236211)
(Telex: 216440) (a/b 216440 LION GR)
(Facsimile: 7241 872)

Ambassador: Sir David Miers, KBE, CMG
*Counsellor, Consul-General and Deputy Head of
Mission:* R N Culshaw, MVO
Counsellor: N N Inkster
Defence and Military Attaché:
Colonel N M Prideaux
Naval and Air Attaché: Captain J J Pearson, RN
Counsellor (Cultural Affairs): Dr J L Munby, OBE
First Secretary (Political/Information):
Ms F C Mooore
First Secretary (Commercial): N J G Bowie
First Secretary (Management): I H Davies
First Secretary (Economic): P H Williams
First Secretary and Consul: D A McKellar
First Secretary (Cultural Affairs British Council
Deputy Director): B P Chenery, OBE
First Secretary (External): T I Priest

Second Secretary (Political/Information):
Miss K L Smith
Second Secretary: J Leonard
Second Secretary (Technical Works): R Clarke
Second Secretary (Economic): D M Landsman
Second Secretary (Economic): S J Wilson
Second Secretary: C J Henson
Third Secretary and *Vice Consul:* G D Beale
Third Secretary: R Steers
Third Secretary (Management): G S Evans
Third Secretary and Vice-Consul: J B Hedley

Corfu
British Consulate
2 Alexandras Avenue, 491 00 Corfu
(Tel: 0661-30.055, 37.995)
(Facsimile 0661 37995)

Consul: Mrs P Hughes

Crete
British *Vice*-Consulate
16 Papa-Alexandrou Street, 712 02 Heraklion
(Tel: 081-224 012)
(Facsimile: 081 243 935)

Vice-Consul: Mrs M Tzanaki

Patras
British Consulate
Post temporarily closed

Rhodes
British Consulate
11 Amerikas Street, (PO Box 47),
851 00 Rhodes
(Tel: 0241-27 247, 27 306)
(Facsimile: (30) (241) 22 615)

Honorary Consul: D E Demetriades, MBE

Salonika
British Consulate
8, Venizelou Street, Eleftheria Square, PO Box
10332, 541 10 Salonika
(Tel: 031-278.006, 269 984)
(Facsimile: (30) (31) 286 610

Honorary Consul: G K Doucas

Samos
British Vice-Consulate
Post temporarily closed

Syros
British Vice-Consulate
8 Akti P Ralli Ermoupolis, Syros 841 00
(Tel: 0281 22232/28922)
(Facsimile: (30) (281) 23 293)

Honorary Vice-Consul: Mrs V Parissi-Thermou

Volos
British Vice-Consulate
4 Iolkou Street Volos 382 21
(Tel: 0421 24642)
(Facsimile: (30) (421) 26 108)

Honorary Vice-Consul: V Anagnostou

GRENADA*

St George's
British High Commission
14 Church Street, St George's
Grenada.
(Tel: 440-3222, 440-3536)
(Telex: 3419 (a/b 3419 UKREP GA))
Telegraphic Address: UKREP GRENADA
(Facsimile: 440 4939)
(All staff resident at Bridgetown unless otherwise
shown)

High Commissioner: E T Davies, CMG
First Secretary and Resident Representative:
A H Drury (Resides in Grenada)
Deputy High Commissioner: J A Noakes
Defence Adviser (Resides at Kingston):
Colonel C S Faith, OBE
Assistant Defence Adviser:
Commander H M Humphreys, RN
First Secretary (Chancery): A ffrench-Blake, OBE
Second Secretary (Management/Consular):
Miss S Kaye
Second Secretary (Chancery/Information):
P G McCrudden
Second Secretary (Technical Works):
J I S McLean
Third Secretary: R M Hardy

GUATEMALA

Guatemala City
British Embassy
Ediicio Centro Financiero, (Seventh Floor),
Tower Two, 7a Avenida 5-10, Zona 4,
Guatemala
(Tel: 321601, 321602, 321604)
(Telex: 5686 BRITON GU)
(Telegraphic Address: BRITON GUATEMALA)
(Facsimile: 341904)

HM Ambassador: J P P Nason, OBE
Defence Attaché (resides at Mexico City): Colonel
A J Dobson
*First Secretary, Consul and Deputy Head of
Mission:* Dr P J Norris
First Secretary (Commercial) *and Director of
Trade Promotion for Central America* (resides at
San José): A S Green, OBE, MVO

Puerto Barrios
British Consulate
7a Calle entre 3a y 4a Avanida
Puerto Barrios, Izabel
PO Box 399
(Tel: 480152)
(Telex: 726 PBB AN GU)
(Facsimile: 480 405)

Honorary Consul: P O Vélez

GUINEA

Conakry
British Embassy (All staff reside at Dakar)

Ambassador: R C Beetham, LVO
First Secretary and Head of Chancery:
M J Hentley

Cultural Attaché and British Council Director:
Ms A Malamah-Thomas
Assistant British Council Director:
J M McCullough
Third Secretary (Chancery, Aid and Information):
Miss S H Jump
Third Secretary (Management) *and Vice-Consul:*
K J Lynch

British Consulate
BP 834, Conakry, Republic of Guinea
(Tel: 461734, 465361, 443442)
(Telex: 22294)
(Facsimile: (224) 44 42 15)

Consul (Resides at Dakar): M J Hentley
Vice-Consul (Resides at Dakar): K J Lynch
Honorary Consul: Mrs V A Treitlein

GUINEA-BISSAU

Bissau
British Embassy (All staff reside at Dakar)

Ambassador: R C Beetham, LVO
First Secretary and Head of Chancery:
M J Hentley
Cultural Attaché and British Council Director:
Ms A Malamah-Thomas
Assistant British Council Director:
J M McCullough
Third Secretary (Chancery, Aid and Information):
Miss S H Jump
Third Secretary (Management) *and Vice-Consul:*
K J Lynch

British Consulate
Mavegro Int., CP100, Bissau
(Tel: 21 15 29)
(Telex: 259 BI) (a/b MAVEGRO BI)
Consul: M J Hentley (Resides at Dakar)
Vice-Consul: K J Lynch (Resides at Dakar)
Honorary Consul: J Van Maanen

GUYANA*

Georgetown
British High Commission
44 Main Street (PO Box 10849), Georgetown
(Tel: 65881/2/3/4)
(Telex: 2221) (a/b 2221 UKREP GY)
(Facsimile: 253 555)

High Commissioner: R D Gordon
Deputy High Commissioner and First Secretary
(Commercial): S J Hiscock
Defence Adviser (Resides at Kingston):
Colonel C S Faith, OBE
Naval Adviser (Resides at Nassau):
Captain A J S Taylor, RN
First Secretary (Aid): Miss A Rowlatt
Third Secretary (Management): P B Harrington
Third Secretary (Chancery/Information/Consular):
A J Ford

HAITI

Port-au-Prince
British Embassy (All staff reside at Kingston)

Ambassador: D F Milton, CMG

Counsellor, Head of Chancery and Consul-General: F Callaghan
First Secretary (Chancery): S M Boldt
First Secretary and Consul: I F Powell
Defence Attaché: Colonel C S Faith, OBE
Naval Attaché (Resides at Nassau):
Captain A J S Taylor, RN
Second Secretary (Commercial/Information):C Q
G Webb
Second Secretary (Chancery): I A Worthington
Second Secretary (Chancery): T V D Manhire
Second Secretary (Technical Assistant): C N
Brazier
Second Secretary (Chancery): F Maynard
Third Secretary (Consular): C D R Smart

British Consulate
Hotel Montana
(PO Box 1302), Port-au-Prince
(Tel: 73969)
(Telex: 2030259)
(Facsimile: 74048)

Consul (Resides at Kingston): I F Powell
Vice-Consul (Resides at Kingston):
C D R Smart
Vice-Consul: Mrs M Guercy, MBE

International Apparel SA, PO Box 13471, Delmas,
Bardancort Rd 24, Port-au-Prince

Honorary Trade Correspondent: D F Chambers

HOLY SEE

British Embassy
91, Viadei Condotti, I-00187, Rome
(Tel: (06) 6789462, 6797479)
(Telex: 626119) (a/b BR EMB I)
Telegraphic Address: PRODROME
(Facsimile 6840684)
Ambassador: A E Palmer, CMG, CVO
First Secretary: F A Doherty

HONDURAS

Tegucigalpa
British Embassy
Edificio Palmira, 3er Piso, Colonia Palmira, PO
Box 290, Tegucigalpa
(Tel: 32-5429; 32-0612; 32-0618)
(Telex: 1234 (a/b 1234 PRODROME HO)
(Facsimile: 32 5480)

Ambassador and Consul-General: P Morgan
First Secretary (Commercial) *and Director of
Trade Promotion for Central America* (Resides at
San José): A S Green , OBE, MVO
Defence Attaché (Resides at Panama City):
Lieutenant-Colonel T A Glen
Second Secretary: I R Lewis
Third Secretary and Vice-Consul: K Burrows

San Pedro Sula
British Consulate
Terminales de Puerto Cortes, Apartado 298, San
Pedro Sula
(Tel: 54-2600)
(Telex: 5513 HT (a/b 5513 TERMCOR HO))

(Cable: TERMCOR San Pedro Sula)
Honorary Consul: F P Barber, MBE

HONG KONG

British Trade Commission
9th Floor, Bank of America Tower,
12 Harcourt Road, Hong Kong
(Tel: (010) (852) 523 0176)
(Facsimile (852) 845 2870)
(Cable Address: UK TRADE Hong Kong)
(Correspondence about passports and visas should
be addressed to the Immigration Department of
the Hong Kong Government, 7 Gloucester Road,
Hong Kong.
(Tel: (852) 523 0176)

Senior Trade Commissioner: S P Day, CMG
Trade Counsellor: J Smith-Laittan
Trade Counsellor: J P Watson
Assistant Trade Commissioner (Hong Kong
Trade): D J Smith
Assistant Trade Commissioner (China Trade):
D J Currie
Senior Information Officer: C W Osborne
Information Officer: Miss R M E Fowler
Management Officer: R T Jarvis

British Diplomatic Service Mail Office
Osborne Barracks, Waterloo Road, Kowloon,
Hong Kong
(Tel: 3-385328 or 3394158)

Officer-in-Charge Mail Office: J Tuke

Hong Kong Government
(See Dependent Territories)
Office of the British Senior Representative,
Sino-British Joint Liaison Group (JLG Hong
Kong) (See Missions & Delegations)

HUNGARY

Budapest
British Embassy
Harmincad Utca 6, Budapest V
(Tel: 266-2888) (266-2046)
(Telex: 22 4527) (a/b 22 4527 BRIT H)
(Facsimile: 266-0907)

Ambassador: J A Birch, CMG
Counsellor and Deputy Head of Mission:
H J S Pearce
Defence and Military Attaché:
Lieutenant-Colonel W B Ibbetson
Air Attaché: Wing Commander M A Gaynor, RAF
First Secretary (British Council Director):
D J Harvey
First Secretary (Commercial): D J R Taylor
First Secretary (Political): Miss S C Rowland-
Jones
First Secretary: P R Nelson
First Secretary (Medical Officer) (Resides at
Warsaw): Dr A C E Stacey
First Secretary (British Council): Dr R Baker

First Secretary (British Council): Ms M H Thomas
First Secretary (Management) *and Consul:*
Miss S M MacTaggart
Second Secretary (Commercial):P D Culligan
Second Secretary (Commercial): Mrs L M Kendall
Second Secretary (British Council): Ms S Bowler
Second Secretary (Chancery): Q J K Phillips
Second Secretary (Chancery): R W Lamping
Second Secretary (Chancery): C J Lonsdale
Second Secretary (Management): I S Wilson
Second Secretary (Information): W H J Blanchard
Third Secretary (Chancery): Miss C M Carden
Attaché (Vice-Consul): Miss N J Alexander

ICELAND

Reykjavik
British Embassy
Laufasvegur 49, 101 Reykjavik
(Postal Address) PO Box 460, 121 Reykjavik
(Tel: 15883-4) (STD (9) 1)
(Telex: 2037) (a/b 2037 UKREYK IS)
(Facsimile: 27940)

Ambassador and Consul-General:
P F M Wogan, CMG
*Second Secretary, Deputy Head of Mission and
Consul:* A Mehmet, MVO

Akureyri
British Vice-Consulate
Glerargata 26, Akureyri
(Tel: 21165 (STD (9) 6))

Honorary Vice-Consul: A Jonsson, MBE

INDIA*

New Delhi
British High Commission
Chanakyapuri, New Delhi 21, 1100-21
(Tel: 601371)
(Telex: 31-65125) (a/b 31-65125 BHC IN)
(Facsimile: 609940)

High Commissioner: Sir Nicholas Fenn, KCMG
Deputy High Commissioner and Minister:
P J Fowler, CMG
Defence and Military Adviser: Brigadier
A F Gordon, CBE
Naval Adviser: Captain P N Galloway, RN
Air Adviser: Group Captain J M Kennell, OBE, RAF
Counsellor and Head of Chancery: L Parker
Counsellor (Economic and Commercial): J E
Holmes
Counsellor: J L Taylor
Counsellor (Management): M J Hardie, OBE
First Secretary (Commercial): Dr G Thom
First Secretary: (Chancery): S P Collis
First Secretary: P J Corgan
First Secretary (Management): R P Smith
First Secretary (Development): J R Drummond
First Secretary (Information): D S Keeling
First Secretary (Engineering Adviser):M McCarthy
First Secretary (Chancery) D J Fitton
First Secretary (Economic): C Clift
First Secretary (Defence Supplies):
D MacLennan

First Secretary (Forestry): Dr E Hanley
First Secretary (Forestry): I Napier
First Secretary (Medical Officer):Dr D A Eggleton
First Secretary (Works): F H Syratt
First Secretary (Supplies): C J Davis
First Secretary (Immigration): M G Hilson
Assistant Defence Adviser:
Lt. Colonel K R Sinclair
Second Secretary (Development): T D Hatton
Second Secretary (Management): W L Rees
Second Secretary (Communications): P S Salkeld
Second Secretary (Supplies): P V B George, TD
Second Secretary (Consular): Miss J A James
Second Secretary (Works): G C Mallery
Second Secretary (Immigration): Miss S J Coker,
MBE
Second Secretary (Trade Policy): J W D Hall
Second Secretary (Immigration): A W Craig
Second Secretary (Commercial): N U Sheppard
Second Secretary (Chancery): C J Sainty
Second Secretary (Political): Ms J W Bird

BRITISH COUNCIL DIVISION

New Delhi
AIFACS Building, Rafi Marg,
New Delhi, 110001
(Tel: 381401, 382004, 383946)
(Telex: 31 65460) (a/b 3165460 BC ND IN)
(Facsimile: (91 11) 378 2016)

Minister (Cultural Affairs): R Arbuthnott, CBE
Counsellor (Cultural Affairs): R L T Sykes
First Secretary (Science and Manpower
Development): Dr I Simm
First Secretary (Libraries and Books): K Spears
First Secretary (Management): Mr I CWinnan, MBE
First Secretary (Cultural): Dr N Gilroy-Scott
First Secretary (Science and Education):
D J Theobald
First Secretary (Science): Dr R I Frome
First Secretary (Manpower Development):
Ms C A Stephens
First Secretary (Science and Technology):
D Cordingly
First Secretary (Science and Education):
K O'Connor
First Secretary (Buildings): A K Dixon
Second Secretary (Information): Miss T Lloyd

Bombay
Office of the British Deputy High Commissioner
Maker Chambers IV, 222 Jamnalal Bajaj Road,
(PO Box 11714), Nariman Point, Bombay,400 021
(Tel: 230517/232330)
(Telex: (011) 82850 (a/b 82850 BHC IN)
(Facsimile: 2027940)

Deputy High Commissioner: A E Furness, CMG
First Secretary (Commercial): L J Friston
First Secretary (Cultural Affairs British Council
Director): R A K Baker, OBE
First Secretary (Education and Science):
N P Willimott
Second Secretary (Immigration): N Johnson
Second Secretary: R Affleck

Second Secretary (Consular/Immigration):
M R Walmsley
Second Secretary (Commercial): R B Smith
Second Secretary (Management): P P Flanagan
Second Secretary (Immigration): D O'Rourke

Calcutta
Office of the British Deputy High Commissioner
1 Ho Chi Minh Sarani, Calcutta, 700 071
(Tel: 44-5171) (After office hours—44-5172)
(Telex: 215983 (a/b UKCL IN))
(Facsimile: 223435)

Deputy High Commissioner: I McCluney, CMG
First Secretary (Cultural Affairs British Council
Director): D J Sloan
First Secretary (Education and Science British
Council Assistant Director): Ms S J Beaumont
Second Secretary (Consular/Management):
C S Gedge

Madras
Office of the British Deputy High Commissioner
in Southern India
24 Anderson Road, Madras, 600 006
(Tel: 473136)
(Telex: 41 7169) (a/b UKMS IN)
(Facsimile: 869004)

Deputy High Commissioner: D Cockerham
First Secretary (British Council Director):
D N Sanderson, MBE
First Secretary (Education and Science British
Council Assisatnt Director): Ms F M Marriott
Second Secretary (Commercial): P F Whiten, MBE
Attaché (Consular/Immigration): J P Geddes

INDONESIA

Jakarta
British Embassy
Jalan M.H. Thamrin 75, Jakarta, 10310
(Tel: 330904 (9 lines))
(Facsimile: 62-21-321824)

Ambassador: R J Carrick, CMG, LVO
Counsellor, (Commercial/Aid) *and Deputy Head
of Mission:* P J Bacon
*Counsellor, Head of Political Sesction and
Consul-General:* Dr P S Collecott
Counsellor (Political): P B Preece
Counsellor (Defence Supply) (Resident in Kuala
Lumpur): B Breslin
Defence and Military Attaché: Colonel B G G
Nicholson, OBE
Naval and Air Attaché:
Commander A C Moore, LVO, RN
First Secretary (Aid): D J C Taylor
First Secretary (Management): R F Taylor
First Secretary: J I Malcolm
First Secretary (Commercial): M B G Plumb
First Secretary (Defence Supply):
C A G Champness
Second Secretary and Consul: P G Baldwin
Second Secretary (Commercial): A F N
Goodworth

Second Secretary: (Political/Information): J Carroll
Second Secretary (Economic): P R Wilson
Third Secretary (Political): I M Donaldson

Medan
British Consulate
PT P.P. London, Sumatra, Indonesia, JL Jend. A
Yani No 2
PO Box 155,
Medan 20111,
Sumatra, Indonesia
(Tel: 518000)
(Telex: 51125 HARCOSIA)
(Facsimile: 513596)

Honorary Consul: J P C Baskett

Surabaya
British Consulate
Jalan Jenderal Basuki Rahmat 33-37,
Surabaya 60011
(Tel: 511 200, 515 101)
(Telex: 32151 HSBCSB IA)
(Facsimile: 515200)

Honorary Consul: R Martin

IRAN

Tehran
British Embassy
143 Ferdowsi Avenue, Tehran 11344,
PO Box 11365-4474
(Tel: 675011 (7 lines))
(Telex: 212493 (a/b 212493 PROD IR))
(Facsimile: 678021)

Chargé d'Affaires a.i.: D N Reddaway, MBE
First Secretary (Commercial): D J Hawkes, MBE
First Secretary (Chancery): A J H Cowell
First Secretary (Management) *and Consul:*
N R I Suter
Second Secretary (Commercial): A M Kent
Third Secretary (Management/Consular):
P J Hickson

IRAQ

Baghdad
British Embassy
House 12, Street 218, Hai Al Khelood
(Tel: 5372121/5) (5 lines)
Telegraphic Address: PRODROME
BAGHDAD
(Telex: 213414 (a/b PRODRM K))

Diplomatic relations were broken off in February
1991.

IRISH REPUBLIC

Dublin
British Embassy
31/33 Merrion Road, Dublin, 4
(Tel: (0103531) 2695211)
(Telex: 93717) (a/b 93717 UKDB EI)
(Facsimile: 2838 423 Group 3)

Ambassador: D E S Blatherwick, CMG, OBE
Counsellor and Deputy Head of Mission: J A Dew
British Council Director: Dr K T Churchill
Defence Attaché: Colonel S D Lambe
First Secretary (Political and Information):
Ms T Gallagher
First Secretary (Commercial): J Mc F Pepper
First Secretary (Chancery): J S McKervill
First Secretary (Chancery): I R Whitting
First Secretary (Management): G R Duff
Second Secretary (Commercial): D S Marsh
Second Secretary (Agric): A Cobden
Second Secretary (Commercial): F D Morris
Third Secretary (Passports/Visas): J D Kenny
Third Secretary: G W Sellars

ISRAEL

Tel Aviv
British Embassy
192 Hayarkon Street, Tel Aviv 63405
(Tel: 03-5249171/8)
(Telex: 33-559) (a/b PRODR IL)
(Facsimile: 291699)

Ambassador: R A Burns, CMG
Counsellor, Consul-General (M) *and Deputy Head
of Mission:* T R V Phillips
Defence & Military Attaché: Colonel J D Andrew,
OBE
Naval and Air Attaché:
Wing Commander J W Landeryou, RAF
Cultural Attaché (British Council Director):
P Sandiford, OBE
First Secretary (Chancery): A J Pearce
First Secretary (Chancery): P D Orwin, OBE, MC
First Secretary and Consul: A S Marshall MBE
First Secretary (Commercial): P A Connolly
Assistant Cultural Attaché (British Council):
Vacant
Assistant Cultural Attaché (British Council):
M Johnson
Second Secretary (Management): E E Dearden
Third Secretary (Chancery): C E Jacobson
Third Secretary and Vice-Consul: Miss M A Abbott
Third Secretary: F M F Thorne, MBE
Third Secretary: N W Dickins

British Consulate General
Migdalor Building (6th floor), 1 Ben Yehuda Street,
Tel: Aviv 63801
(Tel: 03-5100166, 5100497, 5249171/2)
(Facsimile: 03-5101167)

Consul-General: T R V Phillips
Consul: A S Marshall, MBE
Vice-Consul: Miss M A Abbott

Eilat
British Consulate
14 Tsofit Villas, Eilat
(Tel: (0) 59-72344, 74908)
(Facsimile: 74908)

Honorary Consul: Mrs F Morris

ITALY

Rome
British Embassy
Via XX Settembre 80a, 00187 Roma
(Tel: 4825441, 4825551)
(Telex: 626119) (a/b 626119 BREMB I)
(Facsimile: 487 3324)

Ambassador: Sir Patrick Fairweather, KCMG
Minister: D H Colvin
Defence and Military Attaché:
Brigadier A R Jones
Naval Attaché: Captain K F Read, RN
Air Attaché: Group Captain S A Wrigley, RAF
Counsellor (Political and Management):
G M Gowlland, LVO
Counsellor (Political): C L Fransella
Counsellor (Commercial): C R L de Chassiron
Counsellor (Cultural Affairs British Council
Director): K R Hunter, OBE
First Secretary (SocialAffairs/Science and
Technology): D J Hollamby
First Secretary (Agriculture and Environment):
M E Smith
First Secretary (Economic): N K Darroch
First Secretary (Political): J Ashton
First Secretary (Economic): J A Towner
First Secretary (Information): S W Gregson
First Secretary (Commercial): H Kershaw
First Secretary (Consul): G Roberts
First Secretary (Management):
C W G Edmonds-Brown
First Secretary (Political): R J C Allen
Assistant Defence Attaché: Major I W Jefferson
Second Secretary (Political and Information):
Mrs K J Stanton
Second Secretary (Management): C J Ley
Second Secretary: A A Jones
Third Secretary: C M Inglehearn

Florence
British Consulate
Palazzo Castelbarco, Lungarno Corsini 2,
I-50123 Florence
(Tel: 212594, 284133, 287449, Commercial
Office 263556)
(Telex: 570270) (a/b 570270 UKCON I)
(Facsimile: 219112)

Consul: M Holmes (*is also Consul-General for
the Republic of San Marino*)
Vice-Consul: E Masi, MBE

Milan
British Consulate-General
Via San Paolo 7, 20121 Milan
(Tel: (39) (2) 723001
(Emergency numbers: 862490, 8693442)
(Telex: 310528) (a/b 310528 UKCON I)
(Facsimile: (02) 72020153)

*Director General for British Trade Development
in Italy, and Consul-General:* P H D Wetton
Deputy Consul-General and Consul (Commercial):
R J Griffiths, OBE
Consul: W A F Ridout

Consul (Information): J H Halley
Consul (Commercial): J L Blakemore
Vice-Consul (Management): D Lusher

Genoa
British Consulate
Via XII Ottobre, 2/132 16121 Genoa
(Tel: (010) 564 833/6)
(Telex: 270689) (a/b 270689 UKCON I)
(Telegraphic Address: BRITAIN GENOA)
(Facsimile: 5531516)

Consul: M A Wicks, MBE

Turin
British Consulate
Corso Massimo d'Azeglio 60, 10126 Turin
(Tel: (011) 687832/683921)
(Telex: 221464) (a/b 221464 BRITRA I)
(Facsimile: 6699848)

Consul: D H Price

Venice
British Consulate
Accademia, Dorsoduro 1051 30123, Venice
(Tel: (041) 5227207, 5227408)
(Telex: 410283) (a/b 410283 UKCON I)
(Facsimile: (3941) 5222617)

Consul: M H Gluckstern

Trieste
British Consulate
Vicolo Delle Ville 16, 34100 Trieste
(Tel: (040) 302884)

Honorary Consul: Major N J Lister, MBE

Naples
British Consulate-General
Via Francesco Crispi 122, I-80122 Naples
(Postal Address: Consulate, BFPO 8, London)
(Tel: 663511) (3 lines)
(Telex: 710330) (a/b 710330 UKCON I)
(Facsimile: (080) 761 3720)

Consul-General: R C G Harrison
Vice-Consul: D N Broomfield
Vice-Consul: M Burgoyne

Bari
British Consulate
Anglo-Italian Shipping,
Via Montenegro 19, 70121 Bari
(Tel: (080) 521.7859)
(Telex: 812269 ANGLO I)
(Facsimile: (080) 524.4024)

Honorary Consul: D H Gavan

Brindisi
British Consulate
The British School, Via de' Terribile 9,
72100 Brindisi
(Tel/Fax: (0831) 568340)

Honorary Consul: F Gentile

IVORY COAST

Abidjan
British Embassy
3rd Floor, Immeuble "Les Harmonies'',
Angle Boulevard Carde et Avenue Dr Jamot,
Plateau, Abidjan
Postal Address: 01 Boite Postale 2581, Abidjan 01
(Tel: 22.68.50, 22.68.51, 22.68.52, 32.82.09)
(Telex: Abidjan 23706) (a/b PRDRME CI)
(Facsimile: 22 32 21)

Ambassador and Consul-General:
Miss M I Rothwell, CMG *(also Ambassador to the Republics of Niger and Burkina)*
First Secretary (Commercial), *Head of Chancery and Consul:* D R F Flanagan
Defence Attaché (Resides at Accra):
Lieutenant-Colonel T E A Hawkins, MBE
Second Secretary (Commercial): (Vacant)
Second Secretary and Information Officer:
P J Whitehead
Third Secretary (Management) *and Vice-Consul:*
Miss A C Kennedy
Third Secretary Vice-Consul and Attaché ADB:
Miss J A Walder

JAMAICA*

Kingston
British High Commission
PO Box 575, Trafalgar Road, Kingston 10
(Tel: 926-9050)
(Telegrams: UKREPKIN JA)
(Telex: 2110) (a/b UKREPKIN JA)
(Facsimile: 92 97869)

High Commissioner: D F Milton, CMG
Deputy High Commissioner: F Callaghan
Defence Adviser: Colonel C S Faith, OBE
Naval Adviser (resides at Nassau):
Captain A J S Taylor, RN
First Secretary (Chancery): S M Boldt
First Secretary (Management/Consular): I F Powell
Second Secretary (Commercial/Information):
C Q G Jebb
Second Secretary (Chancery): I A Worthington
Second Secretary (Chancery): T V D Manhire
Second Secretary (Chancery): F Maynard
Third Secretary (Consular/Passports): C D R Smart
Third Secretary (Management): Miss V L Lucien
Third Secretary (Immigration): S J Burns

JAPAN

Tokyo
British Embassy
No 1 Ichiban-cho, Chiyoda-ku, Tokyo 102
(Tel: Chancery, Economic, Defence &
Management Sections 3265-5511)
(Facsimile: 5275-3164)
(Tel: Commercial, Information, S & T Atomic
Energy Sections 3265-6340)
(Facsimile: 3265-5580)
(Tel: Consular Section 3265-6340)
(Facsimile: 5275-0346)

(Tel: Visa Section 3265-4001)
(Facsimile: 5275-0346)
(Telex: 22755 (a/b PRODROME J22755))

Ambassador: Sir John Boyd, KCMG
Minister: A C Thorpe
Minister (Financial): J E W Kirby
Defence and Naval Attaché:
Captain C M C Crawford, RN
Military and Air Attaché:
Group Captain A N MacGregor, RAF
Counsellor and Head of Chancery: G H Fry
Counsellor (Management) *and Consul-General:*
D Pragnell, CBE, LVO
Counsellor (Economic): C T W Humfrey
Counsellor (Commercial): P S Dimond
Counsellor: L C R Seeley
Counsellor (Atomic Energy): C Loughlin
Counsellor (Cultural) (British Council Director):
R P Joscelyne
Counsellor (Science & Technology): Dr R Hinder
First Secretary (Inward Investment): C E A Ripley
First Secretary (Science & Technology):
T Salusbury
First Secretary (Chancery): D H Powell
First Secretary (Cultural) (British Council):
J Foley, OBE
First Secretary (Commercial): S J Plater
First Secretary (Information): R E Coghlan
First Secretary (Commercial): R R Cummins
First Secretary (Chancery): M R Everest-Phillips
First Secretary (Economic): A Morgan
First Secretary (Science and Technology):
R S Powell
Second Secretary and Consul: P V Baines
Vice-Consul: Miss A L Johnson
Second Secretary: Miss J M Longbottom
Second Secretary (Commercial): Miss J C Owen
Second Secretary (Commercial): N P Margetts
Second Secretary (Management): A Gerrard
Second Secretary (Economic): M E Cowin
Second Secretary (Economic): G J Prince

Osaka
British Consulate General
Hong Kong and Shanghai Bank Building, 6-1,
3 chome, Awaji-machi Chuo-ku, Osaka 541
(Tel: (81 6) 231-3355)
(Facsimile: (81 6) 202 4312 Group 3)

*Consul-General and Director of Trade
Promotion:* G J B Williams
Consul (Commercial): R A Rayner
Second Secretary (Commercial): S J Fisher

Fukuoka
British Consulate
The Nishi-Nippon Bank Ltd, 1-3-6
Hakata-Ekimae, Hakata-Ku, Fukuoka City
(Tel: (92) 411-2525)
(Telex: 724511)

Honorary Consul: K. Ichikawa
Honorary Vice-Consul: Y Shikata

Hiroshima
British Consulate
Hiroshima Bank Ltd, 3-8, 1-chome, Kamiyacho,
Naka-ku
(Tel: (082) 247 5151)
(Facsimile: (082) 247 3664)

Honorary Consul: O Hashiguchi

Nagoya
British Consulate
Tokai Bank Ltd, 21-24, 3-chome, Nishiki,
Naka-ku
(Tel: (052) 211 1111)
(Facsimile: (52) 211 0920)

Honorary Consul: R Kato

Tokyo
British Consulate-General
No 1 Ichiban-cho,
Chiyoda-Ku, Tokyo 102
(Tel: (33) 265-5511)
(Telex: 22755 (a/b PRODROME J 22755))
(Facsimile: (3) 5275 0346)

Consul-General: D Pragnell, OBE, LVO
Consul: P V Baines
Vice-Consul: Miss D E Lloyd

JERUSALEM

British Consulate-General
19 Nashashibi Street, Sheikh Jarrah Quarter,
PO Box 19690, East Jerusalem 97200
(Tel: 828281)
(Telex: 26260 (a/b UKJM IL))
(Facsimile: 322368)

Consul-General (M): D R MacLennan
Consul: J M Crane
Vice-Consul (Management): Miss E Dow
Vice-Consul (Political): Miss J Adamson
Cultural Attaché (British Council Representative):
C J Woods-McConville, MBE
Assistant Cultural Attaché: P Morison

West Jerusalem Office: Tower House, Kikar
Remez, Jerusalem 93541
(Tel: 717724)

JORDAN

Amman
British Embassy
Abdoun, Amman (PO Box 87)
(Tel: 823100)
(Telex: 22209 (a/b 22209 PRODRM JO))
Facsimile: (6) 813759

Ambassador: P H C Eyers, CMG, LVO
*Counsellor, Consul-General and Deputy Head of
Mission:* J W Watt
Counsellor: M J S Allen
Defence, Naval and Military Attaché:
Colonel B A C Duncan, MBE
Air Attaché: Wing Commander M F Bell, RAF
First Secretary (Commercial/Aid): T M Ellis
First Secretary (Chancery): C B Farr
Consul and First Secretary (Management) (M):
C E Cooper

Assistant Defence Attaché: Major J M Phillips
Second Secretary (Chancery): Viscount Glentworth
Second Secretary (Internal Affairs):
Mrs K Wheatley
Third Secretary (Chancery): M A M Le Goy
Third Secretary: M E Ager
Vice-Consul: Miss A M Marriott

KAZAKHSTAN

Alma Ata
British Embassy

Ambassador: Sir Brian Fall, KCMG (resides at
Moscow)
Consul General and Resident Chargé d'Affaires:
R M Harris
Second Secretary (Political/Information) *and Vice-
Consul:* Miss S K Simon

KENYA*

Nairobi
British High Commission
Bruce House, Standard Street, Nairobi (PO Box
30465)
(Tel: 335944) (all Departments)
(Telex: 22219) (a/b UKREP)
(Facsimile: 333196)
(Telegraphic Address: UKREP Nairobi)
Commercial Department: PO Box 30133
Consular Department: PO Box 48543

High Commissioner: Sir Kieran Prendergast, KCVO,
CMG
Deputy High Commissioner: H B Warren-Gash
Counsellor: A J Hawkes, OBE
Defence and Military Adviser:
Colonel P R Bell
Air and Naval Adviser:
Wing Commander C F W Felger, RAF
First Secretary (Political/Environment):
D E P P Keefe
First Secretary (Commercial): D L Littlefield
First Secretary (Consular): Miss S M G White
First Secretary (Management): P A Heald, MBE
First Secretary (Aid): J D Friend
First Secretary (Aid): P G McCrudden
First Secretary (Works): J G Darlington
Second Secretary (Chancery/Economic):
W T F Tricks
Second Secretary (Chancery): R Vlasto
Second Secretary (Consular): A Summers
Second Secretary (Commercial): D S T Morton
Second Secretary (Works): B W Mitchell
Second Secretary (Works): M J Wood
Second Secretary (Chancery/Information):
R C P Gwynn
Second Secretary: I R Willsher
Third Secretary: D A Parkins

British Development Division
Eastern Africa
c/o British High Commission
(Tel: (254) (2) 335944
(Facsimile: (010) 254 2340 260)
Counsellor and Head of Division: D Sands Smith
Senior Natural Resources Adviser: (Vacant)

Natural Resources Adviser: G A Gilman
Senior Engineering Adviser: H B Jackson
Senior Economic Adviser: E Hawthorn
Engineering Adviser: R J Cadwallader
Programme Adviser: A K C Wood
Programme Adviser: D G Bell
Programme Adviser: A J Gardner
Economic Adviser: W Kingsmill
Economic Adviser: (Vacant)
Senior Economic Assistant: B Killen
Health and Population Manager: Dr M McNeill

Mombasa
Office of the British Honorary Consular
Representative
Greenwood Drive, Nyali, PO Box 84105,
Mombasa
(Tel: (011) 471768)

Honorary Consular Representative: B B Mitchell

KIRIBATI*

Tarawa
British High Commission
PO Box No 61, Bairiki, Tarawa
(Telegraphic Address: UKREP TARAWA)
(Tel: Bairiki 21327)
(Telex: 77050) (a/b UKREP KI 77050)
(Facsimile: 21488)

High Commissioner: D L White
Third Secretary: R Scott

KOREA

Seoul
British Embassy
4 Chung-dong, Chung-ku, Seoul
(Tel: 735-7341/3)
(Telex: 27320) (a/b PRODROM K27320)
(Facsimile: (822) 736 6241 or (822) 733 8368)

Ambassador: D J Wright, CMG, LVO
Counsellor (Economic) *and Deputy Head of
Mission:* P Longworth
Defence and Military Attaché:
Brigadier D P de C Morgan, OBE, RAF
Naval and Air Attaché:
Group Captain R J Springett, OBE, RAF
First Secretary, (Political): Dr M D Reilly
First Secretary (Commercial/Information):
D M Gray
First Secretary (Defence Supply): K Harper
Cultural Attaché: (British Council Director):
T C White, MBE
Assistant Defence Attaché: Major M J Cartwright
Second Secretary (Management):
Second Secretary (Commercial); J K Hague
Second Secretary (Works): D Holmes
Assistant Cultural Attaché: (British Council):
A Jones
Assistant Cultural Attaché (British Council):
M A L Baumfield
Second Secretary (Works) (Resides at Tokyo):
B R Hooker
Vice-Consul: Mrs G Silva
Third Secretary (Political): T W Standbrook

Pusan
British Consulate
Chairman's Room, 12th Floor,
Yoochang Building, 25-2, 4-Ka,
Chungang-Dong Chung-Ku, Pusan
PO Box No 75, Republic of Korea
(Tel: 463-0041 and 463-4630)
(Telex: HYOPSUNG K53323/K53374)
(Facsimile: 051 4625933)

Honorary Consul: S E Wang, CBE
Honorary Vice-Consul: H Guack

KUWAIT

Kuwait
British Embassy
Arabian Gulf Street (PO Box 2 SAFAT), 13001
Safat, Kuwait
(Tel: 24320461/71/81/9 and 2403324/5/6/7)
(Telex: 44614 (a/b PRODROM 44614 KT))
(Facsimile: 240 7395)
Commercial Section PO Box 300, Safat 13001
Kuwait

Ambassador: W H Fullerton, CMG
Deputy Head of Mission: F X Gallagher
Defence Attaché: Colonel C J Squires
First Secretary (Head of Political Section):
B Seddon
First Secretary (Political): P V Wallis
First Secretary (Management) *and Consul* (M):
J Bentley
First Secretary (Commercial): C R Winter, OBE
First Secretary (Defence): A D Young
Second Secretary (Chancery Information): B R
Lowen
Second Secretary (Commercial): R J C Lee
Second Secretary (Management): C Gray
Second Secretary: S Teggert

LAOS

Vientiane
British Embassy (All staff resident at Bangkok)

Ambassador: C C W Adams, CMG
Counsellor and Deputy Head of Mission:
D W Fall
First Secretary (Head of Political Section):
A J Sparkes
First Secretary: P Matthews
First Secretary (Economic/Commercial):
G T Squires
First Secretary and Consul: Miss J C Sharpe
Second Secretary: M S Brown

LATVIA

Riga
British Embassy
3rd Floor Elizabetes Iela, 226010, Riga
(Tel: (7) (0132) 320 737 325 592
(Facsimile: (7) (0132) 322973

Ambassador: R C Samuel, CMG, CVO
First Secretary and Deputy Head of Mission: M C
Bates

First Secretary (British Council): Ms S Maingay
Third Secretary (Consular/Management):
R W Harmer

LEBANON

Beirut
British Embassy
East Beirut: Middle East Airlines Building, Tripoli
Autostrade, Jal el Dib
(Tel: 416112, 410573, 402035, 417007, 410596)
(Telex: 44104) (a/b PRODROM 44104 LE)
West Beirut: Shamma Building, Raouché, Ras
Beirut
(Tel: 812849, 812851, 805898, 804882, 804929)
(Telex: 20465) (a/b PRODROM 20465 LE)

Ambassador: Miss M G Fort, CMG
Defence Attaché: Lieutenant-Colonel E J Gould
Deputy Head of Mission: J A Tucknott, MBE
Attaché: C Brooks, MBE
Vice-Consul: Miss S Wardle
Honorary Consul: W Zard, MBE

Tripoli
British Consulate
Daar Al Ain, Tripoli
(Tel. (06) 621320)

Honorary Consul: A Arida, MBE

LESOTHO*

Maseru
British High Commission, (PO Box Ms 521),
Maseru 100
(Tel: 313961)
(Telex: 4343) (a/b 4343 LO)
(Facsimile: 310120)

High Commissioner: J R Cowling
Deputy High Commissioner: P R Butcher
Second Secretary (Aid/Information/Commercial):
P V O'Connor
Third Secretary/Management Officer:
F X Gallagher

LIBERIA

Monrovia
The Embassy closed on 8 March 1991.

LIBYA

Tripoli
British Interests Section
Italian Embassy, Shara Uahran 1, PO Box 4206,
Tripoli
(Tel: 31191)
(Facsimile: 45753)
(Telex: 20296) (a/b 20296 BRITEMB LY)

Head of Interests Section: A R Brown, MVO
Third Secretary (Management): D S Jones

LIECHTENSTEIN

British Embassy
Thunstrasse 50, 3005 Berne
(Tel: (41) (31) 44 50 21/6)
(Facsimile: (41) (31) 4405 83

Ambassador (resides at Berne): D Bealtie, CMG
Consul-General (Resides at Zurich): T Bryant,
CMG

LITHUANIA

Vilnius
British Embassy, Antakalnio 2, Vilnius 2055
(Tel: (70122) 22 20 70)
Facsimile: (70122) 35 75 79)

Ambassador: M J Peart, LVO
Second Secretary and Deputy Head of Mission:
T P Brownbill
Defence Attaché (resides at London): Wing
Commander D J Holliday, RAF
First Secretary (British Council Director) (resides
at Riga): Ms S Maingay

LUXEMBOURG

Luxembourg
British Embassy
14 Boulevard Roosevelt, L-2450,
Luxembourg Ville
(Tel: (352) 22 98 64/65/66)
(Telex: 3443) (a/b 3443 PRODROLU)
(Facsimile: (352) 22 98 67 Group 2)

Ambassador and Consul-General:
The Hon Michael Pakenham
Counsellor (Commercial) (Resident in Brussels):
B Attewell
*First Secretary, Consul and Deputy Head of
Mission:* S H Palmer
Defence, Naval, Military and Air Attaché
(Resident in Brussels): Colonel J M Craster
Cultural Attaché: (British Council Director)
(Resident in Brussels): Dr M Cooper
First Secretary (Commercial) (Resident in
Brussels): W A Kelly
First Secretary (Labour) (Resident in Brussels):
Miss P J Cruickshank
Second Secretary (Commercial/Information):
P Malone
Attaché: (Management) *and Vice-Consul:* P Jones

MADAGASCAR

Antananarivo
British Embassy
First Floor, Immeuble "Ny Havana"
Cité de 67 Ha, BP167, Antananarivo
(Tel: (261) (2) 27749, 273 70, 337 65)
(Facsimile: (261) (2) 26690
(Telex: 22459 (a/b PRODRO MG))

Ambassador: (Vacant)
Second Secretary: C G R Poole
Defence Attaché (resides at Maputo): Lieutenant
Colonel C W Larkin, OBE
Cultural Attaché (resides at Port Louis): M J
Bootle

Toamasina
Office of the Honorary Consul
c/o Seal Toamasina, Toamasina 501
(Tel: (261) (05) 325 48)
(Facsimile: (261) (05) 339 37)

Honorary Consul: M Gonthier

MALAWI*

Lilongwe
British High Commission
Lingadzi House, (PO Box 30042), Lilongwe 3
(Tel: Lilongwe 731544)
(Telex: 44727) (a/b 44727 UK REPLI MI)

High Commissioner: W N Wenban-Smith, CMG
Deputy High Commissioner: D G Davies
First Secretary (Development): P R O Bromley
Second Secretary (Management): N J Enescott
Second Secretary (Commercial): S J Seaman
Second Secretary (Chancery/Information/Consular):
A J M Dunlop
Second Secretary (Works): R A Reynolds

**British Development Division in
Southern Africa**
Lingadzi House (PO Box 30059, Lilongwe 3)
(Tel: Lilongwe 731544)
(Telex: 447 27 (a/b 44727 UKREPLI MI)
(Facsimile: 734163)

Head of Division: Ms S E Unsworth
Senior Natural Resources Adviser: A J Tainsh
Senior Engineering Adviser: C I Ellis
Senior Education Adviser: M Seath
Senior Health Adviser: Ms S Simmonds
Engineering Adviser: A Barker
Senior Economic Adviser: P Owen
Economic Adviser: Ms R Phillipson
Manpower and Training Adviser: M Blunt
Natural Resources Adviser: A T Barrett
Programme Adviser: M Mallalieu
Programme Adviser: A S Graham
Programme Adviser: C B Austin
Economic Adviser: Ms R Turner

MALAYSIA*

Kuala Lumpur
British High Commission
185 Jalan, Ampang
Kuala Lumpur (PO Box 11030), 50732 Kuala
Lumpur
(Tel: Main Office 2482122,
Consular section 2487122)
(Telex: 35225 (a/b UKREP MA 35225)
(Facsimile: 2480880)

High Commissioner:
D Slater, CMG
Deputy High Commissioner/Counsellor
(Commercial/Economic): B E Cleghorn
Counsellor: A J G Insall
Defence Adviser: Colonel J L Seddon-Brown
Counsellor (Defence Supply): B Breslin
First Secretary: J D Dennis
First Secretary (Management): K A Taylor, OBE
First Secretary (Commercial): A C Gallie
First Secretary (Resident on Bangkok):P Matthews
First Secretary (Defence Supply): P J Sullivan
Assistant Defence Adviser:
Lieutenant-Commander C C Williams, RN
Second Secretary (Commercial): E Mattey
Second Secretary (Economic): Mrs M J F Logan

Second Secretary (resident in Bangkok): M S Brown
Second Secretary (Consular): J K Greengrass
Third Secretary (Information): Ms C A Saunders

Johor
Office of the Honorary British Representative
Lucas Automotive Sdn Bhd, PLO 17, Senai
Industrial Estate KB105, 81400 Senai, Johor
(Tel: (DL) 07-592377, 591301)
(Telex: MA 60762 (LUCMAL))
(Facsimile: (07) 549301)

Honorary British Representative: J W Bradbury

Kuching
Officer of the Honorary British Representative, c/o
Standard Chartered Bank, (PO Box No 12), 93900
Kuching, Sarawak, East Malaysia
(Tel: Kuching (DL) 082-243616, 52233)
(Telex: MA 70117) (a/b CHARTA MA 70117)
(Facsimile: (082) 414299)

Honorary British Representative: I P Beaton

Kota Kinabalu
Office of the Honorary British Representative
The Hong Kong and Shanghai Banking
Corporation, PO Box 11602, 88817
Kota Kinabalu, Sabah, East Malaysia
(Tel: Kota Kinabalu (DL) 088-212622, 223533)
(Telex: MA 80065 (HSBCKK MA 80065))
(Facsimile: (088) 213041)

Honorary British Representative: M K G Scott

Miri
Office of the Honorary British Representative
Sarawak Shell Berhad 98009 Miri, Sarawak
(Tel: 454076/453010)
(Facsimile: 085-452030)

Honorary British Representative: M R E Ellis

Penang
Office of the Honorary British Representative
Plantation Agencies Sdn Bhd,
Standard Chartered Bank Chambers,
Beach Street, 10300 Penang
(Tel: 04-625333)
(Facsimile: (04) 622018)

Honorary British Representative: J W West

The Republic of MALDIVES*

Male
British High Commission (all staff resident at
Colombo)

High Commissioner: E J Field, CMG
*Deputy High Commissioner and Head of
Chancery:* R P Nash, LVO
Defence Adviser: Lieutenant-Colonel
I G Baillie
First Secretary (Economic and Commercial):
Mr J R Albright
First Secretary: B C Walters
Second Secretary (Aid): M R Foord
Second Secretary (Consular and Management): A
J Mayland
Second Secretary: R Affleck (resides at Bombay)

Cultural Attaché: (British Council Director):
R A Jarvis
Assistant Cultural Attaché: (British Council):
Ms H G Liesching
Assistant Cultural Attaché: (British Council):
Dr M Milton

Republic of MALI

Bamako (All staff resident at Dakar)

Ambassador: R C Beetham, LVO
First Secretary and Deputy Head of Mission: M J
Hentley
Cultural Attaché: (British Council Director):
Ms A Malamah-Thomas
Assistant British Council Director:
J M McCullough
Third Secretary (Chancery/Information):
Miss S H Jump
Third Secretary (Management) *and Vice-Consul:*
K J Lynch

British Consulate
BP 2069, Bamako
(Tel: 22 20 64)

Consul (Resides at Dakar): M J Hentley
Vice-Consul (Resides at Dakar): K J Lynch
Honorary Consul: C Jessop, MBE

MALTA

Valletta
British High Commission
7 St Anne Street, Floriana, Malta GC
PO Box 506
(Tel: Malta 233134-8)
(Telex: 1249) (a/b UKREP MW)
(Facsimile: 0356-622001)

High Commissioner: Sir Peter Wallis, KCVO, CMG
Deputy High Commissioner and First Secretary
(Consular/Management): R White
Second Secretary (Management): L R Dalrymple, MVO
Second Secretary (Consular): N Johnson
Third Secretary (Cultural/Information):
Mrs E A Ripard
Third Secretary (Consular): Miss S E Wooten
Third Secretary (Immigration): T J Dearden

MARSHALL ISLANDS

Majuro
British Embassy
PO Box No 61, Bairiki Tarawa
Telegraphic address: UKREP TARAWA
(Tel: (686) 21327)
(Telex: 77050 (a/b UKREPKI 77050)
(Facsimile: (686) 21488

Ambassador: D L White (resides at Tarawa)

MAURITANIA

Nouakchott
British Embassy (All staff resident in Rabat except
the Consul-General and Consul (Commercial) who
reside in Casablanca)

Ambassador: J E C Macrae, CMG
Consul-General: P C F Gregory-Hood
First Secretary (Commercial) *and Deputy Head of Mission:* G A Pirie
Defence Attaché: Lt Col C A Le Hardy
Attaché (Cultural Affairs): D T Baldwin
Consul (Commercial): T M Adams
Second Secretary (Political/Information): J P Bedingfield
Second Secretary and Consul: R Patten
Third Secretary (Management): Miss F Maxton
Vice-Consul: Miss S Sweet

Nouakchott
British Consulate

Honorary Consul: (vacant)

MAURITIUS

Port Louis
British High Commission
King George V Avenue, Floreal, Mauritius
(PO Box 186, Curepipe)
(Tel:(230) 686 5795/6/7/8/9)
(Telex: 4266) (a/b 4266 UKREP IW)
(Facsimile: (230) 6865792)

Commercial Section:
1st Floor, Ken Lee Building,
20 Edith Cavell Street
Port Louis
(Tel: 208 9850/1)
(Telex: 4861 UKCOMM IW)
(Facsimile: 212 8470)

High Commissioner: M E Howell, CMG, OBE
Deputy High Commissioner and First Secretary (Commercial): H L Samuel
Defence Adviser (resides at Nairobi): Colonel P Bell
Attaché: (Immigration/Consular): Mrs K Taylor
Third Secretary (Management): N D M Taylor
Third Secretary (Aid/Chancery): M B Harper

MEXICO

Mexico City
British Embassy
Lerma 71, Col Cuauhtémoc, 06500 Mexico City
DF (PO Box No 96 Bis)
(Tel: (52) (5) 207 2089, 2149, 2449, 2509)
(Telex: 177-3093) (a/b 177-3093 UKEMME)
(Facsimile: (52) (5) 207 7672)

Ambassador: Sir Roger Hervey, KCVO, CMG
Counsellor, Deputy Head of Mission: R D Hart
Counsellor (Cultural): Dr B J Lavercombe
First Secretary (Political): Miss C E Nettleton
Defence Attaché: Colonel A J Dobson
First Secretary (Chancery): Dr J A Brewer
First Secretary (Commercial and Economic): J F Thompson
First Secretary (Scientific and Technological Affairs): A N Martin
First Secretary (Management): M H F Legg
First Secretary (Cultural): Dr P H Williams
Second Secretary and Consul: R E D Deffee, MBE
Secretary Secretary (Commercial): R C Woodward
Second Secretary (Economic): D S Wright
Second Secretary (Cultural): Miss I Monk

Third Secretary (Chancery): P T Moody
Third Secretary (Management): Mrs G Y Woodward

Mexico City
British Consulate
Embassy Consular Section
Río Usumacinta 30, Col. Cuauhtémoc, 06500,
Mexico DF
(Telephones and Telex as for Embassy)

Consul: R E D Deffee, MBE
Vice-Consul: Mrs J C Evans

Acapulco
British Consulate
Hotel Las Brisas (PO Box 281) Acapulco,
Guerrrero
(Tel: (748) 46605)
(Telex: 16837)

Honorary Consul: D B Gore, MBE

Ciudad Juarez
British Consulate
Calle Fresno 185, Campestre Juarez,
Ciudad Juarez, Chihuahua
(Tel: (161) 75791)

Honorary Consul: C R Maingot

Guadalajara
British Consulate
Calz. Gonzalez Gallo 1897,
Guadalajara, Jalisco (Apto. Postal 32-94)
(Tel: (36) 35 82 95, 35 89 27, 39 16 16)

Honorary Consul: S Cohen

Merida
British Consulate
Calle 5853 No 450 (PO Box 89), Merida, Yucatan
(Tel: (992) 16799) (Telex: 753610)
(Facsimile: (992) 282962)

Honorary Consul: Major A Dutton (Retd), MBE
Honorary Vice-Consul: M A Dutton

Monterrey
British Consulate
Privada de Tamazunchale 104, Garza Garcia,
Col. de Valle, Monterrey, Nuevo Leon 66220
(Tel: (83) 569114, 782565)
(Facsimile: 355438)

Honorary Consul: E R Lawrence, MBE

Tampico
British Consulate
2 de Enero 102 Sur-A
Tampico, Tamaulipas
(Tel: (121) 129784 and 129817)

Honorary Consul: D Schulze, MBE

Veracruz
British Consulate
Lloyds Register of Shipping,
Emperan No. 200 P.B., Apdo Postal 724

(Tel: (29) 310955)
(Telex: 151681)

Honorary Consul: Luis Carbajal

MICRONESIA

Pohnpei
British Embassy
PO Box No 61, Bairiki Tarawa
Telegraphic address: UKREP TARAWA
(Tel: (686) 21327)
(Telex: 77050 (a/b UKREPKI 77050)
(Facsimile: (686) 21488

Ambassador: D L White (resides at Tarawa)

MOLDAVIA

Kishinev
British Embassy Moscow

Ambassador: Sir Brian Fall, KCMG (resides at Moscow)

MONACO

British Consulate-General
24 Avenue du Prado, 13006 Marseilles
(Tel: (91) 53 43 32, 37 66 95)
Telex: 420307 (a/b BRITAIN MARSL)

Consul-General (Resides at Marseilles): J Illman
Honorary Consul (Resides at Nice):
Lieutenant-Colonel R 'W Challoner, OBE

MONGOLIA

Ulaanbaatar
British Embassy
30 Enkh Taivny Gudamzh (PO Box No 703)
Ulaanbaatar 13, Mongolia
(Tel: 510331)
(Telex: 79 261 MH(A/B) UKREP MH)
(Facsimile: 1445143)

Ambassador: A B N Morey
Second Secretary: N Hart

MOROCCO

Rabat
British Embassy
17 Boulevard de la Tour Hassan (BP 45), Rabat
(Tel: Rabat (010 212 (7)) 209 051/6, 314 031/4)
(Telex 31022) (a/b PRODROME 31022 M)

Ambassador: J E C Macrae, CMG
First Secretary (Commercial) *and Deputy Head of Mission:* G A Pirie
Defence Attaché: Lieutenant Colonel C A Le Hardy
Cultural Attaché: (British Council Director): E J Weston
Second Secretary (Political/Information): N D Hopton
Second Secretary (Management) *and Vice-Consul:* R Patten
Assistant Cultural Attaché (British Council Assistant Director): D T Baldwin

Third Secretary (Management): Miss F Maxton
Vice-Consul: Miss S Sweet

Tangier
Tangier Office of the British Embassy
Trafalgar House
9 Rue Amerique du Sud
(BP 2122) Tangier
(Tel: (212) 9935 897)

Vice-Consul: W W Page

Casablanca
British Consulate-General
60 Boulevard d'Anfa (BP 13.762), Casablanca
(Tel: 22.16.53/22.17.41/22.31.85)
(Telex: 22781) (a/b BRITAIN 22781 M)
(Facsimile: 26 57 79)

Consul-General (M): P C F Gregory-Hood
Consul (Commercial/Information) (M): T M Adams
Vice-Consul (Commercial): S E Elazar, MBE
Vice-Consul: Mrs L J Adams
Vice-Consul: Mrs C M El Beleidi

Agadir
British Consulate
Hotel Sud Bahia,
Rue des Administrations Publiques, Agadir
(Tel: Agadir 23741)
(Telex: 81070) (a/b BAHIR M)

Honorary Consul: O Benlahcen

MOZAMBIQUE

Maputo
British Embassy
Av Vladimir I Lenine 310, (Caixa Postal 55),
Maputo
(Tel: (258 1) 420111/2/5/6/7)
(Telex: 6-265) (a/b 6-265 PROMA MO)
(Telegraphic Address: PRODROME MAPUTO)
(Facsimile: 421666)

Ambassador: R J S Edis
First Secretary, Consul and Deputy Head of Mission: P January
Defence Attaché:
Lieutenant Colonel C W Larkin, OBE
First Secretary (Chancery): N J L Busvine
First Secretary (Aid): J M Winter
First Secretary (British Council Director): Ms C ffrench-Blake
Second Secretary (Management) *and Vice-Consul:* J Fielder
Third Secretary: (Chancery/Aid): K Shannon

NAMIBIA

Windhoek
British High Commission
116 Leutwein Street, Windhoek 9000
(Tel: (264) 61-223022)
(Facsimile: 264 61-228895)

High Commissioner: H G Hogger
Deputy High Commissioner: J G Rice
First Secretary: R G Bowen, LVO

First Secretary (British Council): D J Utley
Second Secretary: E Taylor
Third Secretary (AMO/Vice Consul): Mrs A Sealy

NAURU*

Nauru
British High Commission (All staff resident at Suva)

High Commissioner: T J David
Deputy High Commissioner, Head of Chancery and First Secretary (Consular): R C B Jones
Second Secretary (Aid and Commercial): Mrs A C Hamilton-Walker
Attaché: (Consular/Management): R Hunter

NEPAL

Kathmandu
British Embassy
Lainchaur Kathmandu (PO Box 106)
(Tel: 410583, 411789, 414588)
(Telex: 2343 (a/b 2342 BRITEM NP))
Telegraphic Address: PRODROME KATHMANDU
(Facsimile: 977 1 411789)

Ambassador: T J B George, CMG
Deputy Head of Mission and Consul: A R Hall
Defence Attaché: Colonel M H Kefford, OBE
First Secretary (Development/Commercial Officer): B W Money
Second Secretary (Management/Consular): H T F Jenkins
Cultural Attaché: (British Council Representative): R P Hale
Vice-Consul: Miss L C Craig
Assistant Cultural Attaché (British Council Assistant Director): J A Mackenzie
Third Secretary (Development): Mrs K McGeough

NETHERLANDS

The Hague
British Embassy
Lange. Voorhout 10, 2514 ED, The Hague
(Tel: 364.58.00)
(Telex: 31600) (a/b 31600 BEMB NL)
(Facsimile: (31) (70) 360 3839)

Ambassador: Sir Michael Jenkins, KCMG
Deputy Head of Mission: R P Flower
Counsellor (Commercial): A D Sprake
Defence and Naval Attaché: Captain H W Rickard, RN
Military and Air Attaché:
Lieutenant Colonel J C Young
First Secretary and Head of Political Section: J D Sawyer
First Secretary (Political): N J G Beer
First Secretary (Labour) (Resides at Brussels): A Tyson
First Secretary (Political/Information): Miss M Gibson
First Secretary (Commercial): J E Mayhew
First Secretary (Management): F McDermott
Second Secretary (Economic/Agriculture/Commercial): G N Loten

Second Secretary (Chancery): C E F Newns
Second Secretary (Chancery): Miss K L Williams
Attaché: S R Titmarsh

Amsterdam
British Consulate-General
Koningslaan 44, 1075 AE, Amsterdam
(PO Box 75488, 1070 AL Amsterdam)
(Tel: 676 43 43)
(Telex: 15117) (a/b 15117 UKAMS NL)
(Facsimile: 761069)

Consul-General: D H Doble
Consul: T C Lamb
Vice-Consul: Miss K E Roskilly
Vice-Consul: P M Barnett
Vice-Consul: M A A Mason

Willemstad
(Curaçao)
(Netherlands Antilles)
British Consulate
Bombadiersweg Z/N, (PO Box 3803), Willemstad, Curaçao, Netherlands Antilles
(Tel: (599) (9) 36 95 33)
(Telex: 3372) (a/EQIPNA)
(Facsimile: (599) (9) 36 95 33)

Consul-General: (Resident at Amsterdam): D H Doble
Consul: (Resident at Caracas): A R J Attryde
Honorary Consul: E J Wilson
Vice-Consul: (Resident at Caracas): M P Johnston

NEW ZEALAND

Wellington
British High Commission
44 Hill Street, Wellington, 1
(Mailing Address: British High Commission, PO Box 1812; Overseas Trade Services (only): PO Box 369)
(Tel: (4726049)
(Telex: NZ3325) (a/b UKREP NZ 3325)
(Telegraphic Address: UKREP Wellington)
(Facsimile: 4711 974 or 499 4176)

High Commissioner: D J Moss, CMG
(also Governor, Pitcairn and High Commissioner to Western Samoa)
Deputy High Commissioner: I C Orr
Counsellor: T H Preston
Defence Adviser and Senior British Defence Liaison Officer: Group Captain D W F Angela, RAF
First Secretary (Chancery/Information): J W Yapp
First Secretary (Commercial): P Rogan
First Secretary (Agriculture and Food): Mrs E A Blackwell
First Secretary (British Council Director): D J F King
Second Secretary (Management/Consular): D Battisby-Dutton
Second Secretary (Works) (Resides at Canberra): J Warrener
Second Secretary (Chancery): Miss B A Proctor
Attaché: (Consular): Mrs A C Harris

Auckland
British Consulate-General
15th Floor, Faye Richwhite Building, 151 Queen
Street, Auckland, 1
(Tel: 30 32-973, 30 32970/1 Immigration only)
(Telex: 2412) (a/b BRITN NZ 2412)
(Telegraphic Address: BRITAUCK)
(Facsimile: 30 31836)
Mailing Address: British Consulate-General,
Private Bag, Auckland, 1

Consul-General and Director of Trade Promotion:
J F Holding
Consul (Commercial): V M Scarborough
Vice-Consul (Immigration/Management): B Conley

Christchurch
British Consulate
2nd floor suite
173 Cashel Street, Christchurch 1
Box 6109, Riccarton,
Christchurch 8004
(Tel: 64 3 655440)
(Facsimile: 64 3 652350)

Honorary Consul: G N Robinson

NICARAGUA
Managua
British Embassy
Reparto "Los Robles"
Primera Etapa
Entrada Principal de la Carretera a Masaya
Cuarta Casa a Mano Derecha, Managua
(Tel: Managua 780014, 780887, 674050)
(Telex: 2166) (a/b PRODROME NK)
(Facsimile: 784085

Ambassador and Consul-General: J H Culver
*First Secretary, Consul and Deputy Head of
Mission* (Resides at San José): R J Hutchings
Defence Attaché (Resides at Panama City):
Lieutenant Colonel T A Glen
First Secretary (Commercial) *and Director of
Trade Promotion for Central America* (Resides at
San José): A S Green, OBE, MVO
Second Secretary (Technical Assistance) (Resides
at San José): Mrs E A Kehoe

NIGER
Niamey
British Embassy (All staff resident at Abidjan)

Ambassador and Consul-General:
Miss M I Rothwell, CMG
First Secretary (Commercial), *Head of Chancery
and Consul:* D R F Flanagan
First Secretary (Education): C Stevenson
Second Secretary and Information Officer:
P J Whitehead
Second Secretary (Commercial) *and Vice-Consul:*
(Vacant)
Third Secretary and Vice-Consul:
Miss A C Kennedy

British Vice-Consulate
BP11168 Niamey. Niger
(Tel: 732015 or 732539)

Honorary Vice-Consul: B Niandou

NIGERIA
Lagos
British High Commission
11 Eleke Crescent, Victoria Island (Private Mail
Bag 12136)
(Tel: Lagos 619531, 619537, 619541, 619543,
619566) (Telex: 21247) (a/b UKREP NG)
(Facsimile: 614021)
Visa Section
Chellaram Building, 54 Marina, Lagos
(Tel: 667061, 666413, 666510, 666513, 666818,
633893, 632903)
(Facsimile: 666909)

High Commissioner: A C D S Macrae, CMG
(also non-resident Ambassador to the Republic of
Benin)
*Deputy High Commissioner and Minister/
Counsellor:* R S Gorham
Defence and Military Adviser: Colonel A C Taylor
Naval and Air Adviser:
Wing Commander A M Carter, RAF
Counsellor (Economic and Commercial): E A
Burner
Counsellor: R I S McGuigan
Counsellor (Management): P M H Young
First Secretary (Commercial): C Jonsen, OBE
First Secretary (Political): A D Kavanagh
First Secretary (Political/Economic): C J B White
First Secretary (Aid): T P N Livesey
First Secretary (Information): T S Rawlinson
First Secretary (Consular/Immigration):
D B McAdam
First Secretary (Management): M J Towsey
Second Secretary (Political): M Denton
Second Secretary (Commercial): P D Jenkins
Second Secretary (Consular): M Keith
Second Secretary (Works): J Sweeney
Second Secretary (Immigration): P A H Benns
Second Secretary (Management): C J Thomas
Second Secretary (Immigration): M J Seery
Second Secretary (Immigration): L C Taylor
Second Secretary (Political): F Cochrane-Dyet

Kaduna
British Deputy High Commission
2/4 Lamido Road, (Private Mail Bag 2096)
Kaduna
(Tel: Kaduna (062) 233380-2)
(Telex: 71104) (a/b 71104 BHCKAD NG)
(Facsimile: 237267)

Deputy High Commissioner: C K Woodfield, OBE
First Secretary (Commercial/Information):
G Fairhurst

NORWAY
Oslo
British Embassy
Thomas Heftyesgate 8, 0244 Oslo 2
(Tel: (02) 55 24 00)
(Facsimile: (02) 55 10 41)

Ambassador: D J E Ratford, CMG, CVO
Consul-General and Deputy Head of Mission:
Miss A J K Bailes
Defence and Air Attaché:
Wing Commander J C W Marshall, RAF
Naval Attaché:
Commander G S Pearson, RN
Military Attaché:
Lieutenant-Colonel G Dodgson
First Secretary (Economic and Commercial):
A L Wotton
First Secretary (Chancery): E R M Davies
First Secretary (Management): R H Tonkin
First Secretary: Mrs G M Walton
First Secretary (Commercial/Economic):
S M Williams
Second Secretary (Information):
C P Winnington-Ingram
Second Secretary (Economic and Commercial):
E C Mason
Second Secretary and Consul: A G Harrison
Second Secretary (Political): A D Jackson
Third Secretary (Commercial): A Hackett
Third Secretary (Resides at Copenhagen):
P S Stevenson
Vice-Consul: J A Webb

Ålesund
British Consulate
Farstadgarden, St Olavs Pl., PO Box 130, 6001
Ålesund
(Tel: (071) 24460)
(Telex: 42755)
(Facsimile: (071) 28530)

Honorary Consul: S A Farstad (Norwegian)

Bergen
British Consulate
A/S Bergens Rørhandel, Carl Konowsgate 34,
Postboks 872, 5001 Bergen
(Tel: (47) (5) 348505)
(Telex: 42248 RENAN)
(Telefax: (47 5) 343 247)

Honorary Consul: R C Hestness (Norwegian)

Harstad
British Consulate
PO Box 322, Strandgate 7,
9401 Harstad
(Tel: (082) 64 631)
(Home) 63 093
(Facsimile: (082) 67745)

Honorary Consul: T O Jacobsen (Norwegian)

Haugesund
British Consulate
Sørhauggt 139, Post Box 128, 5501 Haugesund
(Tel: (04) 72 30 33
(Telex: 42206)
(Facsimile: (04) 723087)

Honorary Consul: K Rasmussen, MBE (Norwegian)

Kristiansund (N)
British Consulate
Vageveien 7, Post Box 148,

6501 Kristiansund N
(Tel: Kristiansund North (073) 75333)
(Telex: 15019)
(Facsimile: (47 73) 753 52)

Honorary Consul: J Leonnechen (Norwegian)

Kristiansand (S)
British Consulate
Tollbodgaten 2, PO Box 300, 461
Kristiansand S
(Tel: (042) 22439)
(Facsimile: 042-22595)

Honorary Consul: J H B Moe, MBE (Norwegian)

Stavanger
British Consulate
Mollegate 23, PO Box 28,
4001 Stavanger
Postal address: PB 178 4001 Stavanger
(Tel: (04) 526020)
(Facsimile: (474) 524340

Honorary Consul: E Mills

Tromsø
British Consulate
c/o L Macks Olbryggeri, Post Box 1103, 9001
Tromsø
(Tel: (83) 84 800)
(Facsimile: (83) 58677)

Honorary Consul: H Bredrup (Norwegian)

Trondheim
British Consulate
Sluppenveien 10, (PO Box 6004) 7003 Trondheim
(Tel: (07) 968211)
(Telex: 55436 (a/b 55436 PROF N))
(Facsimile: (07) 965498) (47 7) 965 498

Honorary Consul: F Kjelsdberg (Norwegian)

OMAN
Muscat
British Embassy
Muscat (PO Box 300)
(Tel: Muscat 738501-5)
(Telex: 5216 (a/b 5216 PRODROME ON))
(Facsimile: 968-736040)
Commercial Section: PO Box 6898 Ruwi
(Tel: 706468)
(Telex: 3743 (a/b 3743 BRITRADE ON))
(Facsimile: 706467)

Ambassador: Sir Terence Clark, KBE, CMG, CVO
Counsellor and Deputy Head of Mission:
N H S Armour
Defence and Military Attaché:
Brigadier M F Bremridge, MC
Naval and Air Attaché:
Wing Commander C B Troke, RAF
First Secretary (Chancery): N H Bates
First Secretary (Commercial): P Nessling
Second Secretary (Management) *and Consul* (M):
G H Davies
Second Secretary (Chancery): A W Turner

Second Secretary (Commercial): J A Begbie
Third Secretary (Political): I P Bailey
Third Secretary (Commercial): P R Seaby
Third Secretary (Management): Mrs J I Begbie
BERS Liaison Officer: L P Taylor
Vice Consul: C Ling

PACIFIC ISLANDS

(See under United States of America)

PAKISTAN

Islamabad
British High Commission
Diplomatic Enclave, Ramna 5, PO Box 1122,
Islamabad
(Tel: 8221311/5)
(Telex: 54122) (a/b 54122 UKEMBPK)
(Facsimile: 823439)

High Commissioner:
Sir Nicholas Barrington, KCMG, CVO
Deputy High Commissioner: J C Harrison, LVO
Counsellor (Economic/Commercial/Aid): P J Dun
Counsellor: J P G Wiseman
Defence and Military Adviser:
Brigadier I McLeod, OBE, MC
Naval and Air Adviser:
Commander D A Scott
First Secretary: G B Reid
First Secretary: P Wilson
First Secretary (Management): G C Livesey, OBE
First Secretary (Consular and Immigration):
F Pett
First Secretary (Commercial/Economic): P J Cole
First Secretary (Economic): J H R Blount
First Secretary (Site Control Officer):
J K Medlen
Second Secretary: M J Bragg
Second Secretary (Consular): D S Adamson
Second Secretary (Immigration): S Lusk
Second Secretary (Immigration): Miss V I Milton
Second Secretary (Immigration): H Rooney
Second Secretary (Management): T M J Collard
Second Secretary (Nurse): Miss A McDonald
Second Secretary (TWG): A Gillott
Second Secretary (Aid): R A W Marshall
Second Secretary (Chancery/Information):
T J Colley
Third Secretary (Chancery): A J Walker
Third Secretary: A P Deane
Third Secretary (Commercial): R L Walters

Lahore
Office of the British Honorary Consul
c/o ICI Pakistan Ltd, 63 Mozang Road, Lahore
(Tel: Lahore 869371-79 (Home 380892))
(Telex: 44851 or 44880)

Honorary British Representative: B A Khan

Karachi
Office of The British Deputy High Commission
Shahrah-e-Iran, Clifton, Karachi 75600
(Tel: 532041-6, 530545)
(Telex: 24180 (a/b 24180 UKREP KA PK))
(Telegraphic Address: Britcongen KARACHI)
(Facsimile: (92 21) 5691512

Deputy High Commissioner: D J Young
First Secretary (Commercial): J G Lindsay, OBE
Second Secretary (Management/Consular): A Mills
Second Secretary: J Dodds
Second Secretary: J M C Ansell
Second Secretary (Immigration): M Sim
Third Secretary (Political/Aid): M K Roper
Attaché (Consular): C J McGill
Attaché (Management): A T McAllister

PANAMA

Panama City
British Embassy
Torre Swiss Bank, Calle 53 (Apartado 889
Zona 1) Panama City, Republic of Panama
(Tel: Panama City 69-0866)
(Telex: 3620) (a/b PROPANA PG), 368.3620
(calls originated in USA only)
(Facsimile: (507) 23-0730)

Ambassador and Consul-General:
T H Malcomson
First Secretary (Commercial) *and Director of
Trade Promotion for Central America* (resides at
San José): A S Green
First Secretary (resides at San José): RJ Hutchings
Defence, Naval, Military and Air Attaché:
Lieutenant-Colonel T A Glen

PAPUA NEW GUINEA*

Port Moresby
British High Commission
Kiroki Street, Waigani,
PO Box 4778, Boroko,
Port Moresby
(Tel: 251677, 251643, 251645, 251659)
(Telex: NE 22142) (a/b UKREP NE 22142)
(Facsimile: 1675253547)

High Commissioner: J W Guy, OBE
*Deputy High Commissioner and Head of
Chancery:* A J Morris
Defence Adviser (Resides at Canberra):
Colonel G A Morris, OBE
Third Secretary (Management/Consular):
Mrs D Hansen

PARAGUAY

Asunción
British Embassy
Calle President Franco 706 (PO Box 404),
Asunción
(Tel: 49-146, 44-472)
(Telex: 139) (a/b PRODROME 139 PY)
(Facsimile: 446 385)

Ambassador and Consul-General: M A C Dibben
Defence, Naval, Military and Air Attaché (Resides
at Montevideo): Captain R A Highton, RN
Commercial/Information Officer: H Silvero
Management Officer/Accountant: Miss C Rea

PERU

Lima
British Embassy
Edificio El Pacifico Washington (Piso 12), Plaza

Washington, Avenida Arequipa
(PO Box 854), Lima 100
(Tel: 33-4738, 33-4839, 33-4932, 33-5032, 33-5137)
(Telex: 25230) (a/b 25230 PU PRODROME)
(Facsimile: 33 47 35) (51 14)

Ambassador: D K Haskell, CMG, CVO
First Secretary, (Commercial) *Deputy Head of Mission and Consul:* F R C Thomson
Defence Attaché: Colonel C H Van de Noot, MBE
Cultural Attaché: (British Council Director):
D J Harvey
First Secretary: G Chalder
Assistant Cultural Attaché: (British Council):
A Mackay
Second Secretary (Chancery/Information) *and Vice-Consul:* R N J Baker
Second Secretary (Management) *and Vice-Consul:*
M K Banham
Vice-Consul: Mrs M A Chesterton

Arequipa
British Consulate
Quesada 107, Yanahuara,
Arequipa
(Tel: 21-37-54)
(Telex: 51031 PE CAMARAQP)
(Facsimile: 21 48 73)

Honorary Consul: J R G Roberts

Piura
British Consulate
Avenida Grau No. 760, Casilla 193, Piura
(Tel: (74) 32 25 32)

Honorary Consul: (Vacant)

Trujillo
British Consulate
Jesus de Nazareth No. 312, Trujillo
(Tel: (44) 235548)

Honorary Consul: W Barber

Iquitos
British Consulate
Jiron Arica 253, Apartado 129, Iquitos
(Tel: 23-4110, 23-4383)
(Telex: 91003 PE-PB)

Honorary Council: L C J Power

Cusco
British Consulate
Hotel San Agustin, Maruri 390, Cusco
(Tel: (51) (84) 22 23 22, 23 10 01)
(Facsimile: (84) 22 11 74)

Honorary Consul: Dr R Delgado

PHILIPPINES

Manila
British Embassy
17/F Locsin Building, 6752 Ayala Avenue,
Makati, Metro Manila 3116, Philippines
(Tel: 816 7116) (16 lines)
Consular/Visa 816 7271 (4 lines)

(Telex: 63282) (a/b 63282 PRODME PN)
(Facsimile: 819 7206 Management/Information)
810 2745 (Consular/Visa) 815 6233 (Chancery/Commercial/Defence)

Ambassador: A E Montgomery
Deputy Head of Mission: A S Collins
Defence Attaché: Lieutenant Colonel J P Clough
First Secretary (Commercial): R J Cork
Cultural Attaché: (British Council Director):
N Bisset
Second Secretary and Consul: J H Fulton
Second Secretary (Management): A A W Loosemore
Second Secretary (Chancery/Information):
R M F Chatterton-Dickson
Second Secretary (Immigration): R J Shead
Third Secretary (Immigration): W B Vincent
Third Secretary (Commercial): M D Walley

Cebu
Office of the British Honorary Consular Agent
35 Paseo Eulalia, Maria Luisa Estate Park,
Banilad, Cebu City 6401
(Tel: 82157)
(Facsimile: (63) (32) 460 269)

Honorary Consular Agent: Mrs M P Jackson

POLAND

Warsaw
British Embassy
Aleja Roz No 1, 00-556 Warsaw
(Tel: (2) 6281001-5)
(Telex: 813694) (a/b 813694 PROD PL)
(Facsimile: 217161)
(Visa and Consular Sections: Wawelska 14, 02-061 Warsaw)
(Tel: 25.80.31/2/3/4/5)
(Telex: 81-61-13 a/b BRITN PL.)
(Facsimile: 250 328)

Ambassador: M J Llewellyn Smith, CMG
Counsellor and Deputy Head of Mission:
R A E Gordon, OBE
Defence and Air Attaché:
Group Captain H H Moses, MBE, RAF
Naval and Military Attaché:
Lieutenant Colonel J R M Pitt
First Secretary (Management): R Leadbeater
First Secretary (Embassy Medical Officer):
Dr A C E Stacey
First Secretary (Political/Economic): M R Etherton
First Secretary: M J Crawford
First Secretary (Economic and Commercial):
A J Gooch
First Secretary (Information): T Clayden
First Secretary and Consul: A E Stead
First Secretary (Chancery): A R Loweth
Assistant Naval Attaché (Resides at Moscow):
Lieutenant Commander G A Newton, RN
Second Secretary (Commercial): J Rutherford
Second Secretary: D A Munro
Second Secretary (Political): M H Davenport
Second Secretary: J E Golding
Third Secretary (Visits): Miss C A J Readdie
Third Secretary (Economic): S J Banks
Attaché and Vice-Consul: A K Pike

PORTUGAL

Lisbon

British Embassy
35-37, Rua de S Domingos Aa Lapa, 37 1200
Lisbon Cedex
(Tel: (351) (1) 3961191, 3961147, 3963181)
(Telex: 12278) (a/b 12278 PROLIS P)
(Facsimile: (351) (1) 3976768)

Ambassador: H J Arbuthnott, CMG
Counsellor and Deputy Head of Mission:
T T Macan
Defence, Naval and Air Attaché: Commander
P M Jones, RN
Military Attaché and Deputy Defence Attaché:
Lieutenant Colonel P N de R Channer
*First Secretary and Head Political/Information
Sections:* B Hopkinson
First Secretary (Political): P J B Roberts
First Secretary (Commercial): D H Turner
First Secretary (Management): R Parkinson, MBE
First Secretary and Consul: D J Ferguson
Second Secretary (Poitical/Information):
S C H Wilson
Second Secretary (Political): Miss J E Bull
Second Secretary (Commercial): Miss K J Baudains
Second Secretary: C Harrison
Third Secretary and Vice-Consul: Miss P Gedney
Third Secretary (Political): A W Ellis

Funchal (Madeira)

British Consulate
Avenida de Zarco No 2, CP417, 9000 Funchal,
Madeira
(Tel: (091) 21221)
(Telex: 72125 a/b BLANDY P)

Honorary Consul: R F Blandy, MBE

Oporto

British Consulate
Avenida da Boavista 3072, 4100 Oporto
(Tel: 02-684789)
(Telex: 26647 (a/b 26647 UKOPO P))
(Facsimile: (3512) 6100438)

Consul: J Thomas

Ponta Delgada (Azores)

British Consulate
Largo Vasco Bensaúde 13,
9500 Ponta Delgada, Sao Miguel, Azores
(Tel: (096) 22201)
(Telex: 82401 (a/b 82401 GRUBEN P))

Honorary Consul: F R Bensaude

Portimão

British Consulate
Rue de Santa Isabel, 21-1py007-Esq, 8500
Portimão
(Tel: 082-27057)
(Telex: (351) (82) 58732 (a/b BRICON P))
(Facsimile: 082-23071)

Honorary Consul: Dr J M T G P de Azevedo, OBE

Macao

British Consulate-General
British Trade Commission, 9th Floor,
Bank of America Tower, 12 Harcourt Road,
Hong Kong (PO Box 528)
(Tel: (852) 523 0176)

Consul-General (Resides at Hong Kong):
S P Day, CMG

QATAR

Doha

British Embassy
PO Box 3, Doha, Qatar
(Tel: 421991)
(Telex: 4205) (a/b 4205 PRODRO DH)
(Telegraphic Address: PRODROME DOHA)
(Facsimile: 438692)

Ambassador and Consul-General: G H Boyce, CMG
First Secretary (Commercial) *and Deputy Head of
Mission:* F G Geere
Naval and Air Attaché: Wing Commander W R
Southcombe, RAF (resides at Abu Dhabi)
Second Secretary (Management) *and Consul* (M):
R J Davies
Third Secretary (Commercial) *and Vice-Consul:*
Miss J Adamson
Third Secretary Vice-Consul: F A Drayton

ROMANIA

Bucharest

British Embassy
24, Strada Jules Michelet, 70154 Bucharest
(Tel: 120303,4,5,6)
(Telex: 011 295) (a/b 011295 PRODM R)
(Facsimile: 595090)

Ambassador: A P F Bache, CMG
Deputy Head of Mission: C J Ingham
Defence, Naval and Military Attaché:
Lieutenant Colonel P G Davies
Air Attaché: (Resident at Budapest):
Wing-Commander M A Gaynor, RAF
Cultural Attaché: C C Henning
First Secretary (Economic): J N M Page ▴
First Secretary (Commercial): W E J Preston
First Secretary (Medical Officer) (Resides at
Warsaw): Dr H M Lipman
Second Secretary (Management): I L Wilson
Second Secretary (Consular): J G Fox
Second Secretary (Resides at Athens):
J V T Bennett
Second Secretary (Works) (Resides at Athens):
R Clarke
Second Secretary: L S C Bristow
Assistant Cultural Attaché: A L O'Dell
Third Secretary: J C Withers
Vice-Consul: Miss S J Hodgetts
Vice-Consul: T J Burke

RUSSIAN FEDERATION

Moscow
British Embassy
Moscow 72, Sosiiskaya, Naberezhnaya
(Tel: 231-85-11 (8 lines)
Commercial and Scientific Departments:
Kutuzovsky Prospekt 7/4, Moscow 121248
(Tel: 248, 2010, 2038)
(International Direct Dialling Lines: Embassy
238-46-86)
(Commercial & Scientific Departments 249-49-36)
(Telex: 413341) (a/b BEMOS SU)
(Facsimile: 2333563 (Embassy), 2318653 (PPAU)
2332766 (Visa Section), 2494636 (Commercial))
British Council tel 2334507
Facsimile: 2302697

Ambassador: Sir Brian Fall, KCMG
Minister and Deputy Head of Mission:
F N Richards, CVO
Minister/Counsellor (Internal): G D G Murrell, OBE
Defence and Air Attaché:
Air Commodore P M Stean, RAF
Naval Attaché: Captain W M Caswell, RN
Military Attaché: Brigadier P Jones, CBE
Political Counsellor: D G Manning, CMG
Counsellor (Commercial): D G Gowan
Counsellor (Science and Technology): Dr P E Potter
Counsellor: J M Scarlett, OBE
Counsellor (Cultural Affairs): T Sandell, OBE
Counsellor (Management) *and Consul-General:*
J Daly
First Secretary: A F Slatter
First Secretary (Commercial): I C Mc D Kelly
First Secretary and Press Attaché:
Ms P A Leslie-Jones
First Secretary (Cultural Attaché): K Allen
First Secretary: R T Montgomery
First Secretary (Public Affairs Unit): N A S Jones
First Secretary (Chancery): Ms P A Major
First Secretary (Embassy Medical Adviser):
Dr H M Carpenter
First Secretary (Economic): R L Turner
Assistant Naval Attaché:
Lieutenant Commander G A Newton, RN
Assistant Naval Attaché:
Lieutenant Commander S E Airey, RN
Assistant Military Attaché: Major S J D Harrison
Assistant Air Attaché:
Squadron Leader A W Kerr, RAF
Assistant Air Attaché (Technical):
Wing Commander N Wiseman, RAF
Assistant Cultural Attaché: M G Bird
First Secretary (Estate Manager):
P J Phelan
First Secretary (Education and Training) (British
Council): K Ghosh
First Secretary (British Council): M G Murphy
Second Secretary: C R G Granville
Second Secretary (Chancery): T E Barrow
Second Secretary (Consul): P F C Massey
Second Secretary (Commercial): R H Astle
Second Secretary (Public Affairs Unit):
W L Le B Egerton
Second Secretary (Management): D J Morley
Second Secretary (Commercial): F W Wheeler

Second Secretary (Comm): G D StJ K Spindler
Second Secretary (Chancery): C D Steele
Third Secretary (Science and Technology):
J Harris
Third Secretary (Public Affairs Unit):
Mrs P J McPhail
Third Secretary (Visits): T J Hedley-Jones

St. Petersburg
British Consulate General
c/o Astoria Hotel, St Petersburg
(Tel: (010) (7) 812 210 5412)
(Facsimile: 871 f44 5137)
(Telex: 0581 1445136 (A/B PRERX)

Consul General: S D M Jack
Consul (Commercial): G E Mearns
Second Secretary and Consul: M G Marshall

Republic of RWANDA

British Embassy (All staff resident at Kinshasa)

Kigali

Chargé d' Affaires and Consul: Ms K W Oliver
Deputy Head of Mission and Vice-Consul: Miss H
M Horn

British Consulate
Avenue Paul VI, BP356, Kigali
(Tel: Kigali 75219 (Office), 75905 (Home))
(Telex: 509 (a/b 09 RWANDEX RW))

Honorary Consul: A D Wood, OBE

St KITTS AND NEVIS*

Basseterre
British High Commission
38 St Mary's Street (PO Box 483), St John's,
Antigua
(Tel: St John's 462 0008/9)
(Telex: UKREP ANTIGUA AK 2 113
(a/b 2113 UKREP AK))
Telegraphic Address: UKREP ST JOHN'S
ANTIGUA
(Facsimile: 462 0008/9 E 14)

†*High Commissioner:* E T Davies, CMG
First Secretary and Representative (Resides at St
John's): I D Marsh
†*Deputy High Commissioner:* J A Noakes
Defence Adviser (Resides at Kingston):
Colonel C S Faith, OBE
†*Assistant Defence Adviser:*
Commander H M Humphreys, RN
†*First Secretary* (Chancery): A ffrench-Blake, OBE
†*Second Secretary* (Management/Consular):
Miss S Kaye
†*Second Secretary* (Chancery/Information):
P Mullee
Second Secretary: T V Manhire (Resides at
Kingston)
†*Third Secretary* (Immigration): Mrs A A Howard
(†Resides at Bridgetown)

ST LUCIA*

Castries
British High Commission
Columbus Square (PO Box 227), Castries, St Lucia
(Tel: 010 1 809 2248)
(Telex: 6314) (a/b 6314 UKREP SLC LC)
(Telegraphic Address: UKREP CASTRIES, ST
LUCIA)
(Facsimile: 31543)

†*High Commissioner:* E T Davies, CMG
First Secretary and Resident Representative:
P T Rouse, MBE
†*Deputy High Commissioner:* J A Noakes
Defence Adviser (Resides at Kingston):
Colonel C S Faith, OBE
†*Assistant Defence Adviser:*
Commander H M Humphreys, RN
†*First Secretary* (Chancery): A ffrench-Blake, OBE
†*Second Secretary* (Management/Consular):
Miss S Kaye
†*Second Secretary* (Chancery/Information):
P Mullee
Second Secretary (Resides at Kingston): T V Manhire
†*Second Secretary* (Technical Works): I Agnew
†*Third Secretary:* R H Wildman
(†Resides at Bridgetown)

ST VINCENT*

Kingstown
British High Commission,
Granby Street, (PO Box 132),
Kingstown, St Vincent and the Grenadines
Telephone: Kingstown 71701/2
Telegraphic Address: UKREP
KINGSTOWN ST VINCENT
(Telex: 7516) (a/b 7516 UKREP SVT VQ)
(Facsimile: 62750)

High Commissioner: E T Davies, CMG
First Secretary and Resident Representative:
A Ferguson
Deputy High Commissioner: J A Noakes
Defence Adviser (Resides at Kingston):
Colonel C S Faith, OBE
†*Assistant Defence Adviser:*
Commander H M Humphreys, RN
†*First Secretary* (Chancery): A ffrench-Blake, OBE
First Secretary (Resides at Port of Spain):
J J Penn
†*Second Secretary* (Management/Consular):
Miss S Kaye
Second Secretary (Chancery/Information):
P Mullee
Second Secretary (Resides at Kingston): G Atkinson
†*Second Secretary* (Technical Works): I Agnew
†*Third Secretary:* R H Wildman
(†Resides at Bridgetown)

SAN MARINO

San Marino
Consul-General (Resides at Florence):
M Holmes
Vice-Consul (Resides at Florence): E Masi
Honorary Vice-Consul (Resides at Florence):
A Crighton, CBE

SAO TOMÉ AND PRINCIPE

Sao Tomé
British Embassy (All staff reside at Luanda)

Ambassador: J G Flynn
Consul: A D F Henderson
First Secretary: S M Noakes
Second Secretary (Commercial): P D Sherar

British Consulate
c/o Hull Blythe (Angola) Ltd,
BP 15, Sao Tomé
(Telex: 220 HBALTD ST)

Honorary Consul: Joao Gomes

SAUDI ARABIA

Riyadh
British Embassy
(PO Box 94351) Riyadh 11693
(Tel: 488 0077 (7 lines) (General enquiries); 488
0088 (3 lines) (Commercial enquiries)) (Telex:
406488 (a/b 406488 BRITEM SJ))
(Facsimile: (1) 488-2373, 488 0623)

Ambassador: Sir Alan Munro, KCMG
Counsellor and Deputy Head of Mission:
J S Laing
Counsellor (Commercial): C E J Wilton
Defence & Military Attaché:
Brigadier M J Holroyd-Smith, OBE
Naval Attaché: Commander T Waddington, OBE(Mil), RN
First Secretary (Commercial): A Walker
First Secretary (Economic): P Gooderham
First Secretary (Management) *and*
Consul-General: C H Woodland, OBE
First Secretary (Chancery): M D K Halsey
First Secretary (Defence Supply): M Tonnison
Second Secretary and Consul (M): P E Owens
Second Secretary (Commercial): P R Barklamb
Second Secretary (Commercial): G G Thomas
Second Secretary (Management): W W Wilson
Second Secretary (Chancery): P V Kennedy
Second Secretary (Chancery): J M Crocker
Third Secretary and Vice Consul: R L Wood
Third Secretary (Management): W S Robertson
Third Secretary (Information): T D Stew
Third Secretary: W S Duncan
Third Secretary: K G Watchorn
Third Secretary and Vice-Consul: N A Kernohan
Third Secretary (Commercial): A Lee
Third Secretary (Management): N J Burns

Jedda
British Consulate-General
(PO Box 393) Jedda 21411
(Tel: (9662) 654-6931, 5796, 6803, 5122, 3969)
(Telex: 601043 (a/b BRITAIN SJ))
(Facsimile: (9662) 654 4917)

Consul-General (M): L E Walker, LVO, OBE
Consul (Commercial): R E Duggan
Consul (Commercial): C Parish
Consul: J F Dimmock
Vice Consul: P Haines
Vice Consul (Management): A F Massey

Al Khobar
British Trade Office
PO Box 88, Dhahran
Airport 31932
(Tel: 857-0595)
(Facsimile: 857 0634)

First Secretary (Commercial): A R J Atryde
Second Secretary and *Consul:* M G Plant

SENEGAL

Dakar
British Embassy
20, Rue du Docteur Guillet, (Boite Postale 6025)
Dakar (Tel: 23.73.92, 23.99.71)
(Telex: 21690) (a/b 21690 PRODROME SG)
(Facsimile: 221 23 27 66)

Ambassador: R C Beetham, LVO
First Secretary and Head of Chancery:
M J Ilentley
Defence Attaché (resides at Rabat): Lieutenant
Colonel C A Le Hardy
Cultural Attaché and British Council Director:
Ms A Malamah-Thomas
Assistant British Council Director:
J H McCullough
Third Secretary (Chancery/Information):
Miss S H Jump
Third Secretary (Management) *and Vice-Consul:*
K J Lynch

SERBIA

Belgrade
British Embassy
Generala Zdanova 46, 11000 Belgrade
(Tel: 645055, 645034, 645043, 645087)
(Telex: 11468 (a/b 11468 PROBEL YU))
(Facsimile: (38-11) 659651)

Ambassador: P E Hall, CMG
*Counsellor, Consul General and Deputy Head of
Mission:* M J Robinson
Defence and Military Attaché:
Colonel A M T Moody
Naval and Air Attaché: Wing Commander
R Parker, RAF
First Secretary (Chancery):
W L Jackson-Houlston
First Secretary (Management) *and Consul:*
G D Reader
First Secretary (Commercial): M H S Thomas
Second Secretary (Chancery/Information):
J N Y Dawbarn
Third Secretary (Management) *and Vice-Consul:*
Miss J A Ashdown
Third Secretary: Miss P L Nobes
Attaché: M A Hyde

SEYCHELLES*

Victoria
British High Commission
Victoria House (3rd Floor) PO Box 161, Victoria,
Mahé
(Tel: 25225)

(Telegraphic Address: UKREP SEYCHELLES)
(Telex: 2269 (a/b UKREP SZ))
(Facsimile: 25127)

High Commissioner: E J Sharland
Deputy High Commissioner: Mrs F L Gristock
Defence Adviser (Resides at Nairobi):
Wing Commander C F W Felger, RAF

SIERRA LEONE*

Freetown
British High Commission
Standard Chartered Bank of Sierra Leone Ltd
Building, Lightfoot Boston Street, Freetown
(Tel: Freetown 223961-5)
(Telex: 3235) (a/b 3235 UKREP SL)

High Commissioner: D K Sprague, MVO
Deputy High Commissioner: Miss M J Martlew, MBE
Defence Adviser (Resides at Accra):
Lieutenant Colonel T E A Jenkins, MBE
Third Secretary (Management): R J Fielder

SINGAPORE*

British High Commission
Tanglin Road, Singapore 1024
(Tel: 4739333)
(Commercial Department, Tanglin PO Box 19,
Singapore 1024)
(Telegraphic Address: UKREP SINGAPORE)
(Facsimile: 474 1958 (Chancery); 475 9706
(Management); 4752320 (Commercial) 4740468
(Consular)

High Commissioner: G A Duggan
Counsellor (Commercial/Economic and Deputy
High Commissioner): P W Ford
Defence Adviser:
Group Captain P G Wildman, RAF
Cultural and Educational Adviser: A G Webster
First Secretary (Political/Coordination):
H R Drake
First Secretary (Commercial): D A Drake
First Secretary (Management): C G Lane
Deputy Cultural and Educational Adviser:
G Millington
Assistant Defence Adviser:
Lieutenant Commander M R D'Cruz, RN
Second Secretary (Commercial): R MacKenzie
Second Secretary: R C Bronson
Assistant Cultural and Educational Adviser:
M Thompson
Assistant Cultural and Educational Adviser:
D Tupper
Second Secretary (Science and Technology):
Mrs S J le Jeune d'Allegeershecque
Second Secretary (Consular): T D McDonald
Second Secretary: G G Causer
Third Secretary: M J Mitchell, MVO
Third Secretary: S I Harston

SLOVENIA

Ljubljana
British Embassy

Ambassador: G M Johnston
Third Secretary (Management): M Louth

SOLOMON ISLANDS*
Honiara
British High Commission
Soltel House, Mendana Avenue, Honiara,
Solomon Islands, (PO Box 676)
(Tel: 21705, 21706)
(Telegraphic Address: UKREP HONIARA)
(Telex: 66324) (a/b UKREP HQ 66324)
(Facsimile: 21549)
Aid Management Office
43 Lengakiki, PO Box 676
(Tel: (677) 20497, 20495)
(Telex: as BHC)
(Facsimile: (677) 20496)

High Commissioner: R F Jones, OBE
Second Secretary: C M Bedwell
Third Secretary (Aid): D A Couper
Third Secretary (Aid): J M McAlpine

SOMALIA
Mogadishu
British Embassy
Waddada Xasan Geedd Abtoow 7/8 (PO Box
1036), Mogadishu (Tel: 20288/9, 21472/3)
(Telex: 3617) (a/b 3617 PRODROME SM)

Staff temporarily withdrawn from post.

SOUTH AFRICA

Pretoria (from approximately July to December)
British Embassy
255 Hill Street, Arcadia, Pretoria, 0002
(Tel: 43-3121)
(Telex: 3-31323) (a/b 31323 BREMB-SA)
(Facsimile: 433207)
Accounts, Management, Communications and
Economic Sections remain at Pretoria throughout
the year.

Cape Town (for Parliamentary Session January to
June)
British Embassy
91 Parliament Street, Cape Town 8001
(Tel: 4617220)
(Telex: 527301 SA (a/b 5-27301 SA))
(Facsimile: 4610017)

Ambassador: Sir Anthony Reeve, KCMG
Counsellor and Deputy Head of Mission: Dr D
Carter
Counsellor: A A Rowell, CMG
First Secretary: R W Kyles
First Secretary (Economic): M M Courtney
First Secretary (Chancery): G D Adams
First Secretary (Management): A E Gay
First Secretary: P Haggie
Second Secretary: P J G Sharp
Second Secretary: D A Slinn
Second Secretary: Miss A M Giles
Second Secretary (Works): D J Evans
Third Secretary: G de Vere Lane, MBE
Third Secretary: A C Holey
Third Secretary: A S Cleary

Johannesburg
British Consulate-General
19th Floor, Sanlam Centre, Cnr Jeppe & Von
Wielligh Sts, Johannesburg, (PO Box 10101,
Johannesburg 2000)
(Tel: (27) (11) 337-8940 (Consular Section only);
337-9420 (all other Sections)) (Telegrams:
BRITCONSUL JOHANNESBURG)
(Telex: 48-7115) (a/b 48-7115 SA)
(Facsimile: (27) (11) 337-7470) Commercial
Information and Management Sections
337-8944 Consular Section
337-8943 Political Section
Consul-General and Director of Trade Promotion:
J F Doble, OBE
Deputy Consul-General: N R Haywood
Cultural Attaché (British Council Director):
W L Radford
Consul (Commercial): M W Powles
Consul (Political): M D Shipster, OBE
Vice-Consul (Political/Aid): C D Wright
Consul: T K Southworth
Vice-Consul (Commercial): Miss S A M Dring
Vice-Consul (Commercial): Mrs M Hubens, MBE
Vice-Consul (Commercial): C Heyns
Vice-Consul: Miss C B Caldwell
Vice-Consul (Commercial): M Cliff
Vice-Consul: J Williams
Vice-Consul: N J K Stucley-Houghton

Cape Town
British Consulate
Southern Life Centre (15th Floor), 8 Riebeeck
Street, Cape Town 8001 (PO Box 500, Cape
Town 8000) (Tel: 25-3670)
(Commercial Section (11th Floor) (PO Box 1346,
Cape Town 8000)
(Tel: 217741)) (Telex: 527447) (a/b 5-27447 SA)
(Facsimile: 251427)
Consul: D L S Coombe
Vice-Consul (Political and Information): I K
Morrison
Vice-Consul: D A McKellar
Vice-Consul (Commercial): E J McEvoy
Vice-Consul: Mrs H L Camp
Vice-Consul: I D Bain
Vice-Consul (Management Officer): J A Dyson

East London
British Consulate
c/o Messrs Coopers Theron Du Toit, First National
Bank Building (7th Floor), Union Street, East London
5201, PO Box 660, East London 5200
(Tel: (0431) 25521/2/3)
(Telex: 25-0920)

Honorary Consul: J L Fletcher

Port Elizabeth
British Consulate
Room 727, Allied Building, 93 Main Street,
Port Elizabeth 6001, Cape Province
(PO Box 213)
(Tel: (27) (41) 552423
(Telex: 24-2326)
Telegraph Address: BRITAIN, Port Elizabeth

Honorary Consul: G P Knowles

Durban
British Consulate
10th Floor, Fedlife House, 320 Smith Street,
Durban 4001 (PO Box 1404)
(Tel: 3052920 and 3052929, 3053041 (Trade and
non-Consular enquiries, 3053060)
(Telex: 622428 SA) (a/b 6-22428 BRITN SA)
(Facsimile: 307 4661)
N.B. All enquiries relating to Consular work in
Natal should initially be referred to Johannesburg.
Consulate does not handle passport, visa or entry
clearance work.
Consul: J Waterton
Vice-Consul: Mrs M C Orr
Vice-Consul (Commercial): D R Sparrow

SPAIN

Madrid
British Embassy
Calle de Fernando el Santo 16, 2800 Madrid
(Tel: 319-0200 (12 lines))
(Telex: 27656) (a/b 27656 INGLA E)
(Facsimile: 319 419 0423)

Ambassador: Sir Robin Fearn, KCMG
Minister and Deputy Head of Mission:
I A Roberts
Counsellor (European Community and
Economic)): A J Longrigg, CMG
Counsellor (Commercial): D F C Ridgway, OBE
Defence and Naval Attaché:
Captain J Gozzard, RN
Military Attaché: Colonel R M Gamble
Air Attaché:
Group Captain H W Farquhar-Smith RAF
Cultural Attaché (British Council Director):
B Vale, OBE
First Secretary and Head of Political Section:
T C Morris
First Secretary (Chancery): J Hedley
First Secretary (Political): N M Jacobsen
First Secretary and Consul-General:
D R S McIntyre
First Secretary (Information): R P Osborne
First Secretary (Management): M E J Herridge
First Secretary (Agriculture): Miss C J Rabagliati
Assistant Defence Attaché: Major R D Peters
Assistant Cultural Attaché (British Council Deputy
Director): A Moore
Second Secretary: J A Pearson
Second Secretary (Management): P A Ramsay, MBE
Second Secretary (Commercial): T M Roberts
Second Secretary (Commercial): C J Edge
Second Secretary (Vice-consul): M J Anderson
Second Secretary (Economic): H S M Elliot
Second Secretary: D J Steward
Second Secretary: A Hill
Third Secretary: K N Edwards
Third Secretary (Chancery): Miss R M Yeoman

Algeciras
British Vice-Consulate
Avenida de las Fuerzas Armadas No. 11,
11202 Algeciras
(Tel: 66 1600, 66 1604)
(Telex: 78079 (a/b BRALG E))
(Facsimile: 632769)
Vice-Consul: Mrs L A Mas

Madrid
British Consulate-General
Centro Colon, Marques de la Ensenada 16, 2o
28004 Madrid
(Tel: 308 52 01)
(Telex: 46664 (a/b BR MAD))
(Facsimile: 308 0882)

Consul-General: D R S McIntyre
Vice-Consul: M J Anderson
Vice-Consul: A Gomez, MBE

Seville
British Consulate
Plaza Nueva 8-B, 41001 Seville
(Tel: (34) (5) 422 8875/74)
(Telex: 72107 (a/b BRSEV E))
(Facsimile: (34) (5) 421 0323)

Consul: C F Formby, MBE
Consul (Commercial): J E D Cooper
Vice-Consul: R Rowe, MBE

Alicante
British Consulate
Plaza Calvo Sotelo 1/2 -1 Apartado de Correos
564, 03001 Alicante
(Tel: (6) 521 61 90, 521 60 22)
(Facsimile: (965) 14 05 28)

Consul: J C A Dove, MBE
Vice-Consul: A A Santolaya Diaz
Honorary Vice-Consul (at Benidorm):
J A Seth-Smith

Barcelona
British Consulate-General
Edificio Torre de Barcelona, Avenida Diagonal 477
(13th Floor), 08036 Barcelona
(Tel: 419 9044 (8 lines), 405 3089 (Direct to
Consul-General's Office)) (Telex: 52799) (a/b
52799 BRBAR E)
(Facsimile: 405 2411)

*Consul-General (also Consul-General for the
Principality of Andorra):* M Perceval
Consul (Commercial): H Wiles
Olympic Attaché: R Daly
British Council and British Institute Director:
Dr P J Spaven
Vice-Consul: I A Bradley
Vice-Consul (Commercial): A F R Patron, MBE
Vice-Consul (Commercial): J H V Hankin
English Language Officer (British Council):
C J Hickey

Tarragona
British Consulate
Calle Real 33, 1°1ª, 43004 Tarragona
(Tel: 220812)
(Telex: 56602 (a/b 56602 INTO E))
(Facsimile: 218 469)

Honorary Consul: I Navarro, OBE

Bilbao
British Consulate-General
Alameda de Urquijo 2-8, Bilbao 8
(Tel: 4157600, 4157711, 4157722)
(Telex: 32446 (a/b 32446 BRBIL E))
(Facsimile: (94) 416-7632)
Consul-General: A W McKenzie, MBE
Consul (Cultural Affairs): Ms K M Board

Santander
British Consulate
Paseo de Pereda, 27, 39004 Santander
(Tel: 220000)
(Telex: 35832 (a/b MPCIA E))
(Facsimile: (942) 222941)

Honorary Consul: M Piñeiro

Las Palmas (Grand Canary)
British Consulate
Edificio Cataluna, C/Luis Morote 6, Third Floor,
35007, Las Palmas (PO Box 2020)
(Tel: 262508)
(Telex: 95276 (a/b 95276 BRTLP E))
(Facsimile: (928) 26 77 74)

Consul: P J Nevitt
Vice-Consul: R C Livingstone

Santa Cruz de Tenerife (Canary Islands)
British Consulate
Plaza Weyler 8-1°, Santa Cruz de Tenerife 38003
(Tel: 28 68 63, 28 66 53)
(Facsimile: (922) 289903)

Consul: G K Hazell

Lanzarote (Canary Islands)
British Consulate
Calle Rubicón No 7, Arrecife, Lanzarote
(Tel: 81 59 28)
(Telex: 96368 (a/b MTEN E))
(Facsimile: (928 814248))

Honorary Consul: B E Key

Málaga
British Consulate
Edificio Duquesa, Calle Duquesa de Parcent 8
29001, Malaga
(Tel. 217-571, 212-325)
(Telex: 77282 (a/b CONBR E))
(Facsimile: (952) 221130)

Consul: M A Bartram
Vice-Consul: I M Smith

Vigo
British Consulate
Plaza de Compostela 23-6° (Aptdo 49),
36201 Vigo
(Tel: 9 86 437133)
(Facsimile: (986) 438899)

Honorary Consul: J M Cogulludo, MBE

Palma
British Consulate
Plaza Mayor 3D, 07002 Palma de Mallorca,

Balearic Islands, Spain
(Tel: 71 24 45, 71 20 85, 71 60 48)
(Telex 69477 (a/b BRPME))
(Facsimile: (971) 717520)
Consul: P Cross
Vice-Consul: M Font Vives, MBE

Ibiza
British Vice-Consulate
Avenida Isidoro Macabich 45-1°, Apartado 307,
07800 Ibiza
(Tel: 30.18.18, 30.38.16)
(Facsimile: (971) 301972)

Vice-Consul: J R Baty

Menorca
British Vice-Consulate
Torret, 28, San Luis, Menorca
(Tel: 15 15 36)

Honorary Vice-Consul: R G Sheridan, OBE, LVO

SRI LANKA*

Colombo
British High Commission
Galle Road, Kollupitiya (PO Box 1433)Colombo 3
(Tel: 437336/44)
(Telex: 21101 (a/b 21101 UKREP CE))
(Facsimile: 437344)

British Council:
49 Alfred House Gardens
Colombo (PO Box 753)
(Tel: 581171/2, 587078/9)
(Telex: 21101 (a/b 21101 UKREPCO CE))
(Facsimile: 587079)

High Commissioner: E J Field, CMG
(Also High Commissioner to the Republic of
Maldives)
*Deputy High Commissioner and Head of
Chancery:* R P Nash, LVO
Defence Adviser: Lieutenant Colonel I G Baillie
First Secretary (Chancery): B C Watters
First Secretary (Economic and Commercial):
J R Albright
First Secretary (resides at New Delhi): P Corgan
Second Secretary (Chancery): J Welsh
Second Secretary (Aid): M R Foord
Second Secretary (Management): A J Mayland
Second Secretary (Immigration/Consular):
B P McMahon
Second Secretary: R Affleck (resides at Bombay)
Cultural Attaché (British Council Director):
R A Jarvis
Assistant Cultural Attaché (British Council):
Ms H G Liesching
Assistant Cultural Attaché (British Council):
Dr M Milton

SUDAN

Khartoum
British Embassy
Off Sharia Al Baladiya, Khartoum East
(PO Box No 801)
(Tel: 70760/66/9, 80127, 80191, 80828, 80856)

(Telex: 22189 (a/b PRDRM SD))
(Facsimile: (010) 249 11 1444137

Ambassador: P J Streams, CMG
First Secretary, Consul General and Deputy Head of Mission: P R Heigl
Second Secretary: J N G Bowden
Second Secretary (Relief): A W J Kerr
Vice-Consul: W M Stevenson
Third Secretary (Management): A W Blyth
Third Secretary: D J Keogh

SURINAME

Paramaribo
British Embassy

Ambassador (Resides at Georgetown):
R D Gordon
First Secretary (Commercial), *Head of Chancery and Consul* (Resides at Georgetown): S J Hiscock
Defence Attaché (Resides at Kingston):
Colonel C S Faith, OBE
Third Secretary and Vice-Consul (Resides at Georgetown): A J Ford

British Consulate
c/o VSH United Buildings, Van't Hogerhuysstraat,
PO Box 1300, Paramaribo, Suriname
(Tel: 72870)
(Telex: 144 (a/b UNITED SN))

Honorary Consul: J J Healy, MBE

SWAZILAND*

Mbabane
British High Commission
Allister Miller Street, Mbabane
Postal Address: Private Bag, Mbabane
(Tel: 42581)
(Telex: 2079) (a/b 2079 WD)
(Facsimile: (268) 42585)
(Telegraphic Address: UKREP MBABANE)

High Commissioner: B Watkins
Deputy High Commissioner: J Chandler
Defence Adviser (resides at Maputo):
Lieutenant-Colonel C W Larkin, OBE
British Council Director: A J Kennedy
Third Secretary (Management and Consular):
B W Gard
Third Secretary (Commercial/Aid/Information):
S A James

SWEDEN

Stockholm
British Embassy
Skarpögatan 6-8, Box 27819, S115 93 Stockholm
(Tel: (Code 08) 667.01.40)
(Telex: 19340) (a/b 19340 BRITEMB S)
(Facsimile: (8) 6629989); 6619766 (Consular/Visa)

Ambassador: R L B Cormack, CMG
Counsellor (Economic/Commercial): B P Austin
Counsellor and Consul-General: M R J Guest
Counsellor: N J MacSween
Defence and Air Attaché:

Group Captain E D Stein, RAF
Naval Attaché: Commander J J M Curtis, RN
Military Attaché:
Lieutenant Colonel C S Harcourt-Smith
First Secretary (Political): D P Spencer, MBE
First Secretary (Commercial): W P Hartshorne
Cultural Attaché (British Council Director)
(resides at Copenhagen): M H Holcroft
First Secretary (Management) *and Consul:*
N F Green
First Secretary (Politica): H D MacPherson
First Secretary (Political): R P R Thompson
Second Secretary (Political/Information): R D Foland
Vice-Consul: I R Cormack

Gothenburg
British Consulate-General

Honorary Consul-General: L Hjörne

Götgatan 15, S-411 05 Gothenburg
(Tel: (31) 15 13 27)
(Telex: 28758 (a/b BRITAIN S))
(Facsimile: 031 153618)

Vice-Consul (Commercial/Consular): A J White

Luleå
British Consulate
SCAB Tunnplåt AB, S-951 88 Luleå
(Tel: (46) (920) 920 00)
(Telex: 50950 (a/b 50950 SSAB S)
(Facsimile: (46) (920) 927 14)

Honorary Consul: J-E Bergmark (Swedish)

Malmö
British Consulate
Gustav Adolfs Torg 8C, 5211 39 Malmö
(Tel: (040) 115525)
(Facsimile: (040) 110203)

Honorary Consul: A Wixell (Swedish)

Sundsvall
British Consulate
SCA Timber AB, S-851 88 Sundsvall
(Tel: (46) (60) 19 32 03)
(Telex: 7192 (a/b 71952 SCATIMB S)
(Facsimile: (46) (60) 19 38 95)

Honorary Consul: O Hildingsson (Swedish)

SWITZERLAND

Berne
British Embassy
Thunstrasse 50, 3005 Berne 15
(Tel: 44.50.21/6)
(Telex: 911929) (a/b 911929 UKBE CH
(Commercial Section))
(Facsimile: (41 31) 44 05 83)

Ambassador: D Beattie, CMG
Counsellor and Deputy Head of Mission: C C Bright
Counsellor (Science and Technology) (Resides at Bonn): Dr R Escritt
Counsellor: I R Cooling
Defence, Naval and Military Attaché:
Lieutenant Colonel W R Thatcher

Air Attaché: Wing Commander H W Hughes, RAF
First Secretary (Information): P Cole
Second Secretary (Political): Dr J E Mitchiner
Second Secretary (Management) *and Consul:*
P A Chatt
Commercial Attaché: B Haessig

Geneva

British Consulate-General
37-39 rue de Vermont (6th Floor), 1211 Geneva 20
(Tel: 734.38.00)
(Telex: 414195 (a/b 414195 UKGV CH))
(Facsimile: (412) 22 734 52 54)

Consul-General: P J Priestley
Consul: Miss C H Bird
Vice-Consul (Commercial): B J Haden, MBE
Vice-Consul: Mrs M K Hainsworth

Montreux

British Vice-Consulate
La Chaumiére 13 Chemin de l'Aubousset, 1806 St
Legier, Vaud
(Tel: 943 32 63)
(Fax: 943 32 63)

Honorary Vice-*Consul:* Mrs S L Darra

Valais

British Vice Consulate
Alusuisse, Swiss Aluminium Limited
CH 3960, Sierra
(Tel: 027 57 56 73)
(Facsimile: 027 2320)

Consular Agent: A Bushnell

Zurich

British Consulate-General and
Directorate of British Export Promotion in
Switzerland, Dufourstrasse 56, 8008 Zurich
(Tel: (01) 261 15 20-6)
(Telex: 816467) (a/b 816467 UKZH CH))
(Facsimile: 1 252 83 51)

Consul-General and Director of Export Promotion:
T Bryant, CMG *(also Consul-General for the
Principality of Liechtenstein)*
Consul (Commercial): M F Smith
Vice-Consul (Consular/Management):
Mrs A Ross McDowell
Vice-Consul (Commercial): E W E Kellner, MBE
Vice-Consul (Commercial): J M Gysin, MBE
Vice-Consul (Commercial): K G Birch
Vice-Consul (Investment): W F Gratz
Vice-Consul (Commercial): B J McKenna

Lugano

British Consulate
Via Motta, 19/via Nassa 32, 6900 Lugano
(Tel: (091) 23 86 06)

Honorary Consul: A Crivelli
Pro Consul: Mrs M Palmesino

SYRIA

Damascus

British Embassy
Quarter Malki, 11 Mohammad Kurd Ali St, Imm
Kotob, Damascus PO Box 37
(Tel: 712561, 712562, 712563, 711179)
(Facsimile: 713592)
(Telex: BRITEM 411049 SY) (a/b BRITEM
411049 SY)

Ambassador: A F Green, CMG
Counsellor and Deputy Head of Mission:
I L Blackley
Defence Attaché: Colonel J J Dumas, OBE
First Secretary (Chancery/Information):
M E Cribbs
First Secretary (Commercial): M J Lowes
Management Officer/Consul: P J Richardson
Vice-Consul (Immigration): P J Blandford
Vice-Consul (Immigration): S Wadvani

Aleppo

British Consulate
PO Box 199
(Tel: 332133)
(Telex: 331 627 ACCO SY)

Honorary Consul: G J A Akras, MBE

TANZANIA*

Dar es Salaam

British High Commission
Hifadhi House, Samora Avenue (PO Box 9200)
(Tel: 29601-5, 46300 46302-4)
(Telex: 41004 (a/b 41004 UKREP))
(Facsimile: 46301)

High Commissioner: R Westbrook, CMG
Deputy High Commissioner: I R Whitehead
Defence Adviser (resides at Kampala):
Lieutenant Colonel E J K O'Brien
First Secretary (Aid): Mrs J Laurence
Second Secretary (Commercial): S J Smith
Second Secretary (Management): G H Piper
Second Secretary (Aid): J G Hall
Second Secretary: The Hon. Alice Walpole
Third Secretary (Aid): S N Crossman
Third Secretary (Consular): Mrs E Marsh

THAILAND

Bangkok

British Embassy
Wireless Road, Bangkok
(Tel: 253-0191)
(Telex: 82263 (a/b PRODROM TH))
(Facsimile: Embassy (662) 2558619, SEADD
(662) 2537124)

Ambassador: C C W Adams, CMG
Counsellor and Deputy Head of Mission: D W Fall
Counsellor and Permanent Representative
(ESCAP): R W H Davies
Defence and Military Attaché:
Colonel J Longman
Naval and Air Attaché: Commander P S Buckley, RN

Counsellor (Hong Kong Affairs): R E Darkin, CPM
First Secretary: A J Sparkes
First Secretary (Management): M F J Ryder
First Secretary (Commercial): D Bleakley
First Secretary and Consul: Miss J C Sharpe
First Secretary (Commercial/Development):
G T Squires
First Secretary: P Matthews
First Secretary (Defence Supply): P R Clark
Second Secretary and Deputy Permanent Representative (ESCAP): Miss L-J O'Neill
Second Secretary: M S Brown
Second Secretary (Political): Miss A M Hall Hall
Second Secretary (Immigration): K J Fuller
Third Secretary: D W Aird
Third Secretary: E Powell
Vice-Consul: Miss M L Childs
Vice-Consul: J H Collins

South-East Asia Development Division
c/o British Embassy

Head of Division: M J Dinham
Senior Natural Resources Adviser and Deputy Head of Division: J R F Hansell
Senior Natural Resources Adviser: D A Trotman
Senior Engineering Adviser: P W D H Roberts
Economic Adviser: J Hoy
Economic Adviser: M P R Lewis
Economical/Social Development Adviser:
Ms J M Walker
Senior Programme Adviser: Ms A C Higginbottom
Programmes Adviser: Dr J Todd
Engineering Adviser: D Robson

TOGO

Lomé
British Embassy (All staff reside at Accra)

Ambassador and Consul-General:
D C Walker
Counsellor and Head of Chancery: M J Greenstreet
Defence Attaché:
Lieutenant-Colonel T E A Hawkins, MBE
First Secretary: S C E Holt
First Secretary (Management/Consular):
Miss D J Walker
First Secretary (Commercial): S S Strong
First Secretary (Aid): Ms R B Stevenson
Second Secretary: D J G Barton
Second Secretary (Consular): S M Pakes

Lomé
British Consulate
British School of Lomé, BP20050 Lomé
(Tel: 21 4606)
(Facsimile: 214989)

Honorary Consul: Mrs J A Sayer

British Commercial Office, BP, 8067, Tokoin, Lomé
(Telex: 5153 AMATO TG)

Commercial Officer: G Fioux

TONGA, Kingdom of

Nuku'alofa
British High Commission
PO Box 56, Nuku'alofa, Tonga
(Tel: 21-020/1)
(Telex: 66226 (a/b 66226 UKREP TS))
(Telegraphic Address: UKREP NUKU' ALOFA)
(Facsimile: (676) 24109)

High Commissioner and Consul for American Samoa: W L Cordiner
Defence Adviser (Resides at Wellington):
Group Captain D W F Angela, RAF
Third Secretary (Consular and Management):
M A Fidler

TRINIDAD AND TOBAGO*

Port of Spain
British High Commission
3rd and 4th Floors, Furness House,
90 Independence Square (PO Box 778), Port of Spain
(Tel: 62-52861-6)
(Telex: 22224 (a/b 22224 UKREP WG))
(Facsimile: 623 0621)

High Commissioner: B Smith, OBE
Deputy High Commissioner: D L Smallman, LVO
Defence Adviser (Resides at Kingston):
Colonel C S Faith, OBE
Naval Adviser (Resides at Nassau):
Captain A J S Taylor, RN
Second Secretary (Management, Consular):
Miss C A Fawcett
Second Secretary (Chancery/Information):
T R Knight

TUNISIA

Tunis
British Embassy
5 Place de la Victoire, Tunis
(Tel: (1) 245-100, 244-805, 245-324, 245-649)
(Telex: 14007 (a/b PRDROM 14007 TN))
(Facsimile: 354 877)
Consular and Visa Sections: 141-143 Avenue De La Liberte, Tunis
(Tel: (216) 1 793 322/794 810/794 005)
(Telex: 15128 (a/b 15218 BRICON TN))
(Facsimile: (216) 792 644)

Ambassador and Consul-General: M L Tait, CMG
First Secretary and Deputy Head of Mission:
A Holmes, MBE
First Secretary: J M Weldin
Defence, Naval, Military and Air Attaché (Resident at Algiers): Group Captain K Gowing, RAF
Cultural Attaché (British Council Director):
D A Handforth
Second Secretary (Commercial and Economic):
Miss R Foxwell
Second Secretary (Management) and *Vice-Consul:*
M Stevens
Vice-Consul and Commercial Officer:
Mrs V Zaoui, MBE

Sfax
British Consulate
Rue de Madagascar, 3000 Bab El Bahr, Sfax,
Tunisia
(Tel: (04) 28 555)
(Telex: 40822 TN)

Honorary Consul: M Bouricha

TURKEY

Ankara
British Embassy
Sehit Ersan Caddesi 461/A, Cankaya
(Tel: (90 4) 127.43.101/15)
(Telex: 942320) (a/b 942320 PROD TR)
(Facsimile: (90 4) 168 3214)

Ambassador: P J Goulden, CMG
Counsellor and Deputy Head of Mission:
W B McCleary
Defence and Military Attaché:
Lieutenant Colonel The Hon S J T Coleridge
Counsellor (British Council and Cultural Affairs):
C Perchard, OBE
Naval and Air Attaché:
Wing Commander A D K Campbell, RAF
First Secretary (Political): S N Evans
First Secretary (Chancery): I F M Lancaster
First Secretary (Commercial): D T Healy
First Secretary (British Council and Cultural
Affairs): A J Mountford
First Secretary (British Council and Cultural
Affairs): Ms R L Varley
First Secretary (Management): J A Francis
Second Secretary (British Council and Cultural
Affairs): K M Bright
Second Secretary (Commercial/Economic):
R Gemmell
Second Secretary (Chancery/Consular):
K L Mowbray
Second Secretary (Defence Sales): D E Bullas
Second Secretary: D Sykes
Third Secretary (Chancery): Ms K A Holgate

Iskenderun
British Consulate
c/o Messrs Catoni Maritime Agencies, Maresal
Cakmak Caddesi 28, Iskenderun
(Tel: (90 881) 30361,2,3)
(Facsimile: (90 881) 30364)

Honorary Consul: H J Beard (resides at Istanbul)
Honorary Vice-Consul: Miss H Koba, MBE

Antalya

British Consulate
Ucgen Mahallesi, Dolaplidere Caddesi, Pirilti
Sitesi, Kat 1 Kilit Sauna Karsisi, Antalya
(Tel: (90 31) 177000, 177002)
(Facsimile: (90 31) 177005)

Honorary Consul: H Pirilti

Bodrum
British Consulate
Iren Sitesi (Turgutreis Road)

No 13 Bodrum
(Tel: (90 6141) 4932 3243)
(Facsimile: (906141) 2289)

Honorary Consul: M A Demirer

Marmaris
British Consulate
c/o Yesil Marmaris Tourism and Yacht
Management Inc
Barbaros Caddesi No 118
Marina PO Box 8, 48700 Marmaris
(Tel: 16486-8)
(Facsimile: 15077)

Honorary Consul: A D Tugay

Mersin
British Vice-Consulate
c/o Catoni Maritime Agencies SA,
Mersin Orta Okulu Sokak 3/B, Cakmak Caddesi,
Mersin
(Tel: (90 741) 12728, 34078)
(Facsimile: 30604)

Honorary Vice-Consul: A Nofal

Istanbul
British Consulate-General
Mesrutiyet Caddesi No 34, Tepebasi, Beyoglu,
PK 33
(Tel: 244 7540 244 7545/49)
(Telex: 24122 (a/b BRIT TR))
(Facsimile: 245 4989)
Commercial Section: 249 88 74)
Office of the Consul for British Council and
Cultural Affairs
Ors Turistik Is Merkezi, Istiklal Cad. 251/253
Kat 2, 3, 5 Beyoglu, 80060 Istanbul
(Tel: 152 7474/78)
(Telex: 23283 (a/b IKIKTR))

Consul-General: M E Cook
Deputy Consul-General: J E Atkinson
Consul (British Council and Cultural Affairs):
W A Lockhart
Consul (Management): M J Shingler
Consul (Information): R Spearman
Vice-Consul: S E F Campbell
Vice-Consul (British Council and Cultural Affairs):
D Codling
Vice-Consul: M J Abel

Izmir
British Vice-Consulate
1442 Sokak No. 49, Alsancak, Izmir PK 300
(Tel: 635151)
(Facsimile: (51) 212 914)

Vice-Consul: A W Buttigieg

TUVALU*

Funafuti
British High Commission (All staff reside at Suva)

High Commissioner: T J David
*Deputy High Commissioner, Head of Chancery
and First Secretary* (Consular): R C B Jones

Second Secretary (Chancery): C P Harvey
Second Secretary (Aid/Commercial):
Mrs A C Hamilton-Walker
Attaché (Consular/Management):
Mrs C M McNeill

UGANDA*

Kampala
British High Commission
101/12 Parliament Avenue, PO Box 7070,
Kampala
(Tel: 2570541/9, 257301/4)
(Telex: 61202 (a/b UKREP KLA))
(Telegraphic Address: UKREP KAMPALA)

High Commissioner: C A K Cullimore
Deputy High Commissioner: P R Whiteway
Defence Adviser: Lieutenant Colonel E J K O'Brien
First Secretary (British Council Director): S Moss
First Secretary (Aid/Commercial):M R Frost
First Secretary (Management/Consular): P Dickson
First Secretary (Chancery): R N E Smith
Second Secretary (Aid/Economic): J A Murray
Second Secretary (British Council): Dr P Brazier
Second Secretary (Commercial/Consular): R
Morton
Third Secretary: A J Carne
Third Secretary (Consular): J A Brown
Third Secretary (Chancery/Information):
Miss C J Cross

UKRAINE

Kiev
British Embassy
Room 1008 Zhovtneva Hotel
Ulitza Rozi Luxembourg
252021 Kiev
(Tel: (010) 7 044 291 8907)
(Facsimile: (010) 873 1445257)
(Telex: 0581 144 5256)

Ambassador: S N P Hemans, CMG CVO
Consul General and Deputy Head of Mission:
D G Martin
Counsellor: Viscount Asquith, OBE
First Secretary (Commercial/Economic): R C C
Cook
First Secretary (Management) W F Somerset
Defence Attaché: Commander C A M Parrish, RN
Second Secretary (Commercial): Miss S J Hinds
Third Secretary (Management): Miss A J Beckett

UNITED ARAB EMIRATES

Abu Dhabi
British Embassy
PO Box 248, Abu Dhabi, United Arab Emirates
(Tel: 326600 (7 Lines), 321364)
(Telex: 22234 (a/b 22234 PRODRO EM))
(Telegrams: PRODROME ABU DHABI)
(Facsimile: 341744/318138)

Ambassador: G S Burton, CMG

First Secretary, Consul and Deputy Head of Post
(M): W R Henderson
First Secretary (Commercial): M K Haddock
First Secretary: I W Baharie
Defence and Military Attaché: Lieutenant Colonel
M A Cullinan
Naval and Air Attaché: Wing Commander W R
Southcombe, RAF
Cultural Attaché (British Council Director):
Dr P J A Clark
Second Secretary (Commercial): D Winter
Second Secretary (Information): Mrs J Perkins
Second Secretary (Management): *and Consul:*
N K Tagg
Third Secretary and Vice-Consul: A H Ingold

Dubai
British Embassy
PO Box 65, Dubai, United Arab Emirates
(Tel: 521070) (Commercial Section
521893/524993)
(Telex: 45426 (a/b 45426 PRODR EM))
(Facsimile: 525750)

Consul-General (M) *and Counsellor:*
R A M Hendrie
First Secretary (Commercial) *and Consul:*
K N Johnson, MBE
First Secretary (Chancery/Economic):
R J Knowlton
Defence, Naval, Military and Air Attaché
(Resident at Abu Dhabi):
Lieutenant Colonel M A Cullinan
Royal Navy Liaison Officer: Commander A
Horton, OBE, RN
*Second Secretary, Vice-Consul and Management
Officer:* D P Gething, MBE
Second Secretary (Commercial): B R Page
Second Secretary (Works): D P Ryan
Second Secretary: K B Howell
Third Secretary (Commercial/Information):
A T Dimbleby
Third Secretary and Vice-Consul: Miss S H Tisdell
Third Secretary and Vice-Consul:
Miss J A Lawson-Smith
Third Secretary: C Weldon

UNITED STATES

Washington
British Embassy
3100 Massachusetts Avenue, NW, Washington
DC 20008
(Tel: HO2-1340/or 462 1340 (Area Code 202))
(Telex: 892370 (a/b PRODROME B WSH),
892384 (a/b PRODROME B WSH))
International calls: Telex 21670 (a/b BRITEM)
211427 (a/b) UKEMB) 64224 (a/b(PROWSH
64224)
(Facsimile: (202) 8984255 Group 3; UKAEA
(202) 8984224 Group 3)

Ambassador: Sir Robin Renwick, KCMG
Minister: C J R Meyer
Minister (Trade Policy): W Marsden, CMG
Minister (Economic): D L C Peretz

Minister (Hong Kong Commercial Affairs): P Lo
Head of British Defence Staff andDefence Attaché:
Air Vice Marshal P Dodworth, OBE, AFC, RAF
Minister (Defence Material): R J Harding, CMG
Counsellor (Defence Equipment): L N Large
Naval Attaché: Rear Admiral
A P Hoddinott, OBE, RN
Military Attaché: Brigadier I B R Fowler
Air Attaché:
Air Commodore S Baldwin, MBE, RAF
Counsellor (Congressional) *and Head of*
Chancery: R P Ralph, CVO
Counsellor: R J Nicholls
Counsellor: R B Dearlove
Counsellor (Defence Supply): B J Limbert
Counsellor (Overseas Development):
R M Graham-Harrison
Counsellor (Trade and Environment): A P Vinall
Counsellor (Management) *and Consul-General:*
A F Smith
Counsellor (Economic): Mrs M E Brown
Counsellor (Science, Technology and Energy):
D A Rolt
Counsellor (Press and Public Affairs): N W Browne
Counsellor (Hong Kong Economic and Trade
Affairs): Mr P C Leung
Counsellor: B R Coleman
Counsellor (Transport): R Griffins
Counsellor (External Affairs): P J Torry
Counsellor (Politico/Military): P L Thomas
Cultural Attaché: G A Tindale, OBE
Attaché (Defence): Dr M F Steeden
Attaché (Defence Equipment) (Air): C Jones
Attaché (Civil Aviation Air Traffic Systems):
V S G Brennan
Attaché (Defence Equipment) (Maritime):
Dr J M Williams
Attaché (Defence Equipment) (Intellectual Property
Rights): H J Muir
Attaché (Defence Equipment) (Land): J Platt
First Secretary (Commercial): E Hosker
First Secretary (Management): F A Blogg
First Secretary: The Hon Dominic Asquith
Attaché (Defence Supply): J D Gutteridge
First Secretary (Trade Policy): V Life
First Secretary (Civil Aviation Shipping):
P Kirk
First Secretary (Political/Military): A M Thomson
First Secretary (Science): R D Jennings
First Secretary: T M Dowse
First Secretary (Chancery): J N Powell
First Secretary (Agricultural and Commercial):
Miss P R Phillips
First Secretary (Economic): A Gibbs
First Secretary (Chancery): A Stones
First Secretary: P L Evans
Education Attaché: Dr D J Cooke
First Secretary (Trade Promotion): B Halliwell
First Secretary: S Pattison
First Secretary: H B Ashton
First Secretary (Technology): R Egginton
First Secretary (Press and Public Affairs):
M A Price, LVO
First Secretary: A J Baxendine
First Secretary: J H Chun
First Secretary (Energy): Dr S Sklaroff

First Secretary (Consul): (Vavant)
First Secretary (Works): J R Chandler
Attaché Defence Supply (Strategic Defence
Initiative): V Starkey
First Secretary Defence Supply (Sea Systems):
H G Thomas
First Secretary Defence Supply (Air Systems):
C McLaughlin
First Secretary Defence Supply (Land Systems):
S Johns
First Secretary (Chancery): Mrs V Life
First Secretary (Hong Kong Economic and Trade
Affairs): R Chan
First Secretary: Miss P D Mitchison
Assistant Naval Attaché:
Captain T M Masterman, RN
Attaché (Joint Warfare) *and Assistant Defence*
Attaché: Colonel G F Smart
Assistant Military Attaché: Colonel J D Sankey
Assistant Air Attaché: Group Captain R S
Peacock-Edwards, AFC, RAF
Second Secretary (Chancery): E G Buchanan
Second Secretary (Transport): R A Foster
Second Secretary: M G Snell, MVO
Second Secretary (Accountant): F Newcomb
Second Secretary (Hong Kong Commercial
Affairs): Mrs D Wai-Sum Wai
Second Secretary: D C Welsted
Second Secretary (Private Secretary to
Ambassador): Ms K E Pierce
Vice-Consul: S J Young, MBE

Atlanta
British Consulate-General
Suite 2700, Marquis I Tower, 245 Peachtree
Center Avenue, Atlanta, Georgia, 30303
(Tel: 524-5856/8 (Area Code 404))
(Telex: 240024) (a/b BRITAIN ATL)
(Facsimile: (404) 524 3153 Group 3)

Consul-General: B T Holmes
Consul (Commercial): P W Ray
Vice-Consul: D A Walters, MVO
Vice-Consul (Commercial): N J Bishop
Vice-Consul (Commercial): L Pranger
Vice-Consul (Commercial): M G Charlton
Vice-Consul: Ms L J Nassar

Miami
British Consulate
Suite 2110, Brickell Bay Office Tower, 1001 S
Bayshore Drive, Miami, Florida 33131
(Tel: (305) 374 1522)
(Telex: 215851 (a/b BRITAIN MIA))
(Facsimile: (305) 374 8196)

Consul: P W Grice, LVO
Vice-Consul (Commercial): R Woods
Vice-Consul (Customs): G Honey

Puerto Rico
British Consulate
San Juan (HC) Taft Street, No 1,
Suite 5E, Santurce 00911
(Tel: (809) 728-6715/1311)
(Telex: 3454325 (a/b CONSUUK))

Honorary Consul: Dr I Court

Boston
British Consulate-General
25th Floor, Federal Reserve Plaza, 600 Atlantic
Avenue, Boston, Ma 02210
(Tel: 248-9555 (Area Code 617))
(Telex: 940994) (a/b BRITAIN BSN)
(Facsimile: (1617) 248 9578 (Group 3))

Consul-General: J W Owen, MBE
Deputy Consul General: A White
Vice-Consul (Commercial): M Harrison
Vice-Consul (Commercial): N J Gaymond
Vice-Consul (Management): Mrs K M Tunsley
Vice-Consul (Press and Public Affairs):
Mrs T Evans

Chicago
British Consulate-General
33 N Dearborn Street, Chicago, Illinois 60602
(Tel: (312) 346.1810)
(Telex: 254432) (a/b BRITAIN CGO)
(Facsimile: (312) 346 7021)

Consul-General: F R Mingay, CMG
Deputy Consul-General: M W Hewitt
Consul (Industrial Development): G M Kidd
Consul: R H Gordon, MBE
Vice-Consul (Commercial): R A Hoffman
Vice-Consul: J L Smith
Vice-Consul (Commercial): Miss E N Brown, MBE
Vice-Consul (Industrial Development): P Marks
Vice-Consul (Commercial Publicity):
Ms F Smeaton
Vice-Consul (Information Officer):Mrs C P Cracaft

Cleveland
British Consulate
55 Public Square, Suite 1650, Cleveland, Ohio
44113-1963
(Tel: 621-7674 (Area Code 216))
(Telex: 980126) (a/b BRITAIN CLV)
(Facsimile: (216) 621 2615 Group 3)

Consul: M C Gathercole, OBE

Houston
British Consulate-General
Suite 2260, 1100, Milam Building, 1100 Milam,
Houston, Texas 77002 5506
(Tel: (Area Code 713) 659-6270)
(Telex: 762-307) (a/b BRITAIN HOU)
(Facsimile: (713) 659 7094)

Consul-General: B J Everett
Deputy Consul-General and Consul (Commercial):
M B Magee
Vice-Consul (Management/Consular): D Hook
Vice-Consul: Mrs H M Tonks
Vice-Consul (Commercial): R F Kleppick
Vice-Consul (Information): Ms H Mann

Dallas
British Consulate
813 Stemmons Tower West, 2730 Stemmons
Freeway, Dallas, Texas 75207
(Tel: (Area Code 214) 637-3600)
(Telex: 730382) (a/b BRITAIN DAL)
(Telegraphic Address: BRITAIN DALLAS)

(Facsimile: (214) 634 9408)

Consul (Commercial): J D Clark, MBE
Vice-Consul (Commercial): Miss S Hess-Cole

New Orleans
British Consulate
10th Floor, 321 St Charles Avenue,
New Orleans, Louisiana, 70130
(Tel: (Area Code 504) 586-1979)
(Facsimile: (Area Code 504) 524 1736)

Honorary Consul: J J Coleman, Jr
Honorary Vice-Consul: Ms A Jeffery

Los Angeles
British Consulate-General
Suite 400, 11766 Wilshire Boulevard, Los
Angeles, California 90025
(Tel: (1) (310) 477 3322)
(Telex: 759365) (a/b BRITAIN LSA)
(Facsimile: (1) (310) 575 1450 Group 3)

Consul-General: M S Baker-Bates
Deputy Consul General and Consul (Commercial):
M T Jones
Consul (Inward Investment): J T Morrison
Vice-Consul: H E Sadler
Vice-Consul (Inward Investment): Miss S Gillett,
MVO
Vice-Consul (Commercial):
P O D McCoy
Vice-Consul (Information): J O Houlton, MBE
Vice-Consul: Ms A Morton
Vice-Consul: Miss A W Bain
Vice-Consul (Commercial): Ms L Colvin
Vice-Consul (Commercial): K C McKivett

New York
British Consulate-General
845 Third Avenue, New York, NY 10022
(Tel: (212) 745 0200)
(Facsimile: (212) 735 3062)

Consul-General: A J Hunter, CMG
Deputy Consul-General: I C Sloane
Consul: M C Carter
Vice-Consul: Mrs J Finnamore-Crorkin
Vice-Consul: A J G Juleff

British Consulate-General
British Trade and Investment Office
845 Third Avenue, New York, NY 10022
(Tel: (212) 745 0495)
(Telegraphic Address: BRITRADEV NEW YORK)
(Facsimile: (212) 745 0456)

*Consul-General, Director-General of Trade and
Investment, USA:* A J Hunter, CMG
*Deputy Consul-General and Director of Inward
Investment:* M E Frost, LVO
*Deputy Consul-General and Director of Trade
Development:* J Thompson
Consul (Commercial): R A Cambridge
Consul (Investment): R G Robinshaw
Consul (Investment) *and Deputy Director Inward
Investment, USA:* I R Whitehead
Vice-Consul (Commercial): U Marthaler

Vice-Consul (Commercial): C W Crorkin
Vice-Consul (Commercial): Mrs R Ballin
Vice-Consul (Commercial): K Abreu
Vice-Consul (Commercial): Mrs J A Faiella
Vice-Consul (Investment): Miss H Williams

British Information Services
845 Third Avenue, New York, NY 10022
(Tel: (212) 745 0200)
(Public Enquiries: (212) 745 0222)
(Media Enquiries: (212) 745 0277/0278)
(Facsimile: (212) 758 5395)

Counsellor and Head of Press and Public Affairs
(Resident at Washington): N W Browne
Director of BIS: P M Innes
Deputy Director of BIS: T Gurney
First Secretary (Information): B E Kirk

Joint Management Office
13th Floor, 845 Third Avenue, New York, NY
10022
(Tel: (212) 745 0200)
(Facsimile: (212) 644 4150)

Counsellor: I C Sloane
Second Secretary (Management):
W G D Johnson, MBE
Second Secretary (Computer Manager): J J Burton

Pacific Islands
US Territories South of the Equator
British Consulate

Consul: W L Cordiner *(also British High
Commissioner in the Kingdom of Tonga* (Resides
at Nuku'alofa))

Philadelphia
British Consulate
Mather & Co, 226 Walnut Street,
Philadelphia, Pa 19106
(Tel: (215) 925-0118)

Honorary Consul: Charles E Mather

Kansas City
British Consulate
8724 Catalina Drive, Prairie Village, Kansas
66207
(Tel: (913) 649-8010)
(Facsimile: (913) 649-8033)

Honorary Consul: Stanley A Hamilton

St Louis
British Consulate
14904 Manor Lake Drive, Chesterfield,
St Louis, Missouri 63017

Honorary Consul: V W Lammert

San Francisco
British Consulate-General
Suite 850, 1 Sansome Street, San Francisco,
California, 94104
(Tel: 981-3030) (Area Code 415)
(Telex: 340628) (a/b BRITAIN SFO)
(Facsimile: (415) 434 2018 Group 3)

Consul-General: A Ford
Deputy Consul-General and Consul (Commercial):
Ms J Elsdon
Vice-Consul (Commercial): C L Bascom
Vice-Consul: Ms P Rumis
Vice-Consul (Information): Ms D Gilmore

Anchorage (Alaska)
British Consulate
University of Alaska, Anchorage College of Arts
and Sciences, 2311 Providence Drive, Anchorage,
Alaska 99508
(Tel: 786 4848 (Area Code 907))

Honorary Consul: Dr D R M Hitchins

Seattle
British Consulate
820 First Interstate Center, 999 Third Avenue,
Seattle, Washington, 98104
(Tel: (206) 622-9255)
(Telex: 329602) (a/b BRITAIN SEA)
(Facsimile: (206) 622 4728 Group 3)

Consul (Commercial): S E Turner
Commercial Officer and Vice-Consul: J Larson

Portland (Oregon)
British Consulate
3515 S W Council Crest Drive,
Portland, Oregon 97201
(Tel: (503) 227-5669)

Honorary Consul: A Hay

Norfolk
British Consulate
Hofheimers, 4554 Progress Road
Norfolk VA 23502
(Tel: 855 9833 (Area Code 804))

Honorary Consul: A V Beachey
Honorary Vice-Consul: Dr Reba N G Bliss

UPPER VOLTA

(See Burkina)

URUGUAY

Montevideo
British Embassy
Calle Marco Bruto 1073, 11300 Montevideo, PO
Box 16024
(Tel: 62 36 30, - 62 36 50)
(Telex: 22249) (a/b PRODROM UY 22249)
(Facsimile: 627815)

Ambassador: D A Lamont
Deputy Head of Mission and Consul:
A T J Lovelock
Defence, Naval, Military and Air Attaché:
Captain R A Highton, RN
Second Secretary (Commercial) *and Vice-Consul:*
J P R Jeffrey
Second Secretary (resides at Buenos Aires): K
Jacobs
Second Secretary (resides at Buenos Aires): D
Corfield
Second Secretary (resides at La Paz): R Gray

VANUATU*

Vila
British High Commission
KPMG House, Rue Pasteur, Vila (PO Box 567)
(Tel: 23100 (3 Lines))
(Telex: 1027 (a/b 1027 UKREP NH))
(Facsimile: 23651)

High Commissioner: T J Duggin
Second Secretary: D R Miller
Third Secretary (Aid): R Hyland

VATICAN CITY (see Holy See)

VENEZUELA

Caracas
British Embassy
Edificio Torre Las Mercedes, (Piso 3) Avenida La
Estancia, Chuao, Caracas 1060
(Postal Address: Embajada Britanica, Apartado
1246, Caracas, 1010-A)
(Tel: 751.10.22, 751.11.66, 751.19.66;Commercial
Section: 92.65.42; Management Section: 91.42.53)
(Telex: 23468 (a/b 23468 PROCA VE))
(Facsimile: 923292)

Ambassador: G E Fitzherbert, CMG
Deputy Head of Mission: M Hickson, LVO
Defence Attaché: Captain R L Perrett, RN
Cultural Attaché (British Council Director):
J A Coope, OBE
First Secretary (Commercial): C Dresser
First Secretary (Chancery): W J Roebuck
Assistant Cultural Attaché (British Council):
P Morris
Second Secretary (Management) *and Consul:*
A R J Attryde
Second Secretary (Commercial): (Vacant)
Second Secretary: F P Devlin
Second Secretary: A R Heyn
Third Secretary: P D Evans
Attaché (Vice-Consul): M P Johnston

Maracaibo
British Vice-Consulate
Avenida 9B Con Calle 66A, No. 66-146,
Maracaibo
(Tel: (061) 78642 or 82794)
(Telex: 62292 and 62446 INSPE VC)

Honorary Vice-Consul: G Z Podolecki

Mérida
British Vice-Consulate
Pedregosa Media, Conjunto Residencial Las
Ardillas, 2a Transversal, Calle Las Dantos, Parcela
No 20-A, Mérida 5101

Honorary Vice-Consul: R G Kirby

VIETNAM, THE SOCIALIST REPUBLIC OF

Hanoi
British Embassy
16 Pho Ly Thuong Kiet, Hanoi
Mailing address: c/o British Embassy, Wireless
Road, Bangkok

(Tel: 425 2349, 425 2510, 425 2620)
(Telex: 4 11 405 (a/b BRITEM VT))
(Telegraphic Address: PRODROME HANOI)

Ambassador: P K Williams, CMG
Consul and Deputy Head of Mission: J R
McCulloch
First Secretary (Political): A J Dean
Third Secretary (Management) *and Vice-Consul:*
S Codd
Third Secretary: J L Parry, MBE

Ho Chi Minh City
British Consulate General

Consul General: D Leith, RVM

WESTERN SAMOA*

Apia
British High Commission (All staff resident in
Wellington)
(Telegraphic Address: UKREP Wellington)
(Telex: NZ 3325 (a/b UKREP NZ 3325))

High Commissioner: D J Moss, CMG
*Deputy High Commissioner and Head of
Chancery:* I C Orr
First Secretary (Chancery/Information): J W Yapp
First Secretary (Agriculture and Food):
Mrs E A Blackwell
First Secretary (Commercial): P Rogan
Second Secretary (Chancery): Ms B A Proctor
Attaché (Consular): Mrs A C Harris

Apia
Office of the Honorary British Representative
c/o (PO Box 2029), Apia Kruse Va'ai and Barlow
(Tel: 21 218 95)
(Cables: EXPEDITION APIA)
(Facsimile: 21407)

Honorary British Consul: R M Barlow

THE REPUBLIC OF YEMEN

Sana'a
British Embassy
129 Haddah Road, Sana'a (Postal Address: PO
Box 1287)
(Tel: 215630-33)
(Telex: 2251 (a/b BRITEM YE))
(Facsimile: 263059)

Ambassador and Consul-General:
M A Marshall, CMG
First Secretary, Head of Chancery: G Kirby
Defence and Military Attaché (Resides at Riyadh):
Brigadier M J Holroyd-Smith, OBE
Naval and Air Attaché (Resides at Riyadh):
Commander T Waddington, RN
Second Secretary (Commercial/Economic/
Political): Mrs G F Simpson
Second Secretary (Management) *and Consul* (M):
G A D Ryan
Second Secretary (Political): D M Simpson
Third Secretary (Aid) *and Vice-Consul:* P L Wyithe
Third Secretary (Information/Press): A P Self

ZAIRE

Kinshasa
British Embassy
Avenue de Trois Z, Gombe, Kinshasa
(Tel: (243) 34775-8)
(Telex: (982) 21689 (a/b 21689 BRITEM ZR))

Chargé d'Affaires and Consul: Ms K W Oliver
Deputy Head of Mission and Vice Consul:
Miss M H Horn

Lubumbashi
British Consulate
c/o Gecamines, BP 450, Lubumbashi
(Tel: (22) 5130 E 728 (Office), E 660 (Home))
(Telex: 41034)

Honorary Consul: P D Ashman

Goma
British Consulate
Sagrim S P R L, 2 Avenue de la Corniche, BP
190, Goma

Honorary Consul: Y G de Bruyn, MBE

Kisangani
British Consulate
BP 504, Kisangani

Honorary Consul: R L F Seneque

ZAMBIA*

Lusaka
British High Commission
Independence Avenue (PO Box 50050), Lusaka
(Tel: 228955) (after hours 251956)
(Telex: 41150 (a/b UKREP ZA 41150))
(Facsimile: 262215)

High Commissioner: P R M Hinchcliffe, CMG, CVO
Deputy High Commissioner: T N Byrne

First Secretary (Development and Economic):
M A Hammond
First Secretary (Political): D F Middleton
First Secretary (Commercial Consular):
K A Neil
First Secretary (Aid): M A Hammond
First Secretary (Management): Miss C Gibson
Second Secretary (Chancery/Information):
T J Andrews
Second Secretary (Aid): J D Hawkes
Second Secretary: M Green
Third Secretary (Development): T M Cayless
Third Secretary (Consular): Miss C L Hopkinson
Third Secretary (Management): Miss L Tufnall

ZIMBABWE*

Harare
British High Commission
Stanley House, Jason Moyo Avenue,
(PO Box 4490), Harare
(Tel: 793781 or 728716)
(Telex: 24607 (a/b 24607 UKREP ZW))
(Telegraphic Address: UKREP HRE)
(Facsimile: 728380)

High Commissioner: R N Dales
Deputy High Commissioner: R S Dewar
Counsellor: D J Woods
Defence Adviser: Colonel A McNeil
First Secretary (Consular): P Colvin
First Secretary (Aid): D G Ward
First Secretary (Chancery/Economic):
J K M Mitchell
First Secretary (Commercial): P Nessling
First Secretary (Management): Miss M H Tough
First Secretary: D J Watson
Second Secretary (Aid): M J Edwards
Second Secretary: M T Whitbread
Second Secretary (Political): S Harkin
Third Secretary (Aid): Miss C Plastow

British Missions and Delegations

UNITED KINGDOM MISSION TO THE UNITED NATIONS

New York
845 Third Avenue, NY 10022
(Tel: (212) 745-0200/0444)
(Facsimile: (212) 745 0316)

United Kingdom Permanent Representative to the United Nations, and United Kingdom Representative on the Security Council (holds personal rank of Ambassador):
Sir David Hannay, KCMG
Deputy Permanent Representative to the United Nations (holds personal rank of Ambassador):
T L Richardson, CMG
Counsellor and Head of Chancery:
D J Plumbly, CMG
Counsellor (Economic and Social Affairs):
J F R Martin
Counsellor (Legal Adviser): M C Wood
Counsellor: I F McCredie
Counsellor (Management): I C Sloane
Counsellor: T C Stitt
First Secretary (Chancery): R N Peirce
First Secretary: I C Cliff, OBE
First Secretary: R D Fenn
First Secretary: R A Barnett
First Secretary: Dr J S C Priest
First Secretary: P W Sprunt
First Secretary: P J Ritchie
First Secretary (Chancery): D Curran
Second Secretary (Press Officer): J A Evans
Second Secretary (Management):
W G D Johnson, MBE
Second Secretary: M T Shryane, MBE
Second Secretary: Mrs C M Cliff
Second Secretary (Chancery): P M A Tissot
Third Secretary (Political): R Shackleton

UNITED KINGDOM MISSION TO THE OFFICE OF THE UNITED NATIONS AND OTHER INTERNATIONAL ORGANISATIONS AT GENEVA

37-39 rue de Vermont, 1211 Geneva 20
(Tel: 734.38.00)
(Telex: 414195 (a/b 414195 UKGV CH))
(Facsimile: (41) (22) 7345254)

UK Permanent Representative (holds personal rank of Ambassador): M R Morland, CMG
Deputy Permanent Representative (Economic Affairs): Miss A E Stoddart
Deputy Permanent Representative and Head of Chancery: E G M Chaplin, OBE
Counsellor (UN): J J R C Harston

First Secretary (UN): G C Perry
Legal Adviser: J J Rankin
First Secretary (UN): M Lonsdale
First Secretary (GATT): D Hayes
First Secretary (Joint Management Officer):
P Newall
First Secretary (UN): D I Campbell
First Secretary (UN): Miss E C Robson
First Secretary (UN): S M McDadd
First Secretary (Environment): A Godson
Second Secretary (GATT): P J A Young
Third Secretary (Management): J Thornton
Third Secretary (UN): Miss S C Boardman
Third Secretary (UN): Miss V S Jennison
Third Secretary (UN): Miss P R Walsh

UNITED KINGDOM DELEGATION TO THE CONFERENCE ON DISARMAMENT

Geneva
37-39 rue de Vermont 1211 Geneva 20
(Tel: (41) (22) 734.38.00)
(Telex: 414195 (a/b 414195 UKGV CH))
(Facsimile: (41) (22) 7345254)

Leader of Delegation (holds personal rank of Ambassador): Sir Michael Weston, KCMG, CVO
Counsellor: I R Kenyon
Military Adviser: Group Captain P Ryan, RAF
First Secretary: Dr G H Cooper
First Secretary (Joint Management Officer):
P Newell
First Secretary: Miss C J Ferguson
First Secretary: The Hon Anthony Monckton
First Secretary (Legal Adviser): J J Rankin
Third Secretary: Miss M A Twigg

UNITED KINGDOM DELEGATION TO THE NORTH ATLANTIC TREATY ORGANISATION

Brussels
OTAN1/NATO, Autoroute Bruxelles Zaventem, Evere, 1110 Bruxelles
(Tel: 242.67.75)
(Telex: 23774 (a/b 23774 UKNATO B))
(Facsimile: 245-2347)

United Kingdom Permanent Representative on the North Atlantic Council (holds personal rank of Ambassador): Sir John Weston, KCMG
Minister, United Kingdom Deputy Permanent Representative: R H Smith
Counsellor and Head of Chancery: J M Cresswell
Counsellor (Defence): E V Buckley

Counsellor (Finance and Infrastructure): J Elliott
First Secretary (European Security): J Miller
First Secretary (Arms Co-operation): G D Magnus
First Secretary (Nuclear Matters): J F M Tesh
First Secretary (Civil and Military Budgets):
R M Milton
First Secretary (Infrastructure): D Whitlock
First Secretary (Infrastructure): S C Routh
First Secretary (Information/Management):
Miss D Skingle
First Secretary (Defence Policy): F M Boland
First Secretary (Political): R V Court
Second Secretary (Arms Co-operation):
M A O'Neill
Second Secretary (Political): G D H Whitaker

UNITED KINGDOM DELEGATION TO THE ORGANISATION FOR ECONOMIC CO-OPERATION AND DEVELOPMENT

Paris
19 rue de Franqueville, 75116 Paris
(Tel: (1) 45 24 98 28)
(Facsimile: 45249837)

United Kingdom Permanent Representative
(holds personal rank of Ambassador):
K G MacInnes, CMG
Deputy United Kingdom Permanent Representative and Counsellor (Economic and Financial):
J Thomas
Counsellor (Management): P A McDermott, MVO
First Secretary: G C Gillham
First Secretary: T J Craddock
First Secretary: A D P Newton
Second Secretary: J J Gimblett

UNITED KINGDOM PERMANENT REPRESENTATIVE TO THE EUROPEAN COMMUNITY

Brussels
Rond-Point Robert Schuman 6, 1040 Brussels
(Tel: 287-8211)
(Telex: 24312 (a/b 24312 UKEC BR B))
(Facsimile: 287/ 8398)

United Kingdom Permanent Representative
(holds personal rank of Ambassador):
Sir John Kerr, KCMG
Minister and Deputy United Kingdom Permanent Representative: D R C Durie
Minister (Agriculture): Miss V K Timms
Counsellor and Head of Chancery:
J R de Fonblanque
Counsellor (Legal Adviser): I D Hendry
Counsellor (External Relations): S J L Wright
Counsellor (Economics and Finance): R J Bonney
Counsellor (Industry): J N Rees
Counsellor (Social Affairs, Environment, Regional Policy and Transport): D J Crawley
First Secretary (Press and Information):
C R V Stagg
First Secretary (External Relations): J D K Grant
First Secretary (Institutions): R Makepeace

First Secretary (Industry and Competition):
Miss C Bradley
First Secretary (Industry): A Holt
First Secretary (Economics and Finance):
N G F Baird
First Secretary (Assistant Legal Adviser):
I Macleod
First Secretary (Agriculture): Miss R E Rawling
First Secretary (Developing Countries): R T Calvert
First Secretary (Economics and Finance):
H R Quinn
First Secretary (Budget and Fiscal): M Neilson
First Secretary (Fisheries and Food): D M Hudson
First Secretary (External Relations): R Madelin
First Secretary (Customs and Excise):
M W Norgrove
First Secretary (Commercial): J Harrod
First Secretary (Social Affairs): K Masson
First Secretary (Presidency Coordinator):
R A W Norton
First Secretary (Regional Policy and Right of Establishment): W D A Haire
First Secretary (Presidency Coordinator):
M A Hatfull
First Secretary (Environment): S M Featherstone
First Secretary (Energy): P J Millett
First Secretary (Transport): N D J Denton
First Secretary (Industry): J C Farrel
First Secretary (External Relations): S J Butt
Second Secretary (Presidency Support/External Relations): J F Clark
Second Secretary (Agriculture and Food):
Miss H Robinson
Second Secretary (External Relations): C Alderton
Second Secretary (Health): Miss C Davis
Second Secretary (External Relations):
N H Moberly
Second Secretary (Institutions): M H Lamport
Second Secretary (Budget): A D McIntosh
Second Secretary (Environment): D Brunnert
Second Secretary (Transport): D Bearfield
Second Secretary (Health): J Mogford
Conference Officer: Miss R Davis
Third Secretary (Management): R J Bryant
Third Secretary: D G Kingdom
Third Secretary (Institutions): Mrs M E Richman

UNITED KINGDOM DELEGATION TO THE COUNCIL OF EUROPE

Strasbourg
18 rue Gottfried, 67000 Strasbourg
(Tel: 88 35 00 78)
(Telex: 890157 (a/b 890157 UKDEL SG))
(Facsimile: (88) 36-74-39)

United Kingdom Permanent Representative to Council of Europe (holds personal rank of Ambassador): N H Marshall, CMG
Deputy United Kingdom Permanent Representative: J R Jamieson
Third Secretary (Chancery) *and Management Officer:* A J Staunton
Third Secretary (Chancery/Visits):
Miss A M Power

UNITED KINGDOM DELEGATION TO THE INTERNATIONAL MONETARY FUND AND INTERNATIONAL BANK FOR RECONSTRUCTION AND DEVELOPMENT

Washington
Room 11-120, International Monetary Fund, 700 19th Street, NW, Washington, DC 20431
(Tel: (202) 623-4562)
(Facsimile: 202 623 4965)

United Kingdom Executive Director of the International Monetary Fund and International Bank for Reconstruction and Development: D Peretz
Alternate Executive Director of the International Bank for Reconstruction and Development:
R M Graham-Harrison
Alternate Executive Director of the International Monetary Fund: P Wright
Assistant (IBRD): S Mills
Assistant (IMF): D Sparkes
Assistant (IBRD): Miss V Harris
Assistant (IMF/IBRD): C J Jarvis

UNITED KINGDOM DELEGATION TO THE NEGOTIATIONS ON CONVENTIONAL ARMS CONTROL IN EUROPE

Vienna
JaurAesgasse 12, 1030 Vienna
(Tel: 7131575/9)
(Telex: 133410 (a/b 133410 BRITEM A), 132810 (a/b 132810 BRITEMB B))
(Telegraphic Address: UKDEL VIENNA)

Head of Delegation (Holds personal rank of Ambassador): T C Wood, CMG
Deputy Head of Delegation: A E Huckle
Counsellor: M W Lingwood
Senior Military Adviser: Brigadier R F Baly
First Secretary: Mrs E A Galvez
Deputy Military Adviser: Group Captain R E Holliday, OBE, RAF
First Secretary (Management): M J Bennett, MBE

UNITED KINGDOM MISSION TO THE INTERNATIONAL ATOMIC ENERGY AGENCY, THE UNITED NATIONS INDUSTRIAL DEVELOPMENT ORGANISATION AND THE UNITED NATIONS (VIENNA)

Vienna
Address and telex numbers as for British Embassy in Vienna
(Tel: 712 24 92)

United Kingdom Permanent Representative (holds personal rank of Ambassador):
G E Clark, CMG
First Secretary and United Kingdom Deputy Permanent Representative: Miss M R McIntosh
First Secretary (IAEA): M H Clements
First Secretary (IAEA): W A Dickson
Second Secretary (UN/UNIDO): A J Hennessy
Third Secretary (Management): J C Steeples

UNITED NATIONS ENVIRONMENT PROGRAMME

Nairobi
United Kingdom Permanent Representative to the United Nations Environment Programme:
Sir Kieran Prendergast, KCVO, CMG

UNITED NATIONS CENTRE FOR HUMAN SETTLEMENTS (HABITAT)

Nairobi
United Kingdom Permanent Representative to the United Nations Centre for Human Settlements (Habitat): Sir Kieran Prendergast, KCVO, CMG

UNITED KINGDOM REPRESENTATION AT THE ASIAN DEVELOPMENT BANK

Manila
6 ADB Avenue, Mandaluyong, Metro-Manila, Philippines
Postal Address: PO Box 789, Manila, Philippines
(Tel: (63) 2 632-4444; 632-6333)
(Cable Address: ASIANBANK, MANILA)
(Telex: RCA 29066 ADB PH); ITT 40571 (ADB PM); ETPI 63587 (ADB PN))
(Facsimile: 632-5557, 6322-741, 632-6816)

Executive Director: Dr H Bühler (German)
Alternate Director: Dr E Stohanzl (Austrian)
Director's Assistant: Ms A Davis (British)

UNITED KINGDOM REPRESENTATION AT THE AFRICAN DEVELOPMENT BANK

Abidjan
rue Joseph Anoma,
01 B.P. 1387, Abidjan
(Tel: 20 44 44, 20 40 23)
(Telex: 22203, 22202, 27717, 23263)

Executive Director: Dr H M Schmidt (German)
Alternate Executive Director: G Duyfjes (Dutch)
Assistant to the Executive Director: S Mattinson (British)

UNITED KINGDOM REPRESENTATION AT THE INTER-AMERICAN DEVELOPMENT BANK

Washington
1300 New York Avenue, NW Washington, DC 20577
(Tel: (202) 623-1054/56/58)
(Cable address: Intambanc, Washington DC)
(Telex: 64141, 44240)
(Facsimile: (202) 623-3605)

Executive Director: F Carpentieri
Alternate Executive Director: Ms A Deckers

UNITED KINGDOM REPRESENTATION TO THE FOOD AND AGRICULTURE ORGANISATION OF THE UNITED NATIONS

Rome

United Kingdom Permanent Representative:
D Sands Smith (c/o British Embassy, Rome)

UNITED KINGDOM REPRESENTATIVE ON THE COUNCIL OF THE INTERNATIONAL CIVIL AVIATION ORGANISATION

Montreal

Suite 928, 1000 Sherbrooke Street West, Montreal, Quebec, Canada, H3A 3G4
(Tel: 285 8302/3)
(Facsimile: (514) 285 8001)

United Kingdom Representative: F A Neal, CMG
Alternate United Kingdom Representative:
S A Hurst

OFFICE OF THE BRITISH SENIOR REPRESENTATIVE, SINO-BRITISH JOINT LIAISON GROUP

Hong Kong

St John's Building, 33 Garden Road,
PO Box 528, Hong Kong

(Tel: (010-852) 8682171)
(Facsimile: (852) 868 2431)

Senior Representative: A C Galsworthy, CMG
Counsellor (Deputy to the Senior Representative):
A R Paul
First Secretary: C W Parton
Second Secretary: C E Garrett

BRITISH MISSION TO THE SUPREME NATIONAL COUNCIL OF CAMBODIA

Cambodiana Hotel, Phnom Penh
(Tel: (010) (873) 144 5255)
(Facsimile: (010) (873) 144 5254)

Head of Mission: D A Burns
First Secretary and Deputy Head of Mission:
B A Thorpe
First Secretary: K J C Sloan
Third Secretary: I D Mason

Governors and Commanders-in-Chief etc, of the Dependent Territories

DEPENDENT TERRITORIES

Anguilla
Government House, Anguilla
(Tel: 2622 (Office/Residence), 2292 (Residence))
(Telegraphic Address: Governor, Anguilla)
(Telex: 9351) (a/b GOV AXA LA)
(Facsimile: 809497 3151)

Governor: A W Shave, OBE
Deputy Governor: H McCrory, MBE

Bermuda
Government House, Hamilton
(Tel: 2-3600 (Deputy Governor's Office: 2-2587)
(Calls from UK: 010 1 809 29 23600 22587))
(Telex: 3202 (a/b 3202 DEPGOV BA))
(Facsimile: 809 29 53823)

Governor and Commander-in-Chief:
The Lord Waddington, PC, DL, QC
Deputy Governor: J P Kelly, MBE

British Antarctic Territory
Foreign and Commonwealth Office, London SW1
(Tel: (071-270 2742)

Commissioner (non-resident): P M Newton
Deputy Commissioner (non-resident): P L Hunt
Administrator (non-resident): Dr M G Richardson

British Indian Ocean Territory
Foreign and Commonwealth Office, King Charles
Street, London, SW1A 2AH

Commissioner (non-resident): T G Harris
Administrator (non-resident): R G Wells

British Virgin Islands
Government House, Tortola, British Virgin Islands
(Tel: (Office) 2345 (Government House) 3400)
(Telegraphic Address: VIRILE, TORTOLA)
(Telex: 7984 (a/b VIRILE VB))
(Facsimile: (1809) 494 5582)

Governor: P A Penfold, OBE
Deputy Governor: E Georges, OBE

Cayman Islands
Government House, Grand Cayman,
Cayman Islands
(Tel: (Office) (1) (809) 94 94 321)
(Telex: 4260 (a/b 4260 CIGOVT CP))
(Facsimile: (809) 94 96556)

Governor: M E J Gore, CBE
Chief Secretary: J L Hurlston, MBE
Deputy Chief Secretary: J M Ryan, MBE

Falkland Islands
Government House, Stanley,
Falkland Islands
(Tel: (500) 27433 (Office); (500) 22210
(Goverment House))
(Telex: 2414 (a/b 2414 GOVERNOR FK))
(Facsimile: (500) 27434

Governor: D E Tatham, CMG
Chief Executive: R Sampson
Government Secretary: C F Redston
First Secretary: R C Huxley
*(See also British Antarctic Territory and South
Georgia and South Sandwich Islands)*

Gibraltar
The Convent, Gibraltar
(Tel: 75908)
(Telex: 2223) (a/b 2223 ADMSEC GK)
(Facsimile: (350) 54586)

Governor and Commander-in-Chief:
Admiral Sir Derek Reffell, KCB, RN (ret'd)
Deputy Governor: A C Carter
Assistant to Deputy Governor: M T Hill

Hong Kong
Government House, Upper Albert Road,
Hong Kong
(Tel: (010) (852) 523 2031)
(Telex: 73380 (a/b 73380 GOVHK HX))
(Facsimile: (010) (852) 526 0995
(Communications Centre, Government House),
(010) (852) 845 2870 (Trade Centre)
(Please note: Correspondence for the Hong Kong
Government should be addressed to the
Government Secretariat, Lower Albert Road,
Hong Kong (Tel: 810 2406/2717)
(Telex: 73380 (a/b 73380 GOVHK HX))

Governor and Commander-in-Chief:
The Rt Hon Christopher Patten
Chief Secretary:
Sir David Ford, KBE, LVO

Montserrat
Government House, Plymouth
(Tel: 2409, 3772 and 2648) (Calls from UK: 010 1
809 491 2409, 3772.and 2648)
(Telex: 5727 (a/b OAG MK))
(Facsimile: 010 1 809 491 4553)

Governor: D G P Taylor

Pitcairn, Henderson, Ducie and Oeno Islands
British High Commission, Wellington,
New Zealand
(Tel: 726-049)
(Telex: 3325) (a/b UKREP NZ 3325)

Governor: D J Moss, CMG (non-resident)

British Consulate-General, Auckland, New Zealand
(Tel: 32 973)
(Telex: 2412 (a/b BRITN NZ 2412))

Commissioner: G D Harraway (non-resident)

St Helena
Plantation House, St Helena
(Telex: 4202 (a/b 4202 GOVT HL))
Governor and Commander-in-Chief:
A N Hoole, OBE
Chief Secretary: M S Hone, MBE

ST HELENA DEPENDENCIES

*Administrator, Ascension Island, The Residency,
Ascension:* B N Connelly
(Telex: 3214 (a/b 3214 GOVT AV) (Dial Code:
2000)) (Calls from UK: 010-247-6311,
010-247-4525)
(Facsimile: 010 247 6152)

*Administrator, Tristan da Cunha, The Residency,
Tristan da Cunha:* P H Johnson

South Georgia and South Sandwich Islands
Government House, Stanley,
Falkland Islands
(Tel: (500) 27433 (Office), (500) 22210
(Government House))
(Telex: 2414 (a/b 2414 GOVERNOR FK))

Commissioner: D E Tatham, CMG (non-resident)
Assistant Commissioner: R C Huxley(non-resident)
*(See also Falkland Islands and British Antarctic
Territory)*

Turks and Caicos Islands
Waterloo, Government House, Grand Turk, Turks
and Caicos Islands
(Tel: Grand Turk 2309 (Office)' 2408
(Residence)) (Calls from UK: 010 1 809 946
2309/2408)
(Telex: 8212 (a/b 8212 GOVTCI TQ))
(Facsimile (1) 809 946 2766)
Chief Secretary's Office, Government Secretariat,
Grand Turk
(Tel: Grand Turk 2702) (Calls from UK: 010 1
809 946 2702)
(Telex: 8212 (a/b 8212 GOVTCI TQ))
(Facsimile: (1) 809 946 2886)

Governor: M J Bradley, CMG, QC
Chief Secretary: M Forrester
Deputy Chief Secretary: M A Capes

INDEX TO NAMES OF PLACES
Where Ambassadors, High Commissioners, and other Diplomatic and Consular Officers normally reside (Part II)

Ibiza, Spain
Innsbruck, Austria
Iquitos, Peru
Iskenderun, Turkey
Islamabad, Pakistan
Istanbul, Turkey
Izmir, Turkey

Jakarta, Indonesia
Jedda, Saudi Arabia
Jerusalem, Jerusalem
Johannesburg, South Africa
Johor, Malaysia
Jyväskylä, Finland

Kabul, Afghanistan
Kaduna, Nigeria
Kampala, Uganda
Kansas City, United States
Karachi, Pakistan
Kathmandu, Nepal
Khartoum, Sudan
Kiel, Germany
Kiev, Ukraine
Kigali, Rwanda
Kingston, Jamaica
Kingstown, St Vincent and the
  Grenadines
Kinshasa, The Republic of Zaire
Kisangani, Zaire
Kishinev, Moldavia
Kota Kinabulu, Malaysia
Kotka, Finland
Kristiansand (S), Norway
Kristiansund (N), Norway
Kuala Lumpur, Malaysia
Kuching, Malaysia
Kuopio, Finland
Kuwait, Kuwait

Lagos, Nigeria
Lahore, Pakistan
Lanzarote (Canary Islands),
  Spain
La Paz, Bolivia
Las Palmas (Grand Canary),
  Spain
Le Havre, France
Libreville, Gabon
Liechtenstein, Liechtenstein
Liege, Belgium
Lille, France
Lilongwe, Malawi
Lima, Peru
Lisbon, Portugal
Ljubljana, Slovenia
Lomé, Togo
Los Angeles, United States
Luanda, Angola
Lubumbashi, Zaire
Lugano, Switzerland
Luleå, Sweden
Lusaka, Zambia
Luxembourg, Luxembourg
Luxor, Egypt
Lyon, France

Macao, Portugal
Madeira (Funchal), Portugal
Madras, India
Madrid, Spain
Majuro, Marshall Islands
Malabo, Equatorial Guinea
Malaga, Spain
Male, The Republic of Maldives
Malmö, Sweden
Managua, Nicaragua
Manaus, Brazil
Manila, Philippines
Maputo, Mozambique, Peoples'
  Republic of
Maracaibo, Venezuela
Mariehamn, Finland
Marmaris, Turkey
Marseille, France
Martinique, France (Fort de
  France)
Maseru, Lesotho
Mbabane, Swaziland
Medan, Indonesia
Medellin, Colombia
Melbourne, Australia
Menorca, Spain
Mérida, Mexico
Mérida, Venezuela
Mersin, Turkey
Mexico City, Mexico
Miami, United States
Milan, Italy
Minsk, Belarus
Miri, Malaysia
Mogadishu, Somalia
Mombasa, Kenya
Monaco, Monaco
Monrovia, Liberia
Monterrey, Mexico
Montevideo, Uruguay
Montreal, Canada
Montreux, Switzerland
Moroní, Comoros
Moscow, Russian Federation
Munich, Germany
Muscat, Oman

Nagoya, Japan
Nairobi, Kenya
Nantes, France
Naples, Italy
Nassau, Bahamas
Nauru, Nauru
Ndjamena, Chad
New Delhi, India
New Orleans, United States
New York, United States
Niamey, Niger
Nice, France
Nicosia, Cyprus
Norfolk, United States
Nouakchott, Mauritania
Nuku'alofa, Tonga
Nuremburg, Germany
Nuuk\Godthaab, Greenland

Odense, Denmark
Oporto, Portugal
Organisation for Economic
  Co-operation and
  Development, Paris
Osaka, Japan
Oslo, Norway
Ottawa, Canada
Ouagadougou, Burkina
Oulu (Uleaborg), Finland

Palma, Spain
Panama City, Panama
Papeete France (French
  Polynesia)
Paramaribo, Suriname
Paris, France
Patras, Greece
Peking, China
Pinang, Malaysia
Perth, Australia
Philadelphia, United States
Phnom Penh, Cambodia
Pitcairn, Pitcairn Islands
Piura, Peru
Plymouth, Montserrat
Pohnpei, Micronesia
Pointe Noire, Congo
Ponta Delgada (Azores),
  Portugal
Pori (Bjorneborg), Finland
Port-au-Prince, Haiti
Port Elizabeth, South Africa
Portimão, Portugal
Portland (Oregon), United States
Port Louis, Mauritius
Port Moresby, Papua New
  Guinea
Port of Spain, Trinidad
Port Said, Egypt
Port Stanley, Falkland Islands
Pôrto Alegre, Brazil
Prague, Czechoslovakia
Praia, Cape Verde
Pretoria, South Africa
Puerto Barrios, Guatemala
Puerto Plata, Dominican
  Republic
Puerto Rico, United States
Punta Arenas, Chile
Pusan, Korea

Quito, Ecuador

Rabat, Morocco
Rangoon, Burma
Recife, Brazil
Reykjavik, Iceland
Rhodes, Greece
Riga, Latvia
Rio de Janeiro, Brazil
Rio Grande, Brazil
Riyadh, Saudi Arabia
Rome, Italy
Rønne (Bornholm), Denmark
Roseau, Dominica

St George's, Grenada
St Helena, St Helena
St John's, Antigua
St Louis, United States
St Malo, France
St Petersburg, Russian Federation
Salonika, Greece
Salvador, Brazil
Salzburg, Austria
Samos, Greece
Sana'a, Republic of Yemen
San Francisco, United States
San José, Costa Rica
San Marino, San Marino
San Pedro Sula, Honduras
San Salvador, El Salvador
Santa Cruz, Bolivia
Santa Cruz, Tenerife, Canary
  Islands
Santander, Spain
Santiago, Chile
Santo Domingo, Dominican
  Republic
Santos, Brazil
São Paulo, Brazil
Sao Tomé, Sao Tomé and
  Principe
Seattle, United States
Seoul, Korea
Seville, Spain
Sfax, Tunisia
Shanghai, China
Singapore, Singapore
Sofia, Bulgaria
Split, Croatia
Stavanger, Norway
Stockholm, Sweden
Stuttgart, Germany
Suez, Egypt
Sundsvall, Sweden
Surabaya, Indonesia
Suva, Fiji
Sydney, Australia
Syros, Greece

Tallinn, Estonia
Tampere, Finland
Tampico, Mexico
Tananarive, Madagascar (see
  Antananarivo)
Tangier, Morocco
Tarawa, Kiribati
Tarragona, Spain
Tbilisi, Georgia
Tegucigalpa, Honduras

Tehran, Iran
Tel Aviv, Israel
Tirana, Albania
Tokyo, Japan
Toronto, Canada
Torshavn, Denmark (Faroes)
Tortola, British Virgin Islands
Toulouse, France
Trieste, Italy
Tripoli, Lebanon
Tripoli, Libya
Tromsø, Norway
Trondheim, Norway
Trujillo, Peru
Tunis, Tunisia
Turin, Italy
Turku, Finland

Ulaanbaatar, Mongolia
United Kingdom Delegation to
  the Council of Europe,
  Strasbourg
United Kingdom Delegation to
  the North Atlantic Treaty
  Organisation, Brussels
United Kingdom Delegation to
  OECD, Paris
United Kingdom Permanent
  Representative to the
  European Communities,
  Brussels
United Kingdom Delegation to
  the Conference on
  Disarmament, Geneva
United Kingdom Mission to the
  United Nations, New York
United Kingdom Mission to
  the Office of the United
  Nations and other
  International Organisations at
  Geneva
United Kingdom Delegation to
  the International Monetary
  Fund and International Bank
  for Reconstruction and
  Development, Washington
United Kingdom Delegation to
  the Negotiations on
  Conventional Arms Control in
  Europe, Vienna
United Kingdom Mission to the
  International Atomic Energy
  Agency, the United Nations
  Industrial Development
  Organisation and the United

Nations (Vienna)
United Kingdom Representation
  at the African Development
. Bank (Abidjan)
United Kingdom lf1620
  Representation at the Asian
  Development Bank (Manila)
United Kingdom Representation
  At the Inter-American
  Development Bank
  (Washington)
United Kingdom Representation
  to the Food and Agriculture
  Organisation of the United
  Nations (Rome)
United Kingdom Representative
  on the Council of the
  International Civil Aviation
  Organisation (Montreal)
United Nations Centre for
  Human Settlements (Habitat)
  (Nairobi)
United Nations Environment
  Programme (Nairobi)

Vaasa, Finland
Valletta, Malta
Valparaiso, Chile
Vancouver, Canada
Venice, Italy
Vera Cruz, Mexico
Victoria, Hong Kong
Victoria, Seychelles
Vienna, Austria
Vientiane, Laos
Vigo, Spain
Vila, Vanuatu
Vilnius, Lithuania
Volos, Greece

Warsaw, Poland
Washington, United States
Wellington, New Zealand
Willemstad (Netherlands
  Antilles)
Windhoek, Namibia
Winnipeg, Canada

Yaoundé, Cameroon
Yerevan, Armenia

Zagreb, Croatia
Zurich, Switzerland

Chronological Lists from 1973 onwards of Secretaries of State, Ministers of State, Permanent Under-Secretaries of State, British Ambassadors etc., High Commissioners and Permanent Representatives to International Organisations

Reference should be made to the Foreign Office and Commonwealth Relations Office Lists of 1965, to the Colonial Office List of 1966 and to the Diplomatic Service List 1992 and earlier Lists for previous lists of officers holding these appointments.

Part III: Chronological Lists

The Foreign and Commonwealth Office was formed in October 1968 by the merger of the former Foreign Office and the Commonwealth Office

SECRETARIES OF STATE FOR FOREIGN AND COMMONWEALTH AFFAIRS 1973-1993

1974   Mar 5 Rt Hon. James Callaghan, MP (later Sir James Callaghan, MP) (later Lord Callaghan)

1976   Apr 9 Rt Hon. Anthony Crosland, MP (died 19 Feb 1977)

1977   Feb 22 Rt Hon. Dr David Owen, MP

1979   May 5 Rt Hon. The Lord Carrington, KCMG, MC

1982   April 5 The Rt Hon. Francis Pym, MC, MP (later Lord Pym)

1983   June 11 The Rt Hon. Sir Geoffrey Howe, PC, QC, MP

1989   July 25 The Rt Hon. John Major, MP

1989   Oct 26 The Rt Hon Douglas Hurd, CBE, MP

MINISTERS OF STATE FOR FOREIGN AND COMMONWEALTH AFFAIRS 1973-1993

1974   March 7 The Rt Hon. David Ennals, MP (later Lord Ennals)

1974   March 7 Roy Hattersley, MP (later the Rt Hon. Roy Hattersley, MP)

1975   Dec 4 The Rt Hon. The Lord Goronwy-Roberts of Caernarvon and of Ogwen

1976   April 14 Ted Rowlands, MP

1976   Sept 13 The Rt Hon. Dr David Owen, MP

1977   Feb 22 Frank Judd, MP

1979   May 5 The Rt Hon. Sir Ian Gilmour, Bt, MP •

1979   May 5 Peter Blaker, MP (later the Rt Hon. Sir Peter Blaker, MP)

1979   May 5 Douglas Hurd, CBE, MP (later the Rt Hon. Douglas Hurd, CBE, MP)

1979   May 5 Neil Marten, MP (later the Rt Hon. Sir Neil Marten, MP)

1979   May 5 Nicholas Ridley, MP (later the Rt Hon. Nicholas Ridley, MP)

1981   Sept 14 The Rt Hon. Humphrey Atkins, MP • (later the Rt Hon. Sir Humphrey Atkins, MP)

1981   Sept 14 Richard Luce, MP

1982   April 5 The Lord Belstead

1982   April 5 Cranley Onslow, MP

1983   June 14 Malcolm Rifkind, MP

1983   June 14 The Rt Hon. Baroness Young

1983   June 14 Richard Luce, MP

1983   June 14 The Rt Hon. Timothy Raison, MP

1984   Sept 11 Timothy Renton, MP

1986   Jan 13 Mrs Lynda Chalker, MP (later the Rt Hon. Baroness Chalker)

1986   Sept 8 Christopher Patten, MP

1987   June 16 The Lord Glenarthur

1987   June 16 David Mellor, QC, MP

1988   July 16 The Rt. Hon. William Waldegrave, MP

1989   July 25 The Hon. Francis Maude, MP

1989   July 25 The Lord Brabazon

1989   July 25 The Hon. Timothy Sainsbury, MP

1990   July 23 Tristan Garel-Jones, MP (later the Rt Hon Tristan Garel-Jones, MP)

1990   July 23 The Rt. Hon. The Earl of Caithness

1990   July 23 The Hon. Mark Lennox-Boyd, MP

1990   Nov 1 The Hon. Douglas Hogg, QC, MP (later the Rt Hon Douglas Hogg, QC, MP)

1992   The Rt Hon Alastair Goodland, MP

ø Chancellor of the Duchy of Lancaster

• Lord Privy Seal

PERMANENT UNDER-SECRETARIES OF STATE FOR FOREIGN AND COMMONWEALTH AFFAIRS AND HEAD OF HM DIPLOMATIC SERVICE 1973-1993

1973   Nov 8 Sir Thomas Brimelow, KCMG (later GCMG) OBE, (later Lord Brimelow)

1975   Nov 22 Sir Michael Palliser, KCMG (later GCMG)

1982   April 8 Sir Antony (Arthur) Acland, (later GCMG), KCVO

1986   June 23 Sir Patrick (Richard Henry) Wright, GCMG

1991   June 28 Sir David (Howe) Gillmore, KCMG

CHRONOLOGICAL LIST OF BRITISH REPRESENTATIVES IN COMMONWEALTH COUNTRIES, TO FOREIGN STATES AND IN THE REPUBLIC OF IRELAND 1973-1993

Afghanistan
1972 John Kenneth Drinkall, amb. ex. and plen. Nov 17
1976 (Kenneth) Roy Crook, amb. ex. and plen. March 20
1979 (William) Norman Hillier-Fry, amb. ex. and plen. Oct 19
1981 John Donald Garner, Chargé d'Affaires a.i. Feb 20
1984 Charles David Stephen Drace-Francis, Chargé d'Affaires a.i. July 18
1987 Ian Warren Mackley, Chargé d'Affaires a.i. January 8
Staff temporarily withdrawn from post February 1989

Albania
1992 Sir Patrick (Stanislaus) Fairweather, amb. ex. and plen. July 20

Algeria
1974 John Armstrong Robinson, amb. ex. and plen. March 2
1977 Richard (later Sir R) (Stanley) Faber, amb. ex. and plen. Nov 30
1981 Benjamin Leckie Strachan, amb. ex. and plen. May 17
1984 Alan (later Sir A) Gordon Munro, amb. ex. and plen. Jan 21
1987 Patrick Howard Caines Eyers amb. ex. and plen. April 12
1990 Christopher Charles Richard Battiscombe amb. ex. and plen. March 6

Angola
1978 John Gerrard Flynn, Chargé d'Affaires. Jan 16
1978 Hugh Campbell Byatt, amb. ex. and plen. Oct 17
1981 Francis Kennedy, amb. ex. and plen. June 10
1983 Marrack Irvine Goulding, amb. ex. and plen. June 29
1985 Patrick Stanislaus Fairweather, amb. ex. and plen. Oct 2
1987 Michael John Carlisle Glaze, amb. ex. and plen. Nov 18
1990 John Gerrard Flynn, amb. ex. and plen. May 9

Antigua and Barbuda
HIGH COMMISSIONERS
1981 James Stanley Arthur. Nov 1
1982 Viscount (John William) Dunrossil. Sept 25
1983 Giles (later Sir G) (Lionel) Bullard. Aug 6
1986 Kevin Francis Xavier Burns. Oct 19
1991 Emrys Thomas Davies. Feb 15

The Argentine Republic
1973 Sir Donald (Charles) Hopson, amb. ex. and plen. Feb 7
1975 Derick (later Sir D) (Rosslyn) Ashe, amb. ex. and plen. March 20
1976 John William Richmond Shakespeare, Chargé d'Affaires a.i. Jan 20
1977 Hugh Michael Carless, Chargé d'Affaires a.i. July 18
1980 Anthony James Williams, amb. ex. and plen. Feb 17

Diplomatic and Consular relations with the Argentine Republic were broken off with effect from 2 April 1982. Consular Relations were resumed on 19 October 1989 and Diplomatic Relations on 15 February 1990.

1989 Alan Charles Hunt Consul General. Oct 19
1989 Alan Charles Hunt Chargé d'Affaires a. 1 and Consul General. Feb 15
1990 The Hon Humphrey (John Hamilton) Maud, amb. ex. and plen. July 15

Armenia
1992 Sir Brian (James) (Proetel) Fall, amb. ex. and plen. July 15

Australia
HIGH COMMISSIONERS
1971 The Rt Hon. Sir (John) Morrice (Cairns) James (later Lord St Brides). May 10
1976 Sir Donald (Claude) Tebbit. May 13
1980 Sir John (Charles Moir) Mason. Apr 29
1984 Sir John (Henry Gladstone) Leahy. Oct 13
1988 (Arthur) John (later Sir J) Coles. March 22
1991 Brian (later Sir B) (Leon) Barder. April 11

Austria
1972 Denis (later Sir D) (Seward) Laskey, amb. ex. and plen. Jan 20
1976 Hugh Travers Morgan. Jan 20
1979 Donald McDonald Gordon, amb. ex. and plen. July 31
1982 Michael O'Donel Bjarne Alexander, amb. ex. and plen. Jan 25
1986 Robert James O'Neill, amb. ex. and plen. Sept 2
1989 Brian Lee Crowe, amb. ex. and plen. May 31
1992 Terence Courtney Wood, amb.ex. and plen. April 30

Azerbaijan
1992 Sir Brian (James) (Proetel) Fall, amb. ex. and plen. July 14

Bahamas
HIGH COMMISSIONERS
1973 (Charles) James Treadwell. July 7
1975 Peter Mennell. Feb 2
1978 John Spenser Ritchie Duncan. Aug 1
1981 Achilles Symeon Papadopoulos. May 2
1983 Peter William Heap. May 23
1986 Colin Garth Mays. Oct 16
1991 Michael Edward John Gore. July 16
1992 Brian Attewell. Sept 16

Bahrain

1972 Robert Mathieson Tesh, amb. ex. and plen. July 29
1975 Edward Ferguson Given, amb. ex. and plen. Oct 14
1979 Harold Berners Walker, amb. ex. and plen. Mar 15
1981 David Gordon Crawford, amb. ex. and plen. Aug 9
1981 (William) Roger Tomkys, amb. ex. and plen. Dec 7
1984 Francis Sidney Edward Trew, amb. ex. and plen. Dec 5
1988 John Alan Shepherd, amb. ex. and plen. April 4
1992 Hugh James Oliver Redvers Tunnell, amb. ex. and plen. Feb 16

Bangladesh

HIGH COMMISSIONERS
1972 Anthony Arthur Golds. April 18
1975 Barry Granger Smallman. Jan 11
1978 (Frank) Stephen Miles. April 17
1980 Sir Michael Scott. Jan 16
1981 Frank (later Sir F) Mills. Oct 23
1983 Terence George (later Sir T) Streeton. Dec 20
1989 Colin (later Sir C) (Henry) Imray. Oct 21

Barbados

HIGH COMMISSIONERS
1973 (Charles) Stuart Roberts. Nov 9
1978 (James) Stanley Arthur. April 25
1982 Viscount (John William) Dunrossil. Sept 25
1983 Giles (later Sir G) (Lionel) Bullard. Aug 6
1986 Kevin Francis Xavier Burns. Oct 19
1991 Emrys Thomas Davies. Jan 13

Belarus

1992 Sir Brian (James) (Proetel) Fall, amb. ex. and plen. July 22

Belgium

1974 David (later Sir D) (Francis) Muirhead, amb. ex. and plen. April 18
1979 Sir Peter (George Arthur) Wakefield, amb. ex. and plen. Jan 20
1982 John (later Sir J) Edward Jackson, amb. ex. and plen. April 30
1985 Peter (later Sir P) (Charles) Petrie, amb ex. and plen. July 7
1989 Robert James O'Neill, amb. ex. and plen. May 10
1992 John Walton David Gray, amb. ex. and plen. June 18

Belize

HIGH COMMISSIONERS
1981 Francis Sidney Edward Trew. Sept 21
1984 John Michael Crosby. Oct 19
1987 Peter Alexander Bremner Thomson. Nov 10
1991 David Patrick Robert Mackilligin. Feb 13

Republic of Benin

1973 Alan James Brown, amb. ex. and plen. March 26
1975 (vacant)
1976 John Robert Williams, amb. ex. and plen. Nov 26
1979 Mervyn (later Sir M) Brown, amb. ex. and plen. Sept 3
1983 William Erskine Hamilton Whyte, amb. ex. and plen. Aug 18
1986 Martin later Sir M (Kenneth) Ewans, amb. ex. and plen. Aug 8
1988 Brian Leon Barder, amb. ex. and plen. Sept 23
1991 (Alastair) Christopher (Donald Summerhayes) MacRae, amb. ex. and plen. June 17

Bolivia

1973 Ronald Christopher Hope-Jones, amb. ex. and plen. Oct 26
1977 Adrian Clarence Buon, amb. ex. and plen. Sept 20
1981 Stanley Frederick St Clare Duncan, amb. ex. and plen. Sept 15
1985 Alan White, amb. ex. and plen. March 9
1987 Colum John Sharkey, amb. ex. and plen. Aug 19
1989 Michael Francis Daly, amb. ex. and plen. June 4
1991 Richard Michael Jackson, amb. ex. and plen. May 15

Botswana

HIGH COMMISSIONERS
1973 Eleanor Jean Emery. June 29
1977 Wilfred Turner. May 14
1981 Wilfred Jones. Sept 3
1986 Peter Albert Raftery. Feb 21
1989 Brian Smith. Feb 18
1991 John Coates Edwards. Nov 19

Brazil

1973 Derek (later Sir D) Sherbourne Lindsell Dodson, amb. ex. and plen. Sept 9
1977 Sir Norman Statham, amb. ex. and plen. Feb 28
1979 George Edmund Hall, amb. ex. and plen. Oct 30
1981 George William (later Sir W) Harding, amb. ex. and plen. March 9
1984 John Burns Ure, amb. ex. and plen. Feb 26
1987 Michael John Newington amb. ex. and plen. Dec 15
1992 Peter Williams Heap, amb. ex. and plen. Aug 4

Brunei

HIGH COMMISSIONERS
1972 Peter Gautrey. Jan 12
1975 James Alfred Davidson. Jan 8
1978 Arthur Christopher Watson. Nov 6
1983 (Robert) Francis Cornish. Aug 5
1986 Roger Westbrook. Sept 8
1991 Adrian John Sindall. April 9

Bulgaria

1973   Edwin Bolland, amb. ex. and plen. May 22
1976   John Cecil Cloake, amb. ex. and plen. Nov 4
1980   Giles Lionel Bullard, amb. ex. and plen. Aug 23
1983   John Michael Owen Snodgrass, amb. ex. and plen. Sep 6
1986   John Harold Fawcett, amb. ex. and plen. Aug 30
1989   Richard Thomas, amb. ex. and plen. May 5

Burkina Faso (formerly Upper Volta)
(Country re-named on 3 August 1984)

1983   John Michael Willson, amb. ex. and plen. July 12
1988   Veronica Evelyn Sutherland, amb. ex. and plen. Jan 26
1991   Margaret Irene Rothwell, amb. ex. and plen.

Burma

1974   Terence John O'Brien, amb. ex. and plen. June 26
1978   Charles Leonard Booth, amb. ex. and plen. Feb 27
1982   Nicholas Maed Fenn, amb. ex. and plen. Oct 20
1986   Martin Robert Morland, amb. ex. and plen. Oct 19
1990   Julian Dana Nimmo Hartland-Swann, amb. ex. and plen. May 5

Republic of Burundi

1975   Richard James Stratton, amb. ex. and plen. Jan 21
1978   Alan Ewen Donald, amb. ex. and plen. Jan 26
1980   John Michael Owen Snodgrass, amb. ex. and plen. July 11
1984   Nicholas Peter Bayne, amb. ex. and plen. Feb 7
1985   Patrick Howard Caines Eyers, amb. ex. and plen. Sept 23
1987   Robert Linklater Burke Cormack, amb. ex. and plen. June 11
1991   Roger Westbrook, amb. ex. and plen.

Cambodia

1973   John Ernest Powell-Jones, amb. ex. and plen. March 14
1975   John Christopher Wyndowe Bushell, amb. ex. and plen. Feb 18
1976   (vacant)
       Staff temporarily withdrawn from post
       Since December 1979 HMG has had no
       representation in Cambodia, but on 7
       November 1991 appointed a Representative
       to the Supreme National Council of
       Cambodia—see Chronological List of
       British Representatives to International
       Organisations

United Republic of Cameroon

1972   Edward Ferguson Given, amb. ex. and plen. June 7

1975   Albert Edward Saunders, amb. ex. and plen. Aug 30
1979   Denis Edward Richards, amb. ex. and plen. April 5
1981   Bryan Sparrow, amb. ex. and plen. Aug 4
1984   Michael John Carlisle Glaze, amb. ex. and plen. July 7
1987   Martin Reith, amb. ex. and plen. Oct 15
1991   William Ernest Quantrill, amb. ex. and plen. April 16

Canada

HIGH COMMISSIONERS

1974   Sir John (Baines) Johnston. June 13
1978   Sir John (Archibald) Ford. May 8
1981   The Lord Moran. June 15
1984   Sir Derek (Malcolm) Day. Aug 1
1988   Sir Alan (Bedford) Urwick. Dec 4
1989   Brian James Proetel Fall. Oct 5
1992   Nicholas (later Sir N) (Peter) Bayne. April 7

Cape Verde

1977   John Ernest Powell-Jones, amb. ex. and plen. April
1979   (Clifford) William Squire, amb. ex. and plen. Sept 24
1982   (Peter) Laurence O'Keeffe, amb. ex. and plen. Sept 15
1986   John Esmond Campbell Macrae, amb. ex. and plen. June 17
1990   Roger Campbell Beetham, amb. ex. and plen. Oct 18

Central African Republic

1977   (Alfred) Ian Glasby, Chargé d'Affaires. Oct 7
1982   Bryan Sparrow, amb. ex. and plen. Jan 28
1985   Michael John Carlisle Glaze, amb. ex. and plen. Feb 9
1987   (vacant)
1988   Martin Reith, amb. ex. and plen. July 2
1991   William Ernest Quantrill, amb. ex. and plen.

Chad (Republic of)

1973   Simon Yelverton Dawbarn, amb. ex. and plen. July 5
1975   Mark Evelyn Heath, amb. ex. and plen. June 17
1978   John Rodney Johnson, amb. ex. and plen. May 10
1980   (vacant)
1982   (Alistair) Christopher (Donald Summerhayes) MacRae, amb. ex. and plen. Feb 2
1985   Michael Francis Daly, amb. ex. and plen. March 20
1987   Maeve Geraldine Fort, amb. ex. and plen. March 7
1990   Charlotte Susanna Rycroft, amb. ex. and plen. March 19
1991   William Ernest Quantrill, amb. ex. and plen. June

Chile

1973	Reginald (later Sir R) (Louis) Secondé, amb. ex. and plen. March 22
1975	(Donald) Keith Haskell, Chargé d'Affaires a.i. Dec 30
1978	Eric Jack Anglin, Chargé d'Affaires a.i. March 11
1980	John Moore Heath, amb. ex. and plen. Feb 20
1982	John Kyrle Hickman, amb. ex. and plen. June 13
1987	Alan White, amb. ex. and plen. July 31
1990	Richard Alvin Neilson, amb. ex. and plen. Aug 31

China

1972	John (later Sir J) (Mansfield) Addis, amb. ex. and plen. March 13
1974	Edward (later Sir E) Youde, amb. ex. and plen. Aug 21
1978	Percy (later Sir P) Cradock, amb. ex. and plen. June 11
1984	Sir Richard (Mark) Evans, amb. ex. and plen. Jan 19
1988	Alan (later Sir A) (Ewen) Donald, amb. ex. and plen. May 14
1991	Robin (later Sir R) Taylor, amb. ex. and plen. June 5

Colombia

1973	Geoffrey Allan Crossley, amb. ex. and plen. June 8
1977	Kenneth James Uffen, amb. ex. and plen. Nov 24
1982	John (later Sir J) Adam Robson, amb. ex. and plen. May 29
1987	Richard Alvin Neilson, amb. ex. and plen. Feb 5
1990	Keith Elliott Hedley Morris, amb. ex. and plen. Sept 26
1991	Dennis Oldrieve Amy, amb. ex. and plen. May 15

Comoros

1984	James Nicholas Allan, amb. ex. and plen. June 7
1986	Richard Borman Crowson, amb. ex. and plen. Aug 29
1989	Michael Edward Howell, amb. ex. and plen. Sept 27
1991	Dennis Oltrieve Amy, amb. ex. and plen. May 14

Congo (People's Republic of)

1973	Mark Echelaz Allen, amb. ex. and plen. March 3
1974	Richard James Stratton, amb. ex. and plen. Nov 9
1977	(vacant)
1978	Alan Ewen Donald, amb. ex. and plen. March 4
1980	John Michael Owen Snodgrass, amb. ex. and plen. Oct 9

1984	Nicholas Peter Bayne, amb. ex. and plen. Feb 7
1985	Patrick Howard Caines Eyers, amb. ex. and plen. June 12
1987	(Thomas) Clive Almond, amb. ex. and plen. June 9
1988	Alfred Ian Glasby, amb. ex. and plen. Aug 14
1990	Peter Warren Chandley, amb. ex. and plen. Aug 21

The Embassy closed on 26 July 1991

Costa Rica

1972	John Kenneth Blackwell, amb. ex. and plen. May 28
1974	Keith Hamylton-Jones, amb. ex. and plen. March 14
1979	(John) Michael Brown, amb. ex. and plen. April 27
1983	Peter Wayne Summerscale, amb. ex. and plen. Jan 24
1986	Michael Francis Daly, amb. ex. and plen. June 6
1989	William Marsden, amb. ex. and plen. April 14
1992	Mary Louise Croll, amb. ex. and plen. July 5

Croatia

1992	Bryan Sparrow, amb. ex. and plen. July 23

Cotê d'Ivoire (see Ivory Coast)

Cuba

1972	Stanley James Gunn Fingland, amb. ex. and plen. Sept 15
1975	(John) Edward Jackson, amb. ex. and plen. Nov 8
1979	John Burns Ure, amb. ex. and plen. Nov 29
1981	David Churchill Thomas, amb. ex. and plen. March 16
1984	(Patrick) Robin Fearn, amb. ex. and plen. Feb 29
1986	Andrew Eustace Palmer, amb. ex. and plen. July 15
1989	(Anthony) David Brighty, amb. ex. and plen. Jan 22
1991	(Arthur) Leycester (Scott) Coltman, amb. ex. and plen. Mar 3

Republic of Cyprus

HIGH COMMISSIONERS

1973	Stephen John Linley Olver (later Sir S). Feb 27
1975	Donald McDonald Gordon. Oct 27
1979	Peregrine Alexander Rhodes. Feb 19
1982	(William) John (Antony) Wilberforce. May 10
1988	The Hon. Humphrey Maud. Sept 7
1990	David John Michael Dain. July 4

Czechoslovakia

1974   Edward Gervase Willan, amb. ex. and plen. July 26

1977   Peter John Ellison Male, amb. ex. and plen. May 11

1980   John Rowland Rich, amb. ex. and plen. Aug 14

1985   Stephen Jeremy Barrett, amb. ex. and plen. March 8

1988   (Peter) Laurence O'Keeffe, amb. ex. and plen. Nov 1

1991   (Anthony) David Brighty, amb. ex. and plen. July 21

Denmark

1976   Anne (later Dame A) (Marion) Warburton, amb. ex. and plen. April 30

1983   James Mellon, amb. ex. and plen. May 7

1986   Peter William Unwin, amb. ex. and plen. July 9

1989   Nigel Christopher Ransome Williams, amb. ex. and plen. Jan 4

Djibouti

1978   Benjamin Leckie Strachan, amb. ex. and plen. Jan 25

1979   Julian Fortray Walker, amb. ex. and plen. Feb 20

1985   David Everard Tatham, amb. ex. and plen. Jan 14

1988   Mark Anthony Marshall, amb. ex. and plen. Jan 18

Dominican Republic

1972   Paul Victor St John Killick, amb. ex. and plen. April 28

1976   Clement Spearman, amb. ex. and plen. Jan 15

1979   Michael A Cafferty, amb. ex. and plen. Sept 27

1983   Roy George Marlow, amb. ex. and plen. July 1

1985   Michael John Newington, amb. ex. and plen. July 7

1988   Giles Eden FitzHerbert, amb. ex. and plen. May 11

Dominica

HIGH COMMISSIONERS

1982   Viscount (John William) Dunrossil. Sept 25

1983   Giles (later Sir G) (Lionel) Bullard. Aug 6

1986   Kevin Francis Xavier Burns. Oct 19

1991   Emmrys Thomas Davies. Feb 20

Ecuador

1974   Norman Ernest Cox, amb. ex. and plen. Oct 12

1977   John Kyrle Hickman, amb. ex. and plen. Sept 29

1981   Adrian Clarence Buon, amb. ex. and plen. April 16

1985   Michael William Atkinson, amb. ex. and plen. June 28

1989   Frank Basil Wheeler, amb. ex. and plen. Aug 18

Egypt (Arab Republic of) (formerly the United Arab Republic)

1973   Sir Philip (George Doyne) Adams, amb. ex. and plen. Jan 17

1975   Willie (later Sir W) Morris, amb. ex. and plen. Nov 25

1979   Michael (later Sir M) (Scott) Weir, amb. ex. and plen. April 4

1985   Sir Alan (Bedford) Urwick amb. ex. and plen. Feb 15

1987   (William) James (later Sir J) Adams, amb. ex. and plen. Dec 14

1992   ChristopherWilliam Long, amb. ex. and plen. April 26

El Salvador

1975   Albert Henry Hughes, amb. ex. and plen. Jan 30

1977   Achilles Symeon Papadopoulos, amb. ex. and plen. Sept 15

1980   (John) Michael Brown, amb. ex. and plen. Feb 8

1982   Colum John Sharkey, amb. ex. and plen. Feb 11

1984   Bryan Oliver White, amb. ex. and plen. Dec 5

1987   David Joy, amb. ex. and plen. Sept 8

1989   Peter John Streams, amb. ex. and plen. Sept 13

1991   Michael Henry Connor, amb. ex. and plen. Nov 25

Republic of Equatorial Guinea

1973   Edward Ferguson Given, amb. ex. and plen. May 10

1975   Albert Edward Saunders, amb. ex. and plen. Nov 5

1979   Denis Edward Richards, amb. ex. and plen. Dec 6

1982   Bryan Sparrow, amb. ex. and plen. Feb 11

1985   Michael John Carlisle Glaze, amb. ex. and plen. April 25

1987   Martin Reith, amb. ex. and plen. Nov 26

1991   William Ernest Quantrill, amb. ex. and plen.

Estonia

1991   Brian Buik Low, amb. ex. and plen. Oct 8

Ethiopia

1972   Willie Morris, amb. ex. and plen. Oct 27

1975   Derek Malcolm Day, amb. ex. and plen. Oct 23

1979   Robert Mathieson Tesh, amb. ex. and plen. April 11

1982   Brian Leon Barder, amb. ex. and plen. Sept 21

1986   Harold Berners Walker, amb. ex. and plen. April 29

1990   Michael John Carlisle Glaze amb. ex. and plen. March 21

Fiji

HIGH COMMISSIONERS

1974   (James) Stanley Arthur. March 24
1978   Viscount (John William) Dunrossil. April 30
1982   Roger Arnold Rowlandson Barltrop. July 30

AMBASSADORS

†1988   Roger Arnold Rowlandson Barltrop, amb. ex. and plen. March 1
1989   (Alexander Basil) Peter Smart, amb. ex. and plen. Aug 19
1992   Timothy James David, amb. ex. and plen. March 14

†From 1 March 1988, the British High Commission became the British Embassy

Finland

1975   James (later Sir J) (Eric) Cable, amb. ex. and plen. Oct 1
1980   Andrew Christopher Stuart, amb. ex. and plen. Aug 8
1983   Alan Brooke Turner, amb. ex. and plen. Jan 25
1986   (Hubert Anthony) Justin Staples, amb. ex. and plen. Feb 25
1989   (George) Neil Smith. Nov 21

France

1975   Sir (John) Nicholas Henderson, amb. ex. and plen. Dec 8
1979   Sir Reginald (Alfred) Hibbert, amb. ex. and plen. April 20
1982   Sir (Major) John (Emsley) Fretwell, amb. ex. and plen. March 4
1987   Sir Ewen Alastair John Fergusson, amb. ex. and plen. June 22

Gabon

1973   Peter John Charles Radley, Chargé d'Affaires. Sept 10
1975   John Keith Gordon, Chargé d'Affaires. Dec 1
1977   (Alfred) Ian Glasby, Chargé d'Affaires. Oct 9
1978   (Alastair) Christopher (Donald Summerhayes) MacRae, amb. ex. and plen. July 13
1980   Terence Grady, amb. ex. and plen. June 3
1982   Alan Hartley Grey, amb. ex. and plen. April 25
1985   Ronald Henry Thomas Bates amb. ex. and plen. Feb 18
1986   Mark Aubrey Goodfellow, amb. ex. and plen. Feb 3
1990   Philip John Priestley, amb. ex. and plen. Nov 22

The Embassy closed on 26 July 1991.

The Gambia

HIGH COMMISSIONERS

1975   Martin Hartley Guy Rogers. Nov 13
1979   Eric Norman Smith. May 18
1981   David Francis Battye Le Breton. Oct 24

1984   John Donald Garner. Nov 6
1988   Alec Ibbott. Feb 20
1990   Alan John Pover. Oct 12

Georgia

1992   Sir Brain (James) (Proetel) Fall, amb. ex. and plen. June 22

Germany (Federal Republic of)

1975   Sir (J) Oliver Wright, amb. ex. and plen. Sept 30
1981   Sir John (Lang) Taylor, amb. ex. and plen. Mar 17
1984   Sir Julian (Leonard) Bullard, amb. ex. and plen. Sept 1
1988   Sir Christopher (Leslie George) Mallaby, amb. ex. and plen. March 20

German Democratic Republic

1973   Peregrine (Alexander) Rhodes, Chargé d'Affaires. May 16
1974   (Herbert Ben) Curtis (later Sir C) Keeble, amb. ex. and plen. Jan 16
1976   Percy (later Sir P) Cradock, amb. ex. and plen. Feb 17
1978   Peter Martin Foster, amb. ex. and plen. April 2
1981   Peter Malcolm Maxey, amb. ex. and plen. Aug 19
1984   Timothy John Everard, amb. ex. and plen. Aug 21
1988   Nigel Hugh Robert Allen Broomfield, amb. ex. and plen. May 10
1990   Patrick Howard Caines Eyers, amb. ex. and plen. Jan 26

On 3 October 1990 the German Democratic Republic ceased to exist.

Ghana

HIGH COMMISSIONERS

1975   Frank Mills. June 24
1978   James Mellon. May 15
1983   Kevin Francis Xavier Burns. May 30
1986   Arthur Hope Wyatt. Oct 24
1989   Anthony Michael Goodenough. Oct 16
1992   David Critchlow Walker. June 14

Greece

1974   (Francis) Brooks (later Sir B) Richards, amb. ex. and plen. Sept 11
1978   Iain (Johnstone Macbeth) (Later Sir I) Sutherland, amb. ex. and plen. May 11
1982   Peregrine (later Sir P) (Alexander) Rhodes, amb. ex. and plen. May 28
1985   Sir Jeremy (Cashel) Thomas, amb. ex. and plen. June 6
1989   Sir (Henry) David (Alastair Capel) Miers, amb. ex. and plen. May 24

Grenada

HIGH COMMISSIONERS

1974   Christopher Ewart Diggines. Feb 7
1977   Henry Sydney Herbert Stanley. Sept 6
1980   (James) Stanley Arthur. April 25

1982	Viscount (John William) Dunrossil. Sept 25
1983	Giles (later Sir G) (Lionel) Bullard. Aug 6
1986	Kevin Francis Xavier Burns. Oct 19
1991	Emrys Thomas Davies. Feb 5

Guatemala

Relations with Guatemala were reduced to Consular level as from 31 July 1963. Consular relations were broken off by Guatemala on 7 September 1981 and resumed on 19 August 1986. Full diplomatic relations were resumed on 29 December 1986.

1987   Bernard Jonathan Everett, amb. ex. and plen. June 25

1991   Justin Patrick Pearse Nason, amb. ex. and plen. March 22

Republic of Guinea

1971   Ivor Forsyth Porter, amb. ex. and plen. May 18

1974   Denzil Inglis Dunnett, amb. ex. and plen. Oct 3

1976   John Ernest Powell-Jones, amb. ex. and plen. Jan 12

1979   (Clifford) William Squire, amb. ex. and plen. Sept 24

1982   (Peter) Laurence O'Keeffe, amb. ex. and plen. Sept 15

1986   John Esmond Campbell Macrae, amb. ex. and plen. May 6

1990   Roger Campbell Beetham, amb. ex. and plen. Nov 29

Guinea Bissau

1975   Denzil Inglis Dunnett, amb. ex. and plen. March 12

1976   John Ernest Powell-Jones, amb. ex. and plen. May 11

1979   (Clifford) William Squire, amb. ex. and plen. Sept 24

1982   (Peter) Laurence O'Keeffe, amb. ex. and plen. Sept 15

1986   John Esmond Campbell Macrae, amb. ex. and plen. May 30

1990   Roger Campbell Beetham, amb. ex. and plen. April 12

Guyana

HIGH COMMISSIONERS

1975   Peter Gautrey. March 26

1978   Philip Louis Victor Mallett. Oct 20

1982   (William) Kenneth Slatcher. Aug 28

1985   John Dudley Massingham. April 6

1987   David Purvis Small, July 16

1990   (Robert) Douglas Gordon, Oct 24

Haiti

1973   John Dunn Hennings, amb. ex. and plen. Feb 26

1976   John Kenneth Drinkall, amb. ex. and plen. Nov 17

1982   Barry Granger Smallman, amb. ex. and plen. Jan 8

1984   (Harold) Martin (Smith) Reid, amb. ex. and plen. Mar 9

1987   Alan Jeffrey Payne, amb. ex. and plen. Oct15

1989   Derek Francis Milton, amb. ex. and plen. June 29

Holy See

1975   Dugald Malcolm, en. ex. and min. plen. May 30

1977   Geoffrey Allan Crossley, en. ex. and min. plen. Dec 15

1980   Mark (later Sir M) (Evelyn) Heath, en. ex. and min. plen. April 18

1982   Sir Mark (Evelyn) Heath, amb. ex. and plen. March 4

1985   David Neil Lane, amb. ex. and plen. May 16

1988   John Kenneth Elliott Broadley, amb. ex. and plen. May 18

1991   Andrew Eustace Palmer, amb. ex. and plen. Aug 21

Honduras

1972   David Morris Pearson, amb. ex and plen. June 1

1975   Keith Hamylton-Jones, amb. ex. and plen. Dec 2

1978   John Barnard Weymes, amb. ex. and plen. May 8

1981   Colum John Sharkey, amb. ex. and plen. June 13

1984   Bryan Oliver White, amb. ex. and plen. Nov 20

1987   David Joy, amb. ex. and plen. July 17

1989   Peter John Streams, amb. ex. and plen. July 30

1992   Patrick Morgan, amb. ex. and plen. Jan 30

Hungary

1973   Hon. John Wilson (later Rt Hon. Lord Moran), amb. ex. and plen. June 7

1976   Richard Edmund Clement Fownes Parsons, amb. ex. and plen. Sept 21

1980   Bryan George Cartledge, amb. ex. and plen. Jan 17

1983   Peter William Unwin, amb. ex. and plen. July 5

1986   Leonard Vincent Appleyard, amb. ex. and plen. July 30

1989   John Allan Birch, amb. ex. and plen. Aug 21

Iceland

1975   Kenneth Arthur East, amb. ex. and plen. April 30

1981   William Roger McQuillan, amb. ex. and plen. March 26

1983   Richard Thomas, amb. ex. and plen. April 30

1986   Mark Fenger Chapman, amb. ex. and plen. Oct 8

1989   Richard (later Sir R) (Radford) Best, amb. ex. and plen. Mar 15

1991   Patrick Francis Wogan, amb. ex. and plen. Sept 16

India

HIGH COMMISSIONERS

1973   Sir (Charles) Michael Walker. Dec 18
1977   John (later Sir J) (Adam) Thomson. Jan 14
1982   Robert (later Sir R) Lucian Wade-Gery. July 31
1986   Sir (Arthur) David (Saunders) Goodall. April 2
1991   Sir Nicholas (Maxted) Fenn. Nov 13

Indonesia

1975   John (later Sir J) (Archibald) Ford, amb. ex. and plen. April 25
1978   Terence John O'Brien, amb. ex. and plen. April 8
1981   Robert Brash, amb. ex. and plen. June 17
1984   Alan Ewen Donald, amb. ex. and plen. May 16
1988   (William) Kelvin (Kennedy) White, amb. ex. and plen. Mar 9
1990   Roger John Carrick, amb. ex. and plen. Aug 3.

Iran

1974   Anthony (later Sir A) (Derrick) Parsons, amb. ex. and plen. March 9
1979   John (later Sir J (Alexander Noble) Graham, amb. ex. and plen. Jan 23
1980   (vacant from June 6)

Iraq

Diplomatic relations with Iraq were broken off with effect from 1 December 1971. They were resumed in 1974

1974   John (later Sir J) (Alexander Noble) Graham, amb. ex. and plen. Sept 5
1977   Alexander (later Sir A) (John Dickson) Stirling, amb. ex. and plen. April 6
1980   Stephen Loftus Egerton, amb. ex. an plen. Sept 21
1982   John (later Sir J) (Campbell) Moberly, amb. ex. and plen. Oct 29
1985   Terence Joseph Clark amb. ex. and plen. March 18
1990   Harold (later Sir H) Berners Walker amb. ex. and plen. Feb 9

Ireland, Republic of

1973   Sir Arthur Galsworthy, amb. ex. and plen. Feb 22
1976   Christopher Thomas Ewart Ewart-Biggs, amb. ex. and plen. July 5
1976   (Walter) Robert (later Sir R) Haydon, amb. ex. and plen. Nov 6
1980   Leonard (later Sir L) (Clifford William) Figg, amb. ex. and plen. June 25
1983   Alan (later Sir A) (Clowes) Goodison, amb. ex. and plen. June 17
1986   Nicholas (later Sir N) Maxted Fenn, amb. ex. and plen. Dec 7
1991   David Elliott Spiby Blatherwick, amb. ex. and plen. Sept 10

Israel

1972   (William) Bernard (later Sir B) (John) Ledwidge, amb. ex. and plen. Oct 31
1975   (Thomas) Anthony (Keith) Elliott, amb. ex. and plen. Nov 17
1976   John (Later Sir J) (Charles Moir) Mason, amb. ex. and plen. Dec 14
1980   John Armstrong Robinson amb. ex. and plen. March 18
1981   Patrick Hamilton Moberly, amb. ex. and plen. July 15
1984   (Clifford) William Squire, amb. ex. and plen. Sept 11
1988   Mark Elliott, amb. ex. and plen. June 19
1992   Robert Andrew Burns, amb. ex. and plen. July 12

Italy

1974   Sir Guy (Elwin) Millard, amb. ex. and plen. June 27
1976   Sir Alan Campbell, amb. ex. and plen. Oct 14
1979   Sir Ronald Arculus, amb. ex. and plen. July 10
1983   The Lord Bridges, amb. ex. and plen. Mar 1
1987   Sir Derek (Morison David) Thomas amb. ex. and plen. Dec 3
1989   Sir Stephen (Loftus) Egerton amb. ex. and plen. Nov 14
1992   Sir Patrick (Stanislaus) Fairweather, amb. ex. and plen. July 5

Ivory Coast

1972   Paul Cecil Henry Holmer, amb. ex. and plen. Sept 28
1975   Joe Booth Wright, amb. ex. and plen. Nov 29
1978   Michael Francis Daly, amb. ex. and plen. Dec 17
1983   John Michael Willson, amb. ex. and plen. Feb 2
1987   Veronica Evelyn Sutherland, am. ex. and plen. June 27
1990   Margaret Irene Rothwell, amb. ex. and plen. Dec 17

Jamaica

HIGH COMMISSIONERS

1973   John Dunn Hennings. Feb 20
1976   John Kenneth Drinkall. April 29
1982   Barry Granger Smallman. Jan 8
1984   (Harold) Martin (Smith) Reid. Mar 9
1987   Alan Jeffrey Payne, June 23
1989   Derek Francis Milton. April 13

Japan

1972   Sir Fred Warner, amb. ex. and plen. July 1
1975   Michael (later Sir M) Wilford, amb. ex. and plen. Sept 22
1980   Sir Hugh Cortazzi, amb. ex. and plen. Oct 13
1984   Sir (Charles) Sydney (Rycroft) Giffard, amb. ex. and plen. Mar 1

1986   Sir John (Stainton) Whitehead, amb. ex.
        and plen. Nov 12
1992   Sir John (Dixon) (Iklé) Boyd, amb. ex.
        and plen. July 7

Jordan
1972   (Hugh) Glencairn Balfour Paul, amb. ex.
        and plen. July 20
1975   John Campbell Moberly, amb. ex. and
        plen. Oct 11
1979   Alan (later Sir A) (Bedford) Urwick, amb.
        ex. and plen. Feb 19
1984   (Arthur) John Coles, amb. ex. and plen.
        Nov 4
1988   Anthony Reeve, amb. ex. and plen. Feb 3
1991   Patrick Howard Caines Eyers, amb. ex.
        and plen. April 27

Kazakhstan
1992   Sir Brian (James) (Proetel) Fall, amb. ex.
        and plen. Sept 14

Kenya
HIGH COMMISSIONERS
1972   (Arthur) Antony (later Sir A) Duff. April 23
1975   Stanley James Gunn Fingland. Oct 4
1979   John (Later Sir J) (Robert) Williams. Sept 15
1982   Sir (Walter) Leonard Allinson. Sept 20
1986   John (later Sir J) (Rodney) Johnson, June 15
1990   (William) Roger (later Sir R) Tomkys,
        Oct 19
1992   Sir Kieran Prendergast. Oct

Kiribati (Republic of)
HIGH COMMISSIONERS
1979   Donald Henry Gair Rose. July 12
1983   Charles Thompson. Sept 26
1990   Derek Leslie White. Jan 17

Korea
1971   Jeffrey Charles Petersen, amb. ex. and
        plen. Sept 30
1975   William Stanley Bates, amb. ex. and plen.
        Feb 13
1980   John Albert Leigh Morgan, amb. ex. and
        plen. Sept 11
1983   (John) Nicholas (Teague) Spreckley, amb.
        ex. plen. May 4
1986   Lawrence John Middleton, amb. ex. and
        plen. Oct 7
1990   David John Wright, amb. ex. and plen.
        April 9

Kuwait
1974   Albert Thomas Lamb, amb. ex. and plen.
        June 18
1977   (Sydney) John (Guy) Cambridge, amb. ex.
        and plen. Nov 29
1982   (Michael) Ramsay Melhuish, amb. ex. and
        plen. Sept 5
1985   Sir Peter (James Scott) Moon, amb. ex.
        and plen. Feb 17
1987   Peter Robert Mossom Hinchcliffe, amb. ex.
        and plen. May 30

1990   Michael (later Sir M) Charles Swift
        Weston amb. ex. and plen. March 18
1992   William Hugh Fullerton, amb. ex. and
        plen. Aug 3

Laos
1973   Alan Eaton Davidson, amb. ex. and plen.
        July 27
1976   Donald Paul Montague Stewart Cape, amb.
        ex. and plen. Jan 3
1978   John Anthony Benedict Stewart, amb. ex.
        and plen. May 24
1980   (William) Bernard (Joseph) Dobbs, Chargé
        d'Affaires a.i. Sept 22
1982   (William) Bernard (Joseph) Dobbs, amb.
        ex. and plen. March 22
1985   (Hubert Anthony) Justin Staples April 25
1986   Derek Tonkin, amb. ex. and plen. June 4
1990   (Michael) Ramsey Melhuish, amb. ex. and
        plen. Jan 24
1992   (Charles) Christian (Wilfrid) Adams, amb.
        ex. and plen. March

Latvia
1991   Richard Christopher Samuel, amb. ex. and
        plen. Oct 8

Lebanon
1975   Peter (later Sir P) (George Arthur)
        Wakefield, amb. ex. and plen. May 28
1978   Benjamin Leckie Strachan, amb. ex. and
        plen. Nov 18
1981   David (later Sir D) Arthur Roberts, amb.
        ex. and plen. May 17
1983   Henry David (later Sir D) Alastair Capel
        Miers, amb. ex. and plen. Nov 11
1985   John Walton David Gray, amb. ex. and
        plen. Nov 28
1988   Allan John Ramsay, amb. ex. and plen.
        June 16
1990   David Everard Tatham, amb. ex. and plen.
        April 28
1992   Maeve Geraldine Fort, amb. ex. and plen.
        July 31

Lesotho
HIGH COMMISSIONERS
1973   Martin John Moynihan. Sept 21
1976   Reginald Herbert Hobden. Feb 7
1978   Owen Glyn Griffith. April 28
1981   Clive Carruthers Clemens. Nov 3
1984   Peter Edward Rosling. Mar 5
1988   John Coates Edwards. May 31
1992   James Roy Cowling. Feb 1

Liberia
1973   John Henry Reiss, amb. ex. and plen. June 27
1978   John Gordon Doubleday, amb. ex. and
        plen. July 16
1980   Dougal Gordon Reid, amb. ex. and plen.
        Oct 28
1985   Alec Ibbott, amb. ex. and plen. April 19
1988   Michael Edward John Gore, amb. ex. and
        plen. Feb 2

Libyan Arab Republic

1974 Donald Frederick Murray, amb. ex. plen.
      Dec 17
1977 Antony James Williams, amb. ex. and
      plen. Jan 12
1980 (John) Michael Edes, amb. ex. and plen.
      Feb 1
1984 (Richard) Oliver Miles, amb. ex. and plen.
      Jan 5

Diplomatic and Consular relations with Libya
were broken off with effect from 30 April 1984.

Lithuania

1991 Michael John Peart, amb. ex. and plen.
      Oct 8

Liechtenstein

1992 David Beattie, amb. ex. and plen. May 21

Luxembourg

1975 Antony (later Sir A) (Arthur) Acland, amb.
      ex. and plen. July 1
1977 Patrick Richard Henry Wright, amb. ex.
      and plen. Aug 19
1979 Jeremy Cashel Thomas, amb. ex. and plen.
      Nov 26
1982 The Hon. Humphrey (John Hamilton)
      Maud, amb. ex. and plen. Sept 20
1985 (Richard) Oliver Miles, amb. ex. and plen.
      Feb 26
1988 Juliet Jeanne d'Auvergne Campbell, amb.
      ex. and plen. Feb 24
1991 The Hon. Michael Pakenham, amb. ex.
      and plen. Oct 19

Madagascar (The Democratic Republic of)

1976 Mervyn Brown, amb. ex. and plen. Feb 19
1978 Peter (later Sir P) (James Scott) Moon,
      amb. ex. and plen. Dec 22
1980 Richard James Langridge, amb. ex. and
      plen. Jan 17
1984 (David) Malcolm McBain, amb. ex. and
      plen. Oct 2
1987 Anthony Victor Hayday, amb. ex. and
      plen. Dec 28
1990 Dennis Oldrieve Amy, amb. ex. and plen.
      April 26

Malawi

HIGH COMMISSIONERS
1973 Kenneth Gordon Ritchie. Sept 7
1977 Michael (later Sir M) Scott. June 17
1980 William Peters. Feb 15
1983 (Arthur) Henry Brind. May 25
1987 Denis Gordon Osborne. Aug 17
1990 (William) Nigel Wenban-Smith, Nov 3

Malaysia

HIGH COMMISSIONERS
1974 Sir Eric (George) Norris. Jan 16
1977 Donald (later Sir D) (Frederick) Hawley.
      Nov 20

1981 William Bentley. March 28
1983 David Howe Gillmore. Sep 17
1986 (John) Nicholas (Teague) Spreckley (later
      Sir N) Oct 31
1992 Duncan Slater. March 10

†Maldives (Republic of)

AMBASSADORS
1973 Harold Smedley, amb. ex. and plen. Jan 20
1976 David Pascoe Aiers, amb. ex. and plen.
      Feb 25
1979 John (later Sir J) (William) Nicholas, amb.
      ex. and plen. Oct 21
HIGH COMMISSIONERS
†1982 John (later Sir J) (William) Nicholas. July 9
1984 John Anthony Benedict Stewart. Nov 11
1987 David Arthur Steuart Gladstone. June 29
1991 Edward John Field. Dec 30
†From 9 July 1982 the British Embassy became a
High Commission

Mali (Republic of)

1974 Denzil Inglis Dunnett, amb. ex. and plen.
      Jan 18
1976 John Ernest Powell-Jones, amb. ex. and
      plen. April 23
1979 (Clifford) William Squire, amb. ex. and
      plen. Sept 24
1982 (Peter) Laurence O'Keeffe, amb. ex. and
      plen. Sept 15
1986 John Esmond Campbell Macrae, amb. ex.
      and plen. March 21
1990 Roger Campbell Beetham, amb. ex. and
      plen. Nov 6

Malta

HIGH COMMISSIONERS
1972 John (later Sir J) (Oscar) Moreton. May 11
1974 (Walter) Robert (later Sir R) Haydon.
      June 15
1976 Norman Aspin. Dec 8
1979 David Pascoe Aiers. Oct 28
1982 Charles Leonard Booth. Oct 9
1985 Stanley Frederick St Clair Duncan. May 3
1988 Brian Hitch. Jan 10
1991 Peter (later Sir P) (Gordon) Wallis. Oct 29

Marshall Islands

1992 Derek Leslie White, amb. ex. and plen.
      July 22

Mauritania (Islamic Republic of)

1973 Denzil Inglis Dunnett, amb. ex. and plen.
      Dec 28
1976 John Ernest Powell-Jones, amb. ex. and
      plen. Feb 17
1979 (Clifford) William Squire, amb. ex. and
      plen. Sept 24
1982 (Peter) Laurence O'Keeffe, amb. ex. and
      plen. Oct 5
1986 John Esmond Campbell Macrae, amb. ex.
      and plen. April 24

Mauritius

HIGH COMMISSIONERS

1974   (Arthur) Henry Brind. Jan 18
1977   (William) Alec Ward. June 13
1981   James Nicholas Allan. Jan 19
1985   Richard Borman Crowson. Dec 11
1989   Michael Edward Howell. Aug 12

Mexico

1972   John (later Sir J) (Edgar) Galsworthy, amb. ex. and plen. July 13
1977   Norman Ernest Cox, amb. ex. and plen. Aug 12
1981   Crispin (later Sir C) (Charles Cervantes) Tickell, amb. ex. and plen. Aug 21
1983   Cynlais (later Sir C) (Morgan) James, amb. ex. and plen. Nov 7
1986   John (later Sir J) Albert Leigh Morgan, amb. ex. and plen. May 21
1989   Michael (later Sir M) Keith Orlebar Simpson-Orlebar, amb. ex. and plen.July 27
1992   Sir Roger (Blaise) (Ramsay) Hervey, amb. ex. and plen. March 2

Moldovia, Republic of

1992   Sir Brian (James) (Proetel) Fall, KCMG. Aug 28

Micronesia

1992   Derek Leslie White, amb. ex. and plen. July 22

Mongolian People's Republic

1974   Myles Walter Ponsonby, amb. ex. and plen. Nov 13
1977   Julian Dana Nimmo Hartland-Swann, amb. ex. and plen. March 5
1979   Thomas Nivison Haining, amb. ex. and plen. Aug 25
1982   James Rupert Paterson, amb. ex. and plen. April 1
1984   Allan Geoffrey Roy Butler, amb. ex. and plen. Oct 11
1987   Guy William Pulbrook Hart, amb. ex. and plen. March 19
1989   David Keith Sprague, amb. ex. and plen. April 20
1991   Anthony Bernard Nicholas Morey, amb. ex. and plen. May 29

Morocco

1975   John Spenser Ritchie Duncan, amb. ex. and plen. March 29
1978   Simon (later Sir S) (Yelverton) Dawbarn, amb. ex. and plen. Aug 19
1982   (Sydney) John (Guy) Cambridge, amb. ex. and plen. Dec 1
1985   Ronald Archer Campbell Byatt, amb. ex. and plen. Jan 28
1987   John William Richmond Shakespeare amb. ex. and plen. Nov 15
1990   John Esmond Campbell Macrae, amb. ex. and plen. June 12

Mozambique (Republic of)

1975   John Henry Lewen, amb. ex. and plen. Oct 15
1979   Achilles Symeon Papadopoulos, amb. ex. and plen. Sept 30
1980   John Anthony Benedict Stewart, amb. ex. and plen. Sept 26
1984   Eric Victor Vines, amb. ex. and plen.Feb 6
1986   James Nicholas Allan, amb. ex. and plen. Feb 21
1989   Miss Maeve Geraldine Fort, amb. ex. and plen. Sept 10
1992   Richard John Smale Edis. amb. ex. and plen. Aug 10

Namibia

HIGH COMMISSIONERS

1990   Francis Neville Richards, June 4
1992   Henry George Hogger. Oct 3

Nauru

HIGH COMMISSIONERS

1978   (James) Stanley Arthur. Jan 30
1978   Viscount (John William) Dunrossil. May 29
1982   Roger Arnold Rowlandson Barltrop. July 30
1990   (Alexander Basil) Peter Smart. March 15

Nepal

1974   Michael Scott, amb. ex. and plen. April 27
1977   John Boyd Denson, amb. ex. and plen. June 1
1983   Anthony (later Sir A) Gerald Hurrell, amb. ex. and plen. Nov 2
1987   Richard Eagleson Gordon Burges Watson, amb. ex. and plen. March 1
1990   Timothy John Burr George, amb. ex. and plen. October 16

Netherlands

1972   (Ernest) John (later Sir J) (Ward) Barnes, amb. ex. and plen. Nov 2
1977   Sir Richard Sykes, amb. ex. and plen. June 19
1979   Sir John (Lang) Taylor, amb. ex. and plen. July 6
1981   Philip (later Sir P) (Robert Aked) Mansfield, amb. ex. and plen. March 14
1984   John (later Sir J) William Denys Margetson, amb. ex. and plen. Nov 30
1988   Michael Romilly Heald (later Sir M) Jenkins, amb. ex. and plen. Jan 23

New Zealand

HIGH COMMISSIONERS

1973   David (later Sir D) (Aubrey) Scott. Jan 26
1976   Harold (later Sir H) Smedley. Feb 9
1980   Richard (later Sir R) (James) Stratton. Sept 17
1984   Terence Daniel O'Leary. July 24
1987   Ronald Archer Campbell Byatt. Dec 15
1990   David Joseph Moss. Sept 27

Nicaragua

1974   David Francis Duncan, amb. ex. and plen.
        Feb 8
1976   Keith Hamylton-Jones, amb. ex. and plen.
        Feb 13
1979   (John) Michael Brown, amb. ex. and plen.
        Nov 14
1983   Peter Wayne Summerscale, amb. ex. and
        plen. Jan 24
1986   Michael Francis Daly, amb. ex. and plen.
        July 14
1989   William Marsden, amb. ex. and plen.
        April 19
1992   John Howard Culver, amb. ex. and plen.
        Nov

Niger

1972   Paul Cecil Henry Homer, amb. ex. and
        plen. Oct 16
1975   Joe Booth Wright, amb. ex. and plen.Dec 16
1979   Michael Francis Daly, amb. ex. and plen.
        June 23
1983   John Michael Willson, amb. ex. and plen.
        Feb 2
1987   Veronica Evelyn Sutherland, amb. ex. and
        plen. Oct 16
1990   Margaret Irene Rothwell, amb. ex. and
        plen. July 10

Nigeria

HIGH COMMISSIONERS
1974   (Charles) Martin (later Sir M) LeQuesne.
        March 30
1976   (vacant)
1977   Sir Sam Falle. Jan 26
1979   Mervyn (later Sir M) Brown. Jan 29
1983   William Erskine Hamilton Whyte. Aug 18
1986   Sir Martin (Kenneth) Ewans. Feb 28
1988   Brian Leon Barder. July 27
1991   (Alastair) Christopher (Donald
        Summerhayes) MacRea. March 7

Norway

1972   Ralph Walford Selby, amb. ex. and plen.
        May 3
1975   (Charles) Peter (later Sir P) Scott, amb. ex.
        and plen. April 5
1978   Albert (later Sir A) (Thomas) Lamb, amb.
        ex. and plen. Jan 16
1981   Gillian (later Dame G) (Gerda) Brown,
        amb. ex. and plen. Jan 12
1983   William (later Sir W) Bentley, amb. ex.
        and plen. Sept 18
1987   John Adam (later Sir J) Robson, amb. ex.
        and plen. March 9
1990   David John Edward Ratford amb. ex. and
        plen. May 7

Oman

1975   (Charles) James Treadwell, amb. ex. and
        plen. March 2
1979   The Hon. Ivor (Thomas) (Mark) Lucas,
        amb. ex. and plen. April 30

1981   Duncan Slater, amb. ex. and plen. Dec 20
1986   Robert John Alston, amb. ex. and plen.
        June 3
1990   Terence Joseph (later Sir T) Clark, amb.
        ex. and plen. Jan 29

†Pakistan

AMBASSADORS
†1972   (John) Laurence (later Sir L) Pumphrey,
        amb. ex. and plen. Jan 30
1976   John Christopher Wyndowe Bushell, amb.
        ex. and plen. July 26
1979   Oliver (later Sir O) (Grantham) Forster,
        amb. ex. and plen. July 11
1984   Richard Alwyne Fyjis-Walker, amb. ex.
        and plen. Oct 12
1987   Nicholas John (later Sir N) Barrington,
        amb. ex. and plen. July 20

HIGH COMMISSIONER
†1989   Nicholas John (later Sir N) Barrington. Oct 1
†From 30 January 1972, the British High
Commission became the British Embassy, then
from 1 October 1989 it reverted to the British
High Commission

Panama

1974   Robert Michael John, amb. ex. and plen.
        Aug 19
1978   John Leslie Yorath Sanders, amb. ex. and
        plen. Oct 8
1981   Stanley Stephenson, amb. ex. and plen. Feb 2
1983   Terence Harry Steggle, amb. ex. and plen.
        May 18
1986   Margaret Bryan, amb. ex. and plen. April 9
1990   John Grant MacDonald, amb. ex. and plen.
        Jan 6
1992   Thomas Herbert Malcolmson, amb. ex. and
        plen. Jan 31

Papua New Guinea

HIGH COMMISSIONERS
1975   George William Baker. Sept 16
1977   Donald King Middleton. May 30
1982   Arthur John Collins. Jan 18
1986   Michael Edward Howell. Jan 27
1989   (Edward) John Sharland. June 11
1991   John Westgarth Guy. July 12

Paraguay

1972   Henry Francis Bartlett, amb. ex. and plen.
        April 30
1976   Charles William Wallace, amb. ex. and
        plen. Feb 8
1979   Derrick Mellor, amb. ex. and plen. Oct 29
1984   Bernard Coleman, amb. ex. and plen. Jan 19
1986   John Grant MacDonald, amb. ex. and plen.
        May 3
1989   Terence Harry Steggle, amb. ex. and plen.
        May 31
1991   Michael Alan Charles Dibben, amb. ex.
        and plen. March 2

Peru

1974   Kenneth Douglas Jamieson, amb. ex. and plen. July 30
1977   (George) William Harding, amb. ex. and plen. Jan 25
1979   Charles William Wallace, amb. ex. and plen. Oct 25
1983   John William Richmond Shakespeare, amb. ex. and plen. Oct 30
1987   Adrian John Beamish, amb. ex. and plen. Dec 16
1990   (Donald) Keith Haskell, amb. ex. and plen. Feb 11

Philippines

1972   James Alexander Turpin, amb. ex. and plen. Nov 9
1976   William Bentley, amb. ex. and plen. Dec 3
1981   Michael Hugh Morgan, amb. ex. and plen. April 9
1985   Robin John Taylor McLaren, amb. ex. and plen. May 15
1987   Keith Gordon MacInnes, amb. ex. and plen. April 27
1992   Alan Everard Montgomery, amb. ex. and plen. July 11

Poland

1972   (Thomas) Frank Brenchley, amb. ex. and plen. June 3
1974   George Frank Norman Reddaway, amb. ex. and plen. July 7
1978   Kenneth Robert Comyn Pridham, amb. ex. and plen. May 24
1981   Cynlais Morgan James, amb. ex. and plen. May 19
1983   John Albert Leigh Morgan, amb. ex. and plen. May 16
1986   Brian Leon Barder, amb. ex. and plen. May 27
1988   Stephen (later Sir S) Jeremy Barrett, amb. ex. and plen. Aug 20
1991   Michael John Llewellyn Smith, amb. ex. and plen. Sept 20

Portugal

1974   Nigel (later Sir N) (Clive Cosby) Trench, amb. ex. and plen. March 29
1976   The Hon. John Wilson (later The Lord Moran), amb. ex. and plen. Nov 15
1981   Hugh (later Sir H) (Campbell) Byatt, amb. ex. and plen. May 30
1986   Michael Keith Orlebar Simpson- Orlebar, amb. ex. and plen. March 15
1989   Hugh James Arbuthnott, amb. ex. and plen. Aug 23

Qatar

1974   David Gordon Crawford, amb. ex. and plen. Nov 5
1978   Colin Turner Brant, amb. ex. and plen. Jan 10
1981   Stephen Peter Day, amb. ex. and plen. Sept 17

1984   Julian Fortay Walker, amb. ex. and plen. Oct 10
1987   Patrick Michael Nixon, amb. ex. and plen. June 11
1990   Graham Hugh Boyce, amb. ex. and plen. Feb 27

Romania

1972   Derick (later Sir D) (Rosslyn) Ashe, amb. ex. and plen. Jan 20
1975   Jeffrey (later Sir J) (Charles) Peterson, amb. ex. and plen. Feb 22
1977   Reginald (later Sir R) (Louis) Secondé, amb. ex. and plen. Jan 21
1979   Paul Cecil Henry Holmer, amb. ex. and plen. Sept 28
1983   Philip McKearney, amb. ex. and plen. Oct 19
1986   Hugh James Arbuthnott, amb. ex. and plen. Nov 14
1989   Michael William Atkinson, amb. ex. and plen. Sept 4
1992   Andrew Philip Foley Bache, amb. ex. and plen. April 15

Russian Federation

1992   Sir Brian (James) (Proetel) Fall, amb. ex. and plen. June 3

Rwanda (Republic of)

1972   (vacant)
1976   James Patrick Ivan Hennessy, amb. ex. and plen. May 20
1976   (vacant)
1978   Alan Ewen Donald, amb. ex. and plen. Jan 19
1980   John Michael Owen Snodgrass, amb. ex. and plen. Nov 13
1984   Nicholas Peter Bayne, amb. ex. and plen. Feb 7
1985   Patrick Howard Caines Eyers, amb. ex. and plen. Aug 20
1987   Robert Linklater Burke Cormack, amb. ex. and plen. June 11
1991   Roger Westbrook, amb. ex. and plen.

Saint Kitts and Nevis

HIGH COMMISSIONERS
1983   Giles (later Sir G) (Lionel) Bullard. Sept 19
1986   Kevin Francis Xavier Burns. Oct 19
1991   Emrys Thomas Davies. Feb 13

St Lucia

HIGH COMMISSIONERS
1979   (James) Stanley Arthur. Feb 22
1982   Viscount (John William) Dunrossil. Sept 25
1983   Giles (later Sir G) (Lionel) Bullard. Aug 6
1986   Kevin Francis Xavier Burns. Oct 19
1991   Emrys Thomas Davies. Jan 29

St Vincent and the Grenadines

HIGH COMMISSIONERS
1979   (James) Stanley Arthur. Oct 27
1982   Viscount (John William) Dunrossil. Sept 25
1983   Giles (later Sir G) (Lionel) Bullard. Aug 6
1986   Kevin Francis Xavier Burns. Oct 19
1991   Emrys Thomas Davies. Feb 11

Sao Tome and Principe

1979   (Alistair) Christopher (Donald Summerhayes) MacRae, amb. ex. and plen. Dec. 3

1980   Hugh Campbell Byatt, amb. ex. and plen. Sept 15

1981   Francis Kennedy, amb. ex. and plen. Nov 20

1983   Marrack Irvine Goulding, amb. ex. and plen. Oct 24

1986   Patrick Stanislaus Fairweather, amb. ex. and plen. June 9

1988   Michael John Carlisle Glaze, amb. ex. and plen. Mar 25

1990   John Gerrard Flynn, amb. ex. and plen. May 22

Saudi Arabia

1972   Alan Keir Rothnie, amb. ex. and plen. May 15

1976   (Arthur) John (later Sir J) Wilton, amb. ex. and plen. March 24

1979   (Albert) James (later Sir J) (Macqueen) Craig, amb. ex. and plen. Nov 12

1984   Sir Patrick (Richard Henry) Wright, amb. ex. and plen. Sept 4

1986   Stephen (later Sir S) (Loftus) Egerton, amb. ex. and plen. April 20

1989   Alan Gordon (later Sir A) Munro, amb. ex. and plen. Aug 16

Senegal (Republic of)

1973   Denzil Inglis Dunnett, amb. ex. and plen. Oct 3

1976   John Ernest Powell-Jones, amb. ex. and plen. Jan 11

1979   (Clifford) William Squire, amb. ex. and plen. Sept 24

1982   (Peter) Laurence O'Keeffe, amb. ex. and plen. Sept 15

1985   John Esmond Campbell Macrae, amb. ex. and plen. Dec 18

1990   Roger Campbell Beetham, amb. ex. and plen. July 7

Serbia

1992   Peter Edward Hall, amb. ex. and plen.

Seychelles

HIGH COMMISSIONERS

1976   John Arthur Pugh. June 29

1980   Eric Young. Sept 14

1983   Colin Garth Mays. Oct 1

1986   (Alexander Basil) Peter Smart. Sept 30

1989   Guy William Pulbrook Hart. June 22

1992   Edward John Sharland. Jan 24

Sierra Leone

HIGH COMMISSIONERS

1972   Ian Buchanan Watt. Oct 18

1977   Michael Hugh Morgan. Oct 5

1981   Terence Daniel O'Leary. May 11

1984   Richard Dennis Clift. Sept 7

1986   Derek William Partridge. June 6

1991   David Keith Sprague. May 30

Singapore

HIGH COMMISSIONERS

1974   (John) Peter Tripp. May 30

1978   John Dunn Hennings. April 26

1982   Sir Peter (James Scott) Moon. June 14

1985   Sir (William Erskine) Hamilton Whyte. March 16

1987   Michael Edmund Pike. July 13 (later Sir M)

1991   Gordon Aldridge Duggan. Jan12

Slovenia

1992   Gordon Mackenzie Johnston, amb. ex. and plen. Aug 25

Solomon Islands

HIGH COMMISSIONERS

1978   Gordon James Augustus Slater. July 7

1982   George Norman Stansfield. June 15

1986   John Bramble Noss. March 17

1988   (David) Junor Young. Oct 10

1991   Raymond Francis Jones. May 12

Somali Democratic Republic

1973   John Dennis Bolton Shaw, amb. ex. and plen. June 12

1977   (Arthur) Henry Brind, amb. ex. and plen. May 19

1980   (Robert) Michael Purcell, amb. ex. and plen. Nov 23

1983   William Hugh Fullerton, amb. ex. and plen. Sept 26

1987   Jeremy Richard Lovering Grosvenor Varcoe, amb. ex. and plen. Feb 15

1989   Ian McCluney, amb. ex. and plen. July 9

South Africa (Republic of)

1972   James (later Sir J) (Reginald Alfred) Bottomley, amb. ex. and plen. Dec 22

1976   Sir David Scott, amb. ex. and plen. Feb 20

1979   John (later Sir J) (Henry Gladstone) Leahy, amb. ex. and plen. July 26

1982   Ewen Alastair John Fergusson, amb. ex. plen. April 29

1984   Patrick (later Sir P) Hamilton Moberly, amb. ex. and plen. Oct 8

1987   Robin (later Sir R) William Renwick, amb. ex. and plen. July 24

1991   Anthony (later Sir A) Reeve, amb. ex. and plen. July 1

Southern Rhodesia* (now see Zimbabwe)

Following the Illegal Declaration of Independence on 11 November 1965, the High Commission was closed

* From 24 October 1964, except for strictly formal purposes, the title Rhodesia was used until 18 April 1980. Now see Zimbabwe

Soviet Union now see Russian Federation

1973   Sir Terence (Willcocks) Garvey, amb. ex. and plen. Nov 12

1976   Howard (later Sir H) (Frank Trayton) Smith, amb. ex. and plen. Jan 9

1978	(Herbert Ben) Curtis (later Sir C) Keeble, amb. ex. and plen. March 28
1982	Sir Iain (Johnstone Macbeth) Sutherland, amb. ex. and plen. Sept 16
1985	Sir Bryan (George) Cartledge, amb. ex. and plen. July 18
1988	Sir Rodric (Quentin) Braithwaite, amb. ex. and plen. Sept 20

Spain
1974	Charles (later Sir C) (Douglas) Wiggins, amb. ex. and plen. Oct 4
1977	Sir Antony (Arthur) Acland, amb. ex. and plen. June 14
1980	Richard (later Sir R) (Edmund Clement Fownes) Parsons, amb. ex. and plen. Jan 20
1984	Lord Nicholas (Charles) Gordon Lennox, amb. ex. and plen. July 2
1989	(Patrick) Robin (later Sir R) Fearn, amb. ex. and plen. Nov 23

Republic of Sri Lanka (Ceylon)
HIGH COMMISSIONERS
1973	Harold (later Sir H) Smedley. Jan 25
1976	David Pascoe Aiers. Feb 21
1979	John (later Sir J) (William) Nicholas. Oct 21
1984	John Antony Benedict Stewart. Nov 11
1987	David Arthur Steuart Gladstone. June 29
1991	Edward John Field. Nov 22

Sudan
1973	John Fleetwood Stewart Phillips, amb. ex. and plen. Dec 14
1977	Derrick Charles Carden, amb. ex. and plen. Oct 17
1979	Richard Alwyne Fyjis-Walker, amb. ex. and plen. Nov 23
1984	Sir Alexander (John Dickson) Stirling, amb. ex. and plen. Sept 1
1986	John Lewis Beaven, amb. ex. and plen. Dec 3
1990	Allan John Ramsay, amb. ex. and plen. June 23
1991	Peter John Streams, amb. ex. and plen. Nov 29

Suriname
1976	Peter Gautrey, amb. ex. and plen. May 5
1979	Philip Louis Victor Mallet, amb. ex. and plen. Jan 11
1982	(William) Kenneth Slatcher. Aug 28
1985	John Dudley Massingham amb. ex. and plen. July 3
1987	David Purvis Small, amb. ex. and plen. July 16
1991	(Robert) Douglas Gordon, amb. ex. and plen. April 27

Swaziland
HIGH COMMISSIONERS
| 1972 | Eric George Le Tocq. Feb 18 |
| 1975 | John Alfred Edwin Miles. Oct 23 |

1979	Desmond Moore Kerr. Aug 16
1983	Martin Reith. July 29
1987	John Gerrard Flynn. May 26
1990	Brian Watkins. May 20

Sweden
1974	Sir Sam Falle, amb. ex. and plen. May 14
1977	Jeffrey (later Sir J) (Charles) Petersen, amb. ex. and plen. Feb 3
1980	Donald (later Sir D) (Frederick) Murray, amb. ex. and plen. July 28
1984	Sir Richard (Edmund Clement Fownes) Parsons, amb. ex. and plen. July 26
1987	Sir John (Burns) Ure, amb. ex. and plen. Dec 7
1991	Robert Linklater Burke Cormack, amb. ex. and plen. June 17

Switzerland
1973	John (later Sir J) (Richard) Wraight, amb. ex. and plen. March 19
1976	Alan (later Sir A) (Keir) Rothnie, amb. ex. and plen. June 14
1980	(Charles) Sydney (Rycroft) Giffard, amb. ex. and plen. June 19
1982	John Ernest Powell-Jones, amb. ex. and plen. May 24
1985	John Rowland Rich, amb. ex. and plen. May 2
1988	Christopher William Long, amb. ex. and plen. July 25
1992	David Beattie, amb. ex. and plen. May 5

Syria
The Syrian Arab Republic severed Diplomatic and Consular Relations with the United Kingdom on 6 June 1967 until 28 May 1973
1973	David Arthur Roberts, amb. ex. and plen. Oct 2
1976	(Albert) James (later Sir J) (Macqueen) Craig, amb. ex. and plen. Sept 7
1979	Patrick Richard Henry Wright, amb. ex. and plen. Nov 26
1982	The Hon Ivor (Thomas Mark) Lucas, amb. ex. and plen. Jan 27
1984	(William) Roger Tomkys, amb. ex. and plen. Nov 13

Diplomatic and Consular relations with the Syrian Arab Republic were broken off with effect from 31 October 1986. They were resumed on 28 November 1990.
| 1991 | Andrew Fleming Green, amb. ex. and plen. Feb 17 |

Tanzania
HIGH COMMISSIONERS
Diplomatic Relations were broken off with Tanzania from 15 December 1965 to 4 July 1968
1973	Arthur Roy Handasyde Kellas. Jan 4
1975	Mervyn Brown. Jan 1
1978	Peter (later Sir P) (James Scott) Moon. April 9
1982	John Anthony Sankey. June 23

1986   Colin (later Sir C) Henry Imray. Jan 6
1989   (John) Thorold Masefield. July 22
1992   Roger Westbrook. Sept 30

Thailand

1973   David (later Sir D) (Lee) Cole, amb. ex. and plen. Nov 26
1978   (John) Peter Tripp, amb. ex. and plen. April 20
1981   (Herbert Anthony) Justin Staples, amb. ex. and plen. April 24
1986   Derek Tonkin, amb. ex. and plen. Feb 18
1989   (Michael) Ramsay Melhuish amb. ex. and plen. Nov 7
1992   Charles Christian Wilfrid Adams, amb. ex. and plen. March 14

Togo

1973   Alan James Brown, amb. ex. and plen. March 26
1976   Frank Mills, amb. ex. and plen. April 1
1978   James Mellon, amb. ex. and plen. May 15
1983   Kevin Francis Xavier Burns, amb. ex. and plen. May 30
1986   Arthur Hope Wyatt, amb. ex. and plen. Oct 24
1989   Anthony Michael Goodenough, amb. ex. and plen. Dec 5
1992   David Crithlow Walker, amb. ex. and plen. June 16

Tonga

HIGH COMMISSIONERS

1973   Humphrey Augustine Arthington-Davy. March 8
1980   Bernard Coleman. Nov 13
1984   Gerald Francis Joseph Rance. Jan 4
1987   Andrew Paul Fabian. March 7
1990   William Lawson Cordiner. April 3

Trinidad and Tobago

HIGH COMMISSIONERS

1973   Christopher Ewart Diggines. July 20
1977   Henry Sydney Herbert Stanley. Sept 6
1980   David Neil Lane. April 10
1985   Martin (later Sir M) Seymour Berthoud. April 11
1991   Brian Smith. Nov

Tunisia

1973   John Ewart Marnham, amb. ex. and plen. March 20
1975   (Hugh) Glencairn Balfour-Paul, amb. ex. and plen. Dec 8
1977   John (later Sir J) (Henry) Lambert, amb. ex. and plen. Sept 27
1981   Alexander (later Sir A) (John Dickson) Stirling, amb. ex. and plen. Jan 27
1984   (William) James Adams, amb. ex. and plen. Aug 21
1987   Stephen Peter Day, amb. ex. and plen. Dec 17
1992   Michael Logan Tait, amb. ex. and plen. July 9

Turkey

1973   Horace (later Sir H) Phillips, amb. ex. and plen. Feb 8
1977   Sir Derek (Sherborne Lindsell) Dodson, amb. ex. and plen. June 15
1980   Peter (later Sir P) (Harold) Laurence, amb. ex. and plen. Jan 30
1983   (Robert) Mark (later Sir M) Russell, amb. ex. and plen. Feb 28
1986   Timothy (later Sir T) Lewis Achilles Daunt, amb. ex. and plen. Nov 1
1992   Peter John Goulden, amb. ex. and plen. Oct

Tuvalu

HIGH COMMISSIONERS

1978   Viscount (John Williams) Dunrossil. Oct 1
1982   Roger Arnold Rowlandson Barltrop. July 30
1989   (Alexander Basil) Peter Smart. Nov 29

Uganda

HIGH COMMISSIONERS

1972   (Arthur) Henry Brind (Acting High Commissioner). Nov 23
1973   James Patrick Ivan Hennessy (Acting later High Commissioner). Sept 12

Diplomatic Relations were broken off on 28 July 1976 until 21 April 1979

1979   Richard Neil Posnett (Acting later High Commissioner) April 15
1979   (Bertram) Anthony Flack. Nov 20
1980   (William) Norman Hillier-Fry. Nov 12
1983   Colin McLean. Sept 14
1986   Derek (later Sir D) (Maxwell) March. June 29
1989   Charles Augustine Kaye Cullimore. Dec 21

Ukraine

1992   David Arthur Stewart Gladstone, Chargé d'Affaires. Jan 17
1992   Simon Nicholas Peter Hemans, amb. ex. and plen. June 4

United Arab Emirates

1973   (Daniel) Donal (John) McCarthy, amb. ex. and plen. June 24
1977   David Arthur Roberts, amb. ex. and plen. Sept 28
1981   Harold Berners Walker, amb. ex. and plen. May 18
1986   Michael Logan Tait, amb. ex. and plen. April 27
1990   Graham Stuart Burton, amb. ex. and plen. Feb 6

United States

1974   The Hon. Sir Peter (Edward) Ramsbotham, amb. ex. and plen. March 3
1977   Peter Jay, amb. ex. and plen. July 21
1979   Sir (John) Nicholas Henderson, amb. ex. and plen. July 12
1982   Sir (John) Oliver Wright. Sept 2
1986   Sir Antony (Arthur) Acland, amb. ex. and plen. Aug 28

1991   Sir Robin (William) Renwick, amb. ex.
        and plen. Aug 20

Upper Volta (Republic of) (now see Burkina)
1972   Paul Cecil Henry Holmer, amb. ex. and
        plen. Oct 16
1976   Joe Booth Wright, amb. ex. and plen.Feb 18
1979   Michael Francis Daly, amb. ex. and plen.
        April 19
1983   John Michael Willson, amb. ex. and plen.
        July 12

Uruguay
1972   Peter Richard Oliver, amb. ex. and plen.
        June 2
1977   William Peters, amb. ex. and plen. June 16
1980   Patricia Margaret Hutchinson amb. ex. and
        plen. March 7
1983   Charles William Wallace, amb. ex. and
        plen. Oct 12
1986   Eric Victor Vines, amb. ex. and plen.
        March 14
1989   Colum John Sharkey, amb. ex. and plen.
        July 14
1991   Donald Alexander Lamont, amb. ex. and
        plen. July 14

Vanuatu (Republic of) (formerly New Hebrides)
HIGH COMMISSIONERS
1980   William Stanton Ashford. July 30
1982   Richard Bostock Dorman. April 25
1985   Malcolm Lars Creek. Aug 27
1988   John Thompson. March 25
1992   Thomas Joseph Duggin. Jan 15

Vatican City (see Holy See)

Venezuela
1973   Sir (Alexander) Lees Mayall, amb. ex. and
        plen. Feb 1
1975   John (later Sir J) (Lang) Taylor, amb. ex.
        and plen. April 25
1979   Reginald (later Sir R) (Louis) Secondé,
        amb. ex. and plen. Sept 20
1982   Hugh (Michael) Carless, amb. ex. plen.
        June 26
1985   Michael John Newington, amb. ex. and
        plen. April 28
1988   Giles Eden FitzHerbert, amb. ex. and plen.
        Jan 18

South Vietnam (Republic of)
1972   (Francis) Brooks (later Sir B) Richards,
        amb. ex. and plen. Jan 24
1974   John Christopher Wyndowe Bushell, amb.
        ex. and plen. March 20
1975   (vacant)
(Vietnam was formally unified in July 1976)

Vietnam (Socialist Republic of)
1974   John Harold Fawcett, amb. ex. and plen.
        Jan 23
1975   John Anthony Benedict Stewart, Chargé
        d'Affaires. Jan 31, then amb. ex. and plen.
        July 25

1976   Robert Matheson Tesh, amb. ex. and plen.
        Feb 7
1978   John (later Sir J) (William Denys)
        Margetson, amb. ex. and plen. May 8
1980   Derek Tonkin, amb. ex. and plen. Sept 3
1982   Michael Edmund Pike, amb. ex. and plen.
        Dec 17
1985   Richard Gilbert Tallboys, amb. ex. and
        plen. June 12
1987   Emrys Thomas Davies, amb. ex. and plen.
        May 27
1990   Peter Keegan Williams, amb. ex. and plen.
        Oct 27

Western Samoa
HIGH COMMISSIONERS
1973   Humphrey Augustine Arthington-Davy.
        April 10
1976   Harold (later Sir H) Smedley. Feb 4
1980   Richard (later Sir R) (James) Stratton.
        Sept 17
1984   Terence Daniel O'Leary. July 24
1987   Ronald Archer Campbell Byatt. Dec 15
1991   David Joseph Moss. Aug 6

Yemen (Republic of)
1973   Derrick Charles Carden, amb. ex. and
        plen. Sept 28
1977   Benjamin Leckie Strachan, amb. ex. and
        plen. Feb 5
1979   Julian Fortray Walker, amb. ex. and plen.
        Feb 4
1984   David Everard Tatham, amb. ex. and plen.
        Sept 19
1987   Mark Anthony Marshall, amb. ex. and
        plen. Nov 23

**Yemen, People's Democratic Republic of
(formerly South Yemen, The People's
Republic of)**
1972   (James) Granville (William) Ramage, amb.
        ex. and plen. May 17
1975   John Single Martyn Roberts, Chargé
        d'Affaires a.i. May 1
1978   Malcolm Towers McKernan, Chargé
        d'Affaires a.i. March 26
1983   Peter Keegan Williams, amb. ex. and plen.
        Feb 23
1986   Arthur Stirling-Maxwell Marshall, amb. ex.
        and plen. Jan 4
1989   (Robert) Douglas Gordon, amb. ex. and
        plen. Jan 29

The People's Democratic Republic of Yemen and
the Yemen Arab Republic merged on 22 May
1990 to become the Republic of Yemen.

Yugoslavia now see Serbia
1977   Robert Alexander Farquharson, amb. ex.
        and plen. June 1
1980   Edwin (later Sir E) Bolland, amb. ex. and
        plen. April 12
1982   Kenneth Bertram Adam Scott, amb. ex.
        and plen. Oct 22

1985   Andrew Marley Wood, amb. ex. and plen.
        Dec 6
1989   Peter Edward Hall, amb. ex. and plen.
        Nov 21

Republic of Zaire
1974   Richard James Stratton, amb. ex. and plen.
        July 21
1977   Alan Ewen Donald, amb. ex. and plen.
        Nov 4
1980   John Michael Owen Snodgrass, amb. ex.
        and plen. May 18
1983   Nicholas Peter Bayne, amb. ex. and plen.
        Nov 23
1985   Patrick Howard Caines Eyers, amb. ex.
        and plen. Feb 24
1987   Robert Linklater Burke Cormack, amb. ex.
        and plen. March 9
1991   Roger Westbrook, amb. ex. and plen. July 30

Zambia
HIGH COMMISSIONERS
1974   (Frank) Stephen Miles. Oct 1
1978   (Walter) Leonard (later Sir L) Allinson.
        Feb 17
1980   John Rodney Johnson. June 30
1984   (William) Kelvin (Kennedy) White. Sept 10
1988   John Michael Willson. Jan 21
1990   Peter Robert Mossom Hinchcliffe. May 19

Zimbabwe (formerly Southern Rhodesia)
HIGH COMMISSIONERS
1980   Ronald Archer Campbell Byatt. April 18
1983   Martin Kenneth Evans. April 9
1985   (Michael) Ramsay Melhuish. Feb 20
1989   (Walter) Kieran (later Sir K) Prendergast.
        Aug 10
1992   Richard Nigel Dales. Sept 21

CHRONOLOGICAL LIST OF BRITISH REPRESENTATIVES TO INTERNATIONAL ORGANISATIONS 1973-1993

UNITED KINGDOM MISSION TO THE UNITED NATIONS

New York
1973   Sir Donald (James Dundas) Maitland,
        Perm. Rep. and Rep. on the Security
        Council. Aug 7
1974   Ivor Seward Richard, amb., Perm. Rep. and
        Rep. on the Security Council. March 25
1979   Sir Anthony (Derrick) Parsons, Perm. Rep.
        and Rep. on the Security Council with
        personal rank of amb. Sept 9
1982   Sir John (Adam) Thomson, Perm. Rep.
        and Rep. on the Security Council with
        personal rank of amb. Aug 17
1987   Sir Crispin (Charles Cervantes) Tickell,
        Perm. Rep. and Rep. on the Security
        Council with personal rank of amb. May 29

1990   Sir David (Hugh Alexander) Hannay Perm
        Rep. and Rep. on the Security Council
        with personal rank of amb. Sept 7

UNITED KINGDOM MISSION TO THE OFFICE OF THE UNITED NATIONS AND OTHER INTERNATIONAL ORGANISATIONS AT GENEVA
1973   David (later Sir D) (Henry Thoroton)
        Hildyard, amb. and Perm. Rep. June 4
1976   Sir James (Reginald Alfred) Bottomley,
        amb. and Perm. Rep. May 7
1978   Sir James Murray, Perm. Rep. with
        personal rank of amb. May 22
1979   Peter Harold Reginald Marshall, Perm.
        Rep. with personal rank of amb. Sept 19
1983   Dame Anne (Marion) Warburton, Perm.
        Rep. with personal rank of amb. May 16
1985   John Anthony Sankey, Perm. Rep. with
        personal rank of amb. Dec 17
1990   Martin Robert Morland, Perm. Rep. with
        personal rank of amb. July 13

UNITED KINGDOM DELEGATION TO THE CONFERENCE ON DISARMAMENT (formerly UK Delegation to the Conference of the 18-Nation Committee on Disarmament)

Geneva
1974   Mark Echalaz Allen, amb., Alternate
        Delegate and Deputy Leader. Sept 15
1977   Derick (later Sir D) (Rosslyn) Ashe, amb.,
        Alternate Delegate and Deputy Leader.
        March 22
1979   David Michael Summerhayes, Leader of
        Del. with personal rank of amb. March 12
1982   (Ronald) Ian (Talbot) Cromartie, Leader of
        Del. with personal rank of amb. Oct 1
1987   Tessa Audrey Hilda Solesby, Leader of
        Del. with personal rank of amb. Oct 10
1992   Sir Michael (Charles) (Swift) Weston,
        Leader of Del. with personal rank of amb.
        April 6

UNITED KINGDOM DELEGATION TO THE NORTH ATLANTIC TREATY ORGANISATION

Brussels
1975   Sir John (Edward) Killick, Perm. Rep. on
        the North Atlantic Council with personal
        rank of amb. Oct 17
1979   Sir Clive (Martin) Rose, Perm. Rep. on the
        North Atlantic Council with personal rank
        of amb. Sept 14
1982   Sir John (Alexander Noble) Graham, Perm.
        Rep. on the North Atlantic Council with
        personal rank of amb. Feb 15
1986   Michael (later Sir M) (O'Donel Bjarne)
        Alexander, Perm. Rep. on the North
        Atlantic Council with personal rank of
        amb. Aug 30
1992   Sir (Philip) John Weston, Perm. Rep. on
        the North Atlantic Council with personal
        rank of amb. Jan 25

UNITED KINGDOM DELEGATION TO THE ORGANISATION FOR ECONOMIC CO-OPERATION AND DEVELOPMENT

Paris

1977   Arthur Frederick Maddocks, amb., Perm. Rep. Mar 19

1982   Kenneth James Uffen, Perm. Rep. with personal rank of amb. May 2

1985   Nicholas Peter Bayne, Perm. Rep. with personal rank of amb. Oct 1

1988   John Walton David Gray, Perm. Rep. with personal rank of amb. July 11

1992   Keith Gordon MacInness, Perm. Rep. with the personal rank of amb. July 1

OFFICE OF THE UNITED KINGDOM PERMANENT REPRESENTATIVE TO THE EUROPEAN COMMUNITY (formerly UK Delegation to the European Communities)

Brussels

1975   Sir Donald (James Dundas) Maitland, Perm. Rep. with personal rank of amb. July 1

1979   Michael (later Sir M) (Dacres) Butler, Perm. Rep. with personal rank of amb. Nov 5

1985   David (later Sir D) (Hugh Alexander) Hannay, Perm. Rep. with personal rank of amb. Oct 14

1990   John (later Sir J) Olav Kerr, Perm. Rep. with personal rank of amb. Sept 2

UNITED KINGDOM DELEGATION TO THE COUNCIL OF EUROPE

Strasbourg

1974   Peter Martin Foster, amb., Perm. Rep. Oct 7

1978   Donald Paul Montagu Stewart Cape, Perm. Rep. with personal rank of amb. April 4

1983   Christopher Duncan Lush, Perm. Rep. with personal rank of amb. Jan 6

1986   Colin McLean, Perm. Rep. with personal rank of amb. Aug 6

1990   Nöel Hedley Marshall, Perm. Rep. with personal rank of amb. Sept 6

UNITED KINGDOM MISSION TO THE INTERNATIONAL ATOMIC ENERGY AGENCY, THE UNITED NATIONS INDUSTRIAL DEVELOPMENT ORGANISATION AND THE UNITED NATIONS (VIENNA) (formerly UK Mission to the IAEA and to UN Organisations at Vienna)

Vienna

1981   (Ronald) Ian (Talbot) Cromartie, Perm. Rep. with personal rank of amb. July 1

1982   Michael Joseph Wilmshurst, Perm. Rep. with personal rank of amb. Aug 16

1987   Gerald Edmund Clark, Perm. Rep. with personal rank of amb. June 3

UNITED KINGDOM DELEGATION TO THE NEGOTIATIONS ON CONVENTIONAL ARMS CONTROL IN EUROPE

Vienna

1989   (John) Michael Edes, Perm. Rep. with personal rank of amb. Mar 6

1990   Paul Lever, Head of Del. with personal rank of amb. May 7

BRITISH MISSION TO THE SUPREME NATIONAL COUNCIL OF CAMBODIA

Phnom Penh

1991   David Allan Burns, British Rep. with personal rank of amb. Nov 11

**Biographical Notes and
List of Staff**

ABBREVIATIONS

m	Married
d	Daughter
s	Son
diss	Dissolved
dec'd	Deceased
AUSS	Assistant Under-Secretary of State
BOTB	British Overseas Trade Board
CDA	Career Development Attachment
CDE	Conference on Confidence- and Security-Building Measures and Disarmament in Europe
CENTO	Central Treaty Organisation
CFE	Negotiations on Conventional Armed Forces in Europe
COI	Central Office of Information
CO	Colonial Office
CRO	Commonwealth Relations Office
CSO	Chief Security Officer
CSBM	Negotiations on Confidence- and Security-Building Measures
CSC	Civil Service Commission
CSCE	Conference on Security and Co-operation in Europe
CSD	Civil Service Department
CSO	Chief Security Officer
CSSB	Civil Service Selection Board
DHC	Deputy High Commissioner
DOE	Department of the Environment
DOI	Department of Industry
DOT	Department of Trade
DSAO	Diplomatic Service Administration Office
DS	Diplomatic Service
DSS	Department of Social Security
DTI	Department of Trade and Industry
DUSS	Deputy Under-Secretary of State
ECGD	Export Credits Guarantee Department
ECSC	European Coal and Steel Community
ENA	Ecole Nationale d'Administration (Paris)
FCO	Foreign and Commonwealth Office
FO	Foreign Office
HCS	Home Civil Service
HMOCS	Her Majesty's Overseas Civil Service
HO	Home Office
IISS	International Institute for Strategic Studies
JSDC	Joint Services Defence College
MBFR	Mutual Reduction of Forces & Armaments Vienna
MECAS	Middle East Centre for Arab Studies
MOD	Ministry of Defence
MPBW	Ministry of Public Buildings and Works
MPNI	Ministry of Pensions and National Insurance
MPO	Management and Personnel Office
NATO	North Atlantic Treaty Organisation
ODA	Overseas Development Administration
OECD	Organisation for Economic Co-operation and Development
OEEC	Organisation for European Economic Co-operation
OMCS	Office of the Minister for the Civil Service
POMEF	Political Office Middle East Forces
PRO	Principal Research Officer
RCDS	Royal College of Defence Studies
SEATO	South East Asia Treaty Organisation
SOAS	School of Oriental and African Studies
SOWC	Senior Officers War Course
SRO	Senior Research Officer
SUPL	Special Unpaid Leave
S1-S3	Secretarial Branch
SO	Security Officer
UN	United Nations
UNHCR	United Nations High Commission for Refugees
WO	War Office

Part IV: Biographical List

Statement concerning the present appointments and some other particulars of the careers of established members of Her Majesty's Diplomatic Service.

A

Aaronson, Andrene Margaret Dundas (née Sutherland); SUPL since May 1992; born 20.10.60; FCO 1985; SUPL 1989; Second Secretary FCO 1990; m 1988 Michael John Aaronson (1d 1989; 1s 1991).

Abbot, David; Kaduna since January 1991; born 6.6.64; FCO 1983; Singapore 1985; Africa/ME Floater 1989; Grade 9; m 1990 Nor Hayati Binte Ibrahim (1d 1992).

Abbot, David John; Second Secretary FCO since January 1974; born 2.1.39; HM Forces 1958-60; FO 1960; Vice-Consul São Paulo 1964; FCO 1968; Milan 1971; m 1963 Catherine Teresa Byrne (3d 1964, 1967, 1970; 1s 1965).

Abbott, Anthony John, MBE (1986); First Secretary FCO since November 1991; born 9.9.41; FO 1959; Khorramshahr 1963; Helsinki 1966; FCO 1969; Lusaka 1972; Second Secretary and Consul Santiago 1976; FCO 1981; on loan to DOT 1982; First Secretary and Consul Lisbon 1983; First Secretary (Commercial) Calcutta 1987; m 1962 Margaret Stuart Green (3s 1963, 1965, 1970; 1d 1968).

Abbott, Milli; FCO since March 1988; born 11.6.56; FCO 1975; Washington 1977; Africa/ME Floater 1981; FCO 1982; Islamabad 1984; Tokyo 1986; Grade 9.

Abbott, Nicholas Robert John; Third Secretary (Econ) Paris since June 1992; born 25.4.63; FCO 1985; Language Training 1986; Third Secretary (Chancery/Inf) Riyadh 1988; Brussels-Stagiare 1991; Grade 9; m 1989 Marcelle Ghislaine Julienne Delvaux.

Abbott, Neil Middleton; Riyadh since December 1990; born 21.6.65; FCO 1987; Grade 10; m 1990 Janet Probyn (1s 1992).

Abbott, Ronald John; Ottawa since December 1991; born 5.11.36; RAF 1954-77; Tehran 1978; Sofia 1979; UKMIS Geneva 1983; Islamabad 1986; Rome 1987; FCO 1989; Grade CSO; m 1961 Nina Dalton (2d 1973, 1978).

Abbott-Watt, Thorhilda Mary Vivia; First Secretary FCO since May 1991; born 11.2.55; FCO 1974; SUPL 1977; FCO 1978; Latin America Floater 1979; Paris 1981; UKREP Brussels 1984; Second Secretary FCO 1986; Second Secretary Bonn 1988.

Abel, Martin Jeremy; Istanbul since August 1988; born 30.4.51; MPBW 1969; FCO 1971; Paris 1974; Madras 1976; FCO 1978; Luxembourg 1979; Peking 1982; FCO 1984; Grade 9; m (1) 1974 Lynne Diane Bailey (1d 1978; 1s 1980); (2) 1992 Nilffer Fasiha.

Abrahams, David William; Second Secretary FCO since August 1983; born 14.7.53; FCO 1974; Geneva 1978; Brussels 1981; m 1978 Susan Joy Denise Gibson (3d 1987, 1988, 1990).

Acheson, Sharon Linda; FCO since March 1992; born 15.2.73; Grade 10.

Ackerman, Erica Alexandra (née Smith); SUPL since April 1989; born 9.4.63; FCO 1983; Caracas 1985; Grade 10; m 1989 Robert Joseph Ackerman.

Adam, Stuart William: Bonn since August 1992; born 20.3.71; FCO 1990; Grade 10.

Adams, Brian David, OBE (1992); First Secretary Dhaka since October 1989; born 17.12.41; CRO 1958; Nairobi 1963; Delhi 1966; Dar es Salaam 1970; FCO 1974; Third later Second Secretary (Tech Co-op) Jakarta 1977; Second later First Secretary UKMIS Geneva 1981; FCO 1986; m 1963 Beryl Pauline Laming (2s 1966, 1971).

Adams, Charles Christian Wilfrid, CMG (1992); HM Ambassador Bangkok since March 1992; born 2.6.39; CRO 1962; seconded to Central African Office 1962; Assistant Private Secretary to Secretary of State for Commonwealth Relations 1965; Second Secretary Rio de Janeiro 1966; seconded to ODA as First Secretary 1970; FCO 1972; First Secretary BMG Berlin 1974; FCO 1978; Counsellor on loan to DOI 1979; Senior Trade Commissioner Hong Kong 1982; Counsellor FCO 1986; Under-Secretary on loan to DTI 1988; m 1965 Elinor Pauline Lepper (3s 1969, 1974, 1978; 1d 1971).

Adams, Geoffrey Doyne; First Secretary (Chancery) Pretoria/Cape Town since March 1991; born 11.6.57; FCO 1979; Language Training 1980; Third, later Second Secretary Jedda 1982; First Secretary ENA Paris 1985; First Secretary FCO 1986.

Adams, Gillian; Africa/Middle East Floater since December 1989; born 10.6.65; MOD 1982; FCO 1984; Nicosia 1986; Grade 9.

Adams, Maurene; Islamabad since July 1992; born 24.6.71; FCO 1990; Grade S2; (1d 1991).

Adams, Paula Andrea; Muscat since June 1989; born 2.10.68; FCO 1987; Grade 10; m 1991 Duncan Campbell Adams.

Adams, Trevor Malcolm; HM Consul Casablanca since June 1988; born 16.4.51; FCO 1971; Paris 1973; Middle East Floater 1976; Bucharest 1977; JAO New York 1979; FCO 1982; Vientiane 1984; Rangoon 1985; m 1979 Linda Jane Burgess (1d 1985).

Adamson, Donald Snaith; Second Secretary (Consular) Islamabad since April 1992; born 3.4.49; Ministry of Social Security 1967; FCO 1968; Khartoum 1971; Brussels (EC) 1972; Wellington 1975; Dacca 1978; loan to ODA 1981; FCO 1983; Cape Town 1985; FCO 1988; m 1970 June Alice Manson Hall (1s 1973; 1d 1977).

Adamson, Joanne; Third Secretary (Chancery/Comm) Doha since June 1992; born 9.7.67; FCO 1989; Language Training Cairo June 1991; Grade 9.

Adamson, Nicholas Clark, OBE(1982); Counsellor on loan to the Private Sector since May 1992; born 5.9.38; HM Forces 1956-69; Second later First Secretary FCO 1969; First Secretary Brussels (EC) 1972; FCO 1975; Islamabad 1979; FCO 1982; First Secretary Paris 1986; Counsellor FCO 1990; m 1971 Hilary Jane Edwards (2d 1976, 1978).

Addiscott, Fraser John; FCO since July 1990; born 4.9.71; Grade 10.

Ager, Keith; FCO since July 1991; born 25.6.48; FO 1965; Bonn 1975; FCO 1977; Lilongwe 1979; FCO 1982; Montevideo 1982; FCO 1985; Rome 1988; Grade 7; m 1969 Ann Simmons (1d 1974).

Ager, Martyn Eric; Amman since February 1990; born 17.6.55; FCO 1972; Moscow 1982; FCO 1985; Grade 8; m 1981 Kathryn Margaret Pierson (1s 1984, 1d 1986).

Agnew, Gail Eileen; Second Secretary FCO since November 1988; born 21.1.48; FCO 1966;

Lisbon 1970; Peking 1973; Bonn 1974; Vientiane 1977; FCO 1980; Nicosia 1982; Budapest 1985.

Aird, Duncan Wishart; Third Secretary Bangkok since February 1989; born 25.8.37; FO 1965; Singapore 1967; FCO 1969; Benghazi 1971; FCO 1972; Nicosia 1974; FCO 1977; Accra 1979; FCO 1981; Seoul 1982; FCO 1983; Kinshasa 1986; FCO 1988; Grade 8; (1) m 1958 Helen Stevenson Lang (1s 1960; 1d 1967) (diss) (2) Choi Chung Soon (1d 1983).

Aitken, Alexandra (née Adams); First secretary (Political) Cairo since may 1990; born 31.10.46; FCO 1971; Sofia 1974; ENA course Paris 1976; Paris 1978; Second Secretary The Hague 1979; Second, later First Secretary FCO 1983; m 1985 James Dean Aitken.

Aitken-Carson, Christine Jane; FCO since May 1992; born 18.8.66; FCO 1985; Kuala Lumpur 1990; Grade 10; m 1990 Richard John Aitken-Carson.

Albright, John Rowland; First Secretary (Comm/Aid) Colombo since December 1989; born 14.7.44; DHSS 1962; DSAO 1966; Havana 1968; Brussels (EC) 1969; Moscow 1972; FCO 1973; Nairobi 1976; Muscat 1979; FCO 1981; Second Secretary (Comm) Manila 1985; m 1969 Gillian Susan Long (1d 1972; 1s 1974).

Alcock, Michael Leslie, MBE (1986); First Secretary FCO since May 1991; born 7.8.50; Ministry of Labour 1967; DSAO (later FCO) 1968, Bangkok 1971; Port of Spain 1975; Tehran 1977; FCO 1979; Second Secretary (Chancery) and Vice-Consul Addis Ababa 1984; Second later First Secretary (Comm/Econ) New Delhi 1987; m 1971 Barbara Ann Couch (2s 1972, 1976).

Alderton, Clive; Third Secretary (External Relations) UKREP Brussels since July 1990; born 9.5.67; FCO 1986; Vice-Consul Warsaw 1988; Grade 9; m 1990 Catriona Mitchell Canning.

Aldridge, Terence John; FCO since October 1988; born 11.9.56; FCO 1980; Darwin 1982; FCO 1984; Tel Aviv 1987; Grade 9; m 1988 Jane Lorna Shore (1d 1991).

Alessandri, Madeleine Kay (née Hateley); Second Secretary (Chancery/Inf) Vienna since November 1990; born 6.3.65; FCO 1988; m 1990 Enrico Alessandri.

Alexander, David Gray, MBE(1984); FCO since July 1990; born 11.3.39; FO 1956; RAF 1958-60; (UK Mission) New York 1961; Bahrain 1963; Baghdad 1964; Kampala 1966; FCO 1969; Second Secretary 1971; Caracas 1972; Second Secretary (Comm) Buenos Aires 1973; Second Secretary Ibadan 1977; First Secretary and Consul Las Palmas 1979; First Secretary

FCO 1984; Head of Chancery and Consul Rangoon 1987; m 1960 Wendy Clowes (2s 1961, 1965).

Aliaga, Deborah Joy; Reinstated FCO 1987; born 8.7.60; FCO 1979; Bonn 1980; La Paz 1983; Resigned 1986; Grade S2; m 1989 KeFernando Aliaga Murillo.

Allan, Duncan Brierton; FCO since July 1989; born 22.11.61; Grade 10.

Allan, Keith Rennie; Gabarone since February 1990; born 25.8.68; MOD 1986; FCO 1988; Grade 10.

Allan, Jane Alison (née Higgs); SUPL since March 1989; born 9.3.63; HCS 1981; FCO 1981; Washington 1984; FCO 1987; Grade 10; m 1987 Ian Allan.

Allan, Justine Rachel Anne; FCO since February 1990; born 15.7.69; Grade 10.

Allan, Moira; Mexico City since May 1989; born 27.5.61; FCO 1983; Prague 1985; FCO 1987; Grade S2.

Allan, Nicholas Edward; FCO since February 1990; born 3.8.65; Grade 10.

Allan, Richard Joseph; Islamabad since January 1990; born 3.10.48; FO (later FCO) 1966; Berlin 1970; Kathmandu 1973; FCO 1977; Milan 1980; FCO 1982; Canberra 1984; Colombo 1987; Grade 9; m (1) 1972 Jeanette Marshall (1s 1974); (2) 1985 Margaret Janette Smylie.

Allcock, Maureen Frances; Sama'a since March 1989; born 28.8.52; FCO 1987; Grade S2.

Allen, Anne; Nairobi since March 1988; born 19.2.63; FCO 1985; Grade S2A; m 1990 Clifford Laurence Allen.

Allen, Keith; FCO since March 1992; born 5.9.72; Grade 10.

Allen, Margaret Rose; Nairobi since June 1990; born 19.6.61; FCO 1987; Grade S2A.

Allen, Mark John Spurgeon; Counsellor Amman since May 1990; born 3.7.50; Third Secretary FCO 1973; Language Student MECAS 1974; Third later Second Secretary Abu Dhabi 1975; Second Secretary FCO 1977; Second later First Secretary Cairo 1978; FCO 1981; First Secretary (Econ) Belgrade 1982; First Secretary FCO 1986; m 1976 Margaret Mary Watson (1s 1978, 1d 1980).

Allen, Roger Edward; First Secretary on loan to DOI since February 1979; born 4.5.45; Second Secretary FCO 1971; Hong Kong 1972; First Secretary (Comm) Peking 1975; FCO 1977; m 1971 Jennifer Jane Ryder (1d 1974).

Allen, Rory James Colclough; First Secretary (Political) Rome since July 1991; born 5.9.48; FCO 1972; Second Secretary Jakarta 1974; First Secretary FCO 1978; Language Training Hong Kong 1981; Bangkok 1982; First Secretary FCO 1985; m 1982 Hazel Rose Dawe (1s 1983).

Allen, Sara Louise; FCO since October 1991; born 31.7.69; Grade 9.

Allen, Sylvia Ann; Tunis since June 1990; born 8.8.60; FCO 1984; La Paz 1986; Grade S2.

Alliott, Jennifer Kate Louise; SUPL since August 1990; born 26.5.64; FCO 1986; Third (later Second) Secretary (Chancery) Pretoria 1988.

Allison, Diana Margaret Jane; FCO since July 1990; born 27.7.46; FCO 1971; Moscow 1973; FCO 1974; Jakarta 1978; Madrid 1980; Kuala Lumpur 1983; FCO 1986; SUPL 1989; Grade S2.

Allmond, Shirley; Washington since November 1991; born 4.2.59; FCO 1984; Karachi 1986; Anguilla 1990; Grade S2.

Alloway, Terence Michael; Kuwait since January 1992; born 18.5.59; FCO 1980; Budapest 1982; Tel Aviv 1983; FCO 1986; SE Asia Floater 1987; FCO 1988; Grade 9; m 1991 Christine Ann Carr.

Almond, Thomas Clive, OBE (1989); Consul-General Bordeaux since October 1992; born 30.11.39; HCS 1960; FCO 1967; Accra 1968; Paris 1971; Second Secretary (Comm) Paris 1972; Second Secretary FCO 1975; Second Secretary (Inf) Brussels Embassy and UKDEL NATO 1978; Second later First Secretary (Chancery) Jakarta 1980; Chargé d'Affaires and Consul Brazzaville 1983; HM Ambassador and Consul Brazzaville 1987; HM Assistant Marshal of the Diplomatic Corps 1988; m 1965 Auriol Gala Elizabeth Annette Hendry.

Alston, Robert John, CMG (1987); On loan to HCS since March 1990; born 10.2.38; FO 1961; Tehran 1962; Third Secretary Kabul 1963; Second Secretary FO 1965; First Secretary FCO 1969; Paris 1970; First Secretary and Head of Chancery Tehran 1974; First Secretary later Counsellor FCO 1977; Head of Chancery UKDEL NATO Brussels 1981; Head of Defence Dept FCO 1984; HM Ambassador Muscat 1986; m 1969 Patricia Claire Essex (1d 1970; 1s 1972).

Altringham, Deborah Elaine; FCO since October 1989; born 4.4.64; FCO 1982; Bonn 1988; Grade 10.

Ambrose, David Alan; Second Secretary FCO since April 1989; born 10.12.42; FO 1965; Bahrain 1966; FO (later FCO) 1967; St Helena

1969; FCO 1970; Peking 1973; FCO 1974; New Delhi 1976; FCO 1977; Sana'a 1977; FCO 1979; Tel Aviv 1981; FCO 1984; Lusaka 1985; Second Secretary Darwin 1987; m 1965 Verna Elizabeth McCormack (2s 1970, 1972).

Ambrose, Philip John; FCO since April 1992; born 3.11.59; FCO 1978; UKREP Brussels 1980; Jedda 1983; Riyadh 1986; South-East Asia Floater 1987; Grade 9.

Amin, Jacqueline Harris; FCO since October 1989; born 2.6.62; FCO 1984; Port Stanley 1985; Luanda 1986; Grade S2; m 1989 Paul John Harms.

Anderson, David Heywood, CMG(1982); Second Legal Advisor FCO since November 1989; born 14.9.37; called to the Bar, Gray's Inn, 1963; Assistant Legal Adviser FO (later FCO) 1960; First Secretary and Legal Adviser Bonn 1969; FCO 1972; Legal Adviser UKMIS New York 1979; Legal Counsellor FCO 1982; Deputy Legal Adviser FCO 1987; m 1961 Jennifer Ratcliffe (1s 1966; 1d 1968).

Anderson, Henry Ian; Vice-Consul Munich since January 1989; born 20.8.52; HO 1974; Dhaka 1983; Second Secretary FCO 1987; m 1976 Janice Irene Leeman (1s 1984; 1d 1987).

Anderson, John; First Secretary FCO since October 1991; born 25.8.49; FCO 1966; Abu Dhabi 1970; Peking 1974; Lagos 1975; FCO 1978; HM Consul Istanbul 1982; Second later First Secretary (Comm) Paris 1987; m 1970 Jacqueline Thorburn (2d 1981; 1990; 1s 1983).

Anderson, Lorraine Michelle; Damascus since February 1992; born 29.12.63; FCO 1989; Grade S2; m 1988 Lawrence Malcolm Reginald Simpson.

Anderson, Michael James; First Secretary UKDIS Geneva since November 1992; born 3.4.61; FCO 1984; Language Training 1986; Second Secretary (Scientific/Econ) Moscow 1988; First Secretary FCO 1989; m 1987 Julie Ann Dickens.

Anderson, Michael John; Vice-Consul Madrid since December 1988; born 1.12.38; FO 1958; SUPL to attend University 1960; FO 1963; Vice-Consul Quito 1965; FCO 1968; Beirut 1974; FCO 1975; Athens 1988.

Anderson, Raymond, MBE(1977); First Secretary FCO since August 1991; born 26.5.37; RAF 1960-64; Agricultural Research Council 1964; DSAO 1965; Lagos 1968; FCO 1969; Ottawa 1972; Second Secretary (Comm) Beirut 1975; Stuttgart 1976; FCO 1977; on loan to DOT 1979; Consul (Comm) Barcelona 1981; First Secretary FCO 1986; First Secretary (Admin) Nairobi 1987; m Teresa Patricia Monks (1d 1963).

Anderson, Thomas Kell; Dublin since September 1991; born 12.5.33; Army 1951-53, 1956-76; Havana 1976; Bangkok 1978; Ankara 1979; Budapest 1980; Bonn 1982; Havana 1984; Tel Aviv 1988; Grade CSO (1s 1963).

Andre, Major John Edward Anthony; Queen's Messenger since 1985; born 11.1.39; HM Forces 1957-1983.

Andrews, Francesca Therese; FCO since July 1989; born 23.2.54; FCO 1973; Cape Town1/ Pretoria 1975; Moscow 1978; FCO 1980; UKDEL Brussels 1982; FCO 1985; Port of Spain 1986; Grade S2.

Andrews, James Ernest; Geneva since January 1987; born 20.11.30; Lagos 1975; Moscow 1976; Tehran 1977; UKMIS New York 1979; Paris 1982; East Berlin 1985; Grade SO; m 1951 Elsie Wears.

Andrews, Timothy John; Second Secretary (Chancery/Inf) Lusaka since September 1990; born 1.8.55; FCO 1976; Dacca 1979; Stuttgart 1982; Bonn 1984; FCO 1987; m 1987 Caroline May Moffat (1d 1989).

Angell, Neil Christopher; Moscow since November 1991; born 31.10.66; FCO 1989; Bangkok 1991; Grade 9.

Angrave, Gillian Linda; Budapest since March 1991; born 16.4.45; FCO 1976; Manila 1976; Lima 1980; Guatemala City 1981; Santiago 1982; FCO 1985; Mexico City 1987; Grade S1.

Ankerson, Dudley Charles; FCO since November 1991; born 4.9.48; Second Secretary FCO 1976; Second Secretary Buenos Aires 1978; First Secretary FCO 1981; First Secretary Mexico City 1985; First Secretary FCO 1988; First Secretary FCO on secondment to the Private Sector 1991; m 1973 Silvia Ernestina Galicia (1d 1985).

Ansell, Carolyn; FCO since April 1991; born 28.12.63; FCO 1984; Warsaw 1989; Grade 10.

Ansell, Michele Helene; FCO since March 1980; born 3.9.40; FCO 1976; Havana 1978; Grade S2.

Ansell, Sarah Louise; Rome since February 1992; born 8.4.70; FCO 1990; Grade S2.

Anstead, Alan Roger Hugh; FCO since September 1991; born 6.2.62; FCO 1980; Moscow 1983; Monrovia 1985; Hamburg 1989; Grade 9; m 1986 Paula Marita Nikkanen (1s 1991).

Anthony, Helen Louise; FCO since June 1988; born 6.12.67; Grade 10.

Anthony, Ian Nicholas; First Secretary FCO since November 1990; born 18.1.60; FCO 1985; Second later First Secretary Lisbon 1988.

Appleyard, Leonard Vincent, CMG (1986); DUSS (Political Director) since October 1991; born 2.9.38; HM Forces 1957-59; FO 1962; Third Secretary Hong Kong 1964; Third later Second Secretary Peking 1966; Second later First Secretary FCO 1969; First Secretary New Delhi 1971; First Secretary (Comm) Moscow 1975; on loan to Treasury 1978; Counsellor (Financial) Paris 1979; Head of ERD FCO 1982; Principal Private Secretary to the Secretary of State 1984; HM Ambassador Budapest 1986; On loan to Cabinet Office 1989; m 1964 Elizabeth Margaret West (2d 1965, 1967).

Arbon, Helen Marie; Jakarta since July 1991; born 21.4.70; FCO 1988; Grade 10.

Arbuthnott, Hugh James, CMG(1984); HM Ambassador Lisbon since August 1989; born 27.12.36; FO 1960; Third Secretary Tehran 1961; Second later First Secretary FO 1964; Private Secretary to Minister of State for Foreign Affairs 1966; Lagos 1968; First Secretary Head of Chancery Tehran 1971; FCO 1974; Assistant later Head of EID (E); Counsellor (Agric/Econ) later Head of Chancery Paris 1978; on loan to International Division ODA (AUSS) 1983; HM Ambassador Bucharest 1986; m 1964 Vanessa Rose Dyer (3s 1965, 1967 (Dec'd 1989), 1970).

Archer, Graham Robertson; Counsellor FCO since June 1990; born 4.7.39; CRO 1962; Delhi 1964; Vice-Consul Kuwait 1966; FCO 1967; Second Secretary Washington 1970; First Secretary FCO 1972; First Secretary and Head of Chancery Wellington 1975; FCO 1979; Rayner Scrutiny 1981; Counsellor and Head of Chancery Pretoria 1982; Counsellor The Hague 1986; m 1963 Pauline Cowan (2d 1965, 1968).

Archer, James Raymond; Second Secretary (Admin) Baghdad since September 1988; born 13.9.43; FO 1963; Rawalpindi 1966; Nicosia 1969; Amman 1970; Brasilia 1973; FCO 1975; MECAS 1977; Lagos 1979; Amman 1982; Second Secretary FCO 1985; m 1972 Kathryn Rose Hughes.

Archer, Nicholas Stewart; PS to the Minister of State since May 1992; born 24.12.60; FCO 1983; Third later Second Secretary (Chancery) Amman 1986; Second later First Secretary FCO 1989.

Arkley, David Ballantine; Management Officer/ Vice-Consul Sao Paulo since June 1992; FCO 1986; born 10.10.66; FCO 1986; Moscow 1988; Floater Duties 1990; Grade 9.

Arkwright, Paul Thomas; First Secretary FCO since June 1991; born 2.3.62; FCO 1986; Second Secretary (Chancery) BMG Berlin since May 1988.

Armour, Nicholas Hilary Stuart; Counsellor and Deputy Head of Mission Muscat since January 1991; born 12.6.51; Third Secretary FCO 1974;

Language Student MECAS 1975 and FCO 1976; Third later Second Secretary Beirut 1977; First Secretary FCO 1980; Head of Chancery Athens 1984; First Secretary FCO 1989; m 1982 Georgina Elizabeth Fortescue (2d 1985, 1987).

Armstrong, Catherine Fraser; FCO since December 1990; born 16.7.53; FCO 1971; Paris 1974; Gaborone 1977; FCO 1980; Manila 1985; Athens 1989; Grade 9; m 1981 Clive Paul Ranson; diss. 1986.

Arnold, Anthony; FCO since January 1990; born 7.8.39; HM Forces 1960-62; HO 1963; FO 1964; MECAS 1966; Baghdad 1968; Tripoli 1971; Second Secretary FCO 1975; Second Secretary (Comm) Jedda 1977; FCO 1980; Second Secretary (Comm) Damascus 1982; Second later First Secretary (Consul/Admin) Prague 1986; m 1963 Janet Mary Alexander (3s 1965, 1966, 1968; 1d 1972).

Aron, Michael Douglas; First Secretary FCO since November 1991; born 22.3.59; FCO 1984; on Secondment to European Commission 1986; Second later First Secretary, FCO 1986; First Secretary Brasilia 1988; m 1986 Rachel Ann Golding Barker (1d 1986; 1s 1990).

Aron, Peter James; First Secretary FCO since January 1990; born 27.2.46; FO (later FCO) 1965; Bonn 1968; Second later First Secretary FCO 1971; First Secretary (Chancery) Singapore 1984; First Secretary (Chancery) Washington 1986; m 1968 Penelope Joan Sebley (2d 1969, 1971; 2s 1976, 1988).

Aron, Dr Rachel Ann Golding (née Barker); SUPL since September 1990; born 18.7.51; First Secretary FCO 1984; Head of Chancery Brasilia 1988; m 1986 Michael Douglas Aron (1d 1986; 1s 1990).

Arrowsmith, Robert Owen; Second Secretary Canberra since October 1989; born 16.9.41; HM Customs and Excise 1959; DSAO 1966; . Freetown 1969; CENTO Ankara 1973; Ankara 1974; FCO 1975; Auckland 1978; Baghdad 1980; Second Secretary FCO 1983; Second Secretary (Comm/Aid) Yaoundé 1987; m 1965 Brenda Florence Battersby (2d 1968, 1970, 1s 1983).

Arroyo, James José Maria; Full-time Language Training Cairo since June 1992; born 25.3.67; FCO 1990; Full-time Language Training 1991; Grade 7.

Arthur, Hilary Jane; Vice-Consul (Consular) Düsseldorf since January 1991; born 28.1.61; FCO 1984; Karachi 1987; Grade 9.

Arthur, Michael Anthony, CMG (1992); Counsellor FCO since June 1988; born 28.8.50; FCO 1972; New York 1972; FCO 1973; Second Secretary UKREP Brussels 1974; Second

Secretary Kinshasa 1976; Second later First
Secretary FCO 1978; PS to Lord Privy Seal
1980; PS to Minister of State 1982; First
Secretary (Chancery) Bonn 1984; m 1974 Plaxy
Gillian Beatrice Corke (2d 1978, 1980; 2s 1982,
1985).

Ash, Elizabeth; FCO since June 1990; born
31.7.52; FCO 1975; New Delhi 1976; UKMIS
Geneva 1978; Peking 1980; FCO 1982; Kingston
1983; FCO 1987; East Berlin 1988; Grade S1.

Ashcroft, Andrew Richard; FCO since
November 1991; Second Secretary 1989; born
28.5.61; FCO 1980; Muscat 1982; Tel Aviv
1987.

Ashdown, Julie Anne; Belgrade since March
1990; born 31.8.57; FCO 1976; Amman 1978;
Asuncion 1982; Brasilia 1983; FCO 1985;
Grade 9.

Ashington-Pickett, Robert Philip; First Secretary
(Chancery) Rome since November 1992; born
12.9.56; Second Secretary FCO 1985; Second
later First Secretary Berlin 1988; First Secretary
FCO 1990; m 1986 Susan Amanda Ward (3s
1987, 1989, 1991).

Ashton, Daniel Anthony; FCO since December
1991; born 18.5.73; Grade 10.

Ashton, John; First Secretary Rome since August
1988; born 7.11.56; FCO 1978; Language
Student Hong Kong 1980; Third later Second
Secretary Peking 1981; FCO 1984; First
Secretary on loan to Cabinet Office 1986; m
1983 Kao Fengning (1s 1986).

Ashton, Richard Henry John; First Secretary
FCO since September 1991; born 1.7.46; ODA
1972-74; Second Secretary FCO 1974; First
Secretary (UN) UKMIS Geneva 1976; First
Secretary (Inf) Athens 1979; First Secretary FCO
1983; First Secretary (Chancery) Ankara 1988; m
(1) 1973 Jean Angela Pooley (2d 1978, 1979);
(2) 1986 Susan Hatfield Young.

Ashworth, Patrick; Vice-Consul (Commercial)
São Paulo since April 1987; born 2.11.50; FCO
1968; Dar es Salaam 1971; Castries 1975;
Moscow 1978; FCO 1980; Valletta 1983; m
1973 Pauline Mary Harrison (1d 1982, 1s 1986).

Aspden, Susan Elizabeth; FCO since April 1989;
born 20.1.57; FCO 1980; Rabat 1981; Jakarta
1983; Havana 1987; Grade 9.

Asquith, Hon Dominic Anthony Gerard; First
Secretary (Political) Washington since June 1992;
born 7.2.57; FCO 1983; Second Secretary and
Head of Interests Section Damascus 1986; First
Secretary (Chancery) Muscat 1987; First
Secretary FCO 1989; m 1988 Louise Cotton.

Asquith, Viscount (Raymond Benedict

Bartholomew Michael), OBE (1992); Counsellor
Kiev since October 1992; born 24.8.52; FCO
1980; First Secretary (Chancery) Moscow 1983;
FCO 1985; on loan to the Cabinet Office 1985;
m 1978 Mary Clare Pollen (1s 1979, 4d 1981,
1984, 1989, 1991).

Astle, Marilia; FCO since August1991; born
14.4.68; Grade 9.

Astle, Richard Howard; Third later Second
Secretary (Comm) Moscow since November
1990; born 24.6.65; FCO 1988; Full-time
language training 1989; Grade 8.

Astley, Philip Sinton, LVO (1979); Deputy Head
of Mission Copenhagen since March 1990; born
18.8.43; British Council 1965-73; First Secretary
FCO 1973; First Secretary Copenhagen 1976;
First Secretary and Head of Chancery East
Berlin 1980; First Secretary FCO 1982;
Counsellor, Home Inspectorate 1984; Head of
Management Review Staff 1985; Counsellor
(Econ/Comm/Aid) and Consul-General Islamabad
1986; m 1966 Susanne Poulsen (2d 1969, 1972)

Atherton, Mary Catherine; FCO since November
1990; FCO 1973; New Delhi 1974; East Berlin
1976; FCO 1978; Algiers 1980; Tunis 1981;
Rome 1983; FCO 1984; Warsaw 1988; Karachi
1988; Grade 9.

Atkin, Patricia Lois; Port Louis since March
1975; born 21.4.44; FCO 1974; Grade S2.

Atkins, Frances Mary; Washington since January
1992; born 2.9.36; FCO 1976; Ankara 1976;
Tunis 1978; Bonn 1980; FCO 1983; East Berlin
1985; Harare 1987; FCO 1990; Grade S1.

Atkinson, James Oswald; First Secretary FCO
since September 1990; born 20.10.44; Board of
Trade 1964; DSA 1966; Commonwealth Office
(later FCO) 1967; Nicosia 1969; Gabarone 1972;
Second Secretary (Comm) Damascus 1976; FCO
1980; First Secretary (Comm) Athens 1984; First
Secretary (Chancery/Inf) Jakarta 1988; m
Annemiek van Werkum (1d 1981).

Atkinson, Jane; Quito since August 1988; born
20.7.60; MOD 1978-87; FCO 1987; Grade S2.

Atkinson, John Edward; Second later First
Secretary FCO since July 1989; born 12.5.46;
FO 1965; Dar es Salaam 1968; Stockholm 1971;
St Vincent 1973; FCO 1977; JAO Brussels 1980;
Second Secretary (Admin) Brussels 1982; Harare
1985; m 1989 Nesia Came.

Atkinson, Simon Mannington; Oslo since May
1992; born 11.5.71; FCO 1989; Grade 10.

Attewell, Brian; High Commissioner Nassau
since September 1992; born 29.5.37; Board of
Trade 1956; SUPL 1958-61; Private Secretary to
Parliamentary Secretary 1964-66; Commonwealth

Office 1966; Second Secretary (Comm) Washington 1967; Buenos Aires 1970; First Secretary FCO 1974; First Secretary (Econ) Canberra 1978; FCO 1980; First Secretary (Comm) Dubai 1984; Counsellor (Comm) Brussels 1988; m 1963 Mary Gillian Tandy (2s 1964, 1969; 1d 1966).

Attryde, Alan Robert James; Second Secretary (Management/Cons) Caracas since July 1990; born 21.8.47; Ministry of Labour 1966; DSAO 1967; FCO 1968; Middle East Floater 1970; Washington 1971; Jakarta 1974; FCO 1978; Cairo 1980; on loan to DTI 1985 (Second Secretary 1985); Consul (Comm) Shanghai 1987; m 1992 Ana Maria Diaz Molina.

Attwood, Ian; Hong Kong since April 1991; born 14.4.62; FCO 1983; Grade 9; m 1987 Tina Louise (1d 1989; 1s 1991).

Attwood, Jane; First Secretary FCO since June 1988; born 15.8.56; FCO 1978; Lisbon 1979; Second Secretary FCO 1981; Second later First Secretary UKMIS New York 1984.

Attwood, Stewart George; First Secretary (Management) Berlin since February 1992; born 18.3.48; HM Forces 1967-70; FCO 1970; Moscow 1972; Kathmandu 1974; Sofia 1975; FCO 1978; Nairobi 1982; FCO 1983; Second Secretary Warsaw 1984; Second Secretary (Comm) Muscat 1987; m 1973 Mary Elizabeth Keegan (née Warren) (2s 1982, 1983).

Augustine, Felicity; Lagos since June 1991; born 10.7.56; MAFF 1972; FCO 1989; Grade S2A.

Auld, Steven James; FCO since March 1990; born 9.7.71; Grade 10.

Aust, Anthony Ivall; Legal Counsellor FCO since September 1991; born 9.3.42; Solicitor 1967; Assistant Legal Adviser Commonwealth Office 1967; Assistant Legal Adviser FCO 1968 (DS Grade 5); Legal Adviser Berlin (BMG) 1976; FCO 1979 (Legal Counsellor 1984); Counsellor (Legal Adviser) UKMIS New York 1988; m (1) 1969 Jacqueline Antoinette Therese Paris (diss 1986) (2d 1974, 1980); (2) 1988 Kirsten Kaarre Jensen.

Austen, Richard James; Second Secretary FCO since July 1990; born 25.5.55; Inland Revenue 1972-77 (SUPL 1974-77); FCO 1981; Dar es Salaam 1983; Third Secretary (Cons) Ottawa 1987.

Auster, Vivian John Whorwood; First Secretary FCO since June 1989; born 11.11.48; FCO 1971; Beirut 1973; Second Secretary (Econ) Dublin 1981; First Secretary FCO 1984; First Secretary UKMIS New York 1987; m 1974 Carol Brown.

Austin, Brian Patrick; Counsellor (Econ/Comm) Stockholm since December 1988; born 18.3.38; CRO 1961; Central African Office 1962; Second Secretary Lagos 1963; The Hague 1966; First Secretary FCO 1969; Consul (Comm) Montreal 1973; FCO 1979; DHC Kaduna 1981; Counsellor FCO 1984; m 1968 Augusta Francisca Maria Lina (1d 1974; 1s 1979).

Austin, David John Robert; Second Secretary FCO since February 1992; born 7.10.63; FCO 1986; Dhaka 1989; m 1990 Emma Jane Carey.

Austin, John Anthony; FCO since February 1983; born 19.10.40; FO 1958; Washington 1963; Dubai 1966; Tehran 1970; FCO 1972; Second Secretary Moscow 1976; Second Secretary (Aid) Gaborone 1979; m 1963 Michele Marie Larcombe (1s 1964; 1d 1965).

Avent, Susan Leslie (neé Smith); Kathmandu since November 1989; born 29.12.63; FCO 1983; New Delhi 1985; Belgrade 1988; Grade 10; m 1992 Geoffrey Philip Avent.

Avery, Raymond Rember; Second Secretary FCO since February 1991; born 31.1.46; DSAO 1965; Port of Spain 1968; Colombo 1972; FCO 1975; Amman 1978; Helsinki 1980; FCO 1982; Second Secretary (Comm) Kuala Lumpur 1987; m 1967 Christine Ruth Floate (1s 1968; 1d 1971).

Axworthy, Michael George Andrew; Second Secretary FCO since April 1991; born 26.9.62; FCO 1986; Third later Second Secretary Valetta 1988.

Aylwin, Robert David; Third Secretary Mexico City since March 1990; born 6.7.37; FCO 1984; Paris 1987; Grade 8; m 1962 Grace Mary Burrell (2s 1963, 1965).

Ayre, Andrew; FCO since July 1991; born 30.4.66; FCO 1986; Warsaw 1988; Rio de Janeiro 1990; Grade 9; m 1990 Bettina Mooseberger.

Ayres, James Winterton; First Secretary FCO since March 1986; born 21.6.38; CRO 1960; Nicosia 1961; Third Secretary and PS to High Commissioner Ottawa 1964; Second Secretary Kingston 1966; Commonwealth Office (later FCO) 1968; Dar es Salaam 1971; Second Secretary (Comm) Nicosia 1974; First Secretary, Head of Chancery and Consul Yaoundé 1977; FCO 1977; Quito 1981; Madrid 1983; m 1960 Ann Bale (2s 1963, 1965).

Ayres, Robert Charles; Second later First Secretary FCO since February 1990; born 12.12.41; CRO 1958; Seconded to Department of Technical Co-operation 1961; CRO 1963; DSAO 1965; Tripoli 1967; Lahore 1969; Islamabad 1971; FCO 1972; Brussels (NATO) 1975; Second Secretary FCO 1978; Second Secretary (Admin) Brussels (JAO) 1985; m 1978 Elizabeth Anne Kirkland (1d 1979).

Ayton, Joanne Addassa; Paris since September 1992; FCO 1991; born 29.7.63; DTI 1988-1991; Grade S2; (1s 1985).

B

Bache, Andrew Philip Foley; (CMG (1992), HM Ambassador Bucharest since April 1992; born 29.12.39; CRO 1963; Third Secretary Nicosia 1964; Second Secretary Commonwealth Office 1966; Second Secretary (Pol and Econ) Sofia 1966; FCO 1968; First Secretary (Chancery) later Head of Information Section Lagos 1971; First Secretary FCO 1974; First Secretary (Comm) Vienna 1978; Counsellor and Head of Chancery Tokyo 1981; Counsellor Ankara 1985; Counsellor FCO 1988; Attached to OMCS (CSSB) 1990; m 1963 Shân Headley (2s 1964, 1966; 1d 1974).

Backhouse, Nigel Antony Richard, MVO (1986); First Secretary FCO since August 1992; born 19.1.56; FCO 1982; Second Secretary Kabul 1984; Second later First Secretary Kathmandu 1985; FCO 1986; First Secretary (Chancery) Madrid 1989; m 1979 Kathleen Helen Gordon (diss 1988) (2s 1983, 1985).

Bacon, Peter James; Counsellor (Comm) Jakarta since July 1992; born 17.9.41; GPO 1958; CRO 1963; Nicosia 1964; Kota Kinabula 1967; Brussels 1970; Beirut 1971; (Second Secretary 1973); Assistant Private Secretary to the Minister of State FCO 1975; Second later First Secretary (Aid/Comm) Suva 1978; First Secretary (Energy) Washington 1980; First Secretary FCO 1984; Consul (Comm) Johannesburg 1988; m 1963 Valerie Ann Colby (1d 1966; 1s 1969).

Bagnall, Andrew William; Attaché Caracas since August 1987; born 28.2.48; GPO 1964-70; FCO 1970; Pretoria 1982; Second Secretary FCO 1985; m 1981 Margaret Christine Bromwich (1s 1981; 1d 1985).

Bagshaw, Charles Kerry, OBE (1992); First Secretary FCO since October 1991; born 5.10.43; Royal Marines 1960-74; First Secretary FCO 1974; First Secretary Gaborone 1977; FCO 1979; UKMIS Geneva 1982; FCO 1987; First Secretary Moscow 1988; m (1) 1965 Janet Mary Bond (diss 1969) (1d 1966); (2) 1970 Pamela Georgina Slater (2d 1973, 1975).

Baharie, Ian Walter; First Secretary Abu Dhabi since May 1991; born 3.5.61; FCO 1982; Language Student SOAS 1983; Third later Second Secretary (Chancery) Cairo 1985; Second later First Secretary FCO 1987; m 1991 Bonaventura Agatha Jasperina Buhre (1d 1991).

Bailes, Alyson Judith Kirtley; Deputy Head of Mission and Consul-General Oslo since August 1990; born 6.4.49; Third Secretary FCO 1969; Budapest 1970; Second Secretary Brussels (NATO) 1974; Second later First Secretary FCO 1976 on loan to MOD 1979; First Secretary (Chancery) Bonn 1981; First Secretary FCO 1984; Language Training 1986; Counsellor Head of Chancery and Consul-General Peking 1987.

Bailey, Ian Peter; Third Secretary (Pol) Muscat since October 1990; born 21.8.57; DTI 1985; FCO 1987; Language Training 1988; Grade 9; m 1990 Teresa Weronika Maria Trosztega.

Bailey, Michael; Third Secretary FCO since January 1991; born 24.2.41; FO 1965; Singapore 1967; FCO 1969; Khartoum 1971; FCO 1973; St Helena 1974; FCO 1976; Muscat 1977; FCO 1980; Peking 1981; FCO 1983; Rangoon 1984; FCO 1986; Third Secretary Rome 1988; Grade 8; m 1967 Wendy Nichol Pocklington (2s 1969, 1970).

Bailey, Rosemarie Anne (née Edwards); SUPL since March 1988; born 20.4.59; FCO 1979; Tokyo 1983; FCO 1986; Grade 9; m 1982 Mark Adrian Stephen Bailey.

Bailey, Stephen; Budapest since October 1990; born 13.4.53; FCO 1971; Mexico City 1975; Gaborone 1977; Sana'a 1981; FCO 1983; Wellington 1987; Grade 9; m 1975 Carol Joan Sterritt (1d 1980).

Bailey, Sylvia Felicity; Second Secretary FCO since December 1988; born 30.4.35; FCO 1970; Mbabane 1971; Tel Aviv 1973; FCO 1975; Peking 1977; FCO 1978; APS to Minister of State 1982; Dhaka 1983; Milan 1986.

Bain, Alison Winifred; Los Angeles since March 1992; born 6.3.38; FO 1965; Kabul 1966; Zomba 1970; FCO 1972; Barcelona 1973; FCO 1976; Dusseldorf 1981; Accra 1984; FCO 1988; Grade 9.

Baines, Paul Vincent; Consul Tokyo since December 1991; born 22.7.47; Inland Revenue 1966; Registrar General's Office 1966; DSAO (later FCO) 1967; Blantyre 1970; Algiers 1973; Warsaw 1976; FCO 1978; Lusaka 1981; FCO 1984; Second Secretary (Admin) Riyadh 1988; m 1969 Edith Lauraine Baer Price.

Baird, Nicholas Graham Faraday; Second Secretary (Econ/Finance) UKREP Brussels since July 1989; born 15.5.62; FCO 1983; Third later Second Secretary Kuwait 1986; m 1985 Caroline Jane Ivett (1s 1989, 2d 1990, 1992).

Baker, Alison Bertha, BEM (1991); Algiers since June 1991; born 9.5.62; FCO 1989; Grade S2.

Baker, Andrew Barrie; Peking since February 1991; born 2.8.66; FCO 1985; Washington 1988; Grade 10.

Baker, Catherine Margaret; FCO since October 1991; born 11.9.68; Grade 9.

Baker, David John; Third Secretary Bangkok since November 1985; born 15.1.50; FCO 1970; Gaborone 1971; FCO 1973; St Helena 1974; FCO 1976; Baghdad 1978; FCO 1980; Attaché Islamabad 1982; FCO 1984; Grade 8; m 1970 Susan June Evans (2d 1971, 1975; 2s 1973, 1982).

Baker, Denise; Brussels since August 1991; born 27.9.67; FCO 1987; Grade S2A.

Baker, Francis Raymond; Second Secretary FCO since August 1991; born 27.1.61; FCO 1980; Panama City 1983; Buenos Aires 1986; m 1983 Maria Pilar Fernandez.

Baker, George Frank; Third Secretary FCO since December 1991; born 26.1.35; GPO 1951; RAF 1953-58; FO 1958; Inland Revenue 1961; FO (later FCO) 1964; Accra 1971; FCO 1972; Singapore 1974; FCO 1976; Gaborone 1978; FCO 1981; BGWRS Darwin 1982; FCO 1985; Helsinki 1986; Third Secretary Khartoum 1987; Third Secretary Tokyo 1991; Grade 8; m Brenda Juliet Phillips (1d 1964; 1s 1966).

Baker, Gordon Meldrum; Counsellor FCO since March 1991; born 4.7.41; Lord Chancellor's Department 1959; Commonwealth Office 1966; FO (later FCO) 1968; Lagos 1969; First Secretary FCO 1973; on secondment to Post-Graduate School of Studies in Industrial Technology, Bradford University 1975; First Secretary FCO 1976; First Secretary Chancery/ Inf later First Secretary Head of Chancery and Consul Brasilia 1978; First Secretary FCO 1982; Counsellor on Secondment to British Aerospace, 1984; Counsellor, Head of Chancery and Consul-General, Santiago 1986; RCDS 1990; m 1978 Sheila Mary Megson.

Baker, James Michael; Singapore since August 1990; born 22.10.35; Royal Navy 1953-84; Havana 1986; Amman 1987; Belgrade 1988; Grade SO; m 1964 Margaret Bennison (1d 1965; 1s 1967).

Baker, Nigel Marcus; Third Secretary (Political/ Econ); Prague since February 1992; born 9.9.66; FCO 1989; Language Training 1991; Grade 8.

Baker, Piers Howard Burton; First Secretary FCO since August 1988; born 23.7.56; Second Secretary FCO 1983; First Secretary (Chancery) Brussels 1985; m 1979 Maria Eugenia Vilaincour (1s 1984).

Baker, Rodney Kelvin Mornington; Third Secretary Madrid since October 1989; born 24.3.49; FO (later FCO) 1966; Warsaw 1974; FCO 1975; Athens 1977; Ankara 1978; FCO 1981; Third Secretary Tokyo 1984; FCO 1986; Grade 7; m 1971 Christine Mary Holt (2d 1979, 1983).

Baker, Russell Nicholas John; Second Secretary (Chancery/Info) Lima since January 1990; born

6.10.53; FCO 1977; Language Training 1979; Prague 1979; Bonn 1982 (Private Secretary to HMA 1982-84); Second Secretary FCO 1986.

Baker, Sheila Ann; Nicosia since September 1990; born 6.6.60; FCO 1984; Peking 1985; FCO 1988; Grade S2.

Baker-Bates, Merrick Stuart; Consul-General Los Angeles since July 1992; born 22.7.39; FO 1963; Third later Second Secretary Tokyo 1963; Second later First Secretary FCO 1968; First Secretary (Inf) Washington 1973; First Secretary later Counsellor Tokyo 1976; Resigned 1981; Reinstated 1985; Deputy High Commissioner Kuala Lumpur 1986; Counsellor FCO 1989; m 1963 Chrystal Jacqueline Goodacre (1s 1966; 1d 1969).

Baldwin, Brian Paul; First Secretary (Comm) Muscat since July 1988; born 7.12.44; Ministry of Transport 1964; Board of Trade 1965; FCO 1967; Johannesburg 1970; Belgrade 1973; FCO 1976; Vice-Consul (Pol) Johannesburg 1979; Second later First Secretary FCO 1983; m Elizabeth Mary Evans (3s 1969, 1970, 1973; 1d 1971).

Baldwin, Peter Graham; Second Secretary (Consular) Jakarta since March 1991; born 28.8.43; Paymaster General's Office 1962; CRO 1963; Lusaka 1964; Calcutta 1967; Vienna 1971; Second Secretary Brussels (UKREP) 1973; FCO 1977; Algiers 1981; Second Secretary FCO 1983; Second Secretary (Immigration/Consular) Colombo 1987; m 1968 Patricia Joyce Carter (2d 1970, 1972; 1s 1980).

Bale, Caroline Margaret; FCO since June 1991; born 25.7.57; FCO 1980; UKMIS Geneva 1981; Moscow 1983; Port Stanley 1986; Sofia 1987; Gaborone 1989; Grade S2.

Balfour, Alison Hannah; Nicosia since September 1992; born 13.5.61; Scottish Office 1980-87; FCO 1987; Mexico City 1989; Grade S2.

Balfour, Andrew; FCO since July 1989; born 26.5.50; FCO 1969; Bridgetown 1972; Durban 1975; FCO 1978; Rabat 1981; Damascus 1985; Dubai 1986; Grade 9; m 1972 Patricia Broomhead (1d 1980; 1s 1983).

Ball, Anthony James; Full-time Language Training since September 1991; born 18.12.68; FCO 1989; Grade 8.

Balls, Anna; Rome since September 1992; born 6.8.70; FCO 1989; Grade S2.

Balmbra, Deborah Elizabeth; Phnom Penh since August 1992; born 9.11.64; FCO 1986; Belgrade 1989; FCO 1990; Grade S2.

Ballett, Sarah Elizabeth; FCO since November 1990; born 31.10.71, Grade S2.

Balmer, Michael Anthony; First Secretary FCO since August 1992; born 21.7.51; MOD (Navy) 1969; FCO 1971; UKMIS Geneva 1973; Moscow 1975; LA Floater 1977; Jedda 1979; Second Secretary (Comm) Warsaw 1981; Second Secretary FCO 1984; Language Training 1987; First Secretary (Comm) Athens 1988; m 1982 Helen Charmian Burgoine (2d 1984, 1987).

Bamber, Major Iain Gordon MacDonald; Superintendent of the Corps of Queen's Messengers since November 1987; born 24.1.38; HM Forces 1957-1984; Queen's Messenger 1984.

Bamford, Victoria Jane; Moscow since January 1992; born 23.12.67; FCO 1989; Grade 10.

Band, Stephen Henry; SUPL since October 1988; born 14.3.48; FCO 1973; Language Student 1974; Second later First Secretary (Comm) Moscow 1975; First Secretary (Chancery) Moscow 1977; FCO 1979; Harkness Fellow at Stanford Business School 1981; First Secretary (Chancery) later Counsellor Washington 1983; m 1975 José Michele Cremaschi (1s 1977; 2d 1979, 1980).

Banham, Michael Kent; Second Secretary (Management/Consular) Lima since May 1990; born 20.9.44; FO 1963; Rawalpindi 1967; Quito 1970; FCO 1974; Tripoli 1976; Nairobi 1980; FCO 1983; Second Secretary (Comm) Bombay 1987; m 1965 Christine Scott (1s 1969; 1d 1971).

Banks, Alison Elizabeth; FCO since July 1992; born 10.1.70; Grade S2.

Banks, David Stewart; Second later First Secretary FCO since December 1984; born 13.12.48; HO 1969; FCO 1971; Bonn 1974; Second Secretary FCO 1976; Second Secretary (Chancery) Singapore 1980; m 1975 Marilyn Joan Paul (2d 1980, 1982).

Banks, Jacinta Mary Catharine (née Cookson); Nicosia since April 1990; born 25.11.57; FCO 1977; Paris 1980; Bombay 1983; FCO 1987; Grade 9; m 1982 Jamie Paul Banks (1d 1992).

Banks, Jamie Paul; Nicosia Since April 1990; born 9.6.57; FCO 1977; UKDEL OECD Paris 1980; Bombay 1983; FCO 1987; Grade 9; m 1982 Jacinta Mary Catharine Cookson (1d 1992).

Banks, Larry, OBE (1991); First Secretary and Consul (Comm) Hamburg since March 1992; born 15.6.42; FO 1961; New York 1963; Lagos 1966; Aden 1968; MECAS 1969; MECAS (Admin Officer) 1971; Muscat 1973; FCO 1975; Second Secretary (Comm) Tripoli 1977; Second Secretary (Admin) and Vice-Consul Sana'a 1980; Second later First Secretary FCO 1984; First Secretary and Consul Kuwait 1988; m 1969 Elizabeth Ann Collins (1d 1970; 1s 1971).

Banks, Simon John; Third later Second Secretary (Economic) Warsaw since January 1991; born 5.4.66; FCO 1988; Language Training 1990; m 1989 The Hon Rowena Joynson-Hicks.

Bannatyne, William Graeme; Canberra since April 1990; born 5.3.67; FCO 1988; Grade 10; m 1990; Caterina Petrigiacomo.

Bannister, Ian; First Secretary FCO since June 1990; born 12.8.61; FCO 1983; Second Secretary (Econ) Brasilia 1987.

Bannister, Irene Marshall; Lusaka since July 1990; born 14.3.67; FCO 1988; Grade S2A.

Barber, Andrew John; First Secretary Addis Ababa since May 1990; born 19.2.59; FCO 1981; Second Secretary Jakarta 1985; Second Secretary FCO 1987; m (1) 1982 Ann Mather (diss 1988); (2) 1990 Caroline Jane Hart (1d 1991).

Barber, Caroline Jane; Full-time language training later Second Secretary (Chancery/Info) Addis Ababa since May 1990; born 5.8.56; FCO 1978; UKMIS Geneva 1980; Jakarta 1983; FCO 1985; m 1990 Andrew John Barber (1d 1991).

Barber, Judith Mary, MBE (1984); FCO since November 1985; born 20.10.47; FCO 1968; Dar es Salaam 1974; FCO 1976; Rome 1977; FCO 1980; Paris 1981; Grade S2.

Barclay, Karl Phillip; First Secretary FCO since July 1992; born 28.5.48; Army 1967-86; First Secretary FCO 1986; First Secretary Hong Kong 1989; m 1974 Gillian Davies (2s 1976, 1983; 1d 1979).

Barder, Sir Brian (Leon) KCMG (1992); High Commissioner Canberra since April 1991; born 20.6.34; HM Forces 1952-54; CO 1957; Private Secretary to Permanent Under-Secretary of State 1960 (Principal 1961); First Secretary UKMIS New York 1964; Diplomatic Service 1965; FCO 1968; Moscow 1971; Counsellor and Head of Chancery Canberra 1973; Sabbatical Canadian National Defence College 1977; Head of Southern African Department FCO 1978; HM Ambassador Addis Ababa 1982; HM Ambassador Warsaw 1986; High Commissioner Lagos, and, concurrently, HM Ambassador (non-resident) to Benin 1988; m 1958 Jane Maureen Cornwell (2d 1961, 1962; 1s 1967).

Barker, Elizabeth Anne, SUPL since November 1988; born 2.12.57; FCO 1978; Belgrade 1980; Pretoria/Cape Town 1983; FCO 1986; Grade S2.

Barklamb, Peter Richard; Second Secretary (Commercial) Riyadh since January 1991; born 18.7.51; FCO 1970; Delhi 1973; Islamabad 1975; Geneva 1976; Brussels 1978; FCO 1981; Warsaw 1984; Second Secretary (Chancery/Inf)

Accra 1985; Second Secretary (Comm/Aid) Bridgetown 1989; m 1974 Jane Bosworth (2d 1979, 1981; 1s 1984).

Barlow, Andrew Watson; FCO since October 1987; born 23.12.54; UKAEA 1977; FCO 1978; UKAEA 1981; PS to Chairman 1983/4; Grade PRO.

Barlow, Claire Heather; FCO since November 1991; born 7.3.72; Inland Revenue 1990; Grade 10.

Barlow, Jacqueline; FCO since June 1990; born 21.7.47; FCO 1969; Berne 1969; Baghdad 1971; Islamabad 1972; Moscow 1973; Phnom Penh and Hanoi 1975; FCO 1976; Moscow 1977; Floater duties 1980; FCO 1984; Tokyo 1987; Grade 9.

Barnard, Ian Clive; FCO since September 1991; born 30.10.65; Grade 8; m 1990 Helen Clare Rothwell.

Barnard, Michael Trevelyan; Dar es Salaam since March 1989; born 15.12.61; FCO 1986; Grade 10.

Barnes, Stewart George; First Secretary FCO since February 1991; born 8.7.48; FCO 1967; Tel Aviv 1973; Resigned 1980; Reinstated 1980; Second Secretary FCO 1980; Second later First Secretary Vienna 1987; m 1975 Jennifer Mary Windebank (1s 1977; 1d 1979).

Barnes Jones, Deborah Elizabeth Vavasseur (née Barnes); First Secretary (Chancery) Tel Aviv since June 1988; born 6.10.56; FCO 1980; Moscow 1983; First Secretary on loan to Cabinet Office 1985; Resigned 1986; Reinstated 1988; m 1986 Frederick Richard Jones (2d (twins) 1991).

Barnsley, Pamela Margaret; Trade Commissioner BTC Hong Kong since January 1989; born 2.6.57; FCO 1982; Second Secretary (Chancery) Brasilia 1983; First Secretary (Comm/Econ) Peking 1987; m 1986 Perry Neil Keller.

Barnett, Robert William; First Secretary (Econ) Bonn since December 1988; born 25.5.54; FCO 1977; Language Training SOAS 1979; Language Student, Kamakura 1980; Tokyo 1981; Second later First Secretary FCO 1984; m 1979 Caroline Sara Weale (2s 1982, 1984).

Barnett, Robin Anthony; First Secretary UKMIS New York since August 1991; born 8.3.58; FCO 1980; Third later Second Secretary Warsaw 1982; Second later First Secretary FCO 1985; First Secretary UKDEL Vienna 1990; m 1989 Debra Marianne Bunt (1step s 1987, 1s 1990).

Baron, Cynthia; Peking since November 1992; born 8.2.40; FCO 1988; Bonn 1991; Grade S2; m 1962 Ernest Roy Baron (2d 1962, 1963).

Baron, Joan Mary; Ankara since September 1989; born 28.5.39; FCO 1974; Khartoum 1976;

FCO 1978; Damascus 1980; FCO 1984; Amman 1986; Grade S1.

Barr, Christopher; FCO since January 1992; born 23.7.57; FCO 1975; Dublin 1979; FCO 1983; Sana'a 1988; Grade 9; m 1982 Bronwyn Patricia Morrison (2s 1983, 1988; 1d 1984).

Barr, Richard Barclay; FCO since April 1992; born 3.5.55; FCO 1975; Freetown 1977; FCO 1980; Prague 1981; Düsseldorf 1983; Accra 1988; Grade 9; m 1977 Jane Anne Greengrass (1s 1978).

Barras, Ian Alexander; Washington since July 1991; born 27.4.50; FCO 1976; Geneva 1979; Peking 1981; Douala 1984; FCO 1986; Athens 1989; FCO 1990; Grade 9.

Barrass, Gordon Stephen, CMG (1992); Counsellor later AUS on loan to Cabinet Office since November 1987; born 5.8.40; Third later Second Secretary FO 1965; Hong Kong 1967; Second later First Secretary Peking 1970; FCO 1972; First Secretary UKMIS Geneva 1974; FCO 1978; Counsellor at RCDS 1983; on loan to MOD 1984; m 1965 Alice Cecile Oberg (dec'd 1984).

Barrell, Mrs Sheila Clare; FCO since June 1992; born 3.8.35; Tehran 1959; Hargeisa 1961; Berlin 1962; Leopoldville 1964; FO 1966; Resigned on marriage 1966; Reinstated 1970; FCO 1970; Kathmandu 1972; Panama City 1975; Seoul 1976; FCO 1978; Floater Duties 1980; FCO 1984; Peking 1984; FCO 1987; CSCE 1988; Grade S1.

Barrett, Brian Andrew; Second Secretary FCO since January 1987; later First Secretary 1989; born 30.11.33; Royal Navy 1952-54; Air Ministry 1954; FO 1960; Athens 1960; Mogadishu 1962; Khartoum 1963; Warsaw 1965; Aden 1967; UKMIS New York 1968; Havana 1969; FCO 1970; Anguilla 1971; Latin America Floater 1973; Second Secretary (Admin) and Consul La Paz 1975; FCO 1979; Vice-Consul Cape Town 1982.

Barrett, Douglas Wilson; Manila since May 1992; born 28.1.56; HCS 1976; FCO 1978; UKREP Brussels 1980; Havana 1983; Latin America Floater 1986; Islamabad 1988; Grade 9.

Barrett, Richard Martin Donne; First Secretary FCO since July 1992; born 14.6.49; MOD 1975-81; First Secretary FCO 1982; Language Training 1983; First Secretary Ankara 1983; First Secretary FCO 1986; First Secretary (ECOSOC) UKMIS New York 1988; m 1973 Irene Hogg (1d 1976; 2s 1980, 1981).

Barrington, Sir Nicholas (John) KCMG (1990); CVO (1975); HM Ambassador Islamabad since July 1987 (later High Commissioner, from 1 October 1989); born 23.7.34; FO 1957; Tehran

1958; Third Secretary Kabul 1959; FO 1961; Second Secretary UKDEL Brussels (EC) 1962; First Secretary Rawalpindi 1965; FO 1968; Private Secretary to PUS Commonwealth Office June 1968; Assistant Private Secretary to the Secretary of State 1968; First Secretary and Head of Chancery Tokyo 1972-75; Counsellor 1973; Chargé d'Affaires, Hanoi 1973; Head of Guidance and Information Policy Department FCO 1976 (later Information Policy Department); Counsellor Cairo 1978; Counsellor (Minister 1982) and Head of British Interests Section Tehran 1981; UKMIS New York (General Assembly) 1983; AUSS (Econ Summit Co-ordinator) 1984; AUSS (Public Departments) 1984.

Barron, Elaine Marie; Phnom Penh since April 1992; Luxembourg 1991; born 30.1.63; FCO 1984; Istanbul 1988; Grade 10.

Barros, Lesley Susan; Paris since February 1990; born 2.5.60; FCO 1980; Brussels 1981; Havana 1982; Brasilia 1984; FCO 1987; Grade S2; m 1989 José Barros Filho (1d 1991).

Barrow, Christine Louise; FCO since February 1991; born 7.9.71; Grade 10.

Barrow, Sarah Jane (neé Green); FCO since August 1991; born 8.6.64; FCO 1982; UKDELOECD Paris 1985; San José 1988; Grade 9; m 1989; Diego Leonardo Barrow Clevas (1s 1991).

Barrow, Timothy Earle; Second Secretary (Chancery) Moscow since September 1990; born 15.2.64; FCO 1986; Language Training 1988.

Barrs, Jeffrey Francis; FCO since October 1991; born 8.9.46; FO 1962; New Delhi 1969; FCO 1971; Warsaw 1972; FCO 1973; Washington 1976; FCO 1979; Kuala Lumpur 1979; FCO 1983;.Munchen Gladbach 1988; Grade 7; m 1966 Jacqueline Lynds (1d 1968; 2s 1970, 1973).

Barrs, Neville Stuart; FCO since March 1987; born 20.5.55; FCO 1971; Nairobi 1978; FCO 1980; Dubai 1983; Grade 7; m (1) 1978 Alison Cambers; m (2) 1983 Susan Rosemary Walker (1s 1985; 1d 1987).

Barson, Jacqueline Anne; FCO since January 1990; born 26.5.59; FCO 1979; Prague 1981; Abu Dhabi 1982; UKMIS Geneva 1986; Grade 9.

Bartlett, Ruth Helen; Johannesburg since July 1992; born 19.3.65; FCO 1988; Riyadh 1990; Grade S2.

Barton, Christopher Richard; Cairo since June 1991; born 31.3.67; FCO 1987; Grade 9.

Barton, David James Gore; Second Secretary (Chancery/Inf) Accra since December 1990; born 8.9.47; DSAO later FCO 1965; Language

Student Seoul 1973; Hong Kong 1974; Kuala Lumpur 1975; Bahrain 1977; FCO 1979; Dacca 1981; The Hague 1982; Second Secretary FCO 1985; m 1974 Kim Hi Su (2s 1974, 1981; 1d 1981).

Barton, Helen Mary; FCO since October 1991; born 5.12.65; Grade 9.

Barton, John; Belgrade since November 1991; born 10.12.33; RAF 1959-82; Warsaw 1983; Pretoria 1985; Baghdad 1987; Stockholm 1989; Grade SO; m 1955 Betty Blaney (2s 1958, 1962).

Barton, Pamela Margaret (née Simpson); SUPL since March 1991; born 7.9.56; FCO 1979; Tokyo 1980; Khartoum 1983; UKREP Brussels 1986; SUPL 1989; FCO 1990; Grade S2; m 1988 Andrew Ronald Barton.

Barton, Philip Robert; On loan to the Cabinet Office since April 1991; born 18.8.63; FCO 1986; Third later Second Secretary Caracas 1987.

Bartram, Michael Antony; Consul Malaga since December 1989; born 8.4.37; FO 1963; Moscow 1964; Tokyo 1965; FCO 1968; Guatemala 1971; Chicago 1973; Anguilla 1976; FCO 1976; Second Secretary (Consular) Islamabad 1980; Havana 1983; Second later First Secretary FCO 1986; m 1965 Raili Orvokki Kompa (1s 1975).

Barwell, David John Frank; Counsellor FCO since June 1989; born 12.10.38; Third Secretary FO 1965; Second Secretary Aden 1967; First Secretary Baghdad 1968; Bahrain 1971; First Secretary (Inf) Cairo 1973; FCO 1976; First Secretary Nicosia 1982; Counsellor Paris 1985; m 1968 Christine Sarah Carter (1s 1976).

Bass, Joan; FCO since November 1990; born 12.3.57; Grade S2A.

Bassnett, Stephen Andrew, MBE (1983); First Secretary (Chancery) Cairo since August 1991; born 24.1.49; Army 1967-86; FCO 1986; m 1980 Judith Christine Anne Whitty.

Bateman, Peter; First Secretary FCO since January 1991; born 23.12.55; FCO 1984; Language Training Tokyo 1986; Second later First Secretary Tokyo 1987; m 1985 Andrea Subercaseaux-Peters (1d 1992).

Bates, Anthony Michael; Private Secretary Bonn since October 1990; born 12.11.58; FCO 1978; Islamabad 1980; Wellington 1982; Bucharest 1985; FCO 1987; Grade 9; Language Training 1990; m 1985 Colette Ann Stewart (1d 1988)

Bates, Kenneth, MBE (1981); Second later First Secretary FCO since July 1989; born 6.5.41; MAFF 1959; FO 1961; Vientiane 1963; Manila 1967; Islamabad 1967; Port Louis 1972; FCO 1973; Madrid 1976; Second Secretary (Admin)

Tripoli 1978; FCO 1982; Second Secretary (Comm) Helsinki 1986; m (1) 1963 Patricia Penny (diss 1974) (1s 1965); (2) 1978 Zara Elizalde (1d 1992).

Bates, Michael Charles; First Secretary Riga since November 1991; born 9.4.48; DSAO later FCO 1966; Delhi 1971; Third Secretary Moscow 1974; Second Secretary FCO 1977; Second, later First Secretary Singapore 1979; First Secretary (Inf/Chancery) Brussels 1983; On loan to No. 10 Downing Street 1987; First Secretary FCO 1990: m 1971 Janice Kwan Foh Yin (1d 1977; 1s 1978).

Bates, Nicholas Hilary; First Secretary (Chancery) Muscat since November 1989; born 5.2.49; Third later Second Secretary FCO 1973; Language Student 1976; FCO 1977; First Secretary UKMIS Geneva 1979; FCO 1983; Cairo 1984; First Secretary FCO 1988; m 1971 Rosemary Jane Seaton (4d 1973, 1975, 1976, 1989).

Batey, Darren Francis; Kampala since August 1990; born 9.1.66; FCO 1984; Rabat 1987; Grade 10.

Batson, Philip David; Bombay since January 1991; born 26.6.68; FCO 1987; Grade 9.

Battisby-Dutton, David; Second Secretary (Management/Consular) Wellington since January 1992;; born 18.1.46; DHSS 1962; FCO 1966; Brussels 1970; New Delhi 1973; FCO 1976; UKMIS Geneva 1981; Lagos 1983; FCO 1987 (Second Secretary 1990); m 1969 Mary Kathleen Clarke (1s 1970; 1d 1971).

Battiscombe, Christopher Charles Richard, CMG (1992); HM Ambassador Algiers since March 1990; born 27.4.40; MECAS 1963; Third Secretary Kuwait 1965; Second Secretary FO (later FCO) 1963; Assistant Private Secretary to the Chancellor of the Duchy of Lancaster 1969; UKDEL OECD Paris 1971; First Secretary UKMIS New York 1974; FCO 1978; Counsellor (Comm) Cairo 1981; Counsellor (Comm) Paris 1984; Counsellor, FCO 1986; Counsellor FCO 1986; m 1972 Brigid Melita Theresa Lunn (1d 1975, 1s 1977).

Battson, Andrew John; Bombay since March 1991; born 8.5.66; FCO 1984; Grade 9.

Batty-Smith, Katharine Amelia Louise; Brasilia since April 1988; born 19.8.64; FCO 1984; Budapest 1986; Grade 9.

Baudains, Karen Jayne; Second Secretary (Commercial) Lisbon since February 1992; born 29.9.55; FCO 1977; Mexico City 1979; South East Asia Floater 1983; Second Secretary FCO 1985.

Bavinton, Sharon Jayne (née Vince); Abu Dhabi since March 1989; born 17.12.58; FCO 1979; UKMIS New York 1981; FCO 1983; Canberra 1984; Grade S2; m 1982 Russell Alexander Bavinton (diss 1992).

Baxendale, James Lloyd; FCO since September 1991; born 23.2.67; Grade 8.

Baxter, Alison Jane; FCO since September 1990; born 15.5.67; Grade 9.

Baxter Amade, Vicki Louise; FCO since December 1990; born 18.3.63; FCO 1982; Lisbon 1984; Maputo 1987;Grade 9; m 1990 Amade Chababe Amade.

Baylis, Robin Grenville, MVO (1981); First Secretary FCO since October 1990; born 9.11.41; Passport Office 1959; CRO 1963; Lagos 1963; Bonn 1967; FCO 1970; Detroit 1973; Canberra 1975; Second Secretary FCO 1978; Colombo 1981; Second Secretary (Comm) Washington 1983; First Secretary Port Stanley 1987; m (1) 1963 Camellia Elizabeth Idris-Jones (diss 1986); (2d 1964, 1966); (2) 1987 Kathleen Dawn Willetts.

Bayne, Sir Nicholas (Peter), KCMG (1992) CMG (1984); High Commissioner Ottawa since April 1992; born 15.2.37; FO 1961; Third later Second Secretary Manila 1963; FO 1966; First Secretary 1967; Bonn 1969; FCO 1972; on loan to the Treasury 1974; Counsellor (Financial) Paris 1975; Head Economic Relations Dept, FCO 1979; Chatham House 1982; HM Ambassador Kinshasa 1983, and concurrently HMA (non-resident) to the Congo, to Rwanda and to Burundi 1984; Attached to MPO (CSSB) 1985; UK Permanent Representative to OECD Paris (with personal rank of Ambassador) 1985; DUSS (Econ) 1988; m 1961 Diana Wilde (3s 1962, 1965, 1968).

Beady, Edward George; Islamabad since July 1991; born 8.8.41; HM Forces 1959-83; FCO (HCS) 1983; FCO 1986; Kaduna 1987; Lagos 1989; Grade 9; m 1963 Sabine Conrad (1s 1967).

Beal, Gordon Kenneth; FCO since September 1988; born 21.10.53; MAFF 1978; FCO 1980; Port of Spain 1981; Paris 1983; Kuwait 1986; Grade 10.

Beale, Gideon David; Third Secretary (Vice-Consul) Athens since October 1990; born 9.7.62; FCO 1986; Grade 9.

Beamish, Adrian John, CMG(1988); AUSS (Americas) since October 1989; born 21.1.39; FO 1962; Third later Second Secretary Tehran 1963; FO (later FCO) 1966; First Secretary UKDEL OECD Paris 1970; First Secretary (Inf) New Delhi 1973; First Secretary FCO 1976; Deputy Head of Personnel Operations Department FCO 1978; Counsellor (Economic)

Bonn 1981; Counsellor, FCO 1985; HM Ambassador Lima 1987; m 1965 Caroline Lipscombe (2d 1966, 1968).

Bean, Peter Lionel; On loan to No 10 Downing Street since October 1989; born 25.7.49; FCO 1969; Tripoli 1971; Brussels (EEC) 1972; Amman 1975; FCO 1978; APS to Minister of State 1980; Ottawa 1982; Second Secretary later First (Chancery/Inf) Bangkok 1985; m 1974 Moira Henderson (2d 1982, 1985).

Beaton, James Simpson Brian; Budapest since September 1991; born 15.2.47; RAF 1962-87; Lagos 1988; Grade SO; m 1966 Margaret Anne Harries (1s 1967; 1d 1976).

Beattie, David, cmg (1989); HM Ambassador Berne since April 1992; additionally HM Ambassador (non-resident) to the Principality of Liechtenstein since May 1992; born 5.3.38; FO 1963; Moscow 1964; FO 1966; Second Secretary 1967; First Secretary 1969; Nicosia 1970; FCO 1974; Counsellor, Head of Chancery, later Deputy Head, UKDEL MBFR, Vienna 1978; Counsellor (Comm) Moscow 1982; Counsellor FCO 1985; Minister and Deputy Permanent Representative UKDEL NATO Brussels 1987; m 1966 Ulla Marita Alha (2d 1968, 1974).

Beattie, Phoebe; Floater Duties since October 1989; born 25.11.59; FCO 1984; Bangkok 1985; Stanley 1988; Grade S2.

Beaumont, David Colin Baskcomb; First Secretary later Counsellor FCO since December 1986; born 16.8.42; CRO 1961; Nairobi 1965; Bahrain 1967; Second Secretary 1969; FCO 1970; Second Secretary (Comm) Accra 1974; First Secretary FCO 1977; First Secretary (Aid) Kathmandu 1981; First Secretary and Head of Chancery Addis Ababa 1983; m 1965 Barbara Morris (1d 1970; 2s 1972, 1973).

Beaven, Keith Andrew; First Secretary FCO since June 1988; born 7.1.61; FCO 1983; Third later Second Secretary (Chancery) Mexico City 1986; m 1986 Jane Marion Wells.

Beckett, Alison Joan; Third Secretary (Management/Cons) Kiev since October 1992; born 1.7.61; FCO 1989; Grade 9.

Beckett, Jemma Roelle; FCO since July 1991; born 18.9.68; Grade S2.

Beckford, Charles Francis Houghton; FCO since September 1991; born 4.11.63; Grade 7.

Beckingham, Peter; First Secretary (Political) Canberra since July 1992; born 16.3.49; BOTB 1974; Director BIS New York 1979; First Secretary FCO 1984; First Secretary (Comm) Stockholm 1988; m 1975 Jill Mary Trotman (2d 1980, 1982).

Bedford, Adrian Frederick; Second Secretary (Chancery and Aid) Bogotá since September 1988; born 30.10.56; Land Registry 1975; FCO 1976; Islamabad 1978; Hanoi 1981; Johannesburg 1982; FCO 1985.

Bedforth, Andrew Kenneth; FCO since September 1991; born 18.2.71; Grade 10.

Bedingfield, Julian Peter; Second Secretary FCO since April 1992; born 23.7.45; FO 1964; Moscow 1969; FCO 1971; Düsseldorf 1971; Bonn 1973; Second Secretary (Comm) Dacca 1975; Ulan Bator 1977; FCO 1978; Second Secretary (Admin) and Consul Berne 1982; Second Secretary (Chancery/Inf) Rabat 1986; m 1975 Margery Mary Jones Davies (2d 1979, 1984; 1s 1982).

Bedwell, Colin Michael; Second Secretary (Consular) Honiara since December 1991; born 24.1.39; MOD 1963; DSAO 1966; Bangkok 1968; Blantyre 1972; FCO 1976; Athens 1978; Colombo 1982; FCO 1984; Freetown 1985; FCO 1988; Second Secretary (Admin) Islamabad 1988; m (1) 1963 Susan Davis (diss 1976) (1s 1963, 1d 1966); (2) 1981 Aliki Loghi (diss 1990) (1d 1981); (3) 1990 Yolande Joachim.

Bee, Stephanie Louise; Moscow since November 1992; born 27.1.67; FCO 1986; UKDEL Brussels 1988; Warsaw 1988; Grade 10.

Beel, Graham; Principal Research Officer, later Senior Principal Research Officer FCO since June 1972; born 22.5.33; HM Forces 1951-53; FO 1956; Second Secretary Moscow 1964; Second later First Secretary FO 1966; Moscow 1971; PRO (DS Grade 5); m 1957 Mary Payne (2d 1963, 1965).

Beels, Jonathan Sidney Spencer; Counsellor Nicosia since May 1992; born 19.1.43; FCO 1965; Prague 1970; Resigned 1979; Reinstated 1988; First Secretary FCO 1988; m (1) 1966 Patricia Joan Mills (diss) (2) Penelope Jane Aedy (1s 1972, 1d 1973).

Beer, Nicholas James Gilbert; First Secretary (Political) The Hague since January 1992; born 6.12.47; Second Secretary FCO 1976; Nairobi 1977; FCO 1979; First Secretary Madrid 1982; First Secretary FCO 1986; m 1975 Diana Eva Brooke (1d 1977; 1s 1980).

Beeson, Elizabeth Ann née Allin; SUPL since October 1988; born 13.12.67; Grade 10; m 1989 Richard John Beeson.

Beeson, Joanne Elizabeth; FCO since September 1991; born 27.9.67; Grade 9.

Beeson, Richard John; Management Officer/Vice-Consul Hamburg since July 1991; born 7.6.54; FCO 1973; East Berlin 1975; Damascus 1976;

FCO 1977; UKREP Brussels 1978; Peking 1980;
FCO 1983; Tripoli 1984; FCO 1986; Singapore
1988; Grade 9; m (1) 1978 Kim Margaret Cotter;
(2) 1989 Elizabeth Ann Allin.

Beetham, Roger Campbell, lvo (1976); HM
Ambassador Dakar since July 1990; and
concurrently, Ambassador (non-resident) to Cape
Verde and to Guinea; additionally Ambassador
(non-resident) to Guinea-Bissau and Mali since
July 1990; born 22.11.37; FO 1960; Third later
Second Secretary UK Delegation to the
Conference of the 18-Nation Committee on
Disarmament Geneva 1962; Second Secretary
(Comm) Washington 1965; First Secretary FCO
1968; First Secretary and Head of Chancery
Helsinki 1972; (SUPL/EC) Brussels 1977;
Counsellor 1978; Counsellor (Econ/Comm) New
Delhi 1981; Counsellor, FCO 1985; m (1) 1965
Judith Mary Yorwerth Rees (diss 1986); (2) 1986
Christine Marguerite Malerme.

Begbie, James Alexander; Third later Second
Secretary (Comm) Muscat since March 1989;
born 10.12.53; FCO 1973; Bahrain 1975; Middle
East Floater 1979; FCO 1980; Tunis 1983;
Shanghai 1986; Grade 9; m 1980 Janice Isobel
Mills (1s 1984; 1d 1985).

Begbie, Janice Isobel (née Mills); Muscat since
July 1989; born 18.4.51; FCO 1971; Lusaka
1973; FCO 1975; Middle East Floater 1977;
FCO 1980; Grade 9; SUPL 1983; m 1980 James
Alexander Begbie (1s 1984; 1d 1985).

Belgrove, David Raymond; FCO since January
1991; born 18.1.62; FCO 1982; Prague 1984;
Kuwait 1986; Grade 9; m 1985 Mette Ofstad (2d
1986, 1989).

Belham, Richard Anthony; Third Secretary
Bangkok since July 1986; born 26.1.50; Home
Civil Service 1976; FCO 1986; m 1987
Chidphan Jaiprasat (1d 1989).

Bell, Charles Frank Leonard; Islamabad since
October 1992; born 13.9.45; Moscow 1990;
Pretoria 1992; Grade SO; m 1967 Christine
Chalker (2d 1968, 1971).

Bell, David Alexander; Second Secretary FCO
since November 1990; born 8.10.45; CRO 1963;
Zomba 1967; Washington 1970; Islamabad 1973;
Dacca 1975; Los Angeles 1978; Brunei 1981;
FCO 1983; Vice Consul (Comm) Cape Town
1986.

Bell, David Mackintosh; Consul-General Lille
since June 1990; born 2.8.39; CRO 1960;
Karachi 1961; Enugu 1963; Havana 1966;
Second Secretary 1967; Mexico City 1968; FCO
1969; Budapest 1971; Second later First
Secretary FCO 1974; Consul (Comm) BTDO
New York 1977; FCO 1981; First Secretary (Inf)
Bonn 1986; m 1963 Ann Adair Wilson (1s 1969;
1d 1976).

Bell, Grahame Colley; FCO since January 1971;
born 16.2.53; Grade 9.

Bell, Harvey Spencer; FCO since August 1991;
born 7.7.45; Royal Navy 1960-72; FCO 1972;
Bonn 1975; Peking 1977; Wellington 1980; FCO
1982; Mogadishu 1985; MIlan 1988, Grade 9; m
1978 Wendy Lydia Frances Ellis.

Bell, Jeremy Paul Turnbull; Third Secretary
(Management/Cons) Gaborone since February
1992; born 4.1.52; FCO 1974; The Hague 1976;
Bahrain 1981; Hanoi 1982; FCO 1985; Tokyo
1988; Grade 9; m (1) 1978 Jane Dorron Lee
(diss 1981) (2) 1991 Setsuko Yamamoto.

Bell, Julie Dawn; Language Training since
October 1990; born 12.11.66; FCO 1989; Grade
9; m 1991 Andrew Michael Bell.

Bell, Karen Ann (née Norris); FCO since
September 1991; born 22.4.66; FCO 1983;
Strasbourg 1986; New Delhi 1988; Grade 9; m
1987 Adrian Bell.

Bell, Kay Beverley; Floater duties since April
1989; born 11.6.57; FCO 1984; Bonn 1986;
Grade S2.

Bell, Melvin; FCO since October 1990; born
14.5.65; FCO 1984; Madrid 1987; Grade 8.

Bellerby, Julie; FCO since September 1985;
born 26.11.60; Grade S3; m 1986 Andrew
Patrick Myers.

Belof, Margaret Mary; FCO since November
1990; born 6.9.61; Grade 9.

Benjamin, Jon; Third Secretary FCO since
February 1992; born 19.1.63; ODA 1986; FCO
1986; Third Secretary Jakarta 1988; Grade 8.

Bennett, Brian Maurice; First Secretary FCO
since February 1992; born 1.4.48; FCO 1971;
Prague 1973; Helsinki 1977; Second Secretary
FCO 1979; Second Secretary (Comm/Aid)
Bridgetown 1983; Second later First Secretary
UKDEL MBFR Vienna 1986; First Secretary
(Chancery/Inf) The Hague 1988; m 1969 Lynne
Skipsey (3s 1974, 1978, 1991).

Bennett, Joan Amy; Vice-Consul Bucharest since
August 1990; born 14.5.38; Baghdad 1967;
Jerusalem 1967; POLAD Singapore 1970; FCO
1972; Warsaw 1973; Colombo 1974; FCO 1976;
Athens 1977; FCO 1980; Copenhagen 1984;
FCO 1986; Grade 9.

Bennett, John Victor Thomas; FCO since August
1989 (First Secretary 1991); born 25.8.41; FO
1957; Moscow 1966; FCO 1969; Prague 1972;
Bangkok 1976; FCO 1979; Caracas 1981;
Second Secretary FCO 1983; Second Secretary
Athens 1986; m 1966 Jacqueline Elizabeth Dawn
Clark (1d 1969).

Bennett, Marylyn; FCO since September 1988; born 16.12.48; New Delhi 1972; Monrovia 1974; FCO 1977; South America Floater 1979; FCO 1982; Floater duties 1983; Panama City 1986; Grade 7.

Bennett, Michael John, MBE (1973); First Secretary (Management) Vienna since April 1992; born 27.11.41; CRO 1959; Karachi 1961; CRO 1963; Salisbury 1965; Hamburg 1968; Kampala 1971; FCO 1974; Second Secretary 1976; Kuala Lumpur 1977; Second Secretary (Commercial) Seoul 1980; First Secretary (Admin) Accra 1984; First Secretary FCO 1988; m 1965 Aileen Kelly Chesney (2s 1967, 1970).

Bennett, Rachel Claire; Kuwait since November 1991; born 10.6.68; FCO 1987; UKDEL Brussels 1989; Grade 10.

Bennett, Stephen Paul; FCO since March 1990; born 28.10.62; FCO 1982; Nairobi 1986; Grade 10; m 1990 Stephanie Cattermole.

Bennett-Dixon, Vanessa May (née Bennett); Stanley since November 1992; born 12.1.57; FCO 1975; Nairobi 1978; Havana 1981; Kuwait 1982; Montserrat 1988; Grade S2; m 1987 Ronald William Dixon.

Bensberg, Mark; FCO since March 1991; born 19.7.62; FCO 1980; Paris 1982; Africa/ME Floater 1985; Vienna 1988; Grade 9.

Bent, Kenneth Thomas; Floater since January 1987; born 3.12.36; Prison Service 1980-82; Warsaw 1982; New Delhi 1983; Grade SO.

Bentley, John; Management Officer/Consul Kuwait since December 1991; born 17.2.35; Inland Revenue 1951; Army 1953-55; FO 1955; Buenos Aires 1956; Khorramshahr 1959; Paris 1963; DSAO 1966; Benin City 1967; FCO 1969; Tel Aviv 1970; Abidjan 1973; Second Secretary FCO 1976; Quito 1978; Vice-Consul (Comm) Atlanta 1982; Second later First Secretary FCO 1986; Deputy High Commissioner Belmopan 1989; (2s 1973, 1978).

Bentley, Joyce Elaine (née Anthony); Montevideo since June 1991; born 10.1.37; UKMIS Geneva 1966; Moscow 1969; Reinstated 1986; FCO 1986; UKDEL Brussels 1988; (2s 1973, 1978).

Berg, Geoffrey, LVO (1976); Counsellor FCO on secondment to the DTI since October 1990; born 5.7.45; CRO 1963; DSA 1965; LA Floater Duties 1968; Bucharest 1970; Second Secretary 1970; FCO 1971; Second later First Secretary (Inf) Helsinki 1975; FCO 1979; First Secretary (Comm) Madrid 1984; First Secretary FCO 1988; m 1970 Sheila Maxine Brown (1s 1975).

Bergne, Alexander Paul A'Court; OBE (1985); Counsellor FCO since July 1987; born 9.1.37;

FO 1959; Third Secretary Vienna 1961; FO 1963; Second Secretary 1964; Tehran 1966; First Secretary FCO 1968; MECAS 1970; Abu Dhabi 1972; Cairo 1975; FCO 1977; Athens 1980; First Secretary FCO 1984; Counsellor Hong Kong 1985; m 1963 Suzanne Juditha Hedwig Wittich (1d 1963; 1s 1966).

Berman, Franklin Delow, CMG (1986); Legal Adviser FCO since November 1991; born 23.12.39; called to the Bar, Middle Temple 1966; Legal Assistant FO 1965; Assistant Legal Adviser FO (later FCO) 1967; First Secretary (Legal Adviser) Berlin 1971; First Secretary (Legal Adviser) Bonn 1972; Legal Counsellor FCO 1974; Counsellor (Legal Adviser) UKMIS New York 1982; Legal Counsellor FCO 1985; Deputy Legal Adviser FCO 1988; m 1964 Christine Mary Lawler (2s 1966, 1968; Triplet d 1972).

Bernard, Gordon Arthur; Second Secretary (Comm) Madrid since June 1986; born 23.6.42 FO 1960; Saigon 1963; DSAO 1964; Bahrain (Res) 1968; Lagos 1971; FCO 1972; Athens 1973; FCO 1974; Düsseldorf 1977; Mogadishu 1980; Second Secretary FCO 1983; m 1980 Christina Louise Downing (1d 1988; 1s 1990).

Berry, Nicola Jane (née Stokes); Bombay since March 1982; born 4.1.58; FCO 1976; UKMIS New York 1979; Grade 10; m 1978 Martin Geoffrey Berry.

Berry, Susanna Gisela; Second Secretary FCO since July 1992; born 6.9.62; FCO 1986; Second Secretary UKDEL Vienna 1989; Second Secretary (Economic) Vienna 1990.

Bersin, Jacqueline; Port Louis since September 1988; born 13.8.58; FCO 1977; SUPL 1978; Islamabad 1979; SUPL 1980; FCO 1981; Rome 1982; Warsaw 1983; FCO1985; Grade 9; m 1990 Alan Maurice Bersin.

Best, Christopher Davey; Second later First Secretary FCO since August 1989; born 3.8.47; Army 1966-69; FCO 1969; Muscat 1971; Jedda 1973; FCO 1974; Sana'a 1975; FCO 1976; Hong Kong 1981; Second Secretary Lagos 1986; m 1971 Mary Elizabeth Cannon (4d 1977, 1979, 1981, 1982).

Bethel, Samantha Claire Risby; FCO since April 1990; born 25.2.70; Grade 10.

Betterton, Judith Anne; Canberra since September 1991; born 2.8.57; FCO 1983; Warsaw 1984; Lilongwe 1987; Bogotá 1989; Grade S2.

Betts, Jonathan, OBE(1983); Consul Munich since June 1988; born 6.12.39; FO 1962; Third Secretary Vienna 1965; Second Secretary FO (later FCO) 1968; Second later First Secretary BMG Berlin 1971; Consul Hamburg 1974; FCO

1978; Cairo 1982; First Secretary FCO 1984; m 1968 Suzanna Elizabeth Camuzzi (2s 1974, 1976).

Bevan, James David; First Secretary FCO since December 1990; born 13.7.59; FCO 1982; Kinshasa 1984; Second later First Secretary UKDEL Brussels 1986; m 1984 Alison Janet Purdie.

Bevan, Terence Richard; First Secretary FCO since May 1992; born 10.4.54; FCO 1970; Bonn 1977; FCO 1980; Second later First Secretary Oslo 1988; m 1978 Gillian Margaret Francis (2d 1981, 1984).

Beveridge, Lesley Ann; Nicosia since February 1990; born 7.8.69; FCO 1987; Grade 10.

Beveridge, Wilhelmina (Wilma) Morrison, MBE (1991); FCO since April 1991; born 16.12.33; Delhi 1970; Belgrade 1972; Wellington 1974; Lusaka 1977; Nicosia 1980; FCO 1983; Oslo 1988; Grade S1.

Beynon, Debra Jane; Dhaka since February 1989; born 22.7.62; Dept of Transport 1978; Dept of Employment 1979; FCO 1983; BMG Berlin 1985; Kingstown 1988; Grade 9; m 1985 Paul Ogwyn Beynon.

Bicker, David Alan; Cairo since August 1991; born 25.10.48; Army 1966-88; UKDEL Brussels 1989; Grade SO; m 1974 Molly Patricia (1d 1976; 2s 1978, 1983).

Bickers, Esmé Lillian; FCO since July 1992; born 18.12.54; FCO 1988; Ottawa 1989; Grade S2.

Bielby, Richard Stephen; FCO since February 1991; born 18.9.65; FCO (HCS) 1989; Grade 10.

Bilimoria, Tehemton Pirosha; Paris since July 1992; born 21.1.46; HM Forces 1964-70; PO 1970-76; FCO 1979; Washington 1984; FCO 1987; Grade 8; m 1980 Tayariez Dastoor (1d 1984; 1s 1986).

Billington, Frances; Second Secretary FCO since May 1988; born 10.5.49; FCO 1975; Bonn 1977; FCO 1979; Kuala Lumpur 1979; Second Secretary FCO 1983; The Hague 1986.

Binnie, Serena Clare; FCO since October 1990; born 4.9.63; FCO 1986; Montevideo 1989; Grade S2.

Binnington, Marian Florence; First Secretary FCO since September 1990; born 13.11.40; CRO 1959; Karachi 1961; CRO 1963; Delhi 1965; Paris 1969; FCO 1971; SUPL 1975; resigned 1976; reinstated 1979; Second later First Secretary FCO 1979; Consul Los Angeles 1985; m 1975; Robert Malcolm Harris (diss 1984).

Binns, Angela June; FCO since September 1990;

born 25.6.69; MOD 1988-1990; Grade 10.

Birch, John Allan, CMG (1987); HM Ambassador Budapest since August 1989; born 24.5.35; Army 1954-56; FO 1959; Third Secretary Paris 1960; Second Secretary Singapore 1963; FO 1964; Second later First Secretary Bucharest 1965; (UK Mission) Geneva 1968; FCO 1970; First Secretary and Head of Chancery Kabul 1973; Counsellor RCDS 1977; Political Adviser UKDEL CTB Geneva 1977; Counsellor and Head of Chancery Budapest 1980; Head of Eastern European Department, FCO 1983; AUSS (Efficiency Scrutiny) FCO, 1986; Deputy Permanent Representative (with personal rank of Ambassador), UKMIS New York 1986; m 1960 Primula Clare Haselden (3s 1962, 1963, 1969; 1d 1967).

Bird, Beverley (née Curtis); FCO since September 1986; born 12.10.62; FCO 1982; Islamabad 1984; Grade 10; m 1986 Peter Franks Bird.

Bird, Charles Philip Glover; Second Secretary Belgrade since August 1992; born 8.10.54; Second Secretary FCO 1986; Language Training 1987; Language Training Cairo 1988; Second Secretary (Chancery) Abu Dhabi 1989; m 1975 Clare St John (2s 1978, 1980; 1d 1982).

Bird, Christabel Helen; Consul Geneva since October 1990; born 18.11.53; Tehran 1978; FCO 1979; Caracas 1980; FCO 1982; Second Secretary UKMIS Geneva 1989.

Bird, Juliette Winsome; Second Secretary (Chancery) New Delhi since July 1992; born 4.10.63; FCO 1990.

Birks, Ian Martin; Second Secretary (Aid) Lagos since January 1992; born 3.6.52; FCO 1971; Canberra 1973; Belgrade 1976; Georgetown 1978; New York 1981; FCO 1984; Islamabad 1988; m 1976 Sheridan Elizabeth Grice (1d 1987).

Birks, Sheridan Elizabeth (née Grice); Lagos since February 1992; born 14.7.54; FCO 1973; Canberra 1974, SUPL 1976; Belgrade 1976; Georgetown 1978; UKMIS New York 1981; FCO 1984; SUPL 1987; Islamabad 1988; Grade 9; m 1976 Ian Martin Birks (1d 1987).

Biscoe, Brian Michael; Consul (Comm) Sao Paulo since June 1991; born 5.8.40; CRO 1959; DSAO 1965; Beira 1967; Rawalpindi (later Islamabad) 1969; Beirut 1973; FCO 1976; Second Secretary (Comm/Aid) Kabul 1978; Accra 1980; Vice-Consul (Comm.) BTDO New York 1984; First Secretary FCO 1988; m 1966 June Owens (1d 1968; 2s 1971, 1975).

Bish, Michael William; Second Secretary FCO since January 1992; born 3.12.42; CRO 1964; DSAO 1965; Rawalpindi 1966; Bonn 1970; FCO

1972; JAO Brussels 1976; Wellington 1979; Second Secretary FCO 1982; Second Secretary (Comm) Johannesburg 1987; m 1966 Patricia June Bedingfield.

Bishop, Ian Roger Aelberry; FCO since June 1990; born 6.7.52; FCO 1972; Lilongwe 1975; Helsinki 1978; FCO 1981; Bangkok 1984; Amman 1988; Grade 9; m 1975 Eileen McAteer (1d 1976; 1s 1980).

Bishop, Kenneth Anthony, OBE(1972); FCO since May 1972 Principal Research Officer (Principal Conference Interpreter (DS Grade 4) 1978); born 22.1.38; HM Forces 1956-58; FO 1961; Third later Second Secretary Moscow 1963; FO (later FCO) 1965; Senior Research Officer 1969; First Secretary Bonn 1971; m 1962 Christine Mary Pennell (1s 1966; 1d 1968).

Biskin, Sally-Ann (née Peters); Harare since March 1988; born 8.2.65; Brussels 1985; Grade 10, m 1991 Cüneyt Cem Biskin.

Black, Geoffrey Whitfield; Tel Aviv since June 1990; born 25.3.48; Army 1962-88; Moscow 1989; Grade SO; m 1981 Lesley.

Black, Peter John William; FCO since June 1990; born 19.12.46; Army 1965-73; Second Secretary FCO 1973; Language Student MECAS 1975 and FCO 1976; Kuwait 1977; First Secretary (Inf) Amman 1980; First Secretary FCO 1983; First Secretary (Chancery) Dhaka 1987; m 1976 Fiona Rosaline Procter (2s 1981, 1982; 3d 1986, twins 1988).

Blackall, Clare Victoria; Dhaka since July 1992; born 17.5.70; FCO 1989; Grade 10.

Blackburn, Derek; Second later First Secretary FCO since August 1982; born 6.12.44; GPO 1961; FO (later FCO) 1968; Beirut 1969; FCO 1972; Islamabad 1973; FCO 1974; Washington 1979; m 1967 Dorothy Margaret Fawcett (1s 1968; 1d 1972).

Blackburne, Alison; Third Secretary (Chancery) Warsaw since March 1989; born 20.6.64; FCO 1987; Grade 8.

Blacker, Catherine Louise; UKDEL Brussels since August 1991; born 15.9.68; FCO 1989; Grade 10.

Blackley, Ian Lorimer; DHM Damascus since March 1991; born 14.12.46; Third Secretary FCO 1969; MECAS 1971; Tripoli 1972; Second Secretary East Berlin 1973; Second later First Secretary Damascus 1974; FCO 1977; First Secretary Head of Chancery/Consul Beirut 1980; First Secretary (Agric) The Hague 1982; First Secretary FCO 1986; Counsellor Kuwait 1988; m 1981 Pamela Ann Helena Belt (1s 1983).

Blackwell, Christopher Robert; Second Secretary

FCO since May 1984; born 11.8.58; FCO 1975; UKMIS Geneva 1978; FCO 1981; Aden 1983; m 1982 Catherine Rose Gallagher (1d 1987; 1s 1989).

Bladen, John; Second Secretary FCO since February 1987; born 8.7.44; FCO 1971; Bangkok 1973; FCO 1975; Accra 1976; FCO 1979; Kingston 1980; FCO 1983; Second Secretary Harare 1984; m 1969 Nina Shaw (1d 1972).

Blair, Camilla Frances Mary; Third later Second Secretary Prague since January 1991; born 23.11.65; FCO 1988; Full-time Language Training 1990.

Blair, Katherine; Tokyo since December 1989; born 11.2.69; FCO 1988; Grade 10.

Blake, Caroline Rosevear (née Weeks); Nicosia since July 1987; born 23.7.57; FCO 1975; UKREP Brussels 1979; FCO 1982; Grade 9; m 1978 Ian Blake.

Blake, Michael David; FCO since April 1984 (Second Secretary 1988)(First Secretary 1991); born 19.1.55; FCO 1971; HCS 1976; FCO 1978; Washington 1979; FCO 1981; Ottawa 1981; m 1978 Audrey Layfield (1s 1983).

Blake, Stanley Clement; Second Secretary FCO since May 1992; born 14.7.44; FO 1964; UK Delegation NATO Paris and Brussels 1966; Amman 1969; FCO 1970; Moscow 1974; Paris 1975; FCO 1978; Tunis 1981 (Second Secretary 1984); Second Secretary (Admin) and Consul Muscat 1984; Second Secretary FCO 1988; Second Secretary (Management) Addis Ababa 1991; m (1) 1967 Marion Lesley Jelly (diss 1972) (1s 1968); (2) 1977 Lindsay Jane Townsend (1s 1981).

Blakemore, John Laurence; First Secretary (Commercial) Milan since February 1990; born 21.1.44; RAF 1961-69; FCO 1969; Mexico City 1972; Caracas 1975; FCO 1978; on loan to DOE 1979; Second Secretary Buenos Aires 1981; Second Secretary (Commercial) Madrid 1982; Second later First Secretary FCO 1986; m 1967 Joan Eileen Black (2s 1972, 1974).

Blakeney, Robin Anthony; Tokyo since January 1990; born 24.12.40; Moscow 1988; Grade SO; m 1963 Maureen Sullivan (2s 1964, 1966; 1d 1968).

Blake-Pauley, Mary Elizabeth (née Whaley); Vice-Consul Munich since March 1989; born 19.3.51; FCO 1968; Belgrade 1972; Bonn 1974; FCO 1976; SUPL 1977; Vice-Consul Frankfurt 1979; FCO 1982; SUPL 1985; Dhaka 1986; SUPL 1988; m 1977 Anthony Frederick Blake-Pauley.

Blanchard, William Hume James; Second

Secretary (Inf) Budapest since September 1992;
FCO 1988; born 8.1.67.

Blatherwick, David Elliott Spiby, CMG (1990);
OBE (1973); HM Ambassador Dublin since
September 1991; born 13.7.41; MECAS 1964;
Third later Second Secretary FO 1966; Kuwait
1968; Dublin 1970; First Secretary FCO 1973;
First Secretary and Head of Chancery Cairo
1977; Counsellor on loan to HCS 1981; Head of
ESSD, FCO 1983; CDA at Stanford University
1985; Counsellor and Head of Chancery UKMIS
New York 1986; AUSS (Principal Finance
Officer and Chief Inspector) FCO 1989; m 1964
Margaret Clare Crompton (1d 1969; 1s 1972).

Bleakley, Derek; First Secretary (Commercial)
Bangkok since February 1990; born 6.4.41; FO
1959; Tokyo 1963; FCO 1970; Second Secretary
Rabat 1970; Valletta 1972; Second Secretary and
Vice-Consul Tokyo 1975; Resigned 1978; Re-
instated 1978; Consul (Comm) Osaka 1979; First
Secretary FCO 1984; Head of Chancery Beirut
1988; m (1) 1964 Maureen Amelia Walters (diss
1979) (2d 1968, 1971); m (2) 1980 Reiko
Tashiro.

Blogg, David John; Second Secretary FCO since
May 1991; born 8.9.48; Board of Inland Revenue
1965; FCO 1971; East Berlin 1973; Khartoum
1974; Dacca 1977; FCO 1979; Jedda 1983;
Athens 1986; Tripoli 1989; m 1973 Susan
Robinia Meloy.

Blogg, Frank Alexander; First Secretary
(Management) Washington since August 1992;
born 22.4.38; CRO 1956; RAF 1957-59; CRO
1959; Karachi 1960; CRO 1962; Lagos 1963;
New York 1966; FCO 1969; Jakarta 1972;
Second Secretary Warsaw 1976; Dubai 1980;
Second later First Secretary FCO 1984; First
Secretary (Admin) and Consul Budapest 1988; m
1964 Jean Powell (1s 1967; 1d 1969).

Bloomfield, Keith George; Counsellor Consul-
General and Deputy Head of Mission; Algiers
since August 1990. born 2.6.47; HCS 1969-80;
UKREP Brussels 1980; First Secretary FCO
1985; Head of Chancery Cairo 1987; m 1976
Genevieve Paul (3d 1979, 1982, 1985).

Blott, Elizabeth; FCO since March 1982; born
7.9.54; FCO 1972; Brussels 1975; Abidjan 1980;
Grade 9.

Blount, James Hubert Rowland; First Secretary
(Econ) Islamabad since August 1992; born
31.8.58; Second Secretary FCO 1985; First
Secretary (Chancery/Economic) Lima 1987; First
Secretary FCO 1990.

Blunt, David Graeme, LVO (1986); First
Secretary (Chancery) Canberra since August
1989; born 19.1.53; FCO 1978; Second later
First Secretary Vienna 1979; First Secretary
(Eernal Affairs) Peking 1983; FCO 1987; m

1975 Geirid Bakkeli (2s 1982, 1984).

Blyth, Alan William; Khartoum since April
1992; born 16.1.52; Foreign Dividends Office
1972-75; FCO 1975; Moscow 1977; Abu Dhabi
1978; Peking 1980; FCO 1982; Islamabad 1984;
Kampala 1988; FCO 1990; Grade 9.

Blyth, Fraser Alexander; FCO since February
1990; born 7.6.69; Grade 10.

Boak, John Desmond; Washington since October
1992; born 27.12.40; RAF 1958-88; Moscow
1988; Tokyo 1989; Havana 1991; Grade SO; m
1964 Philomena Scallan (1s 1965; 1d 1967).

Boardman, Clarence Ronald; Consul (Comm)
Vancouver since May 1989; born 11.12.48;
DSAO1/FCO 1965; Algiers 1970; Ottawa 1972;
Warsaw 1974; FCO 1977; MECAS 1978; Aden
1979; Riyadh 1982; Second Secretary FCO 1986;
m 1973 Marion Lynn Fraser (1s 1991).

Boardman, Sarah Christine; FCO since
September 1990; born 17.8.67; Grade 9.

Boffa, Sandra Jean (née Isaac); FCO since
October 1990; born 22.8.67; Ministry of
Agriculture 1984-1990; Grade S2A; m 1992
Anthony Paul Vincent Boffa.

Boldt, Stuart Murray; First Secretary (Chancery)
Kingston since September 1991; born 15.3.44;
FCO 1969; Second later First Secretary Kuala
Lumpur 1972; FCO 1976; First Secretary Lagos
1977; First Secretary FCO 1981; First Secretary
Singapore 1985; FCO 1987; m 1967 Janice Anne
O'Brien (2s 1972, 1977).

Bolton, Ada Winefride; UKDEL Brussels since
March 1992; born 26.12.44; Jakarta 1973;
Rangoon 1978; FCO 1980; Sana'a 1988; Lagos
1989; Grade S2.

Bolton, Elizabeth Fay; Dhaka since March 1992;
born 25.11.60; FCO 1981; Khartoum 1985;
Valetta 1988; Grade 9.

Bond, Helen; Kuwait since August 1991; born
16.5.55; HM Forces 1973-1986; HCS 1987; FCO
1989; Grade S2.

Bond, Ian Andrew Minton; First Secretary FCO
since December 1990; born 19.4.62; FCO 1984;
Third later Second Secretary (Political) UKDEL
NATO Brussels 1987; m 1987 Kathryn Joan
Ingamells (1d 1989).

Bond, Peter Harold; Vienna since May 1992;
born 2.2.35; Istanbul 1977; Warsaw 1978;
UKDEL NATO Brussels 1980; Lusaka 1983;
Port of Spain 1985; Moscow 1986; Washington
1987; Sofia 1990; Grade CSO; m 1956 Betty
Margaret Elaine Deer (1s 1961; 1d 1965).

Bond, Simon; Third Secretary (Chancery)

Belgrade since September 1992; born 23.4.65; Home Office 1988-89; FCO 1989; Grade 9.

Bonde, Stephen Robin; First Secretary FCO since November 1990; born 14.8.39; FO 1956; HM Forces 1960-62; FO 1962; Tehran 1964; Moscow 1966; FCO 1968; MECAS 1972; Khartoum 1974; FCO 1978; on loan to DHSS 1979; Second later First Secretary and Consul Moscow 1981; First Secretary (Commercial) Al Khobar 1984; on loan to MOD 1988; m (1) 1963 Pamela Brown (diss 1976) (1d 1965); (2) 1976 Maureen Anne Roddan (née Gronguist) (1d 1978).

Bone, Richard Michael; Counsellor FCO since October 1989; born 25.11.34; Army 1956-58; COI 1959; FCO 1966 (PRO 1971); First Secretary UK Mission Geneva 1974; FCO 1975; Regional Director (Asia) Research Department FCO 1978; SPRO 1980; Regional Director (Atlantic) Research Department FCO 1981; m 1963 Margaret Rosetta Phillips (2s 1964, 1967; 1d 1971).

Bone, Roger Bridgland; Auss (Transnational Issues) FCO since December 1991; born 29.7.44; Third Secretary New York UK Mission 1966; FO 1967; Stockholm 1968; Third later Second Secretary FCO 1970; First Secretary (Chancery) Moscow 1973; First Secretary FCO 1975; UKREP Brussels 1978; Asst. Private Secretary to the Secretary of State 1982; CDA Harvard Center for International Affairs 1984; Counsellor Washington 1985; Counsellor FCO 1989; m 1970 Lena Marianne Bergman (1s 1977; 1d 1980).

Bonnicci, Gail Margaret; FCO since May 1991; born 11.12.60; FCO 1984; Madrid 1985; LA Floater 1988; Valletta 1989; Grade S2; m 1990 Martin Mario Bonnicci.

Bonsey, Jennifer Elaine; FCO since July 1989; born 23:12.46; MOD 1964; FCO 1981; Paris 1982; Tunis 1985; UKREP Brussels 1988; Grade S1.

Booker, Jacqueline Alice; FCO since January 1992; born 19.1.62; FCO 1982; Athens 1984; Hanoi 1987; LA Floater 1988; Grade 10.

Boon, George Peter Richard; First Secretary (Political) Dhaka since June 1990; born 2.11.42; CRO 1963; Bombay 1966; Brussels 1969; Second Secretary 1970; Vienna 1971; Seconded to Department of Trade 1974; FCO 1975; The Hague 1978; First Secretary (Inf) BMG Berlin 1981; First Secretary FCO 1986; m 1971 Marie Paule Calicis (1s 1976).

Booth, Mark James; FCO since June 1991; born 13.3.72; Grade 10.

Booth, Peter Parry; Nairobi since July 1987; born 10.5.35; Army 1953-76; Kuala Lumpur 1976; Moscow 1977; Washington 1978; Paris

1983; Warsaw 1985; Grade SO; m 1971 Hilda Christina King (1d 1972; 1s 1974).

Booth, Susan Jane; Warsaw since August 1991; born 3.8.68; FCO 1986; Cape Town/Pretoria 1989; Grade S2; m 1991 Rodney James Booth.

Borley, Salud Maria Victoria; Caracas since May 1992; born 6.5.70; FCO 1989; Grade 10.

Bossley, Edward; FCO since March 1991; born 22.9.71; Grade 10.

Bott, Lindsay Tony; Cairo since August 1987; born 31.10.39; RAF 1956-79; E Berlin 1981; Islamabad 1983; UKDEL NATO Brussels 1985; Montevideo 1986; Grade SO; m 1957 Patricia Doris Nicholas (1s 1962; 2d 1960, 1964)

Bottomley, Patricia Fiona; First Secretary FCO since July 1991; born 29.3.59; FCO 1983 (Second Secretary 1985); Second Secretary and Vice-Consul Havana 1986; First Secretary (Chancery) Mexico City 1988.

Bouakaze-Khan, Najma (née Khan); Addis Ababa since November 1989; born 11.6.67; FCO 1987; Grade S2; m 1992 Didier Bouakaze-Khan.

Bourke, Martin; First Secretary FCO since November 1988; born 12.3.47; Third Secretary FCO 1970; Brussels 1971; Second Secretary Singapore 1974; Second later First Secretary FCO 1975; First Secretary Lagos 1978; FCO 1980; on loan to DOT 1980; Consul (Comm) Johannesburg 1984; m 1973 Anne Marie Marguerite Hottelet (4s 1974, 1977, 1979, 1983).

Bourne, Anthony John; First Secretary FCO since August 1992; born 10.6.60; Second Secretary FCO 1986; Second later First Secretary (Chancery) Cairo 1989.

Bourne, Michael Reginald; Second Secretary FCO since October 1988; born 30.6.38; GPO 1955; HM Forces 1957-59; GPO 1959; FO 1960; Rangoon 1963; FO 1964; Budapest 1965; FO 1966; Brussels 1967; Moscow 1970; Canberra 1973; FCO 1976; Prague 1979; FCO 1981; Second Secretary Paris 1985; m 1963 Sandra Ekin-Wood (3s 1964, 1965, 1972).

Bourne, Katherine Mary; FCO since November 1990; born 3.4.68; Grade 9.

Bousfield, Edward; First Secretary FCO since November 1990; born 9.10.42; FO 1959; Moscow 1964; UK Mission Geneva 1965; Rabat 1968; FCO 1970; MECAS 1973; Kuwait 1974; Abu Dhabi 1976; Paris 1978; Second Secretary FCO 1981; Second Secretary (Aid/Comm) Suva 1984; Second Secretary (Management) Lusaka 1987; m (1) 1975 Madeleine Jean Dart (1s 1979); m (2) 1986 Wan Noor Siha Wan Din.

Bouttell, Elizabeth Anne; FCO since March 1986; born 25.3.48; FCO 1967; Havana 1969; Baghdad 1971; Valletta 1972; FCO 1975; Nairobi 1977; FCO 1980; Washington 1983; Grade S2.

Bowden, Christopher John; Calcutta since January 1991; born 6.7.59; FCO 1977; Copenhagen 1979; Karachi 1982; Bucharest 1983; Paris 1985; FCO 1988; Grade 9; m 1983 Jane Susan Manville (1d 1986).

Bowden, James Nicholas Geoffrey; Second Secretary (Chancery) Khartoum since October 1991; born 27.5.60; Royal Green Jackets 1979-86; Second Secretary FCO 1986; Language Training 1988; Language Training Cairo 1989; Deputy, later Acting Consul-General Aden 1990; m 1985 Alison Hulme.

Bowe, Michael Henry; FCO since February 1990; born 8.3.46; FCO 1971; Lagos 1974; New Delhi 1978; FCO 1981; Second Secretary (Comm) Lilongwe 1982; Second Secretary (Comm) Gaborone 1986; m (1) 1970 Anne Frances Ballard (diss 1985) (1d 1976, 1s 1979); m (2) 1985 Sandra Jean Brown Lassale.

Bowen, Rupert Grenside, LVO (1991); First Secretary Windhoek since May 1990; born 25.10.44; Army 1963-70; MOD 1970-74; First Secretary FCO 1974; First Secretary (Econ) Bonn 1976; First Secretary FCO 1977; Lusaka 1980; FCO 1982; Vienna 1984; First Secretary FCO 1988; m 1972 Sylvia Anne Buzzard (2d 1975, 1977).

Bowes, Jacqueline; FCO since October 1990; born 28.2.60; Inland Revenue 1976-90, Grade S2A.

Bowie, Nigel John Graydon; First Secretary (Comm) Athens since July 1992; born 31.5.51; FCO 1975; Seoul 1977; Paris 1981; Athens 1983; Second Secretary FCO 1985; Second Secretary (Comm/Econ) Oslo 1988; m 1977 Mildred Alice Sansom (2s 1979, 1984; 1d 1982).

Bowman, Victoria Jane (née Robinson); Third later Second Secretary Rangoon since July 1990; born 12.6.66; FCO 1989; m 1991 Mark Andrew Bowman.

Bowskill, Robert Colin; New Delhi since April 1991; born 21.9.43; Army 1959-77; Police 1977-84; Prague 1984; Lusaka 1987; Warsaw 1989; Grade SO; m 1966 Jean Spencer (2s 1967, 1968).

Bowyer, Anthony Harvey; FCO since July 1990; born 21.11.62; FCO 1982; Belgrade 1984; Kaduna 1990; Grade 9; m 1987 Aileen Jane Gemmell (1d 1992).

Bowyer, Aileen Jane (née Gemmell); FCO since July 1990; born 10.9.62; FCO 1983; Belgrade

1985; SUPL 1987; Kaduna 1990; Grade S2; m 1987 Anthony Harvey Bowyer (1d 1992).

Bowyer, Joanne Louise; Bogotá since March 1991; born 30.3.68; FCO 1989; Grade 10.

Boyce, Graham Hugh, CMG (1991); HM Ambassador Doha since February 1990; born 6.10.45; Third Secretary FCO 1968; Third later Second Secretary Ottawa 1971; MECAS 1972; First Secretary Tripoli 1974; (Head of Chancery 1975); FCO 1977; First Secretary (Economic and Financial) Kuwait 1981 (and Head of Chancery 1983); First Secretary FCO 1985; Counsellor and Head of Chancery Stockholm 1987; m 1970 Janet Elizabeth Spencer (1s 1971; 3d 1974, 1980, 1984).

Boyce, Raymond Thomas; FCO since January 1989; born 4.9.38; FO 1962; Montevideo 1963; Berlin 1966; FCO 1969; Dar es Salaam 1973; Port Moresby 1976; FCO 1980; Dhaka 1983; Tokyo 1986; Grade 9; m (1) 1968 Marisa Bellamy (diss 1973) (1s 1969); (2) 1977 Elisa Go (1d 1979).

Boyd, Andrew Jonathan Corrie, OBE (1992); First Secretary FCO since May 1991; born 5.5.50; Royal Navy 1968-80; FCO 1980; First Secretary (Econ) Accra 1981; FCO 1984; First Secretary (Chancery) Mexico City 1988; m 1979 Ginette Anne Vischer (2s 1985, 1987, 1d 1991).

Boyd, Sir John (Dixon) (Iklé), KCMG (1992), CMG (1985); HM Ambassador Tokyo since June 1992; born 17.1.36; FO 1962; Hong Kong 1962; Third later Second Secretary Peking 1965; First Secretary FO (later FCO) 1967; Washington 1969; First Secretary (Chancery) Peking 1973; On loan to HM Treasury 1976; Counsellor (Econ) Bonn 1977; Counsellor UKMIS New York 1981; AUSS, FCO 1984; On secondment to Hong Kong Government as Political Adviser to the Governor 1985; DUSS (Defence) 1987; DUSS (Chief Clerk) FCO 1989; m (1) 1968 Gunilla Kristina Ingegerd Rönngren (diss 1977) (1s 1969; 1d 1971); (2) 1977 Julia Daphne Raynsford (3d 1978, 1979, 1982).

Boyles, Elizabeth; FCO since November 1990; born 28.8.67; Grade 9.

Bradley, Guy; FCO since April 1987; born 3.2.62; FCO 1981; New Delhi 1983; Grade 9; m 1987 Andrea Stannard.

Bradley, Henry Alexander Jarvie; Second Secretary FCO since February 1992; born 23.7.52; HM Customs and Excise 1969; FCO 1971; EC Brussels 1975; Budapest 1978; Bahrain 1979; FCO 1982; Munich 1984; Third Secretary (AO/Vice-Consul) Maseru 1987; m 1979 Gabriella Maria Schwery.

Bradley, Joseph Maxwell; UKDEL Vienna since March 1990; born 14.2.60; FCO 1978; East

Berlin 1981; Resigned 1983 (Reinstated 1986); Lusaka 1987; Grade 9; m 1987 Melanie Rose (2d 1988, 1992, 1s 1990).

Bradley, Richard Marriott; Prague since October 1991; born 3.8.41; FO 1964; Dacca 1966; FO (later FCO) 1967; Singapore 1969; Kampala 1973; FCO 1976; Pretoria 1977; FCO 1980; Tunis 1983; Jedda 1986; FCO 1988; Grade 9; m 1965 Mary Cecilia MacDonald (1s 1968; 1d 1972).

Bradley, Sally Elaine; Rangoon since April 1991; born 22.2.52; FCO 1987; Grade S2.

Bradley, Stephen Edward; Deputy Political Adviser Hong Kong since May 1988; born 4.4.58; FCO 1981; Language Training 1982; Second later First Secretary Tokyo 1983; SUPL 1987; m 1982 Elizabeth Gomersall (1s 1985).

Bradley, Susan Pauline; FCO since November 1987; born 16.5.62; Grade S2.

Bradley, Timothy Gawin, OBE (1991); First Secretary FCO since January 1988; born 3.6.59; FCO 1983; Language Training 1984; Second later First Secretary (Chancery) Kuwait 1986; m 1990 Kathleen Scanlon.

Bradshaw, Philip James; FCO since July 1992; born 11.6.70; FCO 1988; SUPL 1990; Grade 10.

Bradshaw, Ross; FCO since July 1982; born 29.7.46; Royal Signals 1964-67; FCO 1979; Darwin 1980; Grade 9; m (1) 1980 Rachel Ann Bloch (diss 1983) (1d 1981); (2) 1986 Patricia Eve.

Brady, Laura Jane; Full-Time Language Training since September 1991; born 29.4.66; FCO 1989; Grade 8.

Braidford, Lindsey; FCO since February 1988; born 20.4.47; Jedda 1975; Belize 1976; The Hague 1979; Rangoon 1982; Pretoria/Capetown 1984; Grade S1.

Braithwaite, Angela; Moscow since May 1992; born 13.11.1970; FCO 1989; Grade 10.

Bramley, Sheila Jane; FCO since August 1991; born 25.10.63; FCO 1982; Tokyo 1984; Sofia 1987; SE Asia/FE Floater since April 1989; Grade 9.

Bramley, Sheilah Dawn; FCO since July 1990; born 15.4.59; FCO 1979; UKDEL NATO Brussels 1980; Maputo 1982; Floater Duties 1987; Grade 9.

Brammer, Geoffrey Ian; FCO since August 1992; born 9.6.65. FCO 1985; Kaduna 1987; Nassau 1990; Tehran 1991; Grade 9; m 1991 Shelley Diane Chalmers.

Brand, John McHardy; First Secretary FCO since February 1990; born 12.6.50; FCO 1974; Third later Second Secretary on loan to HCS 1975; Second Secretary Accra 1977; Second later First Secretary FCO 1979; UKMIS New York 1981; FCO 1983; First Secretary Kuwait 1986; m 1984 Kyla Jane Windeyer.

Brannigan, Virginia (née Reynolds); Madrid since March 1990; born 16.1.62; FCO 1985; San Jose 1986; Grade S2; m 1992 Stuart Patrick Brannigan.

Brant, Astrid Lorita Sophia; FCO since June 1991; born 27.2.53; DHSS 1980-91; Grade S2.

Braysher, Marion (née Pack); SUPL since July 1989; born 10.12.55; FCO 1976; Paris 1978; E Berlin 1981; Algiers 1983; Prague 1986; FCO 1987; Grade S1; m 1983 Robin Charles Braysher (1s 1989).

Brazier, Colin Nigel; Second Secretary FCO since July 1992; born 31.10.53; FCO 1973; Warsaw 1976; Singapore 1977; Accra 1980; FCO 1982; Dhaka 1985; Third Secretary (Comm) later Second Secretary (Development) Kingston 1989; m 1975 Jane Anne Pearson (1d 1979; 1s 1983).

Breakwell, Kerry Lee; FCO since July 1988; born 22.9.59; FCO 1980; Moscow 1986; Grade 8.

Brear, Andrew James; FCO since September 1991; born 28.1.60; Army 1979-90; Grade 7; m 1986 Jane Susan Matthews (1d 1992).

Breeze, Alastair Jon; CMG (1990); Counsellor FCO since May 1987; born 1.6.34; FO 1958; Third Secretary Jakarta 1960; FO 1962; Second Secretary seconded to Colonial Office for service in Georgetown 1964; First Secretary Tehran 1967; FCO 1971; First Secretary Islamabad 1972; First Secretary Lagos 1976; First Secretary (later Counsellor) FCO 1979; Counsellor UKMIS New York 1983; m 1960 Helen Burns Shaw (2s 1961, 1963; 1d 1970).

Breeze, Christopher Mark; Second Secretary FCO since July 1991; born 13.8.63; FCO 1985; Second Secretary (Chancery) Nicosia 1988; m 1990 Janet Suzanne Champion.

Brennan, Margaret Mary; Ankara since March 1992; born 17.6.38; FO 1968; Accra 1969; Dares Salaam 1970; Washington 1972; Doha 1975; FCO 1978; Baghdad 1979; FCO 1982; Nicosia 1983; FCO 1985; Cairo 1988; Grade 9.

Brenton, Anthony Russell; CDA Harvard University since September 1992; born 1.1.50; FCO 1975; MECAS 1977; First Secretary Cairo 1978; FCO 1981; Presidency Liaison Officer Brussels (Embassy) 1982; FCO 1982; First Secretary (Energy) UKREP Brussels 1985; on loan to European Commission 1986; Counsellor

FCO 1989; m (1) 1971 Susan Mary Blacker (diss 1978); (2) 1982 Susan Mary Penrose (1s 1984; 2d 1987, 1988).

Brett, David Lawrence; Second Secretary (Chancery) Kingston since February 1989; born 20.9.52; FCO 1978; Tehran 1980; Chicago 1983; FCO 1986; m 1984 Carol Sue Lane (1s 1986, 1d 1988).

Brett, Rebecca Louise (née Fenwick); The Hague since March 1990; born 27.11.64; FCO 1984; Washington 1987; Grade 10; m 1987 Paul Brett.

Brett-Rooks, Bedelia; First Secretary (Inf) BMG Berlin since July 1989; born 9.12.46; FCO 1969; On loan to SEATO Bangkok 1972; Copenhagen 1975; Rome 1976; Second Secretary FCO 1978; Second Secretary Accra 1983. UKREP Brussels 1986; First Secretary FCO 1987.

Brettle, Lynda Elizabeth; Islamabad since August 1988; born 2.10.62; FCO 1980; Tokyo 1983; FCO 1985; SE Asia Floater 1987; Grade 9.

Brewer, Jonathan Andrew; First Secretary (Chancery) Mexico City since May 1991; born 20.3.55; FCO 1983; Second later First Secretary Luanda 1986; First Secretary FCO 1988; m 1978 Tessa Alexandra Swiney (diss. 1990).

Brewer, Nicola Mary; First Secretary (Economic) Paris since September 1991; born 14.11.57; FCO 1983; Second Secretary (Chancery) Mexico City 1984; First Secretary FCO 1987; m 1991 Geoffrey Charles Gillham.

Brewis, Joanna Claire; Copenhagen since Febuary 1990; born 22.9.60; FCO 1981; Kuwait 1983; Luanda 1986; FCO 1989; Grade S2.

Brewitt, Jacqueline; Beirut since September 1992; born 2.8.65; FCO 1985; Dublin 1989; FCO 1989; Grade S2A.

Bridge, Richard Philip; First Secretary (Chancery) Moscow since November 1989; born 24.3.59; FCO 1984; Second Secretary (Inf) Warsaw 1986; FCO 1988.

Bridges, Stephen John; Second Secretary FCO since February 1992; born 19.6.60; FCO 1980; Africa/ME Floater 1983; Luanda 1984; Third later Second Secretary (Comm) Seoul 1987; m 1990 Yoon Kyung Mi.

Brier, Simon Richard; SE Asia/Far East Floater since March 1991; born 15.9.67; FCO 1987; Prague 1989; Grade 10.

Brierley, David Anthony; FCO since October 1991; born 14.10.47; Royal Marines 1965; Budapest 1987; Madrid 1989; Grade S0.

Brigden, Neil Stephen; Bucharest since October 1992; born 7.8.68; FCO 1986; Colombo 1989; Grade 9.

Brigenshaw, David Victor; Second Secretary FCO since December 1990; born 1.6.56; FCO 1973; Nairobi 1976; FCO 1981; Kuala Lumpur 1983; Third Secretary (Comm) Quito 1986; m 1977 Yvonne Lesley Bush.

Briggs, Geoffrey; Second Secretary FCO since September 1992; born 20.2.64; FCO 1988, Third Secretary (Econ/Aid) Cairo 1990.

Bright, Colin Charles; Counsellor and Head of Chancery Berne since February 1989; born 2.1.48; Second Secretary FCO 1975; First Secretary Bonn 1977; FCO 1979; on loan to Cabinet Office 1983; Consul BTDO New York 1985; m (1) 1978 Helen-Anne Michie (diss 1990); (2) 1990 Jane Elizabeth Gurney Pease (1s 1992).

Brighty, (Anthony) David, CMG (1984); CVO (1985); HM Ambassador Prague since July 1991; born 7.2.39; FO 1961; Brussels 1963; Havana 1964; FO 1966; Assistant Private Secretary to the Secretary of State for Commonwealth (later FCO) Affairs 1967; Resigned 1969; Reinstated FCO 1971; Head of Chancery Saigon 1973; First Secretary UKMIS New York 1975; Royal College of Defence Studies 1979; Deputy Head of Personnel Operations Department FCO 1980; Head of POD, FCO 1981; Counsellor, Lisbon 1983; on secondment as Directeur du Cabinet, Cabinet of the Secretary-General of NATO Brussels 1986; attached to OMCS (CSSB) 1987; HM Ambassador Havana 1989; m (1) 1963 Diana Porteous (diss 1979) (2s 1964, 1968; 2d 1965, 1970); (2) 1982 Jane Elisabeth Docherty.

Brimfield, Valerie; Dhaka since January 1989; born 27.7.49; FCO 1979; Tunis 1980; Tehran 1983; New Delhi 1985; Grade S1.

Brind, Kevin James; Canberra since July 1990; born 5.10.59; FCO 1977; Bonn 1980; Khartoum 1982; Moscow 1986; FCO 1987; Grade 9; m 1983 Jane Louise Burns.

Brinkley, Robert Edward; First Secretary FCO since September 1992; born 21.1.54; FCO 1977; Language Training 1978; Second Secretary Moscow 1979; First Secretary FCO 1982; First Secretary (Pol/Mil) Bonn 1988; m 1982 Frances Mary Webster (3s 1982, 1984, 1989).

Bristow, Laurence Stanley Charles; Second Secretary (Chancery/Inf) Bucharest since March 1992; born 23.11.63; FCO 1990; Full Time Language Training 1991; m 1988 Fiona McCallum.

Britt, Alan Arthur; FCO since October 1985; born 17.4.44; CRO 1961; Calcutta 1965; Washington 1968; Bogota 1971; FCO 1972; Port of Spain 1975; Second Secretary FCO 1978; Manila 1982; m 1965 Mary Lilian Draper (1s 1965; 1d 1966).

Britton, Catherine Mary; FCO since July 1988; First Secretary 1989; born 13.4.61; FCO 1983; Dar es Salaam 1985; m 1986 Rhodri James Lewis Britton.

Broad, David; Counsellor FCO since April 1992; born 23.5.44; Third Secretary FCO 1968; Third later Second Secretary Blantyre 1969; Second later First Secretary UK Mission New York 1973; FCO 1977; First Secretary (Comm) Head of Chancery and Consul Rabat 1980; First Secretary later Counsellor FCO 1984; Counsellor (Econ/Comm) Lagos 1988; m 1972 Janet Findlay Passmore (1d 1973; 1s 1980).

Brock-Doyle, David John; Counsellor FCO since June 1990; born 31.7.38; FO 1962; HM Treasury 1964; DSA 1965; MECAS 1966; Benghazi 1967; Vice-Consul Khartoum 1968; FCO 1970; First Secretary (Cons) Abu Dhabi 1972; First Secretary FCO 1975; Dar es Salaam 1978; First Secretary FCO 1982; First Secretary later Counsellor Jakarta 1987; m 1962 Jill Marylyn Waters (4d 1963, 1965, 1966, 1968; 1s 1970).

Bromley, Peter Richard Ober; Second later First Secretary (Dev) Lilongwe since August 1989; born 14.10.47; FCO 1966; Kuala Lumpur 1970; Dacca 1973; Georgetown 1976; on loan to DOT 1980; Oslo 1982; Second Secretary (Comm) Dubai 1984; Second Secretary FCO 1987; m 1978 Yasmin Amna Majeed (2s 1981, 1984).

Bronson, Rodney Charles; Second Secretary Singapore since July 1991; born 9.8.46; FCO 1971; Brussels 1974; FCO 1977; Moscow 1977; Copenhagen 1980; Cairo 1984; Second Secretary FCO 1988; m 1968 Margaret Ann Williams (2d 1972, 1974).

Brook, John Edwin; First Secretary FCO since April 1989; born 21.3.45; FO 1964; Moscow 1967; Latin America Floater 1970; Calcutta 1972; Second Secretary FCO 1975; Second Secretary (Comm) Moscow 1978; Second later First Secretary Berne 1981; First Secretary (Comm) East Berlin 1984; First Secretary on attachment to JSDC 1988; m 1981 Moira Elizabeth Lands (1s 1986).

Brook, Sally Anne; SUPL 1990; born 15.11.62; FCO 1985; Nicosia 1988; Grade S2; m 1990 Edward Valletta.

Brook, Simon Douglas; FCO since February 1989; born 5.2.61; FCO 1982; Geneva 1986; Grade 10.

Brooke, Sandra Jane; Bahrain since August 1991; born 21.8.63; FCO 1985; Algiers 1987; FCO 1989; Grade S2; m 1991 Jean-Marc Jefferson.

Brookes, Carter, MBE (1990); Beirut since August 1991; born 13.12.46; FCO 1971; Saigon 1973; FCO 1974; St Helena 1976; FCO 1978; Singapore 1980; FCO 1983; Moscow 1986; New Delhi 1989; Grade 9; m 1971 Margaret Jean Stewart (3s 1974, 1976, 1977).

Brookes, Maurice John; FCO since November 1989; born 14.6.49; FCO 1968; Accra 1971; Aden 1972; Nairobi 1974; Karachi 1976; FCO 1978; Tehran 1981; FCO 1982; Kampala 1982; FCO 1985; Paris 1986; Warsaw 1989; Grade 9.

Brooking, Stephen John Allan; Second Secretary FCO since November 1992; born 13.3.64; FCO 1986; Second Secretary (Econ) Peking 1989.

Brooks, Helen Katherine; FCO since January 1991; born 21.6.67; Research Officer.

Brooks, Shelagh Margaret Jane; FCO since January 1991; FCO 1979; On loan to Hong Kong Government 1987; Legal Counsellor.

Brooks, Stuart Armitage OBE (1991); First Secretary FCO since August 1991; born 15.5.48; Third Secretary FCO 1970; Vice-Consul (Dev) Rio de Janeiro 1972; Second Secretary on loan to HCS 1974; Second later First Secretary Lisbon 1975; FCO 1978; Moscow 1979; First Secretary FCO 1982; Stockholm 1987; m 1975 Mary-Margaret Elliott (2d 1977, 1980).

Broom, David Charles; Paris since December 1989; born 17.9.54; FCO 1973; Islamabad 1975; FCO 1976; UKREP Brussels 1977; Baghdad 1981; Home Civil Service 1982; FCO 1983; Rome 1986; FCO 1989; Grade 9; m 1976 Diana Josephine Hewer (1s 1978; 1d 1989).

Broom, Peter David; Consul (Commercial) Brisbane since November 1991; born 7.8.53; FCO 1970; Oslo 1974; Jedda 1977; Islamabad 1979; FCO 1981; Mbabane 1984; New Delhi 1987; Second Secretary FCO 1989; m 1976 Vivienne Louise Pyatt (2d 1979, 1981).

Broom, Richard Martin; Athens since February 1987; born 6.1.54; FCO 1980; Bangkok 1981; FCO 1984; Grade 9; m (1) 1975 Angela Thornton (1s 1975, 1d 1978); (2) 1987 Susan Clare Jolly.

Broom, Susan Clare (née Jolly); FCO since September 1989; born 15.3.56; FCO 1979; Tripoli 1982; FCO 1984; Athens 1986; Grade S2; m 1987 Richard Martin Broom.

Broomfield, David Norman; Vice-Consul Naples since May 1991; born 21.5.54; FCO 1973; Banjul 1975; LA Floater 1978; Prague 1980; FCO 1983; Tripoli 1986; Second Secretary (Chancery/Inf) Lusaka 1987.

Broomfield, Nigel Hugh Robert Allen, CMG DUSS (Defence) FCO since February 1990; born

19.3.37; Army 1958-68; First Secretary FCO
1969; Bonn 1970; First Secretary and Press
Attaché Moscow 1973; First Secretary FCO
1975; RCDS 1978; Counsellor and Head of
Chancery BMG Berlin 1979; Head of East
European and Soviet Department FCO 1981;
DHC and Minister New Delhi 1985; HM
Ambassador East Berlin 1988; m 1963 Valerie
Fenton (2s 1970, 1976).

Broucher, David Stuart; Counsellor (Econ) Bonn
since April 1989; born 5.10.44; FO 1966; Berlin
1968; Second Secretary on loan to Cabinet
Office 1972; First Secretary 1973; First Secretary
Prague 1975; FCO 1978; First Secretary
(ECOFIN) UKREP Brussels 1983; Counsellor
(Comm/Aid) Jakarta 1985; m 1971 Marion M
Blackwell (1s 1972).

Broughton, Sarah; Lilongwe since November
1990; born 12.8.66; FCO 1984; Ottawa 1987;
Grade 9.

Brown, Alexander Mark; FCO since June 1992;
born 21.7.64; DHSS 1986; FCO 1988; Lagos
1991; Grade 9.

Brown, Allen Roger, MVO (1980); Head of
British Interests Section Tripoli since July 1990;
born 29.12.34; Royal Navy 1953-65; DSAO
1965; Brussels 1967; Benghazi 1969; MECAS
1971; Kuwait 1973; Second Secretary 1975; FCO
1975; Second Secretary Berne 1978; First
Secretary (Comm) Amman 1981; First Secretary
FCO 1985; First Secretary (Comm) Baghdad
1987; m 1956 Brenda Breakwell (1d 1956; twin
s 1960).

Brown, Christine Audrey Frances; Attaché (Aid)
Dhaka since May 1991; born 22.6.51; FCO
1970; New Delhi 1971; Lagos 1973; Bucharest
1975; Kuala Lumpur 1977; FCO 1981; Floater
Duties 1982; FCO 1985; Johannesburg 1988;
Grade 9.

Brown, David Colin; Counsellor FCO since June
1989; born 10.8.39; CRO 1960; Lagos 1960;
Kingston 1964; DSAO 1966; Second Secretary
FCO 1968; Vice-Consul (Comm) Johannesburg
1969; FCO 1974; Deputy High Commissioner
Port Louis 1977; FCO 1981; Deputy Consul-
General Milan 1986; m 1960 Ann Jackson (2s
1961, 1967; 1d 1962).

Brown, Deidre Rebecca (née Herdman); Dhaka
since May 1988; born 19.7.66; FCO 1986; Grade 9;
m 1991 Stephen William Brown.

Brown, Donald Leslie; Counsellor FCO since
March 1992; born 30.6.40; FO 1957; Dakar 1961;
FO 1962; Vice-Consul Moscow 1965; Vancouver
1968; Second Secretary (Comm) Kampala 1969;
FCO 1973; Second Secretary (Commercial)
Moscow 1974; Ottawa 1977; First Secretary and
Consul (Comm) Edmonton 1978; FCO 1982; First
Secretary later Counsellor (Admin) and Consul-

General Tokyo 1984; Counsellor (Comm) Moscow
1988; m 1962 Pamela Patricia Wright (1d 1963; 1s
1969).

Brown, David Thomas; Valletta since August
1992; born 5.2.41; Royal Marines 1958-81;
Moscow 1990; Grade S0; m 1989 Jane Barbara
Maureen (dec'd 1992).

Brown, Edward James Murch, MBE (1991);
Dusseldorf since May 1992; born 27.8.59; FCO
1978; Bonn 1980; Prague 1983; Rabat 1985;
FCO 1987; Grade 9; 1980 Hannah Jane Gibbons.

Brown, Gordon William; Second Secretary
(Cons/Man) Havana since May 1991;; born
17.10.54; Inland Revenue 1975; FCO 1976;
Guatemala City 1979; The Hague 1981; SE Asia
Floater 1983; Kampala 1985; FCO 1988; m 1985
Rosalind Patricia Harwood (1s 1992).

Brown, Helen Ann; Accra since September
1990; born 30.6.67; FCO 1988; Grade S2A

Brown, Helen Charmaine; Second Secretary
FCO since June 1992; born 14.12.41; HM
Customs 1964; DSAO 1965; Seoul 1968; Kuala
Lumpur 1969; Stockholm 1973; Georgetown
1976; FCO 1976; LA Floater 1979; FCO 1981;
Port Louis 1984; Second Secretary (Admin)
Manila 1988; T/D Islamabad 1991.

Brown, Herbert George, MBE (1981); First
Secretary FCO since September 1990; born
2.1.43; FO 1964; Rawalpindi 1966; Kuala
Lumpur 1969; FCO 1973; Barcelona 1975;
Maseru 1978; FCO 1981; Second Secretary and
Vice-Consul Baghdad 1982; on loan to DTI
1985; First Secretary (Comm) Rio de Janeiro
1988; m 1975 Susan Atkin (1d 1977).

Brown, James Andrew; Aden since June 1987;
born 10.4.39; Army 1957-81; Warsaw 1981;
Islamabad 1982; Mexico City 1984; Peking
1986; Grade CSO; m 1961 Agnes Bell Dunbar
(1d 1963).

Brown, James Stanley; Second Secretary FCO
since October 1987; born 24.7.38; GPO 1954;
HM Forces 1957-59; GPO 1959; FO 1962;
Washington 1964; FO (later FCO) 1967; Nicosia
1970; FCO 1973; Bonn 1976; Second Secretary
BMG Berlin 1976; FCO 1981; Second Secretary
Caracas 1983; m 1960 Eveline Brannan (dec'd)
(1s 1961; 2d 1965, 1967); (2) 1979 Valerie May
Jones (diss 1981).

Brown, Jennifer Patricia; UKREP Brussels since
February 1990; born 28.8.64; FCO 1988; Grade
S2A.

Brown, Jeremy Astill; Kampala since January
1990; born 14.3.67; FCO 1987; Grade 9; m 1991
Marie-Louise (Marisa) Alegria Gunner.

Brown, John Mark; Islamabad since March

1990; born 15.5.43; RAF 1962-1984; Grade S0; m 1965 Carole Elizabeth Thompson (2d 1966, 1970)

Brown, John Maurice; First Secretary FCO since August 1992; born 11.6.38; Phnom Penh 1960; Rio de Janeiro 1962; Polad Singapore 1964; FCO 1969; Accra 1970; FCO 1973; Second Secretary 1977; Paris 1980; Second Secretary (Comm) Lusaka 1983; First Secretary (Admin) Ankara 1987; m 1964 Marie Ginette Angamootoo Miniopoo (1s 1969).

Brown, Linda; Rome since May 1992; born 24.12.55; FCO 1974; Bonn 1977; FCO 1980; Budapest 1980; Oslo 1982; FCO 1985; Grade 9.

Brown, Roger Hugh; HM Ambassador Managua since October 1991; born 13.6.37; Royal Marines and Army 1956-58; FO 1960; Leopoldville 1960; FO 1962; SUPL to attend University 1962-63; Jakarta 1964; FO 1966; Yaoundé 1966; Delhi 1970 (Private Secretary to the High Commissioner); Bangkok 1971; Second Secretary FCO 1972; Vice-Consul (Comm) Sydney 1975; First Secretary (Comm) Brasilia 1979; FCO 1983; UKDEL CSCE Vienna 1986; Chargé d'Affaires and First Secretary Managua 1989.

Brown, Stephen David Reid; Consul-General Melbourne since October 1989; born 26.12.45; HM Forces 1964-76; FCO 1976; First Secretary Nicosia 1977; First Secretary (Comm) Paris 1980; FCO 1985; Temporary Duty DTI 1989; m 1966 Pamela Gaunt (1s 1965; 1d 1969).

Brownbill, Timothy Patrick; Deputy Head of Mission Vilnius since September 1992; born 6.2.60; FCO 1979; Lagos 1982; Madrid 1986; FCO 1989; Resigned March 1990; Reinstated July 1990; FCO 1990; Language Training 1992; Grade 9.

Browne, Dr Carolyn; Second Secretary FCO since November 1991; born 19.10.58; FCO 1985; Language Training 1987; Second Secretary (Econ) Moscow 1988.

Browne, Nicholas Walker; Counsellor (Press and Public Affairs) Washington and Head of British Information Services New York since December 1990; born 17.12.47; Third Secretary FCO 1969; Tehran 1971; Second later First Secretary FCO 1975; on loan to Cabinet Office 1976; First Secretary and Head of Chancery Salisbury 1980; First Secretary FCO 1981; First Secretary (Environment) UKREP Brussels 1984; Chargé d'Affaires Tehran 1989; Counsellor FCO 1989; m 1969 Diana Marise Aldwinckle (2s 1970, 1980; 2d 1972, 1976).

Brownhut, Naomi Judith; FCO since July 1990; born 7.6.69; HM Customs and Excise 1988; Grade 10.

Bruce, Dawn Susan; Cairo since March 1989;

born 18.12.61; FCO 1981; Muscat 1983; Peking 1986; Grade 9.

Bruce-Lockhart, James Robert; Counsellor (Bilateral Relations) Bonn since May 1992; born 14.3.41; First Secretary FCO 1973; First Secretary (Inf) Nicosia 1975; FCO 1979; Vienna 1981; Counsellor Lagos 1985; Counsellor FCO 1988; m 1967 Felicity Ann Lee Smith (2s 1968, 1969).

Brummel, Paul; Third later Second Secretary (Chancery) Islamabad since April 1989; born 28.8.65; FCO 1987.

Brundle, Charis Imogen (née Crouch); SUPL since January 1992; born 1.4.63; FCO 1984; UKDEL Strasbourg 1986; FCO 1988; Grade 9; m 1988 Colin James Brundle.

Brunton, Janice Louise; FCO since March 1991; born 19.6.71; Grade S2.

Bryant, Jennifer; FCO since May 1988; born 27.6.34; Islamabad 1972; Athens 1974; Dacca 1977; FCO 1979; UKMIS Geneva 1985; Grade S2.

Bryant, John Edward; FCO since August 1990; born 4.1.51; FCO 1970; Canberra 1972; Kingston 1975; FCO 1977; Bahrain 1978; Cairo 1979; FCO 1983; Nairobi 1986; Grade 9; m 1972 Joyce Anne Barrie (1d 1975; 2s 1985, 1988).

Bryant, Karen Patricia; FCO since March 1991; born 23.3.66; Grade S2.

Bryant, Richard John; UKREP Brussels since March 1990; born 22.9.53; DTI 1973; Dept of Energy 1973; DOT 1975; DTI 1982; FCO 1984; Grade 9; Dhaka 1986; m 1986 Rosalyn Louise Morris.

Bryant, Rosalyn Louise (née Morris); Second Secretary (Economic) Brussels since March 1991; born 15.5.61; FCO 1983; Dhaka 1986; UKDEL Brussels 1989; m 1986 Richard John Bryant.

Bryant, Thomas; Consul-General Zurich since May 1991; born 1.11.38; FO 1957; HM Forces 1957-59; FO 1959; Hong Kong 1963; Peking 1963; Second Secretary and Vice-Consul (Comm) Frankfurt 1966; Second Secretary (Comm) Tel Aviv 1968; Central London Polytechnic Course 1972; First Secretary FCO 1973; First Secretary and Head of Chancery Vienna 1976; First Secretary FCO 1980; Counsellor, Head of Finance Department 1982; Consul-General Munich 1984; Deputy High Commissioner Nairobi 1988; m 1961 Vivien Mary Theresa Hill (twin s 1969; 1d 1972).

Brydon, Nicola; Nairobi since August 1992; born 11.12.69; MOD 1989; FCO 1990; Grade 10.

Bryson, Alan Robert; FCO since September 1991; born 12.3.70; Grade 10.

Bubbear, Alan Keith; Johannesburg since February 1990; born 14.9.64; FCO 1983; Moscow 1985; SUPL 1988; Grade 9; m 1988 Theresa Bernice Allen (2ds twins 1992).

Bubbear, Theresa Bernice (née Allen); Johannesburg since February 1990; born 14.12.62; FCO 1985; Moscow 1987; Grade 9; m 1988 Allan Keith Bubbear (2ds twins 1992).

Buchanan, Craig Robert; FCO since July 1991; born 1.6.72; Grade 10.

Buchanan, Ewen George; Second Secretary (UN) UKMIS Geneva since July 1989; born 18.11.58; FCO 1983; Dhaka 1985; Grade 9.

Buchanan, John Leslie; First Secretary, Consul and Deputy Head of Mission Sofia since November 1990; born 12.10.43; Ministry of Overseas Development 1962; Commonwealth Office 1966; Kaduna 1967; The Hague 1971; FCO 1974; Nicosia 1974; Second Secretary 1975; FCO 1978; Accra 1980; Deputy High Commissioner and Head of Chancery, Port Moresby 1982; First Secretary FCO 1987; m (1) 1967 Lesley Barbara Norfolk (diss. 1971) (1d 1970); (2) 1975 Louise Gertrude Godin.

Buchanan, Kathryn Hilary; UKREP Brussels since March 1992; born 7.7.70; FCO 1989; Grade 10.

Buck, John Stephen; First Secretary FCO since July 1992; born 10.10.53; FCO 1980; Second Secretary Sofia 1982; Second later First Secretary FCO 1983; Head of Chancery Lisbon 1988; m 1980 Jean Claire Webb (1s 1989).

Buckle, Dr Simon James; First Secretary FCO since June 1991; born 29.2.60; MOD 1988-91; Second Secretary FCO 1986; m 1990 Dr Rajeshree Bhatt.

Buckley, Stephan; Second Secretary FCO since August 1992; born 18.6.53; Export Credit Guarantee Department 1972; FCO 1972; Amman 1975; Canberra 1978; FCO 1980; Dakar 1983; Third later Second Secretary (Comm) Seoul 1987; m 1974 Barbara Frances Yelcich.

Budd, Colin Richard, CMG (1991); Counsellor and Head of Chancery Bonn since February 1989; born 31.8.45; Third Secretary FCO 1967; (Assistant Private Secretary to Minister without Portfolio 1968-1969); Third later Second Secretary Warsaw 1969; Second later First Secretary (Chancery) Islamabad 1972; First Secretary FCO 1976; Head of Chancery The Hague 1980; Assistant Private Secretary to the Secretary of State 1984; Counsellor 1986; on loan to the Cabinet Office 1987; m 1971 Agnes Antonia Maria Smit (1d 1979; 1s 1986).

Budden, Alexander James; FCO since August 1991; born 18.4.68; Grade 9.

Buglass, Melvyn James; Rome since June 1989; born 25.9.46; Army 1966-89; Grade SO; m 1973 Sandra Anne Whitehouse (1d 1974; 1s 1975).

Bulcock, Christine Susan; Lusaka since March 1987; born 15.8.61; FCO 1981; Kuala Lumpur 1983; Grade S2.

Bull, David Thomas John; FCO since June 1990; born 20.2.61; FCO 1982; Rio de Janeiro 1983; Lusaka 1986; Grade 9; m 1989 Aisling Maccobb (1d 1989).

Bull, Janet Elizabeth; Second Secretary (Chancery) Lisbon since November 1990; born 22.9.63; FCO 1986; Third later Second Secretary (Chancery) Managua 1988.

Bundy, Rosalind (née Johnson); FCO since August 1987; born 25.1.45; FCO 1977; Paris 1977; Tripoli 1980; FCO 1983; Bonn 1985; Grade S1; m 1984 David Alan Bundy.

Bunn, Justine Mary; FCO since September 1991; born 2.10.64; FCO 1983; Budapest 1986; Doha 1987; Grade 9.

Bunney, John Herrick; First Secretary FCO since November 1990; born 2.6.45; Second Secretary FCO 1971; MECAS 1971; FCO 1973; First Secretary Damascus 1974; FCO 1978; Head of Chancery and Consul Sana'a 1980; First Secretary FCO 1983; Tunis 1987; m 1970 Pamela Anne Simcock (1s 1973; 1d 1976).

Bunten, Roderick Alexander James; FCO since November 1991; born 24.11.59; FCO 1984; SOAS 1985; Language Training 1986; On Secondment to Hong Kong Government as Assistant Political Adviser 1987; SUPL 1990; Grade 7.

Burch, Andrew David; Nairobi since May 1989; born 18.3.57; Department of the Environment 1972; FCO 1976; Nicosia 1980; New Delhi 1982; FCO 1986; Grade 9; m 1982 Sarah Miranda Hodgson Clarke (1s 1989).

Burdekin, Elizabeth Mary; FCO since September 1972; born 16.10.54; Grade S2.

Burdess, Christopher Paul, LVO ; Counsellor FCO since November 1991; born 29.10.42; First Secretary FCO 1973; First Secretary Islamabad 1975; FCO 1979; Head of Chancery Port of Spain 1984; Counsellor (Econ/Comm) Oslo 1987; m 1970 Marion Jane Ball (2s 1970, 1972; 2d 1975, 1977).

Burgin, Allan Lewis; Paris since March 1991; born 22.3.48; Royal Navy 1968-1990; Moscow 1990; Grade SO; m 1970 Susan Hewison (2s 1978; 1982).

Burke, Alison Jane (née Wickham); Bucharest since October 1992; born 25.7.65; SUPL 1991; FCO 1983; Prague 1988; Canberra 1990; Grade S2; m 1991 Thomas John Burke.

Burke, Elizabeth Janet Dwerryhouse; FCO since June 1979; born 13.9.48; FCO 1970; Copenhagen 1972; Aden 1974; FCO 1975; Tel Aviv 1977; Grade S2.

Burke, Thomas John; Vice-Consul Bucharest since October 1992; born 12.12.50; Treasury 1968; FCO 1974; Brasilia 1976; FCO 1979; Islamabad 1983; FCO 1984; Canberra 1987; Vice-Consul Düsseldorf 1991; Grade 9; m (1) 1975 Theresa Ann Herd (diss 1980) (2) 1991 Alison Jane Wickham.

Burner, Edward Alan; Counsellor (Comm) Lagos since January 1992; born 26.9.44; Commonwealth Office (later FCO) 1967; Sofia 1970; Bonn 1972; Second Secretary 1973; Second Secretary (Comm) Bridgetown 1974; Second later First Secretary FCO 1979; Assistant Private Secretary to Minister for Overseas Development 1979; FCO 1981; First Secretary, Head of Chancery and Consul Sofia 1984; On loan to ODA 1987; FCO 1990; m 1969 Jane Georgine Du Port (2d 1970, 1972; 1s 1977).

Burnett, David Edgar, MBE (1979); Singapore since May 1991; born 12.5.37; Royal Navy 1952-64; FO 1964; Karachi1/Rawalpindi 1965; FO 1966; Moscow 1967; FCO 1968; Kampala 1969; FCO 1971; Dacca 1973; FCO 1974; Darwin 1975; FCO 1976; Hanoi 1977; FCO 1978; Gaborone 1979; Tehran 1982; FCO 1986; Singapore 1987; Aden 1988; Grade 8; m Dorothy Sutherland Elliott (1s 1962; 1d 1966).

Burnhams, Robin Edward; Second Secretary (Aid) Dar-Es-Salaam since August 1992; born 10.12.42; CSC 1960; FCO 1967; Buenos Aires 1970; Moscow 1973; FCO 1974; Kingston 1978; Mbabane 1982; Second Secretary FCO 1984; Second Secretary (Admin) and Consul Caracas 1987; Second Secretary FCO 1990; m 1978 Hilda Charlotte Patricia Phibbs (1d 1985).

Burns, David Allan; Head of the British Mission to the Cambodian Supreme National Council, Phnom Penh (with personal rank of Ambassador) since November 1991; born 20.9.37; FO 1955; Army 1956-58; FO 1958; Belgrade 1962; Second Secretary FO 1965; Bangkok 1966; First Secretary FCO 1968; and Washington 1969; First Secretary1/Head of Chancery Belgrade 1973; FCO 1976; Counsellor, Head of Chancery and Consul-General Bangkok 1979; Consul-General Boston 1983; Counsellor FCO 1988; m 1971 Inger Ellen Kristiansson (1s 1971; 1d 1974).

Burns, Nicholas John; Third Secretary (Management) Riyadh since September 1992; born 20.3.62; FCO 1980; The Hague 1983;

Kuala Lumpur 1984; Hanoi 1988; FCO 1989; Grade 9.

Burns, (Robert) Andrew; HM Ambassador Tel Aviv since July 1992; born 21.7.43; Third Secretary FO 1965; SOAS 1966; Third later Second Secretary Delhi 1967; Second later First Secretary FCO 1971; First Secretary and Head of Chancery Bucharest 1976; FCO 1978; Private Secretary to Permanent Under-Secretary of State 1979; CDA Harvard University 1982; Counsellor (Information) Washington and Head of British Information Services New York 1983; Counsellor FCO 1986; AUSS (Asia/Far East) FCO 1990; m 1973 Sarah Cadogan (1 step d 1968; 2s 1975, 1977).

Burns, Sarah Elizabeth; Third later Second Secretary (Chancery) Vienna since June 1991; born 20.4.66; FCO 1988.

Burns, Sean Gilbert Peter; FCO since March 1991; born 19.2.61; FCO 1978; Dar es Salaam 1983; Antigua 1987; Grade 9; m 1983 Marina Higgins; (1d 1989).

Burran, John Eric; Islamabad since March 1992; born 18.5.63; FCO 1982; Bucharest 1987; LA/Caribbean Floater 1989; Grade 9.

Burrett, Louise Victoria; FCO since November 1990; born 16.8.61; FCO 1978; Bridgetown 1981; Dublin 1984; Bombay 1987; Grade 9.

Burrows, Christopher Parker; Second Secretary FCO since August 1989; born 12.9.58; FCO 1980; East Berlin 1982; Africa/Middle East Floater 1985; Bonn 1987 (Second Secretary 1988); m 1988 Betty Cordi; (2d, 1987, 1990).

Burrows, Karl; Tegucigalpa since May 1992; born 8.5.68; FCO 1988; Floater Duties 1990; Grade 10; m 1991 Jane Marie O'Mahoney.

Burt, Nicola Jane; FCO since February 1992; born 6.2.67; FCO 1986; Moscow 1989; Grade S2.

Burton, Austin Charles; FCO since May 1990; born 19.12.38; GPO 1955; HM Forces 1958-60; GPO 1960; FO 1963; Bangkok 1966; Lagos 1968; FCO 1969; Paris 1970; FCO 1972; Hong Kong 1973; Canberra 1978; FCO 1981; Jedda 1981; Second Secretary FCO 1984; Second Secretary Warsaw 1988; Moscow 1989; m 1966 Kathleen Patricia Swan (1d 1969; 1s 1971).

Burton, Graham Stuart, CMG (1987); HM Ambassador Abu Dhabi since February 1990; born 8.4.41; FO 1961; Abu Dhabi 1964; MECAS 1967; Second Secretary (Comm) Kuwait 1969; Second later First Secretary FCO 1972; First Secretary Head of Chancery and Consul Tunis 1975; First Secretary (Chancery) UKMIS New York 1978; Counsellor (Comm) Tripoli 1981; Counsellor FCO 1984; Consul-General San

Francisco 1987; m 1965 Julia Margaret Lappin (1d 1966; 1s 1967).

Burton, John Francis; Pretoria since July 1991; Army 1963-87; New Delhi 1989; Prague 1989; Grade SO; m 1971 Christine (2d 1973, 1974).

Burton, John Jerome; Second Secretary (Computer Manager) BTIO New York since June 1990; born 27.6.40; GPO 1961; DSAO 1965; NATO 1967; Dublin 1969; Budapest 1971; Port Louis 1973; Tripoli 1975; FCO 1978; Wellington 1981; Addis Ababa 1984; Second Secretary FCO 1986; m 1966 Jennifer Charlton (1s 1968; 3d 1969, 1976, 1977).

Burton, Michael St Edmund, CMG (1987), CVO (1979); Minister and Deputy Commandant BMG Berlin since November 1985; born 18.10.37; FO 1960; MECAS 1960; Assistant Political Agent Dubai 1962; Second Secretary 1964; FO 1964 (Private Secretary to Minister of State for Foreign Affairs 1966); Second Secretary (Inf) later First Secretary Khartoum 1967; First Secretary (Inf) Paris 1969; FCO 1972; First Secretary, Head of Chancery and Consul Amman 1975; Counsellor and Head of Chancery Kuwait 1977; Head of Maritime, Aviation and Environment Dept, FCO 1979; Head of South Asian Dept, FCO 1981; on secondment to British Petroleum as Head of Policy Review Unit 1984; m 1967 Henrietta Jindra Hones (1s 1969; 1d 1971).

Bury, Claire Louise; on secondment to the EC Commission since April 1992; born 13.6.65; called to the Bar, Middle Temple 1988; Assistant Legal Adviser FCO 1989; Grade 5.

Busby, George Benedict Joseph Pascale; First Secretary FCO since August 1991; born 18.4.60; FCO 1987; Second later First Secretary (Chancery) Bonn 1989; m 1988 Helen Frances Hurll (1s 1991).

Busvine, Nicholas John Lewis; First Secretary (Chancery) Maputo since September 1991; born 13.5.60; FCO 1982; Third later Second Secretary Kuala Lumpur 1985; FCO 1988; m 1991 Sarah Ann Fergan.

Butcher, Peter Roderick; Deputy High Commissioner Maseru since April 1990; born 6.8.47; FCO 1974; Second Secretary Lima 1979; Second Secretary (Comm) Bombay 1983; First Secretary FCO 1987.

Butler, Christopher Giles Moffat; FCO since November 1982 (Second Secretary 1985); born 13.3.40; HM Forces 1960-77; FCO 1977; Durban 1979; Johannesburg 1980; m 1973 Sandra Ann Barnes (1s 1974; 1d 1978).

Butler, Penelope Margaret; FCO since May 1972; born 14.2.52; Grade 10.

Butler, Sally-Anne; Stanley since July 1990; born 30.3.69; FCO 1988; Grade 10; m 1991 Jonathan Jeffers Butler.

Butler, (Stephen) Patrick; FCO since September 1991; born 18.5.68; Grade 9.

Butler-Madden, Simon Michael Jeremy, OBE (1989); SUPL since July 1989; born 2.8.40; Second Secretary FO (later FCO) 1966; Second later First Secretary UKDEL EC Brussels 1969; FCO 1972; First Secretary Buenos Aires 1975; FCO 1980; Madrid 1984; First Secretary FCO 1989; m 1973 Marcela Eliana Perez (2s 1975, 1978).

Butt, Simon John; Second Secretary FCO since October 1986; born 5.4.58; FCO 1979; Third later Second Secretary Moscow 1982; Second Secretary Rangoon 1984.

Butt, Stephen; FCO since May 1992; born 7.5.63; FCO 1981; Cairo 1986; Athens 1991; Grade 9.

Butterfield, Sarah Jane; FCO since March 1992; born 1.7.72; Grade 10.

Butterworth, Pamela Cynthia Anne, MBE (1987); FCO since December 1988; born 24.4.43; FO 1964; Geneva 1964; Hong Kong 1967; FCO 1969; Peking 1971; FCO 1973; New York 1976; FCO 1978; Washington 1986; Grade S2.

Buxey, Anthony Maurice; Second Secretary FCO since July 1988; born 23.10.36; GPO 1953; HM Forces 1955-57; GPO 1957; FO 1964; Karachi1/ Rawalpindi 1965; FO 1966; Moscow 1967; FCO 1968; Washington 1969; FCO 1971; Bahrain 1979; FCO 1981; Nicosia 1985; m 1963 Grace Amelia Penny (3d 1966, 1967, 1968).

Byne, Bernard Geoffrey; Lusaka since April 1990; born 19.1.33; RN 1948-78; Moscow 1978; Tripoli 1979; Kingston 1981; Bonn 1985; Peking 1988; UKREP Brussels 1989; Grade CSO; m 1954 Gillian Mary (1s 1956).

Byrde, Petronella Leonie Diana; FCO since April 1990; born 20.10.48; DSAO (later FCO) 1967; Gaborone 1971; Dacca 1974; FCO 1977; Second Secretary 1979; Tokyo 1981; First Secretary (Comm) Colombo 1986.

Byrne, Sarah Francis; FCO since June 1992; born 12.4.65; FCO 1987; Lagos 1990; Grade S2.

Byrne, Terence Niall; Counsellor and Deputy High Commissioner Lusaka since January 1990; born 28.4.42; MHLG 1964; MAFF 1971; First Secretary (Agriculture), The Hague 1978; First Secretary FCO 1982; Head of Chancery Quito 1986; m (1) 1966 Andrea Dennison (diss 1977) (1s 1968, 1d 1969); (2) 1981 Susan Haddow Neill (2d 1985, 1987).

Byroo, Jacqueline Sandra; FCO since September 1989; born 30.4.63; FCO 1982; UKREP Brussels 1987; Grade S2A.

C

Caie, Andrew John Forbes; First Secretary later Counsellor FCO since October 1988; born 25.7.47; FCO 1969; SRO (DS Gr. 7) 1972; Second Secretary Manila 1976; PRO(DS Gr. 5) FCO 1980 (First Secretary 1983); First Secretary, Head of Chancery and Consul Bogotá 1984; m 1976 Kathie-Anne Williams (1s 1979; 1d 1987).

Cairaschi, Lucien Marius; FCO since October 1985; born 11.2.65; HCS 1984; Grade 10.

Cairns, Donald Hunter; FCO since May 1992; born 29.10.46; Post Office 1967; FCO 1969; Anguilla 1972; Montevideo 1974; Abu Dhabi 1977; FCO 1980; Second Secretary (Comm) Bogotá 1982; Second Secretary (Admin) and HM Consul Caracas 1984; First Secretary (Comm) Canberra 1988; Deputy Consul General (Comm) Melbourne 1990; m 1972 Judy Francis Woods (1s 1977).

Cairns, Gina Stephanie (née Tart); Bonn since January 1990; born 21.9.65; FCO 1984; Bridgetown 1986; Grade 10; m 1987 William John Cairns.

Cairns, Julie Margaret; Gaborone since February 1990; born 13.3.59; FCO 1977; Bonn 1979; Africa/ME Floater 1982; JAO Brussels 1984; FCO 1986; Grade 9.

Calder, Robert; First Secretary FCO since September 1991; born 27.10.41; CRO 1960; Karachi 1963; Warsaw 1966; Kampala 1968; FCO 1971; Kampala 1972; FCO 1974; Frankfurt 1974; Second Secretary Vientiane 1977; Accra 1978; BMG Berlin 1980; First Secretary FCO 1983; m 1966 Janet Rosemary Allen (2d 1967, 1978; 2s 1968, 1976); Deputy Consul General and First Secretary (Comm) Düsseldorf 1986.

Calder, Stanley Shearer; First Secretary FCO since September 1990; born 7.2.44; Immigration Service 1965; Islamabad 1972; Second Secretary Lima 1975; FCO 1980; Deputy High Commissioner Belmopan 1982; First Secretary Peking 1986; m 1967 Isobel Masson Leith (1s 1968; 1d 1970).

Calder, Tracy Anne; FCO since February 1991; born 24.1.70; Grade 10.

Caldow, Deborah Julia; FCO since March 1992; born 8.9.67; FCO 1987; Accra 1990; Grade S2.

Caldwell, Angela; Floater Duties since February 1992; born 9.3.67; FCO 1986; Washington 1988; Grade 10.

Caldwell, Christine Bernadette; Vice-Consul Johannesburg since February 1991; born 31.7.56; HCS 1973-77; FCO 1977; Warsaw 1979; Ankara 1979; Tripoli 1983; FCO 1984; SUPL 1986; Grade 9; m 1982 Clive David Wright (1d 1989).

Caley, Joanne; FCO since September 1991; born 13.8.65; Grade 7; m 1991 Peter David Morgan.

Callaghan, Francis; Deputy High Commissioner Kingston since March 1991; born 4.9.35; Army 1958-60; MPNI 1960; DSA 1966; Gaborone 1969; Second Secretary (Cons1/Comm1/Inf) Gaborone 1970; Phnom Penh 1972; New Delhi 1974; First Secretary FCO 1977; First Secretary (Comm) and Head of Chancery Banjul 1980; First Secretary (Comm) Harare 1983; First Secretary FCO 1987; m 1963 Nancy Nesbitt (1d 1965).

Callan, Ivan Roy, CMG (1990); Counsellor FCO since December 1990; born 6.4.42; Second Secretary FCO 1969; MECAS 1970; Second later First Secretary Beirut 1972; First Secretary FCO 1975; Ottawa 1980; Counsellor and Head of Chancery Baghdad 1983; Consul-General Jerusalem 1987; m (1) 1965 Hilary Margaret West (née Flashman) (1d 1971); (2) 1987 Mary Catherine Helena Williams.

Callow, Judith Elizabeth; Ottawa since May 1990; born 27.12.48; FCO 1970; Tananarive 1971; UK Mission Geneva 1973; Belgrade 1974; Abidjan 1975; Dakar 1979; Madrid 1983; Paris 1985; UKDEL Brussels 1987; Grade S1.

Callun, Rosemary (née Beckmann); FCO since February 1987; born 17.1.54; FCO 1975; Cairo 1976; Bangkok 1978; Prague 1979; Pretoria 1981; Accra 1983; Port Stanley 1985; Harare 1986; Grade S1.

Callway, Eric Willi; FCO since October 1989; born 30.1.42; FO 1960; CRO 1961; Delhi 1963; Georgetown 1966; Second Secretary FCO 1970; RAF Staff College Bracknell 1972; UK Mission Geneva 1973; First Secretary FCO 1977; First Secretary on loan to MOD 1979; FCO 1980; First Secretary (Comm) E Berlin 1981; First Secretary (Comm) Stockholm 1984; On loan to ODA 1988; m 1965 Gudrun Viktoria Granstrom (2s 1971, 1974).

Calvert, Andrew Paul; FCO since April 1992; born 17.1.69; HCS Cadre of the FCO 1989; Grade 10.

Cambridge, Roger Alan, MVO (1985); Consul (Commercial) BT10 New York since September 1990; born 12.9.52; FCO 1972; Africa Floater 1975; Stockholm 1977; Dar es Salaam 1979; Second Secretary (Chancery/Inf) Port of Spain 1983; Second later First Secretary FCO 1986.

Cameron, James; Bucharest since May 1991; born 21.4.50; Army 1966-90; FCO 1990; Peking

1990; Grade S0; m 1977 Angela Jane Arnold (2d 1977, 1979).

Cameron, Norman James Macdonald; First Secretary FCO since June 1991; born 24.6.46; Second Secretary FCO 1973; Abu Dhabi 1975; Dubai 1975; First Secretary Beirut 1977; First Secretary FCO 1980; Budapest 1981; First Secretary FCO 1984; First Secretary (Chancery) Abu Dhabi 1987; m 1978 Marilyn Cynthia Boughton (twins 1s, 1d 1980).

Campbell, Beresford Ian; Second later First Secretary FCO since September 1985; born 3.3.41; FO 1964; Jedda 1968; FCO 1969; Baghdad 1970; FCO 1971; Second Secretary attached to Hong Kong Government 1981; m 1973 Jean Dolores Gobin (1s 1974; 1d 1977).

Campbell, Christopher John; Jakarta since June 1992; born 12.4.63; FCO 1982; Khartoum 1985; Dhaka 1988; Grade 9; m 1989 Sharon Isabel Hale.

Campbell, Colin Vincent Hayden; FCO since July 1989 (Second Secretary 1991); born 29.7.37; Royal Navy 1953-62; DWS 1962; FCO 1970; Bonn 1973; Dacca 1974; Helsinki 1977; FCO 1979; Nicosia 1986; m 1966 Maureen Ann Herring (1d 1972).

Campbell, David Ian; First Secretary (Humanitarian) Geneva since September 1989; born 9.7.58; FCO 1981; Budapest 1984; Third later Second Secretary Georgetown 1985; Second Secretary FCO 1988.

Campbell, Dorothy May; FCO since October 1991; born 12.6.64; Grade S2.

Campbell, Fiona Jennifer; Cairo since November 1992; born 7.5.68; FCO 1987; Grade S2.

Campbell, Jacqueline Margaret; FCO since April 1990; born 6.6.63; FCO 1983; Cape Town/ Pretoria 1985; UKDEL CSCE Vienna 1987; Grade 9.

Campbell, Josephine Moira; FCO since June 1992; born 17.11.67; FCO 1988;Prague 1990; Grade 9.

Campbell, Linda Margaret; FCO since February 1991; born 12.4.61; Grade S2.

Campbell, Richard, MBE (Mil); Bangkok since June 1990; born 9.12.33; Army 1952-76; HCS 1978-82; Moscow 1982; Baghdad 1983; Bonn 1984; Warsaw 1987; Muscat 1988; Grade SO; m 1955 Catherine Murray Stuart (3s 1956, 1958, 1962).

Campbell, Robert Pius; First Secretary (Political) Helsinki since June 1992; born 19.10.57; FCO 1980; Second Secretary Nairobi 1984; FCO 1985; First Secretary (Economic) Belgrade 1986;

First Secretary FCO 1990; m (1) 1985 Amanda Jane Guy (diss 1992) 1s 1989 (2) m 1992 Ailsa Irene Robinson.

Campbell, Sharon Isabel (née Hale); Jakarta since June 1992; born 12.2.62; FCO 1983; Warsaw 1985; FCO 1986; Dhaka 1988; Grade 9; m 1989 Christopher John Campbell.

Campbell, Stephen; FCO since July 1990; born 26.12.71; Grade 10.

Campbell, Susan Margaret, Brasilia since November 1991; born 28.7.64; FCO 1984; Harare 1986; FCO 1990; Grade S2.

Campbell-Birket, Frances Mary neé Campbell; FCO since August 1990; born 3.4.62 HCS 1981; FCO 1982; Budapest 1984; FCO 1985; Jakarta 1987; Grade S2; m 1992 Christopher Michael Fraser Birkett.

Canale, Philip; Third Secretary Kingston since April 1988; born 23.10.42; RAF 1960-65; FCO 1975; St Helena 1976; FCO 1978; Rome 1980; FCO 1983; Darwin 1985; FCO 1987; Baghdad 1987; Grade 9.

Candlish, Elizabeth Janet Wright; FCO since November 1989; born 16.12.34; Commonwealth Office 1962; Kampala 1962; Accra 1965; FCO 1968; Tegucigalpa 1970; Athens 1972; East Berlin 1975; Lusaka 1975; FCO 1977; Washington 1981; Budapest 1984; Copenhagen 1986; Grade S1.

Candlish, John Michael, OBE (1991); First Secretary (Comm) Peking since September 1990; born 2.4.36; FO 1955; HM Forces 1955-57; Belgrade 1960; Second Secretary 1964; FO 1965; Kuala Lumpur 1968; First Secretary (Comm) Belgrade 1972; FCO 1976; Consul (Comm) Karachi 1978; First Secretary (Science/Industry) Moscow 1982; First Secretary FCO 1986; m 1967 Sheila White (1s 1969).

Cannard, Corrine; FCO since April 1991; born 28.2.70; Grade 10.

Canning, Mark; Second Secretary FCO since November 1988; born 15.12.54; FCO 1974; Freetown 1976; FCO 1978; SUPL 1978; FCO 1981; Georgetown 1982; Chicago 1986; m 1988 Leslie Marie Johnson.

Cannon, Nicholas; FCO since May 1992; Second Secretary Paris 1990; born 29.5.58; FCO 1988; m. Alice Cheung.

Cantor, Anthony John James; On loan to the DTI since June 1992; born 1.2.46; DSAO 1965; Rangoon 1968; Language Training 1971; Tokyo 1972; Second Secretary (Cons) Accra 1977; Second Secretary FCO 1980; Consul (Comm) Osaka 1983; Head of Chancery and Consul Hanoi 1990; m 1968 Patricia Elizabeth Naughton

(2d 1969, 1972, 1s 1980).

Cantrell, Ann Pauline Hester, MBE (1979); FCO since May 1992; born 29.8.41; FO 1962; Düsseldorf 1963; Havana 1966; FO 1967; Salisbury 1968; FCO 1969; Singapore 1969; FCO 1972; Vienna 1974; Hong Kong 1977; FCO 1980; Pretoria 1987; SUPL 1990; Grade S2.

Canvin, Alan Robert; Bucharest since March 1988; Second Secretary 1992; born 23.12.46; FCO 1965; Jedda (later Riyadh) 1984; m 1981 Susan Paviour (1 step d 1963; 1 step s 1966).

Capes, Mark Andrew; Deputy Chief Secretary Grand Turk since August 1991; born 19.2.54; FCO 1971; UKREP Brussels 1974; Lisbon 1975; Zagreb 1978; FCO 1980; Lagos 1982; Vienna 1985; Second Secretary FCO 1989; m 1980 Tamara Rossmanith (2d 1985, 1988).

Carbine, Michael Julian; Second Secretary (Visas) Dusseldorf since April 1990; born 16.1.56; FCO 1975; Budapest 1977; Khartoum 1979; FCO 1982; Budapest 1983; Second Secretary FCO 1986; m 1975 Marian Parkinson (1s 1975).

Carden, Carol Mary; Third Secretary (Chancery) Budapest since August 1992; born 27.3.67; FCO 1989.

Carew-Hunt, Robert Anthony; Second Secretary FCO since September 1988; born 11.10.49; FO (later FCO) 1968; Bonn 1972; FCO 1975; Cairo 1975; FCO 1979; Second Secretary Bandar Seri Begawan 1986.

Carey, Colin Paul; FCO since August 1990; born 21.9.57; FCO 1974; Bonn 1988; Grade 8; m 1981 Janet Coleman (1d 1984, 2s 1986, 1990).

Carey, Joanne Claire; FCO since August 1991; born 6.2.72; Grade 10.

Carlill, Claire Lloyd; FCO since March 1990; born 31.8.62; FCO 1982; Paris 1984; UKMIS New York 1986; Grade S3.

Carlin, Neal Daniel; FCO since July 1990; born 22.3.71; Grade 10.

Carmichael, Steven; Dublin since April 1992; born 5.3.71; FCO 1989; Grade 10.

Carnall, Philippa Jane, MBE (1986); Washington since May 1991; born 31.7.57; FCO 1980; Beirut 1983; Damascus 1984; FCO 1986; Hanoi 1988; Grade S2.

Carne, Alan John MBE (1989); Kampala since August 1991; born 2.10.32; HM Forces 1951-53; FO 1965; St Helena 1967; FCO 1969; Singapore 1970; Darwin 1971; FCO 1972; Addis Ababa 1974; FCO 1976; Darwin 1976; FCO 1978;

Moscow 1979; FCO 1980; Vice-Consul Istanbul 1982; FCO 1984; Havana 1985; FCO 1988; Grade 8; m 1953 Pauline Valerie Manning (3s 1965, 1966, 1970).

Carney, Jonathan Patrick; Islamabad since March 1992; born 23.2.68; DHSS 1986; FCO 1989; Grade 10.

Carr-Alloway, Christine Anne (née Carr); Kuwait since January 1992; born 13.2.60; FCO 1978; Paris 1980; UKREP Brussels 1983; FCO 1986; Grade 9; m 1991 Terry Alloway.

Carr, Julie Anne, Budapest since November 1992; born 5.7.64; FCO 1990; Grade S2.

Carr, Peter Douglas; Second Secretary FCO since October 1988; born 2.5.47; DSAO (later FCO) 1967; Kaduna 1969; FCO 1970; Delhi 1971; Bogotá 1974; FCO 1978; Kuwait 1981; FCO 1984; JAO New York 1985; m 1972 Cynthia Jane Begley (1s 1975; 2d 1977, 1983).

Carrick, Aileen Margaret; Rome since February 1992; born 21.2.69; FCO 1989; Grade 10.

Carrick, Nicholas John; FCO since September 1990; born 1.2.67; Grade 8.

Carrick, Roger John, CMG (1983), LVO (1972); HM Ambassador Jakarta since August 1990; born 13.10.37; FO 1956; Royal Navy 1956-58; FO 1958; Sofia 1962; Second Secretary FO 1965; Second later First Secretary (Econ) Paris 1967; First Secretary and Head of Chancery Singapore 1971; First Secretary FCO 1973; Counsellor 1976; Deputy Head of Personnel Operations Department 1976; CDA University of California Berkeley 1977; Counsellor Washington 1978; Head of Overseas Estate Department FCO 1982; HM Consul-General Chicago 1985; AUSS (Econ) FCO 1988; m 1962 Hilary Elizabeth Blinman (2s 1965, 1969).

Carrington, Merlene Oneata; FCO since July 1991; born 17.1.65; FCO 1983; UKMIS Geneva 1986; FCO 1988; UKDEL Brussels 1991; Grade S2A.

Carroll, John; Second Secretary (Chancery/Inf) Jakarta since October 1990; born 21.5.41; Ministry of Social Security 1959; DSAO (later FCO) 1967; Warsaw 1970; Tonga 1971; Bonn 1973; SUPL Lancaster University 1974; FCO 1977; Vice-Consul Edmonton 1979; Second Secretary BMG Berlin 1982; m 1970 Rosamund Mary Kingon-Rouse (2s 1972, 1975).

Carson, Christine Margaret; JLG Hong Kong since February 1992; born 18.5.65; FCO 1990; Grade S2A.

Carson, Kenneth; Oslo since March 1991; born 16.8.33; Royal Navy 1949-73; Bangkok 1975; Moscow 1977; Lagos 1978; Madrid 1979; Damascus 1982; Kuala Lumpur 1984; Bucharest

1985; Kingston 1987; Grade SO; m 1961 Ann
Pauline (née Evans) (2s 1961, 1966).

Carter, Andrew; Deputy Governor Gibraltar
since October 1990; born 4.12.43; FCO 1971;
Second Secretary Warsaw 1972; First Secretary
1974; Bonn 1975; FCO 1978; on Loan to MOD
1981; FCO 1983; Counsellor, CDA Chatham
House 1984; Counsellor and Head of Chancery
UKDEL NATO Brussels 1986; m (1) 1973 Anne
Caroline Morgan (diss 1986) (1d 1978); (2) 1988
Catherine Mary Tyler (1d 1989).

Carter, Dr David; Deputy Head of Mission
Capetown/Pretoria since September 1992; born
4.5.45; FCO 1970, (Research Cadre); Second
Secretary Accra 1971; FCO 1975; First Secretary
1977; First Secretary and Head of Chancery
Manila 1980; FCO 1983; Deputy High
Commissioner and Head of Chancery Lusaka
1986; Counsellor FCO 1990.

Carter, Dennis Sidney; Second Secretary (Aid)
Addis Ababa since Sseptember 1991; born
12.6.47; Commonwealth Office 1964; DSAO
(later FCO) 1966; Bogota 1969; Moscow 1973;
FCO 1974; Bonn 1978; Washington 1982;
Harare 1984; Second Secretary FCO 1987; m
1968 Catherine Rose (2s 1969, 1975).

Carter, Kevin Robert; Peking since January
1992; born 26.8.55; OPCS 1972-76; Dar es
Salaam (LE) 1979-82; FCO 1983; Warsaw 1984;
Third Secretary (Cons) Valletta 1987; FCO 1989;
Grade 9; m 1976 Sandra Ann McHugh (2d 1985,
1986).

Carter, Michael Charles; Second Secretary New
York since November 1990; born 11.8.46;
Commonwealth Office 1963; Tunis 1968; Accra
1971; Moscow 1974; FCO 1976; Athens 1980;
Dubai 1983; Second Secretary FCO 1986; m
1972 Susan Peta Mills Buffey (2s 1974, 1979).

Carter, Nicholas Paul; First Secretary FCO since
January 1990; born 13.3.46; Commonwealth
Office (later FCO) 1966; Belgrade 1970;
Bombay 1972; Prague 1976; on loan to Midland
Bank 1979; FCO 1981; Second Secretary Bonn
1983; First Secretary (Comm) Kuala Lumpur
1986; m 1970 Gillian Dora Paget (2s 1971,
1978; 1d 1974).

Carter, Peter Leslie; First Secretary FCO since
September 1989; born 19.11.56; FCO 1984;
Second later First Secretary (Chancery) New
Delhi 1986; m 1985 Rachelle Hays (1d 1991).

Carter, Thomas Henry; First Secretary (Science
and Technology) Bonn since November 1990;
born 22.11.53; FCO 1976; ENA Paris 1978;
Paris 1979; Vice-Consul later Second Secretary
(Chancery) Bogotá 1983; Second Secretary FCO
1987; T/D Paris 1990.

Cartwright, George Henry; Moscow since

April 1992; born 1.9.39; Army 1956-79;
Moscow 1981; Cairo 1983; Madrid 1984;
Havana 1987; Bangkok 1988; Grade SO; m
1957 Elizabeth Windsor Charters (2d 1961,
1965; 1s 1962).

Cartwright, Peter John; UKDEL NATO since
January 1990; FCO since December 1986; born
23.3.55; FCO 1975; On loan to Masirah 1978;
Athens 1979; Paris 1982; Kabul 1984; Grade 9;
m 1984 Pamela Jane Edwards (1s 1992).

Cartwright, Stephen Mark; Bombay since
November 1988; born 23.8.64; FCO 1985; East
Berlin 1987; Grade 9; m 1988 Nicola Bjorg
Joyce (1s 1991).

Cary, Anthony Joyce; SUPL as Deputy Chef du
Cabinet, EEC Commission since January 1989;
born 1.7.51; FCO 1973; Third Secretary BMG
Berlin 1975; Second later First Secretary FCO
1978; Harkness Fellow at Stanford Business
School 1980; FCO 1982; PS to the Minister of
State 1984; First Secretary and Head of
Chancery Kuala Lumpur 1986; m 1975 Clare
Louise Katharine Elworthy (3s 1978, 1980,
1983).

Case, Leonard Henry; Khartoum since October
1992; born 1.4.39; Royal Navy 1954-79; Prague
1983; Amman 1985; Kuala Lumpur 1987;
Bucharest 1989; Peking 1991; Grade SO; m
1959 Sheila Ann (née Wills) (1d 1960).

Casey, Kevin Anthony Michael; Second
Secretary (Cons) Canberra since September 1989;
born 18.11.41; FO 1959; New York (UKMIS)
1963; Baghdad 1966; Bonn 1967; FCO 1970;
Addis Ababa 1973; FCO 1977; Islamabad 1979;
Freetown 1981; Georgetown 1984; Second
Secretary FCO 1986; m (1) 1963 Denise Patricia
Byrne (3d 1964, 1967, 1970); (2) 1989 Mrs
Linda Roberts.

Casey, Nigel Philip; FCO since September 1991;
born 29.5.69; Grade 8.

Casey, Sheila Mary; FCO since October 1988;
born 21.7.42; FCO 1971; Tehran 1972; FCO
1974; Lusaka 1976; FCO 1978; Nicosia 1979;
FCO 1982; Prague 1984; UKREP Brussels 1986;
Grade S1.

Castillo, Oscar Luis; FCO since April 1990;
born 5.8.69; Grade 10.

Caton, Michael Malusi, Third Secretary
(Chancery) Canberra since June 1992; born
18.5.64; DHSS 1986-89; FCO 1989; Grade 9; m
1991 Ann Margaret Elliott.

Caton, Dr Valerie; First Secretary (Chancery)
Paris since July 1988; born 12.5.52; FCO 1980;
Second later First Secretary (EC Affairs)
Brussels 1982; First Secretary FCO 1984; m
1987 David Mark Harrison.

Caulfield, Tracy Ann; Vienna since November 1990; born 10.3.70; FCO 1988; Grade 10.

Caughey, Alan Marsh; FCO since November 1990; born 17.11.71; Grade 10.

Causer, Graham George; Second Secretary Singapore since February 1990; born 14.2.46; FO 1964; Castries 1968; Washington 1969; Pro Consul Karachi 1972; FCO 1975; Abu Dhabi 1978; Osaka 1982; FCO 1984 (Second Secretary 1987); m 1969 Hazel Alice Barrett (2d 1974, 1977).

Cavagan, John Raymond; FCO since August 1990; born 9.10.66; Grade 9.

Cavill, David John; Bangkok since November 1991; born 13.6.41; HM Forces 1961-76 HMC and E 1979-84; RUC 1984-89; Moscow 1989; Havana 1990; Grade SO; m 1983 Eve Nicholl.

Cayless, Trevor Martin; Third Secretary (Aid) Lusaka since May 1990; born 18.5.66; DHSS 1985; FCO 1986; Grade 9; m 1989 Rosemary Anne Whiting.

Cazalet, Piers William Alexander; FCO since September 1991; Grade 8.

Cecil, Desmond Hugh; Counsellor FCO since September 1989; born 19.10.41; Second Secretary FCO 1970; First Secretary Bonn 1973; FCO 1974; UKMIS Geneva 1976; FCO 1980; Counsellor Vienna 1985; m 1964 Ruth Elizabeth Sachs (3s 1966, 1968, 1971; 1d 1972).

Ceurvorst, Anthony Paul, MBE (1966); Consul-General Munich since July 1992; born 10.7.35; HM Forces 1954-56; CRO 1956; Delhi 1957; Second Secretary (Admin) Kuala Lumpur 1961 and Salisbury 1964; DSAO (later FCO) 1967; Second Secretary (Comm) Bonn 1970; Consul (Comm) Hamburg 1971; First Secretary (Comm) Madras 1976; FCO 1979; Consul (Comm) BTDO New York 1983; Counsellor (Comm) Cairo 1988; m 1959 Catherine Mary Gilmartin (2s 1960, 1961).

Chadbourne, Karen Maria; FCO since September 1990; born 3.9.70; Grade S2A.

Chadwick, Janine Linda (née Laurence); UKMIS Vienna since May 1991; born 9.4.54; FCO 1983; Brasilia 1987; Grade S2; m 1985 Peter Guy Chadwick.

Chadwick, John Anthony; FCO since September 1992; born 16.12.52; FCO 1971; Malta 1973; Manila 1976; FCO 1980; Islamabad 1983; São Paulo 1988; Grade 9; m 1976 Jane Saliba (3d 1979, 1983, 1986; 1s 1981).

Chadwick, Nigel Spencer; FCO since March 1992; born 17.9.52; FCO 1971; Berne 1973; Buenos Aires 1977; Dacca 1980; Lima 1981; FCO 1984; Bombay 1988; Grade 9.

Chalmers, Ian Pender, OBE (1980); Counsellor FCO since June 1987; born 30.1.39; FO 1963; Second Secretary Beirut 1966; FCO 1968; First Secretary Warsaw 1970; First Secretary FCO 1972; Paris 1976; FCO 1980; Counsellor UKMIS Geneva 1984; m 1962 Lisa Christine Hay (2s 1964, 1971; 3d 1965, 1968, 1976). ·

Chalmers, Kathleen Corbett; FCO since May 1991; born 19.8.59; Brasilia 1981; FCO 1982; Hanoi 1983; FCO 1986; Rome 1987; SUPL 1990; Grade S2.

Chamberlain, Kevin John, CMG (1992); Deputy Legal Adviser FCO since June 1990; born 31.1.42; Called to the Bar, Inner Temple 1965; FCO 1965; First Secretary (Legal Adviser) BMG Berlin 1974; Bonn 1976; FCO 1977; Counsellor (Legal Adviser) UKREP Brussels 1983; Legal Counsellor FCO 1987; m 1967 Pia Frauenlob (1d 1975).

Chambers, David Ian; FCO since June 1987; born 4.12.47; Principal Research Officer; m (1) 1978 Merilyn Figueroa (diss 1990); (2) 1991 Tharinee Plobyon.

Chambers, Karen Ann; FCO since August 1991; born 18.12.67; FCO 1987; Bonn 1989; Grade S2.

Chandler, Julian; Deputy High Commissioner Mbabane since March 1992; born 7.7.50; DSAO (later FCO) 1967; Istanbul 1971; Middle East Floater 1971; FCO 1973; Singapore 1976; Kuala Lumpur 1977; FCO 1979; Port Stanley 1982; Assistant Trade Commissioner Hong Kong 1984; First Secretary FCO 1989; m 1988 Caroline Louise Parkinson; (1d 1980, 2s 1982, 1992).

Chandler, Steven; FCO since April 1991; born 27.1.71; Grade 10.

Chandler, Steven Clive; Dhaka since February 1992; born 16.3.68; DHSS 1986; FCO 1987; BMG Berlin 1989; Grade 10.

Chandler, Vanessa Jane, MBE (1992); FCO since September 1990; born 10.3.62; FCO 1982; Moscow 1984; FCO 1985; New York 1988; Grade 9.

Chandley, Peter Warren, MVO (1981); Deputy Head of Mission Bogota since April 1992; born 24.11.34; RAF 1953-55; Tripoli 1955; Kabul 1958; Havana 1960; Vice-Consul Phnom Penh 1962; Tananarive 1966; FCO 1969; Nairobi 1972; Second Secretary 1973; Kampala 1976; Oslo 1977; First Secretary FCO 1981; First Secretary (Comm) Head of Chancery and Consul Abidjan 1986; HM Ambassador Brazzaville 1990; m 1961 Jane Williams.

Chaplin, Edward Graham Mellish, OBE (1988);

Deputy Permanent Representative and Head of Chancery, UKMIS Geneva since January 1992; born 21.2.51; FCO 1973; MECAS 1974; Third Secretary Muscat 1975; Second Secretary Brussels 1977; ENA Paris 1978; on loan to CSD 1979; First Secretary FCO 1981; First Secretary and Head of Chancery Tehran 1985; First Secretary FCO 1987; Counsellor FCO on secondment to the Private Sector 1990; m 1983 Nicola Helen Fisher (2d 1984, 1989; 1s 1987).

Chapman, Adrian Paul; UKREP Brussels since January 1990; born 14.8.69; FCO 1988; Grade 9.

Chapman, Colin; Third Secretary Rome since June 1991; born 12.1.58; Army 1974-79; FCO 1980; Bonn 1985; FCO 1988; Grade 8; m 1983 Katherine Anne French (1d 1987).

Chapman, Frederick John; Brasilia since June 1990; born 15.10.44; GPO 1961; FCO 1968; Singapore 1969; Bahrain 1972; FCO 1972; Helsinki 1973; FCO 1975; Nairobi 1979; FCO 1982; Addis Ababa 1983; FCO 1986; Grade 8; m (1) 1967 Mary Patricia Clarke (diss. 1988) (1d 1968, 1s 1973); (2) Maria Schuh (née Hedl).

Chapman, Richard Leslie; FCO since June 1990; born 12.10.38; GPO 1953; HM Forces 1957-59; GPO 1959; FO 1963; Geneva 1965; Cairo 1968; FCO 1970; Hong Kong 1971; FCO 1973; Prague 1976; FCO 1979; Second Secretary Nairobi 1984; Second Secretary Pretoria 1987; m 1964 Ruth Vera Garson (1d 1966; 1s 1972).

Chapman, Tracy Michelle; New Delhi since September 1990; born 30.10.68; FCO 1988; Grade S2.

Chapple, Katherine Margaret; FCO since October 1990; born 19.9.64; Home Civil Service 1988; Grade 10.

Charlton, Alan; Counsellor on loan to the Cabinet Office since January 1991; born 21.6.52; FCO 1978; Language Training 1979; Second later First Secretary Amman 1981; First Secretary FCO 1984; First Secretary (Deputy Political Adviser) BMG Berlin 1986; m 1974 Judith Angela Carryer (2s 1979, 1985; 1d 1981).

Chase, Robert John; Counsellor FCO since November 1988; born 13.3.43; FO 1965; Third later Second Secretary Rangoon 1966; FCO 1969; First Secretary (Inf) Rio de Janeiro 1972; FCO 1976; on secondment to ICI Ltd 1980; First Secretary FCO 1982; Counsellor (Comm) Moscow 1985; m 1966 Gillian Ann Shelton (1d 1968; 1s 1969).

Chassels, Lilias Penman Morton; Addis Ababa since February 1991; born 8.5.66; FCO 1988; Grade S2.

Chatt, Paul Anthony; Second Secretary (Managaement/Cons) Berne since July 1990;

born 7.4.56; FCO 1975; Ottawa 1977; East Berlin 1979; Khartoum 1981; FCO 1984; Third (later Second) Secretary (Aid/Comm) Banjul 1987; m (1) 1979 Delyth Hudson (diss. 1988); (2) 1990 Tracie Cavell Heatherington (1d 1992).

Chatterton-Dickson, Robert Maurice French; Second Secretary (Chancery/Information) Manila since October 1991; born 1.2.62; FCO 1990.

Chavasse, Gervase Barrington Bushe; FCO since May 1990; born 20.1.37; HMOCS Zambia 1959-64; DSA 1965; Saigon 1968; Budapest 1971; FCO 1971; Warsaw 1972; Alexandria 1973; FCO 1977; Second Secretary (Admin/Consular) Kampala 1979; Vice-Consul (later First Secretary) Tel Aviv 1980; First Secretary FCO 1983; Deputy High Commissioner and Head of Chancery Maseru 1986; m 1973 Barbara Elizabeth Saunders (2d 1975, 1977).

Cheney, Nicola Ann; Jakarta since September 1991; born 23.11.64; FCO 1987; Moscow 1989; Grade S2.

Cherrie, Yvonne Elizabeth; on secondment to the Birmingham Chamber of Commerce since January 1991; FCO since November 1989; born 31.3.62; FCO 1980; UKREP Brussels 1982; Sana'a 1985; Bahrain 1988; FCO 1989; Grade 9.

Chick, John Charles; Third Secretary (Management) and Vice Consul Quito since September 1990; born 22.10.47; FCO 1971; Baghdad 1973; FCO 1975; Amman 1976; FCO 1979; Darwin 1980; FCO 1984; Hanoi 1985; FCO 1988; Grade 9; m (1) 1971 Denese Irene Smalley; (2) 1989 Tran Thi Thuy Duong.

Chilcott, Dominick John; First Secretary FCO since May 1988; born 17.11.59; Royal Navy 1978-79; FCO 1982; Language Training 1984; Third later Second Secretary Ankara 1984; m 1983 Jane Elizabeth Bromage.

Childs, Marie-Louise; Vice-Consul Bangkok since February 1991; born 23.3.66; FCO 1989; Grade 9.

Chiswell, Jean Anne, MBE (1984); Second Secretary (Immig) Algiers since February 1988; born 16.5.38; Peking 1971; Blantyre 1973; Moscow 1975; Hong Kong 1977; FCO 1981; Prague 1982; FCO 1983; Geneva 1986.

Chittenden, Debra Lorraine; Cape Town/Pretoria since December 1991; born 15.10.66; FCO 1985; Peking 1988; Grade S2.

Chittenden, Geoffrey Martin; Counsellor FCO since September 1991; born 20.5.45; Third later Second Secretary FCO 1969; Delhi 1971; Second later First Secretary FCO 1975; First Secretary Prague 1976; FCO 1978; Hong Kong 1981; FCO 1985; Counsellor New Delhi 1989; m 1967

Frances Mary Fleet (1s 1970; 2d 1972, 1976).

Chivers, George Edward; Bonn since October 1989; born 25.1.31; Army 1948-75; Lagos 19 5; Warsaw 1976; Buenos Aires 1979; Kuala Lum ur 1980; Vienna 1984; Madrid 1987; Moscow 1988; Grade SO; m 1951 Erika Algermissen (2d 1952, 1966; 1s 1956).

Christie, Ian Houston Pritchard; Athens since March 1990; born 26.8.38; RAF 1960-85; FCO 1987; Warsaw 1987; Havana 1989; Grade SO; m 1960 Isabella Sutherland Innes (1s 1960).

Christlow, Thomas William; Lusaka since July 1991; born 7.9.36; Moscow 1978; Istanbul 1979; New York 1983; Pretoria 1985; Prague 1988; Kuala Lumpur 1990; Grade SO; m 1955 Lily Manners (2s 1956, 1961).

Christopher, Duncan Robin Carmichael; Counsellor FCO since October 1991; born 13.10.44; FCO 1970; Second later First Secretary New Delhi 1972; First Secretary FCO 1976; Head of Chancery Lusaka 1980; First Secretary FCO 1983; On loan to Cabinet Office 1985; Counsellor (Comm) Madrid 1987; m 1980 Merril Stevenson.

Chubbs, Sylvia Sharon; Colombo since September 1989; born 9.5.58; FCO 1984; Paris 1986; Grade S2.

Chun, David John; Moscow since August 1992; born 4.4.64; FCO 1985; Lagos 1987; Grade 9; m 1987 Grace Fotheringham.

Chun, Grace (née Fotheringham); Moscow since August 1992; born 24.7.66; FCO 1985; Lagos 1987; Grade 10; m 1987 David John Chun.

Chun, John Henry; First Secretary Washington since January 1990; born 18.4.37; Post Office 1954; RAF 1956-58; Post Office 1958; FO 1963; Moscow 1964; FO 1965; Tokyo 1966; FCO 1969; Ankara 1970; FCO 1972; Third later Second Secretary Pretoria 1977; Second Secretary FCO 1980; Second Secretary Singapore 1981; Second later First Secretary FCO 1984; m 1961 Janice Dorothy May Leech (2s 1964, 1978; 1d 1975).

Church, Bettina Frances; FCO since June 1992; born 30.4.63; FCO 1983; Gaborone 1984; UKMIS Geneva 1987; SUPL 1990; UKMIS New York 1991; Grade S1; m 1990 Julian Andrew Church.

Church, Robert John Paul; Counsellor FCO since May 1992; born 30.4.47; Second Secretary FCO 1973; Language Student SOAS 1975; First Secretary Bangkok 1976; FCO 1979; First Secretary (Chancery) East Berlin 1981; FCO 1984; First Secretary (Chancery) Nairobi 1986; Counsellor and Permanent Representative ESCAP Bangkok 1989; m 1972 Priscilla Mary St

Johnston (3d 1973, 1975, 1984; 1s 1977).

Church, Roger Gilbert; Deputy High Commissioner Nassau since October 1990; born 1.6.46; FO 1965; Abu Dhabi 1968; Bonn 1970; East Berlin 1973; Lusaka 1974; FCO 1976; Madras 1979; Colombo 1980; Quito 1982; Second Secretary (Comm) Madras 1983; Second Secretary FCO 1988; m 1972 Kathleen Wilson Dryburgh (2s 1974, 1977).

Churchill, Nicholas Lovell; First Secretary FCO since May 1989; born 29.5.50; Third Secretary FCO 1973; Language Student 1975; Second Secretary 1976; Language Student Tokyo 1976; Second later First Secretary (Comm) Tokyo 1977; FCO 1980; First Secretary and Head of Chancery Beirut 1983; FCO 1984; Islamabad 1986; m (1) 1977 Julia Charlotte Callaghan (diss 1985); (2) 1985 Diana Mary Lacey (1s 1988, 1d 1989).

Clare, William Geoffrey; Second Secretary (Political/Info) Helsinki since July 1992; born 29.11.58; FCO 1981; Tehran 1983; Los Angeles 1987; Second Secretary FCO 1989; Language training 1991; m 1982 Mandy Wescott.

Claridge, Susan Elisabeth; UKDIS Geneva since February 1990; born 10.5.60; FCO 1984; UKREP Brussels 1987; Grade S2.

Clark, Alan Richard; HM Consul General Montreal since February 1990; born 4.9.39; FO 1958; HM Forces 1960-62; FO 1962; Vice-Consul Tehran 1964; Second Secretary (Admin) Jedda 1966; Second Secretary (Econ) and later First Secretary Paris 1969; First Secretary FCO 1972; First Secretary and Head of Chancery Freetown 1976; FCO 1980; Counsellor Seconded to Vickers Shipbuilders Ltd 1984; Counsellor and Head of Chancery, Bucharest 1986; m 1961 Ann Rosemary Hosford (1s 1976).

Clark, Catherine Elizabeth (née Ferguson); UKDEL NATO Brussels since January 1991; born 12.6.59; FCO 1979; Singapore 1981; Istanbul 1985; FE/SEA Floater 1988; Grade 9; m 1990 Eldred Richard Wraighte Clark.

Clark, Gerald Edmondson, CMG (1989); UK Permanent Representative to IAEA/UNIDO/other UN Organisations, UKMIS Vienna since June 1987; (Holds personal rank of Ambassador) born 26.12.35; FO 1960; Hong Kong 1961; Third Secretary Peking 1962; Second later First Secretary FO 1964; First Secretary and Press Attaché Moscow 1968; FCO 1970; First Secretary and Head of Chancery Lisbon 1973; Counsellor on Loan to the Cabinet Office 1977; Seconded to Barclays Bank International 1979; Counsellor (Comm) Peking 1981; Counsellor, FCO 1984; m 1967 Mary Rose Organ (2d 1970, 1971).

Clark, Hilary Mary; FCO since April 1985; born

10.4.62; FCO 1980; UKREP Brussels 1982; Bonn 1983; Grade 9.

Clark, James Frame; Second Secretary (Presidency Support/External Relations) UKREP Brussels since June 1991; born 12.3.63; FCO 1988; Second Secretary 1989; language training 1989; language training Cairo 1990; FCO 1990; m 1990 Michele Taylor.

Clark, Joseph Denis, MBE (1970); Consul (Commercial) Dallas since September 1991; born 27.8.35; HM Forces 1953-56; HMOCS Kenya 1956-64; Retired as Inspector of Police; FO 1965; Moscow 1967; Lahore 1969; Hanover 1971; FCO 1974; Ulan Bator 1975; Detroit 1977; Consul Gothenburg 1979; Second later First Secretary FCO 1985; First Secretary (Comm) Belgrade 1988; m (1) 1959 June Rose Nobbs (1s 1959); (2) 1982 Ulla Karin Hjalmarsson (3s 1982, 1986, 1988).

Clark, Katherine Margaret (née Storey); FCO since June 1985; born 18.3.50; FCO 1971; Muscat 1972; Budapest 1974; FCO 1975; Peking 1977; UKMIS New York 1978; Rio de Janeiro 1982; Grade 9; m 1987 Richard William Clark.

Clark, Kenneth; Second Secretary (Comm) Gaborone since August 1989; born 18.8.49; Post Office Savings Department 1966; DSAO 1967; Kuwait 1971; Moscow 1974; Rio de Janeiro 1975; FCO 1978; New York 1981; Jedda 1983; Second Secretary FCO 1986; m 1970 Agnes Pearson Elder (3s 1971, 1974, 1978).

Clark, Michael; Second Secretary 1991 (Comm/Cons) Montreal since May 1992; born 21.9.59; FCO 1979; Georgetown 1983; Stockholm 1986; Kuwait 1988; (Second Secretary 1991); m 1983 Jacqueline Anne Wilkins (2s 1985, 1987).

Clark, Michele; SUPL since August 1992; born 25.2.66; FCO 1989; language training 1990; Third later Second Secretary (Community Staffing) UKREP Brussels 1991; m 1990 James Frame Clark.

Clark, Paul Nicholas; Vienna since August 1992; born 26.1.69; Grade 10; FCO 1988; m 1991 Katherine Walsh (1s 1991).

Clark, Peter; First Secretary FCO since September 1992; born 18.4.54; FCO 1982; Principal Research Officer; First Secretary (Chancery) Peking 1988; m 1977 Alison Padgett (1d 1982; 1s 1984).

Clark, Peter; Nairobi since July 1991; born 26.3.47; Royal Air Force 1962-87; FCO 1987; Grade 9 (2s 1974, 1977).

Clark, Richard James; FCO since September 1990; born 10.7.55; FCO 1974; Kingston 1977; BERS Masirah 1980; Bucharest 1981; Maputo 1982; FCO 1983; Doha 1987; Grade 9; m 1981

Lucy Helen Ianelli.

Clark, Roger; First Secretary FCO since May 1985; born 5.9.40; Ministry of Aviation (and Transport and Civil Aviation) 1958; British Airports Authority (on secondment) 1966; BOT 1967; Second Secretary FCO 1969; Vice-Consul (Comm) BTDO New York 1971; First Secretary 1976; First Secretary and Consul Belgrade 1978; First Secretary (Comm) Khartoum 1981; m (1) 1967 Susan Darby (3s 1969, 1970, 1974); (2) 1988 Elizabeth Knott.

Clark, Sandra Jean; Vice-Consul Dusseldorf since January 1989; born 3.12.67; FCO 1985; UKDEL NATO Brussels 1987; Grade 9; m 1990 Mark Stephen Parnell.

Clark, Sir Terence (Joseph) KBE (1990); CMG (1985); CVO (1978); HM Ambassador Muscat since January 1990; born 19.6.34; HM Forces 1953-55; MECAS 1956; Amman 1958; Vice-Consul Casablanca 1961; FO 1963; Commercial Officer Dubai 1965; First Secretary 1966; Assistant Political Agent Dubai 1966; First Secretary (Inf) Belgrade 1969; First Secretary, Head of Chancery and Consul Muscat 1972; FCO 1974; Counsellor (Press and Inf) Bonn 1976; Counsellor (Political) Belgrade 1979; Deputy Leader UKDEL CSCE Madrid 1982; Head of Information Department FCO 1983; HM Ambassador Baghdad 1985; m 1960 Lieselotte Muller (2s 1962, 1966; 1d 1967).

Clark, Teresa Melanie; FCO since November 1990; born 29.5.70; Grade 10.

Clarke, Alison Patricia (née Tierney); SUPL since January 1990; born 12.9.51; FCO 1973; Düsseldorf 1975; Karachi 1979; FCO 1982; Second Secretary (Chancery) Kingston 1986; m 1977 Duncan Clarke.

Clarke, Brian Frank Beverley; FCO since July 1986; born 8.12.33; HM Forces 1952-55; FO 1955; Delhi 1955; FO 1957; Seoul 1958; FO 1960; Tripoli 1962; FO 1965; Junior Attaché Bucharest 1966; FCO 1968; Kaduna 1969; FCO 1970; Anguilla 1971; FCO 1972; Athens 1975; FCO 1978; Sofia 1979; FCO 1982; Sana'a 1983; Grade 8; m 1971 Lucie Broughton.

Clarke, Julie Linda; Moscow since October 1990; born 13.1.64; FCO 1988; Grade S2A.

Clarke, Pauline Joyce; FCO since May 1987; born 8.10.67; Grade 10.

Clarke, Peter Michael; Full-time Language Training Taiwan since October 1991; born 23.8.63; FCO 1988; Language Training 1990; Grade 7.

Clarke, Richard Ian; First Secretary FCO since July 1991; born 7.9.55; FCO 1977; Caracas 1978; Second later First Secretary FCO 1983;

First Secretary Washington 1987; m 1978 Ann Elizabeth Menzies (1s 1984).

Clarke, Roger Stephen Graver, LVO (1991); Deputy Observer later Deputy High Commissioner Windhoek since March 1989; born 8.5.55; FCO 1977; Third Secretary Kinshasa 1978; Second Secretary Paris 1980; First Secretary FCO 1984; on loan to DTI 1986.

Clarke, Rosemary Protase, MBE (1992); Second Secretary (Immigration) Dhaka since June 1992; born 13.2.50; FCO 1977; Port Louis 1978; FCO 1982; Manila 1984; Bahrain 1988; Second Secretary FCO 1991; m 1982 E S M Daniel Sinassamy (1s 1984; 1d 1987).

Clarkin, Jennifer Ann; Vice-Consul Durban since July 1992; born 1.11.60; FCO 1980; BMG Berlin 1982; Mogadishu 1988; Africa/ME Floater 1985; FCO 1989; Grade 9; m 1988 Murray Rex Clarkin.

Claughton, Michael George; Second Secretary FCO since August 1991; born 21.5.39; RAF 1959-62; Colonial Office 1962; FO 1964; Havana 1968; Copenhagen 1969; Belgrade 1971; FCO 1974; Dacca 1978; Suva 1980; FCO 1984 (Second Secretary 1985); Second Secretary (Commercial) Lilongwe 1988; m 1968 Ida Saga.

Clay, Edward; Counsellor FCO since January 1989; born 21.7.45; Third Secretary FO (later FCO) 1968; Nairobi 1970; Second later First Secretary (Chancery) Sofia 1973; FCO 19 5; First Secretary (Comm) Budapest 1979; First Secretary FCO 1982; Counsellor and Head of Chancery Nicosia 1985; m 1969 Anne Stroud (3d 1972, 1974, 1978).

Clayden, Timothy; First Secretary (Information) Warsaw since July 1991; born 28.3.60; Second later First Secretary FCO 1989; m 1984 Katherine Susan Jackson.

Cleary, Anthony Shaun; Third later Second Secretary (Chancery) Pretoria/Cape Town since July 1990; born 27.10.65; FCO 1988.

Clegg, Laura Margaret; FCO since November 1989; born 29.3.65; Grade 9; m 1987 Khalil Salem.

Clegg, Leslie David; MVO (1985); First Secretary (Comm) Madrid since February 1992; born 12.10.49; FO (later FCO) 1967; Banjul (formerly Bathurst) 1971; Wellington 1974; FCO 1977; New Delhi 1980; Second Secretary Lisbon 1984; First Secretary FCO 1988; m 1970 Louise Elizabeth Straughan (3d 1973, 1976, 1984).

Cleghorn, Bruce Elliot; Counsellor and Deputy High Commissioner Kuala Lumpur since January 1992; born 19.11.46; Second Secretary FCO 1974; First Secretary (NATO) Brussels 1976; First Secretary New Delhi 1980; First Secretary

FCO 1983; Counsellor UKDEL CSCE Vienna 1987; m 1976 Sally Ann Robinson (2s 1978, 1981).

Clements, Martin Hugh; First Secretary (IAEA) UKMIS Vienna since April 1990; born 26.7.61; FCO 1983. Second Secretary (Chancery) Tehran 1986; FCO 1987.

Clements, Michael Colin; Counsellor and Deputy High Commissioner Nicosia since November 1990; born 24.8.49; FCO 1974; Second later First Secretary Athens 1976; on loan to the Cabinet Office 1980; FCO 1982; First Secretary and Head of Chancery Singapore 1985; First Secretary FCO 1989; m 1972 Julia Mary Roebuck.

Clemitson, Lynne Dawn; FCO since July 1991; born 4.5.61; FCO 1979; Washington 1982; Dhaka 1985; Wellington 1988; Grade S1; m 1983 Malcolm John Clemitson.

Clephane, James Cavin Alexander; Second Secretary (Chancery) Bandar Seri Begawan since July 1991; Muscat since September 1986; born 3.2.54; FCO 1973; Budapest 1976; Seoul 1977; Jakarta 1980; FCO 1983; Third later Second Secretary Muscat 1986; m 1974 Mary Buchanan Dorman.

Clews, Alison Helen; Manila since April 1992; born 4.11.65; ODA 1987; FCO 1990; Grade S2.

Clews, Anthony Edward; Floater duties since January 1988; born 1.5.38; RAF 1955-78; Lusaka 1978; Havana 1979; Damascus 1980; Ankara 1982; Rome 1983; Kampala 1986; Grade CSO.

Clibborn, John Donovan Nelson dalla Rosa; Counsellor FCO since August 1991; born 24.11.41; Third Secretary FO 1966; Third later Second Secretary (Technical Assistance) Nicosia 1967; Second Secretary FCO 1970; First Secretary (Econ) Bonn 1972; First Secretary UKREP Brussels 1976; SUPL at EC Brussels 1978; FCO 1981; Counsellor Washington 1988; m 1968 Juliet Elizabeth Pagden (1d 1969; 1s 1971).

Cliff, Caroline Mary (née Redman); Second Secretary UKMIS New York since June 1990; born 9.4.55; FCO 1978; Rome 1980; SEA/FE Floater 1983; FCO 1986; (Second Secretary 1987); SUPL 1989; m 1988 Ian Cameron Cliff (1s 1989).

Cliff, Ian Cameron, OBE (1991); First Secretary (Chancery) UKMIS New York since July 1989; born 11.9.52; FCO 1979; Language Training 1980; Second later First Secretary Khartoum 1982; First Secretary FCO 1985; m 1988 Caroline Mary Redman (1s 1989).

Clifton, Timothy David; First Secretary FCO since May 1990; born 25.12.60; FCO 1984;

Second Secretary Luanda 1988; m 1985 Karen Elaine Hurn.

Clissold, Sean Dominic; FCO since September 1990; born 6.4.58; FCO 1975; UKMIS Geneva 1978; Rabat 1981; Ankara 1983; Lagos 1987; Grade 9; m 1986 Belgin Savaci.

Clydesdale, William Reginald; FCO since October 1990; born 12.8.43; MOD 1960; FCO 1980; Lagos 1985; Third Secretary Sofia 1987; Grade 8; m 1969 Noreen Foister (2s 1973, 1976).

Coates, David; Political Counsellor Peking since November 1989; born 13.11.47; Second later First Secretary FCO 1974; Language Student Hong Kong 1977; First Secretary (Comm) Peking 1978; FCO 1981; First Secretary UKMIS Geneva 1986; m 1974 Joanna Kay Weil (2d 1976, 1978).

Cobb, Stanley Owen, MBE (1989); Second Secretary FCO since June 1991; born 15.12.35; Royal Navy 1951-62; CRO 1962; Karachi 1963; Commonwealth Office 1965; Aden 1967; Jakarta 1968; FCO 1968; Bangkok 1969; Rangoon 1971; FCO 1972; Port Moresby 1976; FCO 1976; Dhaka 1979; FCO 1983; Second Secretary (Cons/Admin) Calcutta 1984; Second Secretary and Consul Jakarta 1988; m 1971 Lay Kheng.

Cobden, Alan; Second Secretary (Agric) Dublin since October 1989; born 15.7.54; FCO 1970; Canberra 1975; Tehran 1977; Africa Floater 1978; Bombay 1980; FCO 1983; Third later Second Secretary Sofia 1986; m 1982 Karen Anne Fawn (1s 1985; 1d 1987).

Cochrane-Dyet, Fergus John; Third Secretary (Chancery) Lagos since July 1990; born 16.1.65; FCO 1987; Full-time language training Cairo 1988; FCO 1989; Grade 8; m Susan Emma Aram.

Cockel, Susan Jane; Third Secretary (Comm) Peking since October 1992; born 9.3.66; FCO 1989; Language Training 1990; Full-time Language Training Peking 1991, Grade 9.

Cockerham, David; Deputy High Commissioner Madras since July 1991; born 14.5.44; FO 1962; DSAO 1965; Saigon 1967; Tokyo 1969; Vice-Consul Yokohama 1971; Vice-Consul Tokyo 1972 (Second Secretary 1974); FCO 1975; Vice-Consul (Comm/Inf) BIS New York 1979; Consul (Comm) BTDO New York 1981; First Secretary (Comm) Tokyo 1983; First Secretary on loan to DTI 1987; First Secretary FCO 1989; m 1967 Ann Lesley Smith (2s 1969, 1973).

Cockshott, David John; Second Secretary Paris since January 1991; born 8.3.43; FO 1965; Damascus 1967; Aden 1968; Baghdad 1969; FCO 1971; Cabinet Office 1974; Pretoria 1975; FCO 1978; Vienna 1979; Moscow 1982; FCO

1985; m 1971 Angela Margaret Haldane (1d 1972; 1s 1975).

Codd, Steven; Hanoi since December 1990; born 19.5.61; FCO 1981; Baghdad 1982; FCO 1985; Beirut 1986; FCO 1988; Grade 9.

Codrington, Richard John; First Secretary FCO since December 1988; born 18.12.53; MOD 1975; FCO 1978; Second Secretary (later First Secretary) Dar es Salaam 1980; FCO 1983; New Delhi 1985; m 1985 Julia Elizabeth Nolan (Twin s 1991).

Cody, Kevin Anthony; Third Secretary Sofia since September 1990; born 17.1.37; FO 1966; St Helena 1968; FCO 1969; New Delhi 1971; FCO 1973; Singapore 1975; FCO 1977; Nicosia 1979; FCO 1981; Amman 1986; FCO 1990; Grade 8; m 1964 Anne Bridget Ring (1d 1968; 1s 1970).

Cogan, Claire; Paris since October 1984; born 2.4.62; FCO 1983; Grade 10.

Cogger, Darren Barry; Belgrade since March 1991; born 20.5.63; FCO 1984; Athens 1988; Grade 10; m 1986 Johanna Lesley Payne (1d 1989).

Coggles, Paul James; Third Secretary (Chancery) Sofia since August 1992; born 24.6.66; FCO 1989.

Coghlan, Robert Edward; First Secretary (Information) Tokyo since July 1991; born 18.5.42; Passport Office 1961; FO 1963; Belgrade 1964; Havana 1967; Tokyo 1968; FCO 1973; Zurich 1976; Zagreb 1979; Second Secretary FCO 1981; Second later First Secretary (Comm) Tokyo 1984; First Secretary (Comm) São Paulo 1988; m 1963 Maureen Martha Doris (diss 1976) (2s 1964, 1965).

Coglin, Gillian Joanna; Bucharest since September 1991; born 9.8.67; FCO 1989; Grade 9.

Coker, Sylvia Joan, MBE (1977); Second Secretary (Immigration) New Delhi since August 1990; born 9.12.36; Department of National Savings 1966; FCO 1969; Moscow 1972; Beirut 1973; Ottawa 1976; FCO 1978; Dakar 1981; Rome 1984; Second Secretary FCO 1987.

Colby, Sheila Jean; Kuala Lumpur since July 1990; born 7.5.56; FCO 1979; Lima 1980; FCO 1983; Floater Duties 1984; FCO 1988; Grade S1.

Cole, Alexandra Pamela; FCO since February 1990; born 2.6.70; Grade 9.

Cole, Anne Constance; FCO since March 1988; born 2.10.43; FO 1966; Vientiane 1966; Havana 1968; FCO 1970; Madrid 1972; FCO 1975; Bucharest 1976; New Delhi 1978; FCO 1981;

UKREP Brussels 1982; UKMIS New York 1985; Grade S1.

Cole, Geoffrey Dennis; Second later first FCO since April 1991; born 30.10.53; Dept of Environment 1974; FCO 1983; Second Secretary (Comm) Caracas 1986; Second Secretary (Admin) Doha 1988; m 1980 Anne-Marie Cunningham (2s 1980, 1983; 1d 1985).

Cole, Norman Edward, OBE (1985); First Secretary FCO since January 1992; born 24.4.43; Crown Estate Office 1962; DSAO (later FCO) 1967; Karachi 1969 (Second Secretary 1972); (Vice-Consul 1972); Ottawa 1973; on loan to DOT 1977; Second Secretary FCO 1980; First Secretary (Comm) Lusaka 1981; First Secretary FCO 1984; First Secretary (Management) Rome 1987; m 1966 Loretta Scott (2s 1970, 1972; 1d 1975).

Cole, Peter John; First Secretary (Comm) Islamabad since November 1991; born 26.8.33; RAF 1951-53; HMOCS Kenya 1953-64; retired as Inspector of Police, Karachi 1965; The Hague 1969; Tokyo 1972; Second Secretary FCO 1974; Second Secretary and Vice-Consul Prague 1978; Second later First Secretary FCO 1981; First Secretary (Comm) Khartoum 1985; First Secretary FCO 1988; First Secretary (Commercial) Calcutta 1990; m 1968 Sandra Ann Frances Blackford (2s 1973, 1975).

Cole, Philip; Second later First Secretary (Inf) Berne since January 1989; born 2.6.42; Passport Office 1961; FO 1964; Luxembourg 1966; Istanbul 1968; Bombay 1971; FCO 1975; East Berlin 1978; Second Secretary Kingston 1981; FCO 1984; m 1965 Sonia Louise Scott (1s 1966).

Coleman, Richard Alan; Second Secretary (Consular) Peking since May 1991; born 1.2.45; CRO later FCO 1963; Dacca 1968; FCO 1971; Salisbury 1972; FCO 1972; Freetown 1973; Tehran 1975; FCO 1979; Vientiane 1982; Kingston 1985; Second Secretary FCO 1988; m (1) 1968 Susan Robertson (diss 1973) (1s 1969); (2) 1973 Celia Frances Burnett (1d 1986).

Coleman, Tracey; FCO since March 1990; born 23.1.71; Grade S2.

Coles, Sir (Arthur) John, KCMG (1989), CMG (1984); DUSS (Asia/Americas) since March 1991; born 13.11.37; MECAS 1960; Third Secretary Khartoum 1962; Second Secretary FO 1964; First Secretary and Assistant Political Agent Dubai 1968; On loan to the Cabinet Office 1971; Private Secretary to Lord Balneil 1972; First Secretary and Head of Chancery Cairo 1975; Counsellor (Developing Countries) UKREP Brussels 1977; Head of South Asian Dept 1980; on loan to No 10 Downing Street 1981; HM Ambassador Amman 1984; High Commissioner Canberra 1988; m 1965 Anne Mary Sutherland Graham (2s 1966, 1968; 1d 1970).

Colhoun, Lorraine Elizabeth; FCO since February 1991; born 10.6.69; Grade S2.

Collard, James Malcolm John; Second Secretary (Management) Islamabad since April 1992; born 30.7.43; DSAO 1965; Belgrade 1968; Colombo 1971; East Berlin 1975; FCO 1976; Dacca 1979; Zurich 1981; FCO 1985; Rome 1989; m 1971 Margaret Mary McIver (1d 1980; 1s 1982).

Collard, Timothy Michael; Second Secretary (Science and Tech) Peking since November 1989; born 21.3.60; FCO 1986; Language Training SOAS 1987; Language Training Hong Kong 1988; m 1985 Patricia Polzer (1s 1989).

Collecott, Peter Salmon; Counsellor (Head of Chancery) Jakarta since September 1989; born 8.10.50; Second Secretary FCO 1977; MECAS 1978; (First Secretary 1979); Khartoum 1980; Canberra 1982; FCO 1986; m 1982 Judith Patricia Pead.

Colley, Timothy John; Second Secretary (Chancery/Information) Islamabad since May 1992; born 13.3.65; FCO 1989, (Second Secretary 1991); Full-time Language Training 1991.

Collier, Geoffrey Thomas Grey; FCO since September 1990; born 27.4.68; Grade 9.

Collier, Stephen John, MVO (1991), RVM (1979); Second Secretary Windhoek since March 1989; born 11.1.52; DTI 1968; FCO 1969; Bonn 1972; Aden 1975; Lilongwe 1976; Lagos 1979; FCO 1983; Amman 1985; m 1987 Erica Mary Cholwill Wilson.

Collingridge, Andrew; Lagos since August 1990; born 2.11.62; FCO 1985; Grade 9.

Collings, Barry Anthony; First Secretary (Bilateral Relations) Bonn since June 1991; born 14.6.50; RAF 1968-69; FCO 1970; Holy See 1974; Beirut 1975; Berlin 1976; Budapest 1980; Second Secretary 1981; FCO 1983; Islamabad 1985; FCO 1988; m 1973 Shirley Gibson (1s 1980; 1d 1984).

Collins, Alan Stanley; Counsellor (Commercial) and Deputy Head of Mission Manila since August 1990; born 1.4.48; Ministry of Defence 1970; Private Secretary to Vice Chief of the Air Staff 1973-1975; FCO 1981; First Secretary and Head of Chancery Addis Ababa 1986; m 1971 Ann Dorothy Roberts (1d 1985).

Collins, Helen Laura; FCO since May 1990; born 15.11.70; Grade 10.

Collins, James Robert; Moscow since September 1990; born 9.11.63; FCO 1986; Strasbourg 1988; Grade 10; m 1987 Sheila Marie Barry.

Collins, Margaret Isabel Valerie; FCO since August 1989; born 11.4.40; Tel Aviv 1964; FCO 1966; Rome 1974; FCO 1977; Lisbon 1979; FCO 1981; New Delhi 1988; Grade S1.

Collis, Simon Paul; First Secretary (Political) New Delhi since April 1991; born 23.2.56; FCO 1978; Language Training 1979; Third later Second Secretary Bahrain 1981; First Secretary FCO 1984; UKMIS New York 1986; FCO 1987; First Secretary and Head of Chancery Tunis 1988; FCO 1990; m 1974 Brigitte Stalter (1s 1975; 1d 1980).

Collyer, Nicholas Edwin; Second Secretary (Comm) Seoul since January 1992; born 15.9.52; Forestry Commission 1969; FCO 1971; Moscow 1974; Colombo 1975; Budapest 1979; FCO 1981; UKMIS Geneva 1983; FCO 1986; New Delhi 1987; Second Secretary FCO 1989; m 1973 Kathryn Dobson (2s 1978, 1983).

Coltman, (Arthur) Leycester (Scott); HM Ambassador Havana since March 1991; born 24.5.38; FO 1961; Third Secretary Copenhagen 1963; Cairo 1964; Second Secretary Madrid 1966; First Secretary 1969; Sabbatical year at Manchester Business School 1969; FCO 1970; Brasilia 1974; FCO 1977; Counsellor and Head of Chancery, Mexico City 1979-83; Counsellor and Head of Chancery Brussels 1983; Counsellor FCO 1987; m 1969 Marie Piedad Cantos Aberasturi (1d 1971; 2s 1974, 1978).

Colvin, David Hugh; Minister, Rome since February 1992; born 23.1.41; Assistant Principal Board of Trade 1966; Second Secretary FO 1967; Bangkok 1968; Second later First Secretary FCO 1971; Paris 1975; First Secretary (Press and Information) UKREP Brussels 1977; Counsellor on loan to Cabinet Office 1982; Counsellor and Head of Chancery Budapest 1985; Counsellor FCO 1988; m 1971 Diana Caroline Carew Smith (1s 1983; 1d 1991).

Colvin, Kathryn Frances; FO (later FCO) since July 1968; Principal Research Officer (DS Grade 5) 1980; born 11.9.45; m 1971 Brian Trevor Colvin.

Conley, Brian John; Lusaka since March 1989; born 10.4.67; FCO 1986; Grade 9.

Connelly, Brian Norman; Administrator Ascension Island since January 1991; born 25.12.41; FO (later FCO) 1967; Budapest 1969; Montevideo 1971; FCO 1974; Kuwait 1976; Second Secretary (Admin) Seoul 1980; First Secretary FCO 1984; First Secretary (Comm) Dhaka 1987; m 1965 Theresa Hughes (1d 1966; 1s 1972).

Connelly, Carla Elizabeth; on Floater Duties since April 1991; born 15.6.68; FCO 1988; Grade 10.

Connelly, Daniel Roy; Dhaka since February 1992; born 3.1.66; FCO 1983; Rome 1986; Bombay 1989; Grade 9.

Connolly, Patrick Anthony; First Secretary (Commercial) Tel Aviv since November 1990; born 15.2.45; CO 1964; FO 1966; Salisbury 1967; Pretoria 1969; Islamabad 1970; FCO 1973; Vienna 1976; Baghdad 1979; Second Secretary (Aid) New Delhi 1981; FCO 1984; Second Secretary and Vice-Consul Dubai 1986; m 1967 Teresa Bernadette Crinion (twin s 1969; 1s 1973).

Connolly, Peter Terence; Managua since December 1990; born 2.5.65; FCO 1988; Grade 9.

Connor, Michael Henry; HM Ambassador and Consul-General San Salvador since November 1991; born 5.8.42; FO 1964; Cairo 1968; Vienna 1970; Second Secretary (Comm1/Aid) Kathmandu 1973; FCO 1976; (First Secretary 1979); First Secretary (Comm) and Consul Havana 1981; First Secretary and Head of Chancery Havana 1982; Head of Chancery Ottawa 1983; First Secretary FCO 1988; m 1964 Valerie Jannita Cunningham (3s 1971, 1972, 1975).

Connor, Michael Leslie; First Secretary FCO since October 1991; born 15.11.49; FCO 1971; UKDEL Vienna 1975; Moscow 1975; Tehran 1977; FCO 1980; (APS to Minister of State 1982); Second Secretary Bonn 1983; Second later First Secretary (Comm) Abu Dhabi 1987; m 1973 Linda Helen Woolnough (1d 1984).

Conroy, Anne Elizabeth, MVO (1991); Second Secretary FCO since January 1992; born 30.8.63; FCO 1985; Third later Second Secretary (Chancery) Manila 1988.

Contractor, Robert; Floater Duties since January 1992; born 17.5.68; FCO 1989; Grade 10.

Cook, Michael Edgar; HM Consul-General Istanbul since September 1992; born 13.5.41; DSA 1966; Oslo 1967; FCO 1970; First Secretary and Head of Chancery Accra 1973; First Secretary (Comm) Stockholm 1977; Resigned September 1980; Reinstated August 1981; First Secretary and Head of Chancery Port of Spain 1981; Deputy High Commissioner, Counsellor and Head of Chancery Dar es Salaam 1984; Counsellor FCO 1987; m (1) 1970 Astrid Edel Wiborg (1d 1971; 1s 1974); (2) 1983 Annebritt Maria Aslund.

Cook, Peter Duncan Gifford; Doha since April 1989; born 15.8.63; FCO 1982; Georgetown 1985; Grade 9.

Cook, Roger Charles Colbourne; First Secretary FCO since June 1990; born 27.3.42; FO 1960; Stockholm 1963; Bonn 1967; FCO 1969;

Moscow 1971; FCO 1972; Second Secretary (Comm) Lagos 1976; Moscow 1979; Second Secretary (Cons) Dar es Salaam 1981; on loan to DTI 1984; First Secretary FCO 1986; First Secretary (Tech) Paris 1988; m 1963 Anne May Fountaine (2s 1963, 1966; 1d 1970).

Cook, Sandra Elizabeth;FCO since October 1992; born 12.6.64; FCO 1987; Nicosia 1990; Grade S2.

Cooke, Jill Elaine; FCO since August 1989; born 15.9.58; FCO 1982; Belgrade 1983; FCO 1986; Gaborone 1987; Grade S2.

Cooling, Ian Richard; Counsellor Berne since September 1992; born 24.9.43; Army 1962-74; First Secretary FCO 1975; MECAS 1979; Kuwait 1980; First Secretary and Head of Chancery Tripoli 1983; First Secretary later Counsellor FCO 1984; m 1970 Barbara Joan Wooster (2s 1975, 1979).

Coombe, Donald Lionel Stanley; Consul Cape Town since February 1991; born 20.5.34; Board of Trade 1953; Assistant Trade Commissioner, Lagos 1963; Second Secretary (Econ) Lagos 1965; Board of Trade 1966; Ministry of Technology 1966; FCO 1970; Hong Kong 1973; First Secretary (Comm) Calcutta 1975; First Secretary and Head of Chancery Maseru 1979; FCO 1981; First Secretary (Comm) Dublin 1984; First Secretary FCO 1988; m 1959 Doreen Ada Florence Gay.

Coombs, Kay; First Secretary FCO since December 1991; born 8.7.45; DSAO later FCO 1967; Bonn 1971; Latin America Floater 1973; Second Secretary (Consul) Zagreb 1976; FCO 1979; Second Secretary (Aid/Inf) La Paz 1982; First Secretary (Inf) Rome 1987.

Coombs, Nicholas Geoffrey; Second later First Secretary FCO since December 1989; born 14.12.61; FCO 1984; Language Training 1985; Second Secretary (Chancery) Riyadh 1987; m 1990 Julie Elizabeth Hardman.

Cooper, Andrew George Tyndale; First Secretary FCO since May 1992; born 13.12.53; FCO 1983; First Secretary Canberra 1984; FCO 1987; First Secretary (UN/Press) UKMIS Geneva 1988; m 1981 Donna Mary Elizabeth Milford (1s 1988).

Cooper, Colin Edward; First Secretary (Management/Consular) Amman since November 1991; born 6.5.44; FO 1963; Africa Floater 1966; Lagos 1967; Paris 1971; FCO 1974 (SOAS) 1975; Khartoum 1976; Osaka 1979; Second Secretary FCO 1982; Second Secretary (Aid/Comm) Freetown 1982; FCO 1985; Second Secretary (Aid) Addis Ababa 1988..

Cooper, Derek John William; FCO since November 1992; born 7.1.68; FCO 1986; Islamabad 1989; Grade 10.

Cooper, Elaine; FCO since November 1990; born 11.8.70; Grade 10.

Cooper, Jacqueline Selina; Islamabad since March 1989; born 23.6.41; FCO 1968; Saigon 1969; Rio de Janeiro 1971; Brasilia 1972; Peking 1973; ME Africa Floater 1975; FCO 1977; Warsaw 1978; FCO 1979; Johannesburg 1986; Grade 9.

Cooper, Julia Maria; Dhaka since October 1991; born 3.1.65; FCO 1984; Harare 1986; SUPL 1990; Grade S2; m 1987 Eric Robert Cooper; (1s 1990).

Cooper, Peter; First Secretary FCO since January 1988; born 4.4.38; CRO 1960; Kuala Lumpur 1961; Accra 1963; Abu Dhabi 1966; FCO 1970; Aden and Jedda 1971; Tripoli 1971; Blantyre 1972, Second Secretary 1975; Vice-Consul Bergen 1975; FCO 1980; First Secretary (Chancery/Inf) Wellington 1983; m 1972 Gainor Elizabeth Thomas.

Cooper, Rachel Elizabeth; Vice-Consul Copenhagen since March 1992; born 3.11.65; FCO 1989; Grade 9.

Cooper, Robert Francis, MVO (1975); Counsellor FCO since January 1987; born 28.8.47; Third Secretary FCO 1970; Sheffield University 1971; Tokyo 1972 (Second Secretary 1973; First Secretary 1976); FCO 1977; Seconded to Bank of England 1982; First Secretary (Eernal Trade) UKREP Brussels 1984.

Cooper, Terence Edwin; Geneva since January 1990; born 18.1.34; Home Office Prison Department 1958-75; Rome 1975; Bucharest 1976; Paris 1978; Accra 1980; Oslo 1981; Kampala 1982; Jakarta 1983; Baghdad 1985; Lusaka 1986; Sofia 1988; Grade SSO; m 1956 June Green (1d 1958).

Cope, Brian Roger; Colombo since July 1991; born 1.3.59; Inland Revenue 1975; FCO 1976; Paris 1979; Bucharest 1982; Islamabad 1984; FCO 1988; Grade 9; m 1982 Heather Margaret Frensham (1d 1990).

Cope, John Charles; Second Secretary FCO since September 1991; born 10.8.46; FO 1964; Paris 1968; Moscow 1971; Delhi 1972; Karachi 1974; FCO 1976; Dakar 1978; Warsaw 1981; FCO 1982; Hanoi 1985; FCO 1987; Second Secretary (Admin/Cons) Kathmandu 1988.

Copland, Joanne Catherine; FCO since November 1990; born 2.9.71; Grade S2.

Copleston, John de Carteret; First Secretary FCO since March 1990; born 26.1.52; FCO 1971; Paris 1975; Third later Second Secretary FCO 1978; Second later First Secretary Islamabad 1980; First Secretary FCO 1983; First Secretary (Chancery) Jakarta 1987; m (1) Susan Jane

Ulrich (diss 1986); (2) 1987 Jane Marie
Francesca Wilcox (2d 1988, 1991).

Corbett, Michael Alistair, OBE (1991); First
Secretary FCO since June 1992; born 18.6.38;
FO 1963; Quito 1964; Benghazi 1967; Nairobi
1970; FCO 1973; Sofia 1976; Second Secretary
1977; Strasbourg 1980; First Secretary (Admin)
and Consul Khartoum 1982; FCO 1986; First
Secretary (Comm) Warsaw 1989; m 1965 Maria
Cristina Pinkernell (2s 1965, 1967; 1d 1969).

Cordery, Andrew David; First Secretary FCO
since April 1991; born 2.5.47; Second Secretary
FCO 1974; Nairobi 1975; First Secretary UKMIS
New York 1977; FCO 1981; First Secretary (Econ)
Lusaka 1984; First Secretary BM Berlin 1988; m
1970 Marilyn Jean Smith (2d 1975, 1977).

Cordiner, William Lawson; High Commissioner
Nuku'alofa (and HM Consul for the Pacific
Islands under the United States sovereignty,
South of the Equator) since March 1990; born
9.3.35; Inland Revenue 1952; Seconded East
African Income Tax Department 1960; FCO
1967; Saigon 1968; Addis Ababa 1971; Second
Secretary Kuwait 1974; Baghdad 1976; on loan
to DHSS 1978; FCO 1979; Deputy British
Government Rep Antigua (later BHC Rep
Antigua and Barbuda) and St Kitts Nevis 1980;
Consul (Comm) Seattle 1983; First Secretary
FCO 1988; m 1958 Anne Milton (1s 1974).

Cork, Richard John; First Secretary
(Commercial) Manila since July 1990; born
14.11.42; FO 1960; Kathmandu 1964; Bonn
1968; FCO 1971; Manila 1974; FCO 1976;
Ottawa 1977; Vice-Consul (Admin) Karachi
1980; Second later First Secretary (Comm)
Bahrain 1984; First Secretary FCO 1988; m (1)
1964 Joan Dorothy Seabourne (1d 1969); (2)
1976 Annabelle Alvestir y Empleo (1d 1978; 2
step d 1969, 1974).

Cormack, Ian Ronald; Stockholm since
December 1991; born 20.11.56; FCO 1975;
Nairobi 1978; Havana 1980; Latin America
Floater 1982; Africa/Middle East Floater 1984;
FCO 1986; Shanghai 1988; Grade 9.

Cormack, Robert Linklater Burke, CMG (1988);
HM Ambassador Stockholm since June 1991;
born 29.8.35; HM Forces 1954-56; HMOCS
Kenya 1960; retired as District Officer; CRO
1964; Second later First Secretary and Private
Secretary to Minister of State 1964; First
Secretary (Inf) later Head of Chancery Saigon
1966; First Secretary (Comm) Bombay 1969;
First Secretary Delhi 1970; FCO 1972;
Counsellor, Head of Chancery and Consul-
General Kinshasa 1977; RCDS 1980; Counsellor
(Econ/Comm) Stockholm 1981; Counsellor FCO
1985; HM Ambassador Kinshasa and HMA
(non-resident) to Burundi and to Rwanda 1987;
m 1962 Eivor Dorotea Kumlin (2d 1966, 1969;
1s 1968).

Corner, Diane Louise; On loan to the Cabinet
Office since December 1991; born 29.9.59; FCO
1982; Second Secretary (Chancery) Kuala
Lumpur 1985; Second Secretary FCO 1989;
SUPL 1989; ; First Secretary FCO 1989; m 1986
Peter Timothy Stocker (2d 1989, 1991).

Cornish, (Robert) Francis, LVO (1978);
Counsellor FCO since October 1990; born
18.5.42; HM Forces 1960; FO (later FCO) 1968;
Kuala Lumpur 1970; Jakarta 1971; First
Secretary FCO 1973; First Secretary Bonn 1976;
APS to HRH The Prince of Wales 1980;
Counsellor 1983; High Commissioner, Banda
Seri Begawan 1983; Counsellor (Inf) Washington
1986; m 1964 Alison Jane Dundas (3d 1966,
1969, 1971).

Cornish, Terence Leslie Richard; Hanoi since
October 1991; born 28.10.38; Army 1956-78;
Islamabad 1979; Warsaw 1980; Vienna 1981;
Peking 1984; Athens 1985; Berne 1986; Prague
1989; Grade SO; m 1958 Jennifer Deardrie (3d
1958, 1959, 1964; 1s 1966).

Corrall, Bronwen Mair (née Jones); SUPL since
September 1990; born 3.2.50; FO (later FCO)
1967; Brussels (NATO) 1971; Suva 1973;
Freetown 1975; FCO 1977; FE Floater 1980;
Luxembourg 1982; Nuku'alofa 1984; Second
Secretary FCO 1988; m 1986 Herbert James
Brian Corrall (1s 1987).

Correa, Clive Joel; Rangoon since March 1991;
born 5.11.64; HCS 1988; FCO 1989; Grade 10;
m 1990 Andrea Parker.

Corrigan, Rosalind Mary; FCO since October
1991; born 7.12.66; Grade 9.

Corringham, John Michael; First Secretary FCO
since December 1988; born 18.12.34; Army
1952-72; FCO 1972; First Secretary Georgetown
1975; FCO 1978; Hong Kong 1981; First
Secretary FCO 1984; Attaché Bangkok 1987; m
1961 Caroline Rodney Brown (1s 1962; 1d
1966).

Costello, Susan Carole; FCO since February
1982; born 1.8.44; MOD 1970; FCO 1976;
Santiago 1977; Tehran 1980; Jedda 1981; Grade
S1.

Coton, Michael Christopher; Sofia since
November 1991; born 25.11.39; Fleet Air Arm
1956-79; BMG Berlin 1983; Ankara 1985;
Budapest 1986; UKDEL Brussels 1988; Kuala
Lumpur 1989; Grade SO; m 1980 Judith (1s
1980).

Cotton, David Leslie; Second Secretary
(Commercial) Algiers since January 1992; born
7.8.40; FCO 1968; Anguilla 1970; Berne 1972;
FCO 1974; SUPL 1977; FCO 1978; Stuttgart
1980; Khartoum 1983; FCO 1986; Zurich 1989;
m 1970 Maria Eugenia Leoni.

Coulson, Andrew John, LVO (1984); First Secretary FCO since July 1991; born 17.12.50; FCO 1973; Tel Aviv 1976; Tehran 1978; Second later First Secretary FCO 1980; First Secretary (Inf.) Amman 1983; FCO 1986; First Secretary (Chancery) Harare 1989; m 1978 Merope Jane Wilkinson (1d 1982, 1s 1986).

Coulson, Graham; Sofia since July 1992; born 11.10.46; Army 1962-86; Vienna 1988; New Delhi 1989; Grade SO; m 1971 Maureen Joyce Holiard (1s 1971, 1d 1974).

Coulthard, Deborah Jane; FCO since August 1992; born 23.4.69; FCO 1987; Stockholm 1992; Grade S2.

Coulter, Anthony Julian; Second Secretary FCO since January 1990; born 1.11.61; FCO 1984; Second Secretary (Chancery) Ankara 1987.

Courage, Rafe Philip Graham; Islamabad since September 1991; born 20.10.63; FCO 1986; Third Secretary Brussels 1989; Grade 9; m 1988 Theresa Jayne Pile (1d 1990).

Court, Robert Vernon; First Secretary (Political) UKDEL NATO Brussels since December 1990; born 28.1.58; FCO 1981; concurrently Third Secretary and Vice-Consul Chad; Second Secretary Bangkok 1984; First Secretary FCO 1986; Private Secretary to the Minister of State 1988; m 1983 Rebecca Ophelia Sholl (3s 1986, 1988. 1990).

Courtauld, Captain George; Queen's Messenger since 1985; born 2.5.38.

Couzens, Julie Ann (née Comlay); SUPL since October 1991; born 28.4.65; FCO 1986; Bonn 1988; Grade S2A; m 1990 Michael Christopher Arnold Couzens.

Covill, Peter Stanley; First Secretary (Consul) Harare. since July 1992; born 3.12.36; GPO 1953; HM Forces 1955-57; GPO 1957; CRO 1963; Canberra 1965; Colombo 1968; FCO 1971; Kabul 1972; FCO 1973; Kathmandu 1977; Vice-Consul Jerusalem 1980; Second Secretary FCO 1982; Consul New York 1986; Second Secretary FCO 1991; m 1961 Colleen June Mitchell (1d 1963; 1s 1965).

Cowan, Anthony Evelyn Comrie; First Secretary FCO since July 1991 ; born 28.3.53; Third Secretary FCO 1975; Language Student Cambridge 1977; Language Student Hong Kong 1978; Second later First Secretary Peking 1980; First Secretary FCO 1982; First Secretary (Chancery) Brussels 1987.

Cowan, Shona Mary; Lusaka since August 1992; born 27.11.62; FCO 1984; Paris 1986; Tokyo 1989; Grade S2.

Coward, Ruth Valerie; Mexico City since August 1991; born 18.9.60; FCO 1985; New

Dehli 1988; Grade S2.

Cowe, John McLean; FCO since February 1990; born 7.3.35; HM Forces 1956-61; GPO 1962-64; FCO 1970; Darwin 1971; FCO 1974; Darwin 1976; Singapore 1976; FCO 1980; Lagos 1982; FCO 1985; Seoul 1986; Grade 8; m 1978 Alena Saw Nyunt.

Cowell, (Andrew) (John) Hamish; First Secretary (Chancery) Tehran since October 1992; born 31.1.65; FCO 1987; Third later Second Secretary Colombo 1989.

Cowin, Michael Eugene; Second Secretary (Econ) Tokyo since October 1992; born 29.10.58; FCO 1988; Senior Research Officer; m 1981 Yuko Kosug; (1s 1981; 1d 1983).

Cowley, Aileen Meryl; Second later First Secretary FCO since April 1988; born 30.10.37; FCO 1973; Prague 1976; UKREP Brussels 1978; FCO 1981; Second Secretary (Admin) Paris 1983.

Cowling, Geoffrey Stanley; Deputy Consul General Sao Paulo since July 1991; born 20.9.45; Board of Trade 1964; Colonial Office later Commonwealth Office later FCO 1966; Vice-Consul and Third Secretary Kabul 1970; Vice-Consul and Third Secretary Port Moresby 1974; Second Secretary (Tech Asst) Lima 1976; FCO 1979 (First Secretary 1982); First Secretary (Econ) Copenhagen 1982; Joint Service Defence College 1987; First Secretary FCO 1988; m 1970 Irene Joyce Taylor (1s 1971; 2d 1975, 1980).

Cowling, James Roy; High Commissioner Maseru since February 1992; born 9.2.40; Board of Trade 1957; Paris 1962; Accra 1962; Second Secretary (Comm) Karachi 1964; DSAO (later FCO) 1968; First Secretary (Inf) Buenos Aires 1972; First Secretary (Comm) Copenhagen 1975; FCO 1977; NDC Latimer, 1980; on loan to ODA 1980; First Secretary (Aid) Nairobi 1983; First Secretary, later Counsellor, FCO 1987; m (1) 1962 Monique Lassimouillas; (2) 1983 Janet Bell Barnshaw.

Cowling, Janice; Bandar Seri Begawan since July 1990; born 13.5.64; DHSS 1981-84; FCO 1984; Prague 1985; Africa/ME Floater 1987; Grade 9; m 1990; Maxwell Alfred Timothy Fong.

Cowper-Coles, Sherard Louis, LVO (1991); First Secretary FCO since August 1991; born 8.1.55; FCO 1977; Language Student MECAS 1978; Third later Second Secretary Cairo 1980; First Secretary FCO 1983; Private Secretary to the Permanent Under-Secretary 1985; First Secretary (Chancery) Washington 1987; m 1982 Bridget Mary Elliott (4s 1982, 1984, 1987, 1990; 1d 1986).

Cox, David George; First Secretary FCO since September 1992; born 7.12.61; FCO 1984; Third

Biographical List

later Second Secretary (Chancery) Canberra 1986; Second later First Secretary (Econ) Islamabad 1989.

Cox, David Thomas; First Secretary FCO since January 1990; born 27.4.44; FO (later FCO) 1967; Berlin 1970; FCO 1972; Prague 1974; Munich 1976; FCO 1979; Lusaka 1982; Second Secretary (Commercial) Budapest 1986; m 1975 Claudia Zeillinger (1s 1981).

Cox, Jefferey William; FCO since April 1990; born 26.10.43; Second Secretary FCO 1973; First Secretary Vienna 1975; First Secretary FCO 1978; First Secretary Madrid (CSCE Delegation) 1980; Pretoria 1981; First Secretary FCO 1985; First Secretary BM Berlin 1988; m 1969 Elizabeth Louise Bendle (3d 1971, 1973, 1978).

Cox, Jolyon Nicholas; FCO since August 1988; born 21.9.61; FCO 1979; Bonn 1983; Sana'a 1985; Grade 9; m 1986 Francesca Ann Hindson.

Cox, Julie Ann; Jerusalem since September 1990; born 10.7.62; FCO 1986; Peking 1988; Grade S2.

Cox, Nigel John; FCO since April 1990; born 23.4.54; FCO 1975; Language Student Cambridge 1976; Language Student Hong Kong 1977; Second Secretary Peking 1978; Second later First Secretary FCO 1981; ENA Paris 1984; First Secretary Paris 1985; m1992 Olivia Jane Paget.

Cox, Richard James; FCO since September 1991; born 7.8.67; Grade 9.

Crabbie, Christopher Donald; Counsellor (Financial and European Community) Paris since September 1990; born 17.1.46; Second Secretary FCO 1973; First Secretary Nairobi 1975; Washington 1979; FCO 1983; Counsellor on loan to HM Treasury 1985; Counsellor FCO 1987.

Crabtree, Joanne Elizabeth; Mexico City since February 1990; born 26.9.68; FCO 1988; Grade 10.

Craddock, Timothy James; First Secretary UKDEL Paris since August 1990; born 27.6.56; FCO 1979; Vice-Consul (Information), Istanbul 1981; Second Secretary Ankara 1982; First Secretary FCO 1985.

Craig, David Hamilton; Second Secretary (Chancery) Nicosia since July 1991; born 5.12.61; FCO 1989; Language Training 1990.

Craig, John Jenkinson; Second Secretary FCO since September 1979; born 8.1.49; FCO 1972; Third Secretary Rome 1978; m 1975 Glenys Menai Edmunds (2d 1977, 1984; 2s 1979, 1981).

Craig, Keith Robert; FCO since September 1991; born 28.1.62; Grade 7.

Craig, Lesley; Vice-Consul Kathmandu since February 1991; born 13.5.67; FCO 1988; T/D Islamabad 1990; Grade 9.

Craig, Robyn Jean; Rabat since July 1990; born 9.3.65; FCO 1984; Moscow 1986; Oslo 1987; Grade 10.

Cramman, Ian Pallister; Khartoum since January 1992; born 11.3.70; FCO 1989; Grade 10.

Crane, John Michael; Consul Jerusalem since November 1989; born 14.10.42; CRO 1962; Kampala 1964; FCO 1967; MECAS 1970; Third Secretary Abu Dhabi 1972; Polytechnic Central London 1976; FCO 1977; Second Secretary (Comm) Damascus 1979; British High Commission Representative, Antigua and Deputy British Government Representative, later British High Commission Representative St. Kitts and Nevis 1983; First Secretary FCO 1987; m 1964 Valmai Meredith Jones (3s 1965, 1968, 1985; 1d 1971).

Cranwell, Susan Christine; FCO since August 1990; born 14.7.58; Grade S2.

Craven, Stella Susan; FCO since October 1989; born 24.3.50; WRAF 1967-71; FCO 1972; Suva 1973; FCO 1975; Khartoum 1976; FCO 1977; Resigned 1978; Reinstated 1979; FCO 1979; Islamabad 1981; FCO 1984; Harare 1986; Grade S2A.

Crawford, Alison Flora; FCO 1990; born 22.8.61; FCO 1982; Mexico City 1983; Washington 1987; SUPL 1989; Grade 9; m 1985 Stephen Lawrence Crawford.

Crawford, Charles Graham; First Secretary FCO since June 1991; born 22.5.54; FCO 1979; Language Student 1980; Second later First Secretary (Inf) Belgrade 1981; First Secretary FCO 1984; First Secretary (Chancery) Cape Town/Pretoria 1987; m 1990 Helen Margaret Walsh.

Crawford, Fabiola Magdalena; Damascus since February 1991; born 1.4.66; FCO 1987, UKDEL Vienna 1988; Grade S2.

Crawford, Marilyn Elisabeth; FCO since January 1991; born 16.8.47; FCO 1975; UKDEL NATO Brussels 1977; Antigua 1980; FCO 1982; UKDEL Brussels 1988; Grade S2A.

Crawford, Michael James; First Secretary (Political) Warsaw since March 1992; born 3.2.54; FCO 1981; Second later First Secretary Cairo 1983; First Secretary Sana'a 1985; First Secretary Riyadh 1986; First Secretary FCO 1990; m 1984 Georgia Anne Moylan (twins, 1s 1d 1986, 1s 1989).

Crees, Ian Alec; First Secretary FCO since February 1989; born 31.1.43; Air Ministry 1960;

Passport Office 1961; CRO 1963; Nairobi 1963; Nicosia 1966; FCO 1968; Islamabad 1971; Strasbourg 1975; FCO 1978; Second Secretary Kinshasa 1980; Second Secretary (Comm) Seoul 1984; m 1963 Betty Winifred Kelcher (1d 1965; 1s 1967).

Cressey, David; Pretoria since August 1987; born 30.9.41; Royal Marines 1958-81; Moscow 1981; New Delhi 1983; Paris 1984; Aden 1986; Grade SO; m 1962 Margaret Elizabeth Cassaday (1d 1963; 1s 1965).

Cresswell, Jeremy Michael; Counsellor and Head of Chancery UKDEL Brussels since September 1990; born 1.10.49; FCO 1972; Third later Second Secretary Brussels 1973; Second Secretary Kuala Lumpur 1977; First Secretary FCO 1978; Private Secretary to Parliamentary Under-Secretary, then Minister of State 1981-82; Deputy Political Adviser BMG Berlin 1982; First Secretary FCO 1986; m 1974 Ursula Petra Forwick (1d 1978; 1s 1985).

Cresswell, Sheila Noreen; FCO since August 1990; born 9.8.61; FCO 1984; Bonn 1985; Tokyo 1988; Grade S2.

Cribbs, Michael Edward; First Secretary (Chancery/Inf) Damascus since July 1990; born 8.10.60; FCO 1982; Third later Second Secretary Nicosia 1984; Second Secretary FCO 1987; m 1983 Gillian Corkindale (diss 1991).

Critoph, Tracey Marjorie; Jakarta since July 1990; born 26.8.64; FCO 1988; Grade S2A.

Crocker, John Michael; Second Secretary (Chancery) Riyadh since July 1992; born 27.6.63; FCO 1988; Second Secretary 1989; Full-time Language Training Cairo 1991.

Crockett, Patricia Anne; FCO since August 1991; born 19.11.48; Tokyo 1974; Copenhagen 1977; FCO 1980; Port Louis 1981; FCO 1983; Lusaka 1985; Peking 1989; Grade S1.

Crocombe, Valerie Ann; FCO since May 1992; born 16.7.62; FCO 1980; Washington 1984; Gibraltar 1987; Prague 1989; Grade S1.

Croll, Mary Louise; HM Ambassador and HM Consul General San Jose since July 1992; born 10.9.35; FO 1953; Bahrain 1957; Addis Ababa 1959; UK Mission New York 1961; FO 1964; South America Floater 1967; Bilbao 1969; Second Secretary 1971; Lusaka 1972; FCO 1975; First Secretary (Inf) Madrid 1979; First Secretary FCO 1984; HM Consul Florence and Consul-General for the Republic of San Marino 1988.

Crombie, Anthony Campbell; FCO since August 1990; born 18.10.56; COI 1980; FCO 1985; Second later First Secretary Havana 1987; m 1982 Jane Nicholls Talbot.

Crompton, Angela Louie; Oslo since May 1991; born 4.5.64; FCO 1988; Grade S2A.

Crompton, Michael Robin; First Secretary (Chancery/Info) Vienna since December 1991; born 19.3.38; FCO 1971; First Secretary Lagos 1973; First Secretary FCO 1976; First Secretary Nairobi 1978; First Secretary and Head of Chancery Kinshasa 1983; First Secretary FCO 1987; m 1973 E H Schubert (diss 1977).

Cronin, Martin Eugene; Vice-Consul/AMO Sana'a since November 1990; born 22.1.65; DOE 1987; FCO 1988; Grade 9.

Cronin, Susan Mary (née Hartland); FCO since November 1991; born 16.4.64; FCO 1983; Washington 1986; Riyadh 1988; Grade 9; m 1985 Neil Cronin.

Crooke, Alastair Warren; Counsellor Brasilia since April 1991; born 30.6.49; FCO 1974; Third later Second Secretary (Comm) Dublin 1975; First Secretary (Pol/Press) Pretoria 1978; First Secretary FCO 1981; Islamabad 1985; First Secretary FCO 1988; m 1976 Carole Cecilia Flaxman (1s 1979; twin s 1981).

Cropper, Anthony John; FCO since June 1990; born 3.5.40; FO 1964; Singapore 1965; FO 1967; Mbabane 1968; FCO 1970; Seoul 1972; FCO 1973; Darwin 1975; Kuwait 1976; FCO 1980; Rangoon 1981; FCO 1984; Second Secretary New Delhi 1987; m 1964 Doreen Hall-Strutt (3d 1966, 1970, 1972).

Crorkin, Colin Wynn; Second Secretary BTIO New York since June 1992; born 31.1.57; FCO 1975; Rome 1977; Beirut 1980; UKREP Brussels 1983; FCO 1984; Kinshasa 1987; m (1) 1978 Gillian Smith (diss 1991) m (2) 1991 Joanne Lyn Finnamore (1s 1985).

Crorkin, Gillian (née Smith); FCO since November 1988; (Second Secretary 1992); born 9.1.57; FCO 1976; SUPL 1978; Beirut 1980; SUPL 1980; Beirut 1982; FCO 1982; Brussels 1983; FCO 1984; Kinshasa 1987; Grade 9; m 1978 Colin Wynn Crorkin (diss 1991) (1s 1985).

Crosby, Helen Margaret; FCO since August 1991; born 19.10.63; Grade 9.

Crosland, Jane Margaret; Second Secretary (Political) Copenhagen since February 1992; born 24.11.61; FCO 1989.

Cross, Alan John; FCO since March 1991; born 2.2.72; Grade 10.

Cross, Anthony Keith; Canberra since October 1990; born 8.12.38; RAF 1957-60; MOD 1960-70; Karachi 1970; Bucharest 1972; Kinshasa 1974; Tokyo 1975; Sofia 1978; Baghdad 1980; Nicosia 1981; Bangkok 1984; Brussels 1985; Peking 1986; Khartoum 1988; Grade CSO; m

Rita May Woodcock (1s 1962).

Cross, Bernard William; First Secretary FCO since January 1989; born 18.1.44; CRO1/DSA 1961-68; Freetown 1968; Blantyre 1972; FCO 1974; Moscow 1978; FCO 1981; First Secretary (Commercial) Sofia 1985; m Angela Holthouse Todd (2s 1966, 1973; 1d 1972).

Cross, Caroline Janice, MBE (1991); Third Secretary (Chancery/Info) Kampala since October 1991; born 30.9.64; FCO 1984; Warsaw 1986; Floater Duties 1989; Grade 9.

Cross, Linda Mary (née Guild); Vienna since November 1991; born 15.3.56; FCO 1978; Rabat 1978; Prague 1981; Quito 1983; Paris 1985; FCO 1988; Grade 9; m 1989 Michael John Cross.

Cross, Margaret Christine; SUPL since April 1992; born 13.1.62; FCO 1980; Dhaka 1985; Frankfurt 1989 (Second Secretary 1991); FCO 1991.

Cross, Peter; Consul Palma since January 1990; born 2.2.41; FO 1958; Rome 1962; Khartoum 1965; Lima 1968; FCO 1971; Managua 1974; San Salvador 1976; Second Secretary Doha 1978; On loan to DTI 1982; Vice-Consul later Consul (Commercial) Chicago 1985; m 1962 Elizabeth Anne Widmer (3s 1962, 1964, 1965; 1d 1967).

Cross, Shelley-Anne; FCO since March 1989; born 19.11.59; FCO 1980; Bonn 1982; Floater Duties 1985; Grade 9; m 1990 Robert Simon George Parker.

Crossland, Dudley Stewart; UKREP Brussels since March 1990; born 2.5.63; FCO 1987; Berne 1989; Grade 10.

Crossman, Steven Nigel; Third Secretary (Aid) Dar es Salaam since September 1990; born 16.11.55; FCO 1975; Muscat 1977; Washington 1978; Kuwait 1982; New Delhi 1984; FCO 1987; Grade 9, m 1980 Janet Lynch.

Crosthwaite, Maureen; FCO since November 1990; born 4.5.43; FCO 1987; Vienna 1988; Grade S2.

Croucher, Lance Hans Frederick; FCO since September 1991; born 17.3.40; RAF 1956-83; FCO 1983; Karachi 1985; Pretoria 1988; Grade 9; m (1) 1965 (1d 1966; 1s 1967); (2) 1981 Hildegard Faller (2d 1986, 1987).

Crowe, Brian Lee, CMG (1985); Duss (Economic) FCO since March 1992; born 5.1.38; FO 1961; Third Secretary Moscow 1962; Second Secretary FO 1964; Private Secretary to Minister without Portfolio (Lord Shackleton) for special Mission to Aden 1967; First Secretary Washington 1968; First Secretary Bonn 1973; Counsellor 1976; Head of Planning Dept FCO 1976; Counsellor and Head of Chancery UKREP Brussels 1978; Head of European Community (Eernal) Department FCO 1982; Minister (Comm) Washington 1985; HM Ambassador Vienna 1989; m 1969 Virginia Willis (2s 1972, 1975).

Crowther, Diane Elaine; FCO since November 1981; born 5.9.64; Grade S2A.

Crowther, Kathryn Valerie Bryden; FCO since February 1992; born 14.2.47; FCO 1987; Rabat 1989; Grade S2A.

Crumpton, Douglas William; Berlin since January 1992; born 15.12.33; Army 1950-73; Paris 1974; Warsaw 1975; Amman 1976; Washington 1980; UKDEL NATO Brussels 1983; The Hague 1989; Grade S0; m 1971 Annette Harrison.

Crystal, David Mark, MVO (1974); First Secretary FCO since October 1989; born 30.9.45; FO 1964; Colombo 1967; Sofia 1970; SE Asia floater duties 1972; FCO 1974; Bangkok 1977; Second Secretary FCO 1982; Second Secretary UKDEL Vienna 1984; First Secretary (Comm) Bombay 1986; m 1978 Sulinda Patiya.

Cullen, Carol Dulceta (née Fisher); SUPL since February 1992; born 12.11.56; DoE 1975; FCO 1977; Paris 1979; Dublin 1982; FCO 1985; Nairobi 1988; Grade 9; m 1979 Thomas Cullen (1d 1984).

Cullen, Kevin; First Secretary FCO since May 1992; born 8.11.38; Army 1958-59; National Assistance Board 1962; FO 1964; Karachi 1965; Rawalpindi 1966; Warsaw 1969; FCO 1971; Lilongwe 1974; Second Secretary 1975; Second Secretary (Comm) Tehran 1978; Second later First Secretary (Comm) Harare 1980; First Secretary FCO 1983; First Secretary (Pol/Econ) Copenhagen 1988; m 1962 Margaret Curle (1s 1963; 2d 1966, 1973).

Cullens, Niall James David; LA/Caribbean Floater since May 1990; born 28.2.65; FCO 1986; BMG Berlin 1988; Grade 9.

Culligan, Phillip David; FCO since June 1989; (Second Secretary 1992); born 27.2.61; FCO 1981; Tripoli 1982; Pretoria/Cape Town 1983; Düsseldorf 1986; m 1982 Carole Anne Rouse.

Cullimore, Charles Augustine Kaye; High Commissioner Kampala since December 1989; born 2.10.33; HM Forces 1955-57; HMOCS Tanganyika 1958-61; FCO 1971; First Secretary Bonn 1973; FCO 1977; Counsellor and Head of Chancery New Delhi 1979; Head of Chancery Canberra 1982; Counsellor FCO 1986; m 1956 Waltraud Willemsen (1d 1957; 1s 1961).

Culshaw, Robert Nicholas, MVO (1979); First Secretary and Head of Chancery later Counsellor,

Consul General and Deputy Head of Mission Athens since January 1989; born 22.12.52; Third Secretary FCO 1974; Language Student MECAS 1975 and FCO 1976; Third Secretary Muscat 1977; Second Secretary Khartoum 1979; First Secretary Rome 1980; FCO (APS to the Secretary of State) 1984; m 1977 Elaine Ritchie Clegg (1s 1992).

Culver, John Howard; HM Ambassador and Consul Managua since November 1992; born 17.7.47; Board of Trade 1967; FO later FCO 1968; Latin America Floater 1971; FCO 1973; Third Secretary Moscow 1974; Second Secretary La Paz 1977; Second later First Secretary FCO 1980; First Secretary (Comm) Rome 1983; Head of Chancery Dhaka 1987; First Secretary FCO 1990; m 1973 Margaret Ann Davis (1d 1974; 2s 1978, 1981).

Cumbers, John David; Warsaw since February 1991; born 23.6.40; Army 1960-1991; FCO 1991; Grade SO; m 1969 Aileen Chapman.

Cumming, Melvyn Robert Wilson; First Secretary FCO since July 1992; born 17.3.42; FO 1959; Africa Floater 1963; Abu Dhabi 1965; DSAO (later FCO) 1968; Seoul 1972; Lagos 1975; Naples 1978; Second later First Secretary FCO 1983; First Secretary (Comm) Madrid 1987; m 1971 Pamela Jean Huckle (1d 1975; 1s 1976).

Cummins, John, MBE (1983); First Secretary (Commercial) Prague since May 1992; born 7.9.46; FO (later FCO) 1964; Budapest 1969; Luxembourg 1971; Tunis 1973; FCO 1976; (Second Secretary 1978); Consul and Second Secretary (Admin) Santiago 1980; First Secretary Libreville 1985; First Secretary FCO 1988; Full-time Language Training 1991; m 1969 Gillian Anne Biss (2s 1970, 1972).

Cummins, Rodney Robert; First Secretary (Commercial) Tokyo since April 1992; born 19.10.41; FO 1959; Prague 1963; Buenos Aires 1964; Vienna 1967; San Francisco 1970; Language training 1971; Tokyo 1972; Second Secretary (Inf) and Vice-Consul Osaka 1974; on loan to DOT 1977; FCO 1980; First Secretary (Comm) Mexico City 1982; Deputy High Commissioner Georgetown 1986; First Secretary FCO 1988; m 1964 Sandra Mary Hanmer (2s 1966, 1970; 1d 1967).

Cunliffe, Thomas Johnstone Borthwick; Nairobi since November 1986; born 27.6.34; Army 1952-75; Paris 1975; Peking 1976; Brussels (NATO) 1978; Moscow 1980; Pretoria 1981; Dhaka 1984; Havana 1985; Grade SSO; m 1975 Anne Elizabeth Redmond.

Cunningham, Peter; First Secretary (Admin) Bonn since July 1988; born 10.8.37; FO 1955; RAF 1956-58; Athens 1958; Beirut 1959; Moscow 1961; Bonn 1963; Calcutta 1966; DSAO (later FCO) 1967; Brussels (EC) 1970;

Rome 1972; Second Secretary (Aid) Islamabad 1975; FCO 1979; First Secretary (Admin/Cons) Kampala 1985; m 1965 Eileen Joan Ferguson (1s 1969; 1d 1971).

Cunningham, Raymond Peter; Floater Duties since June 1992; born 21.1.45; Army 1963-1989; FCO 1989; Warsaw 1990; Grade SO.

Curle, Moira Rosemary; Belgrade since November 1990; born 8.10.68; FCO 1986; Grade 10.

Curley, Eugene Gerard, OBE (1991); First Secretary FCO since September 1986; born 30.9.55; FCO 1981; Second later First Secretary Mexico City 1984; m 1982 Joanne England.

Curran, David; First Secretary (Chancery) UKMIS New York since January 1992; born 8.6.60; FCO 1987; Second later First Secretary Manila 1989; m 1989 Lesley Jane Thomas.

Curran, Lynn Marie; UKDEL Brussels since February 1992; born 19.4.66; FCO 1984; Athens 1986; Kinshasa 1989; Grade 9.

Curran, Terence Dominic; Counsellor FCO since May 1990; born 14.6.40; Public Record Office 1960; DSAO 1966; Peking 1968; FCO 1969; Dakar 1970; Assistant Trade Commissioner, later Consul, Edmonton 1973; First Secretary FCO 1978; Pretoria 1980; First Secretary FCO 1984; Counsellor (Econ/Comm) Singapore 1987; m 1969 Penelope Ann Ford (1d 1971; 2s 1973, 1977).

Currie, Colin Robert; Washington since April 1992; born 29.10.69; FCO 1989; Grade 10.

Currie, David James; Assistant Trade Commissioner BTC Hong Kong since January 1989; born 21.10.46; CRO (later FCO) 1963; Peking 1969; Helsinki 1971; FCO 1972; Hanoi 1975; Brussels 1976; Manila 1978; Second Secretary FCO 1982; Second Secretary (Comm) Algiers 1986; m (1) 1968 Valerie Kirk (1s 1970) (diss 1975); (2) 1977 Joyce Rosalie Deacon; (1 step s 1970, 1 foster s 1970).

Curry, Trudy Gay (née Hibbs); SUPL since June 1987; born 9.12.57; FCO 1975; SUPL 1980; Canberra 1981; Brussels 1984; Grade S2; m (1) 1980 Peter Ian Webb (diss 1983); (2) 1983 Peter Lester Curry.

Curtis, Julian Geoffrey Seymour; First Secretary later Counsellor FCO since July 1984; born 27.3.39; FO 1965; Second Secretary Singapore 1966; Bangkok 1967; First Secretary FCO 1971; Jakarta 1973; FCO 1975; First Secretary (Econ) Dublin 1978; First Secretary (Econ) Damascus 1981; m 1966 Victoria Ada Kierulf (2d 1969, 1970; 1s 1981).

Curtis, Penelope Ann; Mexico City since July 1992; born 24.6.68; FCO 1990; Grade S2.

Cushion, Catherine Mary; Kampala since September 1991; born 24.11.60; FCO 1984; Kathmandu 1986; FCO 1989; Warsaw 1989; Grade S2.

Cuthbert, Neil Davidson; FCO since March 1990; born 15.6.71; Grade 10.

Cuxford, Stephanie Anne; FCO since August 1982; born 20.7.65; Grade S3C.

D

Dacey, Alan Treharne; UKDEL Brussels since January 1991; born 10.4.70; FCO 1988; Grade 10.

Davey, Denise; FCO since November 1987; born 8.5.69; Grade 10.

Dain, David John Michael, CMG (1991); High Commissioner Nicosia since July 1990; born 30.10.40; FO 1963; Third Secretary Tehran 1964; Third later Second Secretary and Oriental Secretary Kabul 1965; FCO 1968; Second later First Secretary seconded to the Cabinet Office 1969; First Secretary (Chancery) Bonn 1972; FCO 1975; First Secretary and Head of Chancery Athens 1978; Counsellor and Head of Chancery Nicosia 1981; Counsellor FCO 1985; Attached to OMCS (CSSB) 1989; m 1969 Susan Kathleen Moss (2d 1974, 1979; 1s 1977).

Dales, Richard Nigel; High Commissioner Harare since September 1992; born 26.8.42; FO 1964; Yaoundé 1965; FO (later FCO) 1968; Second Secretary 1969; Copenhagen 1970; First Secretary 1972; FCO 1973; Assistant Private Secretary to the Secretary of State, FCO 1974; First Secretary Head of Chancery and Consul Sofia 1977; FCO 1981; Counsellor Copenhagen 1982; DHC, Counsellor and Head of Chancery Harare 1986; Counsellor FCO 1989; On attachment to the CSSB Recruitment and Assessment Services Agency 1991; m 1966 Elizabeth Margaret Martin (1s 1973; 1d 1976).

Daley, Robyn Jean; FCO since June 1990; born 8.8.69; Grade 10.

Dallas, Emily Margaret; FCO since April 1991; born 27.5.72; Grade 10.

Dallas, Ian Michael; Vice-Consul (Comm) Karachi since March 1989; born 13.12.42; Board of Trade 1961; Commonwealth Office 1966; Peking 1969; Lagos 1971; Accra 1973; FCO 1975; Chicago 1978; Second Secretary FCO 1982; Second Secretary (Admin) Lusaka 1985; FCO 1988; m 1968 Angela Margaret Moore (1s 1971; 1d 1976).

Dalrymple, Leslie Robert, MVO (1992); Second Secretary (Management) Valletta since March 1991; born 29.3.38; FO 1965; Nicosia 1966;

Havana 1969; Suva 1970; FCO 1974; Brussels (NATO) 1978; New Delhi 1981; UKMIS Geneva 1983; FCO 1986 (Second Secretary 1988) m 1965 Elizabeth Cormack dec'd 1991 (2d 1967, 1969).

Dalrymple, Rhona Jane; Tunis since August 1990; born 2.4.65; FCO 1984; Nairobi 1987; Addis Ababa 1989; Grade S2.

Dalton, Andreina; FCO since August 1992; born 12.7.66; FCO 1986; Paris 1988; Warsaw 1991; Grade 10.

Dalton, Maurice Leonard, LVO (1986), MVO (1981); FCO since January 1987; born 18.5.44; Inland Revenue 1961; FO 1965; Enugu/Lagos 1967; FCO 1968; Ankara 1970; East Berlin 1973; Abu Dhabi 1974; FCO 1977; Second later First Secretary (Econ) Oslo 1979; First Secretary (Comm) Kuala Lumpur 1983; First Secretary Peking 1986; m 1982 Cathy Lee Parker.

Dalton, Raymond Glyn; Santiago since September 1992; born 25.4.45; Royal Air Force 1960-85; MOD Police 1985-88; Warsaw 1988; Pretoria 1990; Grade SO; m 1964 Mary Bayfield.

Dalton, Richard John; Counsellor FCO since March 1992; born 10.10.48; Third Secretary FCO 1970; MECAS 1971; Second Secretary Amman 1973; Second later First Secretary UKMIS New York 1975; FCO 1979; First Secretary Head of Chancery and Consul Muscat 1983; First Secretary FCO 1987; Counsellor on loan to MAFF 1988; Counsellor on CDA at Chatham House 1991; m 1972 Elizabeth Keays (2s 1978, 1982; 2d 1973, 1979).

Dalton-Stirling, Michael; Second Secretary Nairobi since November 1992; born 5.4.37; HM Forces 1959-61; FO 1962; Helsinki 1963; Tehran 1966; NATO Brussels 1972; FCO 1974; Mogadishu 1976; Kuala Lumpur 1980; FCO 1983 (Second Secretary 1990); m 1959 Elizabeth Dalton (1d 1962; 1s 1966).

Daltrey, Kim Rowena; SUPL since April 1992; born 5.5.63; FCO 1986; Berne 1988, FCO 1989; Rome 1990; Grade S2; m 1991 Christopher Daltrey.

Daltrey, Christopher; Rome since March 1990; born 21.9.68; FCO 1988; Grade 10; m 1991 Kim Rowena Newson.

Daly, James; Counsellor and Consul-General Moscow since May 1992; born 8.9.40; Royal Marines 1958-67; DSAO later FCO 1968; Accra 1971; Moscow 1973; Second Secretary Karachi 1976; FCO 1979; First Secretary Sofia 1982; First Secretary Paris 1986; First Secretary FCO 1991; m 1970 Dorothy Lillian Powell (2s 1973, 1974).

Daly, Robert; Olympic Attaché Barcelona since

September 1991; born 13.5.47; DHSS 1964; FCO 1970; Dakar 1974; Second Secretary Lima 1978; Second Secretary FCO 1982; Second Secretary (Comm), Consul and Admin. Officer Monrovia 1985; First Secretary (Comm) Havana 1989; m 1968 Nan Desmond (2d 1968, 1972; 1s 1968), (diss 1988); (2) 1989 Linda Ann Czajka.

Damper, Carol Ann; Bucharest since July 1991; born 17.12.44; FCO 1975; Mogadishu 1975; Bonn 1977; Belmopan 1979; FCO 1982; Vienna 1984; FCO 1987; Athens 1988; Grade S1.

Danby, Beryl Anne; FCO since September 1989; born 15.4.42; FCO 1969; Rio de Janeiro 1970; Peking 1972; NATO Brussels 1973; FCO 1977; Prague 1979; Moscow 1980; Bangkok 1982; FCO 1982; The Hague 1985; FCO 1986; Budapest 1988; Grade S1.

Dance, David Peter; FCO since October 1988 (Second Secretary 1989); born 28.6.40; FO 1962; Kuwait 1963; FO 1964; Lourenco Marques 1966; Brussels 1967; FCO 1969; Dacca 1973; Lagos 1976; FCO 1979; Rangoon 1982; Houston 1985; m 1976 Sophi Roberts (1s 1980; 1d 1983).

Daniel, Hamish St Clair, MBE (1992); Second Secretary FCO since July 1992; born 22.8.53; FCO 1973; Algiers 1975; Prague 1977; Lisbon 1978; Islamabad 1980; FCO 1982; San Francisco 1985; Second Secretary (Chancery/Aid) Khartoum 1989; m 1975 Susan Mary Ann Brent (1d 1981; 1s 1985).

Daniels, Malcolm; FCO since September 1986; born 4.9.48; FCO 1965; Singapore 1980; Helsinki 1984; Grade 8; m 1976 Jeannette Susan (2s 1977, 1980).

Daniels, Mark Ian; Washington since August 1989; born 30.8.65; FCO 1982; New Delhi 1985; Grade 10; m 1989 Suzanne Jayne Woodworth.

Daniels, Suzanne Jayne (née Woodworth); FCO since April 1989; born 7.5.63; FCO 1983; New Delhi 1985; Grade S2; m 1989 Mark Daniels.

Daniels, Yvienne; Brussels since March 1990; born 29.12.59; FCO 1988; Grade S2A.

Darby, Lionel Frederick; Second Secretary FCO since April 1980; born 14.3.36; Royal Navy 1951-63; CRO 1963; Canberra 1964; Tamsui 1968; FCO 1971; Secretariat, Pearce Commission on Rhodesian Opinion 1972; FCO 1972; Dubai 1975; Panama City 1978; m 1962 Patricia Jones (1d 1964; 1s 1966).

Darke, John Martin Jamie; First Secretary FCO since August 1991; born 2.5.53; FCO 1975; MECAS 1977; FCO 1979; MBA London Business School 1981, Management Consultant, HAY-MSL 1983; First Secretary FCO 1985; First Secretary (Chancery) Cairo 1988; m 1980 Diana Taylor (1s 1991).

Darroch, Nigel Kim; First Secretary (Econ) Rome since August 1989; (Private Secretary to Minister of State January 1987) born 30.4.54; FCO 1976; Third later Second and later First Secretary Tokyo 1980; FCO 1985; m 1978 Vanessa Claire Jackson (1s 1983; 1d 1986).

Dart, Jonathan; Third Secretary (Science and Technology) Bonn since January 1991; born 14.7.64; FCO 1988; Grade 9; m 1990 Claire Emma Juffs.

Daubeney, Patricia; FCO since September 1991; born 22.12.68; Grade 9.

Daubney, Nicola, Peking since April 1992; born 31.1.70; FCO 1989; Grade 10.

Daunt, Sir Timothy (Lewis Achilles), KCMG (1989), CMG (1982); DUSS (Defence) FCO since September 1992; born 11.10.35; FO 1959; Third later Second Secretary Ankara 1960; FO 1964 (First Secretary 1966); Nicosia 1967; Private Secretary to the Permanent Under-Secretary of State FCO 1970; First Secretary UK Mission New York 1973; Counsellor OECD Paris 1975; Head of Southern European Dept 1978; CERI Paris 1982; Minister and Deputy Perm. Rep. UKDEL (NATO), Brussels 1982; FCO AUSS (Defence) 1985; HM Ambassador Ankara 1986; m 1962 Patricia Knight (1s 1963; 2d 1965, 1969).

Davenport, Ian Hewitt; Second Secretary FCO since October 1981; First Secretary 1990; born 19.1.33; Royal Navy 1948-62; CRO 1963; Delhi 1964; Canberra 1966; FCO 1969; Budapest 1973; Bonn 1974; Warsaw 1977; Dublin 1979; m 1963 Margaret Mary Scannell (1s 1964).

Davenport, Michael Hayward; Second Secretary (Chancery) Warsaw since December 1989; born 25.9.61; Second Secretary FCO 1988; m 1992 Lavinia Sophia Elisabeth Braun.

Davey, Denise; Dubai since January 1990; born 8.5.69; FCO 1987; Grade 10.

Davey, Philip John MVO (1988); FCO since July 1990; born 5.1.39; CRO 1955; HM Forces 1957-59; CRO 1959; Dublin 1960; Lusaka 1964; Paris 1966; NATO Brussels 1967; CENTO Ankara 1968; FCO 1971; Rio de Janeiro 1974; Second Secretary (Admin) and Vice-Consul Brasilia 1976; Second Secretary (Inf) Rome 1977; First Secretary on loan to DTI 1982; Consul (Commercial) Barcelona 1985; m 1960 Molly Kathleen Osborne (2d 1962, 1965).

Davey, Simon James, MBE (1985); First Secretary FCO since June 1992; born 1.2.47; Army 1965-68; FCO 1969; Latin America Floater 1972; Havana 1973; Second Secretary (Aid/Comm) Kathmandu 1976; Second later First Secretary FCO 1980; Consul Durban 1983; First Secretary (Comm) Prague 1988; m 1992 Marcela Eva Dzúrikova.

David, Timothy James; HM Ambassador Suva since March 1992; born 3.6.47; FCO 1974; Second later First Secretary Dar es Salaam 1977; FCO 1980; loan to ODA 1983; First Secretary UKMIS Geneva 1985; First Secretary later Counsellor FCO 1988.

Davidson, Barry Alexander; Freetown since September 1990; born 1.8.64; FCO 1985; UKMIS Geneva 1988; Grade 10; m 1985 Elizabeth Helen Oxley.

Davidson, Brian John; First Secretary On loan to the Cabinet Office since July 1992; born 28.4.64; FCO 1985; Language Training 1986; Third later Second Secretary (Chancery/Inf) Peking 1988.

Davidson, Carolyn Jayne; Tokyo since August 1990; born 18.4.64; FCO 1986; Language Training FCO 1987; Language Training Kamakura 1988; Grade 9.

Davidson, James Gerard; Lagos since March 1991; born 20.5.67; MOD 1985; FCO 1988; Budapest 1989; Grade 10.

Davidson, Susan; Tokyo since January 1990; born 13.12.57; FCO 1987; Grade S2A.

Davies, Carol Anya; Guatemala City since September 1991; born 21.3.65; FCO 1984; Brasilia 1987; FCO 1990; Grade S2.

Davies, Colin Trevor; Berne since August 1991; born 5.1.36; RAF 1953-76; Islamabad 1976; Lisbon 1978; Belgrade 1979; Dublin 1981; Bonn 1983; Paris 1986; Prague 1989; Grade SO; m 1956 Lydia von Pein (1s 1959; 3d 1957, 1962, 1963).

Davies, David Gerald; Deputy High Commissioner Lilongwe since June 1991; born 1.10.40; Ministry of Works 1959; MPNI 1960; DSAO 1966; Brussels (NATO) 1969; Second Secretary (Inf/Admin) Madras 1972; Freetown 1975; FCO 1978; First Secretary (Admin) Athens 1981; First Secretary (Admin) Addis Ababa 1986; First Secretary FCO 1988; m 1969 Pamela Arlotte (2s 1974, 1978).

Davies, Elved Richard Malcolm; First Secretary Oslo since September 1991; born 19.1.51; Army 1972-75; Third later Second Secretary FCO 1975; Language Student 1977; Second later First Secretary Jakarta 1977; FCO 1980; Athens 1984; FCO 1985; First Secretary (Chancery) Nairobi 1989; FCO 1991; m 1976 Elizabeth Angela Osborne (1d 1981; 1s 1984).

Davies, Emrys Thomas, CMG (1988); High Commissioner Bridgetown since January 1991 and concurrently, High Commissioner (non-resident) to Dominica, Antigua and Barbuda, Saint Vincent and the Grenadines, Saint Lucia, Grenada and Saint Christopher and Nevis; born 8.10.34; HM Forces 1953-55; FO 1955; Peking

1956; FO 1959; Bahrain 1960; Second Secretary FO 1962; Seconded to Hong Kong Government as Assistant Political Adviser 1963 (First Secretary 1965); First Secretary Ottawa 1968; First Secretary FCO 1972; Counsellor (Comm) Peking 1976; NDC Rome 1979; Deputy High Commissioner and Head of Chancery Ottawa 1979; Inspectorate FCO 1982; Counsellor (Economic and Finance) UKDEL OECD Paris 1984; HM Ambassador Hanoi 1987; m 1960 Angela Audrey May (1s 1963; 2d 1965; 1971).

Davies, Gerald Howard; Second Secretary (Management) and Consul Muscat since December 1990; born 2.4.48; FCO 1968; Paris 1971; Karachi 1973; Ibadan 1977; FCO 1978; Warsaw 1981; FCO 1984; Melbourne 1986; FCO 1988; m 1972 Yvonne Arnold (2d 1984, 1988).

Davies, Griselda Christian Macbeth (née Todd); FCO since September 1990; born 20.2.59; Budapest 1981; FCO 1982; Buenos Aires 1983; FCO 1985; Damascus 1987; FCO 1988; SUPL 1989; Grade S2; m 1989 John Howard Davies.

Davies, Hugh Llewelyn; Counsellor FCO since March 1990; born 8.11.41; Third Secretary FO 1965; Second Secretary Hong Kong 1966; Second Secretary (later Consul) Peking 1969; Second later First Secretary FCO 1971; First Secretary (Econ) Bonn 1974; First Secretary and Head of Chancery Singapore 1977; FCO 1979; Counsellor Seconded to Barclays Bank International 1982; Counsellor (Comm) Peking 1984; Counsellor (Econ/Financial) UKDEL OECD Paris 1987; m 1968 Virginia Ann Lucius (1d 1970; 1s 1973).

Davies, Ian; Second Secretary FCO since September 1990; born 1.8.56; FCO 1976; Moscow 1978; SUPL 1980; FCO 1983; Paris 1985; Third later Second Secretary Moscow 1988; m 1979 Purificacion Bautista Hervias.

Davies, Ivor Herbert; First Secretary (Management) Athens since June 1990; born 30.11.39; Customs and Excise 1956; Tehran 1961; Berlin 1964; Political Adviser;s Office Singapore 1967; Tokyo 1968; Marlborough House 1972; FCO 1975; Moscow 1978; Second Secretary Georgetown 1979; Vice-Consul (Admin/Cons/Imm) Karachi 1983; First Secretary FCO 1987; m 1963 Mary Diana Gillard (2d 1965, 1971; 1s 1968).

Davies, James Norman, MBE (1975); First Secretary Washington since February 1985; born 11.1.30; HM Forces 1948-50; FO 1950; Beirut 1959; Warsaw 1961; FO 1962; Bonn 1965; FCO 1968; Moscow 1973; FCO 1975; Second Secretary Peking 1978; Second Secretary FCO 1981; m 1952 Buddug Wyn Evans (1d 1954; 1s 1962).

Davies, Jennifer Ann Tudor; Hong Kong since July 1992; born 2.3.50; FCO 1969; Khartoum

1972; Valletta 1974; Singapore 1977; FCO 1979; Buenos Aires 1980; FCO 1982; New Delhi 1984; FCO 1987; Grade S2.

Davies, John Howard; First Secretary FCO since September 1990; born 31.1.57; FCO 1980; Riyadh 1983; Second later First Secretary FCO 1985; First Secretary and Head of Interests Section Damascus 1987; m 1989 Griselda Christian Macbeth Todd.

Davies, Jonathan Mark; Language Training Cairo since June 1992; born 1.12.67; FCO 1990; Grade 8.

Davies, Keith; Moscow since February 1992; born 29.1.41; RAF 1959-82; Warsaw 1983; Vienna 1984; Lagos 1987; Peking 1988; Nicosia 1989; Grade SO.

Davies, Maureen Kerr Stewart (née Paisley); Kathmandu since July 1990; born 12.6.53; FCO 1984; Washington 1987; Grade S2; m 1988 Maxim Philip Davies.

Davies, Paul Ronald; Second Secretary FCO since September 1990; born 30.3.53; FCO 1970; Africa Floater 1974; Dacca 1976; FCO 1979; Tripoli 1982; Kingston 1984; Third Secretary (Comm) Peking 1988; m 1976 Fiona Avril Canning (1d 1979; 1s 1981).

Davies, Peter Brian; First Secretary FCO since July 1992; born 30.12.54; Third Secretary FCO 1977; Language Training Hong Kong 1980; Second Secretary FCO 1981; Second later First Secretary Rome 1983; First Secretary FCO 1987; First Secretary and Consul Peking 1988; m 1981 Charlotte Helena Allman Hall (1d 1984; 1s 1986).

Davies, Peter Douglas Royston; Consul General and Director Trade Promotion, Canada, Toronto since July 1991; born 29.11.36; Third later Second Secretary FO 1964; Nicosia 1966; FO 1967; First Secretary Budapest 1968; FCO 1971; First Secretary (Comm) Rio de Janeiro 1974; Counsellor (Comm) The Hague 1978; Counsellor (Comm) Kuala Lumpur 1982; (Deputy High Commissioner 1983); RCDS 1986; Counsellor FCO 1987; m 1967 Elizabeth Mary Lovett Williams (1s 1968; 2d 1971, 1974).

Davies, Richard William Hardwicke; Counsellor and Permanent Representative (ESCAP) Bangkok since May 1992; born 6.7.42; Second Secretary FCO 1971; Language Student Hong Kong 1973; Trade Commissioner Hong Kong 1976; FCO 1977; First Secretary Hong Kong 1979; FCO 1980; First Secretary (Chancery) Nicosia 1985; First Secretary later Counsellor FCO 1988; m 1965 Prudence Mary Littlechild (2s 1968, 1969).

Davies, Robert Harold Glyn; First Secretary FCO since November 1989; born 23.3.42; FO 1963; Havana 1964; FO 1964; Third later Second

Secretary (Inf) Mexico City 1968; First Secretary FCO 1974; Consul (Comm) Zagreb 1980; First Secretary on loan to Cabinet Office 1983; First Secretary (Comm), Consul and Head of Chancery Luanda 1986; m 1968 Maria Del Carmen Diaz (1s 1970).

Davies, Roger James; Second Secretary (Management/Consular) Doha since April 1991; born 23.9.47; HCS 1965; FO (later FCO) 1967; Moscow 1970; Kampala 1971; Islamabad 1973; Kathmandu 1974; FCO 1978; Baghdad 1981; Vice-Consul (Comm) Johannesburg 1985; Second Secretary FCO 1987; m (1) 1974 Catherine Yvonne Moorby (diss 1990) (1s 1982; 1d 1984) (2) 1990 Jean Heather Theresa Austin.

Davies, Sally Rebekah; FCO since October 1991; born 13.2.67; Grade 9.

Davis, Ashley James; FCO since July 1991; born 23.2.59; FCO 1986; Islamabad 1987; Grade 9; m 1981 Gillian Francis (1d 1984; 1s 1987).

Davis, Doris; FCO since January 1988; born 26.1.47; DSAO 1967; Baghdad 1968; Sofia 1970; FCO 1971; Kuala Lumpur 1972; Peking 1973; Washington 1975; FCO 1978; Cairo 1980; Capetown/Pretoria 1984; Grade 9.

Davis, Joseph Alan; Nicosia since June 1990; born 12.11.64; FCO 1982; Grade 10; m 1990 Joanne Marie Bulheller.

Davis, John Michael, BEM (1990); Cairo since April 1991; born 4.6.34; Royal Marines 1952-66; Beirut 1966; Budapest 1967; Accra 1969; Singapore 1971; Tel Aviv 1973; Valletta 1975; Bangkok 1978; The Hague 1981; Belgrade 1984; Ottawa 1986; Moscow 1989; Grade CSO; m 1956 Sylvia Ambrose (2d 1959, 1962).

Davis, Kevin Roy; FCO since October 1991; born 2.1.65; FCO 1981; Washington 1989; Grade 8; m 1991 Karen Roberts.

Davis, Rosemary; UKREP Brussels since July 1991; born 28.1.63; FCO 1987; Language Training 1988; Language Training Cairo 1989; FCO 1990; Grade 9.

Davis, Stephen Alexander James; Warsaw since February 1990; born 24.9.65; FCO 1983; Mexico City 1986; Grade 9; m 1986 Maureen Patricia Oates.

Davis, Trevor John; First Secretary FCO since April 1981; born 29.5.32; FO 1955; Tehran 1960; FO 1961; Tehran 1962; Second Secretary FO (later FCO) 1966; Lagos 1972; First Secretary FCO 1975; Helsinki 1977; m 1955 Shirley Anne Stock (1s 1959; 2d 1961, 1966).

Davison, Brian William Edward; Cairo since March 1992; born 6.6.45; Royal Marines 1961; MOD Police 1985; HM Prison Service 1986;

Lusaka 1988; Grade SO3; m 1966 Sandra June Thompson (2s 1970, 1971).

Davison, John Paul; First Secretary FCO since April 1989; born 25.6.50; FCO 1974; MECAS 1975; Abu Dhabi 1977; Resigned 1978; Reappointed 1985; First Secretary Dubai 1986; m 1978 Elizabeth Jane Clark (2d 1981, 1986; 1s 1983).

Davison, Nicole April; Dhaka since February 1991; born 6.8.68; FCO 1988; Pretoria/Capetown 1990; Grade 9.

Davy, Lisa Jane; Ottawa since January 1992; born 31.12.67; FCO 1987; Prague 1989; FCO 1990; Grade 10.

Dawbarn, John Nathaniel Yelverton; Third later Second Secretary (Chancery/Inf) Belgrade since November 1990; born 3.5.65; FCO 1987; Language Training 1990; Grade 8; m 1989 Katherine Sarah Urry.

Dawes, Patricia Kathleen; SUPL since September 1989; born 10.11.37; Madrid 1959; Bucharest 1963; FO 1964; Port of Spain 1967; FCO 1970; Paris 1978; Second Secretary FCO 1982.

Dawson, Mark; Seoul since November 1992; born 27.3.65; FCO 1985; Budapest 1987; Bogotá 1989; FCO 1991; Grade 10.

Dawson, Mark; Washington since August 1989; born 3.11.67; FCO 1987; Grade 10.

Day, Martin Charles;Second Secretary (Chancery) Cairo since August 1992; born 4.11.65; FCO 1989; Language Training Cairo 1991.

Day, Rosamund; FCO since October 1991; born 27.6.64; FCO 1983; Bonn 1985; Suva 1987; Africa/ME Floater 1989; Grade 9.

Day, Stephen Peter, CMG (1989); Senior Trade Commissioner Hong Kong and Consul-General Macao since May 1992; born 19.1.38; HMOCS South Arabian Federation 1961-67; retired as Senior Adviser (Federation); Second later First Secretary FO (later FCO) 1967; First Secretary Political Advisers Office, Singapore 1970; First Secretary (Press) UKMIS New York 1972; FCO 1976; Counsellor Beirut 1977; Consul-General Edmonton 1979; HM Ambassador and Consul-General Doha 1981; Counsellor FCO 1984; HM Ambassador and Consul-General Tunis 1987; m 1965 Angela Doreen Waudby (2d 1966, 1968; 1s 1972).

Dean, Alison Fiona; Luanda since December 1991; born 29.1.66; FCO 1987; Athens 1990; FCO 1990; Grade S2.

Dean, Andrew John; First Secretary FCO since November 1992; born 6.2.55; FCO 1982; Second

Secretary (UNIDO/UN) UKMIS Vienna 1984; Second later First Secretary FCO 1986; First Secretary (Chancery) Hanoi 1990; m 1989 Nicola Moreton.

Dean, Catherine Angela; FCO since September 1990; born 22.11.61; FCO 1985; Sofia 1989; Grade S2.

Dean, Lesley Anne; FCO since May 1991; born 22.2.39; FO (later FCO) 1965; Second Secretary Moscow 1979; Second later First Secretary FCO 1981; on loan to the Cabinet Office 1989; m 1972 James Malcolm Dean.

Dean, Nicola Susan; FCO since October 1991; born 19.10.68; Grade 9.

Dean, Robert John; Second Secretary FCO since February 1992; born 21.5.59; MOD 1977; FCO 1978; Second Secretary Copenhagen 1987; m 1981 Julie Margaret Stott (2d 1986, 1988).

Deane, Geoffrey; First Secretary FCO since August 1991; born 19.2.50; FCO 1976; Nairobi 1980; Second Secretary FCO 1984; First Secretary (Chancery) East Berlin 1988; m Karen Aileen Wallace (3d 1980, 1983, 1986).

Deaney, Tina Marie; FCO since June 1991; born 18.4.72; Grade 10.

Dear, Robert Edward; First Secretary FCO since January 1992; born 19.2.55; FCO 1986; First Secretary Vienna 1987; m 1982 Caroline Margaret Reuss.

Dearden, Christopher Robert; FCO since August 1989; born 7.12.59; FCO 1978; Wellington 1981; Ankara 1985; LA/Caribbean Floater 1966; Grade 10.

Dearden, Eric Edwin; Second Secretary (Management) Tel Aviv since February 1992; born 21.12.42; MOD (Army) 1961; FCO 1968; Africa Floater 1970; Algiers 1973; Karachi 1976; FCO 1977; Dhaka 1980; Canberra 1982; FCO 1985 (Second Secretary 1989).

Dearden, Janine Elaine (née Lawrence); SUPL since October 1990; born 18.10.60; FCO 1982; Rome 1983; Nairobi 1985; SUPL 1988; FCO 1989; Grade S2; m 1985 Timothy John Dearden 2s 1987, 1989).

Dearden, Timothy John; Valletta since February 1991; born 29.11.55; HM Forces (Army) 1981-82; FCO 1982; Nairobi 1985; FCO 1988; Grade 9; m 1985 Janine Elaine Lawrence (2s 1987, 1989).

Dearlove, John Gilroy; Counsellor Prague since April 1992; born 17.10.38; Third Secretary FO 1965; Second later First Secretary Tokyo 1966; FCO 1970; Tokyo 1974; First Secretary FCO 1977; First Secretary later Counsellor Brasilia

1981; Counsellor FCO 1984; m 1966 Carol Ann Hetherington (1s 1966; 2d 1973, 1975).

Dearlove, Richard Billing, OBE (1984); Counsellor Washington since August 1991; born 23.1.45; Third Secretary FO 1966; Third later Second Secretary Nairobi 1968; FCO 1971; Second later First Secretary Prague 1973; FCO 1976; First Secretary Paris 1980; First Secretary FCO 1984; Counsellor UKMIS Geneva 1987; m 1968 Rosalind McKenzie (2s 1970, 1978; 1d 1972).

De Chassiron, Charles Richard Lucien; Counsellor (Comm/Econ) Rome since November 1989; born 27.4.48; FCO 1971; Third Secretary Stockholm 1972; First Secretary Maputo 1975; FCO 1978; First Secretary (Comm) Brasilia 1982; First Secretary later Counsellor FCO 1985; m 1974 Britt-Marie Sonja Medhammar (1d 1975; 1s 1976).

Dee, Stewart; Bonn since 1990; born 12.8.69; FCO 1988; Grade 10; m 1991 Claire Duggan.

Deffee, Robert Edward Delves, MBE (1980); Second Secretary (Cons) Mexico City since March 1989; born 10.10.41; FO 1960; Sofia 1962; Phnom Penh 1963; Rome 1965; Lusaka 1966; Vice-Consul Managua 1969; FCO 1970; Khartoum 1974; Dubai 1976; FCO 1980; Second Secretary (Admin) Jedda 1984; FCO 1986; m 1969 Mireya Mayorga Delgado (1d 1972; 2s 1974, 1978).

De Fonblanque, John Robert; Head of Chancery UKREP Brussels since January 1988; born 20.12.43; Third Secretary FCO 1968; Jakarta 1969; Second later First Secretary UKDEL Brussels EEC 1972; on loan to HM Treasury 1977; FCO 1980; Counsellor FCO 1983; Counsellor on loan to the Cabinet Office 1983; Head of Chancery New Delhi 1986; m 1984 Margaret Prest (1s 1985).

De Gier, Helen Marjorie; FCO since January 1989; born 19.2.59; HCS 1976-84; FCO 1984; Freetown 1986; Grade S2A.

Delaney, Michael; Lagos since July 1990; born 14.12.67; FCO 1988; Grade 10; m 1990 Zeliha Doganavsargil.

Delany, Carol Jane; Berlin since August 1990; born 2.7.66; FCO 1986; Grade 10.

Dempster, Sharon Louise; Paris since February 1991; born 13.2.69; FCO 1989; Grade 10.

Deneiffe, Paul Michael; FCO since January 1989; born 21.6.63; FCO 1982 Cairo 1987; Grade 9.

Denham, John Edward; Damascus since August 1991; Royal Navy 1956-78; Budapest 1980; Ankara 1981; Kingston 1984; Moscow 1987; Paris 1989; Grade SO; m 1958 June Dunn.

Denne, Christopher James Alured, CMG (1991); Counsellor FCO since June 1989; born 20.8.45; Diplomatic Service 1967; Delhi 1969; FCO 1972; First Secretary (Inf) Lagos 1974; FCO 1977; Resigned October 1978; Reinstated March 1983; First Secretary FCO 1983; First Secretary and Deputy Permanent Representative UKMIS Vienna 1985; m 1968 Sarah Longman (2s 1971, 1973, 1d 1976).

Dennis, John David; First Secretary Kuala Lumpur since July 1992; born 6.8.59; FCO 1981; Hong Kong 1983; Peking 1985; Second later First Secretary FCO 1987; m 1989 Jillian Margaret Kemp.

Dennison, Greta Mary; FCO since July 1973; born 1.12.33; FCO 1970; UK Mission to the UN New York 1972; Grade S2.

Denny, Ross Patrick; Second Secretary (EC/ Econ) The Hague since October 1992; born 13.9.55; RN 1972-79; FCO 1979; Santiago 1980; Doha 1983; Warsaw 1985; FCO 1988; m 1977 Barbara Harvard (1d 1979; 1s 1981).

Dent, Alastair Ross Möller; FCO since November 1989 (Second Secretary 1991); born 7.2.54; DHSS 1972; FCO 1974; UKREP Brussels 1976; Moscow 1979; FCO 1981; LA Floater 1984; Mexico City 1986; m (1) 1977 (diss 1983); m (2) 1985 Ligia Esperanza Zeledon Castillo (1s 1988).

Dent, Lavinia Pauline (née Graham); Canberra since July 1981; born 13.12.54; FCO 1974; Brussels 1975; Moscow 1979; Grade S2; m 1977 Alastair Ross Möller Dent.

Dent, Shannon Elizabeth; Dubai since April 1985; born 29.3.58; FCO 1979; Lusaka 1979; Peking 1981; Athens 1982; Grade S2.

Denwood, Judith Elizabeth; FCO since October 1991; born 21.10.65; FCO 1986; Bridgetown 1988; Grade 10.

Desloges, Christina Anne (née Sanders); Harare since October 1991; born 30.11.63; FCO 1984; Lagos 1987; FCO 1991; Grade S2A; m 1989 Daniel Albert Joseph Desloges (1d 1990).

De Vere Lane, Graham Vaughan, MBE (1991); Pretoria since September 1990; born 5.5.45; FCO 1968; Singapore 1969; FCO 1971; Lusaka 1973; FCO 1975; Darwin 1976; FCO 1978; Amman 1979; FCO 1983; Khartoum 1984; FCO 1987; Moscow 1988; Grade 8; m 1964 Janet Pine (1s 1964; 2d 1967, 1969).

Devine, John Joseph; FCO since January 1991; born 3.7.70; Grade 10.

Devine, Paul Grahame; Dusseldorf since April 1992; born 19.1.51; DHSS 1973; FCO 1981; Bonn 1983; Riyadh 1985; Suva 1988; Grade 10.

Devlin, Francis Patrick; Second Secretary Caracas since March 1991; born 29.7.41; GPO 1957; FO 1965; Singapore 1967; FCO 1968; Lagos 1969; FCO 1970; Cairo 1974; FCO 1978; Amman 1980; Madrid 1984; Second Secretary FCO 1987; m 1966 Dorothy Daley.

Devlin, Susan; Washington since October 1992; born 4.2.61; FCO 1988; Shanghai 1990; FCO 1991; Lisbon 1992; Grade S2A.

Dew, John Anthony; Counsellor and Deputy Head of Mission Dublin since December 1992; born 3.5.52; FCO 1973; Third Secretary Caracas 1975; Second later First Secretary FCO 1979; First Secretary OECD Paris 1983; First Secretary FCO 1987; m 1975 Marion Bewley Kirkwood (3d 1977, 1980, 1984).

De Waal, James Francis, UKMIS New York since June 1992; born 18.12.68; FCO 1990; Grade 8.

Dewar, Robert Scott; Deputy Head of Mission Harare since April 1992; born 10.6.49; FCO 1973; Third later Second Secretary Colombo 1974; First Secretary FCO 1978; First Secretary (Comm) Head of Chancery and Consul Luanda 1981; First Secretary FCO 1984; First Secretary and Head of Chancery Dakar 1988; m 1979 Jennifer Mary Ward (1d 1988).

Dewberry, David Albert; First Secretary FCO since May 1991; born 27.9.41; CRO 1958; Karachi 1963; Kingston 1966; Warsaw 1970; Brussels 1971; Second Secretary (Aid) Dacca 1972; FCO 1974; Second Secretary Mexico City 1977; First Secretary (Consul/Admin) Buenos Aires 1980; First Secretary FCO 1982; Head of Chancery Dar es Salaam 1987; m 1974 Catherine Mary Stabback (3s 1976, 1977, 1981; 1d 1979).

de Wilton, Christopher Douglas; Second Secretary FCO since February 1991; born 25.10.41; FO 1963; West Africa Floater 1964; Nairobi 1965; Ankara 1968; FCO 1971; Islamabad 1975; FCO 1977; Victoria Seychelles 1978; FCO 1980; Oslo 1984; FCO 1986; Second Secretary (Technical Co-operation) Quito 1988; m 1971 Angela Hunter Pearson (1d 1974; 1s 1978).

Dewsnap, Helen Elizabeth; FCO since May 1992; born 14.1.66; FCO 1985; Rio de Janeiro 1990; Grade S2.

Dibben, Michael Alan Charles; HM Ambassador and Consul-General Asuncion since March 1991; born 19.9.43; CRO 1964; DSA 1966; Montreal 1967; Nassau 1968; Stuttgart 1968; Nassau 1971; FCO 1971; Second Secretary (Grenada Affairs) Port of Spain 1975; Vice-Consul Douala 1979; First Secretary FCO 1981; Consul (Comm) Hamburg 1983; First Secretary FCO 1987.

Dibble, Geoffrey Walter; Moscow since August 1990; born 20.8.35; HCS 1960-74; FCO 1974;

Rome 1976; FCO 1978; Kingston 1980; Islamabad 1983; FCO 1987; Grade 9; m 1980 Hilary Anne Light.

Dibble, Hilary Anne (née Light); Moscow since July 1990; born 17.7.51; FCO 1973; Moscow 1974; FCO 1975; Rome 1976; Kingston 1980; Islamabad 1983; FCO 1987; Grade 9; m 1980 Geoffrey Walter Dibble.

Dicey, Susan Kim; UKMIS Geneva since February 1987; born 7.12.59; FCO 1979; UKMIS New York 1981; Dakar 1983; Moscow 1985; Grade S2.

Dick, Colin John; FCO since September 1990; born 22.6.70; Grade 10.

Dick, Paula Jayne; Amman since October 1990; born 20.6.69; FCO 1988; Grade 10.

Dickerson, Nigel Paul; Second Secretary (Management) and Consul Santiago since April 1992; born 25.4.59; FCO 1978; Bonn 1981; Warsaw 1984; FCO 1987 (Second Secretary 1990); m 1984 Marianne Gay Tatchell.

Dickins, Nicholas William; Tel Aviv since September 1991; born 15.11.56; FCO 1985; Grade 8; m 1991 Marina Papaspyrou.

Dickinson, Barrie; Tel Aviv since October 1991; born 13.8.38; RAF 1956-79; Ankara 1979; Havana 1981; Tokyo 1983; Belgrade 1987; Dublin 1989; Grade SO; m 1965 Beryl Margaret.

Dickinson, Woodman Mark Lowes; First Secretary FCO since January 1991; born 16.1.55; FCO 1976; Second Secretary Ankara 1979; First Secretary FCO 1983; First Secretary (Pol/Inf) Dublin 1987; m 1986 Francesca Infanti.

Dickson, John; Amman since October 1990; born 16.4.33; Royal Navy 1948-73; Beirut 1973; Havana 1974; Paris 1976; Lagos 1978; Kuala Lumpur 1979; Warsaw 1983; The Hague 1985; Bucharest 1988; Grade CSO; m (1) 1958 Michelle Yvonne Jossette Dessaus (diss 1975) (1d 1959; 2s 1962, 1966); (2) 1977 Jean Victoria Levett (1s 1978).

Dickson, Peter Searle; First Secretary (Management/Consular) Kampala since July 1990; born 30.5.34; Royal Navy 1950-64; FO 1964; Tokyo 1966; Düsseldorf 1969; FCO 1972; Accra 1973; Nairobi 1977; FCO 1979; Khartoum 1982 (Second Secretary 1984); Second Secretary (Admin) Oslo 1985; m 1959 Jean Helen (2d 1963, 1965).

Dickson, Susan Jane; FCO since August 1990; born 30.7.64; Assistant Legal Adviser.

Dickson, William Andrew; First Secretary (IAEA) Vienna since May 1989; born 17.12.50; FCO 1969; SUPL to attend University 1970;

FCO 1974; Cairo 1976; Nairobi 1980; Second Secretary FCO 1982; Second Secretary (Comm) Budapest 1982; Second later First Secretary FCO 1986; m 1981 Gillian Ann Hague.

Digby, Simon; FCO since January 1991; born 4.8.55; Crown Agents 1977; FCO 1980; Tehran 1982; LA Floater 1986; FCO 1987; Third Secretary (Admin/Cons) Mbabane 1989; Grade 9.

Dillan, Rachel Elizabeth; Amman since September 1985; born 22.8.63; FCO 1983; Grade S2.

Dillow, Robert Stephen; SUPL since August 1992; born 21.10.62; FCO 1985; Third later Second Secretary (Chancery/Inf) Montevideo 1988; Second later First Secretary FCO 1990; m 1988 Celia Mary Glenny.

Dimbleby, Andrew Timothy; Third Secretary (Comm/Inf) Dubai since June 1989; born 20.5.59; FCO 1979; Freetown 1982; Accra 1981; FCO 1985; Pretoria 1986; Grade 9; m 1981 Susan Irvine (1s 1988, 1d 1991).

Dimmock, John Frederick; Second Secretary (Management/Consular) Jedda since June 1992; born 19.1.45; FO 1962; Baghdad 1966; Enugu 1967; FCO 1968; UN New York 1969; Anguilla 1971; Islamabad 1973; FCO 1975; East Berlin 1979; Bonn 1981; Second Secretary Harare 1983; On loan to the DTI 1988; FCO 1990; m 1972 Edith Schoen.

Dimond, Paul Stephen; Counsellor (Comm) Tokyo since September 1989; born 30.12.44; FO 1963; DSA 1965; Language Training Tokyo 1966; Osaka 1968 (Consul (Comm) 1970); Second Secretary Tokyo 1972; On loan to DTI 1973; Second Secretary FCO 1975; First Secretary (Econ) Stockholm 1977; First Secretary FCO 1980; First Secretary (Comm) Tokyo 1981; First Secretary FCO 1986; on secondment to Smiths Industries plc 1988; m 1965 Carolyn Susan Davis-Mees (2s 1968, 1970).

Dinsdale, Ian McLean Taylor; Second Secretary FCO since October 1989; born 20.10.49; FCO 1969; Nairobi 1972; Colombo 1976; Second Secretary FCO 1979; Second Secretary Santo Domingo 1982; Maseru 1985; Second Secretary Riyadh 1986; m 1975 Elizabeth Ann MontaBut (1 step s 1960; 1 step d 1961).

Dinsley, Andrew; Kiev since July 1992; born 22.8.66; FCO 1990; Grade 10.

Dinwiddy, Bruce Harry; Deputy High Commissioner Ottawa since January 1992; born 1.2.46; Second Secretary FCO 1973; First Secretary UKDEL MBFR Vienna 1975; FCO 1977; First Secretary and Head of Chancery Cairo 1981; First Secretary FCO 1983; Counsellor on loan to the Cabinet Office 1986; FCO 1988; Counsellor Bonn 1989; m 1974

Emma Victoria Llewellyn (1d 1976; 1s 1979).

Dix, Christopher John; FCO since May 1992; born 30.9.64; FCO 1983; UKMIS Geneva 1985; Dhaka 1988; Grade 9; m 1988 Julia Milward.

Dixon, Barry Michael; First Secretary Hanoi since July 1992; born 9.4.38; MAFF 1955; FO 1959; Jakarta 1959; Bangkok 1961; FO 1962; Tokyo 1964; Polytechnic of Central London 1971; Second Secretary FCO 1972; Second Secretary (Inf) Port of Spain 1975; Tokyo 1978; First Secretary FCO 1983; First Secretary (Comm/Inf) Khartoum 1988; m 1966 Daphne Alison Bell (1s 1970; 1d 1974).

Dixon, Carole Valerie; Bangkok since October 1989; born 23.11.41; Paymaster-General;s Office 1964; DSAO 1965; Budapest 1967; Paris 1969; Saigon 1971; FCO 1972; Manila 1978; Athens 1981; FCO 1985; Grade 9.

Dixon, Debra Audrey (née Churchill); SUPL since January 1992; born 6.4.58; FCO 1978; Washington 1980; Sana'a 1983; Dusseldorf 1989; FCO 1986; Grade 9; m 1978 Russell Kenneth Dixon (1d 1985, 1s 1990).

Dixon, Eric Foster; Second later First Secretary FCO since April 1988; born 5.10.32; GPO 1949; HM Forces 1951-53; GPO 1953; FO 1956; Addis Ababa 1957; FO 1959; Colombo 1965; Second Secretary Moscow 1967; FCO 1969; Bonn 1973; FCO 1975; Caracas 1978; FCO 1981; Singapore 1984; m 1964 Brenda Williams (1s 1968; 1 step d 1957).

Dixon, Geoffrey Colin; First Secretary and Deputy High Commissioner Bandar Seri Begawan since September 1991; born 25.2.50; FO (later FCO) 1966; Lagos 1971; FCO 1974; Kuala Lumpur 1978; Abu Dhabi 1981 (Second Secretary 1983); FCO 1984; Head of Chancery, Vice-Consul (Info) and Aid Attaché Panama City 1988; Second Secretary FCO 1989; m 1972 Philippa Margaret Hewett.

Dixon, Hazel; Peking since May 1992; born 19.8.49; HM Forces 1967-77; Ankara 1989; Grade SO.

Dixon, Nicola Claire; FCO since November 1990; born 10.7.68; Grade 9.

Dixon, Russell Kenneth; Düsseldorf since April 1989 (Second Secretary 1992); born 24.1.58; MOD 1976; FCO 1978; Washington 1980; Sana'a 1983; FCO 1985; m 1978 Debra Audrey Churchill (2d 1985; 1992, 1s 1990).

Dixon, Susan; FCO since February 1992; born 24.3.67; FCO 1986; Hong Kong 1989; Grade S2.

Dixon, William James; First Secretary (Information) Canberra since October 1985; born 10.12.31; COI (Northern Region) 1954; Second

Secretary (Inf) Sydney 1961; Second Secretary (Comm/Inf) Rangoon 1965; Second Secretary (Comm) Bombay 1967; FCO 1971; Consul Baghdad 1975; First Secretary Kuala Lumpur 1978; FCO 1982; m (1) 1955 Elizabeth Battell (1d 1960); (2) 1979 Marlene Ellen Mahony.

Doane, Brian Ernest; Second Secretary (Assistant Management Officer) Dhaka since April 1990; born 8.11.38; Customs and Excise Dept 1960; FO 1966; Kota Kinabalu 1967; FCO 1971; Warsaw 1972; Dakar 1973; FCO 1975; Singapore 1978; Tarawa 1981; Kaduna 1983; Second Secretary FCO 1986; m 1966 Joan Christine Beetle (1s 1969).

Doble, Denis Henry; Consul-General Amsterdam since May 1991; born 2.10.36; RAF 1955-57; CO 1960; Assistant Private Secretary to Secretary of State for the Colonies 1964; Second Secretary CRO 1965; Second later First Secretary Brussels 1966; First Secretary (Dev) Lagos 1968; First Secretary FCO 1972; First Secretary (Econ/Aid) Islamabad 1975; First Secretary Head of Chancery and Consul Lima 1978; First Secretary FCO 1982; Acting Deputy High Commissioner Bombay 1985; Deputy High Commissioner Calcutta 1985; Deputy High Commissioner and Head of Chancery Kingston 1987; m 1975 Patricia Ann Robinson (1d 1979; 1s 1981).

Doble, John Frederick, OBE (1981); HM Consul-General Johannesburg since January 1990; born 30.6.41; Army 1959-69; FCO 1969; First Secretary (Chancery) Beirut 1972; Brussels (NATO) 1973; First Secretary FCO 1977; First Secretary Head of Chancery and Consul Maputo 1978; FCO 1981; Counsellor on Secondment to Barclays Bank International 1983; HM Consul General Edmonton 1985; m 1975 Isabella Margaret Ruth Whitbread (1d 1977).

Dobson, Sharon Gail; FCO since September 1991; born 4.1.68; Grade 9.

Dodoo, Ronald Shadrake; FCO since May 1989; born 11.10.36; Kampala 1966; FCO 1973; Strasbourg 1976; Dacca 1979; FCO 1982; Prague 1985; Jakarta 1987; Grade 9; m (1) 1964 Gretal Wilkinson (diss 1973); (2) 1973 Barbara Claire Cooper (2d 1975, 1977).

Doherty, Emer Maria; FCO since September 1990; born 10.1.69; Grade 9.

Doherty, Felicity Mary (née Tebboth); Second Secretary FCO since April 1988; born 24.10.52; FCO 1970; Bonn 1975; SUPL 1976; Moscow 1979; FCO 1981; Second Secretary 1983; Second Secretary (Comm) Lisbon 1986; m 1977 Francis Doherty (2d 1982, 1984).

Doherty, Francis Anthony; Deputy Head of Mission The Holy See since May 1992; born 4.7.41; FO 1960; Brazzaville 1963; Kuching

1965; Saigon 1966; DSAO (later FCO) 1967; Colombo 1970; Peking 1973; Assistant Private Secretary to the PUSS/Minister of State FCO 1976; Second Secretary Hamilton 1979; Second Secretary (Aid) Dar es Salaam 1981; First Secretary (Information) Rome 1983; First Secretary (Information) Milan 1984; First Secretary FCO 1986; First Secretary (Management) Mexico City 1990; m 1964 Noreen Mary Cairns (3s 1971, 1972, 1976).

Doidge, Mary Ellen; on loan to the Home Office since April 1991; born 21.1.46; Bonn 1971; FCO 1974; Warsaw 1975; Tokyo 1977; FCO 1980; Floater duties 1982; Moscow 1983; FCO 1985; Brussels (UKDEL NATO) 1988; Grade 9.

Doig, Amanda Louise; FCO since July 1992; born 7.12.73; Grade S2

Doig, Michael David; Third Secretary (Comm/Econ) Ottawa since September 1990; born 28.5.54; FCO 1973; Tokyo 1975; Karachi 1979; Vienna 1982; Kaduna 1983; FCO 1987; Grade 9; m 1983 Mary Walker McKinnie (1d 1985).

Donald, Douglas Edward; First Secretary (Comm) Dhaka since November 1990; born 27.2.41; DSA 1966; Johannesburg 1967; Second Secretary (Comm) Kabul 1970; Vice-Consul (Inf) Sydney 1974; FCO 1977; Administration Officer and Consul Stockholm 1980; FCO 1985; First Secretary (Information) Ottawa 1986; m 1963 Jane Bell Bardgett (3s 1964, 1967, 1969).

Donaldson, Brian; First Secretary FCO since July 1992; born 6.4.46; Ministry of Aviation 1963; DSAO later FCO 1965; Algiers 1968; La Paz 1971; FCO 1974; Lagos 1975; Luxembourg 1979; Second Secretary FCO 1982; APS to the Minister of State 1983; Second later First Secretary (Aid/Comm) Port Louis 1985; First Secretary (Comm) Head of Chancery and Consul Yaoundé 1989; m 1969 Elizabeth Claire Sumner (3s 1971, 1973, 1979).

Donaldson, Ian Martin; Third later Second Secretary (Political) Jakarta since April 1991; born 21.7.66; FCO 1988; m 1990 Elspeth Jane Chovil Maguire.

Donnelly, Joseph Brian; Counsellor FCO since January 1992; born 24.4.45; Second Secretary FCO 1973; First Secretary (ECOSOC) UKMIS New York 1975; First Secretary and Head of Chancery Singapore 1979; First Secretary FCO 1982; Counsellor on loan to Cabinet Office 1985; Counsellor and Consul-General Athens 1988; RCDS course 1991; m 1966 Susanne Gibb (1d 1970).

Donnelly, Matthew; Lagos since February 1992; born 21.11.61; FCO 1981; Algiers 1985; Nassau 1988; FCO 1990; Grade 10; m (1) 1982 Lesley-Ann Jones (diss 1988); (2) 1988 Tracy May Basnett (1s 1989).

Donnelly, Tracy May (née Basnett); SUPL since January 1988; born 26.3.62; FCO 1982; Berne 1983; Algiers 1985; Grade S2; m 1988 Matthew Donnelly (1s 1989).

Donougho, Pamela Margaret; FCO since October 1981; born 23.5.36; FCO 1971; Vienna 1976; Bonn 1978; Grade 7.

Dooley, John; Belgrade since February 1992; born 31.10.43; Grade SO; m 1968 Susan Hazel Bennett (1s 1973; 1d 1976).

Dorey, Gregory John; First Secretary and Private Secretary to the Minister of State since August 1992; born 1.5.56; MOD 1977; on loan at UKDEL NATO 1982; MOD 1984; First Secretary FCO 1986; First Secretary (Chancery) Budapest 1989; m 1981 Alison Patricia Taylor (1s 1988; 1d 1990).

Douche, Marion Rachel; FCO since August 1991; born 19.3.69; Grade 9.

Dougal, Malcolm Gordon; Counsellor FCO since April 1991; born 20.1.38; HM Forces 1956-58; FCO 1969; First Secretary (Comm) Paris 1972; First Secretary (Comm) Cairo 1976; FCO 1979; Consul-General Lille 1981; Deputy High Commissioner and Head of Chancery Canberra 1986; RCDS 1990; m 1964 Elke Urban (1s 1982).

Douglas, Janet Elizabeth; Second Secretary FCO since September 1991; born 6.1.60; FCO 1985; Language Training 1987; Second Secretary (Chancery/Inf) Ankara 1988.

Douglas, John; Berlin since February 1992; born 13.5.33; Lagos 1979; Havana 1980; Helsinki 1981; New Delhi 1984; Warsaw 1986; Athens 1987; Belgrade 1990; Grade SO; m 1957 Janet Douglas.

Douglas-Hiley, Mark Charles Piers Quentin; JMO New York since February 1991; born 6.11.54; Dept of Employment 1972; DHSS 1973; FCO 1974; Castries 1977; FCO 1979; UKMIS Geneva 1980; FCO 1983; Lagos 1987; Grade 9.

Doust, Stephen Terence; FCO since March 1992; born 4.12.72; Grade 10.

Douthwaite, Ann Mary, MBE (1991); Jakarta since January 1991; born 25.4.40; Düsseldorf 1961; Warsaw 1962; Paris 1963; Moscow 1965; Beirut 1966; FCO 1969; New York (UKMIS) 1970; Muscat 1973; Manila 1976; FCO 1978; Tokyo 1984; Algiers 1987; Grade S1.

Dove, John Henry; Deputy Head of Mission Tallinn since August 1992; born 10.3.65; HM Customs & Excise 1989; FCO 1990; Full-time Language Training 1991; Grade 9.

Dow, Elizabeth Anne; Vice-Consul/MO

Jerusalem since March 1991; born 9.3.58; FCO 1976; New Delhi 1978; Brasilia 1982; FCO 1984; New York (CG) 1988; Grade 9.

Dowse, Timothy Michael; First Secretary (Chancery) Washington since March 1992; born 18.12.55; FCO 1978; Manila 1980; Second later First Secretary Tel Aviv 1982; First Secretary FCO 1986; m 1989 Vivien Frances Life.

Dowsett, Moira; Brussels since May 1991; born 6.11.61; FCO 1988; Grade S2.

Drace-Francis, Charles David Stephen, CMG (1987); on secondment to British Aerospace since January 1991; born 15.3.43; Third Secretary FO 1965; Tehran 1967; Second later First Secretary FCO 1971; Assistant Political Adviser Hong Kong 1974; First Secretary UKREP Brussels 1978; FCO 1980; Counsellor attached to All Souls Oxford 1983; Counsellor and Chargé d'Affaires a.i. Kabul 1984; Counsellor (Commercial) Lisbon 1987; m 1967 Griselda Hyacinthe Waldegrave (2s 1969, 1971; 1d 1979).

Drake, David Allen; First Secretary (Commercial) Singapore since July 1991; born 1.9.47; RAF 1967-75; FCO 1977; Lagos 1979; Kuwait 1982 (Second Secretary 1984); Second later First Secretary FCO 1985; First Secretary (Civil Aviation) Bonn 1989; m 1972 Anne Veronica Paice.

Drake, Howard Ronald; First Secretary (Political/Coordination) Singapore since May 1992; born 13.8.56; FCO 1975; LA Floater 1979; Los Angeles 1981; Second Secretary 1982; Second Secretary FCO 1983; Second Secretary (Chancery/Inf) Santiago 1985; First Secretary FCO 1988; m 1988 Gill Summerfield.

Drayton, Frank Anthony; Vice-Consul Doha since October 1990; born 10.12.54; FCO 1974; Islamabad 1976; Cape Town 1979; Munich 1982; FCO 1985; Prague 1989; Grade 9; m 1988 Fidelma Bernadette Tuohy.

Dresser, Clive; First Secretary (Comm) Caracas since January 1991; born 10.4.37; MPNI 1955; FO 1960; Vienna 1960; Leopoldville 1961; Budapest 1964; Vice-Consul Stuttgart 1966; FCO 1969; Second Secretary Santiago 1971; Lima 1974; Vice-Consul (Inf/Cons) Melbourne 1976; Consul (Comm) Hamburg 1979; First Secretary FCO 1984; First Secretary (Comm) Lagos 1989; m 1961 Wilhelmina Stratton (1s 1967; 1d 1968).

Drew, Alan Clifford; FCO since June 1991; born 4.9.49; Pretoria 1981; FCO 1984; Third Secretary Nairobi 1988; Grade 8; m 1976 Sheila Ann Baldwin (2d 1981, 1983).

Drew, John Mylward; First Secretary FCO since December 1980; born 29.9.39; HMOCS Zambia 1958-69; retired as Senior Principal Ministry of

Power Transport and Works; FCO 1975; First
Secretary (Chancery) Gaborone 1979; m 1963
Judith Anne Finney (1s 1964).

Drew, Richard Arthur, MBE (1982); Second
Secretary Canberra since September 1991; born
31.1.40; GPO 1957; FO 1965; Bahrain 1967;
Nairobi 1968; FCO 1971; Brasilia 1973; FCO
1976; Baghdad1/Beirut 1976; FCO 1978; Bonn
1979; FCO 1982; Second Secretary Peking 1985;
Second Secretary FCO 1989; m (1) (2s 1961,
1965); (2) 1973 Ann Margaret Jeffs (1s 1978).

Drew, Simon Robert; FCO since March 1992;
born 7.5.65; FCO 1981; Pretoria 1989; Grade 8;
m 1991 Katharine Chappell.

Drew, Steven Michael; Manila since September
1992; born 20.12.61; FCO 1989; Grade 10; m
1989 Debra Edie (2d 1989, 1992).

Dring, Sarah Anne Maxwell; Vice-Consul
(Commercial) Johannesburg since November
1991; born 23.11.48; FCO 1974; Sofia 1975;
Nicosia 1977; FCO 1979; South East Asia
Floater 1983; Algiers 1985; FCO 1987 (Second
Secretary 1989).

Drummond, Roderick Ian; First Secretary FCO
since July 1992; born 7.9.62; FCO 1985;
Language Training 1986; Second Secretary
(Comm) Algiers 1988; m 1985 Carolyn Elizabeth
Elliott (1d 1990).

Drummond-Hay, Elisabeth Anne, MBE (1984);
FCO since November 1983 (Second Secretary
1990); born 10.9.42; FO 1962; Oslo 1965;
Warsaw 1967; FCO 1969; UKMIS New York
1969; Dar es Salaam 1973; Nicosia 1975; FCO
1975; Copenhagen 1980.

Drury, Alan Hyslop; Resident Representative St
George;s since November 1989; born 21.2.52;
FCO 1970; Budapest 1973; Dacca 1975; LA
Floater 1977; FCO 1980; Second Secretary
(Comm) Muscat 1983; Second later First
Secretary FCO 1987; m 1980 Joan Lamb (1d
1984; 1s 1986).

Drysdale, Heather; FCO since October 1987;
born 2.6.56; FCO 1977; NATO Brussels 1977;
Tokyo 1980; FCO 1983; Reykjavik 1984; Floater
duties 1987; Grade S1.

Dryden, Paul James, Warsaw since May 1992;
born 15.6.69; FCO 1990; Grade 10.

Dubois, Elaine Joy (née Smith); Washington
since August 1991; born 21.7.63; FCO 1987;
Port of Spain 1989; Grade S2; m1992 Richard
John Lewis Dubois.

Duckett, Keith Dyson; Jakarta since March
1989; born 11.4.58; FCO 1977; Kuala Lumpur
1979; Maputo 1983; Brasilia 1985; FCO 1986;
Grade 9.

Duddy, Fiona Lindsay; FCO since June 1991;
born 30.8.72; Grade 10.

Duff, Graham Reginald; First Secretary (Admin)
Dublin since September 1992; born 27.6.38; FO
1956; HM Forces 1957-59; Benghazi 1959;
Warsaw 1963; Vice-Consul Atlanta 1966; FCO
1968; Second Secretary 1970; Vice-Consul
(Cons1/Imm) Karachi 1972; Washington 1976;
First Secretary FCO 1981; First Secretary
(Admin) Bangkok 1985; First Secretary (Admin)
and Consul Peking 1989; m 1962 Margaret
Dunsden Arnold (2s 1962, 1964).

Duff, Janet Nancy; Full-time Language
TrainingBangkok since May 1992; born 3.12.67;
FCO 1990; Language Training FCO 1991;
Grade 9.

Duff, Morwenna Marion Finlayson; Jakarta since
September 1990; born 6.10.65; HCS 1988; FCO
1989; Grade 10.

Duffield, Linda Joy; First Secretary (Comm)
Moscow since September 1989; born 18.4.53;
DHSS 1976; ENA Paris 1986; First Secretary
FCO 1987.

Duffin, David Robert; FCO since August 1990;
born 4.11.53; FCO 1972; New Delhi 1979; FCO
1981; Singapore 1987; Grade 8; m 1980 Angela
Thicke.

Duffin, Pamela Margaret; Rabat since July 1992;
born 14.3.47; FCO 1987; Rome 1989; Grade S2.

Duffy, Peter John; Second Secretary FCO since
March 1991; born 20.6.50; Ministry of Aviation
(later Ministry of Technology) 1966; FCO 1967;
Addis Ababa 1971; Maseru 1974; Khartoum
1977; FCO 1978; Yaoundé 1982; Johannesburg
1985; Budapest 1989; m 1971 Juliet Heather
Woodward (1s 1972).

Duffy, Sandra Marie; Turks and Caicos Islands
since January 1991; born 21.11.60; FCO 1984;
Algiers 1985; Jerusalem 1987; Grade S2.

Duggan, Gordon Aldridge; High Commissioner
Singapore since January 1991; born 12.8.37;
Third later Second Secretary FO 1963; Second
later First Secretary Canberra 1966; FCO 1969;
First Secretary (Inf) Bonn 1972; First Secretary
and Head of Chancery Jakarta 1974; First
Secretary Canberra 1976; FCO 1979; Counsellor
(Econ/Comm) Lagos 1981; Consul-General
Zurich 1984; Counsellor FCO 1988; on
secondment to Northern Engineering Industries
plc 1989; m 1969 Erica Rose Anderssen (2d
1971, 1973; 1s 1981).

Duggan, Raymond Edward; Consul (Comm)
Jedda since April 1989; born 26.4.43; Board of
Trade 1961; CRO 1963; DSAO 1965;
Christchurch 1965; Berne 1968; Nassau 1969;
Second Secretary 1973; On loan to DOT 1974;

Second Secretary (Pol/Inf) Bangkok 1977; FCO 1979; Vice-Consul (Comm) Hamburg 1982; Second Secretary (Admin/Cons) Bridgetown 1985; m 1963 Ann Shirley Bird (4d 1966, 1967, 1970, 1979).

Duggin, Thomas Joseph; High Commissioner Vila since January 1992; born 15.9.47; Commonwealth Office (later FCO) 1967; Oslo 1969; Bucharest 1973; Assistant Private Secretary to the PUSS, FCO 1977; Second Secretary Bangkok 1979; First Secretary FCO 1982; First Secretary (Comm), Consul and Head of Chancery La Paz 1985; First Secretary and Head of Chancery Mexico City 1989; m (1) 1968 Andrea Nicholson (diss 1983) (2s 1973, 1975); (2) 1983 Jitip Dunlop (née Charernnaimuang).

Duguid, Adam; Third Secretary Riyadh since June 1992; born 11.1.41; HM Forces 1959-67; FO (later FCO) 1967; Bonn 1970; FCO 1972; Nairobi 1973; Tehran 1976; FCO 1978; Nairobi 1981; FCO 1985; Cairo 1987; FCO 1991; m 1967 Alise Vital (1d 1968).

Dun, Peter John; Counsellor (Commercial/Aid) Islamabad since April 1990; born 6.7.47; FCO 1970; Third later Second Secretary Kuala Lumpur 1972; Second later First Secretary FCO 1976; UKREP Brussels 1980; First Secretary UKMIS New York 1983; FCO 1987; RCDS 1989; m 1983 Cheng-Kiak (2s 1987, 1989).

Duncan, Colin; UKREP Brussels since April 1992; born 3.3.70; DSS 1988; FCO 1989; Grade 10.

Duncan, George Rex; FCO since February 1991; Second Secretary 1991; born 20.2.40; DWS St Helena 1965; FCO 1974; Paris 1985; New Delhi 1987; m 1961 Norma Hudson (1s 1962; 3d 1964, 1968, 1969).

Duncan, Guy Charles; Counsellor FCO since July 1988; born 28.4.34; FO 1963; First Secretary Kuala Lumpur 1966; Lusaka 1970; FCO 1973; Athens 1977; FCO 1980; First Secretary later Counsellor Berne 1984; m 1959 Jennifer Jane Crawford (3d 1964, 1966, 1970).

Duncan, John Stewart; NATO Defence College Rome since February 1992; born 17.4.58; FCO 1980; Paris 1982; Khartoum 1985; Second Secretary FCO 1988; on loan to the ODA 1991; m 1984 Anne Marie Jacq.

Duncan, William Sherriffs; Third Secretary Riyadh since January 1991; born 11.5.42; FCO 1971; Delhi 1972; FCO 1975; Cairo 1977; FCO 1980; Darwin 1982; FCO 1984; Rome 1986; FCO 1989; Grade 9; m 1964 Florence Agnes Irene Wilson (2d 1966, 1968).

Duncan-Smith, Louise-Marie Veronica; Victoria since July 1992; born 16.12.62; FCO 1984;

Ottawa 1986; Banjul 1989; FCO 1989; Grade S2; m 1986 Brian David Smith.

Dunkley, Angela Leah; Washington since February 1991; born 27.3.63; FCO 1987; Khartoum 1988; Grade S2.

Dunlop, Alexander James Macfarlane; Second Secretary (Chancery/Info) Lilongwe since August 1989; born 14.6.48; FCO 1968; Ottawa 1971; Vientiane 1974; Sana'a 1980; Vienna 1983; FCO 1986; m 1978 Ortrud Wittlinger.

Dunn, David Hedley; Oslo since January 1992; born 21.9.68; FCO 1989; Grade 10.

Dunn, James Michael; Paris since May 1990; born 7.1.59; FCO 1980; Washington 1984; FCO 1986; Grade 9.

Dunn, Michael George; Second Secretary (Commercial/Aid) Quito since November 1992; born 8.11.48; FO (later FCO) 1966; New York 1971; Lima 1974; FCO 1976; Copenhagen 1980; Harare 1983; Caracas 1986; FCO 1989; m 1983 Mercedes Josefina Fuguet-Sanchez (1d 1987).

Dunn, Phillip Charles, MBE (1987); Aden since September 1985; born 7.7.46; Royal Fleet Auxiliary Service 1964-72; FCO 1972; Singapore 1973; FCO 1975; Darwin 1976; FCO 1978; Harare 1980; FCO 1984; Grade 8; m 1967 Annette Dunn (2s 1968, 1970; 1d 1973).

Dunn, Major Piers Thomas; Queen's Messenger since 1975; born 15.3.33; Army 1952-68.

Dunnachie, Doreen Carole (née Jennings); SUPL simce March 1992; born 20.12.46; FCO 1973; Kinshasa 1974; FCO 1976; Helsinki 1977; Suva 1980; The Hague 1982; FCO 1984; SUPL 1986; FCO 1989; Grade S1; m 1986 Hugh Dunnachie.

Dunnachie, Hugh, MBE (1987); Deputy Consul General Melbourne since March 1992; born 7.12.44; MOD (Navy) 1961-65; DSAO 1965; Singapore (Political Adviser's Office) 1967; Warsaw 1972; Vice-Consul Cairo 1973; Second Secretary FCO 1976; Second Secretary (Comm) The Hague 1980; Consul and Head of BIS Tripoli 1984; First Secretary FCO 1989; m (1) 1963 Elizabeth Mosman Baer (diss 1986) (3d 1964, 1971, 1980; 1s 1965); (2) 1986 Doreen Carole Jennings.

Durham, John Clive; First Secretary FCO since June 1986; born 12.7.39; MPNI 1955; MSS 1966; Commonwealth Office (later FCO) 1967; Wellington 1969; Mogadishu 1972; on loan to DOT 1974; Second Secretary (Comm) Khartoum 1977; Consul (Comm) Frankfurt 1981; m 1962 Sandra Kay Beaumont (1s 1968; 1d 1969).

Durkin, John Edward; FCO since October 1979; born 17.4.35; FO (later FCO) 1962; Accra 1969; FCO 1970; Singapore 1972; FCO 1974;

Islamabad 1977; Grade 8; m 1954 Olive
Simpson (1d 1964).

Dutch, Alastair Keith; Second later First
Secretary FCO since Janaury 1980; born 4.5.52;
FCO 1971; Ankara 1974; Moscow 1977;
Bombay 1978; m 1974 Lesley Joan Carol
Hearsum (2s 1975, 1983).

Duxbury, Julie Annette; UKDEL Brussels since
September 1990; born 5.2.70; FCO 1988; Grade
10.

Dwyer, Michael John; Toronto since March
1990; (Second Secretary 1991); born 29.12.55;
DOE 1972-74; FCO 1974; Ottawa 1977;
Belmopan 1979; Islamabad 1982; FCO 1986; m
1982 Karen Leolin Meighan (2s 1983, 1985).

Dyer, Mairi; FCO since July 1991; born 3.3.71;
Grade S2.

Dyball, Karen Linda; UKMIS New York since
September 1989; born 24.5.60; FCO 1983;
Banjul 1984; Islamabad 1986; Grade S2.

Dyson, John Alva; Vice-Consul (Management
Officer) Cape Town since February 1991; born
15.4.49; DSAO (later FCO) 1966; Port of Spain
1970; Geneva 1973; Yaoundé 1976; FCO 1978;
Nuku'alofa 1982; FCO 1985; Second Secretary
(Comm) Jedda 1987; m 1971 Deirdre Anne
George (2s 1974, 1981).

E

Eade, Arthur John; Washington since August
1989; born 14.1.33; Army 1951-53; Georgetown
1978; Peking 1979; Pretoria 1981; Moscow
1983; New Delhi 1985; Bonn 1986; Grade SO;
m 1973 Margaret Paterson Adie.

Eager, Helen Christine (née Gillings), BEM
(1991); FCO since December 1990; born 10.6.65;
FCO 1985; SUPL 1986; FCO 1988; Baghdad
1988; Grade S2; m 1987 Nigel Dominic Eager.

Eager, Nigel Dominic; FCO since November
1990; born 9.5.62; FCO 1981; Dublin 1986;
Third Secretary/Vice-Consul Baghdad 1988;
Grade 9; m 1987 Helen Christine Gillings.

Eakin, Christopher Howard; FCO since June
1990; born 1.12.64; FCO 1984; East Berlin
1985; Paris 1987; Grade 10.

Ealand, Jane Elizabeth; FCO since November
1991; born 10.8.67; FCO 1986; New Delhi 1988;
FCO 1990; Paris 1990; Grade 10.

Eames, Nigel Anthony; Second later First
Secretary FCO since April 1979; born 19.10.42;
FO 1962; UKDEL NATO Paris 1963; UKDIS
Geneva 1966; FCO 1969; Warsaw 1973; FCO
1974; Paris 1976; m 1966 Jean Morgan Fletcher

(2d 1975, 1981).

Earl, Jane Ann (née Kerr); Luanda since May
1991; born 15.6.68; Grade 10; m 1991 Shaun
Earl.

Earl, Shaun; Luanda since November 1991; born
4.1.70; FCO 1989; Grade 10; m 1991 Jane Ann
Kerr.

Eason, Victor Ernest; First Secretary FCO since
June 1990; born 30.3.38; DWS 1962; FO 1965;
Ottawa 1966; Lagos 1969; Pretoria 1973; FCO
1975; Cairo 1978; FCO 1980; Second Secretary
(Comm) Jedda 1981; First Secretary (Comm)
Singapore 1986; m (1) 1963 Carol Diana Morgan
(1d 1966; 1s 1968); (2) 1982 Valerie Anne
Parkinson.

Easson, Hilary; Algiers since April 1991; born
10.1.68; FCO 1987; Kuwait 1990; Grade S2.

East, Ivan John; FCO since September 1991;
born 12.5.39; Royal Navy 1954-66; FO 1966;
Singapore 1968; FCO 1970; Darwin 1971; FCO
1973; Accra 1975; FCO 1977; Tehran 1979;
FCO 1980; Jakarta 1981; FCO 1984; Mogadishu
1984; Amman 1988; Seoul 1990; Grade 8; m
1965 Gloria Vera Ann MacPherson (2d 1968,
1970).

Eastburn, Malcolm Robert; First Secretary (Inf)
Canberra since May 1989; born 13.6.38; HM
Forces 1957-59; CRO 1959; Karachi 1963;
Blantyre 1967; Vice-Consul Warsaw 1969; FCO
1972; Karachi 1977; Vice-Consul (Inf/Cons) later
Consul (Comm) Toronto 1980; FCO 1985; m
1963 Ann Georgina Burley (1d 1964; 2s 1969).

Easter, Christine Marie; Washington since
October 1991; born 22.11.44; FCO 1975;
Capetown 1975; FCO 1979; Luxembourg 1982;
Anguilla 1985; Rangoon 1987; Budapest 1989;
Grade S1.

Easton, David, BEM (1986); Washington since
October 1992; born 5.1.49; Royal Military Police
1966-1990; Helsinki 1990; Bucharest 1990;
Grade SO; m 1972 Shirley Ann Mainwaring (1d
1973, 1s 1975).

Easton, David John; Counsellor FCO since
December 1989; born 27.3.41; FO 1963; Third
Secretary Nairobi 1965; Second Secretary (UN)
UK Mission Geneva 1967; MECAS 1970; FCO
1972; First Secretary Tripoli 1973; First
Secretary FCO 1977; First Secretary later
Counsellor Amman 1980; FCO 1984; New Delhi
1986; m 1964 Alexandra Julie Clark (2d 1965,
1972; 2s 1969, 1974).

Eastwood, Basil Stephen Talbot; Counsellor
FCO since September 1991; born 4.3.44; Third
Secretary FO 1966; MECAS 1967; Jedda 1968;
Third later Second Secretary Colombo 1969;
Second later First Secretary Cairo 1972; on loan

to Cabinet Office 1976; FCO 1978; Bonn 1980; Counsellor and Head of Chancery Khartoum 1984; Counsellor (Econ/Comm) Athens 1987; m 1970 Alison Faith Hutchings (4d 1972, 1973, 1977, 1979).

Eastwood, Helen; Dubai since January 1992; born 10.12.63; Grade S2A; FCO 1989; m 1990 David Allan Eastwood.

Eaton, Martin Roger; Deputy Legal Adviser FCO since November 1991; born 10.11.40; Admitted to Roll of Solicitors 1968; FCO 1970; Bonn 1977; FCO 1981; Legal Counsellor FCO 1982; Legal Counsellor UKREP Brussels 1987; Legal Counsellor FCO 1991; m 1972 Sylvia Susannah Wellstood White (2s 1974, 1981; 1d 1975).

Eatwell, Jonathan David; FCO since March 1992; born 8.11.67; FCO 1986; Lusaka 1988; Grade 9; m 1991 Lisa Ann Brecknell.

Ebeling, Adrian Stanley Arthur; Paris since October 1989; born 20.1.48; FCO 1984; Grade 8; m 1979 Laura Phipps (1s 1987).

Edge, Christopher James; Second Secretary (Chancery) Madrid since July 1992; born 30.8.53; FCO 1972; Kabul 1975; East Berlin 1977; Rome 1980; Kaduna 1981; FCO 1984; Beirut 1985; Mexico City 1987; Second Secretary Tegucigalpa 1988.

Edgerton, John David; First Secretary FCO since September 1981; born 4.6.33; COI 1963; Colonial Office 1965; Commonwealth Office 1966; Second Secretary (Inf) Quito 1967; and Santiago 1969; FCO 1970; Vice-Consul (Inf) Johannesburg 1972; First Secretary, Head of Chancery and Consul Asunci<l/c o ac>n 1974; FCO 1977; First Secretary (Aid) Nairobi 1979; m 1962 Eileen Pitt Nind (2d 1964, 1966).

Edis, Richard John Smale; HM Ambassador Maputo since August 1992; born 1.9.43; Third Secretary FO 1966; Third later Second Secretary Nairobi 1968; First Secretary Lisbon 1971; FCO 1974; First Secretary (ECOSOC) New York 1977; FCO 1981; Counsellor on secondment to HCS 1982; Deputy Leader UKDIS Geneva 1984; Counsellor FCO and Commissioner British Indian Ocean Territory 1988; Counsellor on CDA at Cambridge University 1991; m 1971 Genevieve Nanette Suzanne Cerisoles (3s 1971, 1972, 1975).

Edmonds-Brown, Cedric Wilfred George; First Secretary (Management) Rome since October 1991; born 24.4.39; CRO 1962; Lagos 1963; CRO 1964; Karachi 1964; Third later Second Secretary (Comm) Buenos Aires 1968; Second Secretary FCO 1973; Second Secretary (Comm) Bucharest 1976; First Secretary (Admin) and Consul Caracas 1980; on loan to ODA 1985; Head of Chancery Ottawa 1988; FCO 1989; Deputy High

Commissioner and Head of Chancery Bridgetown 1989; m (1) 1964 Everild Arline Victoria Hardman (dec'd 1988) (1s 1965; 2d 1967, 1971); (2) 1990 Teiko Watanabe (1s 1990).

Edusei, Charmaine (née Howe); UKDEL Brussels since January 1991; born 17.9.59; FCO 1988; Grade S2; m 1989 Isaac Yaur Edusei.

Edwards, Bernadette Teresa; FCO since July 1991; born 2.3.63; FCO 1983; UKREP Brussels 1985; Shanghai 1987; Rio de Janeiro 1988; Grade S2.

Edwards, Carole Lilian (née Hellier); Washington since October 1989; born 7.7.45; FCO 1973; Freetown 1973; Washington 1975; Prague 1978; Belgrade 1978; FCO 1979; Beirut 1980; Ottawa 1982; Moscow 1985; FCO 1986; Grade 9.

Edwards, Craig Jeremy; FCO since November 1991; born 20.5.70; Grade 10.

Edwards, David Vaughan; Budapest since April 1989; RAF 1961-89; m 1967 Patricia Ann (2d 1968, 1969; 1s 1972); Grade SO.

Edwards, Gillian Rose; FCO since July 1988; born 7.2.64; FCO 1983; Resigned 1987; Reinstated 1988; Grade 10.

Edwards, Jacqueline Wendy; FCO since February 1992; born 4.8.62; FCO 1985; Warsaw 1987; Resigned 1988, Reinstated 1992; Grade S2.

Edwards, John Coates, CMG (1989); High Commissioner Gaborone since November 1991; born 25.11.34; HM Forces 1953-55; Ministry of Supply 1958; CO 1960; PS to Parliamentary Under-Secretary of State 1961; Principal Nature Conservancy 1962; ODM 1965; First Secretary and UK Perm Rep to ECAFE Bangkok 1968; Assistant Secretary ODM 1971; Head of East African Development Division Nairobi 1972; ODM 1976; Head of British Development Division in the Caribbean Bridgetown 1978; Head of West Indian and Atlantic Department FCO 1981; DHC Nairobi 1984; High Commissioner Maseru 1988; m 1959 Mary Harris (1s 1963; 1d 1964).

Edwards, Keith Nigel; Second Secretary Madrid since July 1992; born 9.5.53; FCO 1969; Warsaw 1977; Athens 1978; FCO 1981; Hong Kong 1985; FCO 1988; m 1975 Wendy Ann Carrington (2d 1980, 1982).

Edwards, Mannetta Beverley (née Leigh); UKDEL Brussels since July 1991; born 14.2.59; FCO 1979; Kuwait 1982; FCO 1986; Grade 8; m 1980 Christopher James Edwards (2s 1981, 1986).

Edwards, Peter George; UKDEL Brussels since December 1991; born 25.4.33; Royal Navy 1948-

73; Baghdad 1973; Budapest 1974; Mexico City 1976; Peking 1979; Ankara 1980; Moscow 1982; UKREP Brussels 1983; Montevideo 1984; Havana 1987; Tokyo 1988; Grade CSO; m 1953 Laurel Myrtle Mills (1s 1962).

Eelbeck, Andrew; Third Secretary Pretoria since February 1992; born 2.3.59; FCO 1979; Islamabad 1980; FCO 1982; Singapore 1982; FCO 1986; Third Secretary Prague 1988; Grade 8.

Egerton, William Luke Le Belward; Third later Second Secretary (Chancery) Moscow since April 1991; born 23.8.66; FCO 1988; language training Moscow 1989.

Ehrman, William Geoffrey; on Secondment at Hong Kong as Political Adviser to the Governor since August 1989; born 28.8.50; Third Secretary FCO 1973; Language Student Hong Kong 1975; Third later Second Secretary Peking 1976; First Secretary (ECOSOC) UKMIS New York 1979; First Secretary Peking 1983; FCO 1985; m 1977 Penelope Anne Le Patourel (1s 1981; 3d 1977, 1979, 1986).

Elam, John Nicholas; Counsellor FCO since May 1987; born 2.7.39; FO 1962; Third later Second Secretary Pretoria/Cape Town 1964; FCO 1968; First Secretary Political Residency, Bahrain 1971; First Secretary (Comm) Brussels 1972; First Secretary FCO 1976; Counsellor Salisbury 1979; Deputy High Commissioner Harare 1980; Consul-General Montreal 1984; m 1967 Florence Helen Lentz (2s 1969, 1970; 1d 1974).

El Beleidi, Cecille Maude (née Greaves); Vice-Consul Casablanca since September 1992; born 22.11.62; FCO 1982; Kuwait 1985; FCO 1986; Kathmandu 1989; Grade 9; m 1987 Magdi El Beleidi.

Elder, Andrea Sharron (née Massingham); SUPL since June 1992; born 10.3.71; FCO 1990; Grade 10; m 1991 Alistair Alexander Elder.

Elder, Alistair Alexander; UKREP Brussels since April 1992; born 14.5.71; FCO 1989; Grade 9; m 1991 Andrea Sharron Massingham.

Elder, Peter Edward; FCO since September 1989; born 14.3.68; Grade 10.

Eldon, Stewart Graham, OBE (1991); Counsellor on loan to the Cabinet Office since December 1991; born 18.9.53; UK Mission New York 1976; FCO 1976; Third later Second Secretary Bonn 1978; First Secretary FCO 1982; Private Secretary to Minister of State 1983; First Secretary (Chancery) UKMIS New York 1986; First Secretary FCO 1990; m 1978 Christine Mary Mason (1d 1982; 1s 1985).

Eldred, Josephine Susan; First Secretary later Counsellor FCO since December 1980; born

12.4.39; FO 1962; Singapore 1964; Copenhagen 1967; Second later First Secretary FCO 1969; Valletta 1976.

Eldred, Samantha; Third Secretary Peking since November 1989; born 7.9.63; FCO 1986; Language Training FCO 1987; Language Training Hong Kong 1988; Grade 7.

Elliot, Caroline Margaret; Third Secretary (Chancery) Brussels (Embassy) since July 1991; born 24.8.64; FCO 1987; Peking 1989; Grade 9.

Elliot-de-Larrabure, Jacqueline Mary (née Elliot); LA Floater since March 1989; born 25.1.64; FCO 1984; Lima 1986; Grade S2; m 1991 José Enrique Larrabure Muro.

Elliott, Christopher Lowther; FCO since March 1986; born 26.12.54; DNS 1974; DOE 1975; FCO 1975; Cairo 1979; Bridgetown 1982; Grade 9; m 1975 Julie Lorraine Inman (1s adopted 1975; 1d 1982).

Elliot, Hugh Stephen Murray; Third later Second Secretary (Chancery) Madrid since January 1991; born 21.8.65; FCO 1989; Grade 8; m. 1989 Toni Martin-Elena.

Elliott, Jonathan Andrew; FCO since August 1991; born 3.9.66; Grade 9.

Elliott, Mark, CMG (1988); DUSS (Africa/ Middle East) since May 1992; born 16.5.39; FO 1963; Third later Second Secretary Tokyo 1965; Second later First Secretary FCO 1969; Private Secretary to the Permanent Under-Secretary of State, FCO 1973; First Secretary and Head of Chancery Nicosia 1974; Counsellor (Inf) Tokyo 1977; Counsellor and Head of Chancery Tokyo 1978; Head of Far Eastern Department FCO 1981; Counsellor, later Under-Secretary on loan to HCS 1985; HM Ambassador Tel Aviv 1988; m 1964 Hilary Julian Richardson (2s 1966, 1968).

Elliott, Robert David; Port Louis since June 1988; born 25.11.60; FCO 1980; Prague 1981; Peking 1982; Language Training 1983; Abu Dhabi 1984; Grade 9.

Ellis, Alexander Wykeham; Third Secretary (Political/Economic) Lisbon since July 1992; born 5.6.67; FCO 1990; Grade 8.

Ellis, Ann; FCO since September 1990; born 19.11.47; Grade S2.

Ellis, Amanda Jane; Brussels since February 1989; born 7.12.60; FCO 1987; Grade S2A.

Ellis, Gail Teresa (née Drayton); SUPL since April 1992; born 14.6.60; FCO 1978; Brussels NATO 1981; Peking 1984; FCO 1986; New Delhi 1991; Grade S2; m 1981 Philip Donald Ellis.

Ellis, Hugo; Riydh since July 1992; born 13.9.66; FCO 1988; Grade 10.

Ellis, John Arthur; Second Secretary FCO since October 1989; born 27.3.52; DHSS 1969-71; FCO 1971; Wellngton 1974; Khartoum 1976; Dar es Salaam 1979; FCO 1981; Islamabad 1982; Seoul 1986; m 1974 Law Kwai Chun (1s 1980, 1d 1983).

Ellis, Philip Donld; New Delhi since November 1990; born 9.5.51; FCO 1978; Brussels (NATO) 1981; Peking 1914; FCO 1987; Grade 9; m 1981 Gail Teresa Drayon.

Ellis, Sheila May; FCO since October 1985; born 21.2.33; FCO 1969; Antigua 1970; Bonn 1972; Singapore 1974; Brussels 1976; FCO 1977; UKMIS Gneva 1983; Grade S1.

Ellis, Terence Matthew; First Secretary (Comm/Aid) Amman sime July 1991; born 8.8.34; FO 1962; Berne 1961; Bangkok 1965; FO (later FCO) 1966; Mosow 1969; Bombay 1970; Peking 1972; FCO 1974; Canberra 1977; UKDEL NATO Brussels 1981; Second Secretary (Aid/Inf) Georgeown 1983; Second Secretary FCO 1986; m 1977 Maureen Phoebe Daniels.

Ellwood, Dr Shelgh Margaret; FCO since October 1988; born 21.2.49; Principal Research Officer.

Elmes, Caroline Myfanwy Tonge; Deputy Head of Mission Prague since July 1992; born 20.9.48; Second Secretary FCO 1975; Language Student 1977; First Secrdary Prague 1978; First Secretary FCO 1981; First Secretary (Econ) Rome 1985; Depity High Commissioner and Head of Chancer Colombo 1989.

Elsdon, Judith Ann; Deputy Consul-General and Consul (Comm) San Francisco since June 1989; born 29.4.42; HCS 1960; DSAO 1966; Tel Aviv 1968; Budapest 970; Islamabad 1971; Caracas 1972; FCO 1974; Kathmandu 1977; Latin America Floater 1980; Second Secretary FCO 1982; Second latr First Secretary (Comm) Accra 1985.

Elvin, Leslie Thomas, MBE (1992); Khartoum since August 1988; born 10.3.36; Royal Navy 1951-61; CRO 1161; Freetown 1962; DSAO 1965; Delhi 1961; Belgrade 1969; Stockholm 1970; Bangkok 973; Lagos 1976; FCO 1976; Bridgetown 1978; Athens 1981; FCO 1984; Grade 9; m 1956 Pamela Rose Buckingham (1s 1957; 1d 1965).

Elvins, Christine Patricia (née Pettit); SUPL since October 1988; born 4.6.60; FCO 1979; Bonn 1983; Pretoria 1986; FCO 1987; Grade 10; m 1988 Martyn Andrew Elvins.

Elvins, Martyn Andrew; Warsaw since November 1988; born 13.2.58; FCO 1984; Grade 8; m 1988 Christine P Pettit.

Elvy, Simon David; FCO since July 1992; born 8.12.61; FCO 1983; Baghdad 1985; Stockholm 1989; Grade 9; m 1985 Lesley Jane (1s 1991).

Embleton, Robert Leitch; Second Secretary Washington since June 1984; born 9.10.42; FO 1960; Leopoldville 1964; Bonn 1968; St Vincent 1969; FCO 1973; Stuttgart 1976; Prague 1979; Second Secretary FCO 1980; m 1970 Ursula Biebricher (1d 1975).

Emery, Simon Richard; FCO since June 1985; born 22.8.57; FCO 1981; OECD Paris 1982; Grade 10; m 1981 Dorothy Seery.

Enescott, Nicholas John; Second Secretary (Management) Lilongwe since July 1991; born 6.12.51; FCO 1972; Cape Town 1975; Ankara 1977; Tripoli 1980; FCO 1983; Hanoi 1986; Third Secretary (Comm) and Vice-Consul Dakar 1989.

Engdahl, Denise Jean (née Sanders); Mbabane since November 1989; born 19.9.60; FCO 1982; Wellington 1983; Colombo 1986; Grade S3; m 1989; Göran Magnus Engdahl.

England, Barrie; First Secretary FCO since January 1989; born 22.5.42; Commonwealth Office 1966; MECAS 1968; Kuwait 1970; Athens 1972; FCO 1975; (Second Secretary 1977); Second Secretary Colombo 1977; FCO 1981; Second later First Secretary (Chancery/Inf) Berne 1984; m 1967 Betty Anne Loible (1d 1969; 1s 1972).

Entwistle, Sheila; Singapore since January 1991; born 2.10.37; Post Office 1965; Lahore 1971; Lusaka 1973; Dubai 1975; Kabul 1976; UKREP EEC Brussels 1977; Manila 1980; FCO 1982; Nicosia 1985; Belgrade 1987; Grade S1.

Escritt, Richard Edwin; SUPL on attachment to the European Commission since September 1991; born 18.8.46; Third Secretary FCO 1968; Rawalpindi/Islamabad 1969; Second Secretary 1972; Second later First Secretary (Comm) Prague 1973; First Secretary FCO 1977; First Secretary (Econ) Bonn 1980; First Secretary FCO 1985; on loan to Cabinet Office 1987; Counsellor (Scientific) Bonn 1989; m 1968 Janet Elisabeth Paley (1d 1970; 3s 1972, 1974, 1978).

Etherington, Howard Edmondson; Consulate-General New York since May 1990; born 2.12.38; CO 1966; Lahore 1969; Islamabad 1972; New York CG 1972; Havana 1975; FCO 1977; Bucharest 1979; Dublin 1983; FCO 1986; Grade 9; m 1966 Grace Anne (2d 1968, 1969; 1s 1972).

Etherton, Mark Roy; First Secretary (Political/Economic) Warsaw since June 1991; born 17.3.58; FCO 1983; Second Secretary (Chancery) Paris 1988; m 1991 Suzanne Margaret Miskin.

Evans, Alison Joan; FCO since July 1990; born 30.10.63; FCO 1982; Caracas 1984; African/ME Floater 1988; Grade 9.

Evans, Carol Jeanette (née Kendall); FCO since November 1988; born 10.4.59; FCO 1982; UKDEL Vienna 1984; Warsaw 1987; Grade S2; m 1991 Keith Dennis Evans.

Evans, Claire Elizabeth; Jakarta since June 1989; born 2.11.61; FCO 1987; Grade 9.

Evans, David Hugh; FCO since August 1985; born 27.3.59; SRO (DS Grade 7); m 1988 Nirmala Vinodhini Chrysostom.

Evans, Elined Clare; Second later First Secretary (Economic) Buenos Aires since July 1990; born 22.2.60; FCO 1988.

Evans, Gayle Evelyn Louise (née Sperring) UKMIS New York since July 1992; born 1.9.62; FCO 1983; Accra 1984; Moscow 1986; FCO 1987; Floater Duties 1990; SUPL 1991; Grade S2; m 1991 Julian Ascott Evans.

Evans, Gerald Stanley; Athens since August 1990; born 26.10.51; FCO 1971; Havana 1973; Bonn 1974; Jedda 1977; FCO 1977; Dubai 1979; FCO 1983; Bogota 1986; Grade 9; m 1991 Graciela Elisa Casetta.

Evans, Gillian; Zagreb since November 1992; born 1.9.59; FCO 1981; BMG Berlin 1982; Kinshasa 1984; Africa/Asia/ME Floater 1988; Grade S2.

Evans, Jennifer Mary (née Lewis); Dhaka since July 1989; born 3.3.59; FCO 1978; Far East Floater 1981; SUPL 1983; Vienna 1984; SUPL 1985; Grade 9; m 1982 Wayne Evans.

Evans, Julian Ascott; Second Secretary (Chancery/Press Officer) UKMIS New York since August 1991; born 5.7.57; FCO 1978; Language Training 1980; Moscow 1982; Zurich 1985; Second Secretary FCO 1987; m 1991 Gayle Evelyn Louise Sperring.

Evans, Julie; FCO since February 1991; born 11.6.65; FCO 1986; Stockholm 1988; Grade 10.

Evans, Julie; Ottawa since January 1991; born 22.5.70; FCO 1988; Grade 10.

Evans, Kim Sian; FCO since October 1992; born 2.6.61; FCO 1983; Islamabad 1985; FCO 1988; Kuala Lumpur 1989; Grade S2.

Evans, Laurance Bolton; Second Secretary (Cons) Dar es Salaam since January 1988; born 30.3.43; FO 1962; Saigon 1964; Washington 1968; Brussels (JAO) 1974; Paris 1976; FCO 1979; Vienna 1982; Second Secretary (Dev) Amman 1984; m (1) 1963 Heather Duxbury (dec'd 1986) (2s 1965, 1968); (2) Elizabeth Ann McNab (1s 1989).

Evans, Madelaine Glynne Dervel, CMG (1992); Counsellor FCO since May 1990; born 23.8.44; Second Secretary FCO 1971; Buenos Aires 1972; First Secretary FCO 1975; Private Secretary to PUSS 1976; on loan to UN Secretariat New York 1978; First Secretary UKMIS New York 1979; First Secretary later Counsellor FCO 1982; Counsellor and Head of Chancery Brussels 1987.

Evans, Paul Lawson; First Secretary Washington since July 1992; born 26.5.55; Royal Navy 1973-80; FCO 1983; UKMIS Vienna 1986; First Secretary FCO 1988; m 1986 Judith Mary Stephenson.

Evans, Peter Dering; Third Secretary (Management/Accounts) Caracas since April 1990; born 9.4.57; FCO 1976; Dacca 1978; FCO 1980; Barcelona 1985; San Salvador 1988; Grade 9; m (1) 1979 Anne Deborah Morgan; (2) Susan Elizabeth Parker (1s 1987).

Evans, Rosemary Isabel (née Collier); FO (later FCO) since December 1966 (Second Secretary 1973); born 4.8.44; m 1972 Ronald Evans.

Evans, Stephen Nicholas; First Secretary (Political) Ankara since January 1990; born 29.6.50; Third Secretary FCO 1974; Language Student SOAS 1975; Second Secretary FCO 1976; Head of Chancery and Consul Hanoi 1978; FCO 1980; Language Training Bangkok 1982; First Secretary Bangkok 1983; First Secretary FCO 1986; m 1975 Sharon Ann Holdcroft (2d 1981, 1984; 1s 1986).

Evans, Stewart John Llewellyn; Islamabad since May 1992; born 9.9.52; FCO 1972; Paris 1976; FCO 1979; Lagos 1982; FCO 1984; Budapest 1987; FCO 1990; Grade 9.

Evans, Thomas Alun; Counsellor FCO since December 1982; born 8.6.37; FO 1961; Third Secretary Rangoon 1962; Second Secretary Office of the Political Adviser Singapore 1964; Second later First Secretary FO (later FCO) 1966; First Secretary (UN) UKMIS Geneva 1970; FCO 1974; Counsellor Pretoria 1979; m 1964 Bridget Elizabeth Lloyd (3s 1965, 1967, 1971).

Evans, Walter Frederick; Moscow since April 1992; born 3.12.40; Army 1961-83; Belgrade 1983; Cairo 1986; UKDEL NATO Brussels 1988; Budapest 1990; Grade SO; m 1966 Anita Joy Lavis (3s 1967, 1969, 1972).

Evans, Wayne; Second Secretary (Aid) Dhaka since July 1989; born 29.8.53; FCO 1971; Paris 1974; Maseru 1977; FCO 1979; Baghdad 1981; Vienna 1984; FCO 1987; m 1982 Jennifer Mary Lewis.

Everard, John Vivian; Second Secretary FCO since August 1987; First Secretary 1990; born 24.11.56; FCO 1979; Third later Second Secretary Peking 1981; Second Secretary Vienna

1983; Resigned 1984.

Everest-Phillips, Maxim Roger; First Secretary (Chancery) Tokyo since March 1992; born 4.3.59; FCO 1981; Third later Second Secretary Helsinki 1984; First Secretary FCO 1987; First Secretary on Full Time Language Training at Kamakura 1991.

Everett, Bernard Jonathan; Consul-General Houston since June 1991; born 17.9.43; FO 1966; Third later Second Secretary Lisbon 1967; Second later First Secretary FCO 1971; Consul (Pol) Luanda 1975; First Secretary FCO 1975; First Secretary and Head of Chancery Lusaka 1978; Consul (Comm) Rio de Janeiro 1980; First Secretary FCO 1983; Counsellor on loan to DTI 1984; HM Ambassador Guatemala City 1987; m 1970 Maria Olinda Goncalves de Albuquerque (1d 1974; 2s 1980, 1981; 1d 1976, dec'd 1979).

Everett, Sara Gillian; First Secretary FCO since April 1991; born 6.7.55; FCO 1979; ENA Paris 1981; Caracas 1983; Second Secretary (Econ) UKREP Brussels 1986; Second Secretary (Econ) Brussels (Embassy) 1987; m 1989 Christopher Ian Montague Jones.

Everitt, Oliver Hunter; FCO since March 1992; born 28.12.71; Grade 10.

Everson, Clare Elizabeth; FCO since August 1990; born 20.12.59; FCO 1981; Karachi 1983; SE Asia Floater 1988; Grade 9.

Everson, Mark Stephen; Warsaw since May 1992; born 18.9.68; FCO 1987; Canberra 1989; Grade 10.

Evetts, Keith Derek, OBE (1989); First Secretary FCO since April 1991; born 20.5.48; Third Secretary FCO 1973; Language Student 1974; Second Secretary Warsaw 1975; Language Student FCO 1976; First Secretary Maputo 1977; FCO 1980; UKMIS New York 1983; Kingston 1986; First Secretary (Chancery) Lisbon 1988; m (1) 1971 Bridget Elizabeth Peachey (diss 1988) (2s 1981, 1982); (2) 1988 Lesley Ann Myers (1s 1989, 1d 1990).

Ewan, Valerie; Second Secretary Berlin since May 1991; born 10.12.56; FCO 1979; ENA Paris 1980; Paris 1981; Lagos 1986; Second Secretary FCO 1988.

Ewen, Janice Susan Genevieve; FCO since May 1991; born 23.8.44; FCO 1970; Rome 1973; Budapest 1976; FCO 1978; Madrid 1979; FCO 1981; Moscow 1986; FCO 1988; JMO Brussels 1989; Grade 9.

Ewing, Timothy Robert; Counsellor FCO since November 1990; born 8.5.42; FCO 1970; Second later First Secretary Vienna 1972; First Secretary FCO 1975; Lisbon 1978; First Secretary FCO 1982; Counsellor Brasilia 1987; m 1967

Claudine Marie Huré (1s 1971).

Eyre, Steven Rhys; FCO since Januuary 1991; born 13.3.72; Grade 10.

Eyers, Patrick Howard Caines, CMG (1985), LVO (1966); HM Ambassador Ammman since April 1991; born 4.9.33; MECAS 1959; Dubai 1961; Second later First Secretary Brussels 1964; FO (later FCO) 1966; First Secretary and Head of Chancery Aden 1969 and Abidjan 1970; First Secretary BMG Berlin 1971; FCO 1974; Counsellor Bonn 1977; Head of RID FCO 1981; RCDS course 1984; HM Ambassador Kinshasa; and HMA (non-resident) to the Congo, Rwanda and Burundi 1985; HM Ambassador Algiers 1987; HM Ambassador East Berlin 1990; m 1960 Jutta Lindheide Rusch (2s 1964, 1967; 1d 1966).

Eyre-Wilson, Quintin Gerald; FCO since February 1990; born 16.2.57; FCO 1975; New Delhi 1977; Beirut 1980; Aden 1982; FCO 1983; UKDEL Brussels 1987; Grade 9; m 1982 Julie Mason.

F

Fairhurst, Geoffrey; First Secretary Kaduna since September 1989; born 27.10.42; DSAO 1965; Nairobi 1967; Peking 1970; FCO and Malta 1971; Havana 1971; Milan 1973; FCO 1976; Second Secretary (Aid/Admin) later (Admin/Consular) Bridgetown 1979; FCO 1983; Second later First Secretary (Admin) and Consul Doha 1985; m 1971 Wendy Metcalfe (3d 1973, 1976, 1978).

Fairley, Averil Margaret; FCO since March 1992; born 18.6.67; FCO 1986; East Berlin 1988; Hanoi 1990; Grade 10.

Fairweather, Sir Patrick (Stanislaus), KCMG (1992) CMG (1986); HM Ambassador Rome since July 1992; additionally HM Ambassador (non-resident) to the Republic of Albania since August 1992; born 17.6.36; FO 1965; Second Secretary Rome 1966; First Secretary FCO 1969; Paris 1970; FCO 1973; First Secretary and Head of Chancery Vientiane 1975; First Secretary (Pol) UKREP Brussels 1976; Counsellor (Econ/ Comm) Athens 1978; Head of ECD(I) FCO 1983; HM Ambassador Luanda and concurrently HMA (non-resident) to Sao Tomé and Principe 1985; AUSS (Africa) 1987; DUSS (Africa/ Middle East) 1990; m 1962 Maria Merica (2d 1963, 1965).

Fall, Sir Brian (James) (Proetel) KCMG (1992); HM Ambassador Moscow since June 1992; later additionally HM Ambassador (non-resident) to Belarus, Armenia, Azerbaijan and Moldavia; born 13.12.37; FO 1962; Second Secretary Moscow 1965; Second later First Secretary UKMIS Geneva 1968; Seconded to Civil Service

Department (Civil Service College) 1970; First Secretary FCO 1971; Deputy Director (Industrial Marketing) and Consul (Comm) BTDO; New York 1975; Sabbatical Harvard 1976; Counsellor 1976; Counsellor and Head of Chancery Moscow 1977; Head of Energy Science and Space Department 1979; Head of East European and Soviet Department 1980; PPS to the Secretary of State 1981; On Secondment as Directeur du Cabinet, Cabinet of the Secretary-General of NATO Brussels 1984; AUSS (Defence) FCO 1986; Minister Washington 1988; High Commissioner Ottawa 1989; m 1962 Delmar Alexandra Roos (3d 1964, 1967 (twins)).

Fall, David William; Counsellor Bangkok since March 1990; born 10.3.48; Third Secretary FCO 1971; Language Student Bangkok 1973; First Secretary Bangkok 1976; On loan to Cabinet Office 1977; FCO 1979; First Secretary (Chancery) Pretoria/Cape Town 1981; First Secretary later Counsellor FCO 1985; m 1973 Margaret Gwendolyn Richards (3s 1976, 1977, 1980).

Fallon, Helen Clare; Lagos since February 1990; born 13.6.68; FCO 1987; Grade 9; m 1990 Michael Thomas Fallon.

Farnham, Brian George; FCO since May 1991 (Second Secretary 1991); born 16.4.52; FCO 1968; Paris 1974; FCO 1977; Baghdad 1978; FCO 1980; Tokyo 1981; FCO 1984; Hong Kong 1988; m 1982 Emiko Ishida (2d 1985, 1990).

Farnham, Michael John; FCO since January 1989; born 23.1.59; FCO 1982; Abu Dhabi 1986; Grade 9.

Farnworth, Judith Margaret, FCO since July 1991; born 25.4.66; Grade Research Officer.

Farr, Charles Blanford; First Secretary (Chancery) Amman since March 1992; born 15.7.59; Second Secretary FCO 1985; Second Secretary Pretoria 1987; Second Secretary FCO 1990.

Farr, Dawn Margaret; Nicosia since May 1992; born 5.7.70; FCO 1989; Grade 10.

Farr, Donald Frederick George; FCO since March 1990; born 14.12.36; FO 1956; HM Forces 1956-58; FO 1958; Baghdad 1958; Bangkok 1960; Reykjavik 1964; Second Secretary (Comm) Buenos Aires 1965; FCO 1970; on loan to DTI 1970; First Secretary 1975; Assistant Trade Commissioner 1972 later Trade Commissioner Hong Kong 1975; Consul First Secretary (Comm) and Head of Chancery Abidjan 1977; First Secretary (Inf/Pol) Wellington 1981; First Secretary FCO 1983; First Secretary, Head of Chancery and Consul Luxembourg 1985; m 1964 Ann Camilla Gordon (2s 1965, 1967; 1d 1968).

Farrand, John Percival Morey; Second Secretary FCO since June 1991; born 4.6.54; HM Customs and Excise 1971; FCO 1972; Tokyo 1974; Mexico City 1977; Kuala Lumpur 1981; FCO 1985; San Francisco 1988; m 1979 Sharon Anne Eddie (2d 1980, 1982).

Farrant, David Cornelius; Second Secretary FCO since January 1987; born 5.7.53; FCO 1972; UKMIS Geneva 1976; Moscow 1978; FCO 1980; Athens 1984; m 1976 Anne Laing (2s 1982, 1987).

Farrent, Susan Jennifer; Port of Spain since May 1992; born 17.1.48; FCO 1986; Monrovia 1987; Port Moresby 1991; Grade S2.

Farrington, Angela (née Hunt); FCO since April 1985; born 28.9.62; Grade 10; m 1987 Danny Farrington.

Farrington, Ian Francis; Second later First Secretary FCO since January 1991; born 21.8.63; FCO 1986; Third later Second Secretary (Econ) Athens 1989.

Faulkner, Kevin Paul; FCO since September 1992; born 10.8.61; FCO 1982; Nicosia 1985; Tegucigalpa 1988; Grade 9; m 1987 Sylvana Maria Modrowics.

Faulkner, Leo Gregory; Minister, Consul-General and Deputy Head of Mission, Buenos Aires since June 1990; born 21.9.43; FCO 1968; Second later First Secretary Lima 1972; First Secretary Lagos 1976; FCO 1979; First Secretary and Head of Chancery Madrid 1982; Counsellor on loan to DTI 1984; Counsellor (Comm) The Hague 1986; m 1970 Fiona Hardie Birkett (3d 1973, 1975, 1978).

Faulkner, Nicholas Anthony; FCO since March 1991, born 19.5.72; Grade 10.

Faulkner, Peter; First Secretary FCO since August 1991; born 22.1.38; FO 1955; HM Forces 1958-60; Budapest 1960; Geneva 1962; Cairo 1964; Nairobi 1967; Milan 1973; Vice-Consul Toronto 1975; Second Secretary Ottawa 1976; Rome 1979; FCO 1983; Consul (Cons/Management) Dusseldorf 1987; m 1960 Margaret Maureen Sweeney (3s 1961, 1962, 1966; 1d 1972).

Faulkner, Richard John; Second Secretary FCO since September 1989; born 20.2.48; FCO 1969; Seoul 1972; Dubai 1975; FCO 1979; Islamabad 1983; Rome 1986; m 1973 FranHcoise Marie Christine Armande Trine (1d 1979).

Fawcett, Christine Anne; Second Secretary (Management/Consular) Port of Spain since August 1991; born 17.8.50; FCO 1968; Dar es Salaam 1971; Lima 1973; Havana 1976; Freetown 1977; FCO 1979; SEA Floater 1982; Belgrade 1983; FCO 1986 (Second Secretary 1989).

Fay, Jacqueline Ann (née Builder); FCO since November 1991; born 22.9.61; FCO 1980; Dhaka 1983; Peking 1985; Vice-Consul New York 1987; SUPL 1991; Grade 9; m 1987 Kevin Michael Fay.

Fean, Thomas Vincent; First Secretary FCO since January 1990; born 20.11.52; FCO 1975; MECAS 1977; Third Secretary Baghdad 1978; Second later First Secretary Damascus 1979; FCO 1982; First Secretary UKREP Brussels 1985; m 1978 Anne Marie Stewart (2d 1979, 1981; 1s 1983).

Fear, Harriet Emma; Floater Training since January 1992; born 11.8.68; DO Emp 1986; FCO 1987; Dakar 1989; Grade 9.

Fearis, Timothy Rupert; FCO since July 1989; born 5.2.58; FCO 1979; Accra 1982; FCO 1984; Attaché Islamabad 1987; Grade 9.

Fearn, Sir (Patrick) Robin, KCMG (1991) CMG (1983); HM Ambassador Madrid since November 1989; born 5.9.34; FO 1961; Second Secretary Caracas 1962; FO 1965; First Secretary Budapest 1966; FCO 1969; Vientiane 1972; FCO 1975; Counsellor, Head of Chancery and Consul-General at Islamabad 1976; Head of S America Dept 1979; RCDS Course 1983; HM Ambassador Havana 1984; AUSS (Americas) FCO 1986; m 1961 Sorrell Mary Lynne Thomas (3s 1962, 1964, 1967; 1d 1975).

Fearn, Thomas Daniel; Budapest since December 1992; born 16.9.62; FCO 1991; Grade 9.

Fearne, Eric Alfred; Paris since December 1989; born 20.8.42; FCO 1971; Washington 1974; Tokyo 1977; Vientiane 1979; Budapest 1981; FCO 1982; Colombo 1985; FCO 1988; Grade 9; m 1964 Jean Doris Smith (1s 1965).

Feasey, Susan Catherine; Riga since March 1992; born 8.5.64; FCO 1983; UKMIS Vienna 1985; Dakar 1988; FCO 1990; Grade S2.

Feather, Helen Mary; LA/Caribbean Floater since October 1990; born 2.1.63; FCO 1982; Moscow 1985; Gaborone 1988; Grade 9.

Featherstone, Alan John; Second Secretary FCO since April 1992; born 4.10.37; FO 1954; HM Forces 1956-58; FO 1958; Hanoi 1959; Istanbul 1961; FO 1962; Rome 1964; Rio de Janeiro 1965; DSAO (later FCO) 1967; Muscat 1970; Doha 1972; Tehran 1973; La Paz 1976; FCO 1980; Second Secretary (Comm/Aid) Maputo 1983; Second Secretary (Management) and Consul Rabat 1986; m (1) 1960 Sylviane Jean-Marguerite Cellier de Buraine (1d 1960; 1s 1961); (2) Maria Del Carmen Monroy Vercellone.

Featherstone, Simon Mark; First Secretary (Environment) UKREP Brussels since January

1990; born 24.7.58; FCO 1980; Language Training Hong Kong 1982; Second Secretary (Chancery) Peking 1984; First Secretary FCO 1987; On loan to Cabinet Office 1988; m 1981 Gail Teresa Salisbury (1d 1985).

Fedrick, Geoffrey Courtis; Counsellor, Head of JAO Brussels since September 1989; born 21.8.37; HM Forces 1956-58; Government Actuaries Department 1958; CRO 1960; Salisbury 1961; Peshawar 1964; Second Secretary Washington 1967; Second later First Secretary FCO 1970; Consul (Comm) Toronto 1975; FCO 1980; First Secretary (Admin) Lagos 1983; FCO 1986; m (1) 1961 Elizabeth Louise Moore (2s 1963, 1966); (2) 1984 Margaret Elizabeth Hearnden (née Pawley).

Feeney, Sharon Ann; Warsaw since October 1992; born 11.10.70; FCO 1989; Grade 10.

Fehintola, Adebowale Bamidele; Sana'a since August 1992; FCO 1987; Copenhagen 1989; born 14.11.67; Grade 10.

Feliks, Michael Edward Joseph; Full Time Language Training since September 1992; born 3.9.64; FCO 1990; Grade 7.

Fell, Richard Taylor; Counsellor (Comm/Econ) Ottawa since June 1989; born 11.11.48; FCO 1971; Third Secretary Ottawa 1972; Second Secretary Saigon 1974; Vientiane 1975; Second later First Secretary FCO 1975; Chargé d'Affaires a.i. Hanoi 1979; Brussels (NATO) 1979; First Secretary and Head of Chancery Kuala Lumpur 1983; First Secretary FCO 1986; On secondment to Industry 1988; m 1981 Claire Peta Gates (3s 1983, 1987, 1990).

Fell, William Varley; Counsellor FCO since May 1992; born 4.3.48; FCO 1971; Third later Second Secretary (UNIDO1/IAEA) Vienna 1973; Second later First Secretary (Econ/Comm) Havana 1976; FCO 1978; Warsaw 1979; First Secretary FCO 1982; Counsellor Athens 1988; m 1970 Jill Pauline Warren (1s 1974; 1s, 1d (twins) 1976).

Fellows, Clare Angela; Stockholm since October 1990; born 21.2.56; FCO 1977; Düsseldorf 1979; Luxembourg 1981; Beirut 1982; Santiago 1982; FCO 1984; Floater Duties 1986; FCO 1988; Grade S2.

Felton, Ian; Floater Duties since December 1990; born 16.5.66; FCO 1986; Brussels 1987; Grade 9.

Fenn, Sir Nicholas (Maxted), KCMG (1989), CMG (1980); High Commissioner New Delhi since November 1991; born 19.2.36; FO 1959; Third later Second Secretary Rangoon 1960; Assistant Private Secretary to Secretary of State for Foreign Affairs 1964 (First Secretary 1966); First and Head of Chancery Algiers 1967; First Secretary (Public Affairs) UKMIS New York 1969; Assistant Science and Technology

Department FCO 1972; Deputy Head
(Counsellor) Energy Department FCO 1974;
Counsellor, Head of Chancery and Consul-
General Peking 1975; RCDS 1978; Head of
News Dept 1979; HM Ambassador Rangoon
1982; HM Ambassador Dublin 1986; m 1959
Susan Clare Russell (2s 1962, 1963; 1d 1974).

Fenn, Robert Dominic Russell; First Secretary
UKMIS New York since August 1992; born
28.1.62; FCO 1983; Third Secretary (Chancery)
The Hague 1985; Second Secretary (Chancery)
Lagos 1988; First Secretary FCO 1990.

Fennell, Leigh; FCO since August 1988; born
13.12.60; FCO 1982; Darwin 1986; Grade 9.

Fenner, Margaret Patricia Jean (née Watson);
Lagos since November 1990; born 29.1.66;
Wellington 1986; Warsaw 1988; FCO 1988;
Grade 9; m 1989 Martin David Fenner.

Fenning, Camilla Jane Vance (née Packman);
FCO since October 1990 (Second Secretary
1991); born 29.4.64; FCO 1985; Language
Training 1986; Tokyo 1987; m 1988 Richard
John Fenning.

Fenton, Jennifer Muriel; New Delhi since April
1989; born 30.12.57; HCS 1976; FCO 1977;
Beirut 1980; Floater duties 1982; Singapore
1984; SUPL 1986; FCO 1987; Grade 9; (1d
1986).

Fenwick, Marsha; SUPL since February 1987;
born 7.4.48; FO 1966; Bahrain 1969; FCO 1971;
Abu Dhabi 1973; FCO 1977; SUPL 1984; FCO
1986; Grade 9; m 1983 Michael John Beresford
(1s 1984).

Ferdinand, Derek William; Dublin since
September 1991; born 30.12.37; Royal Navy
1953-67; Prison Service 1968-78; Bucharest
1978; Cairo 1980; Vienna 1981; Bangkok 1984;
Moscow 1986; Washington 1987; Prague 1990;
Grade SO; m 1959 Eva Denise Davison.

Ferguson, Alexander; Resident Representative St
Vincent since September 1992; born 3.6.36; FO
1954; RAF 1955-58; Rangoon 1958; Kuwait
1962; Macao 1964; Beirut 1966; Vice-Consul
Yokohama 1967; FCO 1971; Second Secretary
(Admin) Brasilia 1974; Second Secretary (Aid)
Georgetown 1976; Suva 1980; First Secretary and Consul Baghdad
1981; First Secretary FCO 1984; First Secretary
(Admin) Lisbon 1987; First Secretary FCO 1990;
m 1959 Shirley Ann Rencontre (2s 1960, 1963;
1d 1961).

Ferguson, Christine Julia; First Secretary UKDIS
Geneva since February 1990; born 5.10.57; FCO
1982; Language Training 1983; Second Secretary
Cairo 1985; Second later First Secretary FCO
1987; m 1990 Michael (later Sir Michael)
Charles Swift Weston.

Ferguson, Denis John; Consul Lisbon since
March 1992; born 13.12.39; FO 1960; Rangoon
1961; FO 1963; Düsseldorf 1965; FCO 1970;
Bucharest 1973; Kingston 1975; FCO 1978;
Second Secretary 1980; Second Secretary
(Admin and Consul) Dublin 1983; Second
Secretary (Consular) Nairobi 1985; Second
Secretary FCO 1990; m 1966 Monika Hack (1d
1967; 1s 1968).

Ferguson, Iain; FCO since October 1990; born
18.2.70; Grade 10.

Ferguson, Sandra Kay; FCO since July 1991;
born 11.11.67; FCO 1986; Vienna 1989; Grade
S2.

Fergusson, George Duncan; First Secretary FCO
since September 1991; born 30.9.55; Dublin
1988; HCS 1978-1990; m 1981 Margaret
Wookey (3d 1982, 1986, 1991; 1s 1984).

Ferrand, Simon Piers; Kinshasa since October
1991; born 5.3.68; FCO 1989; Grade 10.

ffrench Blake, Anthony O'Brien, OBE (1991);
First Secretary (Chancery) Bridgetown since
January 1992; born 21.4.42; HM Forces 1962-72;
Second later First Secretary FCO 1972; First
Secretary (Inf/Community Affairs) Bonn 1976;
FCO 1978; First Secretary (Chancery) The
Hague 1983; First Secretary FCO 1988; m (1)
1968 Susanne Bergsoe (diss 1978) (2s 1970,
1974); (2) 1982 Gillian Anne Herbert (2 step d
1970, 1972).

Fidler, Martin Alfred; Third Secretary (Consular/
Management) Nuku'alofa since December 1989;
born 10.12.53; DHSS 1972; FCO 1974;
Belmopan 1977; Africa/ME Floater 1980;
Havana 1981; UKMIS New York 1984;

Field, (Edward) John, CMG (1991); High
Comissioner Colombo since November 1991; born
11.6.36; FO 1963; Second later First Secretary
(Inf) Tokyo 1963; FCO 1968; First Secretary
(Cultural) Moscow 1970; First Secretary (Comm)
Tokyo 1973; FCO 1976; Counsellor on loan to
DOT 1977; Counsellor (Commercial) Seoul 1980;
Centre for International Affairs, Harvard 1983;
Counsellor UKMIS New York 1984; Minister
Tokyo 1988; m 1960 Irene du Pont Darden (1d
1964; 1s 1968).

Field, Robert; Management Officer (Consular)
Addis Ababa since August 1992; born 4.1.53;
FCO 1971; Karachi 1975; Far East Floater 1979;
Second Secretary (Comm) Harare 1982. Second
Secretary FCO 1987.

Fielder, John; Second Secretary (Management/
Consular) Maputo since March 1990; born
27.6.47; CO (later Commonwealth Office) 1966;
HM Forces 1967-73; FCO 1974; Accra 1976;
Nassau 1977; Prague 1980; SE Asia/FE Floater
1982; FCO 1987.

Fielder, Richard John; Freetown since June 1990; born 28.3.52; FCO 1971; Tokyo 1974; FCO 1975; Stockholm 1978; Khartoum 1981; FCO 1982; Dhaka 1985; Chicago 1988; Grade 9; m 1988 Samantha Louise Monton (1d 1988, 1s 1990).

Fielding, Rachel Louise; FCO since April 1991; born 6.12.62; FCO 1984; San José 1986; Dar es Salaam 1989; Grade S2.

Figgis, Anthony St John Howard; AUSS (Protocol), Vice Marshal of the Diplomatic Corps since November 1991; (holds personal rank of Ambassador); born 12.10.40; Third Secretary Belgrade 1963; Commonwealth Office 1965; Second Secretary Bahrain 1968; FCO 1970; First Secretary (Comm) Madrid 1971; FCO 1974; First Secretary and Head of Chancery Madrid 1979; Counsellor (Comm) Madrid 1980; Counsellor Belgrade 1982; Counsellor FCO 1986; Counsellor and Head of Chancery Bonn 1988; Director of Research FCO 1989; m 1964 Miriam Ellen Hardt (1d 1966; 2s 1968, 1972).

Finch, Brian Keith; First Secretary FCO since September 1989; born 1.1.41; Army 1958-78; Second Secretary FCO 1978; Second later First Secretary Hong Kong 1982; m 1968 Gillian Mary Montgomery (1s 1971; 1d 1972).

Finch, Peter Leonard; Tokyo since July 1991; born 1.1.58; FCO 1975; UKMIS Geneva 1978; Tel Aviv 1981; New Delhi 1983; FCO 1986; Grade 9; m 1979 Mitsue Uchida (1d 1990).

Fines, Barry John; New Delhi since March 1991; born 13.9.69; FCO 1988; Grade 10.

Finlay, Norah Ferguson Watson; Singapore since June 1992; born 13.4.70; FCO 1989; Grade 10.

Finlayson, George; Deputy High Commissioner Dhaka since November 1990; Consul (Comm) BTDO New York 1987; born 22.4.43; Inland Revenue 1962; CO 1965; FO 1966; Reykjavik 1967; Prague 1969; Lagos 1971; FCO 1975; Second Secretary New Delhi 1978; First Secretary FCO 1981; First Secretary Head of Chancery Montevideo 1983; Consul (Comm) BTDO New York 1987; m 1966 Patricia Grace Ballantine (2s 1967, 1972).

Finnamore Crorkin, Joanne Lynn; New York since August 1992; born 22.9.63; FCO 1982; Moscow 1984; Colombo 1985; SUPL 1990; Grade 9; m 1991 Colin Wynn Crorkin.

Finnerty, Kevin John; Second Secretary FCO since January 1989; born 1.2.49; FCO 1967; Kuwait 1970; Warsaw 1974; FCO 1976; Mogadishu 1983; FCO 1985; Chicago 1985; m (1) 1970 Sandra Tidy (diss 1982); (2) 1982 Norma Collins.

Firstbrook, Steven Paul; Helsinki since July 1992; born 22.2.70; FCO 1989; Grade 10.

Fish, Norman James; Second Secretary FCO since July 1988; born 11.12.36; FCO 1964; Tel Aviv 1973; Lagos 1978; FCO 1981; Second Secretary Montevideo 1985; m 1971 Beaula Patricia Roberts (1s 1972; 1d 1976).

Fish, Rosemary; Second Secretary FCO since February 1988; born 28.8.49; Ankara 1974; Honiara 1976; Bogota 1978; FCO 1979; Far East Floater 1980; FCO 1982; on loan to DTI 1984; Rio de Janeiro 1986; m 1987 Anthony John Stafford. (1s 1991).

Fisher, Ann; Oslo since January 1991; born 10.2.43; FCO 1971; Falkland Islands 1972; Bonn 1973; FCO 1976; Copenhagen 1980; Ankara 1982; FCO 1984; Bucharest 1986; FCO 1989; Grade S1.

Fisher, Deborah Joan; First Secretary FCO since October 1991; born 4.3.62; FCO 1985; Second Secretary (Chancery) Dar es Salaam 1988.

Fisher, Deryck John; First Secretary FCO since June 1991; born 26.7.46; Inland Revenue 1961; Department of Technical Co-operation ODA 1964; FCO 1973; Kinshasa 1975; Islamabad 1978; Second Secretary FCO 1980; Second Secretary (Consular) Accra 1983; First Secretary (Admin/Consul) Copenhagen 1987; m 1973 Lynda Elizabeth Robinson (2d 1974, 1975; 3s 1976, 1979, 1983).

Fisher, Gary John; Peking since February 1992; born 27.12.69; FCO 1989; Grade 10; m 1992 Claire Louise White.

Fisher, John; First Secretary FCO since September 1986; born 3.8.48; Third later Second Secretary FCO 1974; Language Student SOAS 1975 and Bursa 1976; Second Secretary (Inf) Ankara 1976; First Secretary FCO 1979; UKMIS Vienna (IAEA) 1982; m 1970 Lynette Joyce Corinne Growcott (1d 1978; 1s 1980).

Fisher, Jon Christopher; First Secretary FCO since December 1990; born 5.3.39; Air Ministry 1955; Passport Office 1956; RAF 1958-61; Passport Office 1961; CRO 1963; Lagos 1963; Palma de Majorca 1967; Vice-Consul San José 1967; FCO 1970; Second Secretary Port of Spain 1973; Vice-Consul (Inf) Johannesburg 1977; Second later First Secretary Paris 1979; First Secretary FCO 1983; First Secretary (Comm) Quito 1987; m 1972 Patricia Lorraine Galliford (1d 1976; 1s 1978).

Fisher, Kate; FCO since September 1991; born 12.11.70; Grade S2.

Fisher, Miles Lyndon; FCO since September 1981; born 28.11.61; Grade 9.

Fisher, Simon John; Second Secretary Osaka

since May 1992; born 8.6.59; FCO 1983; Athens 1985; Language Training Kamakura 1989.

Fisher, Susan Maureen; Kuala Lumpur since December 1989; born 7.3.50; DHSS 1977-79; FCO 1979; Budapest 1980; Bermuda 1982; Africa/Middle East Floater 1985; FCO 1987; Grade 9.

Fisher, Theresa Ellen; Manila since May 1987; born 5.6.60; FCO 1977; UKMIS Geneva 1982; Belgrade 1984; Grade S2; m 1985 Ali Gecim.

Fisher, Timothy Dirk Colomb; Third Secretary (Aid) Jakarta since August 1991; born 23.8.47; FCO 1975; Moscow 1976; FCO 1977; Port Moresby 1978; Nairobi 1981; FCO 1985; Colombo 1987; Grade 9; m 1992 Patricia-Jane Van des Voorden.

Fisher, Tracy; Lagos since July 1992; born 15.5.70; FCO 1988; Grade S2.

Fishman, Jason; FCO since July 1990; born 5.10.69; Grade 10.

Fishwick, Nicholas Bernard Frank; First FCO since March 1991; born 23.2.58; FCO 1983; Language Training 1986; First Secretary (Inf) Lagos 1988; m 1987 Susan Teresa Rouane Mendel (1s 1987, 1d 1989).

Fitch, Diana May (née Francis); FCO since May 1988 (Second Secretary 1990); born 26.12.53; FCO 1975; Dar es Salaam 1976; Tortola 1977; FCO 1981; SE Asia Floater 1984; Singapore 1986; m 1991 Geoffrey William Fitch.

Fitchett, Robert Duncan; First Secretary FCO since August 1990; born 10.6.61; FCO 1983; Dakar 1984; Second Secretary (Chancery/Inf) Bonn 1988; m 1985 Adèle Thérèsa Stajjar (1s 1987, 1d 1988)

Fitton, David John; First Secretary FCO since December 1986; born 10.1.55; FCO 1980; Language Training Kamakura 1982; Second later First Secretary (Econ) Tokyo 1983; m 1989 Hisae Iijima.

Fitton-Brown, Edmund Walter; Language Training Cairo since June 1991; born 5.10.62; FCO 1984; Third later Second Secretary Helsinki 1987; Second Secretary FCO 1989 (First Secretary 1991).

Fitzgerald, Antonia Maria; Brasilia since October 1991; born 13.6.71; FCO 1990; Grade S2A.

FitzHerbert, Giles Eden CMG (1985); HM Ambassador Caracas and HMA (non-resident) Dominican Republic since January 1988; born 8.3.35; FO 1966; First Secretary Rome 1968; FCO 1972; Counsellor and later Head of Chancery Kuwait 1975; Counsellor Nicosia 1977;

Head of European Community Dept (Eernal) 1978; Sabbatical at LSE 1982; Inspectorate FCO 1983; Minister Rome 1983; m (1) 1962 Margaret Waugh (dec'd 1986); (3d 1963, 1965, 1967; 2s 1973, 1974); m (2) 1988 Alexandra Eyre (1s 1989).

Flaherty, Shaun David; Lagos since June 1992; born 29.1.66; FCO 1984; Washington 1987; Ankara 1990; Grade 9.

Flanagan, Dermot Richard Francis; Head of Chancery and First Secretary (Comm) Abidjan since February 1990; born 3.5.39; HM Forces 1959-63; CRO 1963; Lagos 1963; Dublin 1965; Dacca 1968; FCO 1971; Second Secretary (Comm) Vienna 1974; Santo Domingo 1979; First Secretary FCO 1982; Deputy High Commissioner Belmopan 1985; m 1975 Madeline Edith Shaw.

Flanagan, Peter Patrick; Second Secretary (Development) Addis Ababa since March 1985; born 18.7.43; FO 1961; Warsaw 1966; Oslo 1968; Jedda 1970; Paris 1972; East Berlin 1975; FCO 1976; Ottawa 1979; FCO 1980; on loan to ODA 1983; m 1967 Ann Austin (2s 1969, 1972).

Flear, Timothy Charles Fitzranulf, MVO (1989); Second Secretary FCO since April 1991; born 22.1.58; FCO 1980; Third Secretary (Comm/Inf) Dubai 1982; resigned and reinstated 1985; FCO 1985; Third later Second Secretary Kuala Lumpur 1987.

Fleming, Susan Jane; FCO since January 1990; born 2.8.64; FCO 1984; UKREP Brussels 1985; Nassau 1988; Grade 9.

Fleming, Thomas; Peking since May 1991; born 30.8.35; RAF 1953-77; Ankara 1977; Bucharest 1979; Washington 1981; Islamabad 1983; NATO Brussels 1985; East Berlin 1989; Grade CSO; m 1957 Catherine Helen Finnegan (1d 1962).

Fleming, Lieutenant Colonel Willoughby Alexander, OBE; Queen's Messenger since 1984; born 7.5.36; Army 1954-84.

Fleming, Wendy Alexandra; FCO since July 1991; born 11.5.70; Grade 10.

Flessati, Francesca Josephine Grovanna; Language Training since September 1991; born 27.10.58; FCO 1990; Grade 9; m 1985 Nicholas John Foster.

Fletcher, Elaine Karen; Floater Duties since April 1992; born 5.1.63; FCO 1984; Budapest 1987; East Berlin 1988; Suva 1989; Grade S2.

Fletcher, James; UKMIS New York since September 1992; born 9.1.40; Prague 1981; Baghdad 1984; Bangkok 1986; Belgrade 1989; Sofia 1990; Grade CSO; m 1962 Sheri Strickland Dearie (2s 1963, 1965).

Fletcher, Patricia May; FCO since August 1991; born 8.9.42; FCO 1983; BMG Berlin 1984; Tortola 1986; FCO 1988; UKDEL Brussels 1990; Grade 9; m 1974 Herbert Fletcher (1s 1978).

Fletcher, Richard George Hopper; Counsellor FCO since August 1988; born 8.11.44; Third Secretary FO 1966; Athens 1968; Second Secretary (Inf) Nicosia 1969; FCO 1972; Second later First Secretary Bucharest 1973; First Secretary FCO 1977; Counsellor Athens 1985; m 1967 Celia Rosemary Soord (2d 1971, 1973).

Fletcher, Robert; Singapore since August 1989; born 18.12.61; FCO 1981; Grade 9.

Fletcher-Cooke, Richard Mark Forrest; SUPL since April 1988; born 31.8.51; MOD 1973; FCO 1978; Language Training Hong Kong 1980; Second Secretary Peking 1982; Second Secretary FCO 1983; Assistant to Civil Commissioner Port Stanley 1985; First Secretary FCO 1986; m 1979 Georgina Anne Southwell.

Flint, David Leonard; Lagos since January 1990; born 21.10.56; FCO 1975; Budapest 1979; Jeddah 1980; FCO 1984; Athens 1986; Grade 9; m 1984 Mary Anne Elizabeth Goodale (3s twins 1986, 1988).

Flisher, Nigel Frederick; FCO since August 1991; born 20.4.53; FCO 1971; Singapore 1974; Vientiane 1978; Colombo 1979; FCO 1982; Islamabad 1984; Third Secretary (Passports/Visas) Dublin 1988; Grade 9; m 1977 Valerie Tay Kim Heok (1d 1978; 1s 1980).

Flower, Robert Philip; Counsellor and Deputy Head of Mission The Hague since April 1990; born 12.5.39; Army 1958-60; Second Secretary Commonwealth Office 1966; Zomba 1967; First Secretary UKDEL NATO Brussels 1970; FCO 1973; First Secretary and Head of Chancery Kuala Lumpur 1977; First Secretary FCO 1979; Counsellor, Deputy Head of PUSD FCO 1981; CDA Munich 1984; Counsellor Bonn 1985; m 1964 Anne Daveen Tweddle (2s 1968, 1972).

Floyd, Linda Vivienne; SUPL since September 1991; born 17.3.65; FCO 1987; New Delhi 1989; Grade S2; m 1990 Neil Floyd; (1d 1992).

Floyd, Neil; Warsaw since September 1991; born 20.5.67; FCO 1987; New Delhi 1989; m 1990 Linda Vivienne Colvin; Grade 9.

Fluck, Peter; Deputy High Commissioner Gabarone since April 1992; born 30.5.36; Royal Navy 1952-66; DSAO 1966; Tehran 1967; FCO 1969; Geneva 1971; Kinshasa 1974; Seoul 1975; Second Secretary 1976; FCO 1979; Second later First Secretary, Head of Chancery and Consul Reykjavik 1981; First Secretary (Comm) Copenhagen 1985; First Secretary FCO 1990; m 1966 Sylvia Elisabet Bergstrom (2s 1968, 1969).

Flynn, John Gerrard; CMG (1992) HM Ambassador Luanda since May 1990; and additionally, HM Ambassador (non-resident) to Sao Tomé and Principe since May 1990; born 23.4.37; FO 1965; Second Secretary Lusaka 1966; FO (later FCO) 1967 (First Secretary 1968); Assistant Director-General, Canning House 1970; First Secretary (Comm) Head of Chancery and Consul Montevideo 1971; FCO 1976; Chargé d'Affaires Luanda 1978; Head of Chancery and Consul-General Brasilia 1979; Counsellor (Comm) Madrid 1982; High Commissioner Mbabane 1987; m 1973 Drina Anne Coates (1s 1984; 1d 1985).

Foakes, Joanne Sarah; Assistant Principal Crown Counsel, Hong Kong since January 1991; born 9.3.57; called to the Bar (Inner Temple) 1979; FCO 1984; SUPL 1990; Assistant Legal Adviser.

Foley, Victoria Beth Louise; FCO since December 1986; born 23.6.60; FCO 1978; Budapest 1982; Paris 1984; Grade 10.

Folland, Richard Dudley; Second Secretary (Political) Stockholm since December 1991; FCO since September 1988; born 10.3.61; FCO 1981; Moscow 1983; Gaborone 1985; FCO 1988; m 1985 Gwen Alison Evans (1s 1989).

Folliss, Anne Mary (née Segar); SUPL since June 1991; born 18.9.62; Mexico City 1984; FCO 1987; Floater Duties 1988; Geneva 1989; Grade S2; m 1991 Tarquin Simon Archer Folliss.

Folliss, Tarquin Simon Archer; First Secretary FCO since June 1992; born 23.10.57; HM Forces 1981-86; Second Secretary FCO 1986; Second later First Secretary (Chancery) Jakarta 1989; m 1991 Anne Mary Segar.

Foord, Michael Robert; Second Secretary (Dev) Colombo since June 1988; born 24.1.42; FO 1966; Dar es Salaam 1968; Sofia 1972; Kuwait 1974; FCO 1975; Jedda 1977; Athens 1979; Tegucigalpa 1982; Second Secretary FCO 1984; m 1968 Christine Edwards (1s 1972; 1d 1974).

Foote, Daniel Edward; Moscow since October 1991; born 11.2.46; Royal Navy 1965-90 Grade SO; m 1967 Carol Elizabeth Combe.

Forbes, Matthew Keith; Colombo since December 1990; born 19.4.66; FCO 1987; Peking 1989; Grade 9.

Forbes-Meyler, John William, OBE (1990); Deputy Head of Mission Vienna since July 1992; born 3.7.42; CRO 1962; Lagos 1964; Chicago 1968; Boston 1968; FCO 1970; Commercial Publicity Officer BIS, New York 1971; FCO 1972; Second later First Secretary Athens 1975; FCO 1980; First Secretary (Econ) Bonn 1983; On loan to MOD 1986; First Secretary (Head of Chancery) Bogota 1988; m (1) 1964 Margaret

Goddard (diss 1979) (1d 1966); (2) 1980 Mary Vlachou.

Ford, Andrew James Ford; Third Secretary (Chancery/Inf/Cons) Georgetown since February 1990; born 21.6.64; FCO 1987; Grade 9.

Ford, Antony; Consul-General San Francisco since February 1990; born 1.10.44; Commonwealth Office 1967; Third later Second Secretary Bonn 1968; Kuala Lumpur 1971; First Secretary FCO 1973; First Secretary (Comm) Washington 1977; First Secretary FCO 1981; Counsellor East Berlin 1984; Counsellor FCO 1987; m 1970 Linda Gordon Joy (1d 1970; 1s 1976).

Ford, Kathleen Margaret; UKREP Brussels since January 1988; born 27.1.58; MOD 1980; FCO 1986; Grade S2.

Ford, Peter William; University of Harvard since September 1990; born 27.6.47; Third Secretary FCO 1970; MECAS 1971; Beirut 1973; Second later First Secretary Cairo 1974; First Secretary FCO 1977; ENA Paris 1980; First Secretary Paris 1981; First Secretary FCO 1985; Counsellor (Comm) Riyadh 1987; m (1) 1975 (diss 1991) Aurora Raquel Garcia Mingo; (2) 1992 Alganesk Haile Beyene.

Forester-Bennett, Charles Anthony Robert; Casablanca since March 1990; born 22.1.60; FCO 1983; Doha 1986; Grade 9; m 1988 Joan Sandra Anthony (1d 1990).

Forrester, Mark Adrian; Dhaka since May 1989; born 29.6.59; FCO 1978; UKMIS Geneva 1980; Santiago 1983; FCO 1986; Grade 9; m 1982 Deborah Cannell (1d 1987, 1s 1990).

Forrester, Stuart Russell; Washington since December 1990; born 10.2.62; FCO 1983; Grade 9; m 1990 Deborah Channon.

Forryan, Anne May; FCO since November 1990; born 3.8.66; Grade 9.

Forsdike, Jack; First Secretary FCO since December 1974; born 6.8.37; HM Forces 1956-58; Second Secretary FO (later FCO) 1966.

Forsdyke, Toby Edward; FCO since Februrary 1992; born 6.1.73; Grade 10.

Forsyth, Brian Gilbert; Dhaka since May 1989; born 27.2.65; FCO 1984; Bucharest 1987; Grade 10; m 1987 Marie Boyle (1s 1989).

Forsyth, Marie (née Boyle); Dhaka since April 1990; born 26.4.66; FCO 1984; Mexico City 1986; SUPL 1987; Grade 10; m 1987 Brian Gilbert Forsyth (1s 1989).

Forsyth, Robert Gilbert; Copenhagen since February 1992; born 31.8.37; HM Forces 1955-

77; Budapest 1982; Dublin 1984; Kuala Lumpur 1986; Paris 1988; Grade SO; m 1958 Margaret Gordon (2s 1959, 1965).

Fort, Maeve Geraldine; CMG (1990); HM Ambassador Beirut since July 1992; born 19.11.40; FO 1963; New York 1964; CRO 1965; Seconded to SEATO Bangkok 1966; Bonn 1968; Lagos 1971; Second later First Secretary FCO 1973; UKMIS New York 1978; FCO 1982; Counsellor on RCDS Course 1983; Head of Chancery Santiago 1984; Counsellor FCO 1986; and later, additionally HM Ambassador (non-resident) to Chad; HM Ambassador Maputo 1989.

Fortescue, Dominic James Lewis; FCO since September 1991; born 9.10.66; Grade 8; m 1990 Miriam Cathleen Rolls.

Foster, Hazel Ankara since October 1991; born 10.4.69; FCO 1989; Grade S2A.

Foster, John Michael; New Delhi since January 1991; born 7.5.55; FCO 1989; Grade 10; m 1986 Julie Bearfoot.

Foster, Julie Maria (née Bearfoot); New Delhi since January 1991; born 19.12.59; FCO 1978; UKDEL NATO Brussels 1981; Doha 1983; FCO 1987; Grade 9; m 1986 John Michael Foster.

Foster, Nicholas John; First Secretary (Pol) Moscow since November 1992; born 3.9.57; Second Secretary FCO 1984; Second later First Secretary (Chancery) Nicosia 1986; First Secretary FCO 1989; m 1985 Francesca Josephine Giovanna Flessati.

Foster, Victoria Evelyn; FCO since November 1990; born 28.12.72; Grade S2.

Foulds, Patricia Lilian; Cairo since May 1990; born 22.12.65; FCO 1985; Kaduna 1987; Windhoek April 1989; FCO 1989; Grade S2A.

Foulds, Sarah Ann; FCO since August 1979; born 10.8.57; PRO (DS Grade 5); m 1981 Ali Reza Fatemi-Shirazi (1d 1985; 1s 1988).

Foulsham, Richard Andrew; First Secretary FCO since March 1990; born 24.9.50; Second Secretary FCO 1982; First Secretary Bandar Seri Begawan 1984; First Secretary (Chancery) Lagos 1986; m 1982 Deirdre Elizabeth Strathairn (1d 1984; 1s 1986).

Fowle, Angela Mary (née Hatcher); SUPL since November 1990; born 25.4.44; FO 1964; Bangkok 1966; Moscow 1968; Athens 1969; FCO 1972; Santiago 1974; FCO 1976; UKMIS Geneva1980; FCO 1983; Düsseldorf 1986; FCO 1989; Grade 9; m 1978 Leslie Thomas Fowle (1s 1983).

Fowler, Joanna; FCO since April 1989; born

12.4.43; FCO 1976; Tehran 1977; Rangoon 1979; FCO 1982; Belgrade 1983; Abu Dhabi 1985; Grade S1.

Fowler, Joseph Villiers; FCO since August 1990; born 23.2.42; GPO 1966-68; FCO 1968; Dacca 1970; Darwin 1971; FCO 1973; St Helena 1975; FCO 1977; Khartoum 1978; FCO 1982; Singapore 1983; FCO 1987; Pretoria 1988; Grade 8; m 1966 Catherine Agnes Brennan (2s 1972, 1978; 2d 1971, 1979).

Fowler, Peter James, CMG (1990); Minister and Deputy High Commissioner New Delhi since February 1988; born 26.8.36; FO 1962; Third Secretary Budapest 1964; Second later First Secretary Lisbon 1965; First Secretary and Head of Chancery Calcutta 1968; FCO 1972; First Secretary and Head of Chancery East Berlin 1975; Counsellor on loan to Cabinet Office 1977; Counsellor Geneva (CTB Delegation) 1980; Counsellor (Bonn Group) Bonn 1981; Counsellor FCO 1985; m 1962 Audrey June Smith (3d 1963, 1968, 1972; 1s 1965).

Fowler, Rosalind Mary Elizabeth; Second Secretary (Info) British Trade Commission Hong Kong since October 1990; born 27.9.65; FCO 1987; Language Training 1988; Language Training Hong Kong 1989; m 1992 Major Jeremy John Robert Tuck.

Fox, Clive Richard; Second Secretary FCO since March 1992; born 5.12.45; GPO 1961-68; FO (later FCO) 1968; Paris 1971; FCO 1973; Athens 1975; Second Secretary FCO 1977; Second Secretary Peking 1988; m (1) Patricia Mary Taylor (diss) (2s 1972, 1974); (2) 1986 Barbara Ann Hogan.

Fox, Ian David; Floater Duties since November 1991; born 2.6.66; FCO 1987; Peking 1988; Grade 10.

Fox, John Graham; Second Secretary (Consular) Bucharest since June 1991; born 19.1.41; HM Forces 1960-66; DSAO 1966; Georgetown 1968; Warsaw 1971; Osaka 1973; FCO 1976; Abidjan 1979; Vientiane 1980; Second Secretary (Comm) Athens 1982; Second Secretary FCO 1987; m 1963 Patricia Mary Goff (2d 1964, 1971; 1s 1968).

Fox, Paul Leonard; New Delhi since February 1990; born 24.7.62; FCO 1987; Grade 9; m 1991 Vicki Ann Rathbun.

Fox, Sarah Victoria; Budapest since May 1992; born 8.10.65; FCO 1985; Warsaw 1987; Hamilton 1989; Grade 10.

Foxwell, Rachael Louise; Second Secretary (Commercial/Consular) Tunis since June 1992; born 29.10.59; FCO 1982; Africa/Middle East Floater 1984; Harare 1985; Third later Second

Secretary Hanoi 1988; Second Secretary FCO 1991.

Frame, Simon Moray; Dubai since May 1990; born 15.8.66; FCO 1984; Paris 1987; Grade 10.

Francis, Catherine Joan; FCO since December 1991; born 1.4.50; FCO 1972; Brussels 1972; Kuala Lumpur 1976; Bonn 1980; FCO 1980; Helsinki 1985; FCO 1987; Riyadh 1989; Grade S1; m 1991 John Treharne Francis.

Francis, Colin William; Second Secretary FCO since October 1991; born 16.6.38; Royal Navy 1953-62; DWS 1962; FCO 1971; Khartoum 1972; Berne 1976; FCO 1979; UKDEL NATO Brussels 1980; FCO 1984; Budapest 1987; Second Secretary (Management) Vice-Consul Dubai 1990; m 1962 Margaret Joyce Perry (2d 1965, 1967).

Francis, John Alexander; First Secretary (Management) Ankara since June 1992; born 14.12.42; FO 1962; Athens 1964; Beirut 1964; Stockholm 1965; Seoul 1968; Malta 1971; Paris 1972; FCO 1972; Dacca 1975; Prague 1979; Kaduna 1981; Second Secretary FCO 1983; Consul Bangkok 1988; m 1981 Grace Engelen.

Francis, Julie Mary; FCO since August 1990; born 21.2.50; FCO 1976; Kabul 1976; FCO 1978; Sofia 1979; UKDEL NATO Brussels 1981; FCO 1984; Kathmandu 1987; Grade S2.

Francis, Paul Richard; FCO since November 1990; born 10.11.53; FCO 1980; Kuwait 1981; Khartoum 1982; Lagos 1986; Abu Dhabi 1988; m 1981 Fenella Wooman.

Franklin, Joanna Mary Clare; Cairo since September 1986; born 12.8.60; FCO 1978; Peking 1981; FCO 1982; Grade 9; m 1988 Habib Elie Gouel.

Franklin, Sarah Louise; FCO since October 1991; born 2.4.66; FCO 1985; UKMIS Geneva 1989; Grade 10.

Franklin-Brown, Alexander; FCO since February 1991; born 30.3.72; Grade 10.

Fransella, Cortland Lucas; Counsellor (Political) Rome since November 1991; born 9.9.48; Third Secretary FCO 1970; Language Student Hong Kong 1971; Assistant Trade Commissioner Hong Kong 1973; Second later First Secretary FCO 1975; Kuala Lumpur 1980; Santiago 1982; FCO 1986; m 1977 Laura Ruth Propper (2s 1978, 1981).

Frape, Neil Jeremy; Paris since March 1990; born 16.11.63; FCO 1984; Addis Ababa 1986; Grade 9; m 1987 Christine Mary Allen (1d 1989).

Frary, Helen Elizabeth; New Delhi since August

1991; born 23.2.69; FCO 1988; Grade 9.

Fraser, Angus Alistair; Second Secretary FCO since November 1990; born 3.7.42; FO 1959; Bonn 1963; Athens 1965; Havana 1968; FCO 1969; Madras 1972; Washington 1976; FCO 1977; Kuala Lumpur 1981; Second Secretary (Admin) Accra 1983; FCO 1985; Vice Consul (Admin/Cons) Karachi 1989; m 1966 Victoria Emily Biggs (1d 1968; 1s 1971).

Fraser, James Terence; FCO since July 1988 (Second Secretary 1991); born 12.4.49; GPO 1966; FCO 1967; Nicosia 1971; Johannesburg 1972; Prague 1974; Africa Floater 1975; FCO 1978; Düsseldorf 1981; Language Training 1983; Baghdad 1984; m 1988 Nada Babić; (1s 1992).

Fraser, Ronald; MVO (1979); FCO since January 1980; born 3.9.49; FCO 1968; Phnom Penh 1971; Tel Aviv 1973; FCO 1976; Lusaka 1978; Grade 9.

Fraser, Shelley; FCO since February 1991; born 21.3.70; Grade 10.

Fraser, Simon James; First Secretary FCO since September 1986 (Private Secretary to Minister of State March 1989); born 3.6.58; FCO 1979; Third later Second Secretary Baghdad 1982; Second Secretary (Chancery) Damascus 1984.

Fraser Darling, Richard Ogilby Leslie; FCO since August 1988; born 2.3.49; Third Secretary FCO 1971; Language Student Helsinki 1973; Third later Second Secretary Helsinki 1974; First Secretary FCO 1978; Washington 1984; m 1991 Nicola Kirkup.

Frate, Maria; Rome since April 1990; born 15.2.59; FCO 1983; Athens 1985; Grade S2.

Frean, Christopher William; Abidjan since May 1992; born 31.7.64; FCO 1988; Grade 10.

Freel, Philip John; Rome since April 1991; born 24.12.55; FCO 1974; Paris 1976; Mogadishu 1979; Lisbon 1980; Addis Ababa 1983; FCO 1985; on loan to CAD Hanslope Park 1986; Lagos 1987; Grade 9; m 1977 Joan Winifred Hill (1d 1979; 1s 1986).

Freeman, John Michael Giles; Second later First Secretary FCO since August 1978; born 18.11.49; FCO 1971; Rome 1975; m 1986 Anne Sarah Holliday (1d 1990).

Freeman, Judith Louise; Floater Duties since May 1991; born 24.3.61; FCO 1984; Berne 1985; East Berlin 1989; Grade S2.

Freeman, Timothy John; Paris since April 1992; born 24.4.65; FCO 1989; Grade 10.

Freeman, Wendy Paula; SUPL since April 1992; born 9.3.61; FCO 1980; Bonn 1982; Africa/ME

Floater 1985; Abidjan 1988; Grade 9.

Freeman, William Henry; First Secretary FCO since January 1985; born 16.12.42; CRO 1961; New Delhi 1964; FO 1966; Saigon 1967; Kota Kinabalu 1969; Paris 1970; Copenhagen 1971; Second Secretary (Comm/Inf) Bombay 1974; FCO 1978; First Secretary Tunis 1980; Marseilles 1981; First Secretary (Inf/Chancery) UKDEL NATO Brussels 1983; m 1970 Veronica Vivien Ratnam (1s 1972).

French, Anna Isabel; FCO since September 1990; born 28.6.71; Grade 10.

French, Roger; First Secretary FCO since September 1988; born 3.6.47; FCO 1965; Havana 1970; Madrid 1971; San Juan 1973; FCO 1977; Second later First Secretary (Chancery), Washington 1980; First Secretary (Comm) Muscat 1985; m 1969 Angela Joyce Cooper (1d 1974, 1s 1980).

Friel, Nicola; Washington since Februrary 1992; born 8.3.70; FCO 1989; Grade 10.

Friend, John David; First Secretary (Aid) Nairobi since November 1988; born 3.1.38; FO 1956; HM Forces 1956-58; Baghdad 1959; Bangkok 1961; Berlin 1964; DSAO 1966; Beirut 1968; Lagos 1971; Second Secretary FCO 1975; New Delhi 1978; Belmopan 1982; First Secretary FCO 1984; East Berlin 1988; m 1966 Margrit Gisela Seime (1s 1968; 1d 1969).

Friis, Andrew Stuart; FCO since October 1988; born 4.4.60; Metropolitan Police 1981; FCO 1982; Kuwait 1986; Grade 9; m 1989 Maria Carina Lumatan Reyes (1s 1991).

Friston, Leonard Joseph; First Secretary (Comm) Bombay since August 1989; born 7.7.35; Admiralty 1953-58; Royal Navy 1954-56; FO 1960; Bahrain 1960; Tokyo-Jakarta-Tokyo 1963; Vienna 1966; Colombo 1968; FCO 1972; Vice-Consul East Berlin 1975; Second Secretary (Admin) New Delhi 1977; FCO 1980; on loan to DOT 1981; Vice-Consul (Comm) Johannesburg 1983; First Secretary (Admin) and Consul Khartoum 1985; m 1965 Barbara Jane McAulay (1d 1969; 1s 1971).

Frost, Albert Edward; Singapore since July 1991; born 13.12.36; Royal Navy 1952-81; Bucharest 1986; Lagos 1988; Grade SO.

Frost, Michael Edward, LVO (1983); Deputy Consul-General and Director of Inward Investment BTDO New York since January 1991; born 5.7.41; FO 1959; Algiers 1962; Kuala Lumpur 1967; FCO 1971; Bucharest 1972; Second Secretary 1973; FCO 1975; Consul (Comm) Seattle 1978; First Secretary FCO 1983; Seconded to ICI 1984; First Secretary, Head of Chancery and Consul Sofia 1987; m Carole Ann Beigel (3s 1964, 1967, 1968)

Frost, Michael Reginald; First Secretary (Aid/Comm) Kampala since January 1991; born 2.12.52; FCO 1971; Prague 1974; Dar es Salaam 1976; Peking 1979; FCO 1982; Washington 1984; Consul (Political/Inf) Cape Town 1986; m 1973 Marie Theresa McGlynn.

Frost, Simon Jaye; FCO since April 1990; born 24.5.70; Grade 10.

Frost, Steven, Alan; Islamabad since November 1992; born 21.9.64; FCO 1987; Grade 10.

Fry, Graham Holbrook; Counsellor and Head of Chancery Tokyo since January 1989; born 20.12.49; FCO 1972; Third later Second Secretary Tokyo 1974; First Secretary on loan to DOI 1979; FCO 1981; First Secretary Paris 1983; FCO 1987; m 1977 Meiko Iida.

Fuguet Debarr, Margaret (née Debarr); Dublin since July 1990; born 2.1.48; Inland Revenue 1964; FCO 1967; UKDEL Brussels EC 1970; FCO 1972; Copenhagen 1974; FCO 1977; Harare 1982; FCO 1985; Grade 9; m 1976 Juan Inocencio Fuguet Sanchez (1s 1977).

Fulcher, Michael Adrian; First Secretary FCO since April 1989; born 15.10.58; FCO 1982; Second later First Secretary Athens 1985; m 1983 Helen Parkinson (1s 1987; 1d 1988).

Full, Ian Francis; Islamabad since January 1989; born 16.8.54; FCO 1972; Paris 1975; San José 1978; Jedda 1981; FCO 1986; Grade 9.

Fuller, Eleanor Mary (née Breedon); Second Later First Secretary FCO since May 1990; born 31.12.53; FCO 1975, ENA course, Paris 1977, Paris 1978, Resigned 1980; Reinstated 1981, FCO 1981; on loan to the ODA 1983; SUPL 1986; m 1984 Simon William John Fuller (3s 1986, 1988, 1991).

Fuller, Martin John; FO (later FCO) since May 1965; born 26.1.41; Principal Research Officer; Senior Principal Research Officer in 1990.

Fuller, Sarah Jane; Rio de Janeiro since April 1991; born 28.3.68; FCO 1986; Paris 1988; Grade S2.

Fuller, Simon William John; Counsellor FCO since April 1990; born 27.11.43; Third Secretary FCO 1968; Second Secretary Singapore 1969; Kinshasa 1971; First Secretary seconded to Cabinet Office 1973; FCO 1976; First Secretary UK Mission New York 1977; First Secretary FCO 1980; Counsellor, Deputy Head of Personnel Operations Department, FCO 1984; Counsellor, Head of Chancery and Consul-General, Tel Aviv 1986; m 1984 Eleanor Mary Breedon (3s 1986, 1988, 1991).

Fullerton, William Hugh, CMG (1989); HM Ambassador Kuwait since August 1992; born

11.2.39; MECAS 1965; Information Officer Jedda 1966; Second Secretary FO (later FCO) 1968; First Secretary and Head of Chancery Kingston (concurrently Port-au-Prince) 1970; First Secretary and Head of Chancery Ankara 1973; First Secretary FCO 1977; Counsellor (Comm/Econ) and Consul-General Islamabad 1980; HM Ambassador Mogadishu 1983; Counsellor on loan to MOD 1987; Governor Falkland Islands, also Commissioner British Antarctic Territory and Commissioner South Georgia and the South Sandwich Islands 1988; m 1968 Arlene Jacobowitz (1d 1970).

Fulton, Craig John; Islamabad since October 1992; born 30.10.67; FCO 1987; Singapore 1990; Grade 9.

Fulton, James Holland; Second Secretary (Consul) Manila since April 1990; born 2.6.35; AMOU (USAF) British Staff Organisation 1954; CRO 1962; Colombo 1963-66; FCO 1967; Wellington 1970; Dacca 1973; FCO 1976; Kathmandu 1979; Bangkok 1983; Second Secretary (Admin) Lagos 1984; Jakarta 1989.

Fulton, Robert Andrew; Counsellor FCO since September 1992; born 6.2.44; Third Secretary FCO 1968; Third later Second Secretary Saigon 1969; FCO 1972; First Secretary Rome 1973; FCO 1977; East Berlin 1978; FCO 1981; Counsellor Oslo 1984; FCO 1987; Counsellor UKMIS New York 1989; m 1970 Patricia Mary Crowley (2s 1972, 1974; 1d 1979).

Furness, Alan Edwin, CMG (1991); Deputy High Commissioner Bombay since May 1989; born 6.6.37; Private Secretary to Parliamentary Under-Secretary of State CRO 1961; Third later Second Secretary Delhi 1962; Second later First Secretary DSAO 1966; First Secretary UKDEL Brussels (EC) 1969; First Secretary and Head of Chancery Dakar 1972; First Secretary FCO 1975; Counsellor and Head of Chancery Jakarta 1978; Counsellor and Head of Chancery Warsaw 1982; Counsellor FCO 1985; m 1971 Aline Elizabeth Janine Barrett (2s 1972, 1975).

Furness, Terence Gordon; Second Secretary FCO since June 1990; born 2.4.39; HM Forces 1958-64; FO 1965; Helsinki 1967; Islamabad 1969; FCO 1973; Washington 1976; Dusseldorf 1980; FCO 1982 (Second Secretary 1984); Second Secretary (Comm) Baghdad 1986; m 1963 Barbara Zietsch (1s 1967; 1d 1978).

Furze, George Philip; First Secretary FCO since October 1987; born 21.3.33; FO 1951; HM Forces 1952-54; FO 1955; Singapore 1956; Tel Aviv 1958; FO 1961; Kuwait 1962; FO 1964; Prague 1965; FO 1966; Accra 1967; FCO 1968; Bahrain 1969; FCO 1970; Darwin 1971; FCO 1973; Nicosia 1974; Nairobi 1977; FCO 1981; Second Secretary Pretoria 1982; FCO 1984; Manager BGWRS Darwin 1984; Grade 6; m

1956 Joyce Patricia Webb (2s 1957, 1962; 1d 1960).

Fussey, Lorraine Helen; Bombay since October 1991; born 30.1.67; FCO 1989; Grade 9.

Fyfe, William McKenzie; Vienna since September 1991; born 29.11.66; FCO 1987; Grade 10.

G

Gaines, Ann; BM Berlin since September 1990; born 24.7.39; FCO 1985; Grade S2A.

Gale, Ian Percy; Manila since June 1992; born 6.12.36; RAF 1957-79; Bucharest 1980; Tripoli 1982; Helsinki 1983; Kuwait 1985; Moscow 1988; Nicosia 1989; Grade CSO; m 1978 Anne Gillian (1d 1965).

Gallacher, Ian Charles; Paris since February 1988; born 2.5.63; FCO 1983; Grade 10; m 1987 Diane Warren.

Gallagher, Francis Xavier, OBE (1986); Counsellor, and Deputy Head of Mission Kuwait since August 1992; born 28.3.46; Third Secretary FCO 1971; MECAS 1972; Second Secretary March 1972; Second Secretary Beirut 1974; Second later First Secretary FCO 1975; Copenhagen 1979; First Secretary and Head of Chancery Beirut 1984; First Secretary FCO 1987; Counsellor, Head of Chancery Khartoum 1989; m 1981 Marie-France Martine Guiller.

Gallagher, Geraldine Mary; FCO since March 1992; born 30.1.60; National Savings Bank 1977; FCO 1979; Prague 1982; Capetown/Pretoria 1984; Dar es Salaam 1985; Peking 1989/Grade 9.

Gallagher, Patricia Ann; Athens since January 1991; born 17.4.65; FCO 1988; Grade S2.

Gallagher, Tracy Anne; First Secretary (Chancery) Dublin since February 1991; born 22.1.58; FCO 1981; Language Training 1982; Third later Second Secretary (Comm) later First Secretary (Econ) Moscow 1983; First Secretary FCO 1988; m 1986 Ian Robert Whitting (1d 1990).

Gallie, Alexander Charles; First Secretary (Comm) Kuala Lumpur since November 1989; born 18.9.40; FO 1960; Dakar 1962; Warsaw 1965; Maseru 1966; FCO 1970; Düsseldorf 1973; FCO 1974; Addis Ababa 1977; Second Secretary (Comm) Vienna 1981; First Secretary on loan to Office of Fair Trading 1987; m 1961 Margaret Louise Keggin (1d 1962; 2s 1966, 1967).

Galsworthy, Anthony Charles, CMG (1985); British Senior Representative J L G Hong Kong since November 1989; born 20.12.44; Third

Secretary FO 1966; Hong Kong 1967; Third later Second Secretary and Consul Peking 1970; Second later First Secretary FCO 1972; First Secretary (Econ) Rome 1977; First Secretary later Counsellor Peking 1981; Counsellor and Head of Hong Kong Department, FCO 1984; Principal Private Secretary to the Secretary of State 1986; Chatham House 1988; m 1970 Jan Dawson-Grove (1s 1974; 1d 1975).

Galvez, Elizabeth Ann (née Sketchley); First Secretary UKDEL Vienna since September 1989; born 24.12.51; FCO 1970; SUPL to attend University 1970; FCO 1973; Helsinki 1974; UKMIS Geneva 1977; FCO 1981; Second Secretary Tegucigalpa 1981; Second Secretary FCO 1985; SUPL 1987; FCO 1988; m 1985 Roberto Arturo Galvez Montes (1d 1987).

Gamble, Adrian Mark; FCO since March 1991; born 30.3.61; Grade 7; m 1990 Jane Brison (1s 1991).

Gamble, Peter John Leeland; FCO since June 1990; born 4.1.40; Royal Navy 1955-67; FO 1967; St Helena 1968; FCO 1969; Freetown 1970; Singapore 1971; Darwin 1973; FCO 1975; Singapore 1977; FCO 1980; Helsinki 1983; FCO 1986; Third Secretary Dhaka 1988; Grade 8; m 1970 Jennifer Mary Sykes (1s 1973; 1d 1976).

Gamble, Judith Christine; Abidjan since March 1992; born 1.12.63; FCO 1987; Washington 1989; Grade S2.

Gameson, Derek; Istanbul since October 1988; born 31.7.35; Army 1953-76; FCO 1976; Cairo 1976; Warsaw 1978; Oslo 1979; Ankara 1982; Havana 1983; Washington 1984; Moscow 1987; Grade SO; m 1957 Edna May Wright (3s 1958, 1961, 1963; 1d 1968).

Ganderton, Jennifer Louise; Stockholm since February 1992; born 15.6.70; Inland Revenue 1988; MOD 1988; FCO 1989; Grade 10.

Gane, Barrie Charles, CMG (1988), OBE (1978); Counsellor FCO since June 1982; born 19.9.35; FO 1960; Third Secretary Vientiane 1961; Seconded to Staff HM Governor Sarawak 1963; Second Secretary Kuching 1963; FO 1966; Second Secretary (Comm) Warsaw 1967; First Secretary Kampala 1967; FCO 1970; Hong Kong 1977; m (1) 1963 Elizabeth Anne Higlett (diss 1974) (2d 1963, 1966); (2) 1974 Jennifer Anne Pitt.

Gard, Brian Walter; Management Officer and Vice-Consul Mbabane since June 1990; born 3.11.38; RAF 1958-70; FCO 1970; LourenHco Marques 1973; Havana 1975; Lisbon 1977; Warsaw 1980; FCO 1982; Bandar Seri Begawan 1986; FCO 1987; Grade 9; m 1959 Lavinia Howes (1d 1963; 1s 1972).

Gardener, Carol Elizabeth; Athens since

September 1990; born 10.8.66; FCO 1988; Grade S2.

Gardiner, James Colin; Second Secretary FCO since February 1992; born 31.1.39; HM Forces 1960-69; FCO 1970; Hong Kong 1983; New York 1989; m 1960 Barbara Jean Tomlinson (2s 1962, 1965).

Gardiner, Yvonne; FCO since July 1992; born 9.1.62; FCO 1987; Caracas 1989; Grade S2.

Gardner, David Martin; Third Secretary (Chancery) Warsaw since January 1991; born 11.11.60; FCO 1978; Mexico City 1981; Tegucigalpa 1984; FCO 1988; Grade 9; m 1983 Ana Luisa Dominguez Ortiz (1s 1992).

Gardner, John Ewart; Lagos since January 1986; born 28.2.53; FCO 1971; Abu Dhabi 1974; Kinshasa 1978; Wellington 1981; FCO 1984; Grade 9; m 1975 Alexandra Marie Donald.

Gardner, Sarah Jayne; Lilongwe since August 1992; born 27.12.68; FCO 1986; Bangkok 1989; Grade 10.

Gardner, Stuart William; FCO since January 1989; born 10.3.70; Grade 10.

Garland, Albert Edward; Athens since August 1992; born 20.8.33; MOD 1952-83; Belgrade 1983; Lagos 1984; Islamabad 1986; Prague 1987; Lusaka 1990; Grade SO; m (1) 1958 Joan Bartlett (1s 1960); (2) 1987 Patricia Walton Turnbull.

Garland, Carol Ann; SUPL since September 1990; born 24.12.64; FCO 1986; Rio de Janeiro 1988; Grade S2.

Garn, Carl Raymond; FCO since May 1990; born 17.10.56; Cabinet Office 1977; CSD 1979; FCO 1981; Dacca 1982; SEA Floater 1985; Vice-Consul Istanbul 1986; Grade 9; m 1987 Lisa Elaine Walter.

Garner-Winship, Stephen Peter; Consul Rio de Janeiro since November 1991; born 26.10.56; FCO 1989; m 1978 Mary Carmel (1s 1979, 1d 1982).

Garnham, Sandra Jayne (née Hibbert); Rome since October 1992; born 15.9.68; FCO 1989; Grade 10; m 1992 Clive Julian Marcus Westbrook Garnham.

Garrett, Charles Edmund; Second Secretary JLG Hong Kong since February 1991; born 16.4.63; FCO 1987; Language Training 1988; Language Training Hong Kong 1989; m 1991 Veronique Frances Edmonde Barnes.

Garrett, Godfrey John, OBE (1982); Counsellor FCO since May 1992; born 24.7.37; FO 1961; Third Secretary Leopoldville 1963; Second

Secretary (Comm) Prague 1965; Second later First Secretary FO (later FCO) 1968; Buenos Aires 1971; FCO 1973; First Secretary later Counsellor Stockholm 1981; Bonn 1983; FCO 1988; Counsellor Prague 1990; m 1963 Elisabeth Margaret Hall (4s 1964, 1967, 1968, 1970; 1d 1974).

Garrett, Martin; Stockholm since May 1990; born 21.2.54; FCO 1974; Honiara 1976; Paris 1979; on loan to Hanslope Park 1981; Tripoli 1982; FCO 1984; Grade 9.

Garry, Josephine Mary; Kuala Lumpur since August 1990; born 7.7.69; FCO 1988; Grade 10.

Garside, Bernhard Herbert; Lagos since September 1990; born 21.1.62; FCO 1983; Masirah 1986; Dubai 1987; m 1989 Jennifer Susan Yard; Grade 9.

Garth, Andrew John; Floater Training since June 1992; born 28.9.69; Inland Revenue 1988; FCO 1988; Warsaw 1990; Grade 10.

Garvey, Kevin Andrew; Phnom Penh since February 1992; born 10.8.60; FCO 1978; Bangkok 1981; Hanoi 1985; Latin America Floater 1986; FCO 1988; Grade 9.

Gass, Simon Lawrence; First Secretary FCO since September 1987; born 2.11.56; FCO 1977; Lagos 1979; Second later First Secretary Athens 1984; m 1980 Marianne Enid Thwaites (1s 1986).

Gates, Helen Deborah; FCO since November 1990; born 31.1.67; Grade 9.

Gathercole, Michael Charles; OBE (1985); Consul Cleveland since February 1989; born 17.1.39; CRO 1962; Port of Spain 1962; Lagos 1966; Nairobi 1970; FCO 1972; Second Secretary 1973; Helsinki 1977; Jedda 1981; First Secretary FCO 1986; m Anne Park (2d 1963, 1968).

Gault, Jean José; Copenhagen since March 1992; born 15.10.45; FCO 1970; Madrid 1971; Warsaw 1974; Rome 1975; FCO 1977; Caracas 1980; Paris 1983; The Hague 1986; FCO 1988; Grade S1.

Gay, Arthur Ernest; First Secretary (Admin) Pretoria since August 1988; born 26.4.38; FO 1960; Bonn 1960; Muscat 1963; Caracas 1965; FCO 1969; Second Secretary (Comm) Bonn 1973; Stuttgart 1977; First Secretary FCO 1980; First Secretary (Admin) Lisbon 1982; First Secretary FCO 1985; m 1961 Margaret Rosalind Cundy (1s 1963; 1d 1966).

Gay, Peter Howard; First Secretary FCO since September 1991; born 15.4.39; COI 1961; CRO 1963; Kaduna 1963; Lagos 1965; Rio de Janeiro 1967; Second Secretary FCO 1971; Assistant Trade Commissioner later Vice-Consul (Comm) Toronto 1974; Second Secretary FCO 1975;

Second Secretary (Chancery) Port of Spain 1976; Grenada 1979; Second later First Secretary FCO 1980; First Secretary (Head of Chancery/Consul) Mogadishu 1983; Consul Oporto 1987; m (1) 1961 Marylea Elizabeth East (diss 1978) (3s 1962, 1964, 1969; 1d 1965); (2) 1987 Angela Susan Kettlety (2s 1988, 1989).

Gebicka, Anna Maria Teresa; Tokyo since July 1992; born 27.1.64; FCO 1990; Grade S3.

Geddes, Jonathan Paul; Madras since July 1990; born 3.9.65; FCO 1985; Rome 1987; Grade 9.

Gedge, Charles Steward; Second Secretary (Consular/Management) Calcutta since January 1992; born 14.8.39; Cairo 1964; Baghdad 1964; Benghazi 1967; Kuwait 1968; New York 1970; FCO 1972; Rio de Janeiro 1976; on loan to DOT 1982; Second Secretary FCO 1987.

Gedny, Philippa; Lisbon since May 1992; born 9.8.59; FCO 1977; Bonn 1979; Montevideo 1982; Antigua 1985; FCO 1987; Grade 9.

Gee, Alan Francis; Second Secretary FCO since July 1992; born 2.12.43; FO 1960; Tokyo 1967; Blantyre 1970; Nicosia 1973; FCO 1975; JAO Brussels 1978; Lagos 1981; Second Secretary FCO 1984; Second Secretary (Admin) Sofia 1988; m 1970 Wendy Rugman (1s 1973).

Gee, Mark Leonard; FCO since November 1991; norn 27.6.70; Grade 10.

Geere, Francis George; First Secretary (Comm) and Deputy Head of Mission Doha since February 1992; born 20.3.44; FO 1961; DSAO 1965; Rawalpindi 1965; Dacca 1966; Khartoum 1968; Bombay 1969; FCO 1973; MECAS 1975; Second Secretary and Consul Jedda 1976; Second Secretary (Inf) Berne 1980; Second Secretary FCO 1985; First Secretary (Comm) and Consul Kinshasa 1988; m (1) 1968 Julie Christine Lawrence (1s 1969; 1d 1971); (2) 1980 Rosalind Jessie Richards (1s 1984, 1d 1989).

Geeson, Paul; Attaché Moscow since May 1989; born 19.2.44; FCO 1970; St Helena 1972; FCO 1974; Darwin 1975; Kinshasa 1977; FCO 1979; Kingston 1984; Grade 9; FCO 1987; m (1) 1971 Janet Ann George (2s 1972, 1974); (2) 1983 Elaine Pybus.

Gemmell, Roderick; Second Secretary FCO since November 1991; born 19.8.50; POSB 1966; DSAO (later FCO) 1967; Bahrain 1971; Washington 1972; The Hague 1975; FCO 1979; Mbabane 1982; Stockholm 1984; Second Secretary (Comm/Econ) Ankara 1987; m 1975 Janet Bruce Mitchell (1d 1981).

George, Andrew Neil; First Secretary and Head of Chancery Bangkok since July 1988; born 9.10.52; Third Secretary FCO 1974; Third later Second Secretary Bangkok 1976; Second later

First Secretary FCO 1980; First Secretary Canberra 1984; m 1977 Watanalak Chaovieng (1d 1979; 1s 1982).

George, Robert Allan; Ankara since March 1992; born 14.9.36; Army 1955-57; RAF 1962-83; Sofia 1983; Nicosia 1984; Cairo 1986; Peking 1989; Budapest 1990; Grade SO; m 1957 Noreen Oliver (1s 1958; 4d 1959, 1960, 1961, 1963).

George, Sarah Jane; Brasilia since May 1992; born 31.1.68; FCO 1989; Grade S2.

George, Timothy John Burr, CMG (1991); HM Ambassador Kathmandu since October 1990; born 14.7.37; FO 1961; Hong Kong 1962; Second Secretary Peking 1963; FO 1966; First Secretary (Econ) New Delhi 1969; Assistant Political Adviser Hong Kong 1972; FCO 1974; Counsellor and Head of Chancery Peking 1978; Sabbatical at IISS 1981; Counsellor and Head of Chancery UKDEL OECD Paris 1982; Counsellor, FCO 1986; m 1962 Richenda Mary Reed (1s 1963; 2d 1965, 1967).

Gerken, Ian, LVO (1992); Deputy High Commissioner and Head of Chancery Valletta since August 1988; born 1.12.43; FO 1962; Budapest 1965; Buenos Aires 1966; FCO 1968; Vice-Consul Caracas 1971; FCO 1975; Second Secretary 1978; Second later First Secretary Lima 1979; First Secretary FCO 1985; m 1976 Susana Drucker (1 step d, 2s 1980, 1982).

German, Robert Charles; Third Secretary Kuala Lumpur since February 1990; born 17.1.58; FCO 1978; Masirah 1985; FCO 1986; Grade 8; m. 1982 Penelope Jane Cooper (2s 1986, 1989).

Gerrard, Anthony; Second Secretary (Management) Tokyo since January 1992; born 25.1.43; HM Forces 1960-70; FCO 1970; Bahrain 1972; Gaborone 1975; FCO 1979; Nicosia 1982; Second Secretary (Admin) Baghdad 1985; Second Secretary FCO 1989; m 1965 Rita Elaine van Heerden (1d 1965, 1s 1968).

Gerrish, Lynn Elaine; Paris since September 1991; born 15.5.58; FCO 1988; Grade S2A.

Gerson, John Henry Cary; Counsellor FCO since July 1992; born 25.4.45; Third Secretary FCO 1968; Hong Kong 1969; Singapore 1971; Second Secretary FCO 1973; First Secretary (Consul) Peking 1974; First Secretary FCO 1978; on loan to HCS 1978; First Secretary later Counsellor FCO 1979; Counsellor Hong Kong 1987; SUPL 1992; m 1968 Mary Alison Evans (1d 1969; 1s 1972).

Gething, David Philip, MBE (1991); Second Secretary (Management/Consular) Dubai since August 1991; born 2.3.46; FO 1965; Cairo 1968; Brussels (NATO) 1970; Moscow 1972; La Paz 1973; Tegucigalpa 1974; Budapest 1975; FCO

1977; Caracas 1979; Manila 1982; FCO 1985; Second Secretary Mogadishi 1990; m 1973 Carmen Noemi Obando (1d 1973).

Gibb, Fionna; FCO since September 1990; born 10.11.63; Grade 9.

Gibbins, Ian Paul; Second Secretary Bonn since January 1990; born 27.6.47; GPO 1963; FCO 1969; Washington 1975; FCO 1977; Brussels 1981; Third Secretary Prague 1984; Grade 7; m 1975 Rose Elizabeth Devlin (2s 1978, 1980; 1d 1983).

Gibbs, Andrew Patrick Somerset, OBE (1992); SUPL since February 1991; born 8.12.51; Third later Second Secretary FCO 1977; Vice-Consul, later Consul (Econ) Rio de Janeiro 1979; First Secretary FCO 1981; Language Training 1983; First Secretary Moscow 1984; First Secretary FCO 1985; First Secretary (Inf) Pretoria 1987; First Secretary FCO 1989; m 1981 Roselind Cecilia Robey (2d 1982, 1986; 2s 1983, 1990).

Gibbs, Timothy; FCO since September 1981; born 20.10.48; FO (later FCO) 1967; Beirut 1974; FCO 1976; Paris 1978; Grade 7; m 1978 Catherine D. MacDougall.

Gibson, Caroline; MVO (1990); Second Secretary (Management) Lusaka since September 1990; born 5.2.41; FO 1961; Ankara 1962; Bahrain 1965; FO (later FCO) 1967; Mexico City 1970; LA Floater 1973; Vice-Consul Budapest 1975; FCO 1975; Vice-Consul Hamburg 1978; FCO 1981; Second Secretary (Aid) Harare 1981; FCO 1985.

Gibson, Graeme Robert; Second Secretary FCO since December 1990; born 11.3.52; FCO 1971; Lagos 1974; Kinshasa 1975; Sofia 1978; FCO 1980; Dhaka 1981; Copenhagen 1984; Mbabane 1987; m (1) 1977 Marie Leota Pringle (2d 1978, 1980); (2) 1987 Pamela Ann O'Hanlon.

Gibson, John Stuart; Second Secretary FCO since January 1991; born 15.3.48; Commonwealth Office 1967; FCO 1969; Moscow 1970; Bonn 1972; Berne 1974; Helsinki 1975; FCO 1977; Cairo 1979; Riyadh 1983; Düsseldorf 1984; Dhaka 1987; m 1972 Grete Sandberg (2d 1975, 1977).

Gibson, Louise Anne; FCO since April 1990; born 20.4.40; Ankara 1962; Cairo 1965; FO 1966; Berlin 1968; Washington 1970; FCO 1972; Peking 1976; FCO 1978; Nairobi 1979; FCO 1982; Islamabad 1988; Grade 9.

Gibson, May Fyfe; First Secretary (Chancery/Information) The Hague since December 1991; born 23.2.40; FO 1962; Washington 1962; Moscow 1965; Lagos 1966; FCO 1968; Kingston 1970; Moscow 1973; FCO 1974; Vice-Consul (Comm) Hamburg 1981; Second Secretary (Comm) Luanda 1985; FCO 1987.

Gibson, Pamela Ann (née O'Hanlon); FCO since October 1990; born 27.9.56; FCO 1975; Geneva (UKMIS) 1978; Kuwait 1981; FCO 1983; Copenhagen 1984; SUPL 1987; Grade S2; m 1987 Graeme Robert Gibson.

Gibson, Robert Winnington; Second Secretary FCO since September 1989; born 7.2.56; FCO 1978; Jedda 1981; Second Secretary UKREP Brussels 1984; Second Secretary (Chancery/Inf) Port of Spain 1986.

Gifford, Michael John; Second Secretary FCO since March 1991; born 2.4.61; FCO 1981; Language Training 1982; Third Secretary (Comm); Abu Dhabi 1983; Second Secretary (Chancery) Oslo 1988; m 1986 Patricia Anne Owen (1d 1989, 1s 1991).

Gildea, John Joseph; FCO since April 1983; born 25.5.41; FO 1958; Bucharest 1963; Rio de Janeiro 1964; FO (later FCO) 1966; New York (UKMIS) 1969; Dar es Salaam 1972; Capetown1/Pretoria 1973; FCO 1976; Islamabad 1980; Grade 9; m 1968 Marilyn Brenda Carruthers (3d 1971, 1973, 1980; 1s 1978).

Giles, Alison Mary; Third later Second Secretary Pretoria since August 1990; born 15.9.64; FCO 1988.

Gill, Anne Frances; UKREP Brussels since March 1992; born 6.7.63; FCO 1988; East Berlin 1989; FCO 1990; Grade S2A.

Gill, Robin Michael; FCO since June 1982; born 3.3.38; CRO 1963; Salisbury 1964; CO 1965; Singapore 1967; FCO 1969; Geneva 1973; Valletta 1976; Accra 1979; Grade 9; m (1) 1962 Veronica Valerie Bolan (diss 1971) (2d 1964, 1967); (2) 1972 Irene May Sheppherd.

Gillett, Sarah, MVO (1986); Vice-Consul Los Angeles since July 1992; born 21.7.56; FCO 1976; SUPL 1978; FCO 1982; Washington 1984; Third later Second Secretary Paris 1987; Second Secretary on secondment to ODA 1990.

Gillham, Geoffrey Charles; First Secretary (Economic) UKDEL Paris since November 1991; born 1.6.54; FCO 1981; Second Secretary Caracas 1983; On loan to the Cabinet Office 1986; FCO 1988; First Secretary (Chancery) Madrid 1989; m 1991 Dr Nicola Mary Brewer.

Gillmore, Sir David (Howe) KCMG (1990); Permanent Under Secretary of State and Head of the Diplomatic Service since June 1991; born 16.8.34; HM Forces 1953-55; FCO 1970; First Secretary (Comm) Moscow 1972; Counsellor and Head of Chancery UKDEL MBFR Vienna 1975; Head of Defence Dept FCO 1979; AUSS FCO 1981; High Commissioner Kuala Lumpur 1983; DUSS (Americas/Asia) FCO 1986; CDA at Harvard University, then Paris 1990; m 1964 Lucile Sophie Morin (2s 1967, 1970).

Gillon, Angela May; FO (later FCO) since September 1964; born 27.9.41; Principal Research Officer; Senior Principal Research Officer in 1990; m 1966 Raanan Gillon (1d 1977).

Gilmore, Jean Doreen; FCO since April 1984; born 10.6.34; GPO 1961-73; Grade S3.

Gilmore, Julie Louise; FCO since September 1986; born 10.12.63; FCO 1981; Bridgetown 1984; Grade 9; m 1983 Brian Gilmore.

Gimblett, Jonathan James; Third later Second Secretary OECD Paris since September 1989; born 3.3.65; FCO 1988; m 1987 Elizabeth Marie Bauer.

Gingell, Colin John; Kiev since September 1992; born 5.3.45; Royal Marines 1966-88; Warsaw 1988; Madrid 1989; Grade SO; m 1964 Sandra Hall.

Girdlestone, John Patrick; Second Secretary FCO since May 1991; born 26.9.46; FO 1964; Khartoum 1968; Mexico City 1971; Cairo 1974; FCO 1976; MECAS 1978; Doha 1979; Madrid 1983; Second Secretary and Consul Al Khobar 1986; m 1975 Djihan Labib Nakhla (1d 1976).

Gladwin, Rob William; UKMIS Geneva since October 1992; born 21.3.64; Home Office 1987; FCO 1989; Grade 10; m 1992 Edwige Denise Danielle Foltête.

Glanfield, Helen Marie; Tokyo since July 1990; born 27.1.69; FCO 1988; Grade S2.

Glass, Colin; Vice-Consul Bahrain since July 1991; born 6.2.55; FCO 1973; Paris 1975; Luanda 1977; Warsaw 1978; Luanda 1981; Stockholm 1985; FCO 1988; Grade 9; m 1981 Ruth Kathleen Elizabeth Pearce (1s 1986).

Glaze, Michael John Carlisle, CMG (1988); HM Ambassador Addis Ababa since March 1990; born 15.1.35; HMOCS Lesotho 1959-70; retired as Deputy Permanent Secretary; Ministry of Finance, HCS (ECGD) 1971; First Secretary FCO 1973; First Secretary (Comm) Abu Dhabi 1975; Rabat 1978; Consul-General (Counsellor) Bordeaux 1980; HM Ambassador and Consul-General Yaoundé 1984; additionally HMA and Consul-General Central African Republic and Equatorial Guinea (non-resident) 1984; HM Ambassador Luanda 1987 and HMA (non-resident) Sao Tomé and Principe 1988; m 1965 Rosemary (2 step d 1954, 1961).

Gledson, Keith; FCO since July 1989; born 7.4.44; HM Forces 1960-70; FCO 1971; Singapore 1977; FCO 1979; Nicosia 1983; FCO 1985; Lusaka 1988; Grade 8; m 1973 Joan Davies.

Glover, Audrey Frances (née Lush); Legal

Counsellor FCO since April 1989; Assistant Legal Adviser FCO 1967; Resigned 1971; Reinstated 1983; Assistant Legal Adviser FCO 1983; First Secretary (Legal Adviser) BMG Berlin 1985; m 1971 Edward Charles Glover (2d 1973, 1976; 2s 1980, 1983).

Glover, Edward Charles, MVO (1976); First Secretary later Counsellor FCO since June 1989; born 4.3.43; Board of Trade 1962; FO 1966; Postgraduate University Research 1968-69; Third Secretary Canberra 1971; Second Secretary Washington 1973; Second later First Secretary FCO 1978; First Secretary FCO (Seconded Guinness Peat) 1980; First Secretary FCO 1983; BMG Berlin 1985; m 1971 Audrey Frances (née Lush) (2d 1973, 1976; 2s 1980, 1983).

Glover, Graham Dingwall; FCO since July 1992; born 14.8.68; FCO 1988; Peking 1989; Grade 9; m 1992 Joanne Whittle.

Glover, Joanne (née Whittle); FCO since July 1992; born 20.4.67; FCO 1986; Peking 1989; Grade 10; m 1992 Graham Dingwall Glover.

Glynn, Christopher Barry; First Secretary FCO since May 1992; born 23.12.49; FO (later FCO) 1967; Bonn 1971; Abidjan 1973; FCO 1975; Alexandria 1978; FCO 1982; Canning House 1983; Vice-Consul (Comm) São Paulo 1985; Second Secretary (Comm) Lisbon 1988; m 1988 Dr. Wilma Sereno Ballat.

Glynn, Vanessa Jane; SUPL since September 1990; born 5.8.60; FCO 1983; SUPL 1985; Second Secretary FCO 1987; Second Secretary (E Trade) UKREP Brussels 1988; First Secretary 1990; m 1984 Colin Thomas Imrie (1d 1985).

Godfrey, Ian David; FCO since August 1989; born 2.10.60; FCO 1980; Washington 1987; Grade 9.

Godfrey, Ronald; First Secretary FCO since November 1991; born 15.1.37; FO 1954; Royal Navy 1956-58; Kuwait 1958; Stockholm 1960; Reykjavik 1960; Luxembourg 1963; Vice-Consul Tegucigalpa 1966; FCO 1970; Beirut 1973; Vice-Consul (Comm) Casablanca 1976; Consul (Comm) 1978; Second Secretary FCO 1980; First Secretary (Aid) Yaoundé 1983; First Secretary and Consul Rome 1985; m 1964 Marie Suzanne Wentzel.

Godson, Anthony; First Secretary (Environment) UKMIS Geneva since August 1991; born 1.2.48; DSAO (later FCO) 1966; Bucharest 1970; Third Secretary Jakarta 1972; Private Secretary to the High Commissioner Canberra 1976; FCO 1979; Second Secretary 1980; Second later First Secretary UKMIS New York 1983; First Secretary (Comm) Kinshasa 1987; First Secretary FCO 1988; Deputy Head of Mission Bucharest 1990; m 1977 Marian Jane Margaret Hurst.

Golding, Terence Michael; FCO since April 1990; later Second Secretary 1992; born 26.7.49; FCO 1969; Washington 1973; Berne 1975; São Paulo 1978; FCO 1981; Budapest 1986; Kaduna 1988; m 1978 Irene Elizabeth Blackett.

Goldsmith, Simon Geoffrey; Paris since November 1992; born 23.1.69; FCO 1990; Grade 10.

Goldthorpe, Debra Kay; Second Secretary Budapest since September 1989; born 30.1.58; FCO 1977; Africa Floater 1981; New York 1982; Second Secretary FCO 1985; Language Training 1989; m 1989 Roger William Lamping.

Golland, Roger James Adam; First Secretary FCO since November 1992; born 8.5.55; FCO 1978; Third later Second Secretary Ankara 1979; FCO 1982; Language Training 1983; First Secretary Budapest 1984; FCO 1986; First Secretary Buenos Aires 1989; m 1978 Jane Lynnette Brandrick (2s 1985, 1987).

Gomersall, Stephen John; Counsellor FCO since April 1990; born 17.1.48; FCO 1970; Language Student Sheffield and Tokyo 1971; Third later First Secretary Tokyo 1972; FCO 1977; Private Secretary to Lord Privy Seal 1979; First Secretary Washington 1982; Counsellor (Econ) Tokyo 1986; m 1975 Lydia Veronica Parry (2s 1978, 1980; 1d 1982).

Gomme, Carol Elizabeth; SUPL since August 1992; born 31.5.66; FCO 1988; Full time language training 1990; Third Secretary (Chancery) Moscow 1990; Grade 9.

Gooch, Anthony John; First Secretary (Comm) Warsaw since May 1992; born 28.11.41; Second Secretary FCO 1970; SEATO Bangkok 1972; Second later First Secretary FCO 1974; First Secretary (Econ) Stockholm 1980; FCO 1983; First Secretary Pretoria 1984; First Secretary FCO 1988; Full-time Language Training 1991; m (1) 1966 Jennifer Jane Harrison (dec'd 1984) (1d 1968); (2) 1988 Cynthia Lee Barlow.

Goodall, Clare; Paris since September 1991; born 8.5.61; FCO 1982; Lima 1983; FCO 1986; Islamabad 1988; SUPL 1991; Grade S2; m 1987 David Spires (1s 1986).

Goodall, David Paul; Third Secretary (Commercial) Accra since September 1990; born 16.4.57; FCO 1976; Wellington 1978; Seoul 1981; SEA Floater 1985; FCO 1987; Grade 9.

Goodenough, Anthony Michael, CMG (1990); AUS (Africa) FCO since March 1992; born 5.7.41; Third Secretary FO 1964; Second Secretary Athens 1967; Private Secretary to the Parliamentary Under-Secretary, FCO 1971 and to the Minister of State, FCO 1972; First Secretary (Econ) Paris 1974; FCO 1977; Counsellor on loan to Cabinet Office 1980; Head of Chancery

Islamabad 1982; Counsellor FCO 1986; High Commissioner Accra and concurrently HM Ambassador (non-resident) to Togo 1989; m 1967 Veronica Mary Pender-Cudlip (1d 1968; 2s 1970, 1979).

Gooderham, Peter Olaf; First Secretary (Econ) Riyadh since January 1990; born 29.7.54; FCO 1983; Second later First Secretary (Chancery) UKDEL NATO Brussels 1985; First Secretary FCO 1987; m 1985 Carol Anne Ward.

Goodman, Jacqueline Amanda; UKMIS Geneva since May 1992; born 2.2.62; FCO 1987; Grade S2.

Goodman, Sean Adrian; FCO since December 1990; born 19.3.64; FCO 1983; Riyadh 1989; Grade 10; m 1991 Sara Ashley Palmer.

Goodwin, Andrew John; Aden since December 1987; born 22.3.59; FCO 1978; Hong Kong 1980; Dhaka 1982; Africa/ME Floater 1984; Grade 9.

Goodwin, David Howard; Second Secretary FCO since November 1990; born 16.8.46; FO (later FCO) 1964; Budapest 1969; Kinshasa 1970; Montevideo 1973; FCO 1975; Moscow 1978; San Francisco 1980; FCO 1983; Second Secretary (Imm) New Delhi 1987; m 1968 Dorothea Thompson (2d 1970, 1976).

Goodwin, Michael Roy; FCO since June 1992; born 17.3.60; FCO 1981; Victoria 1983; FCO 1987; Dublin 1987; Third Secretary (Aid) Banjul 1990; Grade 9; m 1983 Kerry Linda Graney (2d 1986, 1992).

Goodworth, Adrian Francis Norton; Second Secretary (Commercial) Jakarta since November 1992; born 6.7.53; FCO 1982; Seoul 1984; UKREP Brussels 1988 (Second Secretary 1989); Second Secretary FCO 1990; m (1) 1981 Caroline Ruth Steele (diss 1985); (2) 1987 Valerie Ann Chipchase (1s 1990).

Gordon, Diane Eily; Bogotá since March 1989; Second Secretary 1992; born 26.8.43; Lagos 1965; Ankara 1968; FCO 1970; Buenos Aires 1971; FCO 1974; Madrid 1978; FCO 1983; Bridgetown 1985.

Gordon, Jean Francois; First Secretary (Pol) Nairobi since January 1990; born 16.4.53; FCO 1979; Second, later First Secretary Luanda 1981; First Secretary UKDIS Geneva 1983; First Secretary FCO 1988; m Elaine Margeret Daniel (1d 1984).

Gordon, Robert Anthony Eagleson, OBE (1983); Deputy Head of Mission Warsaw since July 1992; born 9.2.52; FCO 1973; Language Student 1974; Third later Second Secretary Warsaw 1975; Second later First Secretary (Head of Chancery) Santiago 1978; First Secretary FCO

1983; First Secretary (Econ) UKDEL OECD Paris 1987; m 1978 Pamela Jane Taylor (2d 1980, 1981; 2s 1985, 1988).

Gordon, (Robert) Douglas; High Commissioner Georgetown since October 1990 and, additionally, HM Ambassador (non-resident) to Suriname; born 31.7.36; HM Forces 1955-57; FO 1957; Amman and FO 1958; MECAS 1959; Abu Dhabi 1961; Vienna 1963; Second Secretary (Comm) Kuwait 1966; Second Secretary FCO 1969; Second later First Secretary, Head of Chancery and Consul Doha 1973; Assistant to the Deputy Governor Gibraltar 1976; FCO 1979; Assistant Marshal of the Diplomatic Corps 1982; First Secretary (Comm) Washington 1984; Consul (Comm) Cleveland 1986; HM Ambassador (later Consul-General) Aden 1989; m (1) 1960 Margaret Bruckshaw (diss 1989) (1s 1961); m (2) 1990 Valerie Janet Brownlee.

Gordon, Robert Hugh, MBE (1980); Consul (Consular/Management) Chicago since March 1991; born 15.10.39; Royal Navy 1956-66; FO 1966; Delhi 1968; FCO 1970; Darwin 1972; FCO 1974; Lusaka 1976; Jakarta 1980; FCO 1983; Third Secretary Tel Aviv 1984; FCO 1986; Vice-Consul later Second Secretary (Chancery) Sofia 1988; m 1976 Heather Christine McCallum (1d 1978; 1s 1982).

Gordon-MacLeod, David Scott; First Secretary FCO since August 1991; born 4.5.48; ODA 1973; Mbabane 1978; Second, later First Secretary FCO 1983; First Secretary and Head of Chancery Maputo 1987; m 1988 Adrienne Felicia Maria Atkins.

Gore, Michael Edward John, CBE (1991); Governor Cayman Islands since September 1992; born 20.9.35; Army 1955-59; Ministry of Defence 1959; CRO 1963; Second Secretary Kota Kinabalu 1963; Commonwealth Office 1966; Head of Chancery and Consul Seoul 1967; Head of Chancery Montevideo 1971; First Secretary and Head of Chancery Banjul 1974; First Secretary FCO 1978; First Secretary (Consular) Nairobi 1981; DHC Lilongwe 1984; HM Ambassador and Consul-General Monrovia 1988; High Commissioner Nassau 1991; m 1957 Monica Marina Shellish (3d 1958, 1960, 1969).

Gore-Booth, The Hon David (Alwyn), CMG (1990); AUSS (Middle East) FCO since January 1989; born 15.5.43; FO 1964; MECAS 1964; Third Secretary Baghdad 1966; Third later Second Secretary Lusaka 1967; FCO 1969; Tripoli 1969; Second later First Secretary FCO 1971; First Secretary UKREP Brussels 1974; FCO 1978; Counsellor (Econ/Comm) Jedda 1980; Head of Chancery UKMIS New York 1983; Counsellor FCO 1987; m (1) 1964 Jillian Sarah Valpy (1s 1968); (2) 1977 Mary Elizabeth Janet Gambetta (née Muirhead).

Gorham, Robin Stuart; DHM, Minister/Counsellor Lagos/Abuja since April 1991; born 15.2.39; CRO 1961; Third Secretary Ottawa 1962; Second Secretary (Econ) Bonn 1965; FO 1967; Private Secretary to the Parliamentary Under-Secretary of State FCO 1968; First Secretary Tokyo 1970; First Secretary (Econ/Comm) Accra 1974; First Secretary FCO 1978; Head of Chancery Helsinki 1980; Deputy High Commissioner and Head of Chancery Lusaka 1983; RCDS 1987; Counsellor FCO 1988; (1) m 1966 Barbara Fechner (diss 1990) (3d 1966, 1969, 1976); (2) 1991 Joanna Bradbury.

Goring, Rebecca Eve; FCO since January 1991; born 12.6.72; Grade 10.

Gosling, James Marshall; Helsinki since August 1989; born 26.3.33; HCS 1957-79; The Hague 1979; Peking 1980; Washington 1981; Moscow 1984; UKDEL NATO Brussels 1985; Sofia 1988; Grade SO; m 1955 Frances Mary Tombs (2s 1958, 1960).

Gosling, Keith Rutherford, OBE (1983); First Secretary FCO since February 1990; born 18.3.44; Second Secretary FCO 1973; First Secretary Singapore 1975; FCO 1977; IAEA Vienna 1978; First Secretary FCO 1982; First Secretary Manila 1986; m 1965 Nadina Susan Perry (2d 1973, 1976).

Gosling, Sarah Elaine; Bonn since June 1992; born 29.7.69; FCO 1990; Grade S2.

Goss, Norman Ernest; FCO since August 1986; born 7.11.49; FO (later FCO) 1966; Singapore 1974; FCO 1976; Canberra 1981; Third Secretary Brussels 1984; Grade 8; m 1971 Susan Mary Eaton (2s 1973, 1975; 1d 1978).

Gostick, Peter Francis; FCO since September 1991; born 8.4.35; FO 1965; Peking 1968; FCO 1969; Tehran 1971; FCO 1973; Lagos 1976; FCO 1978; Hanoi 1979; FCO 1980; Darwin 1980; Sofia 1984; FCO 1987; Kampala 1988; Grade 8; m 1980 Elaine Violet Lindstrom.

Gough, Heather Jean (née Rippeth); Tehran since July 1992; born 28.6.60; FCO 1987; Bonn 1989; Grade S2; m 1988 Kevin Gough.

Gould, Clive Anthony; Second Secretary BM Berlin since March 1990; born 28.6.44; GPO 1960; FO 1968; Brussels 1970; FCO 1972; Vienna 1973; FCO 1976; Budapest 1979; FCO 1982; Hong Kong 1983; Second Secretary FCO 1986; m 1969 Barbara Sheila Austin (1s 1972).

Gould, David Christopher; Washington since March 1982; born 31.12.55; FCO 1976; Grade 8; m 1977 Susan Kensett (2d 1975, (step d) 1980).

Gould, Tina Louise; FCO since January 1991; born 7.6.70; Grade S2.

Goulden, Katherine Lucy; FCO since September 1991; born 20.6.67; Grade 9.

Goulden, (Peter) John, CMG (1989); HM Ambassador Ankara since October 1992; born 21.2.41; Third Secretary Ankara 1963 (Second Secretary 1966); FO (later FCO) 1967; Manila 1969; Second later First Secretary FCO 1971; First Secretary (EEC) and Head of Chancery Dublin 1976; Assistant Head (NATO) of Defence Department FCO 1979; Counsellor 1980; Head of Personnel Services Dept 1980; Head of News Dept FCO 1982; Head of Chancery UKREP Brussels 1984; AUSS (Defence) FCO 1988; m 1962 Diana Margaret Elizabeth Waite (1s 1967; 1d 1970).

Goulding, Marrack Irvine, CMG (1983); SUPL with UN Secretariat, New York since January 1986; born 2.9.36; MECAS 1959; Third later Second Secretary Kuwait 1961; Second later First Secretary FO 1964; First Secretary and Head of Chancery Tripoli 1968; Cairo 1970; Private Secretary to Minister of State FCO 1972; On loan to the Cabinet Office (Central Policy Review Staff) 1975; Counsellor Lisbon 1977; Counsellor and Head of Chancery UKMIS New York 1979; HM Ambassador Luanda and additionally Ambassador (non-resident) to Sao Tome and Principe 1983; CDA at St Antony;s, Oxford 1985; m 1961 Susan Rhoda D'Albiac (1d 1963; 2s 1964, 1967).

Goulty, Alan Fletcher; Deputy Head of Mission Cairo since September 1990; born 2.7.47; Third Secretary FCO 1968; MECAS 1969; Third later Second Secretary Beirut 1971; Khartoum 1972; Second later First Secretary FCO 1975; On loan to the Cabinet Office 1977; Washington 1981; First Secretary later Counsellor FCO 1985; m (1) 1968 Jennifer Wendy Ellison (1s 1970); (2) 1983 Lillian Craig Harris.

Govier, Jane Elizabeth Mary; Second Secretary FCO since March 1992; born 21.3.62; FCO 1984; Language Training 1986; Third Secretary (Comm) Peking 1987; Vice-Consul (Management) Istanbul 1990; Presidency Liaison Officer Luxembourg 1990 (Second Secretary 1991).

Gowan, Davĭd John; Counsellor (Commercial) Moscow since February 1992; born 11.2.49; Ministry of Defence 1970; HCS 1973; Second Secretary FCO 1975; Second later First Secretary (Comm) Moscow 1977; First Secretary FCO 1981; Head of Chancery and Consul Brasilia 1985; on loan to the Cabinet Office 1988; FCO 1989; On loan to the Cabinet Office 1990; m 1975 Marna Irene Williams (2s 1978, 1982).

Gowlland, George Mark, LVO (1979); Counsellor (Political and Management) Rome since February 1990; born 24.2.43; Third Secretary FO 1964; Warsaw 1965; Third later Second Secretary Accra 1967; Lomé 1969; FCO 1970; First

Secretary (Inf) Kuala Lumpur 1973; First Secretary (Comm/Consular) Dubai 1976; First Secretary FCO 1980; Counsellor, Head of Chancery and Consul-General, Algiers 1983; Counsellor, FCO 1986; m 1967 Eleanor Julia Le Mesurier (2s 1968, 1971; 1d 1976).

Gozney, Richard Hugh Turton; APS later PPS to the Secretary of State, FCO, since January 1989; born 21.7.51; FCO 1973; Third Secretary Jakarta 1974; Second later First Secretary Buenos Aires 1978; FCO 1981; Head of Chancery Madrid 1984; m 1982 Diana Edwina Baird (2s 1987, 1990).

Gracey, Colin; FCO since August 1992; born 25.3.47; FCO 1965; Anguilla 1969; Lima 1971; Bombay 1974; FCO 1976; La Paz 1979; FCO 1983; UKMIS Geneva 1986; Islamabad 1989; Grade 9; m 1972 Mercedes Ines Rosenthal (1d 1973; 1s 1977).

Graham, Alison Forbes; Paris since August 1990; born 24.8.59; FCO 1980; East Berlin 1982; FCO 1984; Ottawa 1987; Grade S2.

Graham, David Frank; Second Secretary (Comm/Econ) Berlin since October 1992; born 27.6.59; FCO 1978; Munich 1982; LA Floater 1985; Language Training 1987; Warsaw 1987 (Second Secretary 1990); FCO 1991; m 1990 Anne Marie D'Souza.

Graham, Iain George; Cairo since December 1991; born 1.3.70; FCO 1989; Grade 10.

Graham, Richard Michael John Ogilvie; SUPL since July 1992; born 4.4.58; FCO 1985; Second later First Secretary Nairobi 1986; First Secretary Trade Commissioner (China Trade) and Consul Macau, BTC Hong Kong 1989.

Graham, Robert Glenn; Second Secretary Montevideo since July 1988; born 2.7.40; MOD 1962-69; FCO 1969; Cyprus 1973; FCO 1974; m 1964 Sally Ann Miles (2s 1966, 1967; 1d 1970).

Graham, Steven; FCO since March 1989; born 8.7.68; Grade 9; m 1991 Pauline Lannie.

Graham, Victoria Alexandra; FCO since July 1992; born 24.4.63; FCO 1982; Canberra 1985; FCO 1988; Caracas 1989; Grade 9.

Grainger, David Quentin; Lusaka since October 1992; born 2.2.69; FCO 1990; Grade 10.

Grainger, John Andrew; First Secretary (Legal Adviser) FCO since April 1991; born 27.8.57; called to the Bar (Lincoln's Inn) 1981; Assistant Legal Adviser FCO 1984; First Secretary (Legal Adviser) BMG (later BM) Berlin 1989.

Grainger, Susan Carol; UKMIS New York since August 1989; born 17.6.67; FCO 1987; Grade S2; m 1991 Angus James Robert Steele.

Grant, Ann; Counsellor (ECOSOC) UKMIS New York since August 1992; born 13.8.48; FCI 1971; Calcutta 1973; FCO 1975; on loan to the Department of Energy 1976; First Secretary FCO 1979; Head of Chancery and Consul Maputo 1981; FCO 1984; First Secretary (Energy) UKREP Brussels 1987; resigned 1989; Communications Director OXFAM 1989-91; reinstated FCO 1991.

Grant, Fiona Dorothy; Kuala Lumpur since October 1992; born 7.11.59; FCO 1985; Lagos 1988; FCO 1990; Grade S2.

Grant, John Douglas Kelso; First Secretary (Press) UKREP Brussels since September 1989; born 17.10.54; FCO 1976; Stockholm 1977; Language Training 1980; Moscow 1982; FCO 1984; Resigned 1985; Reinstated 1986; First Secretary FCO 1986; m 1983 Anna Lindvall (1d 1987).

Granville, Christopher Richard; Second Secretary (Chancery) Moscow since October 1991; born 5.3.63; FCO 1989; Language Training 1990; m 1988 Brigitte Deloy (1s 1988).

Gray, Douglas Macdonald; First Secretary (Comm) Seoul since September 1989; born 13.3.54; FCO 1975; Far East Floater 1978; Istanbul 1980; Second Secretary Yaoundé 1983; Second Secretary FCO 1986; m 1980 Alison Ann Hunter (1d 1985).

Gray, John Charles Rodger; First Secretary FCO since February 1989; born 12.3.53; Third Secretary FCO 1974; Language training 1975; Third later Second Secretary Warsaw 1976; FCO 1979; First Secretary FCO 1981. First Secretary UKDEL OECD Paris 1983; on loan to Cabinet Office 1987; m 1988 Anne-Marie Lucienne Suzanne de Dax d'Axat.

Gray, John Walton David, CMG (1986); HM Ambassador Brussels since June 1992; born 1.10.36; HM Forces 1954-56; MECAS 1962; Political Officer Bahrain Agency 1964; Second later First Secretary FO (later FCO) 1967; UKMIS Geneva 1970; Head of Chancery Sofia 1974; Counsellor Commercial, Jedda 1978; Head of Chancery, Jedda 1980; Head of MAED, FCO 1982; HM Ambassador Beirut 1985; UK Permanent Representative OECD Paris 1988 (with personal rank of Ambassador); m 1957 Anthoula Nicolau Yerasimou (2d 1961, 1963; 1s 1971).

Gray, Trudi Elisabeth Mary; Lisbon since August 1992; born 19.7.47; FCO 1978; Buenos Aires 1979; Prague 1982; Port Stanley 1984; Nassau 1985; Lima 1988; Grade S2.

Grayson, William Edward, MBE (1992); Third Secretary Moscow since January 1991; born 11.2.46; FCO 1971; St Helena 1972; FCO 1974; New Delhi 1980; FCO 1983; Peking 1985;

Jakarta 1986; FCO 1989; Cairo 1989; m 1968 Sharon Edith Limmer (3d 1969, 1972, 1977).

Greany, John Terence; FCO since November 1981; born 30.3.42; FO 1961; Singapore 1965; FCO 1967; Rawalpindi 1968; FCO 1970; Nairobi 1975; FCO 1978; Darwin 1979; Grade 8; m 1973 Maria Ann Cushen (2s 1975, 1978).

Greatrex, Avril; Second Secretary (Management) and Vice-Consul Buenos Aires since April 1991; born 17.4.47; DSAO (later FCO) 1967; Kuwait 1971; Lagos 1973; Latin America Floater 1976; FCO 1979.

Greaves, Geoffrey; Resident Representative St Vincent and the Grenadines since April 1988; First Secretary 1989; born 13.6.36; FO 1965; Rome 1966; Tripoli 1969; Athens 1971; FCO 1974; Africa Floater 1976; Cape Town 1978; Second Secretary FCO 1981; DHC Victoria 1984; m 1960 Margaret Eileen Thompson (2d 1967, 1968).

Greavett, Marianne; Islamabad since March 1991; born 7.10.69; FCO 1988; Athens 1989; Grade 9.

Green, Alan Stanley, OBE (1987), MVO (1975); First Secretary, Director of Trade Promotion in Central America, San José, since October 1991; born 28.8.41; HO 1960; DSAO 1966; Washington 1967; Amman 1970; Lahore 1971; Second Secretary Mexico City 1972; Second Secretary FCO 1978; on loan to DOT 1979; First Secretary and Consul (Comm) Tel Aviv/Jerusalem 1982; First Secretary FCO 1987; on loan to Rank Xerox 1987; First Secretary FCO 1989; m 1969 Suzanne Mary Holl (1s 1971; 1d 1976).

Green, Andrew Fleming, CMG (1991); HM Ambassador Damascus since February 1991; born 6.8.41; HM Forces 1962-65; Third Secretary Diplomatic Service (CRO) 1965; MECAS 1966; Aden 1968; Abu Dhabi 1970; First Secretary FCO 1972; Private Secretary to Minister of State FCO 1975 and Parliamentary Under-Secretary of State 1976, First Secretary UKDEL OECD Paris 1977; FCO 1979; Counsellor Washington 1982; Head of Chancery Riyadh 1985; Counsellor FCO 1988; m 1968 Catherine Jane Churchill (1d 1970; 1s 1973).

Green, Andrew Philip; Third Secretary Tokyo since June 1989; born 12.5.58; FCO 1975; Moscow 1982; FCO 1984; Grade 8; m 1982 Susan Mary Merry.

Green, Colin Harvey; UKMIS New York since March 1992; born 22.5.69; FCO 1989; Grade 10.

Green, Derek John; Sofia since October 1980; born 16.2.23; RAF 1941-72; Paris 1972; East Berlin 1974; Tel Aviv 1975; Athens 1978; Grade SO; m 1950 Margery Edith (2s 1953, 1954).

Green, Frances Moira; FCO since April 1991; born 29.4.48; Washington 1975; Georgetown 1977; The Hague 1981; FCO 1984; Maseru 1987; Grade S2.

Green, Helen; FCO since July 1990; born 5.9.71; Grade S2.

Green, Keith William; Second Secretary (Chancery) Buenos Aires since November 1992; born 14.2.64; FCO 1990.

Green, Kelvin Edward; Lilongwe since April 1990; born 19.1.63; Inland Revenue 1981; FCO 1982; Washington 1984; Kampala 1987; Grade 9; m 1984 Gillian Mary Lewis.

Green, Michael; Third Secretary Lusaka since November 1989; born 9.12.40; FCO 1982; UKDEL Brussels 1986; FCO 1988; Grade 8.

Green, Muriel Ruth (née Bailey); FCO since October 1984; born 13.6.49; WRAF 1971-75; FCO 1975; Mexico City 1976; Islamabad 1982; Grade S2; m 1981 William Charles Green (1s 1984).

Green, Noel Frank; First Secretary (Management/Cons) Stockholm since February 1990; born 8.1.49; FCO 1968; Jedda 1971; Brussels (Embassy) 1974; Private Secretary to the Ambassador, UKDEL NATO Brussels 1975; FCO 1977; Second Secretary 1977; Second Secretary (Comm) Lagos 1981; Second Secretary (Admin) Moscow 1985; First Secretary FCO 1987; m 1984 Kerstin Anita Maria Höijer.

Green, Richard Charles Benedict, MBE (1983); First Secretary FCO since November 1990; born 2.5.49; FCO 1971; Kuwait 1975; FCO 1977; Ankara 1978; FCO 1979; Second Secretary Beirut 1980; Second Secretary FCO 1982; Second Secretary (Chancery) Pretoria 1985; Second later First Secretary (Chancery) Bangkok 1988.

Green, Steven John; Third Secretary UKDIS Geneva since January 1989; born 17.5.55; HM Customs and Excise 1972-74; FCO 1974; Peking 1976; Stockholm 1978; SUPL 1980; FCO 1983; Lilongwe 1985; Grade 9; m 1978 Ulla Marianne Nilsson (1s 1980; Twin d 1986).

Greenall, Paula Jane (née Flann); Harare since October 1990; born 22.3.64; FCO 1984; Bangkok 1987; Grade S2; m 1989 Peter Vincent Greenall.

Greene, Bernadette Theresa; UKDEL Geneva since March 1991; born 17.4.66; FCO 1988; Grade S2A.

Greene, Susan Jennifer; Washington since July 1991; born 7.9.57; FCO 1980; New Delhi 1982; FCO 1986; Pretoria/Capetown 1987; Grade S1.

Greenfield, Michael Darren; Colombo since April 1992; born 21.3.70; FCO 1989; Grade 10.

Greengrass, John Kenneth; Kuala Lumpur since November 1989 (Second Secretary 1991); born 19.7.53; Ministry of Housing and Local Government 1970; FCO 1971; UKREP Brussels 1975; Washington 1978; Islamabad 1981; FCO 1983; Lagos 1986; m 1975 Marian Cecilia Williams (3d 1981, 1983, 1986).

Greenlee, James Barry; Second Secretary FCO since October 1989; born 21.12.45; FO (later FCO) 1963; Vienna 1969; Tokyo 1971; FCO 1974; Calcutta 1979; Second Secretary (Admin) and Consul Budapest 1983; Second Secretary (Comm) Lagos 1986; m 1971 Amanda Jane Todd (2d 1979, 1981).

Greenstock, Jeremy Quentin, CMG (1991); Deputy Political Director and AUSS (Western and Southern Europe) FCO since March 1990; born 27.7.43; Second Secretary FCO 1969; MECAS 1970; Second later First Secretary Dubai 1972; First Secretary (Private Secretary to the Ambassador) Washington 1974; FCO 1978; Counsellor (Comm) Jedda (later Riyadh) 1983; Head of Chancery Paris 1987; m 1969 Anne Ashford Hodges (2d 1970, 1975; 1s 1973).

Greenstreet, Michael John; Deputy High Commissioner Accra since February 1991; born 8.6.39; Colonial Office 1956; Brunei 1963; CRO 1964; Zomba 1964; DSAO (later FCO) 1967; Moscow 1970; New Delhi 1971; Commercial Training Post Sydney 1973; Second Secretary 1974; Vice-Consul (Comm) Melbourne 1974; Second later First Secretary FCO 1978; HM Consul Los Angeles 1982; First Secretary (Administration) Dhaka 1985; First Secretary (Immig) and Consul Dhaka 1986; First Secretary FCO 1989; (2d 1967, 1969).

Greenwood, Christopher Paul; Second Secretary FCO since April 1992; born 22.4.53; FCO 1973; Islamabad 1975; Moscow 1977; Manila 1980; FCO 1982; APS to Secretary of State 1982; Los Angeles 1985; Budapest 1988; (Second Secretary 1989); m 1976 Dorothy Gwendolyn Margaret Hughes (1s 1983; 1d 1988).

Greenwood, James Albert; Brasialia since March 1991; born 12.5.37; Kuala Lumpur 1981; Moscow 1982; Tel Aviv 1984; Sofia 1986; New York 1988; Grade SO; m 1966 Elizabeth Anderson (1s 1967).

Greenwood, Jeremy David; FCO since September 1991; born 1.10.70; Grade 10.

Gregg, Colin Arthur; FCO since August 1988; born 13.3.43; FO 1960; Port-au-Prince 1964; Nicosia 1966; Brasilia 1970; Rio de Janeiro 1972; FCO 1974; Second Secretary (Admin) and Vice-Consul Yaoundé 1976; Second Secretary FCO 1978; on secondment to the Development Commission 1986; m 1964 Dorothy Atkins (1d 1966; 1s 1969).

Gregory-Hood, Peter Charles Freeman; Consul-General Casablanca since July 1990; born 12.12.43; Third Secretary CRO 1965; Dakar 1967; Third later Second Secretary Tel Aviv 1969; Second later First Secretary FCO 1972; Paris 1976; First Secretary FCO 1981; First Secretary (Info) New Delhi 1986; m 1966 Camilla Bethell (2d 1968, 1970).

Gregson, Stuart Willens; First Secretary (Information) Rome since September 1991; born 26.4.50; FO (later FCO) 1966; Cairo 1971; Yaoundé 1973; Islamabad 1976; FCO 1978; Gaborone 1982; Vice-Consul Johannesburg 1983; Second Secretary FCO 1987; (First Secretary 1989); m 1976 Anne-Christine Wasser (1d 1976; 1s 1979).

Greig, Rosalind Philippa, Third Secretary Bangkok since January 1992; born 16.4.66; FCO 1989; Grade 9.

Grennan, Gemma Brigid Anne; FCO since September 1986; born 4.7.43; FO 1962; Vientiane 1967; Singapore 1969; Brussels 1971; Special leave 1973; Addis Ababa 1974; FCO 1977; Islamabad 1981; FCO 1983; Ottawa 1984; Grade 9; m 1973 Christopher Roy Heaven (1s 1981).

Gribben, Stephanie Ann (née Smith); FCO since March 1992; born 16.2.65; FCO 1986; Madrid 1988; SUPL 1989; Grade S2; m 1989 Dr Andrew Gribben.

Grice, Philip William, LVO (1991); Consul (Commercial) Miami since September 1990; born 19.1.41; County Courts Branch of Lord Chancellor;s Department 1957; FO 1958; Havana 1962; Monrovia 1965; Bonn 1967; FCO 1969; Khartoum 1972; Nairobi; 1973; Colombo 1973; FCO 1976; Islamabad 1977; Second Secretary FCO 1980; Second Secretary (Comm) Canberra 1983; Consul (Comm) Perth 1985; First Secretary FCO 1988; m 1977 Judith Claire Reeves (3s 1978, 1980, 1988; 2d 1981, 1984).

Griffin, Ryan John; FCO since February 1991; born 9.4.72; Grade 10.

Griffiths, Ralph John; OBE (1985); Deputy Consul-General and Consul (Comm) Milan since July 1989; born 14.5.33; Inland Revenue 1950; RAF 1952-54; HO 1956; Second Secretary DSAO 1967; Moscow 1969; Second Secretary (Comm) Seoul 1973; First Secretary FCO 1977; Holy See 1982; First Secretary (Comm) Warsaw 1985; m 1965 Pamela Evelyn Culver (3d 1966, 1967, 1971; 1s 1976).

Griffiths, Trudy Maureen; FCO since May 1991; born 10.9.70; Grade S2.

Griggs, Kenneth John; FCO since March 1992; born 2.9.61; FCO 1984; Washington 1985; FCO 1988; Athens 1989; Grade 8; m 1986 Leisa Jayne (2d 1988, 1991).

Grime, Ann Kathleen (née Jenkins); Luxembourg since November 1990; born 18.6.51; FCO 1975; Muscat 1976; FCO 1978; Moscow 1979; UKREP Brussels 1981; Resigned 1983; Reinstated 1988; Bucharest 1988; Islamabad 1989; FCO 1990; Grade S2; m 1983 Stephen Howard Grime.

Grimes, Susan (née Metcalfe); Copenhagen since March 1990; born 2.10.65; FCO 1987; Grade S3A; m 1989 Jason Richard Grimes.

Gristock, Frances Lorraine (née Alexander); Second Secretary (Comm/Consular) Victoria since March 1992; born 21.7.59; FCO 1981; SE Asia Floater 1983; FCO 1985; Third Secretary Quito 1986; FCO 1990; SUPL 1991.

Grover-Minto, Helen Katherine (née Grover); Lagos later Abuja since April 1992; born 18.4.65; FCO 1986; Addis Ababa 1988; FCO 1991; Grade S2; m 1991 John Minto.

Grover, John Albert; FCO since February 1984; born 27.1.35; HM Forces 1954-56; FO 1964; Washington 1967; Tehran 1970; Moscow 1974; FCO 1976; Tel Aviv 1981; Grade 7; m 1967 Ann Venetia Simpson (2s 1969, 1971).

Groves, Eliot Siôn; FCO since November 1988; born 17.7.69; FCO 1988; Grade 10.

Growcott, Michael William; First Secretary (Management) Brussels since April 1990; born 15.11.48; FCO 1968; Kampala 1972; Peking 1974; Pretoria 1975; FCO 1978; Assistant to Governor Port Stanley 1979; Second Secretary (Inf/Aid/Econ) Kuala Lumpur 1982; Second Secretary FCO 1986; m 1971 Avril Heather Kemp (2d 1972, 1976; 1s 1974).

Guckian, Alison Clare (née Parker); FCO since April 1990; born 16.5.52; FCO 1982; Jedda 1984; SE Asia Floater 1988; Grade 9; m 1991 Michael Joseph Guckian.

Guckian, Lorna Ruth (née Warren); FCO since August 1990; born 18.6.63; FCO 1983; Port Stanley 1986; Düsseldorf 1987; Africa/ME Floater 1989; Grade 9; m 1990 Noel Joseph Guckian (1d 1992).

Guckian, Noel Joseph; Second later First Secretary FCO since November 1988; born 6.3.55; FCO 1980; Consul (Comm) Jedda 1984; Second Secretary FCO 1987; Paris 1988; m 1990 Lorna Ruth Warren (1d 1992).

Gudgeon, Jonathan Roy; Vienna since July 1992; born 9.5.64; FCO 1984; Moscow 1988; Grade 8; m 1988 Lisa Anne Forte (1s 1992).

Gudgeon, Simon Peter; Moscow since January 1992; born 8.2.66; FCO 1982; Lagos 1987; Grade 8.

Guest, Melville Richard John; Counsellor
Consul-General and Head of Chancery
Stockholm since February 1990; born 18.11.43;
Third Secretary Commonwealth Office 1966;
Third later Second Secretary Tokyo 1967;
Second later First Secretary FCO 1972; Private
Secretary to Parliamentary Under Secretary of
State 1973; First Secretary (Comm) Paris 1975;
FCO 1979; SUPL 1980; Counsellor (Comm)
Tokyo 1986; m 1970 Beatriz Eugenia Lopez
Colombres (4s 1971, 1973, 1974, 1978).

Guest, William Robert; First Secretary Hong
Kong since September 1990; born 5.4.41;
Army 1966-80; Second Secretary FCO 1980;
Hong Kong 1984; FCO 1986; m 1964
Catherine Anne Campbell Ferguson (1d 1968).

Guina, Thomas Noel, MVO (1983); Deputy
Consul-General Toronto since January 1992;
born 21.12.36; Merchant Navy 1954-64; DWS
1964; Baghdad 1965; Diplomatic Service 1968;
FCO 1968; New York 1971; San Francisco
1972; FCO 1976; Warsaw 1979; Second
Secretary (Comm) Nairobi 1980; First Secretary
(Aid/Comm) Kampala 1984; First Secretary FCO
1988; m 1963 Philomena Leahy (1s 1964; 1d
1969).

Gunn, (née Podolier), Janet Frederica; FCO
since October 1985; born 4.10.48; FCO 1970;
SUPL 1976; FCO 1978; Moscow 1984; Principal
Research Officer; m 1975 Ian Gunn (diss 1979)
(1s 1976).

Gunnett, Martin John; Second Secretary Prague
since October 1990; born 1.4.50; FO 1967;
Darwin 1976; FCO 1978; Belgrade 1987; m
1973 Linda Leah (1d 1979, 1s 1981).

Gunson, Joyce Mary Beatriz; Santiago since
October 1990; born 8.4.64; FCO 1988; Panama
City 1989; Grade S2.

Gurney, Tim; Deputy Director and Consul
(Information) BIS New York since January 1991;
born 28.4.55; FCO 1973; Istanbul 1976; Karachi
1979; Montreal 1982; Second Secretary FCO
1985; Second Secretary (Chancery/Inf) Accra
1989; m 1976 Denise Elizabeth Harker (1d 1984;
1s 1986).

Guthrie, Norman James; FCO since November
1978; born 17.12.27; GPO 1944; HM Forces
1947-49; GPO 1949; FO 1954; Warsaw 1968;
FCO 1970; Second Secretary Bonn 1975; m
1963 Iris Violet Green (2d 1970, 1972).

Guy, Frances Mary; First Secretary FCO since
May 1991; born 1.2.59; FCO 1985; Language
Training 1987; Second Secretary (Chancery)
Khartoum 1988; m 1989 Guy Charles Maurice
Raybaudo.

Guy, John Westgarth, OBE (1986); High
Commissioner Port Moresby since July 1991;

born 17.7.41; CRO 1960; Karachi 1961; Calcutta
1964; New York (C-G) 1968; FCO 1970;
Moscow 1972; Jakarta 1974; Second Secretary
1975; Vice-Consul (Inf) São Paulo 1975; FCO
1977; On loan to the DOT 1979; First Secretary
Yaoundé 1981; First Secretary, Head of
Chancery and Consul Maputo 1984; First
Secretary FCO 1987; m 1961 Sylvia Kathleen
Stokes (1s 1962; 1d 1964).

Guymont, Sarah Jean; SUPL since June 1992; born
8.8.52; FCO 1975; Islamabad 1976; FCO 1977;
Moscow 1978; resigned 1980; reinstated FCO
1982; Africa/ME Floater 1983; FCO 1987; Dar es
Salaam 1989; Grade S1; m 1991 Frederick James
Guymont.

Gwynn, Diana Caroline (née Hamblyn); Third
Secretary (Aid) Nairobi since February 1992;
born 15.8.64; DOE 1986-89; FCO 1989; Grade
9; m 1988 Robert Charles Patrick Gwynn.

Gwynn, Robert Charles Patrick, Second
Secretary (Chancery/Inf) Nairobi since April
1992; born 17.3.63; Dept of Employment 1986-
88; FCO 1988; m 1988 Diana Carolline
Hamolyn.

H

Hackett, Anthony John; Oslo since October
1992; born 19.12.55; FCO 1975; Muscat 1977;
FCO 1981; Karachi 1981; FCO 1985; Manila
1988; Grade 9; m 1983 Nilofer Akbar (1d 1986).

Hackett, Paula Geraldine; FCO since November
1990; born 1.1.65; Grade 9.

Haddock, Michael Kenneth; First Secretary
(Commercial) Abu Dhabi since September
1991; born 25.9.50; FCO 1973; UKDEL
Geneva 1978; Moscow 1981; Kuwait 1983;
Second Secretary Damascus 1986; Second
Secretary (Commercial) Prague 1988; m 1972
Irene Doughty (1d 1979).

Hadley, Philippa Ann; Third Secretary
(Chancery) Ottawa since March 1991; born
3.8.62; FCO 1980; Brussels 1983; Bridgetown
1985; FCO 1989; Grade 9.

Hadley, William Gerard; FCO since April 1991;
born 6.11.70; Customs and Excise 1989; MOD
1990; Grade 10.

Hagart, Peter Richard; Consul and Deputy Head
of Mission Rangoon since February 1992; born
11.7.48; Department of Agriculture and Fisheries
for Scotland 1966; FCO 1969; Bucharest 1972;
Quito 1974; Bonn 1975; FCO 1977; FE Floater
1980; Hanoi 1982; Second Secretary (Admin)
and Vice-Consul Brasilia 1983; Second Secretary
FCO 1986; Second later First Secretary (Comm)
Bombay 1990.

Hagger, Philip Paul; Second Secretary (Comm) Riyadh since July 1989; born 5.9.50; FCO 1970; Singapore 1973; FCO 1974; Washington 1975; Nicosia 1978; Casablanca 1981; Lagos 1982; Second Secretary FCO 1987; m (1) 1971 Janet Mary Milnes (dec'd 1975) (1s 1972); (2) 1976 Julie Elizabeth Eastaugh (diss. 1988); (3) 1990 Linda Mary Parmegian; (1d 1977).

Haggie, Paul; First Secretary (Chancery) Pretoria since July 1989; born 30.8.49; Third Secretary FCO 1974; Second later First Secretary Bangkok 1976; FCO 1980; First Secretary (Econ) Islamabad 1982; First Secretary FCO 1986; m 1979 Deborah Frazer (1s 1984, 1d 1986).

Hague, John Keir; Second Secretary (Comm) Seoul since April 1992; born 26.3.47; CO (later FCO) 1966; Dakar 1970; Kuala Lumpur 1973; Munich 1975; Moscow 1977; FCO 1979; Houston 1983; Second Secretary Islamabad 1985; Second Secretary FCO 1989; m 1969 Julie Anne Knight (2d 1972, 1975).

Haigh, Trevor Denton; Moscow since June 1990; born 7.8.44; FCO 1982; Hong Kong 1985; FCO 1988; m 1977 Freda Mary Porritt.

Haig-Thomas, Hugo Alistair Christian; Second Secretary (Press and Information) Bonn since March 1992; born 22.5.47; FCO 1974; MECAS 1975; Language Training Amman 1976; Sana'a 1977; Vice-Consul Düsseldorf 1980; FCO 1982; Second Secretary on loan to ODA 1982; Second Secretary (Chancery) Copenhagen 1989.

Haines, David Michael; Full-time Language Training Cairo since June 1992; born 6.4.63; FCO 1989; Full-time Language Training 1991; Grade 7.

Haines, Paul Anthony; Jedda since November 1990; born 15.1.61; HCS 1980; FCO 1984; Warsaw 1986; Paris 1988; Grade 9.

Hainsworth, Margaret Kay (née Nattrass); Vice-Consul Geneva since January 1991; born 1.3.53; FCO 1972; Budapest 1975; Peking 1975; BMG Berlin 1976; Kampala 1979; FCO 1982; Islamabad 1986; Grade 9; m 1977 Gordon Hainsworth (1s 1985).

Halden, Theresa Victoria; Santiago since December 1990; born 31.10.66; FCO 1987; Grade S2.

Hale, Leslie David, OBE (1979); First Secretary later Counsellor FCO since April 1979; born 2.1.33; HM Forces 1951-53; Colonial Office 1953; HMOCS 1954-62; FO 1963; Hong Kong 1965; First Secretary FO (later FCO) 1967; Kuala Lumpur 1970; FCO 1974; First Secretary New Delhi 1977; m 1960 Susan Marion New (1s 1963; 2d 1961, 1966).

Haley, Anthony Peter; New Delhi since February

1991; born 14.3.59; RAF 1979; FCO 1988; Grade 8; m 1979 Elaine Cuthbertson; (3s 1979, 1982, 1985).

Hall, Andrew Rotely; Deputy Head of Mission and Consul Kathmandu since September 1991; born 3.5.50; SRO, FCO 1980; (PRO 1983); First Secretary New Delhi 1984; First Secretary FCO 1987; m 1973 Kathleen Dorothy Wright (2d 1973, 1978).

Hall, Brian John; UKMIS New York since January 1991; born 29.6.40; RAF 1958-67/71-87; Sofia 1989; Grade SO; m 1963 Lilian May (3d 1966, 1968, 1970).

Hall, Caroline Helen; FCO since May 1992; born 19.1.65; FCO 1987; Third later Second Secretary (Chancery) Oslo 1990; Floater Duties 1991; Grade 8.

Hall, James William, QGM (1974); Karachi since March 1992; born 20.9.49; Royal Marines 1966-89; Bucharest 1990; Grade SO.

Hall, James William David; Second Secretary (Commercial) New Delhi since June 1991; born 1.3.65; FCO 1987; Third later Second Secretary (Economic) Lusaka 1989.

Hall, John George; Second Secretary (Aid) Dar es Salaam since March 1989; born 7.8.51; FCO 1971; Pretoria/Capetown 1976; The Hague 1979; Nairobi 1982; FCO 1986; m (1)1974 Alison Margaret Eden (2s 1976, 1979); (2) 1990 Margaret Elizabeth Bell (1d 1991).

Hall, Martin Vivian; Second Secretary FCO since February 1991; born 10.11.50; FCO 1970; Singapore 1972; FCO 1974; Paris 1975; FCO 1977; Second Secretary (Chancery) Lagos 1989; Second Secretary (Commercial) Baghdad 1990; m 1972 Mary Rawkins (2s 1976, 1980; 1d 1987).

Hall, Mary Eleanor (née Ford); Lagos since April 1992; born 26.9.53; FCO 1978; Aden 1979; UKMIS Geneva 1980; Paris 1983; Ankara 1985; Warsaw 1988; Belgrade 1990; Grade S1; m 1983 Peter Henry Hall.

Hall, Michael Morden; First Secretary FCO since December 1988; born 26.3.42; COI 1969-73; FCO 1973; British Election Commission Rhodesia 1979-80; First Secretary (Chancery/Inf) The Hague 1984; (1s 1974; 1d 1977).

Hall, Peter Edward, CMG (1987); HM Ambassador Belgrade since November 1989; born 26.7.38; HM Forces 1956-58; FO 1961; Third later Second Secretary Warsaw 1962; Second Secretary New Delhi 1966; First Secretary FCO 1969; First Secretary Brussels (EEC) 1972; First Secretary FCO 1976; Counsellor (Econ1/Pol) Caracas 1977; Counsellor and Head of BIS, New York, and Deputy Consul-General 1978;

Counsellor Washington and Head of BIS 1981; Director of Research FCO 1983; Under-Secretary on loan to the Cabinet Office 1986; CDA at Stanford 1988; m 1972 Marnie Kay (1d 1973; 1s 1975).

Hall, Peter Henry; Belgrade since September 1990; born 22.5.40; RAF 1956-64; Paris 1983; Ankara 1985; Warsaw 1988; Grade SO; m 1983 Mary Eleanor Ford.

Hall, Rosalind Anita; FCO since October 1990; born 19.7.65; Grade S2A.

Hall, Rebecca-Jane Victoria; FCO since November 1990; born 27.2.68; Grade 9.

Hall, Simon Lee; on secondment to the DTI since September 1991; born 29.4.63; FCO 1982; Rome 1984; Hanoi 1986; Africa/Middle East Floater 1987; FCO 1990; Grade 9.

Hall, Simon Philip; Singapore since September 1990; born 29.5.70; FCO 1988; Grade 10; m 1991 Deborah Jane Hudson.

Hall, Thomas Mark; FCO since December 1985; born 15.9.47; HM Inspector of Taxes 1964; Commonwealth Office (later FCO) 1967; Tokyo 1970; FCO 1973; Milan 1979; Algiers 1981; Athens 1984; Grade 9.

Hallam, Helen Mary (née Clark); SUPL since February 1992; born 4.7.55; FCO 1973; Bonn 1975; Lima 1978; FCO 1981; Warsaw 1984; FCO 1985; Chicago 1988; FCO 1991; Grade 9; m 1986 Paul Hallam (1d 1990).

Hallett, David Arthur Cyril, LVO (1991), MBE (1980); Deputy Head of Mission La Paz since April 1992; born 16.2.37; GPO 1954; Air Ministry 1956; FO and Hamburg 1962; Moscow 1965; Latin America Floater 1967; Second Secretary (Comm) Budapest 1969; On attachment to East European Trade Council 1973; HM Vice-Consul Guatemala City 1976; Officer I/C St Lucia Office 1980; First Secretary FCO 1983; Consul (Commercial) Dallas 1986.

Hallett, Edward Charles; First Secretary FCO since September 1990; born 15.7.47; FCO 1971; Third Secretary Bonn 1972; PRO (DS Grade 5) 1975; Dublin 1984; FCO 1985; on loan to HCS 1988; m 1972 Audrey Marie Leader.

Halley, James Henry; Consul (Information) Milan since February 1991; born 27.5.53; FCO 1970; The Hague 1973; San José 1976; Vienna 1978; FCO 1980; Third later Second Secretary Seoul 1983; Second Secretary (Consular/Admin) Sana'a 1987; Second Secretary FCO 1989; m 1972 Patricia Catherine Bennett (1d 1977; 1s 1983).

Hall Hall, Alexandra Mary; Full time Language Training Bangkok since April 1989; Second

Secretary 1989; born 1.2.64; FCO 1986.

Hall-Hughes, Rita; On loan to Office of Fair Trading since February 1979; born 31.10.52; FCO 1972; Warsaw 1975; FCO 1976; Grade 10.

Halling, Kathleen (née Stevens); Brussels since September 1991; born 22.9.39; FCO 1984; Grade 10; m 1961 (2s 1964, 1970, 1d 1967).

Halliwell, Bernard, MBE (1981); First Secretary (Trade Promotion) Washington since August 1992; born 31.1.45; FO 1963; Salisbury 1967; Bahrain Residency 1969; Muscat 1970; FCO 1974; Ulan Bator, Geneva and Beirut 1973-74; Addis Ababa 1975; FCO 1975; Hong Kong 1977; Peking 1978; Second Secretary (Chancery/Inf) later (Admin/Cons) Bridgetown 1981; Second Secretary FCO 1985; First Secretary (Management) Bangkok 1988; m 1981 Vanessa Diane Brierley (3s 1984, 1986, 1989).

Hallsworth, Valerie; FCO since November 1988; born 9.11.48; Grade S2A.

Hallworth, Lisa; UKMIS Geneva since May 1991; born 29.7.65; FCO 1987; Madrid 1989; Grade S2A.

Halsey, Michael Deveral Kenhardt; First Secretary (Chancery) Riyadh since March 1990; born 23.10.43; MECAS 1962; Third Secretary FO 1966; Beirut 1968; Second Secretary Tripoli 1969; FCO 1970; Kuwait 1972; First Secretary FCO 1974; Dacca 1975; FCO 1977; First Secretary (Chancery) Berne 1980; First Secretary FCO 1984; m 1973 Jennifer Margaret Haldane (2d 1974, 1976).

Hamblett, Christine; Rome since March 1992; born 8.12.60; FCO 1990; Grade S2.

Hamer, Gillian Doreen; Third Secretary (Comm) Peking since July 1990; born 9.9.61; FCO 1981; Moscow 1983; UKREP Brussels 1984; FCO 1987; Grade 9.

Hamill, Brian William; Paris since July 1992; born 8.1.63; FCO 1981; Masirah 1983; Manila 1983; Grade 9; Budapest 1988; FCO 1989; m 1987 Katrina Lacson Puentevella (1d 1991).

Hamilton, Alasdair Alexander; FCO since May 1990; Born 13.4.71; Grade 10.

Hamilton, Charles Allan; Deputy Head of Mission Yaounde since July 1992; born 5.12.48; DSAO 1968; Vice-Consul Düsseldorf 1970; Third Secretary Prague 1973; Vice-Consul Phnom Penh 1974; Third later Second Secretary Cairo 1975; FCO 1979; Second Secretary Addis Ababa 1981; DHC and Head of Chancery Port Louis 1984; First Secretary FCO 1988.

Hamilton, Gaynor, Santiago since March 1992;

born 13.12.70; FCO 1989; Grade 10.

Hamilton, Jacqueline Ann (née Hopkins); FCO since March 1992; born 10.6.43; Kampala 1983; Amman 1986; SUPL 1989; Grade S2; m 1967 William Hamilton (1s 1968; 1d 1971).

Hamilton, John; UKDEL Brussels since March 1990; born 28.9.68; FCO 1988; Grade 10.

Hamilton, Josephine Anne Temple, MBE (1989); FCO since June 1989; born 15.6.45; FCO 1972; Georgetown 1974; FCO 1976; Ankara 1978; FCO 1982; Kingston 1986; Grade S2.

Hamilton, Leslie; Lagos since July 1990; born 3.12.32; Army 1952-71; Bucharest 1974; Ankara 1976; Kingston 1977; Mexico City 1979; Kampala 1980; Tripoli 1983; Jakarta 1984; Moscow 1985; Colombo 1987; East Berlin 1988; Grade CSO; m 1954 Margot Audrey Bradley (1d 1955; 2s 1956, 1958).

Hamilton, Roger Patrick; First Secretary (Chancery) Copenhagen since August 1989; born 27.5.48; FCO 1971; Second Secretary 1976; First Secretary Jakarta 1978; First Secretary Tokyo 1982; FCO 1983; on loan to the Hong Kong Government 1984; FCO 1986; m 1976 Linda Anne Watson.

Hamilton, William; First Secretary FCO since March 1992; born 13.9.41; Passport Office 1960; CRO 1961; Kuching 1963; Moscow 1966; Georgetown 1967; FCO 1970; Valletta 1974; Helsinki 1977; Second Secretary FCO 1980; Kampala 1983; Second later First Secretary (Comm) Amman 1986; First Secretary (Comm) Helsinki 1989; m 1967 Jacqueline Ann Hopkins (1s 1968; 1d 1971).

Hampson, Fiona Patricia; Santiago since June 1992; born 13.12.67; FCO 1987; Grade 10.

Hancock, Elsa Madeleine; Prague since December 1991; born 4.12.35; FO 1967; Calcutta 1968; Khartoum 1970; Cairo 1970; Inspectorate 1972; FCO 1976; SUPL at EC Brussels 1977; Floater 1981; FCO 1982; JLG Hong Kong 1988; Third Secretary Guatemala City 1989; Grade 9.

Hancock, Janet Catherine; FCO since August 1970; born 5.1.49; SRO 1975; PRO 1983; m 1973 Roger A Hancock (diss 1980).

Hancock, Michael John; FCO since January 1991; born 21.10.62; FCO 1982; Bonn 1984; Belgrade 1987; Islamabad 1989; Grade 9; m 1983 Elizabeth Alison Ormrod.

Hancock, Nicola Jane; Rome since February 1992; FCO 1989; born 30.7.66; Grade 9.

Hancon, John Anthony; FCO since July 1991; born 5.1.48; GPO 1965; FCO 1969; Kuala Lumpur 1971; FCO 1973; Paris 1976; FCO

1978; Sofia 1982; FCO 1984; Nicosia 1988; Grade 7; m 1970 Anne Lesley Hawke (1d 1975; 1s 1980).

Hand, Graham Stewart; First Secretary FCO since October 1990; born 3.11.48; HM Forces 1967-80; FCO 1980; Second later First Secretary Dakar 1982; First Secretary FCO 1984; Language Training 1987; First Secretary and Head of Chancery, Helsinki 1987; m 1973 Anne Mary Seton Campbell (1s 1979; 1d 1984).

Handley, David Thomas; Counsellor Cairo since July 1990; born 31.8.45; Second Secretary FCO 1972; MECAS 1974; First Secretary FCO 1976; First Secretary (Inf) Budapest 1978; FCO 1981; First Secretary and Chargé d'Affaires a.i. Guatemala City 1984; First Secretary FCO 1987; m (1) 1967 Lilian Duff (1s 1974; 1d 1975); (2) 1978 Susan Elizabeth Beale (2s 1980, 1982; 1d 1985).

Handley, Timothy Sean; Tel Aviv since July 1991; born 8.2.51; HCS 1969; FCO 1971; Abu Dhabi 1973; Stockholm 1976; Warsaw 1979; FCO 1981; Georgetown 1985; FCO 1986; Düsseldorf 1988; Grade 9; m 1985 Julie Anne Russell (1d 1989).

Hannaby, Bruce; First Secretary FCO since September 1990; born 20.5.35; Exchequer and Audit Department 1960; FO 1961; Dubai 1964; MECAS 1966; FO 1967; Baghdad 1968; FCO 1971; Copenhagen 1972; FCO 1975; Dubai 1976; Second later First Secretary FCO 1980; Consul Gothenburg 1984; FCO 1985; Consul Amsterdam 1986; m Mary Sheelah Elizabeth Wray (1d 1973; twin s 1976).

Hannah, Craig John; FCO since October 1990; born 2.6.63; Dept of Employment 1980; FCO 1983; Accra 1984; Sofia 1987; Grade 9.

Hannah, Jane Patricia; FCO since February 1989; born 23.9.70; Grade 10.

Hannah, Juliette Sarah; Second Secretary (Chancery) Peking since October 1992; born 29.6.66; FCO 1988; Full-Time Language Training Taiwan 1991.

Hannant, Michael Thomas Moss; First Secretary FCO since February 1991; born 21.11.42; CRO 1963; Dar es Salaam 1964; Karachi 1968; FCO 1972; Second Secretary (Admin/Chancery) Johannesburg 1974; Second Secretary (Comm) Tripoli 1980; First Secretary FCO 1982; First Secretary (Comm) The Hague 1986; m 1966 Penelope Rosann Butcher (1d 1969; 1s 1971).

Hannay, Sir David (Hugh Alexander), KCMG (1986), CMG (1981); UK Permanent Representative to the UN and UK Permanent Representative on the Security Council New York since August 1990 (holds personal rank of Ambassador); born 28.9.35; FO 1959; Tehran 1960; Third Secretary

Kabul 1961; Second Secretary FO 1963; Second later First Secretary UKDEL Brussels (EC) 1965; First Secretary UK Negotiating Team with the European Communities Brussels 1970; First Secretary Brussels (EC) 1972; Counsellor on SUPL to the Commission of the European Communities as Chef de Cabinet to Sir Christopher Soames 1973; Head of Energy Department FCO 1977; Head of Middle East Department FCO 1979; AUSS FCO 1979; Minister Washington 1984; UK Permanent Representative to the EC Brussels 1985; m 1961 Gillian Rex (4s 1963, 1966, 1968, 1972).

Hansen, Caroline (née Thearle); Bangkok since April 1992; born 17.2.66; FCO 1984; Copenhagen 1987; SUPL 1990; Grade 10; m 1989 Jakob Hansen.

Hansen, Diane (née Davies); Port Moresby since March 1991; born 23.7.45; FCO 1974; Lagos 1974; Athens 1977; FCO 1980; Copenhagen 1987; Grade 9; m 1988 Jan Bent Hansen.

Hanson, Timothy Myles; Third Secretary (Aid) New Delhi since January 1991; born 27.6.65; FCO 1984; Third Secretary (Chancery) Muscat 1987.

Hanton, John Christopher; Accra since January 1992; born 9.6.39; Army 1958-83; Prague 1985; Havanna 1989; Grade SO; m 1962 Sylvia Page (1s 1962; twin d 1964).

Harborne, Peter Gale; Counsellor FCO since January 1992; born 29.6.45; DHSS 1966; FCO 1972; Ottawa 1974; Mexico City 1975; Resigned 1979; Reinstated 1981; First Secretary FCO 1981; First Secretary and Head of Chancery Helsinki 1983; Counsellor and Head of Chancery Budapest 1988; m 1976 Tessa Elizabeth Henri (2s 1980, 1981).

Harder, Michael Allan; FCO since May 1987; born 27.10.62; FCO 1983; New Delhi 1986; Grade 9; m 1986 Tracy Rayner (1d 1991).

Hardie, Alexander, OBE (1990); First Secretary FCO since March 1990; born 5.3.47; Second later First Secretary FCO 1973; First Secretary (Inf) Budapest 1977; FCO 1978; Bucharest 1979; FCO 1981; First Secretary Lusaka 1986; m 1971 Jillian Hester Rowlands (1s 1973; 2d 1974, 1978).

Hardie, Alison; Washington since April 1990; born 31.3.65; FCO 1988; Grade S2A.

Hardie, Alison Stewart; FCO since July 1991; born 13.2.66; FCO 1984; UKMIS New York 1987; Warsaw 1989; Grade 9.

Hardie, Michael John, OBE (1989); Counsellor (Management) New Delhi since January 1990; born 14.7.38; FO 1956; HM Forces 1957-59; Bahrain 1959; FO 1962; Elisabethville 1964;

West Africa Floater 1965; Vice-Consul Sofia 1966; Vienna 1968; Munich 1969; Second Secretary FCO 1973; Vice-Consul (Inf) Cape Town 1976; First Secretary (Inf) BMG Berlin 1979; First Secretary (Comm) Valletta 1981; FCO 1983; First Secretary, later Counsellor (Admin) Lagos 1986; m 1967 Patricia Louisa Hulme (diss 1986) (1d 1969; 2s 1970, 1978); m (2) 1990 Jean Fish.

Hardman, Peter James William; Second Secretary Sofia since April 1991; born 28.10.56; FCO 1974; SE Asia Floater 1978; Bombay 1979; Perth 1983; Bangkok 1986; Second Secretary on loan to ODA 1988; Language Training 1990; m 1982 Joëlle Hélène Schneider (1d 1984).

Hardy, Richard Martin; FCO since July 1989; born 7.10.50; FCO 1967; Brussels 1976; FCO 1978; Buenos Aires 1979; FCO 1982; Bridgetown 1986; Grade 7; m 1982 Astrid Posse.

Hare, David Roy; FCO since August 1988; born 26.2.49; Royal Navy 1964-76; FCO 1976; Singapore 1986; Grade 9; m 1970 Susan Elizabeth Allen (1d 1972).

Hare, Paul Webster; LVO (1985); Consul (Econ/Comm) BTDO New York since November 1988; born 20.7.51; FCO 1978; Second Secretary/PS to HMA UKREP Brussels 1979; First Secretary Lisbon 1981 (Head of Chancery 1983); FCO 1985; m 1978 Lynda Carol Henderson (2d 1979, 1982; 3s 1984, 1988, 1991).

Harford, Charlotte Anstice; Second Secretary (Political) Moscow since February 1992; born 12.6.65; FCO 1988; Language Training FCO 1990 (Second Secretary 1991).

Hargreaves, Elaine; FCO since July 1991; born 29.10.71; Grade 10.

Hargreaves, Roger John; Second later First Secretary FCO since May 1990; born 8.12.50; FCO 1968; Hong Kong 1973; FCO 1975; Sana'a 1976; FCO 1977; Second Secretary Hong Kong 1985; m (1) 1973 Susan Florence Chalker (diss 1985); (2) Andrea Margaret Kent; (1s 1989).

Harkin, Simon David; Second Secretary (Political) Harare since August 1992; born 4.10.58; FCO 1989; UKMIS New York 1990; FCO 1991.

Harland, Jeremy; Bridgetown since September 1992; born 8.4.63; FCO 1983; Moscow 1988; FCO 1992; Grade 8.

Harle, Roger William; FCO since August 1988; born 4.2.59; FCO 1982; Darwin 1986; Grade 9.

Harley, Harriett Susanna; Hong Kong since February 1992; born 15.5.65; FCO 1989; Grade S2.

Harmer, Roger William; Third Secretary (Consular/Management) Riga since March 1992; born 5.1.53; FCO 1972; Bucharest 1974; La Paz 1976; Maseru 1978; FCO 1980; Muscat 1983; Ottawa 1986; FCO 1989; Grade 9; m 1976 Cristobalina Lopez Munoz (1d 1977).

Harper, Helen Diane; Muscat since September 1988; born 27.5.65; FCO 1986; Dar es Salaam 1988; Grade S2; m 1991 Paul Kennedy Harper.

Harper, Maurice Bertrand; Port Louis since October 1988; born 3.12.46; FCO 1974; Bangkok 1976; East Berlin 1980; FCO 1981; Bombay 1984; Grade 9; m (1) 1977 Susan Hayward (1s 1979); m (2) 1986 Veera Printer (1d 1987).

Harper, Monica Celia; First Secretary FCO since February 1989; born 18.8.44; FCO 1967; SEATO (Bangkok) 1969; ENA Paris 1972; BMG Berlin 1974; Second Secretary Bonn 1977; FCO 1979; Second Secretary (Admin) Mexico City 1982; First Secretary (Chancery/Info) UKDEL NATO Brussels 1984.

Harper, Robert Geoffrey; FCO since September 1990; born 13.1.57; FCO 1975; UKREP Brussels 1977; Masirali 1979; Kaduna 1980; Paris 1982; FCO 1986; Islamabad 1988; Grade 9.

Harper, Suzanne Rachel; UKDIS Geneva since August 1992; born 30.7.66; FCO 1985; Moscow 1987; FCO 1988; Rome 1989; Grade S2.

Harries, David George, MBE (1990); Beirut since September 1988; born 10.3.60; FCO 1980; Darwin 1982; FCO 1984; Islamabad 1986; FCO 1988; Grade 9.

Harrington, Allison; First Secretary FCO since March 1985; born 15.3.32; CRO 1950; Accra 1956; CRO 1959; Kampala 1962; CRO 1964; Kuching 1967; Second Secretary (Cons) Dar es Salaam 1969; Warsaw 1972; FCO 1974; First Secretary Buenos Aires 1977; Consul Cairo 1981; m 1956 Sheila McLean.

Harrington, Clare Elizabeth; FCO since August 1980; born 30.8.61; Grade S2.

Harrington, David John; Stockholm since February 1984; born 20.9.33; Army 1957-79; FCO 1979; Tel Aviv 1981; Grade 10; m 1956 Sheila Corthorn (1d 1958; 2s 1960, 1962).

Harrington, Peter; Georgetown since August 1990; born 29.9.62; FCO 1981; Baghdad 1984; Stockholm 1988; Grade 9; m 1984 Angela Elizabeth Dent.

Harris, Alison Clare; Wellington since July 1990; born 7.7.60; FCO 1978; Paris 1981; Abidjan 1983; FCO 1987; SUPL 1988; Grade 9; m 1982 John Brent Harris.

Harris, Anthony David, LVO (1979); Counsellor FCO since November 1990; born 13.10.41; Third Secretary CRO 1964; MECAS 1965; Third later Second Secretary and Vice-Consul Jedda 1967; Second Secretary (Inf) Khartoum 1969; First Secretary FCO 1972; First Secretary, Head of Chancery and Consul Abu Dhabi 1975; UKMIS Geneva 1979; Counsellor FCO 1982; on loan to MOD 1983; Counsellor Cairo 1986; m (1) 1970 Patricia Ann Over (1s 1978); (2) 1988 Ann-Sophie Kisling (1s 1988).

Harris, David, OBE (1989); First Secretary (Management) Dublin since November 1989; born 2.5.33; FO 1951; HM Forces 1952-54; FO 1954; Kabul 1955; Leopoldville 1958; Vice-Consul Belgrade 1961; Moscow 1963; Detroit 1965; FCO 1968 (Second Secretary 1969); Tel Aviv 1972; FCO 1976; Consul (Comm) Dallas 1979; First Secretary FCO 1983; First Secretary (Admin), Peking 1986; m 1960 Pauline Anne Plunkett (1d 1961; 3s 1963, 1968, 1969).

Harris, Graham Peter, MBE (1985); Warsaw since August 1992; born 15.10.41; Army 1958-88; Nairobi 1989; Grade SO; m 1965 Tessa E Sharp (1s 1965; 1d 1967).

Harris, Jennifer Anita; The Hague since March 1990; born 10.11.68; FCO 1988; Grade 10.

Harris, Joan; Third Secretary (Science and Tech) Moscow since July 1992; born 27.12.49; FCO 1975; Dakar 1976; Budapest 1978; Oslo 1981; FCO 1983; Paris 1987; FCO 1990; Grade 9.

Harris, Karina Lynn; FCO since December 1990; born 28.2.62; FCO 1983; Cairo 1984; Tokyo 1988; Grade S2.

Harris, Malcolm Harold; Bucharest since December 1987; born 31.12.41; RM 1959-87; Grade SO3; m 1960 Janet Ann Ellis (3d 1961, 1965, 1971).

Harris, Martin Fergus; Second Secretary (CFE) UKDEL Vienna since September 1992; born 17.5.69; FCO 1991.

Harris, Peter Harold Charles; First Secretary Santiago since June 1990; born 25.1.50; FCO 1981; Second later First Secretary (Social and Agriculture) Lisbon 1981; FCO 1984; First Secretary Moscow 1985; FCO 1988; m 1976 Maria Ocazionez (3s 1980, 1982, 1984).

Harris, Robert Malcolm; First Secretary FCO since December 1990; born 9.2.41; FO 1960; Istanbul 1962; CENTO Ankara 1963; Blantyre 1965; FCO 1969; Moscow 1970; FCO 1973; Second Secretary Dublin 1975; National Defence College Latimer 1979; First Secretary FCO 1980; Head of Chancery Brunei 1984; Consul Lyon 1989; m (1) 1961 Edith Joan Kitchener; (2) 1975 Marian Florence Binnington.

Harris, Thomas George; Counsellor FCO and Commissioner British Indian Ocean Territories since September 1991; born 6.2.45; BOT 1966; Third Secretary Tokyo 1969; DOT 1971; Cabinet Office 1976; DTI 1979; Counsellor (Commercial) Washington 1983; Counsellor and Head of Chancery Lagos 1988; Deputy High Commissioner 1990; m 1967 Mei-Ling (3s 1969, 1970, 1984).

Harrison, Anthony Gifford; Second Secretary FCO since January 1992; born 21.2.43; Ministry of Defence (Air) 1964; FCO 1967; Helsinki 1969; Kathmandu 1971; Dacca 1974; Nicosia 1976; FCO 1979; Second Secretary (Admin/ Cons) Colombo 1982; Second Secretary and Consul Oslo 1987; m 1970 (1) Marianne Versteeg (2s 1971, 1973); (2) 1985 Azniv Salakian.

Harrison, Anthony Julian; Second Secretary FCO since May 1981; born 19.3.53; FCO 1975; Pretoria 1978; m 1978 Sharon Readman (1d 1986, 1s 1990).

Harrison, Charles Dale; Islamabad since May 1991; born 23.2.55; MOD 1971; FCO 1976; Accra 1978; Mbabane 1982; FCO 1985; Rome 1988; Grade 9; m 1978 Lorraine Josie Richards (1d 1987, 1s 1990).

Harrison, Guy Andrew: Language Training, Seoul since November 1987; born 30.5.64; FCO 1986; Grade 9.

Harrison, John Clive, LVO (1971); Deputy Head of Mission and Counsellor in Islamabad since July 1989; born 12.7.37; FO 1960; Rangoon 1961; Vientiane 1964; FO 1964; Second later First Secretary (Inf) Addis Ababa 1967; Ankara 1971; Secondment to Cabinet Office 1973; First Secretary FCO 1976; First Secretary, Head of Chancery and Consul Luxembourg 1978; Counsellor and Head of Chancery Lagos 1981; Counsellor, attached to Protocol Department, FCO 1984; Counsellor FCO 1985; m 1967 Jennifer Heather Burston (1s 1968; 2d 1970, 1972).

Harrison, Mark Simon; SUPL since July 1992; born 8.7.68; British Library 1987-88; FCO 1989; Montevideo 1991; Grade 10.

Harrison, Ronald Charles Gully; Consul-General Naples since November 1990; born 11.6.33; HM Forces 1951-53; CRO 1960; Ibadan 1961; Malta 1964 (Second Secretary Comml/Inf 1965); Karachi 1967; FCO 1970; São Paulo 1972; Consul (Comm) BTDO New York 1975; Consul (Comm) Dallas 1977; First Secretary FCO 1979; Deputy Consul-General Milan 1982; Consul-General São Paulo 1987; m Eva Luise Johanne Hornäffer (3s 1960, 1962, 1965; 1d 1966).

Harrison, Stephen Thomas; Third Secretary (Chancery) Bahrain since August 1989; born 14.8.64; FCO 1986; Language Training SOAS 1987; Language Training Cairo 1988; m 1989 Clare Elizabeth Stafford Mackenzie.

Harrison, William Alistair; First Secretary FCO since January 1992; born 14.11.54; FCO 1977; Third later Second Secretary Warsaw 1979; Second later First Secretary FCO 1982; Private Secretary to the Parliamentary Under Secretary 1984; First Secretary UKMIS New York 1987; m 1981 Theresa Mary Morrison (diss 1991).

Harrison, William David; FCO since January 1991; born 28.3.72; Grade 10.

Harrod, Christine Margaret; FCO since December 1984; born 27.12.49; FCO 1967; Paris 1972; Caracas 1975; FCO 1978; Manila 1981; Grade 9; m 1984 David Stanley Martin.

Harrod, Jean (née Geary); Third Secretary (Chancery) UKREP Brussels since January 1992; born 28.4.54; FCO 1972; Geneva (CSCE) 1973; East Berlin 1975; Port Louis 1977; Peking 1980; SUPL 1983; FCO 1986; Grade 9; m 1974 Jeffrey Harrod.

Harrod, Jeffrey; First Secretary (Commercial) UKREP Brussels since February 1990; born 1.4.54; FCO 1970; Geneva (CSCE) 1973; East Berlin 1975; Port Louis 1977; Vice-Consul and later Second Secretary Peking 1980; Consul Shanghai 1984; Second Cater First Secretary FCO 1986; m 1974 Jean Geary.

Harrower, Hazel; Seoul since November 1989; born 18.12.64; FCO 1985; Bucharest 1988; Grade S2.

Harrup, Christine Mary; Colombo since May 1992; born 18.4.49; FCO 1974; Baghdad 1974; Lagos 1977; FCO 1978; Dublin 1981; FCO 1985; Addis Ababa 1987; Grade S1.

Harsent, Susan Elizabeth; UKREP Brussels since August 1989; born 16.6.49; FCO 1970; Bonn 1972; FCO 1975; Suva 1976; FCO 1978; Tel Aviv 1982; FCO 1984; Grade 9.

Harston, Julian John Robert Clive; Counsellor (UN) UKMIS Geneva since July 1991; born 20.10.42; Second later First Secretary FCO 1971; Consul later First Secretary Hanoi 1973; First Secretary FCO 1974; First Secretary Blantyre 1975; FCO 1979; Lisbon 1982; Counsellor Harare 1984; Counsellor FCO 1988; m 1966 Karen Howard Oake Longfield (1s 1978).

Harston, Stewart Ian; Singapore since August 1990; born 3.11.63; Grade 8; m 1990 Marianne Stallard.

Hart, David Peter; Budapest since December 1991; born 20.1.40; RAF 1959-84; East Berlin 1985; Bangkok 1986; Amman 1988; Grade SO; m 1962 Blodwen Martin Williams (1s 1964, 1d 1968).

Hart, Graham Donald; Rio de Janeiro since June 1991; born 25.10.46; FCO 1975; Tokyo 1977; Monrovia 1982; FCO 1985; JMO New York 1988; Grade 9.

Hart, Jeremy Michael; Second Secretary FCO since November 1990; born 24.2.57; FCO 1975; Paris 1978; FCO 1980; Second Secretary FCO 1986; Second Secretary (Vice-Consul) Athens 1986; m 1979 Alison Jane Morrell (1d 1984).

Hart, Neil; Second Secretary Ulaanbaattar since November 1991; born 11.12.47; FO (later FCO) 1966; Tripoli 1970; Reykjavik 1971; Khartoum 1974; Kabul 1975; FCO 1977; Port Moresby 1980; Copenhagen 1984; Second Secretary FCO 1987; m 1974 Solveig Haraldsdottir (1 step d 1967).

Hart, Roger Dudley; Deputy Head of Mission Mexico City since August 1990; born 29.12.43; Third Secretary FO 1965; Third later Second Secretary Berlin 1967; Bahrain 1970; Second later First Secretary FCO 1972; First Secretary (Aid) Nairobi 1975; First Secretary Lisbon 1978; First Secretary FCO 1983; CDA at RCDS 1985; Consul-General Rio de Janeiro 1986; m 1968 Maria de los Angeles de Santiago Jiménez (2s 1969, 1970).

Hart, Simon Charles; FCO since July 1989; born 13.12.57; FCO 1975; Brussels 1978; Tehran 1981; LA Floater 1983; Bogotá 1985; Grade 9; m 1987 Amparo Meza.

Hartland-Swann, Julian Dana Nimmo, CMG (1992); HM Ambassador Rangoon since May 1990; born 18.2.36; FO 1960; Third Secretary Bangkok 1961; Second later First Secretary FO 1965; Head of Eernal Department, BMG Berlin 1968; First Secretary and Head of Chancery Vienna 1971; FCO 1975; Counsellor 1977; HM Ambassador Ulan Bator 1977; Counsellor and Head of Chancery Brussels 1979; Head of South-East Asian Department, FCO 1983; Consul-General Frankfurt 1986; m 1960 Ann Deirdre Green (1s 1961; 1d 1963).

Hartless, Henry; Warsaw since April 1989; born 2.10.32; Army 1951-78; Moscow 1978; Rome 1980; Budapest 1983; Riyadh 1985; Kuwait 1987; Grade SSO; m 1970 Linda Elise Stringman (1s 1972; 1d 1976).

Hartley, David Metcalfe; Third Secretary (Comm) Bangkok since December 1989; born 15.11.55; FCO 1975; Karachi 1977; LA Floater 1980; Kabul 1984; FCO 1986; on loan to DTI 1988; Language Training 1989; Grade 9.

Hartley, James Leslie; Second Secretary FCO since April 1992; born 18.8.49; St Helena 1975; FCO 1977; Lusaka 1978; FCO 1980; LA Floater 1983; Khartoum 1985; Second Secretary and Head of Chancery Ulaanbaattar 1989; m (1)

1973 (diss 1982) Jennifer Parker (1s 1976); (2) 1984 Ann Lesley Oakley.

Hartshorne, William Park; First Secretary (Commercial) Stockholm since June 1992; born 6.6.39; FO 1962; MECAS 1963; Doha 1964; Third Secretary Caracas 1964; Commonwealth Office (later FCO) 1967; Second Secretary Stockholm 1970; Vice-Consul (Comm) Milan 1972; FCO 1977; First Secretary 1978; Assistant to Deputy Governor Gibraltar 1978; First Secretary (Admin) and Consul Caracas 1982; First Secretary FCO 1984; First Secretary (Comm) Abu Dhabi 1986; FCO 1990; m 1966 Yolanda Margaret Stesmans (1s 1967; 1d 1971).

Harvey, Christopher Paul Duncan; First Secretary (Chancery) Brussels since June 1990; born 21.7.56; FCO 1986 (Second Secretary 1986); Second Secretary Suva 1988; m 1989 Anasaini Vesinawa Kamakorewa (1 step d 1987; 1 step s 1988).

Harvey, David; FCO since April 1988; born 10.11.57; FCO 1977; Dublin 1980; Kinshasa 1982; East Berlin 1986; Grade 9; m 1983 Bernadette Louise McMahon (1d 1987).

Harvey, Lindsay; Bridgetown since October 1988; born 31.3.59; FCO 1984; Tehran 1986; Budapest 1987; Grade S2.

Haseman, David Frank; Paris since November 1991; born 25.1.38; Royal Navy 1955-65; FCO 1968-74; Darwin 1972; FCO 1975; Havana 1975; Beirut 1976; New Delhi 1976; BMG Berlin 1979; Nairobi 1982; Bangkok 1984; Mexico City 1986; New York 1987; Peking 1990; Grade CSO; m 1977 Helena Edith Moktan (1s 1978).

Haskell, (Donald) Keith, CMG (1991), CVO (1979); HM Ambassador Lima since February 1990; born 9.5.39; MECAS 1961; Third Secretary Baghdad 1962; Second Secretary FCO 1966; MECAS 1968; First Secretary Benghazi 1969; Tripoli 1970; FCO 1972; Chargé d'Affaires and Consul-General Santiago 1975; Consul-General Dubai 1978; Head of NED, FCO 1981; Head of Middle East Department FCO 1983; Counsellor and Head of Chancery Bonn 1985; on secondment to Industry 1988; m 1966 Maria Luisa Soeiro Tito de Morais (2d 1970, 1979; 2s 1974, 1976).

Haslam, Christopher Peter de Landre; First Secretary (Comm) Copenhagen since July 1989; born 22.3.43; Admiralty and Ministry of Defence (Navy) 1960; DSAO 1966; Jakarta 1969; Sofia 1973; FCO 1974; Canberra 1978; Lagos 1981; Second Secretary FCO 1986; m 1969 Lana Whitley (2s 1971, 1973).

Haspel, Sarah Jane; FCO since October 1991; born 1.5.69; Grade 9.

Haswell, Charles Chetwynd Douglas; Second

later First Secretary FCO since February 1989;
born 18.2.56; FCO 1979; Language Training
Hong Kong 1981; Peking 1982; Third later
Second Secretary (Chancery) Ottawa 1986;
Tokyo 1988.

Hatcher, Margaret Hilary; FO (later FCO) since
August 1964; Second Secretary 1973; First
Secretary 1978; born 11.9.41; m 1968 George
David Hatcher.

Hatfull, Martin Alan; Deputy Presidency Co-
ordinator UKREP Brussels since September
1991; born 7.6.57; FCO 1980; Language
Training 1982; First Secretary Tokyo 1983; First
Secretary FCO 1987; m 1980 Phyllis Morshead
(2s 1984, 1987).

Hatton, Belinda Jane; UKDEL Vienna since
January 1991; born 6.5.65; FCO 1988; Grade S2.

Haveron, Monica; Nicosia since June 1990; born
29.6.67; FCO 1987; Grade S2.

Hawkes, Anthony John, OBE (1988); Counsellor
Nairobi since April 1990; born 24.5.43; FO
1965; Third Secretary Sofia 1966; Third later
Second Secretary FO (later FCO) 1966; Geneva
(UKMIS) 1969; Second later First Secretary FCO
1973; Lusaka 1978; FCO 1982; Islamabad 1984;
First Secretary FCO 1987; m 1979 Jennifer Anne
Collins (1d 1981; 1s 1983).

Hawkes, David John, MBE (1982); First Secretary
(Commercial) Tehran since October 1990; born
13.5.38; DSAO 1965; Moscow 1967; Reykjavik
1969; FCO 1971; Language student MECAS
1974; Kuwait 1975; Second Secretary Baghdad
1979; Second Secretary FCO 1983; First
Secretary (Comm) Amman 1985; First Secretary
FCO 1988; m 1965 Betty Frances Lane (2s
1966, 1971).

Hawkins, Carl McArthur; Bangkok since July
1989; born 25.9.50; FCO 1967; HCS 1974; FCO
1977; Grade 8; m 1987 Yoko Shibuya (1d 1988).

Hawkins, John Mark; First Secretary FCO since
February 1989; born 30.4.60; FCO 1982; Third
later Second Secretary (Chancery) Pretoria/
Capetown 1984; m 1991 Rosemarie Anne
Kleynhans.

Haworth, Carol Yvonne; First Secretary
(Commercial/Aid) Peking since July 1992; born
8.9.61; Second Secretary FCO 1988; Full-time
language training 1989; Full-time language
training Hong Kong 1990.

Haxton, Jennifer Frances; FCO since May 1992;
born 21.4.44; Grade S2; (1s 1970)

Hay, Alexander, MBE (1991); First Secretary
(Management) and Consul Seoul since January
1992; born 3.3.37; Army 1955-57; Ministry of
Labour 1957; Addis Ababa 1961; Kuala Lumpur

1967; FCO 1972; Havana 1975; Seoul 1977;
Second Secretary FCO 1981; Second Secretary
(Comm) Singapore 1983; First Secretary FCO
1987; First Secretary Brisbane 1988; FCO 1988;
m 1957 Evelyn Mary Summerton (4s 1958,
1959, 1964, 1966; 1d 1962).

Hay, Barbara Logan, MBE (1991); St Petersberg
since September 1991; born 20.1.53; FCO 1971;
Language Student 1974; Moscow 1975;
Johannesburg 1978; Second Secretary FCO 1980;
Vice-Consul (Comm) Montreal 1985; First
Secretary (Info) Moscow 1988.

Hay, James Stewart; Ankara since March 1992;
born 2.2.43; Army 1962-84; Moscow 1989;
Grade SO.

Hay-Campbell, (Thomas) Ian; First Secretary,
FCO since July 1990; born 19.5.45; BBC 1972-
84; First Secretary FCO 1984; First Secretary
Head of Chancery and Consul Kinshasa 1987; m
1970 Margaret Lorraine Hoadley (4s 1973, 1974,
1977, 1979).

Hay-Edie, David Olav; First Secretary FCO
since September 1992; born 25.8.43; FCO 1968;
Buenos Aires 1971; Singapore 1973; UKMIS
Geneva 1974; Second Secretary FCO 1976; on
loan to UNHCR Manila 1980; Second Secretary
FCO 1982; First Secretary (Comm/Econ) Oslo
1985; First Secretary (UN) UKMIS Geneva
1989; m 1968 Silviane Veronique Mutrux (1s
1972).

Hayes, Christine Vera; Second Secretary FCO
since January 1990; born 30.3.45; ODM 1964;
DSAO 1967; Paris 1969; Pretoria1/Cape Town
1972; FCO 1975; Warsaw 1978; Houston 1980;
FCO 1983; Peking 1985; Amsterdam 1987.

Hayes, Julie Patricia; Hanoi since March 1991;
born 22.7.59; FCO 1988; Grade S2.

Hayes, Teresa Ann; FCO since July 1980; born
1.4.35; FCO 1971; Lagos 1972; Dacca 1974;
FCO 1976; Kathmandu 1977; Grade 9.

Hays, Carl Downing, BEM (1972); Istanbul since
November 1991; born 28.5.38; RAF 1957-83;
Havana 1983; Cairo 1985; Nairobi 1986;
Belgrade 1989; Grade SO; m 1960 Patricia
Turner (1s 1962; 1d 1965).

Hayward, Christopher Charles; First Secretary
FCO since March 1991; born 22.12.39; MOT
1960; ODM 1963; Vice-Consul Buea 1965;
Tehran 1969; Second Secretary (Comm)
Budapest 1973; FCO 1976; First Secretary
(Development) Khartoum 1979; First Secretary
FCO 1983; Deputy Trade Commissioner Hong
Kong and Consul for Macau 1986; m Margaret
Oney (3d 1966, 1967, 1970).

Haywood, Ian; FCO since April 1989; born
2.10.59; FCO 1978; Kampala 1981; Düsseldorf

1985; Grade 9; m (1) 1984 Angela Jane Kennedy (diss 1988); (2) 1991 June Sandra Tyler.

Haywood, Nigel Robert; Deputy Consul-General Johannesburg since September 1992; born 17.3.55; Army 1977-80; FCO 1983; Second later First Secretary Budapest 1985; First Secretary FCO 1989; m 1979 Mary Louise Smith (3s 1984, 1985, 1991).

Hazell, Rosemary Jane; SUPL since March 1991; born 5.7.53; FCO 1971; Bangkok 1974; FCO 1977; Tokyo 1978; Far East Floater 1981; Africa Floater 1983; FCO 1984; Language Training 1986; Third Secretary (Comm) Bangkok 1987; Second Secretary FCO 1989; m 1989 Arthur Andre Maurel.

Hazlewood, Roger Derek; FCO since September 1990 (Second Secretary 1991); born 10.1.50; FCO 1968; Georgetown 1971; Bonn 1975; Paris 1977; FCO 1980; Cairo 1983; UKREP Brussels 1987; m 1971 Yvonne Helen Betty Johnston McPhee (3s 1973, 1976, 1978).

Head, Ian; Bonn since July 1990; born 21.10.46; Home Civil Service 1987; Grade 9.

Heald, Kenneth, OBE (1991); Consul-General Madrid since March 1989; born 1.3.33; FO 1954; Madrid 1957; Mogadishu 1959; Brussels 1961; FO 1963; Havana 1963; Caracas 1966; Second Secretary Santiago 1970; FCO 1973; Second Secretary (Inf) Ottawa 1976; Consul (Inf) Toronto 1978; First Secretary (Admin) UKMIS Geneva 1981; First Secretary FCO 1985; m 1954 Mary Coulson (1s 1964).

Heald, Peter Andrew, MBE (1981); First Secretary (Management) Nairobi since June 1991; born 27.6.40; FO 1957; Baghdad 1962; Geneva 1963; Lagos 1965; FO 1968; Vice-Consul Tel Aviv 1969; FCO 1971; Second Secretary (Comm) The Hague 1975; Second Secretary and Consul Warsaw 1980; First Secretary FCO 1982; First Secretary (Econ) Tokyo 1984; First Secretary FCO 1987, m 1961 Janet Maureen Bowie (1d 1962; 3s 1964, 1966, 1977).

Healy, Deirdre Elizabeth Margaret; Full-Time Language Training Cairo since May 1992; born 30.4.66; FCO 1990; Language Training FCO 1991; Grade 9.

Healy, Denis Terence; First Secretary (Commercial) Ankara since July 1991; born 18.11.43; FO 1963; DSAO 1965; Belgrade 1967; FCO 1970; Port of Spain 1974; Second Secretary 1975; Vice-Consul Douala 1976; FCO 1979; Second Secretary (Chancery/Aid) Bridgetown 1983; First Secretary (Comm) UKREP Brussels 1985; First Secretary FCO 1990.

Healy, Dora Claire Sarah; FCO since February 1991; born 30.8.52; FCO 1982; Language

Training 1986; Second (later First) Secretary (Chancery/Inf) Addis Ababa 1987; Principal Research Officer; m 1983 Nicholas Guttmann (2d 1976, 1983, 1s 1985).

Healy, Martin Frederick; Hong Kong since August 1990; born 21.10.55; FCO 1972; Moscow 1978; FCO 1979; Third Secretary Pretoria 1984; FCO 1987; Grade 8; m 1977 Jane Catherine Stacey (2d 1981, 1983).

Healy, Robert; Second later First Secretary FCO since November 1991; born 20.1.37; GPO 1953; Bangkok 1964; Cairo 1966; FCO 1968; Tokyo 1969; Washington 1973; FCO 1978 (Second Secretary 1981); Paris 1982; FCO 1985; Second Secretary East Berlin (later Berlin) 1989; m 1964 Donna Marie Dorman (2s 1966, 1969).

Heap, Peter William, CMG (1987); HM Ambassador Brasilia since August 1992; born 13.4.35; HM Forces 1954-56; CRO 1959; Third Secretary Dublin 1960; Third later Second Secretary Ottawa 1960; First Secretary Colombo 1963; Seconded to Ministry of Defence 1966; FO (later FCO) 1968; Deputy Director General BIS New York 1971; Counsellor (Political/Econ) Caracas 1976; (Commercial) 1978; Head of ESSD, FCO 1980; High Commissioner Nassau 1983; Minister Lagos 1986; Senior Trade Commissioner Hong Kong and Consul-General Macao 1989; m (1) 1960 Helen Cutting Wilmerding (diss) (2s 1968, 1969; 2d 1970, 1971); (2) 1977 Dorrit Irene Breitenstein (née Martin); (3) 1986 Ruthann Lind Johnson.

Heath, Amanda Jane; Rio de Janeiro since May 1992; born 10.6.68; FCO 1987; Brasilia 1990; Grade S2.

Heath, Andrew; First Secretary FCO since July 1992; born 17.4.53; FCO 1975; Third Secretary Amman 1978; On loan to Cabinet Office 1981; First Secretary FCO 1983; First Secretary (Financial and Econ) and Head of Chancery Kuwait 1985; First Secretary (Trade Policy) Washington 1988; m 1982 Christina Friday.

Heath, Gillian Carol; Algiers since August 1990; born 21.8.45; FCO 1969; Islamabad 1970; Kampala 1971; San Salvador 1973; Panama 1973; Kuala Lumpur 1975; Brunei 1976; FCO 1978; Havana 1980; Dar es Salaam 1981; Singapore 1984; Washington 1988; Grade S1.

Heathcote, Simon Robert Mark, OBE (1988); First Secretary FCO since January 1991; born 1.3.41; Second later First Secretary FCO 1971; On loan to HCS 1974; Language Student 1975; First Secretary (Inf) Athens 1976; FCO 1979; Buenos Aires 1980; FCO 1982; First Secretary Islamabad 1987; m 1976 Susan Mary Ashley (2s 1977, 1979).

Heather, Tracey Jane; FCO since October 1988; born 4.9.59; Inland Revenue 1986; Grade S2A.

Heaven, Christopher Roy; FCO since December 1986; Second Secretary 1989; born 15.11.44; FO (later FCO) 1961; Brussels 1970; Addis Ababa 1973; FCO 1977; Islamabad 1980; Third Secretary Ottawa 1984; m 1973 Gemma Brigid Ann Grennan (1s 1981).

Hedley, Jason Beal; Third Secretary (Vice Consul) Athens since May 1992; born 23.10.66; FCO 1987; Grade 9.

Hedley, John; First Secretary (Chancery) Madrid since March 1989; born 23.3.50; Third Secretary FCO 1973; Third later Second Secretary Stockholm 1975; Second later First Secretary FCO 1977; First Secretary (Inf) Pretoria 1981; FCO 1985; m 1974 Lesley Joan Holloway (1s 1978; 1d 1981).

Hedley-Jones, Timothy James; Third Secretary (Visas) Moscow since July 1992; born 7.11.68; FCO 1990; Grade 9.

Heffer, John William Charles; Pretoria since August 1991; born 31.7.52; FCO 1971; Kampala 1973; FCO 1974; Victoria (Seychelles) 1975; Bogota 1977; Peking 1980; FCO 1981; Warsaw 1983; FCO 1984; Valletta 1988; Grade 9; m 1975 Lynn Ida Brown (2s 1977, 1980).

Hefford, Brian, Colombo since October 1989; born 10.8.48; FCO 1969; Karachi 1972; Paris 1976; FCO 1979; Islamabad 1983; FCO 1986; Grade 9; m 1971 Susan Mary Gorman (1s 1975).

Heigl, Peter Richard; First Secretary Consul-General and Deputy Head of Mission Khartoum since October 1991; born 21.2.43; Ministry of Power 1963; Ministry of Technology 1968; DTI 1971; on secondment to FCO as Second Secretary (Comm) Kuala Lumpur 1974; Accra 1975; First Secretary FCO 1981; First Secretary (Comm) Riyadh later Consul (Comm) Jedda 1984; First Secretary FCO 1989; m 1965 Sally Lupton (3s 1971, 1973, 1977).

Helke, Jill Beynon (née Barker-Harland) SUPL since December 1990; born 10.4.56; FCO 1978; Language Training Hong Kong 1981; Peking 1983; Second Secretary UKMIS New York 1986; First Secretary FCO 1990; m 1987 Heinz Michael Rudolf Juergen Helke (1s 1988).

Hemans, Simon Nicholas Peter, cmg (1992), cvo (1983); HM Ambassador Kiev since June 1992; born 19.9.40; Third Secretary FO 1964; Second Secretary Moscow 1966; FCO 1968; Deputy Commissioner Anguilla 1969; Second later First Secretary FCO 1969; First Secretary UKMIS New York 1971; First Secretary (Comm) Budapest 1975; First Secretary FCO 1979; Counsellor (Econ/Comm) and Deputy High Commissioner Nairobi 1981; Counsellor and Head of Chancery Moscow 1985; Counsellor FCO 1987; AUSS (Africa) 1990; m 1970 Ursula

Martha Naef (1 step s 1967; 1d 1972, twin s 1974).

Heming, Richard Francis, mbe (1982); Second Secretary FCO since June 1982; born 11.10.39; FO 1963; MOD 1968-71; FCO 1971; Vienna 1978 (Second Secretary 1980); m 1968 Florence Marion Clement (2s 1970, 1973).

Hemingway, Janette (née Hunt); FCO since January 1990; born 17.8.59; FCO 1984; UKDEL Vienna 1986; Grade S2; m 1988 William Piers Hemingway.

Hemingway, William Piers; born 10.11.60; FCO 1979; Kuala Lumpur 1981; Luanda 1985; Vienna 1987; Grade 9; m 1988 Janette Hunt.

Henderson, Andrew David Forbes; Consul and Deputy Head of Mission Luanda since March 1992; born 12.7.52; FCO 1971; Latin America Floater 1975; Rio de Janeiro 1977; Second Secretary (Chancery) Oslo 1980; Second Secretary FCO 1985; Consul, New York (CG) 1987; First Secretary Washington 1988; m 1987 Julia Margaret King (2d 1988, 1990).

Henderson, Lesley; FCO since October 1991; born 21.11.67; FCO 1987; Paris 1989; Grade S2A.

Henderson, Matthew Magnus Murray; First Secretary (External and Press) Peking since June 1992; born 19.7.60; Second Secretary FCO 1986; Second later First Secretary BTC Hong Kong 1988; First Secretary FCO 1990.

Henderson, Victor Joseph; First Secretary (Chancery) Helsinki since October 1989; born 10.1.41; Ministry of Housing and Local Government 1964; Welsh Office 1965; DSAO 1966; MECAS 1967; Jedda 1969; Second Secretary (Comm) Bahrain 1972; FCO 1975; Caracas 1978 (First Secretary 1981); HM Consul Jerusalem 1982; First Secretary FCO 1987; m 1966 Heather Winifred Steed (1d 1967; 1s 1969).

Henderson, William Robert, lvo (1988); First Secretary FCO since March 1989; born 7.11.47; DSAO later FCO 1965; Moscow 1970; Sana;a 1971; Lima 1972; Rio de Janeiro 1973; FCO 1976; MECAS 1977; Dubai 1978 (Second Secretary 1980); FCO 1983; First Secretary (Inf) Madrid 1985; m 1969 Carol Mary Smith (1d 1973; 1s 1976).

Hendrie, Robert Andrew Michie; Consul-General and Counsellor Dubai since September 1990; born 4.5.38; MECAS 1961; Political Residency Bahrain 1962; Tehran 1965; Second Secretary Tripoli 1968; FCO 1969; Lima 1973; First Secretary Buenos Aires 1975; First Secretary FCO 1980; Consul-General Lille 1986; m 1964 Consuelo Liaño Solorzano (2d 1967, 1973).

Hendry, Carol Anne Walls; Tokyo since July 1990; born 7.12.66; FCO 1985; UKREP Brussels 1987; Grade S2.

Hendry, Ian Duncan; Counsellor (Legal Adviser) UKREP Brussels since May 1991; born 2.4.48; Assistant Legal Adviser (DS Grade 5) FCO 1971; First Secretary (Legal Adviser) BMG Berlin 1982; Assistant Legal Adviser, later Legal Counsellor; FCO 1986; m (1)1973 Elizabeth Anne Southall (1d 1975; 1s 1977); (2) 1991 Sally Annabel Hill.

Hennessy, Anthony John; Second Secretary (UN/ UNIDO) UKMIS Vienna since June 1991; born 1.2.55; FCO 1980; Singapore 1981; FCO 1985; Second Secretary (Commercial) Riyadh 1987.

Henson, Clifford James; Second Secretary Athens since July 1992; born 12.8.55; FCO 1973; Singapore 1981; FCO 1983; Islamabad 1985; Third later Second Secretary FCO 1989; m 1979 Ann Tysoe (2s 1981, 1984).

Hentley, Michael Joseph; Deputy Head of Mission Dakar since May 1992; born 13.7.46; CRO 1964; DSAO 1965; Benghazi 1969; Moscow 1972; Lagos 1973; Kaduna 1976; FCO 1978; Second Secretary (Comm) Port of Spain 1982; Second Secretary FCO 1985; First Secretary (Tech) Paris 1987; m 1969 Janice Paterson (1s 1971; 2d 1973, 1979).

Henwood, Jacqueline Susan; Kampala since April 1991; born 10.5.63; FCO 1983; Jakarta 1986; FCO 1989; Grade S2.

Herbert, David; Consul (Comm) Montreal since November 1988; born 13.7.47; CO 1966; Algiers 1969; Baghdad 1970; Tananarive 1971; FCO 1974; Second Secretary Luxembourg 1977; Second Secretary (Comm) Prague 1981; First Secretary FCO 1985; m 1970 Maureen Violet Edmundson (2d 1976, 1978).

Herd, Teresa Ann; FCO since September 1991; born 24.10.54; FCO 1972; Resigned 1974; Reinstated 1980, Warsaw 1981; Lilongwe 1981; FCO 1984; Pretoria 1986; LA/Caribbean Floater 1989; Grade 9.

Herridge, Michael Eric James; First Secretary (Management) Madrid since September 1990; born 23.9.46; DSAO 1966; FCO 1968; Düsseldorf 1969; Prague 1969; Nairobi 1972; FCO 1975; Lagos 1979; Second later First Secretary UKMIS New York 1982; First Secretary FCO 1986; m 1968 Margaret Elizabeth Bramble (1d 1971).

Herring, Julie Ann; FCO since November 1989; born 10.4.65; FCO 1984; Helsinki 1987; Grade 9.

Hervey, Sir Roger (Blaise) (Ramsay), KCVO (1991), CMG (1980); HM Ambassador Mexico City since March 1992; born 3.10.34; HM Forces 1953-55; Third Secretary and Private Secretary to HM Ambassador Bonn 1958; Third later Second Secretary FO 1961; Prague 1963; First Secretary FO 1965; Office of the Political Adviser Singapore 1968; FCO 1970; First Secretary and Head of Chancery Bogota 1974; Counsellor FCO 1976; Counsellor The Hague 1979; Minister (local rank) Madrid 1982; AUSS (Protocol), Vice-Marshal of the Diplomatic Corps with the personal rank of Ambassador 1986; m 1970 Faith Kannreuther (2d 1973, 1975).

Heseltine, Lavinia Pauline; Dhaka since June 1992; born 13.12.54; FCO 1974; Brussels 1975; Moscow 1979; Canberra 1981; Khartoum 1984; Lagos 1986; Grade S1; m 1990 Barry Heseltine.

Hewer, Susan Jane; Kuwait since November 1991; born 18.9.61; FCO 1980; Washington 1982; FCO 1985; New Delhi 1985; UKDEL Strasbourg 1989; Grade S2.

Hewetson, Zoe-Gabrielle; SUPL since November 1991; born 22.4.61; FCO 1987; Brussels 1989; FCO 1991; Grade S2.

Hewett, Peter Geoffrey; FCO since December 1984; born 19.1.31; Forestry Commission 1948; HM Forces 1949-54; Forestry Commission 1954-55; FO 1958; Peshawar1/Delhi 1964; FO 1965; Beirut 1966; FCO 1968; Bangkok 1970; Kinshasa 1973; FCO 1975; Madrid 1976; FCO 1977; Mbabane 1979; FCO 1981; Attaché Belgrade 1982; Grade 8; m Denise Mansfield (2s 1957, 1960; 1d 1965).

Hewitt, Dorothy Lee, MBE (1991); Lagos since July 1990; born 10.12.42; Lord Chancellor;s Department (CC) 1961; FO (later FCO) 1967; Accra 1970; Peking 1973; Sofia 1974; FCO 1976; Lilongwe 1986; FCO 1990; Grade 9.

Hewitt, Gavin Wallace; Counsellor FCO since January 1992; born 19.10.44; Ministry of Transport 1967; On secondment as Third later Second Secretary from Ministry of Transport (later Department of the Environment) to Brussels (EEC) 1970; FCO 1972; First Secretary Canberra 1973; First Secretary FCO 1978; First Secretary and Head of Chancery Belgrade 1981; Counsellor attached to BBC (for Review of Eernal Services) 1984; Counsellor on loan to the HCS 1984; Deputy Permanent Representative (Head of Chancery) UKMIS Geneva 1987; m 1973 Heather Mary Clayton (2d 1975; 1979; 2s 1977, 1982).

Hewitt, Michael Wenham; Deputy Consul-General Chicago since May 1991; born 18.7.33; HM Forces 1954-56; Ankara 1956; Paris 1959; Peking 1962; FO 1963; DSAO 1965; Canberra 1966; Moscow 1969; Second Secretary 1970; UKDEL NATO Brussels 1973; Second Secretary (Comm) Brussels 1975; First Secretary FCO 1979; Consul (Comm) Atlanta 1982; First

Secretary FCO 1987; m 1962 Anne Juliet Sherrington (2s 1963, 1968; 1d 1964).

Hewitt, Norman; FCO since January 1989; born 12.9.46; FCO 1981; Washington 1985; Grade 8; m 1968 Catherine Georgina Sahadeo (1s 1975; 2d 1970, 1983).

Hewitt, Simon; FCO since January 1989; born 31.5.70; Grade 10; m 1992 Jacqueline Mary McQueen.

Hewstone, Myles Alfred; Nicosia since December 1991; born 28.7.40; Moscow 1988; Helsinki 1989; Havana 1990; Grade SO; (1s 1961; 1d 1964); m 1989 Madeline Clare Brown.

Heyn, Andrew Richard; Second Secretary (Chancery) Caracas since February 1991; born 14.1.62; DTI 1985-89; Second Secretary FCO 1989; m 1988 Jane Carmel.

Hickey, Patricia Helen; FCO since March 1991; born 2.2.55; FCO 1975; Bangkok 1977; FCO 1979; Canberra 1981; FCO 1984; New York 1986; Berlin 1988; Grade S2.

Hicking, Nicola Jane (née Boyles); FCO since October 1988; born 28.7.63; FCO 1983; Brasilia 1985; Lagos 1987; Grade S2; m 1992 Robert Hicking.

Hicks, Martin; Second Secretary FCO since January 1986; born 18.11.44; FO 1962; Ottawa 1966; Phnom Penh 1968; FCO 1971; Port Louis 1974; Mbabane 1978; FCO 1980; Second Secretary (Admin) Amman 1982; m 1965 Elizabeth Doris (2d 1966, 1968; 1s 1973).

Hicks-Jones, Claire; FCO since May 1987; born 15.7.68; Grade 10.

Hickson, Albert; Bonn since July 1991; born 3.6.33; Army 1952-75; Bonn 1976; Prague 1977; Stockholm 1979; Dublin 1981; Belgrade 1984; UKDEL NATO Brussels 1986; Berne 1989; Grade SO.

Hickson, Michael, lvo (1986); Deputy Head of Mission Caracas since February 1991; born 13.12.38; Third later Second Secretary (Inf) Caracas 1964; FO (later FCO) 1968; First Secretary Caracas 1973; FCO 1977; Buenos Aires 1981; First Secretary FCO 1982; Head of Chancery and Consul Kathmandu 1985; First Secretary FCO 1988; m 1966 Isobel Hutton McNaughton (2d 1967, 1972; 1s 1971).

Hickson, Philip John; Floater duties since August 1990; born 21.3.65; FCO 1984; Kingston 1986; Grade 9.

Higgins, Kim Catherine; Lagos since August

1989; born 14.10.66; FCO 1987; Grade S2A.

Higgins, Robert Geoffrey; FCO since November 1985; (Second Secretary 1989); born 23.3.48; FCO 1968; The Hague 1971; Phnom Penh 1974; Caribbean Floater 1975; Dacca 1977; FCO 1978; Far East Floater 1980; Bridgetown 1982.

Higginson, Sydney; Nicosia since November 1991; born 14.4.48; Army 1965-1989; Bucharest 1990; Grade SO; m 1968 Thelma Harris (2s 1968, 1971).

Higham, Andrew Bolton; FCO since March 1988; born 28.10.59; FCO 1982; Singapore 1986; Grade 9; m 1989 (1d 1990)

Higley, Rochelle Jane; FCO since July 1991; born 24.1.72; Grade 10.

Hildersley, Sarah Jane; Floater Training since December 1991; born 30.5.68; Third Secretary (Management) JMO Brussels 1990; FCO 1987; UKDEL NATO Brussels 1988; Third Secretary (Management) JMO Brussels 1990; Grade 9.

Hill, Adrian Victor; First Secretary (Comm/Info) Kingston since September 1989; born 28.8.40; Army 1959-62; CRO 1963; Nicosia 1966; Vice-Consul Saigon 1969; FCO 1971; Second Secretary Berne 1974; Second later First Secretary Ottawa 1978; FCO 1983; First Secretary Seoul 1986; m 1976 Regine Landolt (1s 1978; 1d 1981).

Hill, Brenda; Cairo since June 1991; born 27.2.43; DSAO 1965; Washington 1967; FCO 1969; Warsaw 1970; FCO 1971; Seconded to HCS 1972; Bonn 1973; Suva 1975; FCO 1977; Seoul 1979; UKDEL NATO Brussels 1984; FCO 1986; Lilongwe 1989; FCO 1990; Grade 9.

Hill, Charles Edward; FCO since July 1990; born 31.3.63; Grade 9.

Hill, Darryn Scott; FCO since April 1990; born 6.11.70; Grade 10.

Hill, Duncan N; Berlin since August 1991; born 8.12.68; FCO 1989; Grade 10; m 1992 Lisa Pegram.

Hill, Gillian Lynne; Budapest since December 1990; born 12.8.66; FCO 1985; Cairo 1987; Grade S2.

Hill, Jeremy John Leonard; Harare since July 1990; born 3.5.57; FCO 1975; SOAS 1978; Tokyo 1979; Jakarta 1982; FCO 1986; Grade 9; m 1985 Roosnadia Peni Hestiani Roesno (1s 1990, 1d 1992).

Hill, Lauren Sarah; FCO since February 1992; born 14.2.73; Grade 10.

Hill, Michael Thomas; Assistant to Deputy

Governor Gibraltar since July 1988; born 2.1.45; FO 1963; UKMIS New York 1966; Vientiane 1969; Kaduna 1970; FCO 1974; Vice-Consul Ulan Bator 1978; Second Secretary (Cons/Immig/ Aid) Port of Spain 1981; Second later First Secretary FCO 1985; m 1977 Elizabeth Louise Carden (3s 1981, 1988, 1990; 1d 1983).

Hill, Peter Jeremy Oldham; On loan to the Law Officers' Department since January 1991; born 17.4.54; FCO 1982; First Secretary (Legal Adviser) Bonn 1987; Legal Counsellor; m 1981 Katharine Hearn.

Hill, Sally Helen Elizabeth; FCO since September 1990; born 25.10.65; FCO 1987; New Delhi 1988; Grade S2.

Hill, Steven John; FCO since November 1990 (First Secretary 1991); born 7.4.62; FCO 1984; Second Secretary (UNIDO/UN) UKMIS Vienna 1988.

Hillcoat, Hilary Ann; Mexico City since April 1991; born 25.10.46; FCO 1975; Accra 1975; Peking 1978; Quito 1979; FCO 1983; Brasilia 1984; Madrid 1988; Grade S1.

Hillman, John; First Secretary and Deputy Consul-General Sydney since November 1991; born 30.5.48; FO (later FCO) 1967; Dacca 1971; Budapest 1974; Calcutta 1975; Second Secretary (Comm) Dublin 1979; Second Secretary FCO 1983; First Secretary and Consul Cairo 1988; m 1978 Pushp Kanta Sahney (1d 1981).

Hills, Rachel Emma; FCO since March 1990; born 7.4.71; Grade 10.

Hilson, Malcolm Geoffrey; First Secretary (Immigration) New Delhi since February 1990; born 28.9.42; FO 1961; Jakarta 1963; Singapore 1965; FCO 1969; Bombay 1972 (Second Secretary 1975); Second Secretary Kuala Lumpur 1976; FCO 1979; First Secretary Kaduna 1982; First Secretary FCO 1986; m 1965 Marion Joan Freeman (2s 1966, 1968).

Hilson, Marian Joan; New Delhi since February 1990; born 5.2.44; FCO 1988; Grade 9; m 1965 Malcolm Geoffrey Hilson (2s 1966, 1968).

Hilton, Christopher Charles Donald; Budapest since January 1991; born 7.11.69; FCO 1988; Grade 10.

Hilton, Margaret; FCO since September 1990; born 9.8.53; Grade S2.

Hilton, Michael Anthony; First Secretary (Dev/ Comm) Kathmandu since June 1987; born 7.3.50; Department of Employment 1973; FCO 1973; Manchester Business School 1975; Frankfurt 1977; FCO 1979; Second Secretary Ulan Bator 1981; Second later First Secretary FCO 1983; m 1976 Janet Elizabeth Tyler.

Hinchcliffe, Peter Robert Mossom, CMG (1988),

CVO (1979); High Commissioner Lusaka since May 1990; born 9.4.37; Army 1955-57; HMOCS South Arabian Federation 1961-67; Retired as Senior Adviser High Commission (Federation); First Secretary FCO 1969; UKMIS New York 1971; First Secretary and Head of Chancery Kuwait 1974; First Secretary FCO 1976; Counsellor and Head of Chancery Dar es Salaam 1978; HM Consul-General Dubai 1981; Counsellor, FCO 1985; HM Ambassador Kuwait 1987; m 1965 Archbold Harriet Siddall (3d 1967, 1969, 1972).

Hinchley, Carol Ruth; Second Secretary FCO since April 1991; born 9.4.59; FCO 1981; Gaborone 1983; Stockholm 1987.

Hinds, Catherine Rachel; FCO since December 1990; born 21.1.64; FCO 1986; Prague 1989; Grade S2.

Hinds, Sally Jane; Second Secretary (Commercial) Kiev since October 1989; born 1.9.64; FCO 1986; Language Training 1988; Third Secretary (Comm) Moscow 1989.

Hines, Trevor John; Third Secretary (Management/Cons) Belmopan since February 1990; born 10.11.60; FCO 1979; Floater 1982; Jedda 1984; Riyadh 1985; FCO 1987; Grade 9; m 1985 Sandra Bradley (1s 1992).

Hingston-Jones, Elizabeth Rosemary; Moscow since January 1991; born 27.6.63; FCO 1983; Peking 1985; Kuala Lumpur 1986; FCO 1990; Grade S2.

Hirst, Harold Christopher; Peking since January 1991; born 26.12.66; DHSS 1984; FCO 1984; Maseru 1987; Grade 10.

Hiscock, Stephen John; Deputy High Commissioner Georgetown since April 1988; born 16.6.46; Inland Revenue 1963; FO 1965; Kuala Lumpur 1968; Lusaka 1972; FCO 1976; Second Secretary 1977; Islamabad 1978; First Secretary (Comm/Inf) Seoul 1982; First Secretary FCO 1986; m (1) Gillian Denise Roe (diss 1982) (2s 1967, 1971); (2) 1983 Denise Mary Forster (1d 1986; 1s 1989; 1s 1991)

Hitchens, Timothy Mark; Second later First Secretary FCO since December 1989; (Private Secretary to the Minister of State 1991); born 7.5.62; FCO 1983; Language Training Tokyo 1985; Second Secretary Tokyo 1986; m 1985 Sara Kubra Husain (1d 1991).

Hoar, Gareth Keith; Washington since May 1991; born 23.6.65; FCO 1984; Peking 1986; Santiago 1989; Grade 9.

Hoare, James Edward; FCO since February 1992; born 16.4.43; Principal Research Officer (DS Grade 5); FCO 1969; Head of Chancery Seoul 1981; FCO 1985; Head of Chancery Peking 1988; m (1) 1965 Jane Maureen Fletcher (diss) (2s 1968,

1972); (2) 1978 Susan Pares (1d 1978).

Hobbs, Allan, MBE (1980); Second later First Secretary FCO since January 1980; born 17.12.32; GPO 1949; FO 1955; Seconded to WO 1959; Amman 1961; Brussels 1962; FO 1963; Bucharest 1965; FO 1966; Nairobi 1968; FCO 1970; Prague 1971; FCO 1972 (Second Secretary 1973); Moscow 1977; m 1957 Patricia Ann Dwyer (2d 1957, 1960; 1s 1963).

Hobbs, Benjamin James; FCO since March 1992; born 10.2.73; Grade 10.

Hobbs, Jeremy Alexander; FCO since January 1991; born 8.2.61; SRO; m 1983 Ana Maria Eréndira (1s 1990).

Hoddinott, Colin William, MBE (1986); Attaché New Delhi since March 1983; born 25.3.40; GPO 1956; FO 1964; Capetown1/Pretoria 1967; FCO 1970; Nicosia 1975; FCO 1978; Grade 7; m 1966 Gabrielle Crouch (1s 1969).

Hodge, James William; Counsellor FCO since March 1990; born 24.12.43; Third Secretary Commonwealth Office 1966; Tokyo 1967; Second Secretary (Inf) Tokyo 1970; First Secretary FCO 1972; First Secretary (Dev) later (Chancery) Lagos 1975; FCO 1978; First Secretary (Econ) Tokyo 1981 later Counsellor (Commercial); Counsellor and Head of Chancery Copenhagen 1986; m 1970 Frances Margaret Coyne (3d 1973, 1975, 1979).

Hodge, Michael, MBE (1975); Counsellor FCO since July 1992; born 12.6.44; FO 1962; Belgrade 1965; Paris 1968; Bahrain 1970; Second Secretary 1971; Kaduna 1972; Kampala 1973; FCO 1974; First Secretary (Econ) Copenhagen 1978; First Secretary FCO 1983; on loan to ICI 1987; First Secretary (Comm) Paris 1989; m 1966 Wilhelmina Marjorie Glover (1d 1967; 1s 1968).

Hodges, Adele (née Bushnell); Peking since April 1992; born 9.4.70; Grade 10; m 1992 Jeremy Andrew Hodges.

Hodges, Ian Foyle; Paris since December 1990; born 30.10.67; FCO 1987; Budapest 1989; Grade 10; m 1991 Patricia Paule Andreé Seguin (1s 1992).

Hodges, Jeremy Andrew; Peking since April 1992; born 16.7.67; FCO 1988; Floater Duties 1990; Grade 10.

Hodgetts, Susan Jacqueline; Vice-Consul Bucharest since November 1990; born 7.11.48; DSAO (later FCO) 1967; Lagos 1970; Warsaw 1973; Montevideo 1975; FCO 1978; Bridgetown 1981; FCO 1985; Grade 9.

Hodgkinson, Bonita Faye; Lusaka since July 1992; born 30.9.69; DHSS 1986; FCO 1988;

Addis Ababa 1991; Grade 10.

Hodgson, Allen Richard; Geneva since October 1991; born 8.2.60; FCO 1977; Grade 10; m 1989 Sally Maureen Cole-Hamilton.

Hodgson, Arthur Raymond; Paris since July 1991; born 12.4.34; PSA (DOE) 1974; Moscow 1982; Cairo 1984; Tel Aviv 1988; m 1956 Jill Herdman (2s 1957, 1959 (dec'd), 1978; 1d 1958); Grade SO.

Hodgson, George Kenneth; FCO since June 1992; born 15.2.49; FCO 1969; Lagos 1971; Belgrade 1974; Berlin CG 1975; Reykjavik 1976; Karachi 1977; FCO 1979; DHSS 1980-84; FCO 1984; Colombo 1985; Luxembourg 1989; Grade 9; m 1971 Jill Taylor (1s 1975; 2d 1978, 1980).

Hodgson, Kaye Irene; Washington since October 1991; born 7.11.59; FCO 1989; Grade S2.

Hoffman, Robert Anthony; Vice-Consul (Commercial) Chicago since November 1989; born 18.11.49; FCO 1968; Jakarta 1971; Dar es Salaam 1974; FCO 1978; Tunis 1981; Stockholm 1984; Second Secretary FCO 1987; m 1970 Anthea Elizabeth (diss 1986) (1d 1976).

Hogarth, Philip; Paris since February 1991; born 10.5.55; FCO 1970; Damascus 1978; Accra 1982; FCO 1984; Tokyo 1988; Grade 9; m 1978 Monique Marie Thérèse Morand.

Hogarth, Robert, MVO (1979); Second Secretary FCO since February 1992; born 27.5.38; Khartoum 1959; Washington 1962; Seoul 1965; FCO 1968; Tel Aviv 1973; Gaborone 1976; FCO 1980; Douala 1983; Second Secretary (Admin) Seoul 1987; m 1968 Hyun-Key Kim (1s 1971; 1d 1972).

Hoggard, Robin Richard; On loan to DTI since September 1991; born 26.11.56; FCO 1982; Language Training SOAS 1983; Second later First Secretary (Comm) Tokyo 1985; m 1988 Tonoko Komuro; First Secretary FCO 1989.

Hogger, Henry George; High Commissioner Windhoek since September 1992; born 9.11.48; Third Secretary FCO 1969; MECAS 1971; Aden 1972; Second Secretary Caracas 1972; Second later First Secretary Kuwait 1975; FCO 1978; First Secretary, Head of Chancery and Consul Abu Dhabi 1982; FCO 1986; Counsellor and Head of Chancery Amman 1989; m 1972 Fiona Jane McNabb (2d 1979, 1982; 2s 1984).

Hogwood, Jonathan Felix; FCO since April 1992; born 24.7.52; FCO 1971; Warsaw 1974; Islamabad 1975; Luanda 1978; FCO 1981; Dhaka 1986; Tokyo 1989; m 1978 Susan Elizabeth Farmer.

Hogwood, Susan Elizabeth (née Farmer), MBE (1981); First Secretary FCO since April 1992;

born 27.5.52; FCO 1971; Islamabad 1974; SUPL 1978; Second Secretary FCO 1982; Second Secretary (Aid) Dhaka 1986; Second later First Secretary (Consular) Tokyo 1989; m 1978 Jonathan Felix Hogwood.

Holden, Christopher John, OBE (1986); Counsellor FCO since August 1990; born 19.9.47; Third Secretary FCO 1970; MECAS 1971; Third later Second Secretary FCO 1973; Beirut 1974; Second later First Secretary (Econ/Inf) Tripoli 1977; FCO 1980; First Secretary (Chancery) Nairobi 1983; First Secretary (Chancery) later Counsellor Cairo 1986; m 1971 Jennifer Anne Moss (2s 1976, 1978).

Holder, Donald John; Second Secretary (Commercial) Bahrain since November 1990; born 16.8.50; FCO 1976; Bonn 1978; Islamabad 1981; FCO 1984; Auckland 1985; BMG Berlin 1987; FCO 1988.

Holder, Judith Ann, MBE (1974); Second later First Secretary (Management) Prague since August 1989; born 10.11.36; FO 1954; Baghdad 1958; Berlin 1959; FO 1962; Aden 1963; Prague 1965; Tokyo 1967; FCO 1970; Vienna 1976; New Delhi 1979; Second Secretary FCO 1983; Vice-Consul Frankfurt 1986.

Holdich, Patrick Godfrey Hungerford; FCO since May 1985; born 19.9.56; Senior Research Officer; Principal Research Officer 1990; m 1987 Ailsa Elizabeth Beaton.

Holding, John Francis; Consul-General and Counsellor (Commercial) Auckland since December 1990; born 12.8.36; HM Forces 1955-57; Ministry of Housing and Local Government 1957; CRO 1964; Karachi 1964; Second Secretary Rawalpindi/Islamabad 1965; FCO 1966; Second Secretary (Comm) and Vice-Consul, Kinshasa 1970; First Secretary (Econ) Canberra 1973; Deputy High Commissioner Banjul 1978; FCO 1980; Grenada 1984; Head of Chancery Bridgetown 1984; Deputy High Commissioner Dhaka 1987; m 1970 Pamela Margaret Straker-Nesbit (diss 1984) (2d 1971, 1974).

Holgate, Katherine Ann; Third Secretary (Chancery) Ankara since June 1991; born 7.5.66; FCO 1988; Language Training 1990; Grade 8.

Holifield, Martin; Kuwait since September 1991; born 8.9.61; FCO 1979; Islamabad 1986; FCO 1989; Grade 9; m 1985 Morag Catherine Fraser.

Holifield, Morag Catherine (née Fraser); Kuwait since December 1991; born 30.9.63; FCO 1982; SUPL 1986; FCO 1989; Grade S2; m 1985 Martin Holifield.

Hollamby, David James; First Secretary Rome since April 1990; born 19.5.45; CO 1961; DSAO 1964; Beirut 1967; Latin America Floater 1970; Asunción 1972; Second Secretary FCO 1975;

Vice-Consul (Comm) BTDO New York 1978; Consul (Comm) Dallas 1983; First Secretary FCO 1986; m 1971 Maria Helena Guzman.

Holland, Denise Ann; JLG Hong Kong since November 1991; born 13.4.63; FCO 1986; Washington 1989; Grade S2.

Holland, Henry Robert Cumber; First Secretary FCO since September 1989; born 25.11.57; FCO 1984; Second Secretary (Chancery) Nairobi 1986; m 1983 Anne Elizabeth Wardle (1s 1987).

Holland, Patricia Anne; Second later First Secretary FCO since December 1989; born 2.4.64; FCO 1986; Third Secretary (Chancery) Prague 1988.

Holland, Tracey Joanne; Full-Time Language Training Tokyo since August 1992; born 16.7.66; FCO 1990; Language Training 1991; Grade 9.

Hollands, Pamela; Nairobi since August 1991; born 28.6.39; FCO 1984; Belmopan 1986; m 1961 (diss 1979); (2s 1963, 1965); Grade S2.

Hollas, Robert Richmond Maxwell; Second Secretary FCO since August 1984; born 9.4.41; CRO 1959; Salisbury 1962; DSAO 1965; Prague 1966; Kinshasa 1967; Cairo 1970; FCO 1974; Rome 1977; Second Secretary (Admin) The Hague 1980; m 1962 Virginia Christine Watson (3s 1965, 1968, 1974).

Hollis, Anthonia; Bonn since February 1992; born 2.1.66; FCO 1987; Grade 10.

Hollis, Charles John Christian; Second Secretary FCO since August 1992; born 4.4.62; FCO 1984; Language Training 1986; Second Secretary (Chancery) Baghdad 1988; Second Secretary (Chancery) Riyadh 1988.

Hollis, Ian Malcolm; FCO since July 1989; born 16.12.70; Grade 10.

Holloway, Michael John; FCO since January 1991; First Secretary 1992; born 14.1.57; FCO 1976; Dubai 1978, Bucharest 1979; Africa Floater 1981; Mexico City 1983; FCO 1984; Barcelona 1988; Grade 9.

Holmes, Alan, MBE (1984); HM Consul-General Aden since November 1990; born 27.2.40; Ministry of Housing and Local Government 1958; FO 1964; Kabul 1966; Paris 1968; FCO 1970; Moscow 1971; Geneva 1971; FCO 1973; MECAS 1975; Tripoli 1976; Second later First Secretary (Comm) Jedda 1980; First Secretary FCO 1984; HM Consul Durban 1988; m 1964 Patricia Walsingham (1s 1965; 1d 1967).

Holmes, Alan Thomas; Cairo since October 1989; born 28.9.53; FCO 1977; UKDEL NATO Brussels 1980; FCO 1982; Bridgetown 1986; Grade 9; m 1980 Helen Hook.

Holmes, Barbara (née Walsh); SUPL since November 1989; born 2.2.53; Tokyo 1974; Budapest 1977; Aden 1981; FCO 1981; Grade S2; m 1987 Kevin Leslie Holmes (2s 1990, 1991).

Holmes, Cecil Robert LVO (1988); First Secretary FCO since November 1990; born 29.5.40; FO 1957; Moscow 1961; Santiago 1962; Budapest 1965; Bonn 1967; FCO 1970; Nuku'alofa, Tonga 1973; Second Secretary Oslo 1975; Vice-Consul Chicago 1979; Second later First Secretary FCO 1982; First Secretary (Admin) Madrid 1986; m 1962 Margaret Jean Laing (2d 1964, 1967; 1s 1971).

Holmes, Helen (née Hook); Cairo since October 1989; born 26.5.51; Department of Employment and Productivity 1969; FCO 1969; Bangkok 1973; Lagos 1975; FCO 1976; SUPL 1980; FCO 1982; Bridgetown 1986; Grade 9; m 1980 Alan Thomas Holmes.

Holmes, John Dominic; The Hague since June 1991; born 18.8.59; Inland Revenue 1977; FCO 1978; Paris 1984; FCO 1987; Warsaw 1989; Grade 9.

Holmes, John Eaton; Counsellor and Head of Chancery (later Counsellor (Econ/Comm) New Delhi since June 1991; born 29.4.51; Third Secretary FCO 1973; Language training 1975; Third Secretary Moscow 1976; Second later First Secretary FCO 1978; First Secretary (Econ) Paris 1984; First Secretary FCO 1987; Counsellor 1989; on Secondment to the De La Rue Company 1989; m 1976 Margaret Penelope Morris (3d 1981, 1982, 1985).

Holmes, John Philip, BEM; Paris since June 1991; born 12.4.33; RAF 1950-80; Prague 1982; Pretoria 1984; Moscow 1986; Brasilia 1987; Grade SO; m 1959 Jean May Amelia Stuart.

Holmes, Michael, MBE (1981); HM Consul Florence and HM Consul-General to the Republic of San Marino since July 1992; born 23.2.40; FO 1957; Berlin 1961; Baghdad 1964; Latin America Floater 1966; Full-time Language Training 1968; Third Secretary Ulan Bator 1969; Third Secretary (Comm) Budapest 1971; FCO 1972; Second Secretary (Comm) Lusaka 1976; Consul, Moscow 1979; Deputy High Commissioner Nassau 1982; First Secretary FCO 1986; HM Consul Kiev 1991; m 1973 Anne Green (1d 1975; 2s 1979, 1985).

Holmes, Michael, MVO (1991); Second Secretary (Cons/Comm) Melbourne since August 1992; born 3.4.54; FCO 1973; Belmopan 1975; Rio de Janeiro 1978; Baghdad 1981; FCO 1985; Third Secretary Harare 1988; m 1980 Jennifer Margaret Lesley Pike (1d 1982; 1s 1985).

Holmes, Peter Albert Scott; Second Secretary (Management) and Consul Algiers since March

1991; born 13.9.37; FO 1964; Moscow 1966; Benghazi 1966; Rawalpindi1/Islamabad 1969; FCO 1972; Strasbourg 1973; Singapore 1975; FCO 1978; Dhaka 1981; JAO Brussels 1984; FCO 1986; m 1974 Thérese Cecile (1 step d 1969; 1s 1975).

Holmes, Peter Rodney; First Secretary FCO since September 1990; born 29.7.38; FO 1956; Vice-Consul Strasbourg 1959; Vice-Consul Belgrade 1963; Second Secretary (Econ) Paris 1966; Assistant Economic Secretary, CENTO, Ankara 1969; FCO 1971; First Secretary (Inf) Stockholm 1974; Consul Douala 1978; also non-resident First Secretary (Comm) and Consul to Malabo; First Secretary FCO 1980; First Secretary (Comm) and Head of Chancery Bahrain 1983; First Secretary (Comm) Santiago 1987; m 1957 Anne Cecilia Tarrant (1s 1958; 3d 1960, 1962, 1968).

Holmes, Sally Ann; FCO since April 1991; born 7.2.65; FCO 1985; Tokyo 1988; Grade S2.

Holmes, Timothy Charles; First Secretary FCO since September 1990; born 26.4.51; Third Secretary FCO 1974; Language training SOAS 1975; Language training Tokyo 1976; Second later First Secretary Tokyo 1977; on loan to DOT 1981; First Secretary FCO 1983; First Secretary (Chancery) Islamabad 1986; m 1973 Anna-Carin Magnusson (1s 1977).

Holt, Denise Mary (née Mills); SUPL since July 1990; born 1.10.49; FCO 1970; First Secretary (Chancery) Dublin 1984; SUPL 1987; FCO 1988; m(1) 1972 Terence Rollinson (diss 1987); (2) 1987 John David Fletcher Holt (1s 1987).

Holt, (John) David (Fletcher); First Secretary (Chancery) Brasilia since April 1990; born 27.1.38; Royal Air Force 1956-63; Department of Technical Co-operation 1964; FO 1964; DSAO 1965; Delhi 1968; Assistant Private Secretary to the Secretary of State 1972 (Second Secretary 1975); On loan to CSD, PS to the Prime Minister 1976; Vice-Consul (Comm) Rio de Janeiro 1980; First Secretary (Chancery) Dublin 1983; First Secretary FCO 1988; m (1) 1968 Pamela Deirdre Woodroffe-Stacey (diss); (2) 1987 Denise Mary Mills (1s 1987).

Holt, Sean Christopher Eric; First Secretary (Political) Accra since March 1991; born 18.12.49; Army 1968-78; FCO 1978; Second Secretary Havana 1979; First Secretary FCO 1980; Athens 1982; First Secretary FCO 1984; First Secretary (Chancery) Khartoum 1987; First Secretary FCO 1990; m (1) 1973 Jennifer Patricia Trevaskis (diss 1987) (1s 1974; 1d 1976); (2) 1987 Joyce Amanda Anderson.

Holtum, Roger Adrian; Third Secretary (Aid/Comm) Kampala since May 1991; born 2.10.51; FCO 1972; Port of Spain 1975; Tel Aviv 1978; FCO 1981; Dhaka 1983; Helsinki 1986; FCO

1989; Grade 9; m 1983 Nina Lange (1d 1984, 1s 1986).

Holyer, John Albert; Third Secretary (Consular) · Ottawa since May 1990; born 26.4.41; RAF 1958-70; FCO 1971; Freetown 1974; Budapest 1978; Lisbon 1980; FCO 1983; Bombay 1986; Grade 9; m 1964 Morag Reid (2d 1968, 1969).

Homer, Richard David; FCO since June 1992; born 24.12.72; Grade 10.

Hone, Michael Stuart, MBE (1978); Chief Secretary, St. Helena since November 1990; born 19.5.36; Royal Navy 1951-61; CRO 1961; Kingston 1962; CRO 1964; Nairobi 1965; Lisbon 1967; Bridgetown 1970; FCO 1972; Beirut 1976; Baghdad 1978; FCO 1978 (Second Secretary 1979); on loan to DOT 1980; FCO 1982; Canberra 1983; Second later First Secretary and Resident Rep St Vincent and the Grenadines 1985; First Secretary FCO 1988; m (1) 1957 (3s 1962, 1963, 1965); m (2) 1983 Dr Elizabeth Ann Balmer (1s 1983; 1d 1988).

Hood, Laura Elizabeth, FCO since November 1989; born 27.4.63; FCO 1983, Bucharest 1985; Port of Spain 1987; Grade 10.

Hood, Linda Karen; Valletta since February 1991; born 23.2.59: FCO 1985; Bangkok 1987; FCO 1990; Grade S2.

Hook, David; Vice-Consul Houston since August 1991; born 26.5.51; FCO 1971; Kuala Lumpur 1973; Addis Ababa 1974; La Paz 1975; Amman 1976; FCO 1977; Tripoli 1980; Stockholm 1983; FCO 1985; Third Secretary (Admin) and Vice-Consul Kabul 1988; New Delhi 1989; Grade 9; m 1973 (1) Jannette Marie Sharp (diss 1980); (2) 1984 Anna-Karin Bengtsson.

Hook, Neil Kenneth, MVO (1983); First Secretary FCO since August 1992; born 24.4.45; FCO 1968; Moscow 1971; FCO 1972; Language training Sheffield University 1974; Tokyo 1975; Second Secretary (Aid) Dhaka 1980; First Secretary FCO 1984; On loan to DTI 1986; First Secretary (Commercial) Tokyo 1987; m 1973 Pauline Ann Hamilton (1d 1975; 1s 1977).

Hooper, Karen; FCO since June 1990; born 28.5.60; FCO 1980; Port Stanley 1983; Berne 1984; Cairo 1987; Grade 9; m 1984 Thomas Park Rae.

Hope, Marcus Laurence Hulbert; Counsellor (Comm) Jakarta since March 1989; (Deputy Head of Mission August 1989); born 2.2.42; Third Secretary CRO 1965; MECAS 1966; Second Secretary (Inf) Tripoli 1968; FCO 1970; First Secretary Dubai 1974; First Secretary (Comm) Bonn 1976; FCO 1980; Counsellor NDC Rome 1984; Counsellor Beirut 1984; Counsellor FCO 1985; Head of Chancery Berne 1985; m 1980 Uta Maria Luise Müller-

Unverfehrt (1s 1985).

Hopkins, Francis Joseph; New York since November 1991; born 23.9.36; HM Forces (Army) 1959-82; Peking 1984; Lagos 1985; Budapest 1986; Rome 1988; Moscow 1990; Grade SO; m 1959 Judith Ann (3s 1960, 1963, 1971).

Hopkins, Mark Andrew; FCO since September 1990; born 31.8.71; Grade 10.

Hopkinson, Bryan; Second later First Secretary (Chancery) Lisbon since January 1989; born 24.11.56; FCO 1980; Kampala 1981; Resigned 1985; Reinstated 1987; Second Secretary FCO 1987; m 1987 Stephanie Burd.

Hopkinson, Celia Lois; Lusaka since June 1992; born 9.10.59; FCO 1979; UKMIS New York 1982; Sofia 1984; Paris 1986; FCO 1988; Grade 9.

Hopkinson, Moira Elizabeth; FCO since April 1990; born 28.8.59; FCO 1980; Copenhagen 1982; Peking 1985; Islamabad 1986; Grade 9.

Hopper, Colin David; FCO since March 1982; born 31.10.53; FCO 1971; Paris 1979; Grade 7; m 1979 Lesley Greaves.

Hopton, Nicholas Dunster; Second Secretary (Political/Information) Rabat since November 1991; born 8.10.65; FCO 1989; Grade 8.

Horine, Fern Marion; UKDEL Vienna since January 1990; born 28.7.69; FCO 1987; Grade 10.

Horn, Helen Margaret; Second Secretary and Deputy Head of Mission Kinshasa since October 1992; born 27.4.61; FCO 1981; Warsaw 1984; Vice-Consul (Comm) Zurich 1986; FCO 1989.

Horne, Gordon; UKMIS New York since May 1992; born 5.12.66; FCO 1986; Riyadh 1988; Grade 10; m 1989 Susan Lisa Berry.

Horne, Michael John; FCO since August 1992; born 29.5.44; FO 1961; Bucharest 1965; Bangkok 1967; Accra 1971; FCO 1975; Second Secretary (Comm) Kuala Lumpur 1978; Second later First Secretary Libreville 1981; FCO 1985; on loan to No. 10 Downing Street 1985; Consul (Inf) BIS New York 1987; m 1965 Deborah Elaine Hopkinson (1s 1966; 1d 1971).

Horner, Gill Vanessa; UKMIS Geneva since January 1991; born 8.5.61; FCO 1987; Prague 1989; Grade S2.

Horner, Katharine Sarah Julia; FCO since April 1987; born 15.8.52; FCO 1980; Second Secretary Moscow 1985; Senior Research Officer.

Horner, Simon; Nassau since March 1991; born

10.12.69; DHSS 1987; FCO 1988; Grade 10.

Horrell, Roger William, CMG (1988), OBE (1974); First Secretary later Counsellor FCO since March 1980; born 9.7.35; FO 1964; Economic Officer Dubai 1965; First Secretary FO (later FCO) 1967; Kampala 1970; FCO 1973; Lusaka 1976; m 1970 Patricia Mildred Eileen Smith (diss 1975) (1s 1972; 1d 1973).

Hosker, Colin; FCO since January 1983; born 24.1.42; FO 1964; Delhi 1965; FO 1967; Baghdad 1968; FCO 1969; Peking 1970; FCO 1972; St Helena 1974; FCO 1976; Tripoli 1976; FCO 1979; Havana 1980; Grade 8; m 1973 Joan Lavinia Martin (1s 1977; 1d 1979).

Houghton, Jane Louise; FCO since February 1991; born 5.12.64; FCO 1984; Santiago 1987; Grade S2.

House, Gregory Stewart; Lilongwe since March 1991; born 3.6.68; FCO 1988; Grade 10.

Houston, Sharon Linda; Bridgetown since October 1991; FCO 1989; born 14.6.68; Grade 10.

Howard, Alayne Anne (née Whitehouse); Third Secretary (Immig) Bridgetown since May 1989; born 4.6.63; FCO 1982; New Delhi 1985; Grade 9; m 1984 Paul Howard (1s 1987).

Howard, (Charles Andrew) Paul, Bridgetown since May 1989; born 23.9.60; FCO 1983; New Delhi 1985; Grade 9; m 1984 Alayne Anne Whitehouse (1s 1987).

Howard, Richard Leslie Alan; Warsaw since July 1989; born 12.9.33; Royal Marines 1947-73; UKMIS Geneva 1973; Sofia 1974; Washington 1978; BMG Berlin 1981; Accra 1984; Vienna 1986; Grade SO; m (1) Edna May Dudley (2d 1959, 1968); (2) 1984 Helga Rita Shaw.

Howarth, Stephen Frederick; First Secretary later Counsellor FCO since May 1988; born 25.2.47; FCO 1966; Rabat 1971; Washington 1975; Second Secretary 1976; First Secretary FCO 1982; Seconded ENA Paris 1982; FCO 1983; First Secretary and Head of Chancery Dakar 1984; m 1966 Jennifer Mary Chrissop (2d 1966, 1970; 1s 1974).

Howe, Malcolm; New Delhi since October 1990; born 14.2.45; Army 1965; Belgrade 1987; Peking 1989; Grade SO; m 1965 Nancy Crowden Peacock (2d 1966, 1967; 1s 1974).

Howe-Jones, Vanessa Jane; FCO since September 1991; born 23.6.65; Grade 7.

Howel, Iwan Gruffydd ap; Washington since May 1991; born 5.1.68; FCO 1988; Grade 10.

Howell, Kenneth Baxter; Second Secretary Dubai since June 1990; born 22.12.44; HCS 1961; FCO

1969; Cape Town 1972; FCO 1973; Vienna 1976; Rome 1977; FCO 1978; Tel Aviv 1983; FCO 1986 (Second Secretary 1987); m 1970 Josephine Fitzsimmons (2s 1973, 1974).

Howell, Michael Edward, CMG (1989), OBE (1980); High Commissioner Port Louis, since August 1989; (also HM Ambassador to the Comoros (non-resident) 1989-1991); born 2.5.33; HM Forces 1951-53; CO 1953; CRO 1958; Karachi 1959; Second Secretary Bombay 1962; Geneva 1966; First Secretary FCO 1969; Consul (Comm) New York 1973; On loan to National Defence College 1975; First Secretary FCO 1976; Head of Chancery and Consul Kabul 1978; Consul-General Berlin 1981; Consul-General Frankfurt 1983; High Commissioner Port Moresby 1986; m 1958 Joan Little (1s 1962; 1d 1965).

Howell, Commander Richard; Queen's Messenger since 1982; born 30.3.34; Royal Navy 1952-1982.

Howells, Julie (née Satchell); Seoul since April 1991; born 3.6.64; FCO 1982; UKDEL NATO Brussels 1986; Grade S2A; m 1991 David Howells.

Howie, Louise Senga Mary; Prague since March 1992; born 13.9.70; Scottish Office 1989; FCO 1989; Grade 10.

Howitt, Derrick; Colombo since November 1991; born 14.2.43; Royal Navy 1958-83; Moscow 1983; Paris 1985; Singapore 1988; Grade SO; m 1966 Averil E Rose (1d 1968; 1s 1972).

Howlett, David John; FCO since June1982; born 17.1.55; Principal Research Officer; m 1979 Bridget Mary de Boer.

Howlett, John Frederick; Berlin since July 1991; born 22.1.34; HM Forces 1950-79; Prague 1980; New Delhi 1982; Havana 1983; UKDEL NATO Brussels 1985; New York 1988; Grade SO; m 1961 Heidrun von Rode-Diezelsky (1d 1963; 1s 1965).

Howlett, Keith Raymond; FCO since July 1989; born 29.3.50; FCO 1968; Moscow 1980; FCO 1982; Tokyo 1986; Grade 7; m 1984 Claudine Cecile Odette Stedman.

Howley, Maureen Teresa; Second Secretary FCO since April 1989; born 10.1.37; Bahrain 1959; FO 1961; Amman 1962; DSAO later FCO 1965; Delhi 1971; FCO 1973; Cape Town 1980; Warsaw 1983; Atlanta 1985.

Huckle, Alan Edden; Counsellor UKDEL CSCE Vienna since January 1992; born 15.6.48; CSD 1971; HCS 1974; CSD 1975; HCS 1978; First Secretary FCO 1980; Executive Director BIS New York 1983; Head of Chancery Manila 1987; First Secretary FCO 1990; m 1973 Helen Myra Gibson (1s 1981; 1d 1985).

Huckle, Steven Allan; FCO since March 1992; born 24.10.64; FCO 1981; UKREP Brussels 1989; Grade 8; m 1987 Alison Porter (1s 1990, 1d 1991).

Hudman, Anne (née Lister); FCO since July 1992; born 1.9.62; FCO 1987; Helsinki 1989; Grade S3; m 1991 Roger Grenville Hudman.

Hudson, David John; FCO since February 1986; born 3.8.38; RAF 1957-60; Singapore 1961; Ankara 1963; Baghdad 1968; FCO 1969; Accra 1972; Bonn 1973; Khartoum 1976; FCO 1979; Colombo 1982; Grade 9; m 1961 Marlene Violet Victorine Daviot (1d 1966; 1s 1971).

Hudson, Julie Marie; Gaborone since August 1988; born 25.5.65; FCO 1984; Riyadh 1986; Grade S2.

Huggins, Elizabeth Jane; Copenhagen since March 1992; born 25.6.70; DSS 1987-1989; FCO 1989; Grade 10.

Hughes, Antony Joseph; Second Secretary FCO since August 1989; born 23.8.36; FCO 1970; La Paz 1972; Washington 1973; Abu Dhabi 1976; Sofia 1978; FCO 1980; Auckland 1983; Vice-Consul (Admin/Cons) Karachi 1987; m 1975 Elizabeth Anne Stark (2d 1979, 1983).

Hughes, Edgar John; First Secretary later Counsellor FCO since January 1989; born 27.7.47; FCO 1973; On secondment to Cabinet Office 1979; First Secretary CSCE Madrid 1981; FCO 1982; First Secretary and Head of Chancery Santiago 1983; First Secretary (Inf) Washington 1985; m 1982 Lynne Evans (2s 1984, 1988).

Hughes, Ian Noel; First Secretary FCO since March 1991; born 5.12.51; FCO 1971; Latin America Floater 1974; Kabul 1976; Warsaw 1980; FCO 1982; Second Secretary and Vice-Consul Tegucigalpa 1985; First Secretary (Pol) Berne 1988; m 1978 Tereasa June Tinguely (2s 1979, 1981; 1d 1984).

Hughes, Nicola Anna; Manila since February 1992; born 9.3.70; FCO 1988; Grade 9.

Hughes, Peter John; Vice-Consul (Comm) Sydney since June 1989; born 14.9.53; FCO 1976; Islamabad 1978; Rome 1980; Warsaw 1983; FCO 1985 (Second Secretary 1987); m 1978 Jacqueline Alexander (diss 1987).

Hughes, Peter Thomas; First Secretary FCO since May 1991; born 22.12.58; FCO 1982; Second later First Secretary UKMIS Geneva 1985; SUPL 1988; m 1981 Morag Cameron McLure (1d 1991).

Hughes, Richard Farrell; Islamabad since January 1988; born 10.5.33; Army 1948-73; Belgrade 1974; New Delhi 1976; Tehran 1979;

Lagos 1980; Brasilia 1981; Lilongwe 1984; Warsaw 1985; Lagos 1986; Grade SSO; m 1954 Joyce Catherine Grant (1s 1954; 3d 1956, 1959, 1961).

Hulands, Michael Robert; FCO since August 1990; born 29.11.53; FCO 1970; Singapore 1976; Tel Aviv 1978; FCO 1981; Third Secretary Bangkok 1983; Addis Ababa 1986; Grade 7; m 1979 Normah Binti Maznun (1d 1981).

Hulburd, Rachel Kate; Nicosia since October 1992; born 11.2.70; FCO 1989; Grade S2.

Hulse, Christopher, CMG (1992), OBE (1982); Counsellor FCO since May 1988; born 31.7.42; Third Secretary FO 1964; Third later Second Secretary Prague 1967; FCO 1970; First Secretary Bangkok 1972; FCO 1973; UKDEL NATO Brussels 1978; First Secretary Madrid (CSCE Unit) 1980; FCO 1981; Counsellor NDC Rome 1983; Counsellor and Consul-General Athens 1983; m 1966 Dimitra Carayannacou (1d 1969).

Hum, Christopher Owen; AUSS (North Asia) FCO since June 1992; born 27.1.46; FO 1967; Hong Kong 1968; Peking 1971; Second later First Secretary1/Private Secretary to Permanent Representative UKREP Brussels 1973; FCO 1975; First Secretary Peking 1979; First Secretary (Chancery) Paris 1981; First Secretary FCO 1983; Counsellor and Deputy Head of Falkland Islands Department FCO 1985; Counsellor FCO 1986; Counsellor and Head of Chancery UKMIS New York 1989; m 1970 Julia Mary Park (1d 1974; 1s 1976).

Humfrey, Charles Thomas William; Counsellor (Econ) Tokyo since April 1990; born 1.12.47; Third Secretary FCO 1969; Language student Sheffield University 1970; Tokyo 1971 (Second Secretary 1972, First Secretary 1976); FCO 1976; Private Secretary to Minister of State 1979; UKMIS New York 1981; First Secretary FCO 1985; Counsellor Ankara 1988; m 1971 Enid Wyn Thomas (2s 1975; 1983; 1d 1977).

Humphrey, Desmond Keith; First Secretary FCO since January 1990; born 23.9.39; RAF 1956-69; FCO 1970; Hanover 1973; East Berlin 1976; FCO 1979; Second Secretary (Admin) and Vice-Consul Lima 1982; Second Secretary (Comm) Vienna 1986; m 1973 Anne-Marie Berriman (2s 1976, 1979).

Humphries, Eric Henri Edward; Zagreb since June 1992; born 11.10.59; FCO 1978; Islamabad 1982; Nairobi 1984; Victoria 1987; FCO 1990; Grade 9; m 1982 Sara Dorothy Watts (1d 1984).

Hunt, Alan Charles, CMG (1990); Consul-General Dusseldorf and Director-General of Trade and Investment Promotion in Germany since November 1991; born 5.3.41; Ministry of Power

1958; FO 1959; Vice-Consul Tehran 1962; Jedda 1964; Latin America Floater 1965; SUPL to attend University 1967; Second Secretary 1969; FCO 1970; First Secretary Head of Chancery and Consul Panama City 1973; First Secretary FCO 1976; First Secretary (Comm) Madrid 1977; FCO 1981; Counsellor (Econ/Comm) Oslo 1983; Head of British Interests Section Buenos Aires 1987; Counsellor FCO 1990; m 1978 Meredith Margaret Claydon (2d 1980, 1982).

Hunt, Mary Elizabeth; First Secretary and Consul-General Paris since April 1991; born 13.1.35; Paris 1958; London 1960; Vientiane 1963; FO 1965; Jakarta 1967; Rome 1970; SE Asia Floater 1972; FCO 1974; Vice-Consul Strasbourg 1979; Vice-Consul (Comm) Milan 1980; First Secretary (Inf) Paris 1984; First Secretary FCO 1988.

Hunt, Peter Lawrence; FCO since September 1990; born 10.6.45; FO 1962; DSAO 1965; Africa Floater duties 1967; Brussels 1969; Managua 1970; FCO 1973; Second Secretary (Comm) Caracas 1978; First Secretary FCO 1982; Head of Chancery Montevideo 1987; m 1971 Anne Langhorne Carson (2d 1972, 1977; 2s 1974, 1984).

Hunt, Sara Jennifer; Bonn since February 1990; born 29.10.67; FCO 1987; Grade 10.

Hunt, Stephen Anthony; FCO since November 1990; born 3.9.57; MOD 1977; FCO 1978; Lisbon 1981; Prague 1984; Gaborone 1986; Moscow 1988; Grade 9; m 1984 Eileen Crossan.

Hunter, Alistair John, CMG (1985); HM Consul-General New York and Director-General of Trade and Investment Promotion in the USA since December 1991; born 9.8.36; CRO 1961; Private Secretary to Permanent Under-Secretary 1961; Second later First Secretary Kuala Lumpur 1963; First Secretary (Comm) Peking 1965; On loan to the Cabinet Office 1969; FCO 1970; Rome 1973; First Secretary later Counsellor FCO 1975; Head of Personnel Services Department FCO 1976; Counsellor and Head of Chancery Bonn 1980; on loan to DTI (AUSS) 1985; Consul-General Düsseldorf and Director-General of Trade and Investment Promotion in the FRG 1988; m (1) 1963 Gillian Bradbury (2d 1966, 1970; 1s 1970); (2) 1978 Helge Milton (née Kahle).

Hunter, Claire Stewart; FCO since December 1990; born 2.3.69; Grade S2A.

Hunter, Maxine Launa; Bangkok since June 1992; born 9.12.64; FCO 1988; Washington 1989; Grade S2.

Hunter, Paulette Elaine; Peking since June 1990; born 17.10.65; FCO 1985; Lagos 1987; Grade S2.

Hunter, Robert; Vice-Consul (Consular/

Management) Suva since November 1989; born 10.8.47; HM Forces 1964-70; Merchant Navy 1973-74; FCO 1974; Darwin 1975; Beirut 1976; Peking 1977; FCO 1979; Lilongwe 1980; Jedda 1981; FCO 1984; Pretoria 1985; FCO 1988; Grade 9; m 1981 Carol Mary Chorley.

Hunter, Sally; Karachi since January 1985; born 10.12.65; FCO 1985; Grade 10.

Hunter, Wendy; FCO since September 1987; born 9.11.67; Grade 9.

Hurran, Christopher John; First Secretary FCO since June 1990; born 27.8.48; HM Forces 1967-80; FCO 1980; First Secretary Kuwait 1983; First Secretary (Chancery) Caracas 1986.

Hurt, Jane Michelle; Rome since March 1990; born 13.9.65; FCO 1987; Grade 10.

Hustwitt, Justin John; Language Training since September 1992; born 8.9.67; FCO 1991; Grade 8.

Hutchings, Richard Jeremy; First Secretary Consul and Deputy Head of Mission San José since October 1991; born 3.8.34; Army 1955-76; First Secretary FCO 1976; Hong Kong 1980; First Secretary FCO 1983; First Secretary (Chancery/Information) Montevideo 1990; m 1969 Sigrid Slesarenko (3s 1969, 1971, 1976).

Hutson, Sarah; FCO since November 1991; born 28.1.61; FCO 1983; Accra 1985; Ankara 1988; Grade S2.

Hutton, Susan Margaret; Georgetown since March 1989; born 1.4.59; FCO 1984; Grade S2; m 1990 Jonathan Paul McCarthy.

Huxley, John Geoffrey, RVM (1984); Rome since February 1992; born 23.1.35; Amman 1967; Budapest 1968; Pretoria1/Cape Town 1970; Jedda 1972; Islamabad 1973; Caracas 1975; UKDEL NATO Brussels 1978; Prague 1980; Cairo 1982; Amman 1984; The Hague 1985; Warsaw 1988; Ottawa 1989; Grade CSO; m 1961 Monica Wall (dec'd 1987) (1s 1962; 2d 1964, 1966).

Huxley, Roger Christopher; First Secretary Stanley and Assistant Commissioner South Georgia and South Sandwich Islands since June 1990; born 5.12.39; DWS 1965; FCO 1970; Jakarta 1973; Athens 1977; Second Secretary (Comm) Abu Dhabi 1980; Second Secretary FCO 1984; First Secretary Head of Chancery and Consul Mogadishu 1987; m 1966 Enid Mary John (2d 1970, 1971).

Huxter, Rupert James Alexander; First Secretary FCO since January 1991; born 29.10.59; FCO 1985; Language Training 1987; Second Secretary (Info) Belgrade 1987; m 1984 Julia Robson.

Hyde, Dawn Michele (née Broomhead); SUPL since January 1990; born 26.7.62; FCO 1982; Rabat 1983; Dubai 1986; SUPL 1988; Washington 1988; Grade S2; m 1988 Michael Joseph Hyde (1d 1991).

Hyde, Martyn Arthur; Belgrade since July 1990; born 19.3.38; MOD 1965; Metropolitan Police 1976; FCO 1981; Kuala Lumpur 1986; Grade 8; m 1961 Lesley Jackson (3d 1963, 1966, 1968).

Hyde, Richard Damian; Hamilton since December 1991; born 18.9.69; FCO 1989; Grade 10.

Hyde, Richard Wingfield, MBE (1981); Second Secretary (Admin) and Vice-Consul Yaoundé since April 1988; born 29.3.42; Board of Trade 1965; FCO 1968; Vienna 1971; Rangoon 1974; Brussels (EC) 1976; FCO 1980; Second Secretary Antananarivo 1984; m 1965 Brigitte Pachot (diss 1983) (1s 1966; 1d 1969); m 1985 Ana Julie Rasoanaivo.

Hyland, Mark; FCO since November 1990; born 3.7.69; HCS 1986; Grade 10.

Hyland, Susan Margaret; Second Secretary FCO since September 1990; born 30.10.64.

Hyman, Timothy; FCO since December 1990; born 10.10.64; FCO 1982; Washington 1988; Grade 8; m 1988 Michéle Webb.

Hyner, Shelagh Rosalind; New York (CG) since April 1990; born 28.6.42; Tel Aviv 1968; Mexico City 1970; FCO 1972; Athens 1974; FCO 1977; Antigua 1978; FCO 1980; Rabat 1983; FCO 1986; Grade 9; m 1991 John Edward Needham.

I

Idowu, Sandra; UKMIS Vienna since October 1990; born 2.10.60; FCO 1988; Grade S2.

Illman, John; Consul-General Marseilles and for the Principality of Monaco since August 1990; born 26.10.40; FO 1961; Leopoldville (later Kinshasa) 1963; Dublin 1967; Second Secretary (Comm) 1968; Second Secretary (Econ) Paris 1971; First Secretary FCO 1973; First Secretary and Head of Chancery Buenos Aires 1975; Lagos 1979; First Secretary FCO 1982; Counsellor, Head of Chancery, Consul-General Algiers 1986; m 1962 Elizabeth Hunter Frame (2d 1964, 1967; 1s 1972).

Imray, Sir Colin (Henry), KBE (1992), CMG (1983); High Commissioner Dhaka since October 1989; born 21.9.33; Army 1952-54; CRO 1957; Third later Second Secretary Canberra 1958; CRO 1961 (First Secretary 1962); First Secretary (Chancery) Nairobi 1963; Commonwealth Office 1966; DSAO (later FCO) 1967; Trade Commissioner Montreal 1970; Counsellor and Head of Chancery Islamabad 1973; RCDS 1977; Counsellor Tel Aviv 1977; FCO Rayner Project Officer 1980; Deputy High Commissioner Bombay 1980; AUSS (Deputy Chief Clerk) and Chief Inspector FCO 1984; High Commissioner Dar es Salaam 1986; m 1957 Shirley Matthews (1s 1959; 3d 1960, 1962, 1965).

Ingall, Susannah Jane; Bucharest since October 1990; born 27.5.67; FCO 1988; Grade S2.

Ingamells, John Mawgan; Third Secretary (Comm) later Second Secretary (Inf) Buenos Aires since July 1990; born 8.6.61; FCO 1984; Language Training Seoul 1984; Third Secretary (Chancery) Seoul 1987; m 1990 Nicola Jane Dobb (1s 1991).

Ingham, Catherine; Islamabad since May 1989; born 7.9.63; FCO 1988; Grade S2.

Ingham, Christopher John; Deputy Head of Mission Bucharest since August 1991; born 4.6.44; FCO 1968; Moscow 1972; Calcutta 1974; Kuwait 1975; Second Secretary 1976; FCO 1977; First Secretary and Deputy Permanent Representative UKMIS Vienna 1981; First Secretary FCO 1985; First Secretary (Comm) Mexico City 1987; First Secretary FCO 1989; m 1968 Jacqueline Anne Clarke (1s 1971; 2d 1973, 1985).

Ingle, Alan Richmond; First Secretary FCO since January 1988; born 16.10.39; Board of Trade 1957; Accra (Trade Commission Service) 1961; FO 1965; Kingston 1966; Christchurch 1970; FCO 1974; Second Secretary (Comm) Singapore 1977; Second later First Secretary FCO 1981; Consul (Inf) BIS New York 1983; m 1963 Gillian Marsha Hall (1d 1965; 1s 1968).

Inglehearn, Catherine Mary; Rome since October 1992; born 15.5.65; FCO 1990; Grade 9.

Inglis, Thomas; SUPL since November 1990; born 12.12.43; HM Forces 1962-84; Havana 1988; Grade SO; m 1989 Helen Margaret Boutilier.

Ingold, Andrew Henrik; Vice-Consul Abu Dhabi since November 1990; born 30.7.53; Customs and Excise 1972; FCO 1973; Valletta 1975; Monrovia 1978; Paris 1982; FCO 1984; Bombay 1987; Grade 9.

Ingram, Sally Diana (née Wilkins); Second Secretary (Management) Bonn since October 1991; born 16.4.43; WRAF 1960; FCO 1969; Moscow 1972; Ottawa 1973; Valletta 1976; FCO 1978; Belmopan 1983; FCO 1987 (Second Secretary 1989); m 1982 Michael Ingram.

Inkster, Nigel Norman; Counsellor Athens since

May 1992; born 11.4.52; Third Secretary FCO 1975; Language Student1/Third Secretary Kuala Lumpur 1976; Third later Second Secretary FCO 1976; Second later First Secretary Bangkok 1979; FCO 1982; First Secretary and Consul Peking 1983; Buenos Aires 1985; First Secretary FCO 1989; m 1977 Leong Chui Fun (1d 1979; 1s 1981).

Innes, Peter Maxwell; Director BIS New York since July 1992; born 9.8.41; Ministry of Aviation 1960; FCO 1976; Second Secretary (Comm) Seoul 1979; Second later First Secretary FCO 1983; First Secretary (Agric/Cons) Dublin 1985; First Secretary FCO 1989; m 1965 Robina B W Robertson (1d 1970; 1s 1973).

Innes, Stuart Harcourt; First Secretary FCO since August 1989; born 30.10.55; FCO 1980; Doha 1983; Second Secretary Cairo 1986; m 1983 Susan Jane Wood (1s 1987; 1d 1989).

Innes-Hopkins, Christopher Randolph; Second Secretary (Comm/Econ) Tunis since June 1988; born 26.11.53; FCO 1976; Georgetown 1979; Paris 1982; Second Secretary FCO 1985; m 1983 Soraya Nizamodin Dookie (1s 1986).

Insall, Anthony John Godwin LVO (1986); Counsellor Kuala Lumpur since January 1992; born 27.6.49; FCO 1973; Third later Second Secretary (Inf) Lagos 1975; Second later First Secretary FCO 1977; Language Training Hong Kong 1982; First Secretary FCO 1983; First Secretary and Consul Peking 1985; First Secretary FCO 1988; m 1979 Leonie Bridget Meryon (3s 1980, 1982, 1984).

Insall, Christopher Wharton; FCO since October 1984; born 31.12.45; FCO 1966; Jedda 1970; FCO 1971; Paris 1981; Grade 9; m 1982 Lynn Melrose Irvine.

Ives, Malcolm Albert; On loan to the DTI since May 1992; born 10.3.47; MPNI 1964; FO (later FCO) 1966; Dacca 1969; FCO 1971; Sana;a 1973; Addis Ababa 1974; Warsaw 1976; FCO 1978; São Paulo 1981; Jakarta 1985; Second Secretary (Dev) Amman 1987; Second Secretary FCO 1991; m 1973 Susan Robertson (3s 1969, 1974, 1976).

Ivey, Peter Robert; Second Secretary (Inf/Chancery) Helsinki since March 1988; born 25.5.58; FCO 1982; Bahrain 1983; Language Training 1987; m 1987 Philippa Heidi Prince.

Ivins, James; First Secretary FCO since January 1989; born 3.10.42; FO 1962; Jakarta 1963; Vienna 1965; Tokyo 1967; Second Secretary Osaka 1970; Tokyo 1972; First Secretary 1975; On loan to DOT 1975; FCO 1976; Consul Rio de Janeiro 1977; Head of Chancery Maseru 1981; First Secretary on loan to DTI 1983; First Secretary (Comm) Tokyo 1986; m 1963 Patricia Ann Dimmock (1s 1965; 1d 1966).

Ivins, Suzanne Gillian (née Parker); FCO since January 1988; born 5.2.65; FCO 1983; Tokyo 1985; Grade 9; m 1988 James Browell Ivins.

Izzard, Richard Brian George; Accra since March 1992; born 4.1.69; Metropolitan Police 1987; FCO 1988; Sofia 1990; Grade 10.

J

Jack, Stuart Duncan Macdonald; HM Consul-General St Petersberg since September 1992; born 8.6.49; FCO 1972; Third later Second later First Secretary Tokyo 1974; FCO 1979; First Secretary and Press Attaché Moscow 1981; First Secretary FCO 1984; Bank of England 1984; First Secretary (Econ) Tokyo 1985; Counsellor FCO 1989; m 1977 Mariko Nobechi (2d 1980, 1982).

Jacklin, Michael Fraser; Copenhagen since March 1987; born 10.10.29; GPO 1945; HM Forces 1948-50; GPO 1950; FO 1965; Addis Ababa 1967; FCO 1968; New York 1969; FCO 1972; Kuala Lumpur 1973; Athens 1981; FCO 1984; Grade 8; m 1956 Joan Lydia Lester (2s 1964, 1966).

Jackson, Alison Margaret; UKMIS Geneva since November 1991; born 14.1.42; FO 1961; Manila 1970; FCO 1972; Canberra 1972; Brasilia 1975; Ankara 1977; FCO 1980; Mexico City 1982; UKDEL NATO Brussels 1984; FCO 1987; Grade S1.

Jackson, Andrew Jonathan Rupert; Second Secretary (Chancery) Prague since November 1992; born 24.10.61; FCO 1985; Second Secretary Havana 1988; FCO 1989; SUPL 1990; Second Secretary FCO 1990; m 1986 Alison Clare Broughton (diss 1991).

Jackson, Andrew Michael; Second Secretary FCO since July 1991; born 6.11.58; FCO 1984; Third Secretary (Chancery) Bonn 1987; m 1987 Susan Elizabeth Welsh (1d 1989).

Jackson, Carol Anne Pauline; FCO since September 1989; born 22.4.64; FCO 1984; Warsaw 1988; Grade 10.

Jackson, Derek John; First Secretary (Management) and Consul Prague since October 1992; born 19.3.46; HMSO 1967; FCO 1969; Bathurst 1972; Kathmandu 1976; On loan to ODM at Tristan da Cunha 1977; FCO 1980; Wiston House 1982; Second Secretary (Comm) Prague 1984; Consul (Comm) Milan 1988; First Secretary FCO 1989; m 1970 Rosemary Anne Charlton (1d 1976).

Jackson, Elizabeth Anne (née Irwin); SUPL since September 1990; born 8.8.56; FCO 1977;

Moscow 1980; Second later First Secretary UKDEL NATO Brussels 1982; First Secretary FCO 1985; SUPL 1986; First Secretary FCO 1986; m 1981 Richard Charles Edward Jackson (2s 1986, 1988).

Jackson, Helen; FCO since August 1992; born 27.1.62; FCO 1981; Stockholm 1983; Port of Spain 1986; Moscow 1990; Grade S2.

Jackson, John; First Secretary FCO since July 1981; born 20.7.42; FO (later FCO) 1965; Tokyo 1970; FCO 1974; Attachment to Hong Kong Government 1978; m 1966 Ann Marie Phelan (1s 1968; 2d 1970, 1976).

Jackson, Karen Jane; FCO since September 1990; born 20.6.68; Grade 9.

Jackson, Linda Margaret; FCO since June 1989; born 21.12.46; FO 1965; Prague 1968; Santiago 1969; Moscow 1972; FCO 1973; UKDEL Vienna 1976; Peking 1978; FCO 1979; Paris 1981; FCO 1984; Brussels 1986; Grade S1.

Jackson, Nicola Carron; FCO since August 1991; born 1.12.67; Grade 9.

Jackson, Paul Michael; Washington since July 1991; born 5.4.63; HCS 1982; FCO 1983; Islamabad 1985; FCO 1987; Grade 8; m 1984 Cheryl Barrington (1d 1986; 1s 1988).

Jackson, Robert Frederick; FCO since October 1990; born 8.2.57; FCO 1975; Prague 1978; Bandar Seri Begawan 1979; Gaborone 1981; Sana'a 1987; Grade 9; m 1977 Rosalind Barbara Sackett.

Jackson, Rosemary Anne; FCO since December 1989 (reinstated); born 9.1.51; Grade 9; m 1970 Derek John Jackson (1d 1976).

Jackson, Richard Michael, cvo (1983); HM Ambassador La Pax since May 1991; born 12.7.40; Scottish Office 1961; The Hague 1972; FCO 1975; First Secretary (Comm) and Head of Chancery Panama City 1976; First Secretary FCO 1979; Counsellor (Comm) Buenos Aires 1981; Counsellor, Consul-General and Head of Chancery Stockholm 1982; Counsellor (Comm) Seoul 1987; m 1961 Mollie Kitchin (1d 1963; 1s 1968).

Jackson-Houlston, William Lester; First Secretary (Chancery) Belgrade since July 1990; born 6.10.52; FCO 1979; Second Secretary UKREP Brussels 1980; Second later First Secretary FCO 1981; BIS Buenos Aires 1982; FCO 1986; m 1985 Susana Olivia Fitzpatrick (twins, 1s and 1d 1989).

Jacobs, Kenneth Robert; Second Secretary Buenos Aires since October 1991; born 10.1.46; GPO 1963; FCO 1969; Attaché Warsaw 1970; Brussels 1972; FCO 1975; Attaché Addis Ababa 1977; FCO 1980; Attaché Nicosia 1980; FCO

1983; Second Secretary Canberra 1986; Second Secretary FCO 1989; m 1967 Jacqueline Diane Leeks (1d 1969; 1s 1972).

Jacobs, Lisa Claire; Riyadh since September 1990; born 21.3.65; FCO 1986; Moscow 1988; Grade S2.

Jacobsen, Neil Marius; First Secretary (Political) Madrid since August 1992; born 6.6.57; Second Secretary FCO 1984; Second later First Secretary (Econ) Athens 1986; First Secretary FCO 1989; m 1982 Susan Clark (1d 1984; 2s 1988, 1990).

Jacobson, Charles Eugene; Third Secretary (Chancery) Tel Aviv since May 1991; born 17.9.64; FCO 1988; Grade 9.

Jacques, Lorna; Phnom Penh since May 1992; born 15.9.59; FCO 1985; UKDEL CSCE Vienna 1988; Rangoon 1988; Grade S2A.

Jaggard, Stephen Graham; First Secretary FCO since September 1991; born 23.12.42; FCO 1975; First Secretary Dacca 1977; First Secretary (Chancery) Rabat 1980; FCO 1983; First Secretary (Chancery) Bangkok 1988; m (1) 1971 Mary Louise Good (diss 1976) (1s 1973); (2) 1979 Martientje Visse.

Jagpal, Harjit Kaur; Lagos since January 1991; born 8.10.68; FCO 1988; Grade 10.

James, Christopher Noel Mackworth, obe (1987); SUPL since July 1992; born 28.1.46; Army 1964-74; Second Secretary FCO 1975; Second Secretary Nairobi 1976; First Secretary Lagos 1979; FCO 1980; New Delhi 1983; First Secretary FCO 1986; First Secretary later Counsellor Nicosia 1988; m 1970 Charlotte Elizabeth Shepley-Cuthbert (2s 1973, 1974).

James, Janet Ada; Second Secretary (Cons) New Delhi since March 1990; born 4.7.37; Paris 1960; Singapore 1963; Moscow 1967; FCO 1968; Pretoria 1971; The Hague 1974; FCO 1977; Khartoum 1979; Second Secretary FCO 1982; Consul Amman 1983; Second Secretary FCO 1986.

James, Jeffrey Russell; Head of European Council Unit (in Edinburgh) since April 1992; born 13.8.44; Third Secretary Commonwealth Office (later FCO) 1967; Tehran 1969; Third later Second Secretary Kabul 1970; First Secretary FCO 1973; BMG Berlin 1978; FCO 1982; Counsellor on loan to Cabinet Office 1984; Counsellor and Head of Chancery Pretoria/Capetown 1986; Counsellor (Econ/Comm) New Delhi 1988; m 1965 Carol Mary Longden (2d 1965, 1969).

James, Keith Henry; FCO since August 1986; born 11.11.35; HM Forces 1952-65; FO 1965; Singapore 1967; FCO 1969; Baghdad 1971; FCO 1972; Lilongwe 1974; FCO 1977; Peking 1979;

FCO 1981; Attaché Kinshasa 1982; Grade 8; m 1958 Doreen Pattison (2d 1961, 1968).

James, Kevin Charles; First Secretary FCO since February 1992; born 16.11.45; Third Secretary FO (later FCO) 1967; Tokyo 1968; Second later First Secretary FCO 1973; Warsaw 1976; FCO 1979; Tokyo 1981; FCO 1985; First Secretary Colombo 1988; m 1970 Linda Margaret Betts (2d 1972, 1975).

James, Neill; FCO since January 1991; born 6.7.71; Grade 10.

James, Nicola Patricia; Bandar Seri Begawan since September 1988; born 29.9.60; FCO 1980; Peking 1983; Kuala Lumpur 1985; Grade S2.

James, Roger William; First Secretary FCO since November 1988; born 15.9.36; Leopoldville 1960; FO 1963; Nicosia 1966; Chicago 1969; Second Secretary 1970; Vice-Consul (Comm) Los Angeles 1970; Second Secretary (Comm) Brussels 1971; First Secretary (Agric/EC) Dublin 1976; First Secretary (Comm) Caracas 1980; First Secretary (Comm) Bogotá 1984; m (1) 1969 Cynthia Nelson Bender (diss) (1 step s; 1d 1970); (2) 1982 Elisa Amaro Yzaguirre.

James, Stephen Anthony; Third Secretary (Aid/Comm) Mbabane since September 1990; born 1.9.51; Customs and Excise 1968; FCO 1971; Saigon 1973; Peking 1975; Warsaw 1976; Manila 1977; Berne 1981; FCO 1984; Islamabad 1987; Grade 9; m 1979 Nikki Jean Smith (2d 1980, 1982; 1s 1984).

Jameson, Karen Elizabeth; Windhock since October 1989; born 19.11.59; FCO 1980; Madrid 1982; Santiago 1986; Grade 10.

Jamieson, James Richard; Deputy Permanent Representative UKDEL Strasbourg since April 1989; born 26.11.35; COI 1960; Lagos 1962; Rabat 1965; Commonwealth Office 1967; DSAO 1968; Second Secretary FCO 1969; Second Secretary UKDEL EC Brussels 1970; Algiers 1974; Second later First Secretary FCO 1978; First Secretary (Admin) and Consul Helsinki 1981; First Secretary (Comm) Head of Chancery and Consul Abidjan 1983; First Secretary FCO 1987; m (1) 1959 Joan Elizabeth Anderson (diss) (2s 1961, 1964); (2) 1974 Edith Margaret Turkington (1d 1982).

January, Peter; Consul and Deputy Head of Mission Maputo since April 1991; born 13.1.52; FCO 1983; First Secretary (Comm) Budapest 1985; First Secretary FCO 1988.

Jardine, Martine; FCO since April 1990; born 27.9.70; Grade 10.

Jarrett, Anne; Second Secretary FCO since May 1989; born 26.1.60; FCO 1978; Moscow 1981; Africa/ME Floater 1984; UKDEL NATO

Brussels 1986.

Jarrold, Nicholas Robert; Counsellor (Commercial and Economic) Brussels since July 1992; born 2.3.46; Third Secretary FCO 1968; Third later Second Secretary The Hague 1969; Dakar 1972; First Secretary FCO 1975; Nairobi 1979 (Head of Chancery 1983); FCO 1983; Counsellor and Head of Chancery Havana 1989; CDA at Oxford University 1991; m 1972 Anne Catherine Whitworth (2s 1976, 1979).

Jarvie, Carole Marina; UKDEL Brussels since January 1992; born 26.9.54; FCO 1984; The Hague 1986; Canberra 1989; Grade S2.

Jarvis, Russell Thomas; Management Officer BTC Hong Kong since June 1990; born 27.9.47; Commonwealth Office (later FCO) 1964; Sofia 1969; EC Brussels 1972; Sana'a 1972; Islamabad 1973; FCO 1975; Dar es Salaam 1978 (Second Secretary 1979); Vice-Consul (Comm) BTDO New York 1982; First Secretary FCO 1986; m 1969 Joan Ann Wyard (2s 1971, 1986; 1d 1973).

Jay, Michael Hastings, CMG (1992); AUSS (European Community) since September 1990; born 19.6.46; ODM 1969; UKDEL IMF/IBRD Washington 1973; ODM 1975; First Secretary (Dev) New Delhi 1978; First Secretary FCO 1981; Private Secretary to Permanent Under Secretary of State FCO 1982; Counsellor on loan to Cabinet Office 1985; Counsellor (Fin/Comm) Paris 1987; m 1975 Sylvia Mylroie.

Jebb, Christopher Quayle Gladwyn; Second Secretary (Commercial/Information) Kingston since April 1991; born 2.10.50; FCO 1970; Caribbean Floater 1973; Vientiane 1975; Düsseldorf 1978; FCO 1980; Tristan da Cunha 1982; Istanbul 1984; FCO 1987; Second Secretary (Head of Chancery) Asunción 1988; m 1975 Maria Aida Hoyos (1d 1979; 1s 1981).

Jeenes, Kelley Elizabeth; FCO since March 1992; Grade 10.

Jeffrey, John Peacock Reid; Second Secretary (Commercial/Consular/Management) Montevideo since March 1992; born 4.4.53; FCO 1971; Jakarta 1974; Singapore 1975; Africa Floater 1977; FCO 1980; Mexico City 1982; Bucharest 1986; Second Secretary FCO 1988; m 1980 Arlene Elizabeth Watson (1s 1991).

Jeffreys, Stella Ann; Dar Es Salaam since September 1992; born 16.11.62; FCO 1990; Grade S2.

Jenkins, Hayley Rhiannon Jones Davies (née Davies); SUPL since December 1991; born 15.5.63; FCO 1986; Grade S2; Rome 1989; m 1988 Darren Lee Jenkins.

Jenkins, Harold Thomas Fricker; Second Secretary (Management/Consular) Kathmandu since July 1991; born 16.1.40; FO 1961; Brussels 1962; Rangoon 1963; New York 1967; FCO 1969; Bombay 1973; Washington 1976; FCO 1979; Second Secretary (Admin) Dar es Salaam 1983; Second Secretary FCO 1986; m 1962 Margaret T Neyle (1d 1964; 1s 1965).

Jenkins, Janet Lesley (née Bedford); Gibraltar since March 1992; born 28.5.60; FCO 1984; Canberra 1987; Aden 1990; Grade S2; m 1987 William David Jenkins.

Jenkins, John, LVO (1989); First Secretary FCO since August 1992; born 26.1.55; Second Secretary FCO 1980; Second Secretary Abu Dhabi 1983; FCO 1986; First Secretary and Head of Chancery Kuala Lumpur 1989; m 1982 Nancy Caroline Pomfret.

Jenkins, Katherine Patricia; Second Secretary (Chancery) Madrid since May 1991; born 7.11.63; FCO 1987 (Second Secretary 1989).

Jenkins, Sir Michael (Romilly Heald), KCMG, (1990) CMG (1984); HM Ambassador The Hague since January 1988; born 9.1.36; FO 1959; Third later Second Secretary Paris 1961; Second later First Secretary Moscow 1965; FO (later FCO) 1967; Seconded to Industry (GEC) 1969; First Secretary (Econ) Bonn 1970; SUPL to the Commission of the European Communities as Deputy, later Chef de Cabinet to Mr George Thomson 1973; Counsellor 1974; Head of European Integration Dept (Eernal) FCO 1977; SUPL with EC Brussels 1978; AUSS (Europe) FCO 1983; Minister Washington 1985; m 1968 Maxine Louise Hodson (1d 1971; 1s 1975).

Jenkins, Owen John; FCO since August 1991; born 21.8.69;Grade 8.

Jenkins, Paul David; Second Secretary (Commercial) Lagos since July 1992; born 22.6.51; FCO 1968; Bonn 1972; FCO 1974; Prague 1974; Monrovia 1976; Kaduna 1978; FCO 1981; Nairobi 1984; Gaborone 1986; Second Secretary FCO 1990; m 1972 Jennifer Whitmarsh (2s 1976, 1979).

Jenkins, Peter Redmond; Minister/Counsellor, Consul-General and Deputy Head of Mission Brasilia since April 1992; born 2.3.50; FCO 1973; Third later Second Secretary (UNIDO/IAEA) Vienna 1975; Second later First Secretary FCO 1978; First Secretary and PS to HM Ambassador Washington 1982. First Secretary FCO 1984; First Secretary (Econ) Paris 1987.

Jenkins, Richard Thomas, OBE (1986); Counsellor (Cultural Affairs) Moscow since January 1988; born 19.8.43; FCO 1967; Warsaw 1970; FCO 1970; Second later First Secretary East Berlin 1976; FCO 1979; First Secretary (Comm) Warsaw 1983; PRO (DS Grade 5) FCO 1985; m 1976 Maurizia Marantonio (2s 1977, 1982).

Jenkinson, Eric; First Secretary, Consul and Deputy Head of Mission Bahrain since January 1992; born 13.3.50; FO 1967; EC Brussels 1971; Islamabad 1973; Second Secretary (Comm) Jedda 1978; Second Secretary FCO 1982; First Secretary (Econ) Bonn 1986; m 1973 Kathleen Forster (2s 1980, 1981).

Jenkinson, Gale Louise; FCO since February 1992; FCO 1984; born 24.11.63; FCO 1984; Islamabad 1986; Ottawa 1989; Grade 9.

Jenner, Donald Paul Robert; Second Secretary FCO since July 1992; born 3.8.49; FCO 1968; Prague 1971; Colombo 1972; FCO 1976; Mogadishu 1978; Islamabad 1980; FCO 1983; DHC Victoria 1987; m 1971 Margaret Lilian Fielder (2s 1976, 1978).

Jennings, Colin Brian; Deputy High Commissioner Nicosia since September 1992; born 27.11.52; MOD 1976; UKDEL NATO 1980; MOD 1982; FCO 1983; First Secretary Lagos 1986; First Secretary FCO 1989; m 1978 Jane Barfield.

Jennings, Katharine Mary; Language Training since September 1992; born 20.9.65; FCO 1990; Grade 7.

Jennison, Vanessa Sandford; Third Secretary (UNCTAD) UKMIS Geneva since November 1990; born 25.2.64; 1988; Grade 9; m 1989 G J Peck.

Joad, Katie Louise; Tokyo since October 1992; born 18.3.69; FCO 1990; Grade 10.

Johns, Selby Colmer; First Secretary (Comm/Econ) Budapest since November 1988; born 1.12.37; RAF 1960-63; FO 1966; Warsaw 1967; Lusaka 1971; Second Secretary FCO 1973; Language training London University 1975; Second later First Secretary Budapest 1976; First Secretary (Comm) Brussels (UKREP) 1980; First Secretary FCO 1985; m 1966 Virginia Ann Werring (2s 1967, 1970 (dec'd 1972); 2d 1968, 1973).

Johnsen, Emma Louise (née Williams); FCO since November 1990; born 23.2.66; Grade 9; m 1992 Per-Arne Johnsen.

Johnson, Alison Louise; Vice-Consul Tokyo since June 1992; FCO 1989; Grade 9.

Johnson, David John; Counsellor FCO since May 1990; born 2.3.38; HM Forces 1957-59; FO 1959; Moscow 1962; Dakar 1965; Second Secretary (Inf) 1966; Temporary Chargé d'Affaires Ulan Bator January to March 1969; Second Secretary UKMIS Geneva 1969; First Secretary UKDEL MBFR Vienna 1973; First Secretary and Press Attaché Moscow 1975; FCO 1978; NATO Defence College Rome 1982; SUPL with NATO Secretariat Brussels 1982;

Counsellor and Head of Chancery Islamabad 1985; m 1976 Kathleen Johanna Hicks (3d, twin d 1981, 1983).

Johnson, George Michael; First Secretary (Admin) Brasilia since November 1988; born 10.1.43; Post Office 1960; FO 1961; Kinshasa 1965; Moscow 1967; Paris 1968; FCO 1971; Lagos 1973; Sofia 1976; FCO 1979 (Second Secretary 1980); Vice-Consul (Comm) Toronto 1984; m 1971 Anne Marion Little (1s 1971).

Johnson, Julie Michelle; FCO since May 1991; born 12.11.63; FCO 1983; Port Stanley 1985; FCO 1986; Vienna 1987; Hong Kong 1990; Grade 9.

Johnson, Karen Marguerite; Bonn since May 1992; born 26.11.68; FCO 1987; Tel Aviv 1989; Grade 10.

Johnson, Katrina; FCO since April 1990; born 10.3.66; FCO 1985; Paris 1987; Grade 9.

Johnson, Kenneth Neil, MBE (1982); First Secretary (Comm) Dubai since November 1988; born 12.4.44; FO 1961; Ibadan 1965; Accra 1966; Caracas 1969; FCO 1971; Detroit 1975; Second Secretary (Comm) Lagos 1977; First Secretary FCO 1983; First Secretary (Comm) Doha 1985; m 1963 Veronica Jones (1s 1971).

Johnson, Matthew Alfred; Cape Town/Pretoria since December 1990; born 11.6.70; FCO 1988; Grade 10.

Johnson, Nicholas; Second Secretary (Consular) Valletta since April 1990; born 11.1.58; FCO 1980; Islamabad 1983; FCO. 1986; m 1991 Michela Aloysio (1d 1992).

Johnson, Peter Seguin; BTC Hong Kong since February 1990; born 7.1.27; GPO 1941; FO 1959; Budapest 1960; FO 1961; Seconded to Ministry of Defence 1962; FO 1964; Moscow 1965; FO (later FCO) 1966; Brussels 1969; FCO 1972; Second Secretary Peking 1980; FCO 1983; m 1951 Molly Munro Jenkins (1d 1952; 1s 1954).

Johnson, Philip Hughes; Administrator Tristan Da Cunha since January 1992; born 2.10.35; Army 1953-56; Passport Office 1957; CRO 1961; Kingston 1962; Lusaka 1967; Second Secretary FCO 1971; Prague 1975; Vice-Consul (Comm) Houston 1978; Second later First Secretary FCO 1982; Parliamentary Clerk FCO 1983; Deputy High Commissioner Nassau 1986; First Secretary FCO 1990; m 1959 Diana Ruth Chase (4d 1960, 1962, 1964, 1965).

Johnson, Sandra Lissenden; Helsinki since February 1992; born 13.2.43; FCO 1970; Washington 1971; Resigned 1973; Reinstated 1982; UKDEL CSCE Madrid 1982; Moscow 1983; Rangoon 1984; FCO 1987; Grade S1.

Johnson, Simon William; Istanbul since November 1989; born 26.3.64; FCO 1983; Budapest 1987; Grade 10.

Johnson, Tamsin Jane; Addis Ababa since February 1991; born 15.1.70; FCO 1989; Grade 10.

Johnson, Walter George Devon, MBE (1982); Second Secretary (Management) JMO New York since December 1990; born 28.6.44; FO 1963; Mexico City 1965; Sofia 1968; FCO 1969; Wellington 1970; Bogota 1973; FCO 1975; UKDEL Brussels 1978; Caracas 1981; Second Secretary, Bursar, Wiston House 1983; Second Secretary (Comm) Abidjan 1987; m 1989 Margaret Murray-Lee (2d .1969, 1972).

Johnston, Elizabeth Ann (née Barker); SUPL since October 1987; born 2.12.57; FCO 1978; Belgrade 1980; FCO 1982; Pretoria/Cape Town 1983; FCO 1986; Grade S2; m 1987 Paul Neville Johnston.

Johnston, Gordon Mackenzie; HM Ambassador Ljubljana since August 1992; born 24.6.41; FO 1959; Berne 1963; Tamsui 1966; FO (later FCO) 1967; Islamabad 1971; FCO 1972; Paris 1974; Second Secretary Georgetown 1978; Second Secretary FCO 1981; First Secretary (Comm) Belgrade 1984; First Secretary (Econ) Dublin 1989; First Secretary FCO 1990; m 1963 Barbara Glenis Christie (1s 1965; 1d 1966).

Johnston, Martin Paul; Third Secretary (Chancery/Vice-Consul) Caracas since August 1991; born 4.1.64; FCO 1990; Grade 9.

Johnston, Stuart Allen; First Secretary FCO since December 1989; born 20.5.56; Royal Navy 1974-1985; Second Secretary FCO 1985; Second later First Secretary Harare 1987; m (1) 1980 Morag Donald-Scot (diss 1987); (2) 1988 Caroline Mary Thornton.

Johnstone, James; UKMIS Geneva since August 1992; born 16.3.44; Army 1966-88; New York 1988; Grade SO; Peking 1991; m (1) 1967 Patricia Anne Strong (1d 1968; 2s 1969, 1974) (diss 1983); (2) 1986 Rachel Baliti.

Johnstone, Lauren Clair (née Blagburn); SUPL since July 1991; born 21.7.70; FCO 1989; Grade 10; m 1992 Andrew Brian Johnstone.

Johnstone, Peter; FCO since September 1991; born 30.7.44; FO 1962; Berne 1965; Benin City 1966; Budapest 1968; Maseru 1969; FCO 1973; Second Secretary 1975; Second Secretary (Chancery) Dacca 1977; Dublin 1979; First Secretary FCO 1983; First Secretary (Comm) Harare 1986; HM Consul-General Edmonton 1989; m 1969 Diane Claon (1s 1971; 1d 1977).

Jones, Alison Elizabeth; FCO since October 1990; born 11.2.72; Grade S2.

Jones, Alyson Claire; Maputo since August 1989; born 15.5.68; FCO 1987; Grade 9.

Jones, Andrew Martin; FCO since January 1989; born 14.12.59; FCO 1980; Darwin 1981; FCO 1984; Singapore 1986; Grade 8; m 1985 Amanda Wainer (1s 1988, 1d 1990).

Jones, Annabel Nicole (née Russ) FCO since November 1988 (Second Secretary 1990); born 26.10.60; FCO 1981; Floater duties 1983; Washington 1986; m 1989 Gareth Richard Jones.

Jones, Barrie Samuel, LVO (1985); Consul General Brisbane since December 1988; born 10.8.40; Crown Agents 1959; CRO 1962; Calcutta 1962; CRO later Commonwealth Office 1964; Karachi 1967; Rio de Janeiro 1970; Second Secretary 1970; Vice-Consul (Comm) Los Angeles 1971; FCO 1976; First Secretary and Head of Chancery Mbabane 1979; FCO 1984; m 1962 Pamela Anne Trowman (2s 1965, 1973; 1d 1968).

Jones, Brian Russell; Second Secretary FCO since March 1992; born 23.9.41; Inland Revenue 1959-62; Commonwealth Office 1967; Tokyo 1968; FCO 1974; Warsaw 1976; Second Secretary (Admin) and Consul Caracas 1977; Second Secretary (Comm) Tokyo 1980; FCO 1984; Second Secretary (Comm/Aid) Luanda 1989; m 1972 Yoshiko Aoji (2d 1974, 1975).

Jones, Caitlin Olga; FCO since November 1990; born 3.6.67; Grade 9.

Jones, Catherine Helen Courtier; Second Secretary FCO since January 1989; born 13.9.56; FCO 1976; Moscow 1979; Latin America Floater 1982; Bogotá 1984 (Second Secretary 1985).

Jones, Ceinwen Jane; FCO since July 1992; born 2.5.50; FCO 1976; Bangkok 1977; Moscow 1979; UKDIS Geneva 1981; FCO 1984; Banjul 1990; Grade 9.

Jones, David; Prague since March 1991; born 17.11.31; Army 1952-77; Moscow 1977; Paris 1978; Washington 1980; Montevideo 1982; Warsaw 1985; Lilongwe 1986; Helsinki 1988; Grade SO; m 1957 Winifred Anne Coupar (2s 1959, 1963).

Jones, David Alan; First Secretary FCO since December 1989; born 26.10.53; Lord Chancellor;s Department 1970; FCO 1971; Tehran 1975; Islamabad 1978; Second Secretary on loan to MOD 1981; Second Secretary FCO 1983; First Secretary (Comm) Cairo 1986; m 1975 Jennifer Anne Wright.

Jones, David Stephen; Tripoli since July 1991; born 19.9.51; Public Record Office 1970-73; FCO 1976; Port of Spain 1978; Peking 1981; Africa/ME floater 1982; FCO 1984; Brasilia 1988; Grade 9; m 1973 Jane Martin (diss 1978).

Jones, Elaine Frances; SUPL since Maay 1992; born 29.9.59; Port Stanley 1979; SUPL 1981; Kathmandu 1984; FCO 1986; Peking 1988; Grade S2; m 1979 Peter Jones.

Jones, Eric Malcolm; First Secretary FCO since January 1990; born 7.10.45; Passport Office Liverpool 1963; DSAO 1966; Middle East Floater 1969; Düsseldorf 1970; Peking 1973; FCO 1974; Kuwait 1976; FCO 1980; Second Secretary (Aid) Dhaka 1982; Second Secretary (Comm) later First Secretary (Dev) Lilongwe 1985; m (1) 1974 Jane Elizabeth Petherbridge (diss 1986); (2) 1988 Sylvia Margaret Hayhurst.

Jones, Frances Myfanwy; FCO since September 1990; born 24.5.51; FCO 1973; Karachi 1975; Jakarta 1975; FCO 1978; Valletta 1978; FCO 1981; Amman 1984; FCO 1987; SUPL 1989; Grade S2.

Jones, Frank; Second Secretary (Visas) Paris since August 1989; born 7.9.48; FO (later FCO) 1967; Kaduna 1970; NATO Brussels 1974; Sana'a 1977; FCO 1978; Ottawa 1982; FCO 1984; m 1982 Elizabeth Mary Lendrum (1s 1991).

Jones, Jacqui Ann (née Currie); LA Floater since February 1992; born 8.3.67; FCO 1987; Bagdad 1989; FCO 1991; Grade 10; m 1991 Henry Lee Jones.

Jones, Jacqueline; FCO since February 1991; born 3.10.71; Grade S2.

Jones, Jack Henry; On loan to ODA since September 1991; born 23.10.50; FCO 1984; Second later First Secretary Colombo 1986.

Jones, Jennifer Ann (née Wright); Second Secretary FCO since January 1990; born 7.8.49; DSAO (later FCO) 1967; Kathmandu 1970; Delhi 1970; Tripoli 1972; Lisbon 1972; Tehran 1975; Islamabad 1978; FCO 1981; Cairo 1986; m 1975 David Alan Jones.

Jones, Joan Elizabeth, BEM (1991); Belmopan since May 1991; born 6.11.43; FCO 1988; Grade S2.

Jones, John Derek, BEM (1984); FCO since May 1978; born 16.8.37; HM Forces 1955-57; FO 1965; Singapore 1967; FCO 1969; Saigon 1974; Singapore 1975; FCO 1975; Tel Aviv 1977; Grade 9; m 1963 Iris Roberts (1s 1970; 1d 1963).

Jones, Lesley Anne; Moscow since August 1990; born 31.7.65; FCO 1985; Washington 1987; Grade S2.

Jones, Leslie Norman; Moscow since November 1991; born 26.5.48; Army 1964-88; Cairo 1988; Grade SO; m 1972 Dorothy Alma Tanner (1s 1977; 1d 1978).

Jones, Llinos Dawn; UKMIS New York since June 1992; born 27.3.68; FCO 1988; Kuwait 1989; Warsaw 1990; Grade S2.

Jones, Lloyd Howell; Washington since May 1992; born 6.5.68; FCO 1989; Grade 10.

Jones, Mervyn Thomas; Consul (Commercial) Los Angeles since March 1990; born 23.11.42; CRO 1964; Calcutta 1966; Bonn 1967; Language Training RAF North Luffenham 1970; Warsaw 1970; Second Secretary FCO 1973; Second Secretary (Chancery) Oslo 1977; First Secretary (Admin) Bangkok 1981; First Secretary and Head of Chancery Bangkok 1982; JSDC course 1985; Seconded to Commonwealth Secretariat 1985; m 1965 Julia Mary Newcombe (2s 1966, 1969).

Jones, Neale Robert; Istanbul since October 1992; born 20.2.63; FCO 1986; Islamabad 1989; Grade 9; m 1992 Catherine Ingham.

Jones, Noel Andrew Stephen; First Secretary (Information) Moscow since May 1991; born 22.12.40; FO 1962; Zagreb 1963; Hamburg 1965; Bangkok 1968; Taiwan 1970; FCO 1972; Third Secretary (Comm) Belgrade 1975; Second Secretary (Chancery) Bonn 1979; Second Secretary FCO 1983; Language Training Sussex University 1984; Head of Chancery Ulan Bator 1985; Consul (Comm) Seattle 1987; m 1963 Jean Rosemary Cheval (1s 1966; 1d 1968).

Jones, Pamela Edna Palmer; FCO since February 1981; born 25.10.34; Berne 1960; Moscow 1963; FO 1964; Salisbury 1966; FCO 1967; Ankara 1970; Bonn 1972; FCO 1975; Paris 1978; Grade 9.

Jones, Patricia Anne; Bonn since May 1991; born 12.5.70; FCO 1989; Grade S2.

Jones, Peter; Luxembourg since May 1992; born 23.7.57; FCO 1976; Port Stanley 1979; Madrid 1981; Kathmandu 1984; FCO 1986; Peking 1988; Grade 9; m 1979 Elaine Frances Scott.

Jones, Peter Edward; First Secretary FCO since July 1992; born 28.8.61; FCO 1985; Second later First Secretary UKDEL CACN Vienna 1989.

Jones, Phillip Roy; FCO since May 1985; born 18.2.50; FO (later FCO) 1966; Washington 1976; FCO 1979; Attaché Muscat 1982; Grade 8; m (1) 1972 Lesley Pamela Goody (diss 1981) (2s 1973, 1978; 1d 1975); m (2) 1982 Karen Patricia Lyle; (1s 1985; 1d 1987).

Jones, Ralph Mahood; Riyadh since February 1992; born 4.5.69; FCO 1989; Grade 10.

Jones, Randolph Thomas; Third Secretary (Cons/Immigration) Port of Spain since November 1989; born 12.9.56; FCO 1976; Islamabad 1978; Colombo 1982; FCO 1985; Peking 1989; Grade

9; m 1980 Kathryn Rosemary Smith (2s 1984, 1987).

Jones, Raymond Francis, OBE (1986); High Commissioner Honiara since May 1991; born 15.11.35; FO 1953; HM Forces 1954-56; Amman 1956; Singapore 1958; Tokyo 1959; Cairo 1964; Accra 1967; Second Secretary FCO 1970; Vice Consul later Consul Seattle 1973; First Secretary on loan to DOI 1979; First Secretary New Delhi 1983; Deputy Consul-General Chicago 1986; m 1957 Maurag Anna (2d 1959, 1961).

Jones, Richard Alexander Owen; FCO since June 1990; born 19.4.71; Grade 10.

Jones, Richard Christopher Bentley; First Secretary FCO since June 1992; born 22.3.53; Second Secretary FCO 1978; PS to HM Ambassador Tokyo 1980; First Secretary FCO 1984; First Secretary (Head of Chancery) Suva 1988.

Jones, Richard Hugh Francis; Second later First Secretary FCO since November 1989; born 28.9.62; FCO 1983; Third later Second Secretary Abu Dhabi 1986.

Jones, Robert Edward; FCO since May 1988 (Second Secretary 1989); born 30.5.47; FCO 1966; Singapore 1973; FCO 1974; Belgrade 1978; FCO 1981; Prague 1985; m 1972 Linda Joan Edith Watts (1d 1974, 1s 1977).

Jones, Timothy Aidan; First Secretary FCO since March 1992; born 5.9.62; FCO 1984; Language training 1986; Second Secretary (Chancery) The Hague 1988.

Jones Parry, Emyr, CMG (1992); Counsellor FCO since June 1989; born 21.9.47; FCO 1973; Second later First Secretary (Comm) Ottawa 1974; FCO 1979; First Secretary (Energy) later First Secretary (Information, Press and Institutions) UKREP Brussels 1982; Counsellor on SUPL-EC Brussels 1987; m 1971 Lynn Noble (2s 1977, 1979).

Jonsen, Cyril, OBE (1987); First Secretary FCO since July 1987; born 13.1.35; FO 1952-53; RAF 1953-55; Bangkok 1955; Singapore 1957; Kabul 1959; Madrid 1962; FO 1963; DSAO 1965; Prague 1966; Kuching 1969; Second Secretary Dakar 1972; FCO 1974; Nairobi 1978; First Secretary (Comm) Quito 1983; m 1959 Beryl Anne Wilson (1s 1961).

Jordan, Carole-Ann; FCO since November 1990; born 28.4.64; Grade S2.

Jordan, Jacqueline (née Curtis); SUPL since November 1989; born 20.2.59; FCO 1984; Valletta 1986; Grade S2; m 1989 Arthur William Jordan.

Joy, Arthur Anthony; Consul-General Vancouver

since April 1990; born 3.6.36; HM Forces 1957-59; CRO 1960; Delhi 1961; Salisbury 1965; Lusaka 1965; CRO 1966; Vice-Consul Damascus 1966; Vice-Consul Strasbourg 1967; Second Secretary (Cons/Tech Ass) Ibadan 1969; FCO 1970; Vice-Consul (Comm) Rio de Janeiro 1972; First Secretary (Energy) Washington 1976; First Secretary FCO 1980; Counsellor Overseas Inspectorate FCO 1985; Counsellor (Finance and Admin) New Delhi 1986; m (1) Jeanette Strafford (diss 1971) (4s 1957, 1959, 1960, 1963); (2) Lena Elsa Warner (née Svanberg) (1 step s 1966, 1s 1979).

Joy, David, CBE (1983); Consul-General Barcelona since July 1989; born 9.12.32; HMOCS Northern Rhodesia1/Zambia 1956; Retired as Under-Secretary, Cabinet Office; FCO 1971; First Secretary (Inf) Caracas 1973 and Head of Chancery 1975; Assistant Head, Mexico and Caribbean Department 1977; Counsellor and Head of Chancery Warsaw 1978; Counsellor Buenos Aires and Head of British Interests Section 1982; Counsellor FCO 1984; HM Ambassador and Consul-General Tegucigalpa and (non-resident) El Salvador 1987; m 1957 Montserrat Morancho Saumench (1s 1958; 1d 1961).

Joy, Rupert Hamilton Neville; Full-Time Language Training Cairo since May 1992; born 5.9.63; FCO 1990; Full-Time Language Training 1991.

Juleff, Andrew John Gerent; Vice-Consul CG New York since August 1991; born 3.5.60; FCO 1986; Third Secretary (Aid/Comm) Kampala 1989; Grade 9.

Jump, Sophie Harriet; Third Secretary (Chancery/Information) Dakar since December 1991; born 29.4.67; FCO 1989; Grade 9.

Jupp, Anita Lorraine; SUPL since August 1992; born 11.3.58; FCO 1979; Madrid 1980; Bucharest 1981; Athens 1983; Riyadh 1985; FCO 1986; Hamilton 1987; Washington 1988; FCO 1992; Grade S1.

Jupp, Sheridan Arlene; FCO since October 1990; born 2.1.57; Grade S2.

K

Kahlow, Bonita; FCO since October 1989; born 23.1.66; Grade 10.

Kane, Jacqueline; Athens since June 1990; born 25.3.67; FCO 1987; Grade S2.

Karmy, Peter John; Second Secretary (Cons/Inf) Ankara since March 1989; born 1.7.47; FO (later FCO) 1967; Benghazi 1969; San José 1970; Seoul 1973; Kuwait 1976; FCO 1977; Sofia 1980; FCO 1984; Second Secretary (Admin) Manila 1985; m 1977 Eui Jong Han (1d 1979).

Kavanagh, Anthony; First Secretary (Chancery) Lagos since February 1990; born 26.3.57; Second Secretary FCO 1984; Second Secretary BMG Berlin 1986; FCO 1988; m 1992 Joanna Mary McKie.

Kavanagh, Neil Richard; FCO since February 1992; born 28.3.72; Grade 10.

Kay, Anthony Paul; FCO since April 1992; born 29.6.72; Grade 10.

Kay, Kathleen Ursula; First Secretary FCO since August 1984; born 31.3.40; FCO 1979; First Secretary Guatemala City 1982.

Kay, Martin Paul; Suva since November 1991; born 21.3.68; FCO 1987; UKMIS New York 1989; Grade 10; m 1990 Alison Jane Howell.

Kay, Ronald, MBE (1981); First Secretary FCO since April 1991; born 29.11.40; FO 1959; Muscat 1962; Bahrain 1963; Washington 1964; DSAO 1966; Salisbury 1969; Kathmandu 1969; Jakarta 1969; Tokyo 1971; Latin America Floater 1972; FCO 1974; Dublin 1974; FCO 1975; Kuala Lumpur 1976; Second Secretary Dar es Salaam 1980; FCO 1983; First Secretary (Admin) and Consul Amman 1985; First Secretary (Comm) Sana'a 1988.

Kaye, Alan Robert; First Secretary FCO since June 1984; born 3.9.29; FO 1953; Bahrain 1954; Bonn 1956; Prague 1959; Luxembourg 1961; FO 1963; DSAO 1965; Vice-Consul Jerusalem 1967; Ottawa 1969; FCO 1972; Second Secretary 1973; Singapore 1977; First Secretary (Consular) Lusaka 1981; m 1956 Judith Helen Benstead (1s 1960; 2d 1965, 1966).

Kaye, Stella; Second Secretary (Management/Consular) Bridgetown since November 1991; born 22.7.35; FO 1954; Tehran 1958; Panama 1960; Baghdad 1964; Canberra 1966; Luanda 1969; New Delhi 1971; Moscow 1973; FCO 1974; Islamabad 1977; FCO 1979; New York 1980; Atlanta 1982; Second Secretary FCO 1984; Second Secretary (Cons/Immig) Bombay 1988.

Kazer, Kathleen; FCO since September 1970; born 1.6.47; Principal Research Officer (DS Grade 5).

Kealy, Robin Andrew, CMG (1991); Counsellor, Director of Trade Promotion and Investment Paris since November 1990; born 7.10.44; Third Secretary FO 1967; MECAS 1968; Tripoli 1970; Second later First Secretary Kuwait 1972; First Secretary FCO 1975; Head of Chancery Port of Spain 1978; Political Adviser Belmopan 1978; First Secretary (Comm) Prague 1982; First Secretary later Counsellor FCO 1986; Counsellor Consul-General and Deputy Head of Mission Baghdad 1987; m 1987 Annabel Jane Hood (2s 1989, 1992).

Kearns, William John; First Secretary FCO since

March 1984; born 28.2.34; Ministry of Supply 1951; HM Forces 1952-55; Board of Trade 1958; Nairobi 1963; Second Secretary (Comm) Brisbane 1967; Second Secretary (Comm) Lagos 1972; FCO 1976; First Secretary and Head of Chancery Reykjavik 1979; First Secretary (Comm) Washington 1982; m 1962 Maura F Cahill (2d 1963, 1968; 1s 1964).

Keating, Gillian; UKREP Brussels since January 1991; born 1.6.66; FCO 1988; Grade S2A.

Keech, Joseph Anthony; Third Secretary Nairobi since March 1983; born 22.5.45; FCO 1974; Bonn 1977; FCO 1980; m (1) 1970 Margaret Bickerstaffe (1d 1975); m (2) 1983 Elizabeth Marion Sibley (1s 1988).

Keefe, Denis Edward Peter Paul; First Secretary (Political/Environment) Nairobi since July 1992; born 29.6.58; FCO 1982; Language Training 1984; Second Secretary (Chancery) Prague 1984; First Secretary FCO 1988; m 1983 Catherine Ann Mary Wooding (1d 1985; 3s 1987, 1989, 1991).

Keegan, David Barclay; Second Secretary FCO since November 1991; born 4.4.63; FCO 1986; Second Secretary and Vice-Consul (Econ) Rio de Janeiro 1989; m 1987 Susan Amanda Line.

Keeling, David Stuart; First Secretary (Inf) New Delhi; born 5.7.43; FO 1960; Ankara 1964; Budapest 1967; FCO 1968; Delhi 1970; Second Secretary FCO 1975; Secretary to Lord Shackleton;s Economic Survey of The Falkland Islands 1975-76; SUPL 1978; FCO 1979; Victoria 1980; First Secretary (Inf) Lagos 1980; First Secretary FCO 1985; m 1974 Gauri Charatram Sriram (1s 1975).

Keith, Deborah Jeanne; Tokyo since July 1990; born 1.7.68; FCO 1988; Grade 9.

Keith, Michael; Second Secretary (Consular) Lagos since August 1992; born 22.9.42; CRO 1961; Dar es Salaam 1964; Rawalpindi 1966; Lagos 1968; FCO 1969; Phnom Penh 1970; Bangkok 1971; Muscat 1971; FCO 1974; Hanoi 1976; Amman 1976; Valletta 1977; Seoul 1979; Second Secretary FCO 1982; Second Secretary (Admin) Madrid 1987; m 1979 Evelyn Briffa (1s 1987).

Kellachan, Siobhan Jane; Berne since December 1989; born 23.11.69; FCO 1987; Grade 10.

Kelly, Brian Patrick; Second Secretary and Consul Oslo since October 1991; born 3.3.43; HM Forces 1960-64; DSAO (later FCO) 1965; Wellington 1967; Dakar 1969; Helsinki 1973; FCO 1976; Vienna 1979; Lusaka 1982; Second Secretary FCO 1985; Second Secretary (Commercial) Madras 1988; m 1964 Marianne Bruce (1s 1965; 1d 1967).

Kelly, Edward Michael; First Secretary FCO since December 1987; born 10.9.39; Second Secretary FCO 1964; Hong Kong 1981; Second later First Secretary Bangkok 1984; m 1969 Anne Edwards (1d 1971; 1s 1974).

Kelly, Iain Charles MacDonald; Vice-Consul (Comm) Los Angeles since December 1990; born 5.3.49; FCO 1974; Language training 1975; Moscow 1976; Kuala Lumpur 1979; FCO 1982 (Second Secretary 1984); Consul Istanbul 1986; Second Secretary FCO 1988; m 1981 Linda Clare McGovern (4s 1984, 1986 (dec'd), 1988, 1989).

Kelly, John Philip, MBE (1984); Deputy Governor Hamilton since August 1989; born 25.6.41; FO 1959; Leopoldville 1962; Cairo 1965; Bonn 1968; FCO 1970; Canberra 1973; Antwerp 1977; Second Secretary FCO 1978; on loan to DOTI 1980; Resident Representative Grenada 1982; First Secretary FCO 1986; m 1964 Jennifer Anne Buckler (1s 1968).

Kelly, Mark; FCO since November 1990; born 17.9.71; Grade 10.

Kelly, Norman James; First Secretary Management Officer and Consul Helsinki since June 1990; born 19.5.42; Department of Employment and Productivity 1966; FCO 1968; Monrovia 1971; Cairo 1971; Atlanta 1975; Second Secretary FCO 1978; Second Secretary (Comm) Kaduna 1983; Second Secretary (Admin) Sofia 1986; First Secretary FCO 1988; m 1970 Mary Angela Callaghan (1d 1971).

Kelly, Patricia Mary, MBE (1977); HM Consul-General Rio de Janeiro since May 1990; born 6.1.38; Department of Economic Affairs 1964; Assistant Private Secretary to the Secretary of State for Foreign Affairs 1966; Singapore High Commission 1968; FCO 1972; Second Secretary The Hague 1974; First Secretary FCO 1978; Consul Rio de Janeiro 1980; On loan to Cory Coal Ltd 1982; First Secretary (Comm/Energy) Caracas 1984; FCO 1988; m 1984 William Edward Drysdale.

Kelly, Paul John, MBE (1984); FCO since June 1989; born 11.3.64, FCO 1982; Pretoria 1987; Grade 9.

Kelly, Peter Joseph; FCO since June 1987 (Second Secretary 1989); born 16.10.41; HM Forces 1958; FCO 1968; Washington 1971; FCO 1974; Tel Aviv 1975; Ankara 1976; FCO 1978; Bahrain 1981; Third Secretary Copenhagen 1984; m 1969 Pamela May King (2s 1972, 1976).

Kelly, Robert Anthony; Third later Second Secretary Hong Kong since March 1990; born 10.12.59; FCO 1986; m 1986 Heather Erica Christina Smith (1s 1992).

Kelly, Robert Mitchell Forrest; First Secretary (Chancery) Helsinki since June 1989; born

12.8.46; Second Secretary FCO 1972; Nairobi 1974; First Secretary FCO 1977; First Secretary (Chancery) Ankara 1981; FCO 1984; m 1973 Helen Glencairn Hart.

Kelly, William Antony; First Secretary and Consul Brussels since January 1989; born 1.1.42; FO 1959; Geneva 1963; Hanoi 1965; Rio de Janeiro 1967; Caracas 1969; FCO 1971; New Delhi 1975; Second Secretary Accra 1978; Second Secretary FCO 1982; Consul Rio de Janeiro 1985; m 1968 Christina Ann Johnson (2s 1970, 1974).

Kelly, William Charles; FCO since June 1990; born 5.1.61; FCO 1980; Jedda 1982; Lisbon 1985; Warsaw 1988; Grade 9; m 1983 Carol Ann Villis (2s 1985, 1987).

Kemp, Michael Scott; FCO since August 1988; born 4.11.38; HM Forces 1956-64; CSC 1964; DSAO 1965; Lusaka 1967; Calcutta 1971; Lahore 1972; Brunei 1974; FCO 1978; Lagos 1981; Port Louis 1985; Grade 9; m 1974 Shangrila Bernadette Eva Singha (1d 1975).

Kendall, Pamela; Copenhagen since September 1992; born 26.11.62; FCO 1986; Moscow 1989; FCO 1990; Grade S2.

Kendall, Louise Margaret (née Wood); Third Secretary (Commercial) Budapest since August 1992; born 16.1.63; FCO 1981; Prague 1984; Tel Aviv 1986; FCO 1988; Language Training 1991; Grade 9; m 1988 Philip Gary Kendall (1d 1992).

Keningale, Jacqueline; Jedda since July 1992; born 18.2.66; FCO 1986; Moscow 1987; Grade 10; SUPL 1990; m 1990 Paul Bevan Downing.

Kennedy, Alison Cranston; Management Officer/ Vice-Consul Abidjan since August 1991; born 21.8.62; FCO 1983; Third Secretary (Aid) Khartoum 1987; FCO 1991; Grade 9.

Kennedy, Paul Vincent; Second Secretary (Chancery) Riyadh since November 1991; born 18.4.57; FCO 1989; m 1984 Najia Ben Salah (1d 1990).

Kenny, John David; Third Secretary (Passports/ Visas) Dublin since May 1991; born 7.6.55; FCO 1973; Vienna 1976; Georgetown 1978; E Berlin 1982; FCO 1984; Cairo 1987; Grade 9; m 1979 Pamela Bernadette Baptiste (1s 1981; 1d 1985).

Kent, Andrew Magnus; Second Secretary (Commercial) Tehran since May 1992; born 30.11.65; FCO 1989; m 1991 Sarah Louise Mills.

Kent, Kathleen Mary; FCO since February 1988; born 23.3.33; Ankara 1961; FO 1963; Copenhagen 1964; Bonn 1966; FCO 1967; Mogadishu 1969; FCO 1971; Washington 1972;

FCO 1975; The Hague 1979; Vienna 1982; Bonn 1985; Grade S1.

Kent, Mark Andrew Geoffrey; Third later Second Secretary (Chancery/Inf) Brasilia since July 1989; born 14.1.66; FCO 1987; m 1991 Martine Delogne

Kent, Sarah Louise (née Mills); SUPL since April 1992; born 28.1.65; FCO 1983; Prague 1987; FCO 1989; Grade 9; m 1991 Andrew Magnus Kent.

Kenwrick-Piercy, Theodore Maurice; First Secretary FCO since January 1992; born 16.1.48; Third later Second Secretary FCO 1971; Second later First Secretary (Press) UKREP Brussels 1974; FCO 1977; Nicosia 1982; First Secretary FCO 1986; First Secretary (Chancery) The Hague 1988; m 1976 Elisabeth Barbara Kenwrick-Cox (1s 1981; 1d 1983).

Kenyon, Ian Roy; Counsellor UKDIS Geneva since June 1988; born 13.6.39; FCO 1974; First Secretary UKDIS Geneva 1976; Bogota 1979; FCO 1982; Head of Nuclear Energy Department, FCO 1983; Counsellor FCO 1986; m 1962 Griselda Rintoul (1d 1963; 1s 1966).

Keogh, David John; Khartoum since October 1988; born 24.6.56; FCO 1979; Ankara 1980; Abu Dhabi 1981; FCO 1983; Islamabad 1984; FCO 1988; Grade 9; m 1987 Carolyn Ann Connolly.

Keogh, Michael Christopher; New York since March 1990; born 19.6.37; Army 1954-77; Washington 1977; Bucharest 1979; The Hague 1980; Jakarta 1983; Lusaka 1984; Copenhagen 1986; Prague 1988; Grade CSO; m 1962 Rona Sparrow (1s 1964; 1d 1965).

Kerby, Michael Adam; Stockholm since July 1983; born 5.5.37; RN 1954-67; MOD Police 1970; Jakarta 1980; Lusaka 1981; Grade SO; m 1956 Barbara Mary Lilley (2d 1957, 1960).

Kerly, David Ernest George; First Secretary (Admin) Warsaw since July 1988; born 26.2.37; FO and Bonn 1959; Moscow 1961; Geneva 1963; Nairobi 1965; DSAO (later FCO) 1968; Port Louis 1971; Munich 1975; Budapest 1976; Second Secretary FCO 1978; Second Secretary Honiara 1981; Second Secretary FCO 1984; m 1959 Lesley Ann Davies (1s 1961; 1d 1962).

Kernohan, Neil Alexander; Riyadh since June 1992; FCO 1989; born 20.9.65; Grade 9.

Kerr, Alistair William Jackson; Second Secretary (Political Information Aid) Abidjan since September 1987; born 22.6.53; FCO 1975; Paris 1978; Nairobi 1981; FCO 1984.

Kerr, Christine; Cape Town/Pretoria since June 1991; born 7.4.60; FCO 1989; Grade S2.

Kerr, Douglas James; FCO since February 1991 (Second Secretary 1991); born 4.11.58; FCO 1980; Bucharest 1982; Kampala 1984; Tel Aviv 1988.

Kerr, James Alexander David; FCO since December 1986; born 22.7.43; CRO 1962; Moscow 1965; Geneva 1966; Ibadan 1969; UKDEL NATO Brussels 1972; FCO 1975; MECAS 1977; Cairo 1978; Vice-Consul Berlin 1981; Consul (Comm) Berlin CG 1982; m (1) 1966 Marja Terhikki (diss 1979); (2d 1967, 1971); (2) 1980 Jeanne Bonner (1d 1981).

Kerr, Sir John (Olav), KCMG (1991), CMG (1987); UK Permanent Representative with personal rank of Ambassador, to the EC Brussels since September 1990; born 22.2.42; Third Secretary FO 1966; Third later Second Secretary Moscow 1967; Second Secretary (Econ) Rawalpindi/ Islamabad 1969; First Secretary 1971; FCO 1972; Private Secretary to the PUS 1974; Counsellor and Head of DM Division HM Treasury 1979; PPS to the Chancellor of the Exchequer 1981; Counsellor and Head of Chancery Washington 1984; AUSS (European Community) FCO 1987; m 1965 Elizabeth Mary Kalaugher (2s 1967, 1968; 3d 1970, 1976 (twins)).

Kerr, Kathleen Mary; Amman since March 1991; born 18.4.56; FCO 1983; Kuwait 1984; Canberra 1986; Berlin 1989; Grade S1.

Kerr, Michael John; Oslo since March 1989; born 12.8.49; RAF 1969-73; FCO 1973; Islamabad 1975; FCO 1977; Dakar 1979; FCO 1983; Cairo 1985; Grade 9; m 1975 Linda Ruth Campbell.

Kerr, Susan Caroline; Prague since July 1990; born 9.4.69; FCO 1988; Grade 10.

Kerrigan, Alison (née Durkin); SUPL since November 1991; born 10.4.59; FCO 1978; UKREP Brussels 1982; FCO 1984; Washington 1988; FCO 1991; Grade S2; m 1984 Christopher Kerrigan.

Kerrigan, Joseph; Dublin since December 1991; born 6.7.69; FCO 1989; Grade 10.

Kerr-Smiley, Lieutenant Colonel Peter Simon; Queen;s Messenger since 1984; born 9.6.34; Army 1952-1984.

Kerry, Catherine; Lagos since July 1991; born 31.7.65; FCO 1988; Grade S2A.

Kershaw, Alexander Richard; FCO since September 1991; born 15.1.67; Grade 8.

Kershaw, Harry; First Secretary (Commercial) Rome since June 1990; born 25.9.38; FO 1960; Vientiane 1961; DSAO 1965; Karachi 1967; FCO 1972; La Paz 1975; Second Secretary (Comm) Seoul 1979; Second Secretary on loan to DOT 1983; Second Secretary FCO 1986; Second later First Secretary (Commercial) Jakarta 1986; m Anong Sonsip (1s 1962; 1d 1964).

Kershaw, Roger; First Secretary (Political) Bonn since February 1992; born 18.3.58; FCO 1982; Language Training 1983; Second Secretary (Comm) Tehran 1984; First Secretary FCO 1987; m 1983 Annick Marie Jeanne Renée Gourley.

Ketchen, Paul Thomas; Brasilia since April 1992; born 24.2.69; FCO 1987; Rome 1989; Grade 10.

Kettle, Mark Brian; Vienna since August 1990; born 22.10.66; FCO 1985; Grade 10.

Kidd, John Christopher William; Deputy Head of Mission Addis Ababa since June 1990; born 4.2.57; FCO 1978; Third later Second Secretary Nicosia 1980; Second Secretary and PS to HM Ambassador Paris 1984; (First Secretary 1985); First Secretary FCO 1986.

Kidner, James Hippisley; First Secretary FCO since February 1990; born 26.2.61; FCO 1985; Second Secretary Kuala Lumpur 1987.

Kilford, Yvonne; FCO since December 1988; born 8.1.70; Grade S2.

Kilvington, Sally Louise; Santiago since March 1991; born 20.2.67; FCO 1989; Grade S2.

Kimmins, Lieutenant Colonel John Michael Carew; Queen's Messenger since 1979; born 16.7.34; Army 1952-79.

Kinchen, Richard, MVO (1976); Counsellor (Finance) UKMIS New York since March 1988; born 12.2.48; Third Secretary FCO 1970; (temporary secondment to British Commission on Rhodesian Opinion 1972); MECAS 1972; Kuwait 1973; Second Secretary FCO 1974; Second later First Secretary Luxembourg 1975; First Secretary (Econ) Paris 1977; FCO 1980; PS/Parliamentary Under-Secretary of State 1982; First Secretary and Head of Chancery Rabat 1984; m 1972 Cheryl Vivienne Abayasekera (1s 1976; 3d 1973 (dec'd 1980), 1979, 1982).

King, Albert Norman, LVO, (1983); First Secretary FCO since June 1992; born 29.3.43; Customs and Excise 1963; Government Actuary;s Department 1963; CRO 1964; DSA 1965; Ibadan 1967; BMG Berlin 1971; Second Secretary (Comm) Singapore 1973; Second Secretary (Comm) Muscat 1976; First Secretary Dacca 1980; First Secretary FCO 1984; First Secretary (Admin) Vienna 1987; m 1969 Dympna Mary Farren (1s 1971; 2d 1973, 1979).

King, Alison Jane; Mexico City since October 1989; born 11.6.66; FCO 1984; UKREP Brussels

Biographical List

1987; Grade 10.

King, David John Buckingham; FCO since November 1976 (Second Secretary 1989); born 13.3.39; FO 1965; Aden 1968; Amman 1970; Georgetown 1971; Cairo 1974; Jedda 1974.

King, Julian Beresford; FCO since January 1992; born 22.8.64; FCO 1985; Paris (ENA) 1987; Second Secretary Paris 1988; Presidency Liaison Officer Luxembourg 1991.

King, Larry; FCO since August 1988; born 1.7.62; FCO 1982; Amman 1985; Grade 9; m 1988 Elaine Margaret Neeve.

King, Peter William; FCO since March 1992; born 29.7.40; RAF 1958-70; MOD 1974; Bucharest 1984; Bonn 1985; Moscow 1986; Kingston 1988; Vienna 1989; Grade SO; m 1970 Jean Lewis (2d 1972, 1973; 1s 1975).

Kingdom, David George; Third Secretary Brussels since February 1992; born 19.8.46; FCO 1986; Grade 8; m 1968 Janice (2s 1972, 1981).

Kingston, Iain Conger; Maseru since December 1991; born 30.5.50; DOE (PSA) 1975; FCO 1976; Cairo 1979; Lilongwe 1983; FCO 1985; Houston 1988; Grade 9; m 1978 Georgia Georgiou (2s 1982, 1983).

Kinoshita, Susan Margaret (née Copnell); FCO since October 1989; born 28.7.61; FCO 1983; Language Training Tokyo 1985; Tokyo 1986; Grade 9; m 1989 Makoto Kinoshita (1d 1991).

Kinsey Helen Jane; FCO since August 1990; born 23.2.71; Grade 9.

Kirby, Diane (née Tallon); Muscat since July 1988; born 25.1.67; FCO 1986; Grade 10; m 1988 Sean William Kirby.

Kirby, Gordon; First Secretary/Head of Chancery Sana'a since May 1989; born 22.2.43; GPO 1960; Ministry of Technology 1968; FCO 1970; Amman 1972; MECAS 1975; Beirut 1976; Language Training 1977; Jedda 1977; Language Training 1981; Second Secretary (Comm) Belgrade 1982; FCO 1985; m 1972 Kathleen Margaret Dawn (2d 1978, 1982).

Kirk, Andrew Phillip; Second Secretary FCO since July 1991; born 26.2.54; FCO 1972; Yaoundé 1975; Havana 1979; FCO 1981; Lisbon 1985; Nairobi 1987; m 1978 Cheryl Jeanne Nichols (2d 1983, 1987).

Kirk, Anna Therese (née Macey); First Secretary FCO since February 1988; born 1.6.59; FCO 1982; Language Training 1984; Third later Second Secretary Oslo 1984; m 1989 Matthew John Lushington Kirk.

Kirk, Malcolm; Paris since July 1990; born

10.4.59; FCO 1978; Nassau 1980; Dakar 1981; FCO 1984; Havana 1985; FCO 1987; Grade 9; m 1982 Linda Patricia Greenwood (1s 1983).

Kirk, Matthew John Lushington; Second later First Secretary FCO since January 1988; born 10.10.60; FCO 1982; Language Training 1984; Third later Second Secretary (Pol/Inf) Belgrade 1984; m 1989 Anna Thérèse Macey.

Kirkpatrick, Andrew John; Third Secretary (Chancery) Budapest since October 1990; born 1.1.63; FCO 1988; Grade 9.

Kirkpatrick-Smith, Adrian; First Secretary FCO since September 1991; born 12.9.45; Army 1960-71; FCO 1975; Beirut 1977; Second Secretary FCO 1978; Seconded to MOD 1989; m 1968 Olive Anne Bailey (1s 1982 (adopted)).

Knapp, Maria Grace; Madrid since June 1992; born 3.4.70; FCO 1989; Grade S2.

Knight, Casimir Stephen Bower; Full-Time Language Training since May 1992; born 4.3.67; FCO 1990; Grade 8.

Knight, Joan Evelyn; UKDIS Geneva since September 1988; born 11.7.38; FCO 1987; Grade S2.

Knight, John David; Second Secretary (Comm) Dar es Salaam since July 1987; born 2.8.43; DSAO later FCO 1966; Baghdad 1968; Bangkok 1970; FCO 1975; Vientiane 1977; Cairo 1980; FCO 1984; m 1975 Panee Wongcharoenrat.

Knight, Roger William; Second later First Secretary FCO since June 1987; born 16.4.47; FO (later FCO) 1966; Jedda 1969; Singapore 1970; FCO 1973; Second Secretary Jedda (later Riyadh) 1984; m 1969 Gillian Elizabeth Newberry (3s 1973, 1975, 1985).

Knight, Terence Ronald; Third later Second Secretary (Chancery) Port of Spain since July 1989; born 3.9.51; FCO 1973; Rabat 1976; Lima 1978; Islamabad 1981; FCO 1983; Oslo 1986; Grade 9; m 1971 Jane Willcocks (2d 1975, 1980; 2s 1977, 1982).

Knight Smith, Ian; Counsellor on loan to the DSS since December 1991; born 18.6.38; HM Forces 1957-59; FCO 1962; Mexico City 1964; Second Secretary Calcutta 1967; Second Secretary (Inf) Caracas 1969; First Secretary FCO 1972; First Secretary (Regional Policy) UKREP Brussels 1982; FCO 1987; On Secondment to the EEC Brussels as Counsellor (National Expert) 1989; m (1) 1964 Glenys Audrey Hayter (dec'd 1981) (1s 1967); (2) 1989 Ellen Ragnhild Sweet-Escott.

Knightson, Jean Lesley; FCO since April 1992; born 22.10.63; FCO 1984; Sofia 1987; FCO 1989; Lagos 1990; Grade S2.

Knott, Graeme Jonathan; Third later Second Secretary (Chancery) Havana since May 1991; born 2.11.66; FCO 1988.

Knott, Paul Robert; Bucharest since May 1992; born 30.6.70; FCO 1989; Grade 10.

Knowles, George; FCO since November 1979; born 23.9.24; HM Forces 1943-47; FO (later FCO) 1966; Brussels 1967; Bahrain 1970; Helsinki 1971; FCO 1974; Washington 1977; Grade 8; m 1952 Joyce Anne Hickling (2s 1957, 1959; 1d 1970).

Knowles, John Samuel; Third Secretary Kingston since September 1989; born 29.2.36; HM Forces 1952-66; FO 1966; Singapore 1968; FCO 1970; Kaduna 1972; FCO 1973; Maseru 1975; Darwin 1978; FCO 1981; Kabul 1982; FCO 1985; Baghdad 1985; FCO 1989; Grade 8; m 1959 Patricia Gregson (2s 1965, 1967; 1d 1959).

Knowlton, Richard Jonathan; First Secretary (Chancery/Econ) Dubai since November 1991; born 25.3.50; Third later Second Secretary FCO 1973; Language Student FCO and Finland 1977; Second later First Secretary Helsinki 1978; First Secretary FCO 1981; Harare 1984; FCO 1989; m (1) 1973 Julia Lister (diss 1990) (1d 1976; 1s 1981); (2) 1990 Vanessa Baldwin.

Knox Müller, Margaret; Third Secretary (Chancery) Vienna since January 1989; born 6.10.61; FCO 1981; Bonn 1984; LA/Caribbean Floater 1987; Grade 9; m 1991 Karl Michael Müller.

Kolinska, Anna Maria; Madrid since November 1990; born 3.3.62; FCO 1983; Johannesburg 1986; Grade 10.

Korad, Mark David; FCO since January 1991; born 19.6.69; Grade 10.

Kotak, Sheetal Arun; Madrid since January 1991; born 27.8.69; FCO 1988; Grade 10.

Krickser-Grier, Frances (née Grier); SUPL since May 1989; born 4.11.46; British-Council Tehran 1970-73; FCO 1975; Brussels 1981; Madrid 1984; Second Secretary FCO 1987; m 1989 Hans Theoder Krickser.

Kydd, Ian Douglas; First Secretary (Econ/ Comm) Ottawa since June 1988; born 1.11.47; CO 1966; DSAO (later FCO) 1966; New Delhi 1970; Second Secretary (Radio/TV) BIS New York 1975; FCO 1979; First Secretary on loan to 10 Downing Street 1981; Language Training 1983; First Secretary (Chancery) Lagos 1984; m 1968 Elizabeth Louise Pontius (1s 1971; 1d 1973).

Kyle, Michael Anthony; First Secretary FCO since January 1991; born 20.7.48; FCO 1970;

Third later Second Secretary Saigon 1972; Second later First Secretary FCO 1975; Washington 1978; FCO 1981; First Secretary (Pol/Econ) Accra 1984; First Secretary (Chancery) Dar es Salaam 1988; m 1976 Wendy Suzanne Sloan (1d 1979; 1s 1981).

Kyles, Raymond William; First Secretary (Chancery) Pretoria since August 1991; born 10.3.56; FCO 1980; UKMIS Geneva 1982; Second Secretary UKREP Brussels 1985; First Secretary FCO 1987; m 1981 Christine Jane Thompson.

L

Lacey, Jane-Frances; Algiers since February 1990; born 20.9.63; FCO 1984; East Berlin 1985; Dublin 1987; Grade 10.

Lacey, John Herbert Laurence; First Secretary and Consul Paris since July 1988; born 11.7.33; HM Forces 1951-53; FO 1954; UKDEL Luxembourg 1957; Latin America Floater 1960; Consul Guayaquil 1962; Second Secretary and Consul Quito 1965; Consul Strasbourg 1966; Commonwealth Office (later FCO) 1968; Second Secretary Bogota 1971; First Secretary (Cons1/ Imm) Lagos 1975; Consul Frankfurt 1979; First Secretary (FCO) 1983; First Secretary and Consul Paris 1986; First Secretary FCO 1986.

Ladd, Michael John; Vienna since January 1990; born 23.10.54; FCO 1971; Washington 1980; FCO 1983; Baghdad 1986; Grade 8; m 1979 Christine Jane Tate (1s 1983; 1d 1986).

Ladva, Sharad Raiya; Yaoundé since March 1989; born 12.7.60; FCO 1978; Belmopan 1985; Grade 10; m 1988 Ellen Louis Santana (1s 1991).

La Fontaine, Hilary Dawn, MBE (1974); Second later First Secretary FCO since September 1982; born 19.10.37; Kaduna 1969; Blantyre 1971; FCO 1973; Second Secretary and Vice-Consul Hanoi 1981.

Laffey, Susan; Second Secretary FCO since July 1987; born 9.10.61; East Berlin 1987; Senior Research Officer (DS Grade 7).

Laidlaw, Christine Margaret; First Secretary On loan at 10 Downing Street since August 1992; born 11.3.44; FO 1961; Oslo 1965; Abidjan 1968; Bahrain 1971; FCO 1973; LA Floater 1974; Language Student 1976; Tehran 1977; Second Secretary FCO 1981; Second Secretary (Comm) Nicosia 1983; First Secretary (Comm) Sofia 1988.

Laing, (John) Stuart; Counsellor and Deputy Head of Mission Riyadh since June 1992; born 22.7.48; Third Secretary FCO 1970; MECAS

1971; Third later Second Secretary Jedda 1973; Second later First Secretary UKREP Brussels 1975; FCO 1978; First Secretary and Head of Chancery Cairo 1983; First Secretary FCO 1987; Counsellor and Head of Chancery Prague 1989; m 1972 Sibella Dorman (1s 1974; 2d 1979, 1985).

Laing, Paul James; First Secretary Berlin since March 1990; born 1.12.53; HM Customs and Excise 1974-80; FCO 1980; New Delhi 1983; Second later First Secretary FCO 1985; m 1982 Dawn Myerscough (2d 1986, 1990, 1s 1992).

Lake, Robin Duncan; Berlin since October 1991; born 15.12.70; FCO 1989; Grade 10.

Lake, Samantha; FCO since July 1992; born 28.2.74; Grade S2.

Lamb, Jonathan Charles; First Secretary FCO since January 1991; born 20.4.55; Second Secretary FCO 1981; First Secretary Montevideo 1984; FCO 1986; First Secretary (Econ) Bucharest 1988; m 1986 Beatriz Clara de Pace Sampietro (1d 1989).

Lamb, Robin David; FCO since 1988; born 25.11.48; FCO 1971; Language Student MECAS 1974; Research Officer (DS Grade 7); FCO 1977; Second Secretary Jedda 1979; Principal Research Officer FCO 1982; First Secretary (Econ) Riyadh 1985; PRO (DS Grade 5); m 1977 Susan Jane Moxon (1d 1982; 1s 1986).

Lamb, Timothy Charles; Consul Amsterdam since August 1990; born 12.10.37; Royal Navy 1955-62; DWS 1962; FCO 1971; Pretoria 1973; Rangoon 1976; FCO 1980; Karachi 1982; Nairobi 1986; Second Secretary FCO 1989; m 1964 Patricia Keenan (2d 1971, 1974).

Lambert, David George, MBE (1977); First Secretary FCO since September 1988; born 16.8.41; Board of Trade 1959; FCO 1969; Kuwait 1970; Lagos 1973; Second Secretary Khartoum 1974; FCO 1977; Second Secretary (Comm) Paris 1980; First Secretary FCO 1982; Copenhagen 1983; m 1965 Mary Ann McGarrigle (3d 1965, 1966, 1968).

Lambert, Jason Edward; FCO since October 1990; born 27.9.71; Grade 10.

Lamont, Donald Alexander; HM Ambassador Montevideo since July 1991; born 13.1.47; Second later First Secretary FCO 1974; First Secretary (UNIDO/IAEA) Vienna 1977; Moscow 1980; First Secretary FCO 1982; Counsellor on Secondment to IISS 1988; Counsellor and Head of Chancery BMG (later BM) Berlin 1988; m 1981 Lynda Margaret Campbell (1d 1983; 1s 1986).

Lampert, Sarah Jane; Third later Second Secretary (Chancery) Sofia since January 1991;

born 8.11.65; FCO 1988; Language Training 1990.

Lamport, Martin Henry; Third Secretary (Institutions) UKREP Brussels since July 1990; born 22.11.52; HM Forces 1972; FCO 1975; SUPL 1976; FCO 1979; Tripoli 1980; Caracas 1983; FCO 1987; Grade 9; m 1990 Catherine Pricilla Maxwell.

Lamport, Stephen Mark Jeffrey; First Secretary later Counsellor; FCO since October 1988; born 27.11.51; UKMIS New York 1974; Third Secretary FCO 1975; Third later Second Secretary Tehran 1975; First Secretary FCO 1980; PS to Minister of State 1981; First Secretary (Chancery) Rome 1984; m 1979 Angela Vivien Paula Hervey (2s 1983, 1985; 1d 1990).

Lancaster, Ian Francis Millar; First Secretary (Chancery) Ankara since September 1991; born 23.9.47; Second Secretary FCO 1974; Second later First Secretary and Consul Hanoi 1975; First Secretary FCO 1977; Prague 1978; First Secretary FCO 1981; First Secretary (Chancery) Brussels 1983; First Secretary FCO 1987; m 1972 Simone Daniel (1d 1978; 1s 1981).

Lance, Andrew Robert; First Secretary FCO since June 1981; born 13.8.43; FO 1962; SUPL 1962-65; DSAO 1965; Prague 1969; Second Secretary (Chancery) The Hague 1972; FCO 1976; First Secretary (Comm) East Berlin 1977; m 1966 Sandra Rosemarie Jackson (1d 1967).

Landman, Sheryl; FCO since January 1991; born 5.12.71; Grade S2.

Landsman, David Maurice; Second Secretary (Economic) Athens since March 1991; born 23.8.63; FCO 1989; m 1990 Catherine Louise Holden (1s 1992).

Lane, Bari Albert; Second later First Secretary FCO since July 1985; born 6.5.48; Ministry of Technology 1965; FO, DSAO and FCO 1966; Vice-Consul Aden 1970; Warsaw 1973; Bombay 1974; FCO 1975; Second Secretary (Admin) Peking 1978; Vice-Consul (Comm) Sydney 1980; m 1971 Jacqueline Mary Chatt.

Lane, Colin George; Second later First Secretary FCO since November 1987; born 8.3.42; FO 1959; Leopoldville (later Kinshasa) 1964; Warsaw 1967; Consular attachment at Hamburg 1970; Vice-Consul Chicago 1970; FCO 1973; Antigua 1975; Second Secretary FCO 1979; Second Secretary (Cons) Harare 1983; m (1) 1965 Carole Anne (née Shrubb) (diss) (1d 1966; 1s 1971); m (2) 1983 Brenda Ivy Taylor.

Lane, Jillian; Bonn since August 1992; born 29.1.69; FCO 1989; Grade 10.

Lang, Susan Margaret; Bonn since March 1984;

born 30.4.48; Beirut 1970; Brussels 1972; FCO 1978; Dublin 1979; E Berlin 1982; Grade S1.

Langford, Clare Alexandra; Caracas since July 1991; born 2.4.67; FCO 1985; Kuwait 1988; FCO 1990; Grade S2.

Langham, Elizabeth Jane (née Webb); FCO since May 1991; born 4.8.61; FCO 1984; Moscow 1986; Washington 1988; Grade 9; m 1989 Peter Andrew Langham (1d 1992).

Langham, Peter Andrew; FCO since May 1991; born 26.9.64; FCO 1983; Moscow 1985; Hamilton 1988; Washington 1990; Grade 9; m 1989 Elizabeth Jane Webb (1d 1992).

Langley, Anthony Haydn; FCO since June 1990; born 26.3.45; FO (later FCO) 1961; Bonn 1967; Tel Aviv 1970; FCO 1973; Accra 1973; Moscow 1976; FCO 1978; Helsinki 1981; FCO 1984; Second Secretary Dubai 1987; m 1966 Carole Joy Weaver (3d 1966, 1969, 1973).

Langman, Nicholas John Andrew; First Secretary FCO since July 1991; born 1.11.60; FCO 1983; Second Secretary Montevideo 1986; Second later First Secretary UKMIS New York 1988.

Langridge, Pauline Anne; Madrid since May 1990; born 17.8.63; FCO 1988; Grade S2.

Langridge, Richard James, CVO (1992); HM Consul-General Bordeaux since December 1989; born 29.10.32; HM Forces 1951-53; FO 1953; Assistant Private Secretary to Secretary of State for Foreign Affairs 1956; Second Secretary New York 1958; Leopoldville 1961; FO 1962; First Secretary (Inf) Athens 1965; First Secretary and Head of Chancery Dakar 1969; First Secretary (Inf) Paris 1972 (Counsellor 1976); DS Inspector FCO 1976; HM Ambassador Antananarivo 1980; Rayner Scrutiny FCO 1985; Deputy High Commissioner and Head of Chancery Colombo 1985; m 1965 Jeannie Louise Joosen (1d 1967).

Larkins, Christopher Paul; Warsaw since December 1991; born 2.10.63; FCO 1986; Grade 10.

Larmouth, Helen Dorothy; Washington since February 1992; born 22.8.63; FCO 1989; Grade S2.

Larner, Jeremy Francis; Second Secretary FCO since March 1992; born 12.11.49; Inland Revenue 1967; FCO 1968; Cairo 1971; Benghazi 1972; Abu Dhabi 1972; Moscow 1975; Seoul 1975; Manila 1976; Monrovia 1977; FCO 1980; Third later Second Secretary (Comm) Tunis 1983; Second Secretary (Comm) Port Louis 1989; m 1975 Sally Dewhurst (2s 1978, 1980).

Lassey, Christine Anne; FCO since January

1992; born 3.12.56; FCO 1978; EC Brussels 1979; Moscow 1982; UKMIS New York 1986; Bonn 1988; Grade S2.

Last, Christopher Paul; Moscow since October 1991; born 27.3.60; FCO 1981; BGWRS Darwin 1984; FCO 1986; Riyadh 1987; FCO 1988; Grade 9; m 1983 Julia Frances.

Latta, Marie Louise; FCO since June 1992; born 25.5.67; MOD 1986; FCO 1988; Berne 1989; Grade 10.

Latter, Edwin John Scott; FCO since September 1991; born 16.2.68; Grade 8.

Lattin-Rawstrone, Howard; Second Secretary (Commercial/Aid) Cairo since April 1991; born 23.3.55; FCO 1975; Buenos Aires 1977; Maputo 1981; Brussels 1982; FCO 1984; Cairo 1988; m (1) 1980 Sylvia Christine Waller (diss 1987); (2) 1987 Caroline Sarah Lattin (2 adopted d 1976, 1978; 1s 1987).

Laurie, Amanda Katharin; Vienna since July 1991; born 1.3.66; FCO 1989; Grade S2.

Lavender, Fiona Jayne; FCO since April 1991; born 12.6.70; Grade S2.

Lavers, Richard Douglas; Deputy Head of Mission and Consul-General Santiago since January 1990; born 10.5.47; Third Secretary FCO 1969 and Buenos Aires 1970; Second later First Secretary Wellington 1973; FCO 1976; First Secretary (Pol/Econ) Brussels 1981; on secondment to Guinness Mahon 1985; First Secretary FCO 1987; NATO Defence College Rome 1989; m 1986 Brigitte Anne Julia Maria Moers (2s 1988, 1989).

Lavery, Creena Christina Maureen; FCO since September 1991; born 17.5.62; Grade 9.

Lavery, Derek John; Islamabad since June 1989; born 1.6.68; FCO 1987; Grade 10.

Lawler, Michelle; Third Secretary and Vice-Consul Bogata since January 1990; born 8.6.64; FCO 1987; Grade 9.

Lawrence, Margaret Ann Maureen; First Secretary FCO since March 1991; born 26.12.42; FO 1960; Kabul 1964; Bangkok 1966; Bonn 1969; FCO 1972; Pretoria 1975; Assistant in the Governor;s Office Port Stanley 1978; Second Secretary (Inf) Rio de Janeiro 1979; on loan to DOT 1981; FCO 1982; First Secretary and Consul Athens 1987.

Lawrence, Paul David; FCO since November 1989; born 10.4.68; Grade 10.

Lawrie, Archie Duncan; Ankara since May 1991; born 2.6.41; Army 1957-83; East Berlin 1983; Islamabad 1985; Belgrade 1986; Dhaka

1987; Grade CSO; m 1966 Janet Stead (2d 1963, 1977; 2s 1970 and 1 dec'd 1977).

Lawrie, James Malcolm, MBE (1985); Accra since April 1990; born 1.6.44; FCO 1970; Jedda 1972; FCO 1973; Islamabad 1975; FCO 1977; Kuwait 1979; FCO 1983; Third Secretary Peking 1984; FCO 1986; Grade 8; m 1971 Anne Margaret Martin (3s 1974, 1977, 1982).

Lawson, John Warren; Second Secretary FCO since August 1989; born 21.7.35; GPO 1951; HM Forces 1954-56; GPO 1956; FO 1962; Helsinki 1964; FO 1966; Budapest 1967; FCO 1968; Beirut 1969; FCO 1972; Ankara 1974; FCO 1976; Singapore 1976; FCO 1978; Second Secretary East Berlin 1985; m 1960 Maureen Ann Clay (1d 1963).

Lawson, Mary; FCO since August 1992; born 18.2.50; FCO 1984; Bogota 1985; FCO 1986; UKDEL Vienna 1987; Rabat 1990; Grade S2A.

Lawson-Smith, Jacqueline Alison; Dubai since November 1988; born 13.2.57; FCO 1976; Berne 1977; Hanoi 1980; Ottawa 1982; FCO 1983; Grade 9.

Lawton, Barbara Joyce; Canberra since June 1992; born 14.1.37; MOD 1967; FCO 1974; Tripoli 1974; East Berlin 1977; Tel Aviv 1978; Paris 1983; Sofia 1983; Ottawa 1986; FCO 1985; FCO 1989; Grade 9.

Lay, Christopher James; Kingston since December 1989; born 26.6.42; Royal Marines 1961-83; Moscow 1983; BMG Berlin 1984; Baghdad 1987; Grade SO; m 1971 Mary (2s 1972, 1973).

Layden, Anthony Michael; Counsellor (Comm/ Econ) Copenhagen since March 1991; born 27.7.46; Third Secretary FCO 1968; MECAS 1969; Second Secretary Jedda 1971; Second later First Secretary Rome 1973; FCO 1977; First Secretary and Head of Chancery Jedda 1982; First Secretary FCO 1982; Head of Chancery Muscat 1987; m 1969 Josephine Mary McGhee (3s 1973, 1974, 1977; 1d 1982).

Lea, Stuart John; Second Secretary Peking since February 1992; born 21.8.43; GPO 1959; FCO 1969; Washington 1970; FCO 1973; Attaché Mexico City 1977; Addis Ababa 1980; Third Secretary FCO 1983; Budapest 1986; Grade 8; m 1966 Jane Partridge (2d 1969, 1971).

Leach, Michael; First Secretary (Admin) Cairo since February 1988; born 6.9.40; CRO 1960; Nicosia 1963; Lagos 1966; Singapore 1969; Second Secretary FCO 1972; Bogota 1976; Lusaka 1980; First Secretary FCO 1983; m 1963 Sandra Virginia Mole (1d 1967, 1s 1976); (diss 1991); (2) m 1992 Judith Parkinson.

Leach, Patricia Kathleen; UKREP Brussels since

February 1983; born 15.1.53; DOI 1973-76; FCO 1978; East Berlin 1978; UKMIS New York 1981; Grade S2.

Leadbeater, Raymond; first Secretary (Management) Warsaw since September 1992; born 13.3.44; FO 1964; Jakarta 1966; Lusaka 1968; FCO 1972; Istanbul 1975; New Delhi 1978; Second Secretary (Admin) Lagos 1981; FCO 1985; Second later First Secretary (Admin/Cons) Wellington 1989; m (1) 1968 Joyce Marie Chapman (diss 1973); (2) 1974 Sheila Sanderson (2s 1978, 1980).

Leafe, Gordon, MSM (1984); Tunis since June 1991; born 4.11.35; RAF 1954-57; Army 1960-84; Moscow 1984; Dhaka 1985; Lilongwe 1988; Grade SO; m 1959 Marina Olga Sterriker (2s 1960, 1961, 1d 1963).

Leatherbarrow, Barbra Ann; Peking since August 1992; born 6.3.66; FCO 1987; Grade S2.

Le Breton, Paul John Woodhouse; Counsellor (Commercial/Economic) and Deputy High Commissioner Singapore since May 1990; FO1/ Commonwealth Office 1965; Berlin 1967; FCO 1969; First Secretary 1972; First Secretary (Capetown1/Pretoria) 1974; First Secretary (Comm) Prague 1979; FCO 1982; Consul (Comm) Zurich 1986; m 1971 Dirksje Sieling (1s 1974; 1d 1977).

Leck, George; FCO since July 1991; born 6.4.56; FCO 1979; Ankara 1980; Africa/Middle East Floater 1984; Latin America/Caribbean Floater 1986; Islamabad 1987; Grade 9.

Lee, Adrian Jonathan; Riyadh since October 1992; born 24.10.68; FCO 1989; Full-Time Language Training Cairo 1991; Grade 9.

Lee, Richard John Clifton; Second Secretary (Commercial) Kuwait since March 1992; born 26.9.51; FCO 1971; Copenhagen 1973; Addis Ababa 1976; Moscow 1979; FCO 1982; Accra 1984; Lusaka 1987; FCO 1989; Grade 9; m 1973 Lesley Eleanor McConnell (1d 1980; 1s 1982).

Lee, Sydney Norman, MBE (1980); First Secretary (Management) Cairo since March 1991; born 25.2.34; Ministry of Supply 1950-55; RAF 1952-54; Colombo 1957; Kaduna 1960; Bombay 1964; DSAO (later FCO) 1967; Vice-Consul San José 1970; Sana'a 1974; Second Secretary (Admin) Lusaka 1979; First Secretary FCO 1982; Consul Chicago 1986; m (1) 1956 June Eileen Tobin (diss 1990), (3s 1957, 1963, 1964), (2) 1990 Marion Clare Louise Winter (1stepd 1976).

Lee, Thomas David; FCO since June 1990; born 9.5.63; FCO 1983; Nicosia 1987; Grade 10.

Lee-Gorton, Victoria (née Lee); FCO since September 1990; born 5.3.70; Grade 9; m 1992

Christopher John Gorton.

Leech, Mary Theresa; The Hague since July 1991; born 24.10.44; CRO 1962; Bonn 1966; Accra 1969; FCO 1971; Antananarivo 1972; Rabat 1974; FCO 1977; Prague 1978; Strasbourg 1980; FCO 1983; Vienna 1985; Paris 1988; Grade S1.

Lees, Andrea Margaret; FCO since June 1989; born 19.7.68; Grade 10.

Lees, Diana Jane; Valletta since August 1989; born 8.3.44; FCO 1977; New Delhi 1978; Moscow 1981; Bonn 1983; FCO 1985; Grade 9.

Legg, Judy; FCO since September 1991; born 29.4.67; Grade 8.

Legg, Michael Henry Frank; First Secretary FCO since February 1989; born 11.3.43; CRO 1961; DSAO 1965; Beira 1967; Delhi 1968; Belgrade 1972; FCO 1976; on loan to DOT 1978; Second Secretary (Comm) Madras 1980; Consul (Comm) Milan 1984; m 1972 Chantal Violette Gonthier (2s 1976, 1979).

Legg, Rufus Alexander; FCO since September 1990; born 13.3.68; Grade 9.

Leggatt, Alison Elaine; FCO since May 1988; born 6.12.43; FO 1965; Bonn 1967; Frankfurt 1969; Munich 1969; Islamabad 1972; FCO 1973; Bridgetown 1974; FCO 1976; Washington 1977; FCO 1977; Helsinki 1979; FCO 1981; Caracas 1985; Grade S2.

Legge, Jeremy John; First Secretary On loan to the Cabinet Office since December 1989; born 19.5.61; Second Secretary FCO 1985; Second Secretary Lusaka 1987; Second later First Secretary FCO 1989; m 1990 Melanie King.

Le Goy, Mark; Full-time language training Cairo since May 1990; born 29.6.64; FCO 1988; Full-time language training 1989; Grade 9.

Leicester, Graham Hansford; First Secretary FCO since April 1991; born 3.12.61; FCO 1984; Language Training Taiwan 1986 (Second Secretary 1987); FCO 1987; Second Secretary JLG Hong Kong 1988; m 1988 Margaret Clare Hannah.

Leigh, David John; Second Secretary FCO since August 1987; born 3.7.48; Post Office 1964; FCO 1969; Lagos 1974; FCO 1975; Third Secretary Tokyo 1978; FCO 1981; Third Secretary Sofia 1984.

Leigh Phippard, Dr Helen Thérèse; FCO since December 1990; born 8.11.64; SRO; m 1990 Anthony David Phippard.

Leith, Dennis, RVM (1975); Consul-General Ho Chi Minh City since November 1992; born 10.12.48; FCO 1967; Moscow 1971; Mexico

City 1972; Sofia 1975; FCO 1976; Guatemala City 1979; Vienna 1982; Second Secretary FCO 1984; Second Secretary (Comm) Bahrain 1987; on secondment to the London Chamber of Commerce 1991; m 1971 Barbara Mary Hum (1s 1974; 1d 1979).

le Jeune d'Allegeershecque, Susan Jane (née Miller); Second Secretary (Econ/Inf) Singapore since March 1992; born 29.4.63; FCO 1985; UKREP Brussels 1987 (Second Secretary 1987; m 1991 Stephane Hervé Marie le Jeune d'Allegeershecque.

Lennard, Sarah-Jill; First Secretary FCO since December 1985; born 19.4.56; FCO 1981; Third Secretary Montevideo 1982; Second Secretary FCO 1983; UKREP Brussels 1983; m 1987 Mark Kilroy (1s 1989).

Lennie, Helen Jane; FCO since July 1992; born 20.11.69; FCO 1988; Bucharest 1990; Grade 10.

Leon, Judith Mary; Bangkok since March 1992; born 17.7.63; Home Office 1984; FCO 1988; UKMIS New York 1989; Grade 9.

Leonard, James; Second Secretary FCO since July 1992; born 30.3.39; GPO 1955; HM Forces 1958-60; GPO 1960; FO 1963; Washington 1965; FO 1967; Nairobi 1968; FCO 1970; Accra 1971; Bucharest 1973; FCO 1977; Pretoria 1979; Second Secretary Bridgetown 1982; Second Secretary Athens 1989; Grade 7; m 1964 Catherine Anne Rowan (1s 1968; 2d 1965, 1981).

Leppard, Peter Brian; Prague since October 1991; born 24.5.38; Ankara 1969; Budapest 1970; Lagos 1972; Mbabane 1974; New Delhi 1977; East Berlin 1980; Athens 1982; Colombo 1985; Warsaw 1987; Cairo 1988; Grade CSO; m 1960 Barbara Pocock (twin d 1962; 1d 1970).

Leslie, Alison Mariot (née Sanderson); Paris (quai d'Orsay) since September 1990; born 25.6.54; Scottish Office 1975; FCO 1977; Singapore 1978; Second later First Secretary Bonn 1982; First Secretary FCO 1986; m 1978 Andrew David Leslie (2d 1987, 1990).

Leslie, Thomas Gary; Karachi since July 1991; born 27.4.69; FCO 1989; Grade 10.

Leslie-Jones, Philippa Anne; First Secretary (Chancery) Moscow since January 1991; born 19.7.59; FCO 1984; Second Secretary Warsaw 1986; First Secretary FCO 1989.

Letchworth, Lieutenant Colonel Robert Charles; Queen;s Messenger since 1986; born 3.8.37; Army 1956-1986.

Levenson, Brenda Susan; Second Secretary FCO since April 1982; born 26.5.44; FO 1962; UKDEL to the Council of Europe Strasbourg

1965; Kampala 1968; FCO 1972; Warsaw 1975; Dar es Salaam 1976; FCO 1979; Second Secretary Belmopan 1981.

Lever, Paul, CMG (1991); AUSS (Defence) FCO since August 1992; born 31.3.44; Third Secretary CO 1966; Third later Second Secretary Helsinki 1967; UKDEL NATO Brussels 1971; First Secretary FCO 1973; Assistant Private Secretary to Secretary of State 1978; SUPL with EC Commission Brussels 1981; Head of United Nations Department FCO 1985; Counsellor FCO 1986; Head of Delegation UKDEL CFE/CSBM Vienna (with personal rank of Ambassador) 1990; m 1990 Patricia Anne Ramsey.

Lever, Simon Jeffrey; Peking since November 1991; born 4.1.63; FCO 1983; Doha 1985; SE Asia/FE Floater 1988; Full-time language training FCO 1989; Language Training Hong Kong 1990; Grade 9.

Levi, Andrew Peter Robert; Second Secretary (Chancery) Bonn since April 1990; born 4.3.63; FCO 1987; (Second Secretary 1989).

Levitt, Kirstie Jane; FCO since November 1992; born 4.7.69; FCO 1988; Cairo 1991; Grade S2.

Le Verrier, Anne Shellagh D'Arcy; FCO since April 1986; born 2.11.40; FCO 1964; Manila 1965; Jedda 1966; FCO 1968; Kingston 1969; FCO 1971; Ankara 1972; FCO 1977; Addis Ababa 1978; FCO 1979; Valletta 1984; Grade S2.

Levoir, Derek Charles; Second Secretary FCO since July 1991; born 8.8.46; DSAO 1965; Latin America Floater 1969; Rome 1971; FCO 1974; Second Secretary 1976; Asuncion 1978; Lisbon 1982; Vice-Consul Naples 1986; m 1973 Liana Annita Ugo (2d 1975, 1976).

Lewington, Richard George; First Secretary FCO since January 1991; born 13.4.48; DSAO (later FCO) 1968; Attached to Army School of Languages 1971; Ulan Bator 1972; Second Secretary (Chancery/Inf) Lima 1976; FCO 1980; Second Secretary (Comm) Moscow 1982; Second later First Secretary FCO 1983; First Secretary (Comm) Tel Aviv 1986; m 1972 Sylviane Paulette Marie Cholet (1s 1982; 1d 1984).

Lewis, Alan Edward; Counsellor Ottawa since April 1992; born 18.2.44; Second Secretary FCO 1971; Language Student Tokyo 1972; Second later First Secretary Tokyo 1973; FCO 1975; First Secretary (Econ) Pretoria 1985; First Secretary FCO 1989; m 1966 Linda Mary Goffrey (1s 1979, 1s 1d (twins) 1981).

Lewis, Ann Walford; Principle Research Officer FCO since June 1985; born 2.5.40; FCO 1966; Second Secretary Moscow 1970; FCO 1971; Helsinki 1972; FCO 1974; Principal Research Officer (DS Grade 5); on loan to Cabinet Office

1979; First Secretary and Head of Chancery East Berlin 1982; (1s 1975).

Lewis, Beverley Elizabeth; Africa/ME Floater since October 1991; born 22.7.66; HCS 1985; FCO 1985; Grade 10.

Lewis, Claire Samantha; FCO since September 1990; born 3.6.66; Grade 9.

Lewis, Ian Roger; Second Secretary Tegucigalpa since June 1992; born 29.10.43; Ministry of Overseas Development 1964; Commonwealth Office DSAO and FCO 1966; Warsaw 1968; Nicosia 1969; Dacca 1972; FCO 1975; LA Floater 1978; FCO 1979; Paris 1981; Athens 1982; FCO 1984; HM Consul and Second Secretary (Admin) Santiago 1984; Second Secretary FCO 1989; m 1978 Marina Rosa Diez.

Lewis, Dr John Ewart Thomas; First Secretary (Chancery) Bonn since August 1991; born 5.11.55; FCO 1987; m 1992 Joy Suzanne Spalding.

Lewis, Joy Suzanne (née Spalding); SUPL since September 1991; born 1.8.60; FCO 1980; Rio de Janeiro 1983; Buenos Aires 1986; FCO 1988; Grade 9; m 1992 Dr John Ewart Lewis.

Lewis, Siân; UKDEL NATO Brussels since February 1988; born 23.12.65; FCO 1986; Grade S2A.

Lewis, Susanna Mary; Second Secretary FCO since February 1972; born 13.11.34; FO 1957; Brussels 1958; Mexico 1960; Guatemala 1961; Hong Kong 1963; FO 1965; Cairo 1967; FCO 1968; Paris 1969.

Lewis, Trevor James; Washington since July 1991; born 8.10.60; FCO 1979; UKREP Brussels 1982; Accra 1984; FCO 1988; Grade 9.

Lewty, (David) Ian; Counsellor FCO since September 1989; born 27.7.43; Third Secretary FO 1965; MECAS 1966; Third later Second Secretary Ottawa 1967; Second Secretary and Head of British Interests Section Baghdad 1971; First Secretary FCO 1972; First Secretary and Head of Chancery Jedda 1976; ENA Paris 1979; UKDEL OECD Paris 1980; First Secretary FCO 1984; Counsellor, Head of Chancery and Consul-General Khartoum 1987; m 1968 Mary Law (2d 1969, 1970).

Lewzey, Alice June; FCO since November 1991; born 4.3.36; Baghdad 1964; FO 1965; Rawalpindi 1966; FO 1968; Berlin 1969; FCO 1971; Geneva 1972; FCO 1975; Lisbon 1979; Peking 1981; FCO 1982; Luxembourg 1987; Warsaw 1990; Grade 9.

Ley, Carol Anne, (née Buchan); FCO since October 1989; born 25.2.61; FCO 1983; Cairo 1986; Grade S2; m 1988 Graham John Ley (1d 1991).

Ley, Christopher John; Second Secretary (Admin) Rome since August 1989; born 14.1.46; FO 1964; Sofia 1968; Rawalpindi1/Islamabad 1970; Chicago 1973; Ottawa 1974; FCO 1976; Madrid 1980; Bombay 1983; Second Secretary FCO 1984; m 1969 Joan Marie Lager (2s 1971, 1972).

Ley, Graham John; Second later First Secretary FCO since October 1989; born 31.5.61; FCO 1984; Second Secretary Cairo 1987; m 1988 Carol Anne Buchan (1d 1991).

Liddell, James; Consul (Commercial) Perth since June 1992; born 20.6.45; FCO 1970; Buenos Aires 1973; Blantyre 1975; FCO 1977; Seoul 1980; Suva 1984; Second Secretary FCO 1988; m 1978 Jillian Stella Coventry.

Lidstone, Jeremy Michael Howard; First Secretary FCO since March 1990; born 23.1.48; Army 1966-80; FCO 1980; First Secretary (Chancery) Lagos 1981; First Secretary FCO 1983; First Secretary (Inf) Nicosia 1986; m 1972 Annette Elizabeth Spurway (diss 1991), (2s 1975, 1978).

Lillie, Stephen; Third Secretary (Chancery/ Information) Peking since January 1992; born 4.2.66; FCO 1988; Full-time language training 1989; Full-time language training Hong Kong 1990; Grade 7; m 1991 Denise Chit Lo.

Lillington, Leisa; FCO since January 1991; born 23.1.65; Home Office 1985; Grade S2.

Linacre, Joanne Tracy; Peking since September 1987; born 22.10.64; DHSS 1981; FCO 1985; Grade 10.

Lindfield, John Richard; FCO since July 1989; born 12.5.59; DHSS 1978; FCO 1978; Cairo 1981; Floater duties 1984; Karachi 1985; Grade 9; m 1985 Judith Christine Brown.

Lindley, Graham; Brussels since June 1992; born 18.3.46; Royal Navy 1964; HOPD 1982; Bucharest 1988; Prague 1990; Grade SO; m 1967 Anita Wood (1s 1969; 1d 1976).

Lindsay, Angela Millar; Paris since October 1991; born 17.8.66; FCO 1989; Grade S2.

Lindsay, Bridget Clare (née O'Riordan); SUPL since June 1991; born 13.8.59; FCO 1980; Warsaw 1982; Tokyo 1984; SUPL 1986; Canberra 1987; FCO 1989; Grade 9; m 1983 Iain Ferrier Lindsay (1s 1991).

Lindsay, Dawn Novelle; FCO since September 1991; born 6.6.62; FCO 1985; Lagos 1988; Grade 9.

Lindsay, Iain Ferrier; Second Secretary FCO since October 1989; born 9.3.59; FCO 1980; Warsaw 1982; Tokyo 1983; Canberra 1986

(Second Secretary 1988); m 1983 Bridget Clare O'Riordan (1s 1991).

Lindsay, James Grant, OBE (1987); First Secretary (Commercial) Karachi since April 1991; born 7.9.41; Scottish Home and Health Department 1964; DSAO (later FCO) 1966; Monrovia 1969; Benin City 1970; Cairo 1973; Second Secretary 1975; on loan to DOT 1975; Second Secretary (Econ) The Hague 1979; First Secretary (Cons/Immig) Lagos 1982 (concurrently First Secretary and Consul (non-resident) People's Republic of Benin); First Secretary FCO 1986; m 1965 Helen Mackinnon (3s 1965, 1969, 1970; 1d 1967).

Lines, Aidan Arthur Swithin; First Secretary (Arab League) Cairo since May 1991; born 23.4.55; FCO 1979; Second Secretary Kuala Lumpur 1981; FCO 1983; Language Training Hong Kong 1984; Trade Commissioner and Consul for Macau, BTC Hong Kong 1986; FCO 1988; on loan to HCS 1989; m (1) 1983 Joanna Mary Green (diss 1987); (2) 1988 Joann Phillipa Seddon (1d 1989, 1s 1991).

Ling, Jeffrey, CMG (1991); AUSS (Director of Communications and Technical Services) since October 1989; born 9.9.39; Second Secretary FO 1966; Second later First Secretary and Private Secretary to HM Ambassador at Washington 1969; First Secretary UKDEL OECD Paris 1974; FCO 1977; Counsellor, Special Adviser to Sultan of Brunei 1979; Counsellor Paris 1982; Director of Research, FCO 1986; later AUSS (Comms/IT Review in FCO); m 1967 Margaret Anne Tatton (1s 1974).

Ling, Norman Arthur; Deputy Consul-General Johannesburg since June 1988; born 12.8.52; Second Secretary FCO 1978; Second Secretary Tripoli 1980; Second later First Secretary Tehran 1981; First Secretary FCO 1984; m 1979 Selma Osman.

Lingwood, David Michael; Cairo since October 1991; born 10.5.68; FCO 1989; Grade 9.

Link, Joan Irene (née Wilmot); First Secretary (Information) Bonn since March 1990; born 3.3.53; FCO 1974; Third Secretary Bonn 1975; Third later Second Secretary FCO 1977; Second later First Secretary UKDIS Geneva 1980; First Secretary FCO 1983; m 1975 David Gerard Link (2s 1977, 1985).

Linnell, Aidan John; FCO since November 1989; born 13.4.60; FCO 1982; Canberra 1987; Grade 8.

Little, Alison Jane; Lusaka since March 1990; born 3.4.68; FCO (HCS) 1986; FCO (DS) 1988; Grade 10.

Little, Jennifer Margaret; FCO since July 1989; born 21.6.47; FCO 1970-72; Senior Research Officer.

Little, Margaret Cambridge; FCO since May 1989; born 5.3.49; FCO 1973; Warsaw 1974; Tehran 1976; Hanoi 1979; Rome 1979; FCO 1982; Colombo 1986; Grade S2.

Little, Robert George MacGregor; Lagos since April 1990; born 3.8.37; Army 1956-79; Istanbul 1981; Bucharest 1981; Rome 1983; Amman 1987; Moscow 1989; Grade SO.

Littlefield, David Leslie; On loan to the DT1 since September 1990; born 22.5.40; Ministry of Housing and Local Government 1958; Customs and Excise 1959; CRO 1961; Dacca 1962; Kampala 1964; Beirut 1967; Second Secretary (Admin) 1969; Second later First Secretary FCO 1972; National Defence College 1978; Consul (Inf) Sydney 1978; First Secretary and Resident Rep St Lucia 1983; First Secretary FCO 1987; m (1) 1961 Georgina MacDonald McKay Provan Allan (diss 1978) (1s 1966); (2) 1978 Marian Peacock Pochin (diss 1981); (3) 1981 Mary Patricia Holman (née Fee).

Livesey, Geoffrey Colin, OBE (1989), MBE (1968); First Secretary (Management) Islamabad since May 1989; born 21.12.43; FO 1962; West Africa Floater 1965; Hanoi 1967; Montevideo 1968; Panama City 1969; FCO 1972; Warsaw 1975; Abidjan 1977; Second later First Secretary FCO 1982; First Secretary (Comm) and Consul Havana 1985; m (1) 1969 Elisa Jane Pullen (diss 1983) (2s 1973, 1975); (2) 1985 Linda Ann Lowe.

Livesey, Timothy Peter Nicholas; Second later First Secretary (Aid) Lagos since October 1989; born 29.6.59; FCO 1987; Rabat 1988; FCO 1988; m 1986 Catherine Eaglestone (1d 1990).

Livingston, Catherine Mary (née Bramley); SUPL since September 1991; born 22.6.56; FCO 1975; Cairo 1977; Resigned 1980; Reinstated 1982; FCO 1982; Rome 1984; Muscat 1986; SUPL 1990; FCO 1991; Grade S1; m 1985 Richard Ian Livingston.

Llewellyn Smith, Michael John, CMG (1989); HM Ambassador Warsaw since September 1991; born 25.4.39; FCO 1970; First Secretary and Cultural Attaché Moscow 1973; First Secretary (Inf) Paris 1976; FCO 1977; RCDS 1979; Counsellor (Pol) and Consul-General Athens 1980; Counsellor FCO 1984; Minister Paris 1988; m 1967 Colette Gaulier (1s 1970; 1d 1971).

Lloyd, Andrew; FCO since September 1990; (Second Secretary 1992); born 22.10.64; FCO 1982; Washington 1984; Kaduna 1987; m 1987 Sandra Leigh Craven.

Lloyd, Arthur Jeffrey; First Secretary (Management) Sofia since April 1992; born 13.5.37; RAF 1955-58; Ministry of Labour 1958; National Insurance Board 1959; Ministry of Aviation 1960; FCO 1966; Kampala 1969; Delhi

1972; FCO 1976; Innsbruck 1979; Moscow 1980; Consul (Cons/Admin) Hamburg 1981; FCO 1985; m 1963 Helene Margarete Einberger (1s 1966; 1d 1970).

Lloyd, David Andrew; First Secretary (Comm) Al Khobar since August 1988; born 24.12.40; FO 1964; MECAS 1969; Kuwait 1970; Second Secretary Bogota 1973; FCO 1976; Second Secretary (Comm) Madrid 1979; First Secretary FCO 1983; m (1) 1965 Janet Elizabeth Rawcliffe (diss) (1d 1969; 1s 1971); (2) 1979 Patricia Villa (diss); (3) 1987 Katherine Jane Smith (3d 1987, 1988, 1991).

Lloyd, Diane Elizabeth; Vice-Consul tokyo since December 1991; born 27.2.68; FCO 1987; Warsaw 1989; Full-time Language Training FCO 1989; Full-time Language training Tokyo 1990; Grade 9.

Lloyd, Susan Jacqueline; Harare since December 1991; born 28.2.70; FCO 1989; Grade 10.

Loader, Edward, MVO (1980); First Secretary (Management) Peking since July 1992; born 7.9.35; RAF 1957-59; HCS 1959; Islamabad 1970; Second Secretary (Imm) New Delhi 1971; Second Secretary FCO 1975; Berne 1978; First Secretary (Admin) Cairo 1982; UKMIS Geneva 1985; First Secretary (Cons/Immig) Dhaka 1989; m 1958 Judith Anne Robinson (1s 1960; 3d 1964, 1966, 1973).

Lock, Jennifer Hazel; Tunis since September 1991; born 9.7.59; FCO 1978; Jakarta 1982; Stockholm 1985; FCO 1988; Grade 9.

Lockhart, Ian Sinclair, MBE (1969); First Secretary (Commercial/Aid) Cairo since March 1992; born 4.1.37; CRO 1959; Lahore 1959; Wellington 1962; FO 1964; Khartoum 1965; MECAS 1968; Second Secretary (Comm) Jedda 1970; Tripoli 1974; Second later First Secretary (Comm) The Hague 1977; FCO 1980; First Secretary (Comm) Doha 1983; Head of Chancery and HM Consul Abu Dhabi 1986; First Secretary FCO 1989; m 1959 Joyce Margaret Robinson (1d 1960; 1s 1962).

Lockton, Guy Patrick, MBE (1975); HM Consul-General Lyon since September 1992; born 24.7.36; HM Forces 1955-57; FO 1957; Moscow 1959; Bonn 1961; Second Secretary 1964; Vice-Consul (Comm) Chicago 1964; MECAS 1967; Second Secretary (Comm) Dubai 1969; FCO 1971; First Secretary (Comm) East Berlin 1975; First Secretary Head of Chancery and Consul Seoul 1978; First Secretary Head of Chancery and Consul Luxembourg 1981; Consul-General Jedda 1985; Deputy Consul-General and Director of Trade Development BTIO New York 1989; m 1959 Mavis Kerridge (3s 1962, 1963, 1971; 1d 1966).

Lockyer, Michael Henry; Amman since

November 1991; born 23.8.38; Army 1953-78; Nairobi 1978; Dacca 1981; Washington 1982; Tokyo 1983; Kingston 1986; East Berlin 1988; Prague 1990; Grade SO.

Lodge, John Martin; First Secretary FCO since October 1991; born 9.1.42; HM Customs and Excise 1958; FO 1964; UKDEL EFTA later UK Mission Geneva 1965; Aden 1968; Peking 1969; Vancouver 1971; Seattle 1972; FCO 1973; Dacca 1976; Second Secretary (Comm) Lilongwe 1979; FCO 1983; Second Secretary Kathmandu 1986; Second Secretary Bandar Seri Begawan 1988; m 1971 Valerie Turnbull (diss 1990); (1s 1977).

Lodge, Katherine Rosemary; FCO since January 1990; Second Secretary 1992; born 3.8.59; FCO 1984; Language Training Tokyo 1985; Third Secretary Tokyo 1986.

Logan, David Brian Carleton, CMG (1991); AUS (Central and Eastern Europe) FCO since June 1992; born 11.8.43; Third Secretary Istanbul 1965; Third later Second Secretary Ankara 1967; Private Secretary to the Parliamentary Under-Secretary of State 1970; First Secretary 1971; First Secretary UKMIS New York 1973; FCO 1977; Counsellor, Head of Chancery and Consul-General Oslo 1982; Counsellor FCO 1986; CDA at Oxford University 1988; Minister Moscow 1989; m 1967 Judith Margaret Walton Cole (1d 1968; 2s 1970 (dec'd 1988), 1976).

Logan, Jane; FCO since August 1992; born 11.10.64; FCO 1984; Pretoria 1986; Port of Spain 1989; Grade S2.

Logan, (née Tandy) Marilla Joy Fiona; Second Secretary Kuala Lumpur since July 1992; born 12.9.53; FCO 1974; Moscow 1977; FCO 1978; Düsseldorf 1980; FCO 1983; m 1986 Allan Robert Logan.

Lomax, Michael Leslie; FCO since January 1990; born 26.3.39; Army 1956-79; FCO 1979; Mexico City 1980; Jakarta 1983; Lagos 1987; Grade 9; m 1975 Sally-Ann (1d 1967).

Long, Christopher William, CMG (1986); HM Ambassador Cairo since April 1992; born 9.4.38; Third Secretary FO 1963; MECAS 1964; Third later Second Secretary Jedda 1965; FO 1967; Second later First Secretary Caracas 1967; FCO 1969; First Secretary and Head of Chancery Budapest 1974; Belgrade CSCE Meeting 1977; Counsellor and Head of Chancery Damascus 1978; Counsellor and Head of Chancery UKMIS Geneva 1980; Head of Near East and North Africa Department FCO 1983; AUSS (Deputy Chief Clerk and Chief Inspector) FCO 1985; HM Ambassador Berne 1988; HM Ambassador (non-resident) to the Principality of Liechtenstein 1991; m 1972 Patricia Ann Eleanor Stanbridge (1d 1974; 2s 1977, 1982).

Long, Jeremy, OBE (1988); First Secretary FCO

1989; born 9.7.43; FO 1962; DSAO 1965; Baghdad 1965; Vice-Consul Alexandria 1967; Vice-Consul Sofia 1968; Fiji 1970; Second Secretary FCO 1972; Vice-Consul (Comm) Brisbane 1976; FCO 1981; First Secretary (Admin) Islamabad 1986; m 1965 Monica Mary Wade (2s 1970, 1971).

Long, Michael John; First Secretary FCO since November 1987; born 13.2.40; FO 1958; Moscow 1963; Vice-Consul Belgrade 1966; Second Secretary FO (later FCO) 1967; Karachi 1970; Second Secretary and Consul Moscow 1973; First Secretary 1975; Consul New York (Consulate General) 1975; FCO 1980; First Secretary Holy See 1985; m 1965 Elizabeth Mann Ewing.

Longbottom, Julia Margaret; Second Secretary (Chancery) Tokyo since October 1990; born 13.7.63; FCO 1986; Language Training 1988; Language Training Kamakura 1989; m 1990 Richard James Sciver (1d 1992).

Longdon, Catherine Mary; FCO since November 1990; born 15.12.64; Grade 9.

Longhurst, William Jesse; Seoul since January 1992; born 7.2.67; FCO 1990; Grade 8; m 1991 Eriko Niimi (1d 1991).

Longrigg, Anthony James, CMG (1992); Counsellor (Econ/EC Madrid since June 1991; born 21.4.44; FCO 1972; Second later First Secretary (Pol) Moscow 1975; FCO 1978; Brasilia 1981; First Secretary FCO 1985; Counsellor (Internal) Moscow 1987; m 1968 Jane Rosa Cowlin (2d 1970, 1973).

Longworth, Peter; Deputy Head of Mission Seoul since March 1991; born 26.5.42; First Secretary FCO 1974; First Secretary (Econ) Bonn 1977; First Secretary, Head of Chancery and Consul Sofia 1981; First Secretary FCO 1984; Counsellor (Comm) Copenhagen 1987; m (1) 1967 Ann Louise Miriam Summerson (diss); (2) 1975 Christina Margareta Wallin.

Lonsdale, Charles John; Third later Second Secretary (Budapest) since April 1990; born 5.7.65; FCO 1987; Vienna CSCF 1988; FCO 1989; Grade 8.

Lonsdale, Michael James; First Secretary (UN) UKMIS Geneva since May 1990; born 11.3.43; CO 1960; Malta 1964; FCO 1967; Third Secretary (Inf) Nassau 1973; Third Secretary (Econ) New Delhi 1975; FCO 1979; Second Secretary (Comm) Lagos 1981; Second Secretary (Head of Chancery) and Consul Reykjavik 1985; Second Secretary FCO 1986; (First Secretary 1989); m 1973; Glenys Margaret Ritchie.

Loosemore, Anthony Arthur William; Second Secretary (Management) Manila since May 1991; born 20.10.34; FCO 1972; Lagos 1974; Rabat

1977; FCO 1980; Tristan da Cunha 1981; Warsaw 1982; Muscat (BERS Liaison Officer) 1985; Second Secretary FCO 1987; m 1970 Christiane Paulette Babayou (1d 1972).

Lo Prinzi, Clare Julia (née Nicholls); Rome since January 1991; born 26.3.69; FCO 1988; Grade 10; m 1992 Fabio Felice Lo Prinzi.

Loran, Kenneth Charles; FCO since July 1986; born 7.3.30; Royal Navy 1946-55; FO 1955; Singapore 1956; FO 1957; Benghazi 1958; Tripoli 1960; Bucharest 1961; Singapore 1963; FO 1965; Accra 1966; FO 1967; Delhi 1968; Istanbul 1971; FCO 1973; Madrid 1975; FCO 1977; Mogadishu 1977; FCO 1979; Kabul 1980; FCO 1982; Attaché Abu Dhabi 1982; Grade 8; m Mary Theresa Monteith (1s 1955; 1d 1956).

Lorimer, Eamonn Barrington; Washington since June 1989; born 11.12.64; FCO 1985; Grade 10.

Losack, Sheila June; FCO since August 1982; (Second Secretary 1992); born 13.6.33; Jakarta 1958; Moscow 1959; UKMIS New York 1961; Addis Ababa 1963; FCO 1967; Bangkok 1969; UKDEL NATO Brussels 1970; FCO 1973; Valletta 1975; FCO 1977; Vienna 1981.

Loten, Graeme Neil; Second Secretary (Econ/ Agric) The Hague since July 1988; born 10.3.59; FCO 1981; UKDEL NATO Brussels 1983; Khartoum 1986.

Lott, Ann Veronica (née Lewis); Canberra since July 1989; born 22.11.55; FCO 1978; Algiers 1979; Montevideo 1982; FCO 1984; Latin America Floater 1987; FCO 1988; Grade 9; m 1989 Justin Karl Lott.

Louth, Michael; Third Secretary (Management/ Comm/Cons) Ljubljana since October 1992; born 21.5.63; FCO 1981; Lagos 1984; East Berlin 1988; FCO 1989; Grade 9.

Love, Darren Mark; Accra since July 1991; born 26.2.68; FCO 1988; Warsaw 1989; Grade 10.

Loveday, Christine; FCO since May 1991; born 15.8.59; FCO 1984; Muscat 1986; Kingston 1989; Grade S2.

Lovelock, Anthony Thomas John; Deputy Head of Mission Montevideo since May 1990; born 16.2.40; MPNI 1960; Commonwealth Office 1966; Chittagong 1968; Budapest 1968; Ibadan 1969; Second Secretary (Comm) and Vice-Consul Vientiane 1973; FCO 1976; Vice-Consul (Comm) Sydney 1979; Consul (Inf) Melbourne 1980; First Secretary (Admin) and Consul Copenhagen 1982; First Secretary FCO 1986; m 1962 Janet Marion Evans (3d 1967, 1970, 1977).

Lovett, Simon Joseph; Second Secretary FCO since November 1990; born 11.8.57; DHSS 1977; FCO 1981; Bombay 1983; Ottawa 1987;

m 1985 Amita Rani Sarwal (1s 1986).

Low, Brian Buik; HM Ambassador Tallinn since October 1991; born 15.11.37; RAF 1956-61; FO 1962; Sofia 1965; Sydney 1967; Second Secretary (Comm) Kuala Lumpur 1969; Moscow 1973; Second later First Secretary FCO 1974; Singapore 1978; Consul (Comm) BTDO New York 1981; First Secretary FCO 1984; Head of Chancery Lima 1988; m 1960 Anita Joan Allum (3d 1961, 1963, 1968).

Lowen, Barry Robert; Third Secretary (Chancery) Kuwait since June 1989; born 9.1.64; FCO 1986; Language Training Cairo 1987; Grade 8; m 1989 Karin Rhiannon Blizard.

Lowes, Merrick John; First Secretary (Comm) Damascus since April 1991; born 14.11.44; RAF 1962-74; FCO 1975; Vienna 1978; Maseru 1981; Vice-Consul Naples 1983; Second Secretary FCO 1986; First Secretary on loan to Office of Fair Trading 1989; m 1970 (Christine) Wendy Ralley (1s 1975; 1d 1978).

Loweth, Alan Robert; First Secretary (Chancery) Warsaw since September 1991; born 12.12.52; FCO 1973; Language Student 1977; Copenhagen 1978; FCO 1981; Language Student 1984; Second Secretary Moscow 1985; First Secretary FCO 1988; m 1986 Linda Susan Parr.

Lowis, Joanna Jill; Third later Second Secretary FCO since March 1992; born 2.8.42; Warsaw 1965; Düsseldorf 1966; FCO 1969; Wellington 1972; UKDEL OECD Paris 1974; FCO 1977; Pretoria/Capetown 1978; FCO 1981; Kathmandu 1984; FCO 1988; Third Secretary (Cons) Ottawa 1989.

Lownds, Mathew John; Third Secretary (Aid/ Chancery) Luanda since November 1992; born 6.8.65; FCO 1987; Dublin 1989; Dusseldorf 1990; Grade 9.

Lowson, Christine Ruth; SUPL since May 1992; born 14.4.63; FCO 1982; Nairobi 1985; Islamabad 1988; FCO 1990; Grade S2; m 1991 Kevin Joseph Carnegie Sloan.

Lucas, Stephen John; Paris since October 1992; born 30.6.62; DTI 1986-1990; FCO 1990; Grade 9.

Lucien, Valerie Linda; Assistant Management Officer Kingston since September 1990; born 12.8.47; FCO 1977; Lagos 1978; UKREP Brussels 1981; Africa/ME Floater 1984; FCO 1987; Grade 9.

Luckett, Jane Elizabeth; FCO since May 1992; born 11.11.64; Grade S2.

Ludlow, David; on secondment to the European Commission Brussels since November 1990; born 19.11.63; FCO 1985; Language training 1986;

Private Secretary to HM Ambassador Moscow 1987; (Second Secretary 1989).

Luff, Frances Marjorie; Third Secretary (Chancery) Bahrain since October 1992; born 13.10.65; FCO 1989; Language Training Cairo 1991; Grade 9.

Lumsden-Bedingfeld, Ann; Colombo since August 1990; born 11.8.62; FCO 1985; East Berlin 1987; FCO 1989; Grade S2.

Lusher, David; Vice-Consul Milan since April 1991; born 27.12.55; DOE 1973; FCO 1975; Belgrade 1977; Seoul 1978; Accra 1982; FCO 1984; Islamabad 1987; Grade 9; m 1978 Soon-Ja Chung (1s 1983).

Lusty, Gregor Malcolm; Full-Time Language Training since September 1992; born 12.3.69; FCO 1991; Grade 9.

Lyall, Michael David; Warsaw since February 1992; born 9.9.43; Royal Navy 1961-1989; Moscow 1991; Grade S0; m 1967 Janet Haugh (1s 1969).

Lyall Grant, Mark Justin; First Secretary (Chancery) Paris since January 1990; born 29.5.56; FCO 1980; Second Secretary Islamabad 1982; First Secretary FCO 1985; m 1986 Sheila Jean Tresise.

Lyall Grant, Sheila Jean (née Tresise); Vice Consul Paris since March 1990; born 16.12.60; FCO 1980; Islamabad 1982; FCO 1985; Grade 9; m 1986 Mark Justin Lyall Grant.

Lycett, Nadine Claire; Washington since October 1992; born 19.4.65; FCO 1984, UKDEL NATO Brussels 1986; FCO 1988; Grade S2.

Lygo, Clifford George; FCO since September 1982; born 2.2.51; FCO 1967; Rome 1976; FCO 1979; Khartoum 1980; Grade 9; m 1976 Sandra Francida Wilson (2d 1978, 1983).

Lynch, Cheryl Vinetta; Peking since July 1991; born 4.11.66; FCO 1988; Grade S2A.

Lynch, Kevin Joseph; First Secretary (Commercial) Kinshasa since August 1991; born 6.1.41; Passport Office 1958; CRO 1964; Lusaka 1964; FO 1967; Kuala Lumpur 1967; FCO 1968; Beirut 1970; Georgetown 1973; FCO 1976; Third later Second Secretary Bucharest 1979; Second Secretary (Comm) Brussels 1983; Second Secretary FCO 1987; m 1963 Margaret Ann Childs (2s 1964, 1965).

Lynch, Thomas Desmond; FCO since September 1982; born 6.7.36; GPO 1952; HM Forces 1954-56; GPO 1956; FO 1965; Paris 1967; Capetown/Pretoria 1970; FCO 1972; Bangkok 1973; FCO 1976; New York 1980; Grade 7; m 1969 Carole Jacqueline Jones (1s 1965).

Lyne, Kevin Douglas; Second Secretary (Chancery) Santiago since September 1991; born 6.11.61; FCO 1988 (Second Secretary 1989); m 1988 Anne Francoise Dabbadie (1d 1989).

Lyne, Richard John; First Secretary FCO since January 1992; born 20.11.48; FCO 1970; Belgrade 1972; Algiers 1974; Damascus 1977; FCO 1980; on loan to DTI 1981; Second Secretary (Comm) New Delhi 1984; Second later First Secretary (Chancery/Inf) Stockholm 1988; m 1977 Jennifer Anne Whitworth (1d 1982; 1s 1985).

Lyne, Roderic Michael John, CMG (1992); Counsellor FCO since October 1990; born 31.3.48; FCO 1970; Attached to Army School of Languages 1971; Moscow 1972; Second Secretary Dakar 1974; FCO 1976; Assistant Private Secretary to Secretary of State 1979; First Secretary UKMIS New York 1982; Chatham House (CDA) 1986; Counsellor (Head of Chancery) Moscow 1987; m 1969 Amanda Mary Smith (2s 1971, 1974; 1d 1981).

Lyons, Julian Michael; FCO since August 1991; born 17.12.65; FCO 1984; UKDEL NATO Brussels 1986; Africa/ME Floater 1989; Grade 9.

Lyons, Lesley Anne (née Martin), UKMIS New York since December 1986; born 7.9.55; FCO 1975; Barcelona 1975; Singapore 1981; SUPL 1983; Grade 9; m (1) 1979 Henry Philip Harris; (2) 1985 John Thomas Lyons.

Lysaght, Stephen Peter; Washington since February 1992; born 17.5.70; FCO 1989; Grade 10.

Lyscom, David Edward; Counsellor (Science and Technology) Bonn since September 1991; born 8.8.51; FCO 1972; Third later Second Secretary Vienna 1973; Second Secretary Ottawa 1977; Second (later First Secretary) FCO 1979; First Secretary 1980; First Secretary Bonn 1984; First Secretary (Economic) Riyadh 1988; m 1973 Nicole Jane Ward (2d 1983, 1987; 1s 1985).

Lyster-Binns, Benjamin Edward Noël; Lilongwe since August 1991; born 19.10.65; FCO 1989; Grade 9.

M

McAdam, Douglas Baer; First Secretary (Consular/Immigration) Lagos since September 1990; born 25.6.44; FO 1961; Ulan Bator 1966; Vice-Consul Luanda 1969; Delhi 1972; FCO 1975; Second Secretary Ulan Bator 1978; Vice-Consul (Comm) Rio de Janeiro 1979; Second later First Secretary and Head of Chancery UKDEL Vienna 1983; FCO 1986; m 1965 Susan Clare Jarvis (1s 1970; 1d 1975).

McAdam, Susan Clare (née Jarvis); Lagos since September 1990; born 4.10.42; FO 1961; resigned 1965; reinstated 1984; Vienna 1984; FCO 1986; Grade 9; m 1965 Douglas Baer McAdam (1s 1970; 1d 1975).

Macadie, Jeremy James; FCO since December 1991; born 10.7.52; FCO 1972; Dakar 1975; Addis Ababa 1980; FCO 1981; Sana'a 1984; Antananarivo 1988; Grade 9; m 1975 Chantal Andrea Jacqueline Copiatti.

Macaire, Robert Nigel Paul; Second Secretary Bucharest since January 1992; born 19.2.66; MOD 1987-90; FCO 1990; Language Training FCO 1991.

McAllister, Andrew Thornton; Karachi since August 1990; born 30.11.67; FCO 1988; Grade 9.

McAllister, Dominic James; Full-Time Language Training since September 1992; born 12.2.64; FCO 1990; Grade 9.

McAllister, Susan Peta; Latin America Floater since November 1990; born 28.5.67; FCO 1985; Paris 1987; Grade 10.

Macan, Thomas Townley; Counsellor and Deputy Head of Mission Lisbon since July 1990; born 14.11.46; FCO 1969; Third later Second Secretary Bonn 1971; Second later First Secretary Brasilia 1974; FCO 1978; First Secretary (Press and Inf) Bonn 1981; First Secretary later Counsellor FCO 1986; m 1976 Janet Ellen Martin (1s 1981; 1d 1984).

McArdle, Leo Michael; Bucharest since February 1992; born 29.8.36; Army 1955-78; Lagos 1978; Moscow 1979; UKMIS Geneva 1981; UKREP Brussels 1984; Peking 1987; Montevideo 1988; Paris 1991; Grade CSO; m 1968 Kathleen Lee.

McAree, Kevin Thomas; FCO since May 1989; born 27.6.52; FCO 1971; Caracas 1974; FCO 1974; Honiara 1974; Moscow 1977; Georgetown 1979; FCO 1983; Munich 1988; Grade 9; m 1975 Susan Margaret Humphrey.

McAree, Patrick Sean; FCO since March 1991; born 30.12.53; FCO 1971; Cairo 1975; Calcutta 1978; FCO 1982; Tehran 1984; Düsseldorf 1988; Grade 9; m 1975 Maureen Alexander.

Macartney, Glen Patrick Charles; Second later First Secretary FCO since February 1975; born 24.9.49; Third Secretary FCO 1971; Language Student Sheffield University 1972; Third later Second Secretary Tokyo 1973.

Macaulay, Donald Alistair Robert, MBE (1991); First Secretary FCO since May 1991; born 26.6.37; Royal Navy 1958-59; CRO 1963; Freetown 1963; (Second Secretary (Inf) 1964);

Bombay 1967; FCO 1970; Lourenco Marques 1973; FCO 1975; Vice-Consul (Cons/Admin) Munich 1976; Second Secretary (Comm) Washington 1981; Second later First Secretary FCO 1985; First Secretary (Comm) Kuwait 1988; m (1) 1964 Bonnie Robin King (dec'd 1984) (2s 1971, 1973), (2) 1991 Pamela Lesley Wyatt.

McCafferty, Catherine Sarah; FCO since December 1991; born 7.4.73; Grade 10.

McCafferty, Marie Claire; Bonn since November 1990; born 17.5.65; FCO 1988; Grade S2A.

McCairn, John; Warsaw since December 1991; born 10.9.35; Army 1951-76; Baghdad 1981; Moscow 1982; Paris 1984; Tel Aviv 1986; Grade CSO; m 1959 Marigold Phyllis Swain (2s 1963, 1976; 1d 1967).

McCall, Gary; Bridgetown since December 1989; born 8.2.69; FCO 1987; Grade 10; m 1990 Patricia Ann Chin.

McCallum, Louise Mary; UKDEL Vienna since November 1992; born 26.4.69; FCO 1990; Grade 10.

McCallum, Robert Campbell; UKMIS New York since January 1991; born 4.11.45; Moscow 1989; Grade SO.

McCann, Alec; Rome since April 1991; born 4.11.70; FCO 1988; Grade 10.

McCann, Gerry; Bangkok since July 1990; born 24.9.68; FCO 1988; Grade 10.

McCarron, Helen Paula; UKMIS Geneva since June 1992; born 29.6.68; FCO 1986; New Delhi 1989; Grade 9.

McCarthy, Helen Grace; Luxembourg since June 1988; born 1.2.64; FCO 1983; Paris 1985; Grade S2.

McCarthy, Nicholas Melvyn, OBE (1983); Deputy Head of Mission Brussels since May 1990; born 4.4.38; FO 1961; Vice-Consul Saigon 1962; Tokyo 1964; Second Secretary (Comm) 1966; FCO 1970; Second later First Secretary (Inf) Brussels 1973; FCO 1978; First Secretary (Comm) and Head of Chancery Dakar 1980; FCO 1984; Consul-General Tokyo 1985; HM Consul-General and Director of Trade Promotion Osaka 1985; m 1961 Gillian Eileen Mary Hill (1d 1963; 3s 1964, 1968, 1970).

McCarthy, Tina Ann; Dar es Salaam since September 1990; born 25.1.66; FCO 1984; Peking 1987; FCO 1988; Grade 10.

McCleary, William Boyd; Counsellor and Deputy Head of Mission Ankara since January

1990; born 30.3.49; HCS 1972; First Secretary (Agric later Chancery) Bonn 1975; First Secretary FCO 1981; First Secretary Head of Chancery and Consul Seoul 1985; First Secretary FCO 1988; m 1977 Susan Elizabeth Williams (2d 1983, 1985).

McCluney, Ian, cmg (1990); DHC Calcutta since March 1991; born 27.2.37; HM Forces 1958-62; Addis Ababa 1964; FCO 1967; Assistant Private Secretary to the Secretary of State 1969; Second Secretary 1970; MECAS 1971; Baghdad 1972; FCO 1975; First Secretary 1977; First Secretary and Head of Chancery Kuwait 1979; HM Consul-General Alexandria 1982; Counsellor FCO 1986; HM Ambassador Mogadishu 1989; m 1962 Elizabeth Mary Walshe (1d 1962; 2s 1965, 1967).

McCluskie, Matthew William; Tunis since February 1990; born 6.5.65; FCO 1984; Bonn 1986; Prague 1988; Grade 10.

McCole, Alan; Second Secretary and Vice-Consul Paris since August 1987; born 13.3.40; HM Forces 1958-63; GPO 1963; FO 1965; Prague 1966; Lagos 1968; FCO 1971; Islamabad 1975; FCO 1977; BTDO New York 1979; FCO 1981; m 1960 Patricia Mary Painter (2s 1964, 1965).

McColl, Sir Colin (Hugh Verel), kcmg (1990); FCO since May 1977; born 6.9.32; FO 1956; Third Secretary Bangkok 1958; Vientiane 1960; Second Secretary FO 1962; First Secretary Warsaw 1966; FCO 1968; Consul Geneva 1973; m (1) 1959 Shirley Marian Curtis (dec'd 1983) (2s 1962, 1963; 2d 1960 (dec'd), 1967) (2) 1985 Sally Morgan (1s 1990).

McColl, Lorraine Helen; Bonn since January 1990; born 20.8.57; FCO 1989; Grade S2.

McColl, Sally Ann; FCO since February 1990; born 27.11.64; FCO 1983; UKREP Brussels 1987; Grade S2A.

McColm, Sean; FCO since November 1990; born 10.7.72; Grade 10.

McCombe, Iain Stewart; FCO since July 1988; born 22.11.69; Grade 10.

McConnell, Gillian Anne; FCO since January 1988; born 10.5.68; Grade S3A.

McConnell, Mary Ellen; FCO since September 1986; born 14.7.48; FCO 1974; Amman 1975; FCO 1976; Valletta 1978; Dar es Salaam 1981; FCO 1984; The Hague 1985; Grade S2.

McCormick, Patrick Joseph; First Secretary The Holy See since September 1987; born 16.10.35; HM Forces 1954-56; FO and Belgrade 1956; Reykjavik 1958; Baghdad 1961; Madrid 1963; Rio de Janeiro 1966; Assistant Private Secretary

to Secretary of State, FCO 1970; Vice-Consul Guatemala City 1973; Consul Milan 1977; First Secretary FCO 1981; First Secretary, Head of Chancery and Consul San José 1984; First Secretary FCO 1987; m 1956 Margaret Mary Madden (2d 1959, 1961).

McCormick, Stephen; FCO since September 1990; born 5.9.67; Grade 9.

McCoy, Anne Jennifer; FCO since August 1984; born 14.6.48; FCO 1970; Accra 1970; Manila 1972; FCO 1974; UKDIS Geneva 1976; FCO 1978; Nicosia 1982; Grade S2.

McCoy, Peter Owen David; Vice Consul (Commercial) Los Angeles since October 1992; born 28.4.52; FCO 1971; New Delhi 1974; Kaduna 1977; FCO 1981; Maseru 1984; AO/Vice Consul/Comm Montreal 1987 (later Second Secretary); Second Secretary FCO 1990; m 1975 Sally Ann Lord (2d 1976, 1978; 1s 1982).

McCredie, Ian Forbes, obe (1984); Counsellor UKMIS New York since September 1992; born 28.12.50; Third Secretary FCO 1975; Third later Second Secretary (Econ) Lusaka 1976; FCO 1979; First Secretary (Econ/Comm) Tehran 1981; FCO 1983; Copenhagen 1985; First Secretary FCO 1989; m 1976 Katherine Lucy Frank (1s 1981; 1d 1983).

McCrory, Henry, mbe (1979); Deputy Govenor Anguilla since November 1991; born 14.10.38; Crown Agents 1957-62; HM Forces 1958-60; CRO 1962; Zomba 1964; Baghdad 1968; FCO 1971; Second Secretary Tehran 1975; HM Consul Lisbon 1980; Consul (Comm) BTDO New York 1983; HM Consul New York 1985; First Secretary FCO 1987; m 1963 Diane Frances Endersby (1d 1965; 2s 1967, 1974).

McCrory, Iain; First Secretary FCO since November 1987; born 29.3.40; POSB 1958; CRO 1963; Ibadan 1963; DSA 1966; Oslo 1968; Yaoundé 1970; Second Secretary Dar es Salaam 1974; FCO 1978; Second Secretary (Comm) Paris 1982; m 1968 Ann Elizabeth Morgans (2d 1968, 1978; 1s 1970).

McCrudden, Patrick Gerald; First Secretary (Aid) and Deputy Permanent Representative UNEP/UNCHS Nairobi since September 1991; born 22.4.50; FCO 1969; Saigon 1971; Mexico City 1974; Bahrain 1976; FCO 1977; Tristan da Cunha 1980; Brussels 1981; Pretoria 1982; Second Secretary FCO 1985; Second Secretary (Chancery) Bridgetown 1988; m 1973 Anne Maureen Dolan (diss 1989); (1s 1974; 2d 1974, 1976).

McCulloch, James Rae; Deputy Head of Mission Hanoi since February 1992; born 29.11.40; FO 1958; Bamako 1962; New York 1964; Lusaka 1967; FCO 1969; Algiers 1972; Kabul 1973; Second Secretary FCO 1977; Luanda 1980;

Second later First Secretary (Comm) Bangkok 1982; First Secretary (UN) UKMIS Geneva 1986; First Secretary FCO 1990; m 1965 Margaret Anderson (2s 1965, 1970).

McCulloch, Susan Geddes; Berne since June 1992; born 29.6.70; FCO 1989; Grade 10.

McCusker, Joan; FCO since July 1991; born 3.10.70; Grade 10.

McDadd, Stephen Mark; First Secretary (UN) UKMIS Geneva since February 1991; born 17.1.60; FCO 1981; Third Secretary Nicosia 1982; Second later First Secretary FCO 1985; Language Training 1986; FCO 1987; m (1) 1982 Susanne Pantall (diss); (2) 1987 Elizabeth Comstock Smith.

MacDermott, Alastair Tormod; First Secretary FCO since September 1991; born 17.9.45; FO (later FCO) 1966; Kabul 1971; FCO 1973; Accra 1973; FCO 1977; Language Training Tokyo 1978; Second Secretary Tokyo 1979; Colombo 1983; First Secretary (Inf) Tokyo 1986; m 1968 Helen Gordon (2d 1969, 1971).

McDermott, Andrew Muir Miller; Second later First Secretary FCO since October 1991; born 24.12.43; Ministry of Transport 1959; MOD (Navy) 1961; FO 1964; Phnom Penh 1965; Pretoria/Cape Town 1969; Dacca 1971; Yaoundé 1974; FCO 1975; MECAS 1977; Kuwait 1978; Second Secretary FCO 1983; Second Secretary (Admin) and Consul Berne 1986; m 1979 Catherine Michelle Brunet.

McDermott, Frank; First Secretary (Management) The Hague since November 1989; born 29.1.43; FO 1960; DSAO 1965; Port of Spain 1965; Lusaka 1969; Abu Dhabi 1972; FCO 1975; Lagos 1978; Second Secretary (Admin) (JAO) Brussels 1980; FCO 1985; m (1) 1964 (1s 1967; 1d 1969); m (2) 1983 Hilary Jean McGregor (1d 1984).

McDermott, Patrick Anthony, MVO (1972); Counsellor (Management) Paris since December 1990; born 8.9.41; FO 1960; Mexico City 1963; New York (UKDEL) 1966; Belgrade 1971; FCO 1973; Bonn 1973; Paris 1976; Second later First Secretary FCO 1979; Consul-General and Economic and Financial Adviser to BMG Berlin 1984; First Secretary FCO 1988; m (1) 1963 Patricia Hunter-Naylor (2s 1967, 1970); (2) 1976 Christa Herminghaus (2s 1977, 1981).

MacDonald, Catriona MacLeod; FCO since March 1992; born 18.4.64; FCO 1988; Belgrade 1990; Grade S2.

McDonald, David Christopher; Washington since June 1990; born 12.5.64; FCO 1984; Grade 9.

McDonald, John Douglas; Second Secretary (Consular) Singapore since January 1991; born

5.6.34; FCO 1969; Peking 1971; Madras 1973; Warsaw 1976; FCO 1979; Dusseldorf 1982; Second Secretary Tehran 1985; Second Secretary FCO 1988; m 1963 Mary Patricia O'Neill.

MacDonald, John William; Consul-General Shanghai since January 1991; born 13.6.38; FO 1955; Royal Navy 1957; FO 1959; Cairo 1960; Tokyo 1964; (Second Secretary (Comm) 1967); FCO 1970; Second later First Secretary Dacca 1972; First Secretary (Comm) Tokyo 1974; on loan to DOT 1979; NDC Latimer 1981; Dhaka 1982; First Secretary (Comm/Dev) Dar es Salaam 1983; First Secretary FCO 1987; m 1960 Margaret Millam Burns.

MacDonald, Kay (née Moore); UKREP Brussels since March 1989; born 5.7.58; FCO 1982; Prague 1983; Mexico City 1984; Washington 1986; Grade S2; m 1988 Thomas John MacDonald.

McDonald, Simon Gerard; First Secretary FCO since September 1990; born 9.3.61; FCO 1982; Language Student SOAS 1983; Third later Second Secretary Jedda (later Riyadh) 1985; Second Secretary (Chancery) Bonn 1988; m 1989 Olivia Mary Wright (1s 1990; 1d 1992).

MacDougall, David; FCO since December 1991; born 7.7.73; Grade 10.

McDuff, Nicholas Frederic; Second Secretary on loan to the DTI since December 1990; born 22.7.50; MOD (Navy) 1967; FCO 1970; Muscat 1972; UKDEL NATO Brussels 1972; BMG Berlin 1975; Karachi 1978; Islamabad 1980; FCO 1982; Athens 1983; UKDEL NATO Brussels 1984; Bandar Seri Begawan 1987; m 1978 Jennifer Mary Cain (3s 1981, 1985, 1986).

McEvoy, Edward James; Vice-Consul (Commercial) Cape Town since September 1990; born 6.2.46; CRO later FO 1962; Belgrade 1968; Mbabane 1970; FCO 1972; Aden 1975; Luxembourg 1977; Addis Ababa 1979; on loan to Home Office 1982; Second Secretary (Immig) Dhaka 1985; Second Secretary (Comm) Manila 1989; m 1967 Patricia Gibbs (diss 1991); (1s 1972).

McEwan, Elizabeth Ann; Vice-Consul San José since June 1991; born 29.4.52; FCO 1972; Suva 1975; EEC Brussels 1977; Budapest 1979; Montserrat 1981; FCO 1985; Anguilla 1986; FCO 1988; Grade 9.

McEwen, Christine Elizabeth; FCO since August 1990; born 4.10.58; FCO 1978; BMG Berlin 1981; Peking 1984; Bombay 1987; Grade 9.

McFarlane, Jacqueline (née Stewart); FCO since July 1992; born 1.11.67; FCO 1986; Manila 1988; Grade S2A; m 1988 Neil Ross McFarlane.

McFarlane, Neil Ross; FCO since May 1991;

born 26.3.69; Grade 10; m 1988 Jacqueline Stewart.

McFarlin, Andrew John; FCO since March 1990; born 30.8.70; Grade 10.

McGarrity, Sharon; FCO since March 1992; born 22.2.66; FCO 1987; Harare 1990; Grade S2.

McGhee, John; Second Secretary (Aid/Inf) La Paz since September 1990; born 26.4.38; FO 1964; Peking 1966; Freetown 1967; FCO 1971; Latin America Floater 1975; Havana 1977; Cairo 1979; Second Secretary and Consul Montevideo 1980; Second Secretary on loan to ODA East Kilbride 1984; Second Secretary (Admin) and Vice-Consul Lima 1986; m (1) 1961 Catherine McFall (diss 1976) (1d 1962; 1s 1964); (2) 1976 Helen Nimmo Grant.

McGill, Clive John; Karachi since July 1991; born 9.10.58; FCO 1978; Belmopan 1982; Stockholm 1985; FCO 1988; Grade 9; m (1) 1983 Thelma Garcia; (2) 1988 Angela Raw.

McGinley, Francis John; Second Secretary FCO since July 1989; born 12.1.49; FCO 1971; NATO Brussels 1974; Nairobi 1977; FCO 1980; Banjul 1982; Second Secretary (Inf) Oslo 1984.

MacGlashan, Maureen Elizabeth; On attachment to the CSSB Recruitment and Assessment Services Agency since September 1992; born 7.1.38; FO 1961; Second Secretary Tel Aviv 1964; FCO 1967 (First Secretary 1968); First Secretary and Head of Chancery East Berlin 1973; First Secretary (E Trade) UKREP Brussels 1975; Counsellor on loan to the Home Civil Service 1977; Counsellor Bucharest 1982; SUPL 1986; Deputy Head of Mission and Consul General Belgrade 1990; Counsellor FCO 1991.

McGlone, Jane Mary; UKREP Brussels since September 1988; born 7.12.61; FCO 1987; Grade S2A.

McGowan, Fiona Ure; UKREP Brussels since August 1989; born 23.2.65; FCO 1988; Grade S2A.

Macgregor, John Malcolm, CVO (1992); Counsellor and Head of Chancery Paris since February 1990; born 3.10.46; FCO 1973; Second later First Secretary New Delhi 1975; First Secretary FCO 1979; Private Secretary to Minister of State 1981; Counsellor and Head of Chancery Prague 1986; m 1982 Judith Anne Brown (1d 1984; 3s 1986, 1987, 1990).

MacGregor, Judith Anne (née Brown), LVO (1992); SUPL since January 1986; born 17.6.52; FCO 1976; First Secretary (Chancery/Inf) Belgrade 1978; FCO 1981; m 1982; John Malcolm Macgregor (1d 1984; 3s 1986, 1987, 1990).

McGregor, Alexandra Davenport (née Gillies); SUPL since May 1992; born 13.9.57; FCO 1978; Prague 1979; FCO 1981; Kabul 1982; FCO 1984; Paris 1985; FCO 1988; New Delhi 1989; FCO 1981; Grade S1; m 1991 Peter McGregor (1d 1991).

McGregor, Peter; New Delhi since July 1989; later Second Secretary 1992; born 30.5.50; FCO 1970; Jedda 1972; Lusaka 1976; FCO 1979; Damascus 1982; Port of Spain 1986; m (1) 1972 Vanessa Avril Utteridge (dec'd 1989) (1s 1980); (2) 1991 Alexandra Davenport Gillies (1d 1991).

McGuigan, Rupert Iain Sutherland; Counsellor Lagos since January 1989; born 25.6.41; First Secretary FCO 1972; First Secretary New Delhi 1974; First Secretary (Econ) Kingston 1978; First Secretary FCO 1981; Bridgetown 1985; m 1968 Rosemary Rashleigh Chaytor (2d 1970, 1972).

McGuinness, Mark Andrew; Islamabad since June 1990; born 25.8.67; FCO 1988; Grade 10.

McGuinness, Patrick Joseph; Second Secretary FCO since July 1991; born 27.4.63; FCO 1985; Language Training 1986; Second Secretary (Chancery) Sana'a 1988.

McGurgan, Kevin; FCO since April 1990; born 31.5.71; Grade 10.

McGurk, Gerard; Athens since January 1991; born 22.12.70; FCO 1988; Grade 10.

McHugh, Susan Mary; Second Secretary FCO since July 1983; born 12.2.44; FCO 1971; on loan to SEATO Bangkok 1974; New Delhi 1977; SUPL 1980; Victoria (Seychelles) 1981.

McIlveen, Siobhan Theresa; Madrid since February 1992; born 11.3.64; FCO 1988; San José 1989; FCO 1991; Grade S2.

MacInnes, Keith Gordon, CMG (1984); Head of Delegation OECD Paris (with the personal rank of Ambassador) since June 1992; born 17.7.35; HM Forces 1953-55; FO 1960; Third later Second Secretary Buenos Aires 1961; FO 1964; (First Secretary 1965); Private Secretary to Permanent Under-Secretary Commonwealth Office 1965; First Secretary (Inf) Madrid 1968; FCO 1970; Counsellor and Head of Chancery Prague 1974; Counsellor and Head of Chancery Geneva 1977; also Deputy Permanent Representative 1979; Head of Information Department FCO 1980; AUSS (Principal Finance Officer) FCO 1983; HM Ambassador Manila 1987; m (1) 1966 Jennifer Anne Fennell (diss 1980); (1d 1968; 1s 1970); (2) 1985 Hermione Anne Felicity Pattinson.

Macintosh, Anne; Third Secretary (Comm) Buenos Aires since July 1991; born 15.4.61; FCO 1980; Rome 1982; Havana 1985; FCO 1988; Grade 9.

Macintosh, Kenneth Gilbert; FCO since October 1990; born 29.3.72; Grade 10.

MacIntosh, Sarah; FCO since September 1991; born 7.8.69; Grade 9.

McIntosh, Elaine; Luxembourg since July 1991; born 2.9.68; FCO 1988; Grade S2A; m 1990 Angus Lyon McIntosh.

McIntosh, Martin Howard; First Secretary (Commercial) Buenos Aires since June 1990; born 26.12.47; FO (later FCO) 1966; Jakarta 1970; Tokyo 1970; Moscow 1972; Beirut 1973; FCO 1976; Madrid 1979; Second Secretary Bogota 1982; Second later First Secretary (Comm) Nairobi 1984; First Secretary FCO 1989; m 1970 Erika Wagner (2d 1983, 1985).

McIntosh, Miriam Rose; First Secretary and Deputy Permanent Representative UKMIS Vienna since June 1989; born 30.5.39; FO 1958; Rangoon 1961; UK Mission New York 1963; Latin America Floater 1966; Second Secretary (Inf) Delhi 1968; Secondment to Polytechnic of Central London 1972; FCO 1973; First Secretary Athens 1976; FCO 1981.

McIntyre, Bruce Alexander; Second Secretary FCO since May 1992; born 17.8.44; FO 1962; Malta 1966; Accra 1968; Dublin 1971; Caracas 1973; Madrid 1976; FCO 1979; Mexico City 1982; Second Secretary (Comm/Aid) Maputo 1986; Second Secretary (Comm) and Vice Consul Montevideo 1988; m 1973 Norma Ann Harrison (1d 1975).

McIntyre, Douglas Robert Stuart; Consul-General Madrid since February 1991; born 10.5.41; FO 1959; Khartoum 1964; La Paz 1967; Tripoli 1969; Rome 1971; FCO 1974; Second Secretary Mexico City 1977; Vila 1982; First Secretary and Consul Las Palmas 1984; First Secretary FCO 1988; m (1) 1964 (diss 1968) (1s 1964); (2) 1971 Catherine Campbell Tweed (1d 1974; 1s 1976).

McIver, Damian John; Second Secretary On T/D EC MIS Zagreb since June 1992; born 2.11.61; HM Customs and Excise 1986; FCO 1986; Belgrade 1987; Second Secretary FCO 1991.

Mackay, Gavin Anderson; Second Secretary Nicosia since September 1989; born 1.11.49; FCO 1973; Wellington 1975; Suva 1978; Dhaka 1981; FCO 1983; Dubai 1986; (Second Secretary 1988); m 1975 Glenys Pickup (1d 1977; 2s 1980, 1984).

McKay, Robert, MBE (1986); Paris since January 1992; born 22.12.39; Army 1957-1988; Belgrade 1990; Grade SO; m 1960 Betty Alice Rose Morris (1d 1961).

McKeith, Brian, MBE (1991); Lagos since March 1987.

1988; born 22.6.38; HM Forces 1957-81; Prague 1983; Havana 1986; Moscow 1986; Prague 1987; Grade SO.

McKellar, Dugald Aitken; First Secretary and Consul Athens since October 1990; born 27.6.37; CO 1963; Malta 1964; Cyprus 1966; Saigon 1969; FCO 1972; Peking 1975; New York 1976; Tehran 1979; Freetown 1980; Second Secretary (Aid) Accra 1981; Second Secretary FCO 1983; Second Secretary (Consular) Cape Town 1986; m 1966 Gillian Virgo.

McKelvey, Diane Elizabeth; Third Secretary (Political) Copenhagen since April 1992; born 6.7.67; FCO 1989; Grade 9.

McKelvey, Thomas Stanley; Vienna since January 1990; born 18.3.40; RAF Regiment 1957-82; Prague 1988; Grade SO; m 1964 Patricia Elizabeth Green (1s 1965; 2d 1968, 1972).

McKendrick, Ian; FCO since September 1991; born 4.10.70; Grade 10.

McKenzie, Alistair William, MBE (1980); Consul-General Bilbao since January 1990; born 19.2.45; DSAO 1965; Budapest 1967; Singapore 1969; Brasilia 1972; FCO 1975; San Salvador 1978; San José 1980; Commercial Attaché Madrid 1982 (Second Secretary 1983); Second Secretary FCO 1984; Deputy High Commissioner and Head of Chancery Banjul 1986; m 1968 Margaret Emily Young (2s 1970, 1974).

MacKenzie, Catherine Louise Hay; Language Training Cairo since August 1992; Second Secretary 1992; born 9.8.66; FCO 1989; Language Training FCO 1991.

Mackenzie, Dorothy (née Byers); SUPL since January 1990; born 1.3.56; FCO 1974; The Hague 1976; Lusaka 1979; FCO 1982; Ottawa 1985; Grade 9; m 1978 Robert Mackenzie.

MacKenzie, Hilary (née Grace); FCO since January 1992; born 1.3.59; FCO 1980; Islamabad 1982; Oslo 1984; Bombay 1987; Amsterdam 1989; Grade 9; m 1989 Ian James McKenzie.

MacKenzie, Ian Johnston; Washington since August 1990; born 30.8.42; RAF 1958-86; Budapest 1988; Grade SO; m (1) 1963 Frances Mary Giles (diss) (1s 1964; 2d 1966, 1968); (2) 1984 Ingeborg Wilhelmine Therese Schmitz (3 adopted d 1972, 1974, 1976).

MacKenzie, Kenneth John Alexander; First Secretary Vienna since August 1992; born 9.9.49; FCO 1973; Brussels 1975; Second later First Secretary FCO 1978; Buenos Aires 1981; First Secretary FCO 1982; First Secretary (Econ) Bucharest 1985; First Secretary FCO 1988; m 1980 Alison Mary Linda Sandford (1d 1983; 1s 1987).

Mackenzie, Lorimer William Peters; FCO since October 1989; born 4.12.59; FCO 1983; Riyadh 1985; Grade 9.

MacKenzie, Neil Clark; Second later First Secretary FCO since November 1981; born 29.11.37; FO 1955; RAF 1957-59; Moscow 1959; West Africa Floater 1961; Geneva 1963; DSAO 1965; Berlin 1968; Seoul 1971; Second Secretary and Consul Warsaw 1974; FCO 1976; Washington 1979; m 1967 Jacqueline Olive Archer (1d 1969; 1s 1974).

McKenzie, Philip; San José since January 1991; born 26.4.65; FCO 1986; Lusaka 1987; Grade 10.

Mackenzie, Robert; Second Secretary (Commercial) Singapore since March 1990; born 5.3.54; Dept of National Savings 1973; FCO 1974; The Hague 1976; Lusaka 1979; FCO 1982; Ottawa 1985; Second Secretary FCO 1988; Second Secretary (Commercial) Mexico City 1988; m 1978 Dorothy Byers.

MacKenzie-May, Mary Faith Arbuthnott (née MacKenzie); FCO since July 1984; (Second Secretary 1988); born 22.5.47; FCO 1975; Moscow 1977; FCO 1978; Bahrain 1982; m 1989 David Robert May.

McKeogh, Fiona (née Sutherland) UKREP Brussels since September 1989; born 17.9.59; FCO 1983; Bonn 1984; Cape Town 1987; Grade S2; m 1992 Paul Nicolas McKeogh.

McKeown, Patricia; Banjul since April 1992; born 13.5.69; FCO 1987; UKDIS Geneva 1989; Grade 10.

MacKerras, Carl Anthony; FCO since October 1990; born 13.11.69; Grade 10; Land Registry 1988-1990.

McKerrow, Elizabeth Mary (née Foot); FCO since August 1991; born 18.1.67; FCO 1986; Buenos Aires 1990; Grade 10; m 1991 Ian Bernard Harry McKerrow.

Mackie, Anne Bernadette; SUPL since April 1990; born 24.10.59; FCO 1983; Cairo 1985; Lagos 1988; FCO 1990; Grade S2.

McKie, Margaret Stevenson; Prague since May 1991; born 7.8.62; FCO 1988; Grade S2A.

Mackilligin, David Patrick Robert; High Commissioner Belmopan since February 1991; born 29.6.39; CRO 1961; Salisbury 1962; Karachi 1962; Rawalpindi 1965; Assistant Private Secretary to the Secretary of State, Commonwealth Office 1966; Private Secretary to the Minister without Portfolio 1968; FCO 1969; Deputy Commissioner Anguilla 1969; Accra 1971; First Secretary and Head of Chancery Phnom Penh 1973; FCO 1975; Counsellor

(Comm/Aid) Jakarta 1980; NATO Defence College Rome 1985; Counsellor (Econ/Comm) Canberra 1986; m 1976 Gillian Margaret Zuill Walker (2d 1979, 1980).

McKinlay, Ian Leonard; Addis Ababa since October 1989; born 17.9.58; FCO 1978; UKMIS Geneva 1980; Tehran 1983; FCO 1986; Grade 9; m 1984 Ann Hugoline Cameron (1s 1989).

Mackintosh, Leila Ailsa, MBE; Rabat since November 1985; born 21.2.30; Zagreb 1960; Conakry 1962; Brussels 1964; FO 1965; Kinshasa 1967; Vienna 1971; FCO 1974; Bonn 1976; Tehran 1979; FCO 1980; Havana 1981; Beirut 1983; Grade S1.

Mackley, Ian Warren, CMG (1989); Deputy High Commissioner Canberra since November 1989; born 31.3.42; FO 1960; Saigon 1963; APS to Minister of State FO 1967 (Second Secretary 1968); Second later First Secretary Wellington 1969; FCO 1973; New Delhi 1976; FCO 1980; Seconded to ICI 1982; Counsellor CDE Stockholm 1984; Chargé d'Affaires Kabul 1987; m (1) 1968 Jill Marion Saunders (diss 1988); (3s 1970, 1973, 1983); (2) 1989 Sarah Anne Churchley (1d 1989, 1s 1991).

McKnight, Elisabeth Eithné; UKREP Brussels since November 1985; born 2.8.41; FCO 1973; Dacca 1974; FCO 1975; Mbabane 1976; FCO 1978; Grand Turk 1980; UKMIS New York 1983; Grade S1.

Mackrell, William Michael; Bonn since June 1992; born 11.8.42; Grade SO.

McLachlan, Malcolm Orde; Guatemala City since March 1988; born 10.9.63; FCO 1981; Karachi 1984; Grade 9; m 1989 Maricruz Mendia Moynes.

The MacLaren of MacLaren, Donald; Deputy Head of Mission Havana since September 1991; born 22.8.54; FCO 1978; Third later Second later First Secretary BMG Berlin 1980; Language Training 1983; First Secretary and Press Attaché Moscow 1984; First Secretary FCO 1987; m 1978 Maida-Jane Aitchison (3s 1980, 1981, 1984; 1d 1987).

McLaren, Donald Stuart; Third Secretary (Commercial) Kuala Lumpur since July 1992; born 1.8.44; FCO 1971; Jakarta 1973; FCO 1975; St Helena 1976; FCO 1977; Pretoria 1979; FCO 1982; Third Secretary Darwin 1984; FCO 1986; Accra 1988; Grade 9; m 1968 Glenys Catherine Bryant (1d 1971; 2s 1973, 1979).

McLaren, Marilynn; Tehran since December 1990; born 20.7.47; Scottish Office 1963; FCO 1981; Dacca 1981; Tehran 1985; Lisbon 1987; FCO 1989; Grade S1.

McLaren, Sir Robin (John Taylor), KCMG (1991),

cmg (1982); HM Ambassador Peking since June 1991; born 14.8.34; Royal Navy 1953-55; FO 1958; Hong Kong 1959; Third Secretary Peking 1960; FO 1961; Assistant Private Secretary to the Lord Privy Seal 1963; Second later First Secretary Rome 1964; Assistant Political Adviser Hong Kong 1968; FCO 1970; Deputy Head of Western Organisations Department 1974; Counsellor and Head of Chancery Copenhagen 1975; Head of Hong Kong and General Department FCO 1978; Head of Far Eastern Department FCO 1979; Political Adviser Hong Kong 1981; HM Ambassador Manila 1985; AUSS (Asia/Far East) FCO 1987; DUSS (Americas/Asia) 1990; m 1964 Susan Ellen Hatherly (2d 1965, 1966; 1s 1973).

Maclean, Alistair; First Secretary FCO since November 1991; born 18.3.37; FO 1961; Washington 1961; Vice-Consul Lomé 1964; Bonn 1967; Melbourne 1970; Perth 1970; Manila 1971; Second Secretary 1972; DTI 1972; Second Secretary (Comm) Lagos 1975; First Secretary and Consul Tel Aviv 1979; First Secretary FCO 1983; First Secretary (Head of Chancery and Consul) Kathmandu 1988; m 1961 Ann Galloway Hamilton (2s 1962, 1971).

MacLean, Clayton; Islamabad since August 1992; born 30.6.69; FCO 1990; Grade 10.

Maclean, Janet May; FCO since February 1992; born 3.7.47; Grade S2.

McLean, Philip Alexander; Minister Consul-General and Deputy Head of Mission Peking since December 1991; born 24.10.38; HM Forces 1956-58; Second later First Secretary FCO 1969; First Secretary (Comm) La Paz 1970; Head of Chancery 1973; First Secretary FCO 1974; Consul (Comm) and Deputy Director Industrial Marketing BTDO New York 1976; Counsellor Head of Chancery and Consul-General Algiers 1981; Counsellor Overseas Inspectorate FCO 1983; Counsellor FCO 1985; Consul-General Boston 1987; m 1960 Dorothy Helen Kirkby (2s 1963, 1967; 1d 1964).

McLeman, Malcolm; Attaché Ankara since February 1988; born 27.5.39; GPO 1963; FO 1965; Singapore 1967; FCO 1969; Jedda 1970; Delhi 1974; FCO 1975; Darwin 1976; FCO 1977; Tokyo 1979; FCO 1982; Grade 8; m 1963 Joyce Vyner (3d 1965, 1967, 1969).

MacLennan, David Ross; HM Consul-General Jerusalem since November 1990; born 12.2.45; FO 1963; DSAO 1965; MECAS 1966; Aden 1969; Civil Service College 1972; Second later First Secretary FCO 1972; First Secretary UKDEL OECD Paris 1975; First Secretary Head of Chancery and Consul Abu Dhabi 1979; First Secretary FCO 1982; on secondment to European Commission 1984; Counsellor (Comm) Kuwait 1985; Counsellor and Head of Chancery Nicosia 1989; m 1964 Margaret Lytollis (2d 1964, 1966).

MacLennan, Paul Andrew; Moscow since May 1992; born 18.5.66; FCO 1987; Grade 10.

MacLeod, Alister; FCO since May 1989; born 5.8.41; CO 1960; CRO 1963; Delhi 1964; Paris 1966; FCO 1968; Accra 1970; Johannesburg 1973; FCO 1975; Milan 1976; Bombay 1978; FCO 1980; Mbabane 1987; Grade 7; m 1975 Katharine Marguerite Searle.

MacLeod, Fiona; FCO since April 1992; born 19.10.70; Grade S2.

MacLeod, Frances Ann; FCO since August 1991; born 4.12.59; FCO 1983; Warsaw 1985; Maputo 1988; Grade 9; m 1989 James Robert McDougall.

MacLeod, Gordon Stewart; New Delhi since November 1988; born 15.2.52; FCO 1971; Ankara 1973; Washington 1977; Dacca 1979; FCO 1982; Valletta 1985; Grade 7; m 1978 Susan Raggatt (2d 1981, 1984).

McLeod, Hudson Hugh, mbe (1982); First Secretary FCO since March 1991; born 13.3.49; HM Forces 1967-81; First Secretary FCO 1981; Islamabad 1983; First Secretary FCO 1985; First Secretary (Pol/Econ) Accra 1988; m 1982 Elizabeth Jane Fitzgerald (1s 1984; 1d 1987).

MacLeod, Iain; First Secretary (Assistant Legal Adviser) UKREP Brussels since January 1991; born 15.3.62; Assistant Legal Adviser FCO 1987; m 1988 Dr Alison Mary Murchison.

MacLeod, Jean; Second Secretary (Management) Berlin since May 1991; FCO 1983; born 4.12.37; DSAO 1965; Karachi 1966; Bahrain 1967; Moscow 1969; Lagos 1970; FCO 1974; Far East Floater 1978; Dar es Salaam 1981; Second Secretary FCO 1983.

MacLeod, Sian Christina; Second later First Secretary FCO since May 1992; born 31.5.62; FCO 1986; Language Training 1987; Second Secretary (Chancery) Moscow 1988; m 1987 Richard Anthony Robinson (1d 1992).

McLoughlin, Michael John; First Secretary (Commercial) Quito since June 1990; born 13.12.38; HM Forces 1957-59; FO 1960; Dakar 1960; Bamako 1961; Athens 1963; Berlin 1964; Reykjavik 1966; Madras 1968; FCO 1972; Second Secretary Lusaka 1975; La Paz 1978; Mid-Career Development Course 1983; First Secretary FCO 1984; HM Consul Palma 1985; m 1964 Rachel Ward Morris (2d 1965, 1967; 2s 1970, 1973).

McLoughlin, Peter Edward Francis; Second Secretary FCO since February 1988; born 29.5.37; FO 1963; West Africa Floater 1964; Zagreb 1965; Mbabane 1968; FCO 1972; UKREP Brussels 1974; Wellington 1976; FCO 1979; Second Secretary (Admin) UKREP

Brussels 1984; m 1965 Susan Ruth Pierce (2s 1966, 1968; 2d 1971, 1973).

McMahon, Anthony Gordon; First Secretary FCO since August 1990; born 29.6.35; Admiralty 1951; FO 1952-53; HM Forces 1954-55; POMEF Cyprus 1956-57; Ankara and Beirut 1958; Moscow 1959; Antwerp 1960; Düsseldorf 1961; Tegucigalpa 1963; DSAO (later FCO) 1967; Durban 1969; FCO 1971; Second Secretary 1973; Vice-Consul (Comm) Karachi 1975; Consul (Comm) Berlin 1979; FCO 1982; HM Consul-General Bilbao 1985; m 1958 Gillian Dockerill (2s 1960, 1964).

McMahon, Brian Patrick; Second Secretary (Immigration/Consular) Colombo since May 1990; born 26.3.46; CRO and DSAO 1963; Prague 1968; Bonn 1969; Kabul 1972; FCO 1975; Islamabad 1978; UKMIS Geneva 1981; Second Secretary FCO 1984; m 1967 Eileen Marian (1d 1970; 1s 1975).

McMahon, Ian Irvine; First Secretary FCO since May 1992; born 8.6.55; Army 1973-83; Second Secretary FCO 1983; Second later First Secretary (Chancery) Islamabad 1985; First Secretary FCO 1987; First Secretary (Chancery) New Delhi 1989; m 1979 Anne Elizabeth Baker (1d 1981).

McMahon, John George; Islamabad since January 1991; born 23.7.61; DHSS 1987; FCO 1988; Grade 9.

McMahon, Keith David; Lusaka since October 1990; born 10.3.68; FCO 1988; Grade 10.

McManus, John Andrew; Second Secretary FCO since February 1992; born 20.5.55; FCO 1977; Paris 1980; Algiers 1983; FCO 1985; Language Training FCO 1987 (Second Secretary 1987); Second Secretary Moscow 1988.

McManus, Rosaleen Mary; Brussels since June 1991; born 15.1.62; FCO 1987; Oslo 1988; Grade S2.

McMillan, Margaret Eileen; FCO since April 1981; born 12.2.33; Singapore 1963; Kaduna 1965; Berne 1968; FCO 1969; Hanover 1972; Berlin 1973; Reykjavik 1975; FCO 1977; East Berlin 1978; Grade S1.

McMillan, Norman Hamilton, OBE (1984); Counsellor (Chancery) Vienna since August 1989; born 28.10.46; Third Secretary FCO 1968; Third later Second Secretary Vienna 1970; Second later First Secretary FCO 1972; Rome 1977; Dhaka 1981; Cairo 1984; FCO 1986; m 1969 Carolyn Vivienne Barltrop (1s 1982; 1d 1983).

McMurtrie, Aileen; FCO since April 1990; born 12.4.69; Grade 10.

McNair, Richard Andrew; Cairo since November 1991; born 18.2.59; FCO 1979; Lagos 1980; FCO 1982; Ankara 1984; FCO 1987; Grade 8; m 1978 Julie Elaine Stephen (1d 1981; 1s 1983).

McNally, Paula Amanda; FCO since September 1990; born 28.3.68; Grade S2.

McNeill, Alasdair Morrell; Istanbul since August 1992; born 13.11.67; FCO 1988; Grade 10.

McNeill, Christine Mary; Second Secretary FCO since January 1991; born 12.3.62; FCO 1979; Cairo 1983; Suva 1987; m 1982 Scott Robertson McNeill.

McNeill-Ritchie, Simon Laird; First Secretary FCO since January 1992; born 10.4.61; FCO 1984 (Second Secretary 1987); Second later First Secretary (Econ) Tokyo 1988.

McNess, Anne Patricia; FCO since September 1992; born 1.4.53; Principal Research Officer; FCO 1979; SUPL 1986; m 1980 Stephen Christopher Rossides.

Macphail, John Patrick Nicholson; Second Secretary (Comm) Lagos since July 1989; born 21.5.48; FCO 1968; Middle East Floater 1971; Moscow 1973; Georgetown 1974; FCO 1976; Budapest 1979; Mexico City 1980; UKDEL NATO Brussels 1983; Second Secretary FCO 1985; m 1981 Joy Chambers (1d 1983).

MacPhail, Pamela Joanne (née Davies); Third Secretary) Public Affairs) Moscow since July 1992; born 3.12.62; FCO 1990; Grade 9; m 1989 Alastair David McPhail.

McPherson, Alison Francis Mary; Tunis since December 1988; born 5.6.52; Ottawa 1974; Aden 1977; St Vincent 1978; Port of Spain 1980; FCO 1983; SE Asia Floater 1986; Grade 9.

MacPherson, Hugh David; First Secretary (Political) Stockholm since February 1992; born 17.2.53; FCO 1974; Language Training 1975; Ankara 1976; Sao Paulo 1980; FCO 1982; Research Sabbatical 1985; First Secretary FCO 1989.

Macpherson, John Bannerman; First Secretary FCO since April 1990; born 23.6.51; Third later Second Secretary FCO 1975; Language Student MECAS 1977; Second Secretary Khartoum 1979; Second later First Secretary Sana'a 1980; FCO 1983; Language Training 1985; First Secretary Sofia 1987; m 1985 Monica Jane Lancashire (2s 1986, 1988; 1d 1992).

MacPherson, Kara Isobel; FCO since February 1992; born 3.8.60; FCO 1981; Islamabad 1983; Prague 1986; Africa/ME Floater 1988; Grade 9.

Macqueen, Christine Ann; First Secretary Paris since May 1990; born 24.5.59; FCO 1982; Second Secretary (Econ) Brasilia 1984; Second later First Secretary FCO 1987.

McQueen, Jacqueline Mary; SUPL since May 1992; born 27.12.63; Inland Revenue 1980, FCO 1985; Bonn 1986; FCO 1989; Grade S2A.

McQuibban, Peter James; First Secretary on loan to the Cabinet Office since September 1992; born 7.11.55; Third later Second Secretary FCO 1981; Second Secretary (Econ) Brasilia 1982; First Secretary FCO 1985; First Secretary (Political) Warsaw 1988; First Secretary FCO 1992; m 1982 Susan Jennifer Magdalen Hitch.

McQuigg, Harold; Lagos since September 1987; born 9.6.40; Royal Marines 1955-80; Prison Service 1980; Havana 1984; New Delhi 1986; Grade SO; m 1961 Nora Shilliday (3s 1962, 1964, 1968; 1d 1970).

MacRae, (Alastair) Christopher (Donald Summerhayes), CMG (1987); High Commissioner Lagos and concurrently, HM Ambassador (non-resident) to Benin since February 1991; born 3.5.37; HM Forces 1956-58; CRO 1962; Third later Second Secretary Dar es Salaam 1963; MECAS 1965; Beirut 1967; First Secretary FO (later FCO) 1968; First Secretary and Head of Chancery Baghdad 1970; First Secretary and Head of Chancery Brussels 1972; SUPL to the Commission of the European Communities (DGVIII) 1976; HM Ambassador Libreville 1978; also HMA (non-resident) to São Tomé and Principe 1979; Head of West African Department FCO 1980 and later also HMA (non-resident) to Chad 1982; Counsellor and Head of Chancery Paris 1983; Minister and Head of British Interests Section Tehran 1987; CDA at the IISS 1987; Scrutiny of DS/FCO Administration and Support Services 1988; on loan to the Cabinet Office 1988; m 1963 Mette Willert (2d 1963, 1967).

MacSween, Norman James; First Secretary (Chancery) later Counsellor Stockholm since August 1991; born 22.1.48; FCO 1970; Third later Second Secretary Nairobi 1972; FCO 1975; Language Student SOAS 1976 and Shiraz 1977; First Secretary Tehran 1977; FCO 1979; First Secretary (Chancery) Bonn 1983; First Secretary FCO 1987; m 1983 Julia Jane Reid (1s 1988, 1d 1990).

MacTaggart, Sheila Margaret; First Secretary (Management) Budapest since March 1992; born 18.8.41; Admiralty later MOD 1963; FO 1966; Copenhagen 1968; UKMIS Geneva 1969; FCO 1971; Pretoria 1972; Brussels 1975; FCO 1978; Second later First Secretary (Management) Bonn 1986.

McVey, Andrea; Paris since January 1991; born 28.1.64; FCO 1988; Grade S2A.

Machin, Barbara Elizabeth; FCO since May 1988; born 24.1.55; FCO 1976; Honiara 1976; Moscow 1978; UKMIS New York 1980; FCO

1983; Abidjan 1984; Grade S1.

Madden, David Christopher Andrew; Counsellor, FCO since January 1990; born 25.7.46; Third Secretary FCO 1970; Third later Second Secretary BMG Berlin 1972; First Secretary on loan to Cabinet Office 1975; First Secretary Moscow 1978; First Secretary and Head of Chancery Athens 1981; FCO 1984; Counsellor, Head of Chancery and Consul-General Belgrade 1987; m 1970 Penelope Anthea Johnston (1s 1972; 2d 1974, 1975).

Madeley, Anthony Andrew; Second Secretary FCO since April 1991; born 10.3.52; FCO 1970; Accra 1973; Budapest 1976; Dar es Salaam 1978; FCO 1981; Amsterdam 1984; Alexandria 1987.

Madge, Victoria Jane; Sofia since December 1991; born 12.10.66; FCO 1990; Grade S2.

Madisons, Alexander Emil; Peking since August 1990; born 9.11.62; FCO 1983; Grade 8.

Magee, Helen Sarah Anne; FCO since September 1990; born 18.10.67; Grade 8.

Magee, Michael; Consul (Comm) Houston since May 1991; born 30.10.38; FO 1956; RAF 1958-61; Hanoi 1961; Phnom Penh 1961; Bahrain 1962; Brasilia 1966; FCO 1970; UKMIS New York 1971; Second Secretary FCO 1975; On loan to DOT 1976; Lisbon 1978; First Secretary (Comm) Colombo 1983; First Secretary FCO 1986; m (1) 1963 Carole Ann Griffiths (2s 1964, 1967; 1d 1974) (diss); m (2) 1982 Susan Elizabeth Ball.

Magor, William Wavell; Second Secretary (Comm) Dubai since September 1987; born 11.7.43; CRO later Commonwealth Office 1961; Accra 1966; UKMIS New York 1969; FCO 1971; Algiers 1971; FCO 1973; Caracas 1976; Nassau 1979; FCO 1981; Second Secretary (Admin) (later Admin/Cons) Port of Spain 1983; m 1965 Avril Anne Swalwell (1d 1966; 1s 1973).

Maguire, John; Second Secretary and Consul (Comm) Perth since February 1988; born 4.6.49; SHHD 1967; FCO 1968; Moscow 1971; Belmopan 1972; New Delhi 1974; Tokyo 1978; FCO 1982; Alexandria 1985; m 1978 Mette Lucie Konow Monsen.

Maher, Heather Kirsten Maria; Bangkok since July 1990; born 12.11.70; FCO 1988; Grade S2.

Major, Pamela Ann; First Secretary FCO since February 1988; born 4.3.59; FCO 1982; Language Training SOAS 1983; Second Secretary (Chancery) Peking 1986.

Makepeace, Richard Edward; First Secretary (Environ) UKREP Brussels since January 1989;

born 24.6.53; FCO 1976; Language Student
MECAS 1977; Third later Second Secretary
Muscat 1979; Second later First Secretary
(Chancery) Prague 1981; FCO 1985; Private
Secretary to the Parliamentary Under-Secretary
of State 1986; m 1980 Rupmani Catherine
Pradhan.

Makin, John; Floater Training since January
1992; born 13.1.64; DHSS 1984; FCO 1985;
Kaduna 1987; Dusseldorf 1990; Grade 9.

Malcolm, James Ian; First Secretary (Pol/Econ)
Jakarta since November 1987; born 29.3.46;
MPBW 1964; FO 1966; UKDEL NATO Brussels
1969; Rangoon 1972; FCO 1974; Nairobi 1977;
Damascus 1980; Second Secretary (Comm)
Luanda 1983; Second Secretary FCO 1985; m
1967 Sheila Nicholson Moore (1s 1976; 1d
1980).

Malcomson, Thomas Herbert; HM Ambassador
Panama City since January 1992; born 9.10.37;
FO 1961; Bangkok 1963; Vice-Consul (Comm)
São Paulo 1967; FCO 1971; Second Secretary
(Inf) Colombo 1972; Consul Chiang Mai 1975;
Second later First Secretary FCO 1978; First
Secretary/Head of Chancery Brunei 1981; Acting
High Commissioner Solomon Islands 1984; First
Secretary (Comm) Lima 1985; First Secretary
FCO 1989; m (1) 1960 Barbara Hetherington
(diss 1985) (1s 1964; 2d 1966, 1970); m (2)
1986 Blanca Ruiz de Castilla (1 step s 1973;
twin d 1989).

Maley, Lisa Helen; Brussels since May 1990;
born 28.8.67; FCO 1988; Grade 10.

Malin, Carl Spencer; Ottawa since October
1989; born 7.7.69; FCO 1987; Grade 10.

Malin, Keith Ian; First Secretary (Chancery/
Econ) Sofia since April 1990; born 11.12.53;
FCO 1976; Third Secretary (Developing
Countries) UKREP Brussels 1978; Second later
First Secretary FCO 1979; First Secretary on
secondment to HCS 1983; First Secretary (UN/
Press) UKMIS Geneva 1984; FCO 1986; m 1977
Gaynor Dudley Jones (1s 1985).

Mallaby, Sir Christopher (Leslie George), KCMG
(1988), CMG (1982); HM Ambassador Bonn since
April 1988; born 7.7.36; FO 1959; Third
Secretary Moscow 1961; Second Secretary FO
1963; First Secretary Berlin 1966; FCO 1969;
Consul (Comm) New York 1971; Counsellor and
Head of Chancery Moscow 1975; Head of Arms
Control and Disarmament Dept FCO 1977; Head
of Eastern European and Soviet Department
1979; Head of Planning Staff 1980; Minister
Bonn 1982; On loan to Cabinet Office as a
Deputy Secretary 1985; m 1961 Pascale
Francoise Thierry-Mieg (1s 1964; 3d 1967, 1971,
1972).

Malone, Philip; Third Secretary (Commercial/

Information) Luxembourg since March 1992;
born 3.12.61; FCO 1981; Buenos Aires 1983;
Guatemala City 1986; FCO 1989; Grade 9; m
1989 Ana Lorena Pullin.

Manley, Ernest George; FCO since July 1990;
born 15.2.51; FCO 1970; Aden 1973; Milan
1975; East Berlin 1978; FCO 1980; Kuala
Lumpur 1983; Consul Milan 1986; Grade 7; m
1973 Mary Catherine Whelan (1s 1975).

Manley, Philip Ernest; FCO since February
1990; born 17.6.44; GPO 1960; FCO 1969;
Washington 1971; FCO 1974; Amman 1975;
FCO 1976; Attaché Moscow 1978; FCO 1980;
Third Secretary Lagos 1981; FCO 1984; Second
Secretary Bonn 1987; m 1967 Christine Anne
Kellett (1s 1970; 1d 1972).

Manley, Simon John; FCO since November
1990; born 18.9.67; Grade 8.

Manley, Suzanne Marie Theresa; La Paz since
April 1990; born 12.12.64; FCO 1987; Grade S2.

Mann, Brian Keith; Third Secretary Peking since
December 1988; born 12.1.37; Royal Navy 1952-
63; FO 1964; Delhi 1966; FCO 1968; Moscow
1969; FCO 1970; St Helena 1971; FCO 1973;
Baghdad 1975; FCO 1976; Baghdad 1977; Beirut
1978; FCO 1981; Seoul 1983; FCO 1986; Sana'a
1986; Grade 8; m 1958 Rita Pamela Edmunds.

Manning, David Geoffrey, CMG (1992); Political
Counsellor Moscow since September 1990; born
5.12.49; Third Secretary FCO 1972; Language
course 1973; Third later Second Secretary
Warsaw 1974; Second later First Secretary New
Delhi 1977; FCO 1980; Paris 1984; Counsellor
on loan to the Cabinet Office 1988; m 1973
Catherine Marjory Parkinson.

Manning, Vicky June; FCO since June 1988;
born 29.3.67; Grade S3.

Manooch, Sharon; FCO since July 1992; born
28.5.74; Grade S2.

Mansell, Julie; Washington since February 1990;
born 16.4.66; FCO 1987; Grade S2.

Mansfield, Clive; FCO since August 1988; born
8.4.54; FCO 1973; Beirut 1975; Bombay 1976;
Mexico City 1979; Rome 1981; FCO 1984;
Islamabad 1987; Grade 9; m 1980 Gail Denise
Purvis (diss 1989).

Mansfield, James Charles; Washington since
August 1992; born 10.9.34; Royal Navy 1950-77;
Oslo 1977; Moscow 1983; Kampala 1984;
Valletta 1986; Havana 1989; Belgrade 1990;
Grade CSO; m 1956 Catherine Harkin (1s 1957,
1d 1959).

Mansley, Janette Margaret; Suva since April
1992; born 14.7.64; FCO 1983; New Delhi 1985;

Luanda 1989; Grade S2.

Mansley, Phillip John Francis; Counsellor FCO since July 1990; born 4.3.39; FO 1958; HM Forces 1958-60; FO 1960; Vice-Consul Shanghai 1963; Bahrain 1965; (Second Secretary 1967); MECAS 1968; Assistant Political Agent Doha 1970; Second Secretary and Head of Chancery Doha 1971; First Secretary FCO 1973; First Secretary Hong Kong 1974; FCO 1978; Abu Dhabi 1981; First Secretary FCO 1984; Counsellor Amman 1986; m 1968 Elizabeth Mary Bennett (1d 1971; 1s 1972).

Mantle, Shirley Mair; Nicosia since September 1988; born 11.7.37; FCO 1975; Maseru 1976; Bandar Seri Begawan 1978; FCO 1981; Georgetown 1982; FCO 1986; Baghdad 1988; Grade S1; m 1965 (diss 1971).

Marcelin, Hamilton David; First Secretary (Admin) and Consul Belgrade since February 1989; born 16.11.41; FO 1960; Kuwait 1963; Nairobi 1966; Rio de Janeiro 1967; MECAS 1969; Khartoum 1971; FCO 1974; Second Secretary (Comm) Sydney 1977; First Secretary (Comm) Muscat 1982; FCO 1985; m (1) 1966 Mona Druce (diss 1977) (1d 1969); (2) 1977 Pamela Foxall.

March, Shirley Elizabeth; First Secretary FCO since May 1990; born 4.2.61; FCO 1984; Second Secretary (EC Affairs) Brussels 1988; m 1984 Paul Louis March (1s 1990).

Marchant, Trixie Jane (née Farmer) FCO since February 1991; born 1.3.65; FCO 1987; UKMIS Geneva 1989; Grade 9; m 1989 Andrew John Marchant.

Marden, Nicholas; First Secretary (Chancery) Paris since December 1988; born 2.5.50; Army 1971-74; Third later Second Secretary FCO 1974; Second Secretary Nicosia 1977; First Secretary FCO 1980; Warsaw 1982; FCO 1985; m 1977 Melanie Gaye Glover (2d 1980, 1982).

Mardlin, Robert Andrew; Dhaka since October 1992; Born 13.1.65; FCO 1984; Lima 1986; Sofia 1990; Grade 10; m 1988 Amanda Karen Morall.

Marlow, Susan Joy; Munich since December 1992; born 15.9.53; FCO 1975; Vienna 1978; FCO 1980; Peking 1981; FCO 1983; Bonn 1984; Floater duties 1986; FCO 1987; Floater Duties 1987; Oslo 1989; Grade S2.

Marlowe, Alan James; First Secretary FCO since July 1989; born 15.4.39; RAF 1958-60; Second later First Secretary FCO 1965; Hong Kong 1972; FCO 1976; Caracas 1978; FCO 1980; Helsinki 1985; m 1964 Valerie Street.

Marr, Elisabeth Ward Henderson; Second Secretary FCO since October 1987; born 16.12.39; FO 1963; South Africa 1964; Dubai 1967; Caribbean Floater 1970; Nicosia 1972; FCO 1973; Manila 1976; Melbourne 1980; Second Secretary FCO 1982; Second Secretary (Admin) and Vice-Consul Lima 1985.

Marren, Marrena Ruby; Prague since April 1992; born 15.1.68; FCO 1987; Paris 1989; Grade S2.

Marriott, Allison Mary; Vice-Consul Amman since April 1990; born 31.3.66; HMSO 1985; FCO 1987; Sofia 1989; Grade 9.

Marriott, Anne Stuart Murray (née Corbett); Bangkok since October 1988; born 29.10.57; FCO 1979; Brasilia 1982; FCO 1984; Abu Dhabi 1985; Grade S2; m 1988 Paul James Marriott.

Marsden, Ian Thomas; FCO since April 1990; born 5.10.69; Department of Social Security 1989; Grade 10.

Marsden, Rosalind Mary; Counsellor on secondment to the National Westminster Bank since March 1991; born 27.10.50; Third Secretary FCO 1974; Language training SOAS 1975; Third, Second and later First Secretary Tokyo 1976; First Secretary FCO 1980; First Secretary (Econ) Bonn 1985; First Secretary FCO 1989.

Marsden, William, CMG (1991); Minister (Trade Policy) Washington since May 1992; born 15.9.40; FO 1962; Third Secretary UKDEL NATO 1964; Private Secretary to HM Ambassador Rome 1966; Second Secretary (Comm/Econ) Rome 1967; On secondment to Joseph Lucas Ltd 1970; First Secretary FCO 1971; First Secretary and Cultural Attaché Moscow 1976; FCO 1978; Counsellor UKREP Brussels 1981; Counsellor FCO and Commissioner British Indian Ocean Territory 1985; HM Ambassador and Consul-General San José and HM Ambassador (non-resident) to Nicaragua 1989; m 1964 Ursula ("Kaia") Collingham (1d 1966; 1s 1970).

Marsh, David Sydney; Second Secretary (Commercial) Dublin since April 1990; born 9.3.46; CO 1963; FO (later FCO) 1966; Brussels 1969; Bangkok 1971; FCO 1975; Bucharest 1978; Beirut 1980; Dacca 1982 (Second Secretary 1983); FCO 1986; m 1976 Chanidapan Raksanaves.

Marsh, Elaine (née Skinner); Third Secretary (Consular) Dar Es Salaam since June 1992; born 6.1.57; FCO 1976; Port of Spain 1978; Bucharest 1982; Valletta 1984; FCO 1987; New Delhi 1989; Grade 9; m 1985 Andrew Peter Marsh; (diss 1989).

Marsh, Ian Dudley; Resident Representative Antigua since January 1990; born 17.3.45; FO 1965; Algiers 1967; Benin City 1970; Accra

1971; Kuala Lumpur 1972; FCO 1976; Second Secretary (Aid) Yaoundé 1978; FCO 1980; Vice-Consul (Pol/Inf) Cape Town 1983 (First Secretary 1986); First Secretary FCO 1987; m (1) 1969 Susan Mary Walsh (dec'd 1985) (1d 1977); (2) 1991 Margot Anita Gonsalves.

Marsh-Collings, Terence; Jakarta since May 1989; born 12.9.40; Geneva 1971; Warsaw 1972; Bangkok 1973; FCO 1975; Lilongwe 1976; Dacca 1980; UKREP Brussels 1981; Grade 9; FCO 1984; m 1966 Maureen Patricia Evans (1d 1974).

Marshall, Alan Christie, MBE (1987); Second Secretary FCO since September 1991; born 22.8.46; FO (later FCO) 1965; Bathurst 1969; UKDEL NATO Brussels 1972; Sana'a 1976; FCO 1977; Accra 1979; Athens 1981; FCO 1982; Colombo 1983; FCO 1987; Second Secretary Singapore 1989; m (1) 1968 Margaret Patricia Millar (diss 1983) (2d 1971, 1974); (2) 1983 Christie Margaret Hepburn.

Marshall, Alan John; Luanda since February 1990; born 11.9.52; FCO 1971; Cairo 1973; Lilongwe 1975; Salisbury 1978; Sana'a 1980; FCO 1981; Islamabad 1983; Vice-Consul Lisbon 1987; Grade 9; m (1) 1975 Shirley Heather Monaghan (1s 1979; 1d 1986); (2) Ana Paula do Santos Marques.

Marshall, Albert Selwyn, MBE (1968); First Secretary and Consul Tel Aviv since March 1990; born 26.9.34; FO 1955; Army 1956-57; New York 1961; Prague 1964; Kingston 1965; FCO 1968; Addis Ababa 1972; Belgrade 1976; Second Secretary and Vice-Consul Tokyo 1977; FCO 1981; First Secretary (Admin) Washington 1986; m (1) 1960 Joan Margaret Lashwood (dec'd 1985) (1s 1961; 1d 1963); (2) Marion Rose Willmott.

Marshall, Angela Rosemary; Maseru since January 1991; born 22.8.60; FCO 1988; Grade S2.

Marshall, Bernard Alan; First Secretary (Comm) Bucharest since June 1989; born 23.3.48; FCO 1968; Bombay 1971; Islamabad 1971; Moscow 1973; Anguilla 1974; Bonn 1976; FCO 1978 (Second Secretary 1979); Vice-Consul (Comm) Melbourne 1982; Second Secretary FCO 1986.

Marshall, Brian; Second Secretary FCO since April 1985; born 13.12.51; FCO 1971; on loan to HCS 1974; FCO 1977; Second Secretary Muscat 1984; m 1975 Susan Joyce Bishop (1d 1976).

Marshall, Francis James; Second Secretary (Management Officer) JMO Brussels since August 1991; born 10.8.46; CRO 1963; Commonwealth Office (later FCO) 1965; Mogadishu 1969; Singapore 1971; FCO 1974; Port Louis 1977; Tripoli 1981; Addis Ababa

1983; FCO 1984; Vice-Consul Toronto 1987; m 1971 Clare Wray (1s 1972; 1d 1976).

Marshall, Hermione Marie (née Roberts); FCO since November 1991; born 2.5.52; Grade S2; m 1983 Allan William Marshall.

Marshall, Mark Anthony, CMG (1991); HM Ambassador and HM Consul General Sana'a and concurrently HMA (non-resident) to Djibouti since November 1987; born 8.10.37; MECAS 1958; Third Secretary Amman 1960; FO 1962 (Second Secretary 1963); Commercial Officer Dubai 1964; FO/Commonwealth Office 1965; Aden 1967; First Secretary 1968; Assistant Director of Treasury Centre for Administrative Studies 1968; UK Delegation to the Brussels Conference 1970; First Secretary1/Head of Chancery, Rabat 1972; FCO 1976; Counsellor (Econ/Comm) Tripoli 1979; Head of Chancery Damascus 1980; Counsellor FCO 1984; m 1970 Penelope Lesley Seymour (2d 1973, 1975).

Marshall, Michael Gavin; FCO since June 1990; born 13.9.60; FCO 1980; Moscow 1982; Baghdad 1983; Floater Duties 1988; Grade 9.

Marshall, Noël Hedley, CMG (1986); UK Permanent Representative to the Council of Europe, Strasbourg (with personal rank of Ambassador) since September 1990; born 26.11.34; FO 1957; Third Secretary Prague 1959; FO 1961; Second Secretary Moscow 1963; First Secretary CRO 1965; Karachi 1966; Rawalpindi 1967; Chargé d'Affaires Ulan Bator 1967; Rawalpindi 1968; FCO 1970; UKREP Brussels 1974; NATO Defence College Rome 1977; Counsellor UKDIS Geneva 1978; Head of North America Department FCO 1982; Counsellor Overseas Inspectorate 1985; Minister Moscow 1986; FCO 1989.

Marshall, Peter James; First Secretary FCO since October 1988; born 25.6.44; Ministry of Aviation 1963; CRO 1964; DSAO 1965; Seconded to Commonwealth Secretariat 1965; Malta 1967; Johannesburg 1970; Second Secretary Kaduna 1970; Vice-Consul (Comm) San Francisco 1974; First Secretary FCO 1979; Deputy High Commissioner, Head of Chancery and First Secretary (Comm) Valletta 1983; m 1966 Roberta Barlow (1s 1967; 3d 1969, 1972, 1974).

Marshall, Peter William; SUPL since August 1986; born 25.1.49; FCO 1968; Tehran 1971; FCO 1973; Dacca 1977; SUPL 1979; FCO 1982; Peking 1983; FCO 1985; Grade 9.

Marshall, Robert; First Secretary FCO since November 1986; born 21.8.44; First Secretary FCO 1975; First Secretary (Inf) Rome 1977; First Secretary FCO 1980; First Secretary (Chancery) Lagos 1986; m 1971 Patricia Daly.

Marshall, Robert John; Kamakura on language training since August 1991; born 19.6.68; FCO

1988; Grade 7.

Martin, Angus Charles Trench; FCO since September 1991; born 27.12.71; Grade 10.

Martin, Ann Louise; FCO since November 1990; born 4.11.72; Grade S2.

Martin, Arthur; UKMIS Geneva since July 1989; born 15.8.41; HCS 1968; FCO 1970; Kathmandu 1972; East Berlin 1976; Singapore 1977; Kuala Lumpur 1979; FCO 1981; Nairobi 1983; Grade 9; FCO 1985; m 1965 Lesley (née McCaa) (1d 1969; 1s 1971).

Martin, Christopher Nichols; FCO since July 1981; born 4.5.62; Grade 9.

Martin, Dominic David William; Third later Second Secretary (Chancery) New Delhi since August 1989; born 25.11.64; FCO 1987.

Martin, Douglas George; Consul-General and Deputy Head of Mission Kiev since May 1992; born 1.10.47; Third Secretary FCO 1970; Hong Kong 1971; Second Secretary Peking 1974; Second later First Secretary FCO 1976; First Secretary (Chancery) Moscow 1977; FCO 1980; On loan to Cabinet Office 1982; First Secretary and Head of Chancery Lisbon 1985; Counsellor and Deputy to the Senior Representative JLG Hong Kong 1988; m 1970 Jill Cambridge (2s 1973, 1974; 1d 1978).

Martin, Frances Edith Josephine; Washington since January 1987; born 20.2.48; MOD 1965; FCO 1973; Montevideo 1973; Peking 1976; Tehran 1977; Moscow 1979; FCO 1981; Grade 9.

Martin, Francis James; First Secretary FCO since September 1991; born 3.5.49; DSAO later FCO 1968; Reykjavik 1971; Stuttgart 1973; FCO 1976; Second Secretary 1978; Vice-Consul (Pol/ Inf) Cape Town 1979; Second later First Secretary (Institutions) UKREP Brussels 1983; FCO 1988; Deputy High Commissioner Freetown 1988; m 1970 Aileen Margaret Shovlin (2s 1973, 1975; 2d 1976, 1978).

Martin, James; FCO since August 1972; born 22.5.39; Tehran 1962; Peking 1965; Tel Aviv 1966; FCO 1968; Doha 1971; Grade 9.

Martin, John Francis Ryde; Counsellor (ECOSOC) UKMIS New York since February 1988; born 8.2.43; Third Secretary Commonwealth Office 1966; Third later Second Secretary Buenos Aires 1968; Language Student 1970; Second later First Secretary Athens 1971; First Secretary FCO 1974; Private Secretary to the Minister of State FCO 1976; Head of Chancery Nicosia 1978; FCO 1982; Counsellor on loan to DTI 1983; Head of Chancery Lagos 1983; m (1) 1966 Heléne Henriette Raymonde Pyronnet (2s 1967, 1969); (2) Kathleen Marie White (1s 1988).

Martin, John Robert; FCO since February 1987; born 5.5.58; FCO 1979; Baghdad 1980; FCO 1982; Darwin 1985; Grade 9; m 1984 Jill Catherine Walker.

Martin, Neil Richard; Sofia since December 1991; born 14.3.67; FCO 1987; Tunis 1989; Grade 9.

Martin, Nicholas Jonathan Leigh; First Secretary FCO since July 1991; born 29.1.48; First Secretary FCO 1979; First Secretary (Chancery) Nairobi 1981; First Secretary FCO 1984; First Secretary (Chancery) Rome 1987; m 1980 Anna Louise Reekie (1s 1983; 2d 1985, 1987).

Martin, Reginald Charles; FCO since January 1989; born 3.4.30; HM Forces 1946-1970; FCO 1970; Darwin 1979; Rome 1986; Grade 8; m 1956 Hilary Wheatley (2s 1957, 1963; 1d 1960).

Martin, Rosemary Sheila; FCO since January 1986; born 25.3.59; FCO 1981; BMG Berlin 1983; Grade S2.

Martin, Simon Charles; Second later First Secretary FCO since October 1990; born 15.5.63; FCO 1984; Language Training 1986; Third later Second Secretary and Vice-Consul Rangoon 1987; m 1988 Sharon Margaret Joel.

Martin, Stanley William Frederick, LVO (1981); HM Assistant Marshal of the Diplomatic Corps since July 1972; born 9.12.34; Army 1953-55; CRO 1958; Assistant Private Secretary to Secretary of State 1959; First Secretary (Defence) Canberra 1962; First Secretary (Eernal Affairs and Defence) Kuala Lumpur 1964; Commonwealth Office (later FCO) 1967; Seconded to CSD 1970; FCO 1971; m 1960 Hanni Hansen (1s 1962; 1d 1964).

Martin, Stephen Robert; On loan to the Hong Kong Bank, Hong Kong since May 1990; born 9.9.53; FCO 1972; SE Asia Floater 1975; Peking 1977; Language Training 1979; Muscat 1981 (Second Secretary 1982); Second Secretary FCO 1984; Consul Jerusalem 1987; m 1986 Wendy Susan Kent (1d 1992).

Martinez, Paul Lawrence; FCO since February 1990; born 6.11.53; FCO 1972; Paris 1975; Kingston 1977; Chicago 1981; FCO 1984; Second Secretary (Chancery/Inf) Lima 1986; m 1978 Ann Elizabeth Stokes (2d 1982, 1985).

Martlew, Margaret June, MBE (1974); Second Secretary and Deputy High Commissioner Freetown since January 1991; born 20.6.35; FO 1963; Bonn 1963; Kinshasa 1966; Amman 1969; Belmopan 1971; FCO 1973; Buenos Aires 1975; Santiago 1977; FCO 1979; East Berlin 1980; FCO 1982; Belmopan 1986; Prague 1990.

Marzouk, Helen (née Matthews); FCO since February 1991; born 27.3.62; FCO 1981; Dhaka

1984; Moscow 1985; Tunis 1985; Berne 1988; Grade 9; m 1987 R B L Marzouk.

Masefield, (John) Thorold, cmg (1986); AUS (South and South East Asia) since July 1992; born 1.10.39; CRO 1962-64; Private Secretary to Permanent Under-Secretary of State 1963; Kuala Lumpur 1964; Second Secretary Warsaw 1966; FO (later FCO) 1967; First Secretary UKDEL Disarmament Conference, Geneva 1970; FCO 1974; Counsellor, Head of Chancery and Consul-General Islamabad 1979; Head of Personnel Services Dept FCO 1982; Counsellor FCO 1985; CDA at Harvard 1987; Attached to OMCS (CSSB) 1988; High Commissioner Dar-es-Salaam 1989; m 1962 Jennifer Mary Trowell (2s 1964, 1970; 1d 1966).

Mason, Bryon John; FCO since May 1991; (Second Secretary 1991); born 12.4.38; FO 1964; Copenhagen 1966; Bombay 1968; Prague 1972; Mexico City 1974; Rio de Janeiro 1975; FCO 1977; Port Louis 1980; Cairo 1984; Kathmandu 1987; Grade 9; m 1965 Jennifer Linda (1d 1964).

Mason, Colette Hazel; Port of Spain since May 1991; born 15.7.65; FCO 1987; Grade S2A.

Mason, Edward Charles; FCO since August 1990; born 11.5.68; Grade 8.

Mason, Ian David; on Floater Duties since March 1991; born 26.10.67; FCO 1987; Mogadishu 1989; Grade 10.

Mason, James Muir Angel; FCO since July 1989; born 13.8.69; Grade 10.

Mason, Louise; FCO since October 1986; born 30.8.63; Grade 10.

Massey, Andrew Fraser; Jedda since July 1989; born 24.7.63; FCO 1984; Bangkok 1987; Grade 10.

Massey, Paul Francis Cobden; Second Secretary (Consular) Moscow since April 1990; born 25.7.39; FCO 1977; Colombo 1979; Brasilia 1983; FCO 1985 (Second Secretary 1988); m 1960 Jacquita Jill Durk (3s 1961, 1963, 1966).

Massingham, Carol May; Havana since October 1990; born 17.6.66; FCO 1985; Pretoria/Cape Town 1988; Grade 10.

Masterman, Margaret Alice (née Neal); FCO since June 1988; born 5.6.63; FCO 1984; Warsaw 1985; Grade 9; m 1989 Graham Paul Masterman.

Mather, David Livingstone; FCO since January 1991; born 5.2.41; FO (later FCO) 1963; Moscow 1969; FCO 1971; Third Secretary Canberra 1975; FCO 1978; Second Secretary East Berlin 1982; FCO 1985; Second Secretary Paris 1988; m 1966 Anne Roberts (1s 1967; 1d 1972).

Mathers, Peter James; FCO since October 1991; born 2.4.46; HM Forces 1968-71; FCO 1971; SOAS 1972; Tehran 1973; Bonn 1976; FCO 1978; Copenhagen 1981; First Secretary (Comm) Tehran 1986; FCO 1987; First Secretary (on Secondment to UN Offices) UKMIS Vienna 1988; m 1983 Elisabeth Hoeller (1s 1984; 1d 1986).

Mathewson, Iain Arthur Gray; First Secretary FCO since January 1989; born 16.3.52; HM Customs and Excise 1974-77; DHSS 1977-80; FCO 1980; First Secretary UKMIS New York 1981; FCO 1985; Warsaw 1985; m 1983 Jennifer Bloch (1s 1984; 1d 1986).

Mathieson, John David; Madrid since February 1992; born 19.6.35; Colombo 1958; Baghdad 1967; Nicosia 1967; Sofia 1969; Kinshasa 1972; Singapore 1974; Islamabad 1976; Stockholm 1979; Moscow 1981; Dublin 1984; Paris 1990; Grade CSO; m 1956 Esther Lois Ferdinands (3s 1957, 1961, 1963; 1d 1966).

Mattey, Eric; Second Secretary (Comm) Kuala Lumpur since December 1990; born 26.3.49; FCO 1968; Bucharest 1971; Rabat 1973; Moscow 1975; FCO 1977; Vienna 1980; Port Louis 1983; Second Secretary FCO 1985; m 1970 Janet Walker (1s 1971; 1d 1974).

Matthews, Andrew John; Paris since August 1992; born 28.4.55; FCO 1974; Bonn 1976; Singapore 1979; FCO 1982; Dublin 1982; FCO 1985; Grade 9; Colombo 1988; m (1) 1976 Carole Susan Thomson (diss 1986) (1d 1976); (2) 1988 Denise Ann Mary Carroll (1d 1992).

Matthews, Mark Julian; FCO since August 1990; born 24.8.68; Grade 9.

Maud, The Hon Humphrey (John Hamilton), cmg (1982); HM Ambassador Buenos Aires since July 1990; born 17.4.34; HM Forces 1953-55; FO 1959; Third Secretary Madrid 1961; Second later First Secretary Havana 1963; FO 1965; (on secondment to the Cabinet Office 1968); First Secretary Paris 1970; Sabbatical at Nuffield College Oxford 1974; Head of Financial Relations Dept FCO 1975; Minister (Local Rank) Madrid 1979; HM Ambassador and Consul-General Luxembourg 1982; AUSS (Econ) FCO 1985; High Commissioner Nicosia 1988; m 1963 Maria Eugenia Gazitua (3s 1964, 1966, 1972).

Maudsley, Patrick Nelson; FCO since March 1987 (Second Secretary 1990); born 12.5.43; CRO later Commonwealth Office 1964; Paris 1966; Lusaka 1969; Prague 1972; FCO 1973; Dacca 1976; Durban 1978; Salisbury 1980; FCO 1982; Rabat 1985; m 1972 Vyvian Elaine St John (1d 1973).

Mawby, Sally Ann; Georgetown since October 1992; born 29.7.60; FCO 1979; Washington 1984; FCO 1987; FCO 1987; Tortola 1988; Grade S2.

Maxton, Fiona; Third Secretary (Management) Rabat since October 1989; born 19.12.67; FCO 1985; Bonn 1988; Grade 9.

Maxwell, Jacqueline Murray; The Hague since June 1990; born 6.11.64; FCO 1983; UKMIS New York 1986; FCO 1989; Grade S2.

Maxwell, Letitia Kelso; Copenhagen since August 1989; born 12.2.42; FCO 1977; Helsinki 1979; Doha 1981; FCO 1984; Grade S1.

Maxwell, Mary Josephine; First Secretary FCO since February 1990; born 5.11.39; Board of Trade 1957; DSAO 1966; SE Asia Floater 1969; Phnom Penh 1971; Rangoon1/Valletta 1973; Second Secretary FCO 1976; Second Secretary (Inf) Castries 1976; Bridgetown 1977; Port of Spain 1981; FCO 1983; First Secretary (Admin) The Hague 1986.

May, Philip; Tehran since June 1992; born 12.11.60; Ottawa 1982; Moscow 1985; Islamabad 1986; FCO 1988; Grade 9; m 1985 Susan Ann Checketts; (2d 1989, 1990).

May, Susan Ann (née Checketts); SUPL since November 1989; born 18.8.56; FCO 1978; Peking 1980; Ottawa 1982; Moscow 1985; Islamabad 1986; Grade 9; m 1985 Philip May (1d 1989).

Mayer, Helen; FCO since June 1991; born 24.8.71; Grade S3.

Mayhew, Michael John Ernest; First Secretary (Commercial) The Hague since August 1992; born 6.11.46; DSAO (later FCO) 1966; Mexico City 1969; Algiers 1972; Tokyo 1974; FCO 1975; Prague 1978; Second Secretary (Inf) Oslo 1981; Second Secretary FCO 1985; First Secretary (Comm/Dev) Bangkok 1987; m 1976 Elizabeth Carol Owen.

Mayland, Alan John; Second Secretary (Admin) Colombo since August 1989; born 5.11.46; FO 1965; Warsaw 1968; Cairo 1970; Brussels 1971; Calcutta 1974; Budapest 1975; FCO 1976; Paris 1981; Ottawa 1982; Second Secretary FCO 1986.

Mayman, Shelley Liann; FCO since November 1991; born 2.5.70; Grade S2.

Maynard, Ivan Trevor; Berlin since September 1992; born 13.9.58; FCO 1975; Pretoria 1984; Grade 8; FCO 1987; m 1984 Susan Jane Parritt.

Mayne, Edward Patrick; Second Secretary FCO since August 1990; born 25.12.42; MAFF 1960; FO 1962; Khartoum 1964; Pretoria 1965; Tehran 1968; FCO 1971; Gaborone 1974; Islamabad 1976; Paris 1978; FCO 1981; Second Secretary (Consular) Accra 1987; m 1969 Marion North (1d 1971; 1s 1973).

Mayne, Julie Ann; Caracas since May 1992; born 3.4.58; FCO 1989; Grade S2.

Mealor, Michelle Louise; Riyadh since September 1991; born 8.4.68; FCO 1988; SUPL 1990; Grade 10.

Mearns, George Ewen; Consul (Comm) St Petersberg since October 1992; born 18.1.41; FO 1958; Pretoria1/Cape Town 1962; Jedda 1964; Stockholm 1966; Bahrain Residency 1969; FCO 1972; Language Student 1974; Moscow 1975; Second Secretary (Admin) Port of Spain 1978; FCO 1981; Second Secretary (Comm) Warsaw 1984; Consul (Comm) Hamburg 1987; m 1961 Elsie Crossley (1) dec'd 1989 (1d 1966; 1s 1968) (2) Sylvia Jeanette Mueller.

Mearns, Stuart; FCO since January 1989; born 21.11.58; FCO 1982; Khartoum 1985; Grade 8; m 1983 Andrea Chapman.

Measures, Helen Elizabeth; FCO since June 1992; born 23.6.66; Grade S2.

Meath, Caroline Melanie Cherry; Canberra since January 1992; born 16.9.69; FCO 1990; Grade S2.

Meath Baker, William John Clovis; First Secretary and Consul Prague since December 1989; born 11.5.59; FCO 1985; Second later First Secretary (Chancery and Inf) and Consul Kabul 1988; FCO 1989; m 1985 Elizabeth Diana Woodham-Smith (2d 1988; 1990).

Medcalf, Jane Elizabeth; FCO since September 1990; born 13.10.54; Grade S2.

Medlin, Alexadra Lynn (née Russon); Cairo since March 1990; born 15.10.61; FCO 1980; Cape Town/Pretoria 1983; Port Moresby 1986; Grade S1; m 1986 Shaun Lincoln Medlin.

Mee, Jeffery Bryan; Vice-Consul Vienna since March 1991; born 8.7.56; Passport Office 1975; FCO 1976; Kathmandu 1978; FCO 1980; Khartoum 1982; Peking 1985; Vancouver 1987; FCO 1987; Grade 9; m 1986 Patricia Maria (Suk Yee) Wong; (1s 1990).

Megson, Sheila Mary; FCO since February 1974; born 28.11.37; Rio de Janeiro 1964; Dakar 1966; Vientiane 1969; Caracas 1973; Grade S1.

Mehmet, Alper, MVO (1990); Second Secretary (Head of Chancery) Reykjavik since July 1989; born 28.8.48; Immigration Service 1970; Lagos 1979; FCO 1983 (Second Secretary 1986); Bucharest 1986; m 1968 Elaine Susan Tarrant (2d 1969, 1971).

Meiklejohn, Dominic Francis; FCO since November 1990; born 14.11.67; HM Customs and Excise 1989-90; Grade 8.

Melbourne, Sean; Maputo since January 1990; born 9.12.68; FCO 1988; Grade 10.

Melling, Scott Richard; FCO since November 1990; born 10.5.72; Grade 10.

Mellor, John; Ankara since March 1990; born 9.2.52; Department of National Savings 1968; FCO 1971; Belgrade 1973; Middle East Floater 1975; Dar es Salaam 1977; FCO 1979; Strasbourg 1980; FCO 1982; Washington 1987; Grade 9; m 1987 Mary Bridget Ann McGettigan.

Meredith, Richard Evan; Second later First Secretary FCO since January 1989; born 31.1.61; FCO 1983; Third Secretary Bridgetown 1985; Second Secretary Managua 1987; m 1986 Louisa Jane Oriel.

Merriman, Eva; FCO since November 1991; born 16.9.57; FCO 1983; Paris 1984; Tunis 1987; Brussels 1989; Grade S2.

Merry, David Byron; First Secretary FCO since January 1989; born 16.9.45; Ministry of Aviation 1961; CRO (later Commonwealth Office, later FCO) 1965; Bangkok 1969; Second Secretary (Inf) Budapest 1974; Second later First Secretary FCO 1977; First Secretary (Civil Air Attaché) Bonn 1981; Head of Chancery East Berlin 1985; m 1967 Patricia Ann Ellis (2d 1969, 1972; 1s 1971).

Mesarowicz, Anthony David; FCO since October 1991; born 28.7.70; Grade 10.

Messer, Terence George; Belgrade since June 1991; born 7.11.39; Army 1958-82; Istanbul 1982; Cairo 1983; Moscow 1985; Singapore 1986; Grade SO.

Metcalfe, Caryl Aileen; FCO since January 1987; FCO 1977; Baghdad 1978; Stockholm 1980; FCO 1983; Lilongwe 1985; New Delhi 1988; Grade S1; m 1991 Duncan Richard Mackinnon.

Metcalfe, Julian Ross; First Secretary FCO since April 1991; born 24.2.56; Economic Adviser FCO 1983; First Secretary Cairo 1987; m 1985 Rachel Mai Jones.

Metcalfe, Susan; FCO since September 1987; born 2.10.65; Grade S3A.

Meyer, Christopher John Rome, CMG (1988); Minister (Comm) later Minister Washington since May 1989; born 22.2.44; Third Secretary FO 1966; Third later Second Secretary Moscow 1968; Madrid 1970; First Secretary FCO 1973; UKREP Brussels 1978; Counsellor and Head of Chancery Moscow 1982; Counsellor FCO 1984;

Harvard University 1988; m 1976 Francoise Elizabeth Hedges (2s 1978, 1984).

Meyer, Fenella Jane (née Cracroft), SUPL since April 1991; born 20.10.62; FCO 1983; Vienna 1986; Nicosia 1989; FCO 1990; Grade S2; m 1990 David Meyer.

Miah, Faruk; FCO since June 1990; born 18.12.70; Grade 10.

Michael, Alan Rhys; First Secretary FCO since October 1988; born 2.1.48; FCO 1971; MECAS 1973; Jedda 1975; Jedda1/Riyadh 1976; FCO 1978; Second Secretary UKMIS Geneva 1982; First Secretary (Comm) Kuwait 1986; m 1973 Anita Ruth Ford (1s 1973; 1d 1977).

Middel, Julie; SUPL since June 1990; born 26.4.58; DHSS 1976; FCO 1979; Copenhagen 1982; Floater Duties 1985; Sofia 1986; Brussels 1987; FCO 1990; Grade 9; m 1988 Wolfgang Middel.

Middleton, David Farquharson; First Secretary Lusaka since February 1991; born 21.11.53; FCO 1982; Language Training Kamakura 1984; First Secretary Tokyo 1985; First Secretary FCO 1988; m 1984 Georgina Mary Housman (1s 1987, 2d 1989, 1992).

Midgley, John Barrington, OBE (1990); First Secretary (Management) Canberra since October 1992; born 1.5.38; Board of Trade 1960; Canberra 1963; Enugu 1966; Tehran 1968; FCO 1970; Second Secretary (Comm) Helsinki 1972; Second Secretary (Comm) Nicosia 1977; First Secretary Ankara 1980; First Secretary FCO 1983; First Secretary (Admin) and Consul-General Riyadh 1986; First Secretary FCO 1990; m 1961 Maureen Tobin (2s 1964, 1971; 1d 1966).

Miers, Sir (Henry) David (Alastair Capel), KBE (1985), CMG (1979); HM Ambassador Athens since May 1989; born 10.1.37; Army 1955-57; FO 1961; Third later Second Secretary Tokyo 1963; Second later First Secretary (Comm) Vientiane 1966; FCO 1968 (Private Secretary to the Minister of State 1968 and the Parliamentary Under-Secretary of State 1969-70); Paris 1972; FCO 1975; Counsellor and Head of Chancery Tehran 1977; Head of MED FCO 1979; Chatham House 1983; HM Ambassador Beirut 1983; AUSS (Middle East) FCO 1986; m 1966 Imelda Maria Emilia Wouters (2s 1967, 1971; 1d 1968).

Milburn, Roi; First Secretary (Management) Bonn since October 1992; born 9.4.45; FO 1963; DSAO 1965; Sofia 1967; Cairo 1968; FCO 1970; Bonn 1970; Islamabad 1973; FCO 1976; Second Secretary and Vice-Consul Rangoon 1979; Second later First Secretary FCO 1984; Deputy High Commissioner Mbabane 1987; m 1970 Marguerita Gabriel Corker (1d 1972; 1s 1978).

Miles, Joanne Denise; San José since November 1991; born 10.6.57; FCO 1980; Prague 1982; FCO 1984; Bandar Seri Begawan 1986; Guatemala City 1988; Grade S2.

Miles, (Richard) Oliver, CMG (1984); AUSS (Econ) since July 1990; born 6.3.36; MECAS 1960; Acting Political Officer Abu Dhabi 1961; FO 1962; Second Secretary Amman 1964; FO 1966; First Secretary Mukalla 1966; Private Secretary to High Commissioner Aden 1967; First Secretary and Head of Chancery Aden 1967; FO (later FCO) 1968; Nicosia 1970; First Secretary FCO 1973; Counsellor Jedda 1975; Counsellor and Consul-General Athens 1977; Head of NENAD FCO 1980; HM Ambassador Tripoli 1984; UKMIS New York (UNGA) 1984; HM Ambassador and Consul-General Luxembourg 1985; on loan to HCS 1988; m 1968 Julia Lyndall Weiner (3s 1972, 1973, 1977; 1d 1979).

Millan, George Edward Kraus; Peking since November 1991; born 24.11.36; HM Forces 1954-76; Cairo 1982; Bucharest 1984; Oslo 1986; Tel Aviv 1989; Grade SO; m 1958 Melinda Rose (1d 1959; 1s 1962).

Millar, Lindsey; FCO since January 1991; born 18.6.67; Scottish Office 1984-90; Grade S2A.

Miller, Anne Virginia; FCO since September 1991; born 16.1.72; Grade 10.

Miller, David Ivimey, OBE (1991); Principal Research Officer (DS Grade 5) FCO since September 1990; born 26.3.37; FO 1964; Moscow 1966; FCO 1968; Moscow 1971; FCO 1971; BMG Berlin 1972; CSCE (Geneva) 1974; FCO 1974; CSCE (Belgrade) 1977; FCO 1981; First Secretary and Head of Chancery Belgrade 1978; on loan to Cabinet Office 1982; Principal Research Officer seconded to NATO Secretariat Brussels 1985; m 1966 Caroline Ethel Jackson (2d 1970, 1973).

Miller, David Roland; Second Secretary Vila since February 1990; born 1.11.52; FCO 1972; Bucharest 1975; Tripoli 1976; Rome 1979; FCO 1982; Kuala Lumpur 1985; Second Secretary FCO 1989; m 1976 Gillian Mary Cornthwaite (2s 1980, 1983).

Miller, Emma Kate; FCO since November 1991; born 6.8.70; Grade 10.

Miller, Geoffrey Francis; Queen's Messenger since 1973; born 21.5.30.

Miller, Iain Walter; Sana'a since August 1991; born 26.6.70; DHSS; FCO 1989; Grade 10.

Miller, Julian Peter; Language Training Kamakura since August 1989; born 27.12.64; FCO 1987; Language Training 1989; Grade 9.

Miller, Julie; Jakarta since August 1991; born 21.11.70; FCO 1988; Grade 10.

Miller, Kerri-Lyn; Port Louis since May 1990; born 11.11.64; FCO 1987; Shanghai 1989; Grade S2A.

Miller, Nicholas Michael; FCO since July 1990; born 10.10.62; FCO 1982; Bangkok 1984; Peking 1987; Grade 9.

Miller, Peter Charles William; FCO since November 1989; born 27.8.46; FCO 1964; Madrid 1987; Grade 7; m (1) 1970 Jennifer O;Toole (diss 1984) (1s 1971; 1d 1973); (2) 1985 Jean Ward (3s 1974, 1976, 1977).

Miller, Shirley; UKREP Brussels since February 1992; born 6.12.56; FCO 1976; Reykjavik 1981; UKDIS Geneva 1984; Port Stanley 1987; FCO 1988; Grade S2.

Millett, Peter Joseph; First Secretary (Energy) UKREP Brussels since January 1989; born 23.1.55; FCO 1974; LA Floater 1976; Caracas 1978; Doha 1981; Second Secretary FCO 1985; m 1981 June Harnett (2d 1984, 1987).

Millington, Anthony Nigel Raymond; SUPL since March 1990; born 29.1.45; Third Secretary FCO 1968; Second later First Secretary Tokyo 1969; First Secretary FCO 1976; Paris 1980; CDA at Japanese NDC 1984; Counsellor and Head of Chancery Tokyo 1985; Counsellor FCO 1989; m 1969 Susan Carolyn Steilberg (2s 1976, 1978).

Mills, Anthony; Second Secretary (Management) Karachi since October 1990; born 29.5.43; Inland Revenue 1966; FCO 1970; Addis Ababa 1973; UKREP Brussels 1975; Prague 1977; Dacca 1979; FCO 1981; Freetown 1982; FCO 1986; m 1978 Christine Mary Napp (2s 1979, 1982).

Mills, David Paul; Cairo since July 1989; born 2.10.67; FCO 1987; Grade 10.

Mills, Hilary Clare; FCO since August 1991; born 5.6.46; FCO 1978; Dakar 1978; Rio de Janeiro 1980; Brasilia 1982; Moscow 1984; FCO 1985; Bonn 1987; Grade 9.

Millson, Tony; First Secretary FCO since December 1991; born 25.11.51; FCO 1970; MECAS 1973; Third Secretary (Comm) Tripoli 1974; Third later Second Secretary (Development) Amman 1976; FCO 1980; Second Secretary BMG Berlin 1983; First Secretary FCO 1986; Head of Chancery Kuwait 1988.

Milne, Hilary Taylor; FCO since November 1991; born 7.6.65; FCO 1984; Rome 1985; Freetown 1988; FCO 1990; Grade 10.

Milton, Derek Francis, CMG (1990); High Commissioner Kingston and HM Ambassador (non resident) Haiti since April 1989; born 11.11.35; RAF 1954-56; Colonial Office 1959-63; Assistant Private Secretary to Commonwealth and Colonial Secretary 1962; First Secretary CRO later FO 1964; First Secretary (Economic and Social Affairs) New York (UK Mission) 1967; First Secretary Rome 1972; FCO 1975; Counsellor Sabbatical at Glasgow University 1977; Counsellor (Pol/Econ) Caracas 1978; on loan to DOT 1980; Overseas Inspectorate FCO 1982; Minister/Counsellor Mexico City 1984; RCDS 1988; m (1) 1960 Helge Kahle (diss 1975) (2s 1963, 1965); (2) 1977 Catherine Walmsley.

Milton, Guy Hugh; On Secondment to the ODA as Assistant Private Secretary to the Minister of State since February 1992; born 7.5.61; FCO 1983; Language Training 1984; FCO 1985; Paris 1989; (Second Secretary 1991); m 1984 Ann Richardson.

Milton, Verity Iris; Tel Aviv since June 1990; born 4.8.38; FCO 1973; Moscow 1974; Guatemala 1976; FCO 1978; Milan 1980; FCO 1983; Africa/Middle East Floater 1985; Jerusalem 1988; Grade 9.

Minshull, Heidi Jane; FCO since November 1990; born 2.3.67; Grade 8.

Minshull, Simon Peter; Islamabad since August 1992; born 21.11.68; FCO 1988; Moscow 1990; Grade 10.

Minter, Graham Leslie, LVO (1983); First Secretary (Econ/Agric) Canberra since March 1990; born 4.1.50; FCO 1968; Anguilla 1971; Latin America Floater 1973; Asuncion 1975; FCO 1978; First Secretary (Econ) Mexico City 1979; First Secretary FCO 1984; m 1975 Peter Anne Scott (1s 1978).

Mistry, Hemlata; FCO since October 1990; born 7.6.62; (FCO Home Civil Service 1988); Grade 10.

Mirtle, Catherine Grace; FCO since June 1989; born 8.1.69; Grade 10.

Mitchell, Amanda Elizabeth; Muscat since November 1989; born 3.6.59; FCO 1977; Paris 1979; Cayman Islands 1982; FCO 1986; Riyadh 1987; Grade S1.

Mitchell, Andrew Jonathan; FCO since September 1991; born 7.3.67; Grade 8.

Mitchell, Arthur Edward, BEM (1985); UKMIS New York since March 1985; born 12.9.23; Colombo 1968; Sofia 1969; UKDEL NATO Brussels 1971; Saigon 1973; Georgetown 1974; Washington 1975; Moscow 1978; Vienna 1979; Bucharest 1982; Grade SSO; m 1950 Myrtle Vera (1d 1951).

Mitchell, Carole, RVM (1990); The Hague since November 1991; born 7.6.57; Scottish Office 1975; FCO 1987; Reykjavik 1988; Grade S2.

Mitchell, Edward John; Counsellor FCO since May 1992; born 21.4.39; FO 1962; Vice-Consul Düsseldorf 1963; Second Secretary FO 1965; Bangkok 1967; First Secretary Bonn 1972; FCO 1976; First Secretary Bangkok 1979; First Secretary FCO 1983; Counsellor Bonn 1988; m 1973 Belinda Mary Ponsonby (3s 1976, 1978, 1981).

Mitchell, Frederick John, MBE (1991); Third Secretary Islamabad since March 1991; born 30.5.38; HM Forces 1953-65; FO 1965; New Delhi 1967; FCO 1968; Benghazi 1969; FCO 1971; Singapore 1973; FCO 1975; Rome 1976; FCO 1979; Sana'a 1979; FCO 1983; Bucharest 1984; Riyadh 1987; Grade 8; m 1961 Rosa Leona Vereecke (1s 1964; 1d 1962).

Mitchell, John Steven; FCO since March 1992; born 28.11.67; FCO 1985; Tokyo 1988; Stockholm 1990; Grade 9; m 1989 Margaret Rose Howie.

Mitchell, Jonathan Kenneth Milton; First Secretary (Chancery) Harare since September 1991; born 18.12.59; Second Secretary FCO 1987; Second later First Secretary (Info) Amman 1989; First Secretary FCO 1990; m 1986 Joyce Ann Henderson (1d 1990).

Mitchell, Margaret Rose (née Howie); Stockholm since October 1990; born 7.3.66; FCO 1985; Tokyo 1988; Grade S2; m 1989 John Steven Mitchell.

Mitchell, Margareta (née Richmond); FCO since September 1991; born 28.11.46; Commonwealth Office 1968; Kinshasa 1971; Stockholm 1971; Brussels 1973; Vienna 1975; Bridgetown 1977; FCO 1980; Valletta 1983; FCO 1986; SUPL 1987; Grade 9; m 1985 Stephen Robert Mitchell.

Mitchell, Michael James, MVO (1989); Third Secretary (Chancery) Singapore since May 1989; born 7.8.54. HM Customs & Excise 1980; FCO 1985; Third Secretary (Aid) Kampala 1986; Grade 9; m 1982 Dominique Steggle.

Mitchell, Robert; Second Secretary FCO since September 1983; born 20.10.43; GPO 1967; FCO 1969; Islamabad 1972; Milan 1975; FCO 1978; Second Secretary (Admin) Kabul 1981; m 1981 Janet Frances Booth.

Mitchell, Wendy Agnes; BMG Berlin since March 1988; born 13.7.66; FCO 1985; Grade S2A.

Mitchiner, John Edward; Second Secretary (Political) Berne since January 1991; born 12.9.51; FCO 1980; Third later Second Secretary Istanbul 1982; Second Secretary FCO 1985; Second Secretary (Dev) New Delhi 1987; m

1983; Elizabeth Mary Ford.

Mitchison, Pamela Denise; First Secretary (Chancery) Washington since December 1991; born 28.12.58; FCO 1978; Far East Floater 1981; Moscow 1982; Paris 1985; Second Secretary FCO 1988.

Moakes, Nicholas David; Deputy Political Adviser Hong Kong since September 1988; (Second Secretary 1989); born 11.4.64; FCO 1985; m 1987 Elizabeth Fay Nuttall (1s 1989; 2ds 1990, 1992).

Moberly, Nicholas Hamilton; Third Secretary UKREP Brussels since August 1989; born 11.5.63; FCO 1987; Dublin 1988; FCO 1988; Grade 8; m 1991 Margaret Fiona Clare Callan.

Mochan, Charles Francis; FCO since September 1991; born 6.8.48; MOD (Navy) 1966; FCO 1967; Port Elizabeth 1970; Kingston 1972; FCO 1974; Second Secretary 1975; Seoul 1977; FCO 1980; Second later First Secretary (Comm) Helsinki 1981; First Secretary FCO 1984; DHC and Head of Chancery Port Louis 1988; m 1970 Ilse Sybilla Carleon Cruttwell (1d 1971; 1s 1974).

Monckton, Anthony Leopold Colyer; First Secretary FCO since December 1992; born 25.9.60; HM Forces 1979-87; Second Secretary FCO 1987; Second later First Secretary UKDEL Geneva 1990; m 1985 Philippa Susan Wingfield (1s 1988, 1d 1989).

Money, Brian Walter; First Secretary (Dev/ Comm) Kathmandu since April 1991; born 4.1.41; Board of Trade 1960; DSAO (later FCO) 1967; Bonn 1970; Second Secretary BMG Berlin 1971; Kingston 1974; FCO 1978; Second Secretary (Cons/Admin) Dublin 1981; First Secretary (Comm) Jakarta 1984; on loan to MOD 1988; m (1) 1969 Margaret Askew (1s 1971); (2) 1984 Audrey Josephine Pakenham (1d 1985).

Montgomery, Alan Everard; HM Ambassador Manila since July 1992; born 11.3.38; First Secretary FCO 1972; Dacca 1974; Ottawa 1977; FCO 1980; Counsellor (GATT) UKMIS Geneva 1983; Head of Chancery Jakarta 1987; Counsellor FCO 1989; m 1960 Janet Barton (1s 1971; 1d 1976).

Montgomery, Robert Thomas; First Secretary Moscow since September 1990; born 27.6.34; GPO 1951; FO 1963; Vienna 1963; Lagos 1966; FO 1967; Belgrade 1968; FCO 1970; Nairobi 1973; FCO 1975; Canberra 1983; Second later First Secretary FCO 1986; m 1957 Alma Georgina Magee (1s 1969; 2d 1958, 1960).

Moodey, Jeremy Michael; First Secretary FCO since April 1991; born 27.1.62; FCO 1983; Third later Second Secretary Islamabad 1985; Second

Secretary (Chancery) Rome 1988; m 1987 Sally Clare Marsh (1d 1988; 1s 1990).

Moody, John Edward, MBE (1976); FCO since September 1983; born 25.1.37; GPO 1953; HM Forces 1955-57; GPO 1957; FO 1960; Singapore 1962; Bangkok 1963; FO 1964; Belgrade 1965; FO (later FCO) 1966; Bucharest 1970; Beirut 1972; FCO 1976; on loan to MOD 1980; Grade 7; m 1961 Jean Mary Wilson (3s 1962, 1963, 1965).

Moody, Patrick Thomas Robert; Third later Second Secretary (Chancery/Info) Mexico City since November 1990; born 17.3.66; FCO 1988.

Moon, Dorian Laurence; Moscow since March 1992; born 2.1.59; HCS 1985; BEMRS Cyprus 1986; HCS 1989; FCO 1990; Grade 10; m 1989 Joanne Ashley (1d 1989; 1s 1991).

Moon, Michael Yelland; FCO since September 1990; born 19.8.59; FCO 1977; UKREP Brussels 1979; Khartoum 1982; Africa/Middle East Floater 1986; Grade 9.

Moon, Rhoda Jacqueline; FCO since September 1984; born 5.2.66; Grade 10.

Moon, Richard John; First Secretary FCO since July 1988; born 3.1.59; FCO 1983; Second Secretary Jakarta 1985; m 1987 Sandra Sheila Francis Eddis (1s 1990).

Moon, Sandra Sheila Francis (née Eddis), MVO (1984); FCO since August 1988; born 11.3.56; FCO 1980; Washington 1982; Jakarta 1984; Grade 7; m 1987 Richard John Moon (1s 1990).

Mooncie, Alan Rasheed; Second Secretary FCO since October 1988; born 27.10.49; FCO 1969; Ankara 1972; Luxembourg 1974; Belgrade 1977; FCO 1979; Stockholm 1982; Second Secretary FCO 1984; Second Secretary (Econ/Comm) Oslo 1986; m 1969 Linda Payne (3s 1969, 1970, 1977).

Mooney, Julie Anne; UKDEL Brussels since July 1991; born 21.4.71; FCO 1990; Grade S2A.

Mooney, Peter West; FCO since April 1990; born 31.10.39; HM Forces 1958-63; GPO 1963; FO (later FCO) 1964; Singapore 1966; FCO 1968; Addis Ababa 1969; FCO 1971; Darwin 1973; FCO 1979; Darwin 1987; Grade 9; m 1964 Helen Kay Alcock (1s 1965; 1d 1969).

Moonlight, Julie Anne (née Thorpe); FCO since September 1992; born 12.8.68; FCO 1986; Paris 1989; Grade S2; m 1991 Philip Lindsay Moonlight.

Moore, Alison Jean, FCO since September 1991; born 24.2.68; Grade S2.

Moore, Charles Jonathan Rupert; FCO since

December 1991; born 14.4.63; FCO 1982; Harare 1984; Masirah 1987; Gaborone 1987; Grade 9; m 1988 Deborah Mary Ford (1s 1989; 1d 1992).

Moore, David; FCO since September 1992; born 18.6.59; HO 1977; FCO 1978; Moscow 1980; Wellington 1982; FCO 1986; Vice-Consul Osaka 1990; Grade 9; m 1981 Annette May Gardner (1d 1982; 1s 1985).

Moore, Deborah Mary (née Ford); FCO since December 1991; born 15.4.63; FCO 1982; Muscat 1985; SUPL 1988; Grade 10; m 1988 Charles Jonathan Rupert Moore (1s 1989; 1d 1992).

Moore, Fiona Charlotte; First Secretary (Chancery) Athens since July 1991; born 15.8.59; FCO 1981; Third later Second Secretary Warsaw 1983; Second later First Secretary FCO 1987.

Moore, Geraldine Fiona; FCO since July 1976; born 6.6.54; Grade 9.

Moore, Gillian Elizabeth; Wellington since April 1991; born 1.7.59; FCO 1980; Maseru 1984; UKMIS New York 1988; Grade S2; m 1982 Patrick Richard Moore.

Moore, Ian Anthony; Stockholm since August 1991; born 15.10.32; Inland Revenue 1949-54; RAF 1951-54; Devon and Cornwall Constabulary 1954; Warsaw 1979; Bangkok 1980; Belgrade 1982; Peking 1984; UKREP Brussels 1985; Havana 1988; Baghdad 1989; Grade SO; m 1969 Diane Mons Charles (2d 1973, 1975).

Moore, Karen; FCO since September 1992; born 15.7.64; FCO 1987; Peking 1990; Grade S2.

Moore, Richard Peter; First Secretary FCO since October 1992; born 9.5.63; Second Secretary FCO 1987; Second Secretary Ankara 1990; Consul (Inf) Istanbul 1991; m 1985 Margaret Martin (1s 1989, 2d 1991, 1992).

Moore, Trevor Charles; FCO since September 1989; (First Secretary 1992); born 19.1.58; FCO 1980; Belgrade 1982; Vice-Consul New York 1986; Second Secretary Washington 1987; m 1991 Diane Elizabeth Burns.

Moores, Amias Steven; FCO since March 1990; born 31.3.71; Grade 10.

Moorhead, Michelle Anne; Washington since November 1991; born 2.2.70; FCO 1988; Grade S2; m 1990 Ian William Moorhead.

Moorhouse, Derek, OBE (1992); First Secretary (Admin) Canberra since December 1988; born 21.11.32; CRO 1951; RAF 1951-53; CRO 1953; Delhi 1956; CRO 1958; Accra 1959; CRO 1961; Delhi 1963; Ankara (CENTO) 1965; Brussels 1967; FCO 1970; Second Secretary (Admin) Beirut 1974; Second Secretary (Admin) and Vice-Consul Doha 1976; Vice-Consul (Comm)

Toronto 1979; First Secretary FCO 1982; m 1960 Cynthia Agnes Mackertich (1d 1962; 1s 1967).

Moran, Karen (née Pinkney); Seoul since November 1989; born 2.3.65; National Savings Dept 1984; FCO 1984; Washington 1986; Grade 10; m 1986 Sean Moran.

Moran, Sean; Seoul since November 1989; born 6.3.64; Inland Revenue 1984; FCO 1984; Washington 1987; Grade 10; m 1986 Karen Pinkney.

Moran, Terence, RVM (1991); Harare since March 1990; born 20.5.41; Sofia 1985; Helsinki 1987; Grade SO; m 1962 Lesley Williams (1s 1963; 1d 1967).

Morey, Anthony Bernard Nicholas; HM Ambassador Ulaanbaattar since May 1991; born 6.12.36; FO 1955; HM Forces 1955-57; FO 1957; Kuwait 1960; Vice-Consul 1961; FO 1962; Madras 1965; Second Secretary FO 1966; Tehran 1967; Second Secretary (Comm) Kabul 1968; FCO 1971; Second later First Secretary (Comm) Washington 1972; Consul (Comm) Zagreb 1976; First Secretary (Admin) Lagos 1980; Seconded to Guinness Mahon 1983; Counsellor (Admin) and Consul-General Moscow 1985; Deputy High Commissioner Madras 1989; m 1961 Agnes Campbell Kerr (1d 1962; 2s 1965, 1970).

Morgan, Angela Merril; Warsaw since April 1991; born 14.3.68; FCO 1989; Grade 10.

Morgan, Deborah Edith; FCO since July 1985; born 31.5.64; Grade S3C.

Morgan, Glyndwr Hugh Warren; First Secretary and Deputy High Commissioner Belmopan since June 1991; born 23.7.42; Supreme Court of Judicature 1959; DSAO 1964; Peking 1967; Luxembourg 1968; Jakarta 1971; Budapest 1974; FCO 1976; Frankfurt 1979; Sana'a 1982; Second Secretary FCO 1985; Second Secretary (Admin) and Consul Addis Ababa 1988; m 1964 Pamela Helen Foster (1s 1965).

Morgan, Lemuel Charles; Bangkok since February 1992; born 26.11.43; FO (later FCO) 1967; St Helena 1968; FCO 1969; Singapore 1970; FCO 1971; Tripoli 1971; FCO 1973; Jakarta 1974; FCO 1976; Lagos 1978; FCO 1982; Gaborone 1982; FCO 1986; Third Secretary (Chancery/Inf) Kampala 1988; Grade 9; m 1991 Patricia Anita Ball.

Morgan, Mark Scott Thomas; Second Secretary FCO since July 1990; born 26.4.58; FCO 1976; Geneva 1984; FCO 1986; Second Secretary and Vice-Consul Aden 1988.

Morgan, Patrick; HM Ambassador Tegucigalpa since January 1992; born 31.1.44; Board of Trade 1963; CRO 1964; FO 1965; Bonn 1967;

Kuwait 1969; on loan to DTI 1972; La Paz 1972; FCO 1975; Second Secretary Washington 1979; First Secretary (Chancery/ Econ) Jakarta 1983; First Secretary FCO 1987; m 1966 Marlene Collins Beaton (2s 1967, 1968; 2d 1973, 1982).

Morgan, Richard de Riemer; First Secretary FCO since January 1991; born 9.5.61; FCO 1984; Language Training Tokyo 1986; Second Secretary (Comm) Tokyo 1987; m 1987 Susan Carolyn McGaw.

Morgan, Richard Edwin; FCO since February 1990; born 9.7.43; CRO 1961; Dar es Salaam 1963; Bahrain (Residency) 1967; FCO 1969; Islamabad 1971; FCO 1974; Pretoria 1977; Algiers 1980; Second Secretary FCO 1983; Second Secretary (Comm) Bridgetown 1986; m 1970 Carole Ann Price (3d 1972, 1975, 1981; 2s 1983, 1992).

Morgan, Steven Leonard; Guatemala City since November 1990; born 14.1.65; Department of Employment 1983; FCO 1984; Budapest 1986; FCO 1987; Paris 1988; Grade 10.

Morgan, Stuart John; FCO since December 1990; born 2.12.63; FCO 1983; Khartoum 1988; Grade 10.

Morham, James Smith; BM Berlin since January 1990; born 18.6.35; Army 1953-1978; Islamabad 1985; Bucharest 1986; Grade SO; m 1954 Irene Dawson.

Morland, Martin Robert, CMG (1985); UK Permanent Representative (with personal rank of Ambassador) to the Office of the United Nations Geneva since July 1990; born 23.9.33; HM Forces 1954-56; FO 1956; Third later Second Secretary Rangoon 1957; FO 1961; Common Market Delegation Brussels 1962; FO 1963; First Secretary 1964; UKDEL to the Conference of the 18 Nation Committee on Disarmament Geneva 1965; Private Secretary to Minister of State FO 1967 and First Secretary FO (later FCO) 1968; Deputy Head of European Integration Department 1973; Counsellor (Econ) Rome 1973; Head of Maritime, Aviation and Environment Dept FCO 1977; Head of Chancery Washington 1979; Counsellor (Rayner Scrutiny) 1982; Seconded to Hardcastle & Co Ltd 1982; on loan to the Cabinet Office as an Under-Secretary 1984; HM Ambassador Rangoon 1986; m 1964 Jennifer Hanbury-Tracy (2s 1965, 1967; 1d 1966).

Morley, David John; Second Secretary (Management) Moscow since April 1991; born 23.10.54; MAFF 1972; FCO 1973; UKMIS Geneva 1975; Port Stanley 1978; Kuala Lumpur 1980; FCO 1981; Kaduna 1984; FCO 1988; m 1978 Jacqueline Ann Wells.

Morley, Jacqueline Ann (née Wells), MBE (1991); Moscow since April 1991; born 20.7.55; FCO

1973; UKMIS New York 1974; UKMIS Geneva 1975; Port Stanley 1978; SUPL 1980; Kuala Lumpur 1981; FCO 1981; SUPL Kaduna 1984; FCO 1988; Grade S1; m 1978 David John Morley.

Morley, Michael Donald; Second Secretary (Commercial) Santiago since December 1991; born 18.2.53; FCO 1973; Moscow 1975; Kuala Lumpur 1977; Latin America Floater 1981; Beirut 1983; FCO 1984; La Paz 1987 (Second Secretary 1990); m 1983 Carmen Gloria Del Prado (2s 1987, 1989).

Morley, Stuart Richard; First Secretary (Chancery) Bridgetown since November 1990; born 26.1.59; Second Secretary FCO 1988; Second later First Secretary (Chancery/ Information) San Jose 1989; m 1987 Janet Henry.

Morphet, Sarah Francis; FO (later FCO) since November 1966; born 8.7.40; COI 1963; Principal Research Officer; Senior Principal Research Officer in 1990; m 1965 Richard Edward Morphet (2d 1967, 1969).

Morrell, Susan Mary; FCO since January 1992; born 7.11.50; FCO 1977; UKMIS New York 1978; Budapest 1981, Khartoum 1982. Islamabad 1985; Moscow 1988; Grade S1.

Morrice, Philip; On Secondment to the Anglo Taiwan Trade Committee as Director since May 1992; born 31.12.43; Scottish Office 1960; CRO 1963; Kuala Lumpur 1964; Third Secretary Commonwealth Office (later FCO) 1968; Third later Second Secretary Caracas 1969; First Secretary UKDEL OECD Paris 1973; First Secretary (Energy) UKREP Brussels 1975; FCO 1978; First Secretary (Comm) later Counsellor Rome 1981; Counsellor (Econ/Comm) Lagos 1986; Minister/Counsellor and Consul-General and Director of Trade Promotion Brasilia 1988; m (1) 1975 Gillian Jane Mather; (2) 1989 Margaret Clare Bower (1d 1988; 1s 1989).

Morris, Andrew James; Deputy High Commissioner Port Moresby since October 1989; born 22.3.39; Army 1960-64; FO 1964; Kuwait 1965; Salisbury 1969; Sofia 1969; FCO 1971; Muscat 1973; San Francisco 1976; Consul Los Angeles 1978; Second Secretary FCO 1982; First Secretary Kaduna 1986; m 1961 Ann Christine Healy (2s 1964, 1971).

Morris, David Derek; FCO since July 1991; born 18.6.39; FCO 1969; St Helena 1970; FCO 1972; Accra 1973; FCO 1975; Bangkok 1977; FCO 1981; BGWRS Darwin 1982; FCO 1984; Warsaw 1986; FCO 1987; Dar es Salaam 1988; FCO 1988; Abu Dhabi 1989; Grade 8; m 1969 Jean Margaret Dixon (4d 1970, 1971, 1973, 1976).

Morris, John Charles; First Secretary FCO since

September 1989; born 2.10.51; FCO 1984; Second later First Secretary (Chancery) Brasilia 1986; m 1982 Mary Teresa Graham (1d 1983).

Morris, Keith Elliot Hedley, CMG (1988); HM Ambassador Bogota since September 1990; born 24.10.34; FO 1959; Dakar 1960; Second Secretary (Inf) Algiers 1962; FO 1963; Second Secretary Paris 1964; First Secretary Bogota 1967; (Head of Chancery 1969); First Secretary FCO 1971; Counsellor (Comm) Warsaw 1976; Minister/Counsellor Mexico City 1979; Counsellor, Head of Personnel Policy Department FCO 1984; CDA RCDS 1986; Director-General for British Trade Development in Italy, and Consul-General Milan 1987; m Maria del Carmen Carratala (2s 1963, 1970; 2d 1966, 1972).

Morris, Norman James; First Secretary FCO since April 1992; born 12.5.38; FO and Brussels 1959; Berlin 1962; Hanoi 1966; Frankfurt 1967; FCO 1968; Africa Floater 1970; Kampala 1971; Nassau 1973; Second Secretary FCO 1976; Second later First Secretary (Admin) Vienna 1985; First Secretary and Consul Brussels 1990; m 1973 Rotraud Ingrid Teinzer (dec'd 1991).

Morris, Richard Charles; FCO since November 1990; born 1.11.67; Grade 9.

Morris, Richard Peter; FCO since October 1991; born 8.9.64; FCO 1983; Bucharest 1988; Grade 9; m 1990 Diane Jacqueline Harvey.

Morris, Rose Marie June Townson; (née Bennett); FCO since May 1979; born 21.11.45; FCO 1970; Singapore 1971; Beirut 1973; FCO 1976; Lagos 1977; Grade S1; m 1980 Jeremy Robin David Morris.

Morris, Sara Joanne; FCO since April 1991; born 19.10.62; FCO 1983; Mexico City 1987; Grade S2.

Morris, Timothy Colin; First Secretary (Political)Madrid since September 1991; born 12.9.58; FCO 1981; SOAS 1982; Language Student Tokyo 1983; Second Secretary (Comm) Tokyo 1984; First Secretary FCO 1987; on loan to DTI 1990.

Morris, Warwick; First Secretary FCO since November 1991; born 10.8.48; FCO 1969; Paris 1972; Language Student Seoul 1975 (Second Secretary 1977); FCO 1979 (PS to Deputy PUS 1979-80) First Secretary 1982; First Secretary (Comm) Mexico City 1984; First Secretary and Head of Chancery Seoul 1988; m 1972 Pamela Jean Mitchell (1s 1976; 2d 1978, 1982).

Morrish, Diane Elizabeth (neé Sproule); FCO since April 1988; born 19.12.56; Grade S2; m 1989 John Richard Morrish.

Morrish, Geoffrey, BEM (1988); UKDEL NATO

Brussels since June 1992; born 15.7.39; HM Forces 1960-88; Moscow 1988; Ankara 1989; Grade SO; m 1970 Pamela Roberts (2s 1962, 1964).

Morrison, Alan; Islamabad since March 1992; born 4.1.70; FCO 1989; Grade 10.

Morrison (née Hutchison), Anne; Second Secretary later First Secretary FCO since March 1980; born 30.9.35; CRO 1960; Nicosia 1960; CRO 1964; DSAO 1965; Nairobi 1968; FCO 1971; Moscow 1972; FCO 1973; Lagos 1974; New York 1975; Paris 1977; m 1984 Alastair George Angus Morrison.

Morrison, Fiona-Margaret; Third Secretary (Chancery) UKDEL Brussels since September 1991; born 23.1.67; FCO 1989; Grade 9.

Morrison, Ian Kenneth; Vice-Consul (Pol/Inf) Cape Town since January 1991; born 27.12.54; Inland Revenue 1974; FCO 1977; Budapest 1979; Islamabad 1981; Madrid 1983; FCO 1986; Third Secretary Accra 1988; Grade 7; m 1978 Gillian Winifred Turk (1d 1982).

Morrison, James Thorburn; Consul (Investment) Los Angeles since March 1990; born 2.4.35; CRO 1953-58; HM Forces 1954-56; Calcutta 1958; CRO 1960; Accra 1962; Benghazi 1965; Miami 1969; Second Secretary 1969; Toronto 1970; on loan to DOT 1974; Trade Commissioner (First Secretary) Hong Kong 1977; FCO 1982; Consul (Inward Investment), New York since February 1986; m 1960 Patricia Anne (1d 1965).

Morrison, Jonathan James Howard; FCO since August 1991; born 31.12.67; Home Office 1989-91; Grade 9.

Morrissey, Gillian Lesley (née Worrall); FCO since February 1990; born 2.2.60; FCO 1979; Helsinki 1981; Doha 1984; Bonn 1988; Grade 9; m 1984 Patrick John Morrissey.

Mortimer, Hugh Roger; First Secretary (Chancery) Berlin since February 1991; born 19.9.49; FCO 1973; Rome 1975; Singapore 1978; FCO 1981; Second later First Secretary UKMIS New York 1983; First Secretary FCO 1987; on attachment to the Auswärtiges Amt 1990; m 1974 Zosia Cecylia Rzepecka (2d 1976, 1980).

Morton, David Stanley Thomas; Second Secretary (Commercial) Nairobi since September 1991; born 6.12.45; FO 1963; Kinshasa 1967; Cairo 1967; Wellington 1969; UKREP Brussels 1972; FCO 1975; Beirut 1977; Washington 1979; Dacca 1982; Second Secretary FCO 1985; Second Secretary (Commercial) Baghdad 1990; m (1) 1972 Judith Anne Amies (diss 1983) (1s 1973); (2) 1987 Beverley Anne Sheppard (2s 1988, 1991).

Morton, Ralph Christopher; Second Secretary (Comms/Cons) Kampala since October 1992; born 13.12.55; FCO 1979; Khartoum 1982; UKDEL NATO Brussels 1984; Third later Second Secretary (Chancery) East Berlin 1987; Second Secretary FCO 1991.

Morton, Susan Elizabeth; First Secretary (Chancery) Peking since June 1992; born 25.2.62; FCO 1986; Senior Research Officer.

Moscrop, George; FCO since August 1985; born 21.5.32; HM Forces 1948-57; FO 1957; Singapore 1958; FO 1960; Baghdad1/Basra 1961; Delhi 1963; Francistown 1965; FO 1966; Istanbul 1967; Tripoli 1967; FCO 1969; Mogadishu 1972; FCO 1973; Islamabad 1975; FCO 1977; Tel Aviv 1978; FCO 1981; Accra 1981; Grade 8; m (1) 1954 Ivy Amelia Butler; (2) 1975 Margaret May Chatterton (1s 1968).

Moser, Andon Barbara; FCO since September 1991; Grade S2.

Moss, David Joseph, CMG (1989); High Commissioner Wellington since September 1990 and concurrently, Governor (non-resident) of the Pitcairn, Henderson, Ducie and Oeno Islands; Also High Commissioner (non-resident) Western Samoa; born 6.11.38; CSC 1956; FO 1957; RAF 1957-59; FO 1959; Third Secretary Bangkok 1962; (Second Secretary 1965); FO 1966; Assistant Private Secretary to Minister of State for Foreign Affairs 1967; FCO 1968; First Secretary (Comm) La Paz 1969; FCO 1970; First Secretary and Head of Chancery The Hague 1974; First Secretary later Counsellor FCO 1978; Deputy Head of Permanent Under-Secretary;s Department FCO 1979; Head of Permanent Under Secretary;s Department FCO 1981; Counsellor, Head of Chancery and Deputy Permanent Representative, UKMIS Geneva 1983; Additional AUSS, FCO 1987; AUSS (Deputy Chief Clerk) 1988; m 1961 Joan Lillian Tyler (1s 1970; 1d 1971).

Moss, Keith Cyril; First Secretary FCO since August 1991; born 11.6.46; FO 1965; Moscow 1968; Tokyo 1969; Budapest 1973; FCO 1974; Paris 1977; Vice-Consul Douala 1981; Second Secretary FCO 1983; Second later First Secretary (Chancery) UKMIS Vienna 1987; m 1969 Lynn Butler (2s 1971, 1975).

Moss, Kylie Joanne; FCO since July 1990; born 22.10.71; Grade 10.

Mott, Alan Lawrence; FCO since August 1991; born 5.10.65; FCO 1984; Washington 1989; Grade 8; m 1988 Tina Michaela.

Mountford, Claire; Berne since January 1992; born 19.10.68; FCO 1989; Grade S2.

Mowbray, Fiona (née Roberts); Ankara since September 1991; born 8.11.63; FCO 1983;

Washington 1984; Addis Ababa 1986; Nassau 1990; Grade S2; m 1986 Kevin Lewis Mowbray.

Mowbray, Kevin Lewis; Second Secretary (Chancery/Consular) Ankara since June 1991; born 5.4.59; FCO 1977; UKREP Brussels 1979; ME Floater Africa 1982; FCO 1984; Addis Ababa 1986; Nassau 1990; m 1986 Fiona Roberts.

Moyse, Jacqueline Arlette; FO (later FCO) since November 1959; born 25.5.35; FO 1951; Tripoli 1958; Grade 9.

Muat, David Andrew; Second Secretary FCO since January 1988; born 8.5.42; Post Office 1960; FO 1962; Jakarta 1964; Manila 1964; Buenos Aires 1967; FCO 1970; UKREP Brussels 1974; Paris 1977; FCO 1980 (Second Secretary 1982); Second Secretary (Admin) and Consul East Berlin 1984; m 1988 Susan Jean Grear (1s 1991).

Mugridge, Helen; FCO since March 1987; born 12.10.68; Grade 10.

Muir, Richard John Sutherland; AUSS (Principal Finance Officer and Chief Inspector) since July 1991; born 25.8.42; FO 1964; MECAS 1965; Second Secretary (Comm) Jedda 1967; Second Secretary (Comm) Tunis 1970; FCO 1973; First Secretary Washington 1975; First Secretary, later Counsellor, Riyadh 1981; Counsellor FCO 1985; m 1966 Caroline Simpson (1d 1970, 1s 1972).

Mulcahy, Colin Paul Peter; First Secretary (Admin) Khartoum since January 1989; born 21.6.44; CRO 1963; Freetown 1966; DSAO (later FCO) 1968; Bombay 1972; Second Secretary (Chancery) Wellington 1976; Second Secretary FCO 1981; Vice-Consul (Comm) Toronto 1985; m 1969 Josephine Ann Molly Smyth.

Muldoon, Julie Aileen; Accra since May 1986; born 4.5.61; FCO 1984; Grade S2.

Mullee, Patrick; Second Secretary (Chancery/ Information) Bridgetown since July 1991; born 8.10.54; FCO 1974; Prague 1976; Caracas 1977; Africa Floater 1980; Latin America Floater 1983; FCO 1985; Third later Second Secretary San José 1988; m 1987 Joanna Louise Johnson (1d 1989).

Mulvaney, Isabella Maria; Karachi since March 1991; born 18.3.68; FCO 1986; UKDEL Brussels 1988; Grade 10.

Munro, Sir Alan (Gordon), KCMG (1990); CMG (1984); HM Ambassador Riyadh since August 1989; born 17.8.35; Army 1953-55; MECAS 1958; FO 1960; Third Secretary (Inf) Beirut 1960; Kuwait 1961; Third later Second Secretary Beirut 1961; FO 1963; First Secretary and Head of Chancery Benghazi 1965 and Tripoli 1966;

First Secretary DSAO (later FCO) 1968; Consul (Comm) Rio de Janeiro 1973; Consul-General Rio de Janeiro 1974; Head of East Africa Dept FCO 1977; Head of Middle East Dept FCO 1979; Head of Personnel Operations Dept FCO 1979; On loan to MOD 1981; HM Ambassador Algiers 1984; DUSS (ME/Africa) FCO 1987; m 1962 Grania Bacon (2d 1963, 1965; twin s 1970).

Munro, Catriona Mairi; Brussels since August 1991; born 6.3.65; FCO 1988; Grade S2.

Munro, Colin Andrew; HM Consul-General Frankfurt since April 1990; born 24.10.46; Inland Revenue 1968; Third Secretary FCO 1969; Bonn 1971; Second later First Secretary Kuala Lumpur 1973; FCO 1977; Private Secretary to Minister of State 1979; First Secretary and Head of Chancery Bucharest 1981; First Secretary FCO 1983; Counsellor East Berlin 1987; m 1967 Ehrengard Maria Heinrich (2s 1967, 1978).

Munro, Donald Alexander; Second Secretary Warsaw since May 1990; born 2.8.38; GPO 1954; HM Forces 1957-59; GPO 1959; FO 1960; Colombo 1967; Singapore 1968; FCO 1970; Bucharest 1971; BMG Berlin 1973; FCO 1977; Second Secretary Lagos 1984; Second Secretary FCO 1989; m Marit Saether (1s 1967; 1d 1972).

Muras, Keith Watson; First Secretary FCO since September 1991; born 16.11.45; First Secretary FCO 1976; Consul (Econ) Johannesburg 1977; FCO 1980; First Secretary Moscow 1982; on loan to HCS 1984; First Secretary FCO 1986; First Secretary (Chancery) Kingston 1988; m 1968 Joan Sheila Perkins (1s 1973).

Murphy, Clare Elizabeth; Peking since January 1991; born 5.5.67; FCO 1987; Madrid 1988; Grade 9.

Murphy, Ralph; First Secretary FCO since April 1985; born 27.3.43; Third Secretary FO 1965; Buenos Aires 1968; Second Secretary (Comm) Havana 1970; First Secretary FCO 1973; First Secretary Washington 1974; FCO 1978; First Secretary (Energy) Mexico City 1981; m 1969 Gay Norwood (1s 1970; 1d 1972).

Murphy, Sandra; Second Secretary (Commercial) Addis Ababa since March 1991; born 9.4.50; FCO 1968; UKREP Brussels 1972; Resigned 1975; Reinstated 1978; FCO 1978; Harare 1981; Second Secretary FCO 1984; Second Secretary (Aid) Kingston 1987.

Murphy, Shaun Henderson; FCO since October 1986; born 24.4.62; FCO 1981; BGWRS Darwin 1984; Grade 8.

Murphy, William John, MBE (1991); Nicosia since January 1992; born 14.4.38; Royal Navy 1953-78; Budapest 1984; Montevideo 1986; Amman 1989; Grade SO; m 1977 Jennifer Milne

Gauldie (1s 1978).

Murray, Andrew Robin; Counsellor FCO since February 1991; born 21.9.41; First Secretary FCO 1973; First Secretary Islamabad 1975; Head of Chancery Buenos Aires 1979; FCO 1982; Counsellor UKMIS New York 1984; Counsellor and Head of Chancery Caracas 1988; m 1965 Irene Dorothy Foy (1d 1967; 1s 1970).

Murray, Ann Marie Catherine; UKMIS New York since January 1992; born 20.6.66; FCO 1990; Grade S2.

Murray, Clare Philomena, MBE (1985); FCO since June 1985; born 21.7.33; Bahrain 1955; FO 1957; Belgrade 1958; FO 1959; Oslo 1960; FO (later FCO) 1962; Moscow 1972; FCO 1973; Ottawa 1974; FCO 1976; Washington 1982; Grade 9.

Murray, Craig John; First Secretary FCO 1990; born 17.10.58; FCO 1984; Second Secretary (Comm) Lagos 1986; m 1984 Fiona Anne.

Murray, Fiona Mary; Munich since June 1992; born 23.2.66; FCO 1988; Moscow 1989; Grade 9.

Murray, Gillian; Paris since February 1992; born 18.9.69; FCO 1990; Grade S2.

Murray, Iain Richard, OBE (1991); First Secretary FCO since February 1992; born 13.8.44; CRO 1963; Sabbatical leave at University 1965; Commonwealth Office (later FCO) 1968; Accra 1970; Second Secretary Addis Ababa 1972; Vice-Consul (Comm) Rio de Janeiro 1975; Consul Oporto 1979; First Secretary on loan to No 10 Downing Street 1983; Chargé d'Affaires San Salvador 1987; m (1) 1967 Victoria Crew Gee (1d 1969; 1s 1971); (2) 1984 Judith Ann Wilson.

Murray, June; Johannesburg since January 1990; born 9.6.50; FCO 1986; Tegucigalpa 1988; Grade S2.

Murray, Michael Thomas; First Secretary FCO since January 1987; born 13.10.45; FO DSAO 1964; Prague 1967; Vienna 1971; Vice-Consul (Comm) Frankfurt 1973; Second Secretary (Dev) Khartoum 1977; FCO 1980; First Secretary and Head of Chancery Banjul 1983; m 1968 Else Birgitta Margareta Paues (1s 1974; 1d 1981).

Murray, Rosemary Elizabeth; FCO since February 1986; born 24.12.51; FCO 1974; Havana 1975; FCO 1977; Aden 1978; Bangkok 1979; FCO 1981; Mexico City 1984; Grade 9.

Murray, Winston Anthony; Bonn since April 1991; born 4.7.64; OFT 1985; FCO 1985; Grade 10; m 1990 Judith Muponda.

Murrell, Geoffrey David George, OBE (1987);

Minister/Counsellor (Internal) Moscow since April 1991; born 19.12.34; FO 1959; Third Secretary Moscow 1961; FO 1964; Second Secretary Moscow 1968; FCO 1970; PRO 1970; First Secretary (Inf) Belgrade 1975; SPRO 1980; Regional Director Research Department 1978; Counsellor Moscow 1983; FCO 1987; m 1962 Kathleen Ruth Berton (3d 1964, 1970, 1978; 1s 1967).

Musgrave, David William; First Secretary FCO since March 1989; born 12.5.53; FCO 1983; Second later First Secretary Copenhagen 1985; m 1978 Madeleine Nnomo Assembe (2d 1979, 1991; 1s 1981).

Mycroft, Sally Margrit; Prague since May 1992; born 2.6.65; FCO 1989; Grade S2.

Myers, Sharon Theresa; Moscow since September 1988; born 19.4.65; FCO 1987; Grade S2.

N

Nalden, Philip Nigel; Lagos since October 1989; born 30.3.45; Army 1963-68; Moscow 1988; Grade SO3; m 1982 Heather McIntosh (1s 1967).

Napthen, Florence Wilson; FCO since June 1991; born 25.10.61; Crown Office, Edinburgh 1978; FCO 1986; Wellington 1988; Grade S2; m 1990 Stephen Kenneth Napthen.

Nash, Ronald Peter, LVO (1984), MVO (1983); Deputy High Commissioner Colombo since June 1992; born 18.9.46; FCO 1970; Second later First Secretary Moscow 1974; First Secretary UKDEL Vienna 1976; FCO 1979; New Delhi 1983; First Secretary FCO 1986; Counsellor and Head of Chancery Vienna 1988; m 1976 Annie Olsen (3s 1979, 1981, 1983).

Nash, Stephen Thomas, First Secretary FCO since January 1992; born 22.3.42; British Council Baghdad 1965; FO 1967; Third Secretary Caracas 1968; Third later Second Secretary (Chancery) Bogotá 1970; Sabbatical at Oxford University 1972; FCO 1973; SEATO Bangkok 1975; FCO 1977; First Secretary and Deputy Head of Post Guatemala City 1979; Deputy High Commissioner Belmopan 1981; First Secretary FCO 1982; Chargé d'Affaires a.i. and First Secretary Managua 1986; On Secondment to British Aerospace 1989; m (1) 1967 Rose-Marie Bornstrand (diss 1973); (2) 1977 Boonying Permkasikam (1s 1971; 2d 1977, 1985).

Nason, Justin Patrick Pearse, OBE (1980); HM Ambassador Guatemala City since March 1991; born 29.3.37; HM Forces 1956-58; FO 1963; Third later Second Secretary Prague 1965; FO

(later FCO) 1967; First Secretary Pretoria1/Cape Town 1971; First Secretary and Head of Chancery Saigon 1974; FCO 1975; Deputy High Commissioner and Head of Chancery Kampala 1979; CDA at Canadian National Defence College 1981; DHC and Head of Chancery Colombo 1982; on secondment to Barclays Bank PLC 1986; Minister/Counsellor Mexico City 1988.

Naughton, Dawn Karen; UKDEL Brussels since September 1990; born 22.8.69; FCO 1988; Grade 10.

Naylor, David George; Frankfurt since January 1992; born 31.3.52; HM Forces 1967-79; FCO 1979; Kabul 1981; Jakarta 1984; FCO 1987; Grade 9; m 1982 Elizabeth Jean Cameron (1s 1987; 1d 1992).

Neale, Paul Gilroy; Dublin since July 1992; born 17.10.41; Royal Navy 1957-82; FCO 1986; 1989 transferred to Security Officer Branch; Nairobi 1989; Grade SO; m 1963 Mary McKenzie (2s 1964, 1966).

Neave, Pamela; Lagos since August 1988; born 3.6.65; FCO 1985; Grade 9.

Neblett, Sharon Annette Therese; Accra since July 1988; FCO 1986; born 16.11.60; DTI 1978; Grade S2A.

Neil, William John; UKDEL NATO Brussels since January 1990; born 23.5.67; FCO 1988; Grade 10.

Neill, Kenneth Andrew; First Secretary (Comm/ Cons) Lusaka since September 1992; born 6.11.44; FO 1961; Tripoli 1967; Moscow 1970; Vientiane 1970; FCO 1974; Hanoi 1977; Karachi 1979; Second Secretary (Chancery/Inf) Lilongwe 1982; Second later First Secretary Honiara 1988; m 1977 Julie C Brown (1s 1981).

Neilson, James George Lovie; Budapest since March 1992; born 27.7.44; Army 1965-88; Geneva 1988; Moscow 1991; Grade SO; m 1967 Lorraine (1d 1968; 1s 1971).

Neilson, Kim; FCO since June 1991; born 30.9.71; Grade 10.

Neilson, Richard Alvin, CMG (1987), LVO (1968); HM Ambassador Santiago since August 1990; born 9.7.37; FO 1961; Third later Second Secretary Leopoldville 1963; FO 1966; Second later First Secretary (Inf) Santiago 1966; Canberra 1969; FCO 1973; Counsellor on loan to HCS 1977; DHC and Counsellor Lusaka 1979; Deputy Governor and Political Adviser Gibraltar 1981; Counsellor FCO 1984; HM Ambassador Bogotá 1987; m 1961 Olive Tyler (1s 1963).

Nellthorp, Helen Rosemary; Second Secretary (Commercial) Prague since May 1991; born

10.5.62; FCO 1980; Athens 1984; Floater Duties 1987; Third Secretary (Comm) Washington 1989.

Nelson, David George; Second Secretary FCO since April 1988; born 24.7.40; Inland Revenue 1959; DSAO 1967; FCO 1968; Moscow 1970; Bonn 1972; Islamabad 1974; FCO 1978; on loan to DOT (Second Secretary) 1980; Consul (Comm) Boston 1982; on loan to the Office of Fair Trading 1986; m 1968 Juliette Theresa Brogan (1s 1973; 1d 1977).

Nelson, Diana June (née Gordon); FCO since April 1992; born 17.6.58; FCO 1981; Paris 1984; Algiers 1987; Second Secretary FCO 1989; SUPL 1991; m 1985 Miles Christopher Nelson (1d 1991).

Nelson, Emma Sutherland; FCO since June 1990; born 20.3.70; Grade 10.

Nelson, Kay Alison (née Starling); SUPL since November 1988; born 24.3.55; FCO 1974; Moscow 1978; Paris 1980; loan to Office of Fair Trading 1982; Second Secretary and Vice-Consul Abidjan 1984; FCO 1987; m 1988 Dr Niall Charles William Nelson.

Nelson, Philip Raymond; First Secretary Budapest since January 1991; born 7.4.50; FCO 1972; Third later Second Secretary (Comm) Budapest 1974; Second later First Secretary Paris 1976; FCO 1979; Rome 1980; First Secretary FCO 1983; First Secretary (Chancery) Manila 1989; m (1) 1971 Cynthia Elson (diss 1978); (2) 1992 Lyndsay Ann Halper.

Nessling, Paul William Downs; First Secretary (Comm) Harare since August 1989; born 26.9.45; Bahrain 1975 (From DOI); Second Secretary FCO 1979; Lisbon 1981; Warsaw 1982; First Secretary (Aid) Nairobi 1984; FCO 1987; m 1975 Kathryn Freeman.

Nethersole, Jonathan Sebastian; Pretoria since September 1990; born 7.11.69; FCO 1988; Grade 10.

Nettleton, Catherine Elizabeth; First Secretary (Political) Mexico City since September 1991; born 13.3.60; FCO 1983; Language Training 1984; Peking 1987; (Second Secretary 1988); Second Secretary FCO 1989.

Nevile, Major David Richard; Queen;s Messenger since 1985; born 9.9.36; Army 1956-1985.

Neville-Jones, (Lilian) Pauline, CMG (1987); On loan to the Cabinet Office since October 1991; born 2.11.39; FO 1963; Third Secretary Salisbury 1965; Third later Second Secretary Singapore 1966; Second later First Secretary FCO 1968; Washington 1971; FCO 1975; First Secretary and later Counsellor on SUPL as Deputy, subsequently Chef de Cabinet to

Christopher Tugendhat, Commissioner (subsequently Vice President) of the European Commission 1977; Sabbatical at Chatham House and IFRI, Paris 1982; Counsellor FCO 1983; Minister (Econ), later Minister, Bonn 1987.

Newall, Peter; First Secretary (Management) UKMIS Geneva since November 1990; born 20.3.47; DSAO (later FCO) 1966; Tehran 1970; Delhi 1972; FCO 1976; Second Secretary (Comm) Belgrade 1979; First Secretary (Comm) Kuwait 1982; FCO 1986; HM Consul Marseilles 1989; m 1969 Marina Joy McHugh (2d 1972, 1973; 1s 1976).

Newbury, Gillian; Budapest since June 1989; born 23.3.63; FCO 1987; Grade S2.

Newcomb, Francis; Second Secretary (Accountant) Washington since March 1991; born 1.6.38; CRO 1963; Benin City 1964; Singapore 1967; FCO 1971; Karachi 1974; FCO 1978; New Delhi 1982; FCO 1985; m 1967 Joan English.

Newell, Clive Dare; FCO since June 1990; born 22.12.53; FCO 1976; Third Secretary (Comm) later Second Secretary Tehran 1979; FCO 1980; Second later First Secretary Kabul 1982; First Secretary FCO 1984; First Secretary Addis Ababa 1986.

Newey, Cyril Alwin; Paris since November 1986; born 16.1.40; Delhi 1965; Calcutta 1966; Bonn 1966; Aden 1968; Budapest 1969; Calcutta 1971; Madrid 1973; UKDEL NATO Brussels 1975; Washington 1978; Salisbury 1980; Warsaw 1982; Cairo 1983; Madrid 1985; Grade SSO; m Constance Graham (2s 1966, 1967; 1d 1971).

Newlands, Andrew; Bonn since April 1990; born 10.2.68; DHSS 1984; FCO 1988; Grade 10; m 1989 Eileen Mitchell.

Newman, NG Deborah; Washington since October 1989; born 11.7.63; FCO 1985; Paris 1987; Grade S2; m 1991 Victor NG.

Newman, George William; FCO since March 1983; (Second Secretary 1991); born 16.6.54; FCO 1972; Munich 1976; FCO 1978; Moscow 1981; m 1975 Elaine Haron Turner (1s 1983; 1d 1987).

Newman, James Michael; Cairo since September 1992; born 31.3.70; Metropolitan Police 1989; FCO 1990; Grade 10.

Newman, Pauline Agnes; FCO since September 1978; born 7.4.48; FO 1966; Addis Ababa 1969; Sofia 1971; Islamabad 1972; FCO 1973; Tokyo 1975; Grade S1.

Newman, Peter James; First Secretary (Commercial) Nicosia since July 1992; born 29.5.46; FO 1963; Muscat 1968; Bahrain

Residency 1970; Tokyo 1971; FCO 1975; Dacca 1978; Second Secretary UKDEL MBFR Vienna 1980; Second Secretary (Econ) Oslo 1983; First Secretary FCO 1987; Deputy High Commissioner and Head of Chancery Gaborone 1989; m 1966 Kathryn Yvonne Alcock (1d 1969; 1s 1972).

Newns, Carl Edwin Francis; Second Secretary (Political) The Hague since February 1992; born 30.6.68; FCO 1989; Grade 8.

Newton, Alan Peter; Second Secretary FCO since December 1989; born 21.6.46; Inland Revenue 1963; DSAO 1965; Tel Aviv 1969; Accra 1969; San José 1973; Dacca 1976; FCO 1980; Montevideo 1983; Copenhagen 1987; m 1976 Mayra Rosa Antonia Camacho.

Newton, Alastair Dan Barr; First Secretary UKDEL Paris since April 1992; born 8.1.54; FCO 1985; Second Secretary later First Secretary Kinshasa 1986; First Secretary FCO 1989; m 1988 Vivienne Jane Ivanich (2d 1979, 1980).

Newton, Peter Marcus; Counsellor FCO and Commissioner (non-resident) British Antarctic Territory since May 1992; born 16.9.42; Third Secretary CRO later Commonwealth Office 1965; Kinshasa 1967; Third later Second Secretary Lima 1968; First Secretary FCO 1972; First Secretary (Econ) Tokyo 1975; First Secretary and Head of Chancery Caracas 1979; First Secretary later Counsellor FCO 1981; Consul-General Montreal since June 1987; Deputy High Commissioner Ottawa 1989; m 1972 S m Freire de Castilho (2s 1974, 1977; 1d 1976).

Nicholas, Barry Stuart; FCO since September 1991; born 1.11.62; FCO 1981; East Berlin 1984; Dubai 1986; Warsaw 1988; Grade 9; m 1989 Susan Jane Parker (1s 1992).

Nicholas, Susan Jane (née Parker); FCO since September 1991 (Second Secretary 1991); born 17.9.62; FCO 1981; Warsaw 1984; Bonn 1987; Düsseldorf 1988; Warsaw 1989; m 1989 Barry Stuart Nicholas (1s 1992).

Nicholls, Gary Patrick; Tokyo since February 1990; born 4.10.68; FCO 1988; Grade 10.

Nichols, John Roland; First Secretary FCO since February 1989; born 13.11.51; Third later Second Secretary FCO 1977; Second later First Secretary Budapest 1979; FCO 1982; First Secretary (Comm) Brasilia 1985; m 1983 Angela Suzanne Davies (1s 1987; 1d 1989).

Nichols, Mark Andrew; Washington since July 1989; born 5.2.65; FCO 1984; Grade 9; m 1989 Deborah Lisle.

Nichols, Martin Christopher; New Delhi since August 1991; born 4.5.62; FCO 1981; Tel Aviv 1984; FCO 1987; Darwin 1988; FCO 1990; Grade 9; m 1983 Julie Marie Wilkins (2s 1983,

1988; 1d 1992).

Nicholson, Martin Buchanan; Principal Research Officer on loan to the Cabinet Office since January 1987; born 12.8.37; FO 1964; Moscow 1965; FO (later FCO) 1968; Conference Interpreter (DS Grade 5) Research Officer 1969; First Secretary Moscow 1971; FCO 1971; First Secretary Prague 1972; First Secretary FCO 1975; First Secretary UKDEL MBFR Vienna 1978; PRO FCO 1981; m 1964 Raili Tellervo Laaksonen (1d 1965; 1s 1968).

Nicholson, Peter David; Peking since March 1992; born 25.1.38; Royal Navy 1953-63; BOT 1963; Bonn 1970; Warsaw 1971; Vientiane 1972; Athens 1975; Brussels 1977; Madrid 1980; Lusaka 1983; New Delhi 1986; New York 1987; Moscow 1990; Grade SO; m 1958 Ann Fuller (2d 1959, 1964; 1s 1969).

Nicolopulo, Evangelo Paul; Vice-Consul (Comm) Montreal since February 1988; born 14.1.50; FCO 1969; LourenHco Marques 1972; Saigon 1973; FCO 1974; Kingston 1977; Madrid (CSCE) 1980; Alexandria 1982; Second Secretary FCO 1985; m 1981 Kareen Elizabeth Sun.

Nithavrianakis, Michael Stephen; Moscow since September 1990; born 30.4.67; FCO 1984; Kuala Lumpur 1987; Grade 9.

Nixon, Patrick Michael, CMG (1989), OBE (1984); Counsellor FCO since January 1990; born 1.8.44; Third Secretary FO 1965; MECAS 1966; Cairo 1968 (Second Secretary 1969); Lima 1970; Second later First Secretary FCO 1973; First Secretary and Head of Chancery Tripoli 1977; Director and Consul (Inf) BIS New York 1980; First Secretary later Counsellor FCO 1983; HM Ambassador and Consul-General Doha 1987; m 1968 Elizabeth Rose Carlton (4s 1970, 1971, 1975, 1978).

Noakes, Jonathan Arnott; Deputy High Commissioner Bridgetown since July 1991; born 4.1.44; FO 1965; Third Secretary Ankara 1966; FO 1967; Second Secretary FCO 1971; First Secretary FCO 1974; First Secretary (Econ) Oslo 1981; First Secretary FCO 1985; m 1973 Nicola Jane Macaulay Langley.

Noakes, Stephen Martin; First Secretary (Chancery) Luanda since September 1990; born 6.2.57; Home Civil Service 1979-88; Second Secretary FCO 1988; m 1989 Hazel Clarke.

Nobes, Paula Louise; Third Secretary (Chancery) Belgrade since January 1991; born 1.8.69; FCO 1988; Language Training 1990; Grade 9.

Noble, Andrew James; First Secretary FCO since November 1989; born 22.4.60; FCO 1982; Bucharest 1983 (Second Secretary (Chancery/Inf) Bonn 1986).

Noble, Barry Paul; Counsellor Paris since June 1989; born 17.10.38; FO 1962; Dakar University 1964; Third later Second Secretary (Leopoldville) Kinshasa 1965; Second Secretary (Comm) Kaduna 1967; First Secretary FCO 1969; Warsaw 1972; FCO 1975; Counsellor UKMIS Geneva 1980; FCO 1984; m 1965 Alexandra Helena Giddings (1s 1966).

Noble, David John, MVO (1983); Deputy Head of Mission Suva since December 1991; born 15.6.38; CRO 1961; CO 1961; Port of Spain 1962; CRO (later Commonwealth Office) 1963; Vienna 1968; Vice-Consul Cape Town 1972; Johannesburg 1974; Second Secretary FCO 1977; Second Secretary Stockholm 1980; First Secretary (Dev) Lilongwe 1984; FCO 1988; m (1) 1982 Barbara Margarete Hildegard Maria Klosterschulte (diss 1991) (1s 1983) (2) 1991 Yvonne Brown (1 step son 1974; 1 step daughter 1976).

Noble, Robert Antony; Islamabad since March 1989; born 24.8.66; FCO 1984; Lisbon 1986; Grade 9.

Noble, Richard Adam; Second later First Secretary FCO since June 1989; born 9.6.62; FCO 1987; Third later Second Secretary (Chancery) Moscow 1987.

Noel, Louisa Veronica; Kuala Lumpur since December 1989; born 24.4.62; FCO 1988; Grade S2.

Noel-Clarke, Michael Richard Fulke; Counsellor FCO since November 1990; born 28.2.40; FO 1964; Third later Second Secretary Paris 1965; FO 1967; Beirut 1968; Second later First Secretary Tehran 1970; FCO 1974; Cairo 1977; First Secretary later Counsellor FCO 1981; Counsellor Brussels 1986; m 1971 Vashti Bayat Makoui (1d 1972; 1s 1976).

Nolan, Julia Elizabeth; FCO since January 1989 (Second Secretary 1989); born 2.1.59; FCO 1983; Bangkok 1984; SUPL 1986; New Delhi 1987; m 1985 Richard John Codrington.

Noon, Paul David; Damascus since May 1991; born 1.6.68; FCO 1989; Grade 10.

Norman, Duncan Charles; FCO since April 1990; born 12.10.71; Grade 10.

Norman, Sarah Caroline; New Delhi since November 1991; born 16.12.70; FCO 1990; Grade 9.

Norris, Peter James; Deputy Head of Mission and Consul Guatamala City since July 1990; born 22.12.55; FCO 1982; First Secretary Lagos 1985; FCO 1988; m 1982 Dilvinder Kaur Dhaliwal (2d 1986, 1990).

Norsworthy, Sean Francis; Tunis since October 1992; born 18.4.68; FCO 1987; Islamabad 1989; Grade 10.

Northern, Richard James, MBE (1982); First Secretary (Econ/Comm) Ottawa since November 1992 ; born 2.11.54; FCO 1976; MECAS 1978; Language Student; FCO 1978; Jedda 1980; Second later First Secretary Rome 1983; First Secretary FCO 1987; m 1981 Linda Denise Gadd (2s 1983, 1986).

Northover, John Charles; First Secretary (Commercial) Sofia since June 1992; born 11.6.45; HCS 1964-1978; FCO 1978; Second Secretary Yaoundé 1980; Second Secretary FCO 1983; First Secretary (Inf) Brussels 1987; m 1972 Eileen Christina Wells (1d 1972; 1s 1975).

Norton, Redmond; Second later First Secretary (Comm) Helsinki since October 1988; born 30.4.46; Board of Trade 1962; FCO 1969; Rio de Janeiro 1972; Caracas 1975; Dacca 1977; FCO 1980; Second Secretary (Admin) Tripoli 1984; Second Secretary (Tech Co-op) Quito 1985; m 1969 Jean McGarrigle (1d 1974; 1s 1979).

Noss, John Bramble; Consul-General Perth since October 1991; born 20.12.35; FO 1954; HM Forces 1955-57; Beirut 1957; Copenhagen 1960; FO 1964; Moscow 1965; (Second Secretary 1966); Second Secretary (Comm) Santiago 1968; FCO 1970; Second, later First Secretary (Econ) Pretoria 1973; First Secretary (Comm) Moscow 1977; FCO 1978; Consul (Inward Investment) New York 1981; Counsellor 1986; High Commissioner Honiara 1986; Counsellor (Comm) Helsinki 1988; m 1957 Shirley Andrews (1d 1959; 2s 1961, 1966).

Nuttall, (Andrew) Roger; First Secretary FCO since August 1992; born 9.6.43; FO 1962; DSAO 1965; SE Asia Floater 1966; Calcutta 1968; Second Secretary 1970; Secretary, DS Whitley Council Staff Side 1969; Academic year for Management Studies at London Polytechnic 1971; Second Secretary (Comm) Brussels 1972; First Secretary FCO 1977; On secondment to CBI 1978; FCO 1979; First Secretary (Comm) Head of Chancery and Consul Abidjan 1981; First Secretary FCO 1983; Consul-General/ Economic Adviser Berlin (CG)1988; m 1967 Colette Marie Dastrevigne (2s 1969, 1972).

Nye, Richard Paul; Karachi since July 1990; born 29.2.64; FCO 1982; Vienna 1984; Algiers 1987; Grade 9; m 1985 Alison Claire Edwards.

Nye, Alison Claire (née Edwards); Karachi since July 1990; born 18.12.64; FCO 1983; SUPL 1985; Algiers 1987; Grade 9.

O

Oakden, Edward Anthony; First Secretary FCO since February 1992; born 3.11.59; FCO 1981; Third later Second Secretary (Chancery) Baghdad 1984; Second Secretary (Chancery) Khartoum 1985; First Secretary and Private Secretary to HM Ambassador Washington 1988; m 1989 Stephanie Mary Liston.

Oakley, Caroline Jane; Floater Duties since November 1990; born 16.9.64; FCO 1984; Santiago 1987; Grade 10.

Oakley, Matthew Edward; Vice-Consul Riyadh since October 1990; born 19.7.65; FCO 1983; Athens 1985; Jedda 1988; Grade 9.

O'Brien, Gareth David; FCO since October 1991; born 27.7.65; FCO 1982; Copenhagen 1985; Warsaw 1988; Africa/ME Floater 1990; Grade 9; m 1991 Lisa Margaret Donagher.

O'Brien, Lisa Margaret (née Donagher); FCO since September 1991; born 30.10.66; FCO 1984; BMG Berlin 1986; Floater Duties 1989; Grade 9; m 1991 Gareth David O'Brien.

O'Brien, Patrick Thaddeus Dominic; Second Secretary FCO since December 1988; born 3.11.49; Post Office 1966; FCO 1968; Lagos 1971; Georgetown 1975; FCO 1978; JAO Brussels 1982; Abidjan 1984; m 1970 Maureen Mortimer (3d 1970, 1971, 1979; 1s 1973).

O'Brien, Sally Anne (née Knatchbull-Hugessen), MVO (1989); SUPL since June 1990; born 15.3.59; FCO 1983; UKREP Brussels 1985; Washington 1987; Grade 9; m 1987 Dr Thomas Patrick O'Brien.

O'Callaghan, John Matthew; Second Secretary (Information) Santiago since May 1992; born 27.4.66; FCO 1990; Grade 8.

O'Connell, Philip; FCO since September 1991; born 14.11.66; FCO 1985; Nairobi 1990; Grade 10

O'Connell, Sarah Thérèse; Second Secretary FCO since January 1992; born 13.2.56; Second Secretary FCO 1986; Second Secretary (Chancery) Kuala Lumpur 1988.

O'Connell, Terry; FCO since December 1990; born 19.9.58; MOD 1976; FCO 1978; Stockholm 1980; Tripoli 1983; FCO 1984; Santiago 1984; Bombay 1987; Grade 9; m 1991 Valerie Anna-Maria Gonsalves.

O'Connor, Marie; Bangkok since July 1991; born 3.1.38; Brasilia 1961; Baghdad 1962; Tokyo 1964; FCO 1966; Mogadishu 1968; Jedda 1970; Kinshasa 1971; FCO 1972; Mexico City 1973; Tehran 1974; FCO 1977; Muscat 1982; Washington 1987; FCO 1989; Grade S1.

O'Connor, Paul Vincent; Second Secretary (Aid/Commercial) Maseru since October 1991; born 29.6.56; FCO 1975; Jedda 1977; Washington 1980; Floater Duties 1983; FCO 1985; Istanbul 1987; m 1985 Georgina Louise Jayne (1d 1991).

O'Connor, Sheila Mary; Prague since August 1991; born 28.12.60; FCO 1982; UKREP Brussels 1983; Yaoundé 1986; Rangoon 1989; Grade S1.

O'Flaherty, Stephen John; First Secretary FCO since August 1992; born 15.5.51; Third Secretary FCO 1975; Language Student India 1977; Second Secretary New Delhi 1978; First Secretary FCO 1980; Prague 1981; First Secretary FCO 1984; First Secretary (Chancery) Vienna 1988; m 1975 Sarah Louise Gray (2d 1979, 1987; 1s 1983).

Ogden, Michael Geoffrey; First Secretary FCO since May 1990; born 12.4.48; Second later First Secretary FCO 1977; Pretoria 1980; First Secretary FCO 1981; First Secretary (IAEA) UKMIS Vienna 1986; m 1976 Carolyne Bryant (1d 1979; 1s 1980).

Ogg, Fiona; Warsaw since April 1992; born 25.7.70; FCO 1989;Grade 10.

Oglethorpe, Barbara Ruth (née Freeman); SUPL since November 1988; born 12.2.58; FCO 1983; SUPL 1985; FCO 1986; Grade 9; m 1981 William Justin Oglethorpe (1d 1985).

O'Hara, Violet Brown McGregor (née Steele); Consul (Comm) Rio de Janeiro since July 1990; born 22.9.42; FO 1961; Tokyo 1964; Singapore 1964; Kinshasa 1967; FCO 1970; Strasbourg 1971; Jakarta 1975; Hanoi 1978; FCO 1980; Second later First Secretary (Comm) Washington 1985; m 1986 Basil Austin Samuel O'Hara.

O'Hara, William; FCO since July 1992; born 9.1.39; FO 1960; Bahrain 1960; Lisbon 1963; DSAO 1966; Khorramshahr 1968; Phnom Penh 1970; Paris 1973; FCO 1975; (Second Secretary 1977); Vice-Consul (Comm) São Paulo 1979; Second later First Secretary (UN/UNIDO) UKMIS Vienna 1983; SUPL 1987; m 1964 Monique Marcelle Georgette Gentzbourber (2d 1964, 1968).

O'Keeffe, Deanna Maureen; FCO since October 1991; born 24.9.61; FCO 1980; Vienna 1989; Grade 10.

Oliver, David John; New Delhi since March 1991; born 31.7.35; Army 1953-81; Budapest 1982; Tel Aviv 1983; Peking 1986; Riyadh 1987; Grade CSO; m 1970 Peggy Muriel Eve.

Oliver, Geoffrey Harold; Madrid since January 1991; born 11.6.48; HM Forces 1965-88; Moscow 1989; Grade SO.

Oliver, Kaye Wight; First Secretary Consul and

Deputy Head of Mission, later Chargé d'Affaires Kinshasa since June 1990; (additionally Chargé d'Affaires non-resident to Burundi and Rwanda); born 10.8.43; Customs and Excise 1962; CO 1965; DSAO (later FCO) 1966; Kuala Lumpur 1970; Second Secretary FCO 1974; Lilongwe 1978; Paris 1981; First Secretary Nairobi 1983; First Secretary Head of Chancery and Consul Yaoundé 1984; First Secretary, FCO 1987.

Oliver, Matthew Keith; Istanbul since October 1989; born 16.8.51; Blantyre 1973; Washington 1975; Belgrade 1978; FCO 1979; Bombay 1980; Warsaw 1983; FCO 1984; Auckland 1986; Grade 9.

Olver-Osman, Tesca Marie (née Osman); SUPL since October 1988; born 6.1.62; FCO 1981; Warsaw 1983; Düsseldorf 1984; SUPL 1987; Düsseldorf 1988; Grade 9; m 1985 Robert Owen Olver.

O'Mahony, Daniel Lawrence; Paris since August 1990; born 2.10.61; FCO 1984; Grade 10.

Oman, Magnus Paul; Valletta since August 1991; born 5.8.68; FCO 1989; Grade 10.

O'Neill, Douglas Matthew; FCO since September 1990; born 13.6.69; Grade 10.

O'Neill, Louisa-Jayne; Second Secretary (Political) Bangkok and Deputy Permanent Representative (ESCAP) since March 1992; born 3.7.66; FCO 1987; Language Training Bangkok 1991.

Onn, Anthony Wilfred; Bonn since May 1989; born 16.4.44; Royal Navy 1959-84; Sofia 1987; Grade SO.

Orchard, Kevin John; FCO since September 1992; born 19.6.60; MOD 1977; FCO 1979; Jedda 1981; Islamabad 1982; Dakar 1984; FCO 1987; Third Secretary (Admin) Ottawa 1989; Grade 9; m 1984 Virginia Ann Brown (1d 1987).

Orchard, Kirsty Jen; New Delhi since February 1991; born 26.8.69; FCO 1988; Grade S2.

Ord-Smith, Robin Jeremy; Bucharest since November 1991; born 8.10.65; FCO 1989; Grade 9.

Ormiston, Ewan Kenneth; Brussels since February 1992; born 27.8.68; FCO 1989; Grade 10.

O'Rourke, Peter Vincent; FCO since September 1990; born 26.9.60; FCO 1980; Maputo 1981; Lisbon 1984; Rabat 1987; Grade 9.

Orr, Dermot John David; Riyadh since December 1990; born 7.5.48; Army 1964-88; Sofia 1988; The Hague 1990; Grade SO; m 1969

Adrianne Katherine Edith Sherwood (1d 1970; 2s 1972, 1975).

Orr, Iain Campbell; Counsellor and Deputy High Commissioner Wellington since January 1991; born 6.12.42; Third later Second Secretary FCO 1968; Hong Kong 1969; Second later First Secretary Peking 1972; FCO 1974; Assistant Political Adviser Hong Kong 1978; Dublin 1981; First Secretary FCO 1984; Consul-General Shanghai 1987; m 1978 Susan Elizabeth Gunter (1d 1983; 1s 1984).

Orrell, Sarah Christine; FCO since June 1986; born 1.7.37; FO 1966; Buenos Aires 1967; FCO 1969; Colombo 1979; Amman 1983; Grade S1.

Orwin, Peter David, OBE (1992), MC (1966); First Secretary (Chancery) Tel Aviv since July 1989; born 20.12.44; Army 1963-75; First Secretary FCO 1975; First Secretary Athens 1977; FCO 1981; Brasilia 1984; FCO 1987; m 1977 Pamela Jane Heath (2d 1980, 1987; 1s 1982).

Osborn, Andrew Robert; Moscow since July 1992; born 13.2.64; FCO 1982; Lagos 1987; Budapest 1990; Grade 10; m 1988 Karyn Lindsay Heraty.

Osborn, Derek Clive; FCO since June 1986; born 13.4.30; GPO 1968; FCO 1969; Lagos 1970; FCO 1971; Abu Dhabi 1973; FCO 1975; Darwin 1976; FCO 1979; Warsaw 1983; Grade 8; m 1956 Nina May Binnee (2d 1959, 1962).

Osborn, Karyn Lindsay, (née Heraty); Budapest since November 1990; born 12.2.66; FCO 1986; Lagos 1988; Grade 10; m. 1988 Andrew Robert Osborn.

Osborn, Sally Mary; SUPL since November 1988; born 26.1.57; FCO 1976; Dacca 1978; Amsterdam 1982; Second Secretary FCO 1984; Second Secretary (Inf/Chancery) Lisbon 1988; m 1988 Neil Gordon Haddock (1s 1990).

Osborne, Christopher Wyndham; First Secretary (Inf) BTC Hong Kong since November 1989; born 18.6.46; CO 1964; Commonwealth Office (later FCO) 1966; Lusaka 1968; Kampala 1970; Bridgetown 1973; FCO 1976; Second Secretary Dacca 1979; Second Secretary (Comm) Caracas 1982; First Secretary FCO 1986; m 1967 Gillian Mary Hawkey (3s 1967, 1974, 1979).

Osborne, David Allan; First Secretary FCO since March 1991; born 31.8.42; CRO 1961; Department of Technical Co-operation 1961; CRO 1963; Accra 1963; DSAO 1965; Guatemala 1968; Second Secretary (Inf) Bonn 1973; Second Secretary Valletta 1974; Central London Polytechnic 1977; First Secretary FCO 1978; First Secretary Head of Chancery and Consul San José 1980; First Secretary FCO 1984; First Secretary (Comm) São Paulo 1988; m 1966 Joan Marion Duck (1s 1970; 2d 1971, 1973).

Osborne, John Stuart, MBE (1991); Third
Secretary FCO since December 1990; born
18.7.42; FCO 1968; Singapore 1969; FCO 1971;
Kuwait 1973; FCO 1974; Jedda 1977; FCO
1980; Rome 1983; FCO 1986; Attaché Kabul
1988; FCO 1989; Third Secretary Baghdad 1989;
Grade 8; m (1) 1965 Deborah Ann Cecile
Battersby (diss 1979) (2d 1969, 1971); (2) 1979
Yvonne Valerie Keirle.

Osborne, Roy Paul; First Secretary (Chancery/
Inf) Madrid since February 1989; born 13.7.51;
FCO 1970; Oslo 1972; Islamabad 1974; Vice-
Consul Rome 1978; Second Secretary FCO 1981;
Second Secretary (Comm/Dev) later First
Secretary, Head of Chancery and Consul
Yaoundé 1985; m 1977 Vivienne Claire Gentry
(2d 1983, 1984).

O'Shaughnessy, Jonathan Edward; FCO since
June 1991; born 7.10.71; Grade 10.

O'Sullivan, John Richard, MBE (1992); NATO
Brussels since March 1989; born 1.1.32; RAF 1950-
60; Mexico 1966; Belgrade 1968; Cairo 1969; Paris
1971; Peking 1973; Bangkok 1975; Valletta 1978;
Moscow 1980; Peking 1981; Lagos 1982; Vienna
1984; New Delhi 1987; Grade CSO; m 1954 Jean
Margaret (1s 1962; 1d 1964).

Oswald, David; Second Secretary FCO since
March 1990; born 15.6.46; FO 1965; Amman
1968; Zomba 1970; Blantyre 1971; Tokyo 1973;
FCO 1976; Gaborone 1978; FCO 1982; Jedda
1986; m 1972 Jane Avril Bennett Edmunds (2d
1974, 1977).

Ouassine, Angela Susan (née Wright); Lilongwe
since May 1989; born 17.1.67; FCO 1985; Grade
10; m 1988 Mahammed Ouassine (diss 1992).

Oulmi, Sally Teresa (née Cashman); Stockholm
since October 1990; born 4.10.52; FCO 1974;
UKREP Brussels 1975; Abidjan 1979; Strasbourg
1983; FCO 1986; Ottawa 1987; Grade S1; m
1976 Hocine (Frank) Oulmi.

Owen, Caroline Jane; Washington since April
1990; born 29.10.66; FCO 1986; Grade S2A.

Owen, Gareth Wynn; Prague since February
1992; born 24.11.69; FCO 1989; Grade 10.

Owen, Helen Patricia; FCO since August 1987;
born 9.4.49; FCO 1974; Sana'a 1974; FCO 1976;
Bandar Seri Begawan 1981; Manila 1982;
Madrid 1984; Grade S1.

Owen, Jane Caroline; Language Training
Kamakura since August 1989; born 15.4.63; FCO
1987; Language Training 1988; Second Secretary
1989.

Owen, John Wynne, MBE (1979); Consul-General
Boston since January 1992; born 25.4.39; FO
1956; Army 1958-60; Jakarta 1960; Saigon 1961;

Paris (NATO) 1962; San Salvador 1963; Resigned
1967; Reinstated 1970; FCO 1970; Tehran 1973;
Second Secretary 1974; Vice-Consul (Comm) São
Paulo 1978; Admin Officer and Consul Peking
1980; First Secretary FCO 1983; SUPL 1985;
Counsellor FCO 1989; m (1) 1962 Thelma
Margaret Gunton (dec'd 1987) (2d 1964, 1969; 1s
1970) (2) 1988 Carol Edmunds (1 step d. 1977).

Owen, Richard Lloyd; First Secretary FCO since
November 1988; born 21.4.48; Second Secretary
FCO 1975; Language Student 1976; Language
Student MECAS 1977; First Secretary Abu
Dhabi 1980; Beirut 1980; FCO 1981; San José
1983; BMG Berlin 1986; m 1985 Eva Maria
Steller (1d 1986).

Owens, Judith Caroline Elizabeth; SUPL since
July 1992; born 17.8.64; FCO 1984; Washington
1986; Warsaw 1988; Floater Duties 1990; Grade
S2.

Owens, Patrick Eldred; Riyadh since April 1988
(Second Secretary 1990); born 20.4.53; FCO
1972; Muscat 1974; Bucharest 1977; Algiers
1979; FCO 1981; Jakarta 1984; m 1978 Merle
Quirine Decevninck van Capelle (1d 1980, 2s
1982; 1985).

Owens, Ruth Mary; Nairobi since June 1989;
born 28.3.67; FCO 1987; Grade 10.

Oyler, Diane Margaret (née Evans); SUPL since
October 1988; born 25.5.59; FCO 1978; New
Delhi 1981; Bandar Seri Begawan 1985; Grade
S2; m 1988 Cpt. Richard Geoffrey Torin Oyler.

Oxley, Anthony, BEM; New York since June
1989; born 9.9.42; Royal Navy 1961-83;
Baghdad 1983; Bucharest 1984; Montevideo
1986; East Berlin 1987; Grade SO.

P

Pacey, Mary Margaret; FCO since October 1982;
born 17.9.40; FO 1962; Geneva 1963; Nicosia
1966; FO (later FCO) 1967; Lusaka 1969; Beirut
1971; FCO 1974; Stockholm 1975; Washington
1977; Cairo 1980; Grade S2.

Packer, Deborah (née Wilde); reinstated FCO
March 1991; born 10.5.66; FCO 1985; resigned
1986; NEDO 1986-1987; Grade S2; m 1990
Phillip Anthony Packer.

Packwood, Sarah Anne; Bonn since May 1991;
born 22.5.68; FCO 1989; Grade S2.

Paddington, Ian; Second Secretary FCO since
September 1983; born 3.4.37; FO 1963;
Salisbury 1965; Lusaka 1965; Yaoundé 1967;
Frankfurt 1971; FCO 1972; Santo Domingo
1975; Second Secretary (Vice-Consul (Comm))
Sydney 1979; Vice-Consul (Comm) Brisbane
1980; m 1966 Judith Louise Harte (1d 1969).

Page, Andrew John Walter; Full-Time Language Training since September 1991; born 17.9.65; FCO 1990; Grade 8.

Page, Alexander Simon; Dhaka since September 1989; born 20.10.64; FCO 1987; Warsaw 1989; Grade 9; m 1989 Isabella Lynn Marshall.

Page, Brian Ronald; Second Secretary (Comm) Dubai since March 1992; born 5.3.49; FCO 1968; Helsinki 1971; Doha 1973; Capetown 1976; FCO 1978; Muscat 1979; Singapore 1983; FCO 1986 (Second Secretary 1988); m 1973 Susan Frances Vinall (2s 1975, 1979).

Page, Derek Alan; FCO since September 1990; born 29.9.50; FCO 1975; Pretoria 1977; Bombay 1979; FCO 1981; Frankfurt 1984; Montevideo 1987; Grade 9; m 1972 Inger Merete Ebbesvik (2s 1977, 1981).

Page, Isabella Lynn (née Marshall); Dacca since April 1990; born 6.1.64; FCO 1981; Kuala Lumpur 1984; Prague 1987; SUPL 1989; Grade 9; m 1989 Alexander Simon Page.

Page, John Nathaniel Micklem; First Secretary (Economic) Bucharest since January 1991; born 16.12.53; Second later First Secretary FCO 1981; SUPL 1983; FCO 1983; Bangkok 1985; First Secretary FCO 1988; m 1985 Lady Katharine Asquith.

Page, Julie Elizabeth (née Hall); SUPL since October 1988; born 29.6.59; FCO 1983; Nairobi 1985; Grade S2; m 1989 William Page.

Page, Martin; Second Secretary FCO sinceSeptember 1990; born 16.11.51; MOD 1969; FCO 1970; Beirut 1973; FCO 1976; Lima 1976; Warsaw 1979; FCO 1982; Vila 1983; Dar es Salaam 1987; m 1975 Christine Mary Ogilvy (1s 1979; 1d 1984).

Page, Michael Keith; First Secretary (Comm) Washington since April 1988; born 15.2.43; CRO 1960; Dacca 1964; FCO 1966; Manila 1969; Wellington 1972; FCO 1974; New York 1979; Second Secretary (Vice-Consul and Admin) Prague 1985; on loan to ODA 1985; m (1) 1966 Marina Kathleen Hyde-Gomes (diss 1977) (1d 1970); (2) 1980 Frances Lenio (née Gladwin) (1s 1984).

Page, Simon David; Language Training Peking since September 1992; born 22.2.67; FCO 1990; Language Training FCO 1991; Grade 8.

Page, Simon Graham; Third Secretary (Chancery) New Delhi since July 1992; born 22.11.61; FCO 1979; Kuala Lumpur 1983; Floater Duties 1987; Dublin 1988; FCO 1990; m 1985 Sharon Ann Murphy (1s 1990).

Page, William James Oliver; FCO since November 1990 born 4.8.65; FCO 1984; Riyadh

1986; Floater Duties 1989; Grade 9.

Paget, Norman John; First Secretary (Commercial) Paris since July 1992; born 2.2.37; FO 1962; MECAS 1963; Vice-Consul Khartoum 1964; DSAO 1965; Manila 1968; Second Secretary (Comm) Manila 1970; Cairo 1971; Second Secretary FCO 1973; Consul Bordeaux 1976; First Secretary (Comm) Brussels 1980; First Secretary (Comm) Bucharest 1986; First Secretary FCO 1989; m 1965 Kiriaki Evangelia Hadimina (1s 1974).

Paget, Olivia Jane; SUPL since October 1992; born 31.7.57; FCO 1978; Mexico City 1980; FCO 1982; Third Secretary (Chancery) Paris 1987; FCO 1990; (Second Secretary 1991); m 1992 Nigel John Cox.

Pagett, Christopher Robert Geoffrey, OBE (1990); First Secretary FCO since September 1991; born 13.6.52; Third Secretary FCO 1975; Second Secretary Havana 1978; Second later First Secretary (Econ) Lusaka 1979; First Secretary FCO 1984; First Secretary (Chancery) Maputo 1988; m (1) 1974 Anne-Marie Roberts; (2) 1988 Diane Brown.

Pagett, Ian William; Khartoum since December 1989; born 19.9.69; FCO 1988; Grade 10.

Pagett, Wayne Norman; New Delhi since August 1990; born 26.3.67; FCO 1988; Grade 10; m 1990 Kay Louise Clements.

Paginton, David Alan; FCO since October 1991; born 1.4.51; Board of Inland Revenue 1968; FCO 1971; Istanbul 1973; UKREP Brussels 1976; Sofia 1979; FCO 1981; São Paulo 1984; Islamabad 1988; Grade 9; m 1986 Marcia Rosana Antonio (1s 1986, 1d 1987).

Paice, Anthony John; First Secretary FCO since September 1990; born 5.10.42; Second Secretary FCO 1969; First Secretary Calcutta 1972; FCO 1975; First Secretary (Econ) Bonn 1977; FCO 1980; First Secretary UKDEL MBFR Vienna 1982; FCO 1984; First Secretary Kuwait 1988; m 1968 Christine May Symons (4d 1971, 1974, 1978, 1983).

Pain, Warren David; FCO since April 1992; born 17.5.71; Grade 10.

Painting, Julia; FCO since November 1989; born 24.4.60; FCO 1981; Prague 1983; SEA/FE Floater 1985; Grade 9.

Pakenham, The Hon Michael (Aidan); HM Ambassador and Consul-General Luxembourg since October 1991; born 3.11.43; Third Secretary FO 1966; Third later Second Secretary Warsaw 1967; Second Secretary FCO 1970; Assistant Private Secretary later Private Secretary to the Chancellor of the Duchy of Lancaster 1971; On secondment to Cabinet Office 1972;

(First Secretary 1972); UKDEL CSCE Geneva 1974; First Secretary New Delhi 1974; Washington 1978; Counsellor FCO 1983; Counsellor (External Relations) UKREP Brussels 1987; m 1980 Meta Landreth Doak (2d 1981, 1985).

Pakes, Stuart Murray; Second Secretary (Immig/ Cons) Accra since April 1990; born 8.5.49; FO 1967; FCO 1968; Aden 1970; Anguilla 1973; Reykjavik 1973; East Berlin 1976; FCO 1977; Madrid 1981; Cairo 1984; FCO 1987 (Second Secretary 1989); m 1972 Linda Anne Rawlings (2d 1977, 1981; 1s 1984).

Palmer, Andrew Eustace, CMG (1987); CVO (1981); HM Ambassador to the Holy See since August 1991; born 30.9.37; HM Forces 1956-58; FO 1962; La Paz 1963; Second Secretary (Comm) 1964; Second Secretary Ottawa 1965; Treasury Centre for Administrative Studies 1967; First Secretary FO (later FCO) 1968; First Secretary (Inf) Paris 1972; FCO 1976; RCDS 1978; Counsellor Head of Chancery and Consul-General Oslo 1979; Head of Falklands Islands Department FCO 1982; CDA Harvard Center for International Affairs 1985; HM Ambassador Havana 1986; On secondment to the Duke of Kent;s Household 1988; m 1962 Davina Cecil Barclay (2s 1963, 1977; 1d 1965).

Palmer, Lucy Kate; FCO since September 1990; born 7.7.69; Grade 9.

Palmer, Neil Roger; FCO since January 1983; born 18.8.47; DSAO later FCO 1966; Canberra 1970; Bonn 1973; Düsseldorf 1974; Moscow 1974; FCO 1975; Dacca 1978; FCO 1980; JAO New York 1982; Grade 9; m 1970 Penelope Wraight (1s 1976).

Palmer, Peter Hughes; Second Secretary FCO since June 1987; born 15.4.33; Royal Navy 1948-58; Ministry of Labour 1958; FO 1959; Bahrain (Agency) 1959; Tripoli 1962; Vice-Consul Durban 1967; FCO 1969; Vice-Consul Buea 1972; Third Secretary1/Vice-Consul Mogadishu 1974, Montreal 1976; FCO 1978; Second Secretary (Admin/V-C) Abu Dhabi 1983; m (1) 1958 Marion Annette Loon (2s 1958, 1966; 2d 1960, 1963); (2) 1976 Sara Elizabeth Barr.

Palmer, Sara (née Abbots-Darbyshire);SUPL since October 1991; FCO 1991; born 16.11.64; FCO 1983; UKMIS Geneva 1985; Montevideo 1988; Grade 9; m 1991 Christopher John Palmer.

Palmer, Sidney Hodgson; First Secretary Head of Chancery and Consul Luxembourg since December 1989; born 8.6.40; FO 1960; Belgrade 1961; Bangkok 1964; Rangoon 1967; FCO 1971; Baghdad 1974; Assistant to Resident Commissioner Vila 1978; Second Secretary Vila 1980; First Secretary FCO 1983; DHC and Head of Chancery Port Moresby 1986; m 1962

Jacqueline Germaine Albiser (1s 1975).

Panter, Sarah Jane; FCO since July 1992; born 5.10.68; FCO 1987; Prague 1990; Grade S2.

Papaspyrou, Marina; Tel Aviv since February 1992; born 17.1.64; FCO 1984; Berne 1986; Budapest 1989; FCO 1990; Grade 10.

Parfitt, Alan Frank; FCO since January 1989; born 6.8.66; Senior Research Officer.

Paris, Bridget Jennifer; FCO since October 1991; born 18.4.67; Grade 9.

Parish, Colin; Consul (Commercial) Jedda since September 1990; born 27.11.43; Royal Navy 1961-70; FCO 1970; Phnom Penh 1973; Accra 1974; SUPL 1978; FCO 1982; Belgrade 1986; Grade 9; m (1) 1966 Carole Grace; (diss. 1978); (2) 1978 Fairroligh Janet Lee Syme (2s 1985, 1989).

Parish, Paul Edward; SUPL since October 1992; born 10.8.63; FCO 1983; Vienna 1986; FCO 1989; Grade 10.

Parker, David John; First Secretary FCO since September 1990; born 12.2.43; BOT 1960; Salisbury 1964; Brunei 1967; Beira 1970; FCO 1971; New Delhi 1975; Baghdad 1978; Second Secretary FCO 1981; HM Consul Jakarta 1984; Second Secretary (Admin) Freetown 1988; m 1965 Valerie Ann Mitchell (1d 1966; 1s 1968).

Parker, David John; FCO since November 1989; born 2.6.57; FCO 1978; Mexico City 1987; Grade 8; m 1987 Mary Elizabeth Garner.

Parker, Gordon Alistair Gillespie; Second Secretary FCO since April 1992; born 2.2.50; FCO 1969; Tehran 1973; FCO 1976; Jedda 1980; FCO 1984; Second Secretary (Chancery) Nairobi 1988; m 1973 Mary Elizabeth Smith (1s 1987).

Parker, John Andrew; FCO since October 1986; born 19.5.51; FCO 1972; Nairobi 1975; FCO 1978; Budapest 1982; Grade 8; m 1973 Rosalind Jane Trimmer (2s 1978, 1983; 1d 1980).

Parker, Katherine Clare; Georgetown since February 1992; born 14.7.67; FCO 1988; Registry/ Cypher Floater Moscow 1990; Grade 10.

Parker, Lyn; Counsellor and Head of Chancery New Delhi since February 1992; born 25.11.52; FCO 1978; Second later First Secretary Athens 1980; FCO 1984; Counsellor on loan to the Cabinet Office 1989; m 1991 Jane Elizabeth Walker.

Parker, Nigel Denis; Assistant Legal Adviser FCO since March 1988; born 25.8.61; Grade 5.

Parker, Nigel Graham; Budapest since August

1990; born 13.9.56; FCO 1982; Kingston 1985; FCO 1988; Grade 9; m 1983 Paula Northwood (1s 1987, 1d 1991).

Parker, Penelope Estelle; SUPL since July 1989; born 27.9.62; FCO 1985; Lagos 1987; Grade S2.

Parker, Susan Caroline; Vienna since December 1990; born 1.7.63; FCO 1985; UKREP Brussels 1987; FCO 1988; Grade S2.

Parker, Valerie Ann; FCO since October 1990; born 21.2.42; Grade S2; m 1965 David John Parker (1d 1966, 1s 1968).

Parker-Brennan, Catherine Mary (née Parker); FCO since October 1988; born 2.5.51; FCO 1975; Lusaka 1976; Peking 1978; FCO 1979; Bonn 1982; FCO 1985; Lagos 1988; Grade S1; m 1982 Michael Brennan.

Parkhouse, Heather Ann; Dublin since July 1990; born 25.10.33; Ankara 1963; Moscow 1966; Aden 1967; Kathmandu 1969; Saigon 1973; FCO 1975; Amman 1978; Harare 1983; Cairo 1987; Grade S1.

Parkins, David Alan; Nairobi since August 1989; born 7.5.64; FCO 1984; Grade 8.

Parkinson, Guy Paul, Budapest since May 1992; born 5.6.70; FCO 1989; Grade 10.

Parkinson, Howard; First Secretary FCO since November 1991; born 29.3.48; BOT 1967; FCO 1969; LA Floater 1972; Tegucigalpa 1974; Buenos Aires 1975; Second Secretary 1977; Maputo 1978; Second later First Secretary FCO 1981; First Secretary (Comm) Lisbon 1985; First Secretary on loan to British Gas 1989; m 1974 Linda Wood (1d 1979; 1s 1982).

Parmley, Jane Helen (née Buchanan); Lagos since October 1984; born 18.8.63; FCO 1982; Grade S2; m 1987 Nigel William Kenneth Parmley.

Parris, Stephen Christopher; First Secretary (Economic) Copenhagen since September 1991; born 6.8.40; FO 1958; Stockholm 1962; Bonn 1964; Consulate General and BTDO New York 1967; FCO 1970; East Berlin 1973; Blantyre 1974; Lilongwe 1975; Second Secretary and Consul Oslo 1978; FCO 1983; Second later First Secretary, Head of Chancery and Consul Reykjavik 1986; First Secretary (Comm) Cairo 1989; m 1967 Anette Tengberg Hansen (1d 1967, 1s 1971).

Parry, John Leonard, MBE (1986); Hanoi since March 1988; born 23.2.39; HM Forces 1957-60; GPO 1961; FO 1965; Singapore 1967; FCO 1969; Islamabad 1972; FCO 1973; Amman 1975; FCO 1976; Darwin 1978; FCO 1980; Attaché Ankara 1982; FCO 1987; Grade 8; m 1957 Joan Templeton Williams (2s 1958, 1965;

1d 1963).

Parsons, Henry Edward Goodman; FCO since October 1991; born 22.11.70; Grade 10.

Parsons, Tanya Suzanne; Lagos since January 1991; born 4.2.65; FCO 1984; Warsaw 1987; UKDEL Vienna 1989; Grade 9.

Parton, Charles William; First Secretary Joint Liaison Group Hong Kong since August 1990; born 23.3.56; FCO 1979; Language Training Hong Kong 1982; Second Secretary FCO 1983; First Secretary (Econ) Peking 1985; First Secretary FCO 1987; m 1983 Charmian Constance Denman (1d 1987, 1s 1990).

Partridge, Andrew Warren; Islamabad since January 1989; born 26.4.68; FCO 1986; Grade 10; m 1988 Margaret Robertson.

Partridge, Colin Douglas; First Secretary FCO since November 1989; born 12.12.55; FCO 1978; Third later Second Secretary (Chancery) New Delhi 1980; Second later First Secretary FCO 1983; Language Training 1986; Head of Chancery and Consul Hanoi 1987; m 1983 Gita Sahgal (diss 1989).

Partridge, Diane Freda; Third Secretary (Aid) Belmopan since September 1989; born 29.11.44; OECD Paris 1966; Yaoundé 1969; Lagos 1970; Rio de Janeiro 1971; FCO 1972; Antananarivo 1974; FCO 1976; Buenos Aires 1977; FCO 1979; Brasilia 1981; FCO 1985; Grade 9.

Partridge, Margaret (née Robertson); Vice-Consul Moscow since November 1992; born 3.3.66; FCO 1986; Islamabad 1989; Grade 9; m 1988 Andrew Warren Partridge.

Pasquill, Derek James; Maseru since November 1990; born 11.1.59; HCS 1984; FCO 1986; Kampala 1988; Grade 10.

Patel, Shofia; FCO since February 1990; born 3.2.69; DSS 1988; Grade 10.

Patel, Varsha; On loan to the ODA since April 1992; born 17.6.66; FCO 1987; Prague 1990; Grade 10.

Paterson, David Michael; Riyadh since July 1992; born 8.10.68; FCO 1988; Grade 10; m 1991 Shona MacDonald Alexander.

Paterson, Fiona; Second later First Secretary (Info) Paris since October 1990; born 6.4.51; FCO 1977; Bogota 1979; Ottawa 1983; Second Secretary FCO 1987; Second Secretary (Chancery/Info) Bangkok 1989.

Paterson, William Neil Carlton; Second Secretary FCO since March 1989; born 19.10.50; FCO 1978; Sofia 1980; FCO 1981; Düsseldorf

1983; Second Secretary (Comm/Aid) Yaoundé 1986; m 1975 Margaret Christine Schmidt-Feuerheerd (1s 1976; 3d 1978, 1981, 1983).

Patey, William Charters; First Secretary FCO since August 1992; born 11.7.53; FCO 1975; MECAS 1977; Abu Dhabi 1978; Second Secretary (Comm) Tripoli 1981; First Secretary FCO 1984; First Secretary (Chancery) Canberra 1988; m 1978 Vanessa Carol Morrell (2s 1987, 1991).

Patrick, Andrew Silas; Third later Second Secretary (Chancery) Nicosia since February 1991; born 28.2.66; FCO 1988.

Patten, Roger; Second Secretary (Consular/Visa) Rabat since November 1991; born 24.7.43; CRO 1963; Bombay 1966; Pretorial/Cape Town 1970; Warsaw 1973; FCO 1974; San Juan 1976; FCO 1978; Prague 1980; Düsseldorf 1982; Second Secretary FCO 1987; Nicosia 1989; Second Secretary FCO 1989; m 1966 Anna Jones (2s 1967, 1970).

Patterson, Ernest Mark; FCO since October 1989; born 22.2.69; Grade 10.

Patterson, Hugh William Grant; First Secretary FCO since July 1990; born 17.10.50; FCO 1979; First Secretary BMG Berlin 1980; First Secretary FCO 1984; First Secretary (Head of Chancery) and Consul Guatemala City 1987; m 1981 Philippa Anne Colbatch Clark (1d 1986).

Patterson, Michael Anthony; First Secretary FCO since May 1988; born 7.5.41; FO 1961; Warsaw 1964; Dacca 1966; Accra 1970; Second Secretary FCO 1974; First Secretary Beirut 1982; Consul (Comm) Perth 1983; First Secretary (Comm) Canberra 1986; m (1) 1965 Dorothy Howe (diss 1977) (1s 1971; 1d 1973); (2) 1990 Beverley Lynette Wilton.

Pattinson, Christine Mary; UKDEL Brussels since November 1991; born 11.12.61; FCO 1988; Grade S2.

Pattison, Stephen Deer; First Secretary (Chancery) Washington since September 1989; born 24.12.53; HCS 1980; Second Secretary FCO 1981; Second Secretary Nicosia 1983; FCO 1986.

Patton, Geoffrey Joseph Laurence; Floater duties since December 1991; born 24.4.62; MOD 1985-86; FCO 1986; Warsaw 1989; Floater Training 1991; Grade 10.

Paul, Alan Roderick; Counsellor JLG Hong Kong since September 1991; born 13.5.50; Third Secretary FCO 1972; Language Student Cambridge 1973; Hong Kong 1974; Third later Second Secretary FCO 1975; Second later First Secretary (Comm) Peking 1977; FCO 1980; First Secretary and Head of Chancery The Hague

1984; First Secretary, later Counsellor FCO 1987; m 1979 Rosana Yuen Ling Tam (1d 1981; 1s 1985).

Paver, James Edward Luke; FCO since August 1991; born 2.10.63; Grade 9; m 1992 Rebecca Jane Ash.

Pawley, Michael James; First Secretary FCO since November 1991; born 14.10.39; CRO 1961; Kuala Lumpur 1964; Vientiane 1968; LA Floater 1971; Second Secretary FCO 1973; Nicosia 1974; Freetown 1977; FCO 1980; First Secretary (Inf/Chancery) Caracas 1984; First Secretary (Commercial) Lima 1989.

Paxman, Timothy Giles, LVO (1989); Counsellor on loan to the Cabinet Officer since March 1992; born 15.11.51; Department of Environment/Transport 1974; First Secretary UKREP Brussels 1980; FCO 1985; First Secretary Head of Chancery Singapore 1989; m 1980 SégolAene Claude Marie (2d 1982, 1984).

Peacock, Kathryn Louise Carmel; FCO since August 1991; born 16.7.60; FCO 1984; New Delhi 1985; UKREP Brussels 1988; Grade S2.

Peake, Philippa Jane; FCO since October 1990; born 30.3.64; Grade S2.

Pearce, Andrew John; First Secretary (Chancery) Tel Aviv since September 1992; born 7.10.60; FCO 1983; Language Training 1984; Third later Second Secretary Bangkok 1986; First Secretary FCO 1988; m 1986 Pornpun Pathumvivatana.

Pearce, David Avery; Consul Douala since August 1991; born 17.2.52; FCO 1971; UKMIS New York 1973; Rome 1976; FCO 1979; Dhaka 1982; FCO 1986; Paris 1987 (Second Secretary 1987); Second Secretary and Deputy Head of Mission Libreville 1990; m (1) 1973 Anne Mathews (dec'd 1986) (1d 1980, 1s 1984); (2) 1988 Virginia Martin (1d 1991).

Pearce, Howard John Stredder; Deputy Head of Mission Budapest since June 1991; born 13.4.49; FCO 1972; Buenos Aires 1975; First Secretary FCO 1978; First Secretary and Head of Chancery Nairobi 1983; First Secretary later Counsellor FCO 1987; Language Training 1990.

Pearce, Jessica Mary; First Secretary FCO since August 1990; born 1.9.57; FCO 1985; Second Secretary (Chancery) Dakar 1987.

Pearey, David Dacre; First Secretary later Counsellor FCO since June 1990; born 15.7.48; Ankara 1979 (on secondment from MOD); First Secretary FCO 1983; First Secretary & Head of Chancery Kampala 1987.

Pearey, (Dorothy) Jane, MBE (1980); FCO since September 1989; (Second Secretary 1991); born 31.5.45; OECD Paris 1969; Moscow 1972; FCO

1973; Belgrade 1977; FCO 1980; UKMIS New York 1983; Seconded to NATO 1984; Seconded to 21st Century Trust 1988.

Pears, Thomas Stanley; Third Secretary Islamabad since July 1983; born 27.6.39; GPO 1955; HM Forces 1959-61; GPO 1961; FO 1965; Warsaw 1966; FO 1967; Geneva 1968; FCO 1970; Nairobi 1971; FCO 1973; Kuala Lumpur 1976; FCO 1979; m 1963 Linda Evelyn Farquhar (3d 1965, 1968, 1972).

Pearson, Frances; UKREP Brussels since May 1991; born 17.7.54; FCO 1987; Washington 1988; Grade S2.

Pearson, John Anthony; FCO since November 1990; born 28.4.68; Grade 8.

Pearron, Julian Christopher; Third Secretary (Chancery) Madrid since June 1992; born 8.7.69; FCO 1990; Grade 9.

Pearson, Nigel John; Peking since February 1992; born 4.3.69; FCO 1987; Grade 9.

Pearson, Patricia Ann (née Thomas); FCO since September 1991; born 2.6.42; FCO 1969; Beirut 1972; Islamabad 1975; SUPL 1979; FCO 1982; Lilongwe 1988; Grade 9; m 1977 B S Pearson.

Peart, Michael John, LVO (1983); HM Ambassador Vilnlus since October 1991; born 15.12.43; Home Office 1960; CO 1966; FO DSAO and FCO 1967; Blantyre 1969; on attachment to RAF North Luffenham 1972; Warsaw 1973; Second Secretary (Pol) Mexico City 1975; Second later First Secretary FCO 1980; First Secretary and Head of Chancery Dhaka 1983; First Secretary FCO 1987; m 1968 Helena Mary Stuttle (1d 1972 (dec'd 1979); 1s 1975).

Pease, Simon Robert Hellier; First Secretary FCO since April 1992; born 20.2.52; FCO 1972; Ibadan 1975; SUPL 1978; FCO 1981, (Second Secretary 1982); Second later First Secretary UKDEL CDE Stockholm 1984; First Secretary FCO 1986; First Secretary and Head of Chancery Rabat 1988; m 1975 Catherine Elizabeth Bayley (1d 1981, 1s 1983).

Peaston, Walter Robert Gordon; First Secretary (Admin) JAO Brussels since July 1984; born 15.4.28; Army 1946-60; Brazzaville 1960; Prague 1963; Second Secretary FO 1966; Second Secretary (Inf) Sydney 1969; Bombay 1970; FCO 1973; Assistant Economic Secretary CENTO Ankara 1977; Second later First Secretary FCO 1979; m 1954 Muriel Dorothy French (diss 1976) (1s 1955; 1d 1958).

Peate, David James, OBE (1989); First Secretary (Comm) East Berlin since March 1989; born 2.7.44; FO 1964; DSAO 1965; Delhi 1967; Warsaw 1971; Second Secretary Lomé 1972;

FCO 1975; Melbourne 1978; FCO 1983; First Secretary Brussels 1984; m 1971 Siri Jean Jessica Elizabeth Zetter (1d 1973; 1s 1975).

Peel Yates, Julian David Hugh; SUPL since November 1990; born 2.12.50; HM Forces 1975-82; Second Secretary FCO 1982; First Secretary Nairobi 1984; First Secretary FCO 1987; m 1985 Caroline Anne Nelson.

Peers, Gary Clive; Third Secretary Bonn since August 1990; born 6.12.58; FCO 1985; Grade 8; m 1979 Pamela Jane Tailby (1d 1981, 2s 1983, 1985).

Pegler, Gillian Harriet; Second Secretary FCO since June 1986; born 6.10.47; CO 1965; CO 1967; FCO 1968; Warsaw 1970; Rotterdam 1970; Port of Spain 1971; FCO 1972; Kampala 1972; Nicosia 1973; Budapest 1974; Kuala Lumpur 1974; FCO 1978 (Second Secretary 1979); Vice-Consul (Inf) Johannesburg 1982.

Peirce, Robert Nigel; First Secretary (Chancery) UKMIS New York since August 1990; born 18.3.55; FCO 1977; Language Student Cambridge 1978; Language Student Hong Kong 1979; Second later First Secretary (Chancery) Peking 1980; First Secretary FCO 1983; on loan to Cabinet Office 1985; on Secondment to Hong Kong Government as Deputy Political Adviser 1986; Assistant Private Secretary to the Secretary of State 1988; m 1978 Christina Anne Skipworth Davis (1s 1986; 1d 1988).

Pellew, Mark Edward, LVO (1980); Counsellor FCO since November 1991; born 28.8.42; FO 1965-67; Third later Second Secretary Singapore 1967; Second Secretary Saigon 1969; Second later First Secretary FCO 1970; First Secretary (Inf) Rome 1976; First Secretary FCO 1980; Counsellor (Pol) Washington 1983; Counsellor on Secondment to Hambros Bank 1989; m 1965 Jill Thistlethwaite (2s 1966, 1968).

Pemberton, Rhonda Karen (née Leps); SUPL since April 1991; born 21.1.61; FCO 1985; Lagos 1987; FCO 1989; Grade S2A; m 1988 Robert John Pemberton (1d 1991).

Pemberton, Robert John; FCO since May 1989; born 11.6.63; FCO 1982; Lagos 1985; Grade 9; m 1988 Rhonda Karen Leps (1d 1991).

Pendered, Joanne Michelle; FCO since January 1992; born 2.11.65; FCO 1984; Bombay 1987; Santiago 1990; Grade 10.

Penfold, Peter Alfred, OBE (1986); Governor British Virgin Islands since October 1991; born 27.2.44; FO 1963; Bonn 1965; Kaduna 1968; Latin America Floater 1970; Canberra 1972; FCO 1972; Second Secretary Addis Ababa 1975; Second Secretary (Inf) Port of Spain 1978; FCO 1981; First Secretary January 1983; DHC and Head of Chancery Kampala 1984; First Secretary

FCO 1987; m 1972 Margaret Quigley (diss 1983) (2d 1963, 1974; 2s 1973, 1980); (2) Celia Delores Koenig.

Penney, John Anthony; FCO since May 1972; born 30.10.40; FO 1966; Second Secretary (Dev Asst) Lima 1968; Principal Research Office; Senior Principal Research Officer in 1990; (DS Grade 5); m 1968 Mary Perpetua Hurley.

Penrith, Alan Paul; Third later Second Secretary (Chancery) Ottawa since October 1988; born 24.5.58; Inland Revenue 1977; FCO 1978; Mexico City 1980; Yaoundé 1983; FCO 1985; m 1982 Karen Cooper (2s 1987, 1991).

Pepper, James McFadyen; First Secretary (Comm) Dublin since June 1992; born 10.6.36; MOD (Navy) 1954; MAFF 1963; DSAO 1967; Pretoria1/Cape Town 1968; Tehran 1972; On loan to DOI 1974; Vice-Consul (Comm) Adelaide 1977; Second later First Secretary JAO Brussels 1980; First Secretary FCO 1984; on loan to MOD 1986; First Secretary Islamabad 1988; m 1967 Sheila McDonald David (1s 1969; 1d 1972).

Perceval, Michael; HM Consul General Sao Paulo since March 1990; born 27.4.36; RAF 1956-60; First Secretary FCO 1970; UKREP Brussels 1972; First Secretary, later Head of Chancery Nicosia 1974; First Secretary FCO 1978; Counsellor and Head of Chancery Havana 1980; Brasilia 1982; Counsellor (Comm) Rome 1985; m 1968 Allessandra Grandis (1d 1969; 1s 1971).

Percy, Michael Vivian; FCO since January 1989; (Second Secretary 1991); born 9.8.50; DSAO (later FCO) 1968; Paris 1972; Brasilia 1975; Budapest 1977; FCO 1980; Quito 1983; Warsaw 1987; m 1972 Susan Roslyn Penrose (2d 1974, 1981; 1s 1977).

Perin, Susan Elsie; FCO since September 1991; born 4.11.52; FCO 1987; UKDEL Vienna 1989; Grade 2A.

Perkins, Graham Ernest; FCO since October 1989 (Second Secretary 1990); born 16.4.42; FCO 1972; Lagos 1974; Budapest 1977; FCO 1981; Kathmandu 1983; Frankfurt 1986; m 1970 Anastasia Simone (2s 1971, 1978; 1d 1984).

Perkins, Jacqueline Louise (née Gage); Second Secretary (Chancery/Information) Abu Dhabi since June 1992; born 3.10.64; FCO 1989; Second Secretary 1990; Language Training Cairo 1991; m 1991 Stuart Blair Perkins.

Perks, Adam Cecil; Third Secretary (Cons) Ottawa since October 1991; born 3.5.66; FCO (HCS) 1984; FCO 1987; Kuwait 1988; FCO 1991; Grade 9; m 1990 Nicola Rose Wardle.

Perks, Nicola Rose (née Wardle); Ottawa since

October 1991; born 16.9.65; FCO 1987; Amman 1989; SUPL 1990; FCO 1991; Grade S2; m 1990 Adam Cecil Perks.

Perrin, Geoffrey Gordon; Second later First Secretary FCO since October 1978; born 12.8.49; FCO 1971; Geneva 1975; m 1977 Heather Beryl Robson (2s 1979, 1984).

Perrott, John Gayford; First Secretary FCO since October 1988; born 5.7.43; CRO 1962; Karachi 1966; Ankara 1970; Calcutta 1972; Second Secretary (Cons1/Admin) Calcutta 1974; Second Secretary FCO 1976; Second later First Secretary Kathmandu 1979; Consul (Comm) Istanbul 1984; m 1964 Joan Wendy Lewis (1d 1964; 1s 1966).

Perry, Anthony John; Second Secretary Brussels since October 1990; born 5.3.39; GPO 1956; HM Forces 1959-61; GPO 1961; FO (later FCO) 1965; Singapore 1971; FCO 1973; Tokyo 1974; Third Secretary Brasilia 1983; FCO 1986; m 1971 Hendrika Huiberdina Vos (1s 1973; 1d 1976).

Perry, Christopher Ian; FCO since January 1990; born 27.5.70; Grade 10; m 1992 Charlotte Dawson.

Perry, Geoffrey Colin; First Secretary (UN/Press) UKMIS Geneva since May 1992; born 13.1.51; Third Secretary FCO 1973; Language Student Cambridge University 1975; Language Student1/Second Secretary Kuala Lumpur 1976 and Singapore 1977; Second later First Secretary FCO 1977; Trade Commissioner Hong Kong 1981; First Secretary FCO 1986; m 1975 Barbara Elisabeth Gysin (née Kaestlin) (2d 1977, 1979).

Perry, Mary; Helsinki since August 1989; born 6.12.36; FCO 1974; Belgrade 1975; Jakarta 1977; UKREP Brussels 1980; Peking 1986; FCO 1984; Grade S1.

Perry, Susan; FCO since January 1990; born 7.3.44; HCS 1965; FCO 1977; Havana 1979; Tunis 1980; Warsaw 1983; Kathmandu 1986; Grade 9.

Perry, Thomas Ian; Islamabad since November 1991; born 29.3.55; MOD 1972; FCO 1974; UKMIS New York 1976; Dubai 1979; Africa/ME Floater 1979; Jakarta 1981; FCO 1983; The Hague 1986; FCO 1988; Grade 9; m 1982 Jeannie Bell.

Persighetti, Stephen Victor; Second Secretary FCO since November 1991; born 31.3.56; FCO 1975; Moscow 1977; Beirut 1978; Tokyo 1981; Floater duties 1983; on loan to ODA 1985; Third Secretary (Aid) Jakarta 1988.

Peters, David Silvester; Lagos since June 1991; born 14.5.36; Army 1955-77; FCO 1977; Jedda

1978; Warsaw 1983; FCO 1986; BDSMO Hong Kong 1989; Grade 9; m 1963 Ursula Hopp (1s 1965; 1d 1969).

Petherbridge, Richard Sidney; Riyadh since July 1992; born 23.8.55; DHSS 1975; FCO 1980; Nicosia 1982; Seoul 1985; FCO 1987; Prague 1990; Grade 10; m 1982 Pauline Joan Mulvey (1s 1984; 1d 1986).

Pethick, Mark Julian; FCO since September 1990; born 3.4.68; Grade 9.

Pett, Frederick, LVO (1991); First Secretary (Consular) Islamabad since February 1992; born 19.12.40; GPO 1956; Passport Office 1960; CRO 1960; Lahore 1961; CRO 1963; Colombo 1964; Dubai 1967; Cairo 1971; FCO 1971; Dacca 1974; Second Secretary (Cons1/Immig) Bridgetown 1977; Second Secretary (Comm) Jakarta 1979; Second Secretary FCO 1983; First Secretary on loan to Office of Fair Trading 1985; First Secretary (Management) Harare 1987; m 1961 Iris Bailey (1d 1963).

Petty, Alan Edwin; First Secretary FCO since May 1990; born 4.11.46; Second later First Secretary FCO 1975; Consul Johannesburg 1980; FCO 1980; SUPL 1988; m 1988 Judith Rosemary Anne Barthram.

Phenna, Gillian; Buenos Aires since November 1991; born 3.12.68; FCO 1986; Cape Town/ Pretoria 1988; Grade 10.

Phillips, Alison Jane (née Francis), OBE (1991); First Secretary FCO since September 1990; born 18.4.56; FCO 1974; UKMIS New York 1981; Second Secretary FCO 1982; First Secretary Paris 1986; m 1978 Richard Charles Jonathan Phillips, QC.

Phillips, Duncan Keith; FCO since July 1989; born 7.3.69; Grade 10.

Phillips, Gillian Lynne (née Murray); SUPL since July 1989; born 8.5.63; FCO 1983; Brussels 1985; FCO 1987; Grade S2; m 1989 Quentin James Kitson Phillips.

Phillips, Quentin James Kitson; Second Secretary FCO since December 1992; born 20.10.63; FCO 1986; Second Secretary (Info) Budapest 1989; m 1989 Gillian Lynne Murray.

Phillips, Russell James; FCO since December 1991; born 24.2.64; FCO 1983; Georgetown 1985; Khartoum 1988; Grade 9.

Phillips, Sarah Louise; FCO since April 1988; born 17.12.39; FCO 1969; Delhi 1970; FCO 1971; Vientiane 1972; Washington 1975; FCO 1978; Rabat 1979; Belgrade 1982; FCO 1983; UKMIS Geneva 1985; Grade S1.

Phillips, Tom Richard Vaughan; Counsellor,

Consul-General and Deputy Head of Mission Tel Aviv since March 1990; born 21.6.50; DHSS 1977; FCO 1983; First Secretary Harare 1985; First Secretary FCO 1988; m 1986 Anne Renee Marie de la Motte (1s 1987; 2s 1989).

Philpott, Hugh Stanley; FCO since October 1990; (Second Secretary 1992); born 24.1.61; FCO 1980; Oslo 1982; Budapest 1985; Language Training 1987; Third Secretary (Comm) Baghdad 1988; m 1984 Janine Frederica Rule.

Philpott, Janine Frederica; FCO since October 1990; born 30.1.60; FCO 1980; UKDEL NATO Brussels 1982; Budapest 1985; FCO 1986; Baghdad 1988; Grade 9; m 1984 Hugh Stanley Philpott.

Pickering, Helen Mary; Third Secretary UKMIS Geneva since June 1990; born 10.7.64; FCO 1986; Moscow 1988; Algiers 1989; Grade 9.

Pickering, Sara Elizabeth; Vice-Consul Budapest since January 1991; born 22.4.67; FCO 1988; Grade 9.

Pickles, Carolyn; FCO since September 1991; born 1.3.61; FCO 1986; Pretoria 1988; Grade S2.

Pickup, Lawrence; FCO since September 1991; born 10.9.52; FCO 1976; Dar es Salaam 1980; Dubai 1982; SEA Floater 1986; On loan to the DT1 1989; Grade 9.

Picton, Joanne; Wellington since February 1992; born 7.10.69; FCO 1989; Grade 10.

Pierce, Anne Nicholson (née Creighton); Riyadh since June 1992; born 20.7.65; ODA 1984-89; FCO 1989; Grade S2; m 1991 Timothy Karl Pierce.

Pierce, Karen Elizabeth; PS to HM Ambassador Washington since December 1991; born 23.9.59; FCO 1981; Language Training 1983; Tokyo 1984; FCO 1987; (Second Secretary 1989); m 1987 Charles Fergusson Roxburgh.

Pigott, Carsten Orthöfer; First Secretary FCO since February 1991; born 31.5.53; FCO 1972; Lagos 1975; Language Student MECAS 1977 and FCO 1978; Third Secretary (Comm) Khartoum 1979; Second Secretary (Comm) Tripoli 1982; Second Secretary FCO 1984; First Secretary (Chancery) Peking 1987; m 1976 Susan Kathlyn Pugh (1d 1981; 1s 1983).

Pike, Andrew Kerry; Warsaw since January 1990; born 6.6.64; Dept of Transport 1982; FCO 1984; Sana'a 1985; Grade 9.

Pilmore-Bedford, Jeremy Patrick; FCO since September 1990; born 22.8.67; Grade 9.

Pindred, David; UKREP Brussels since September 1991; born 20.4.39; Rome 1980;

Dublin 1988; Pretoria 1990; Grade SO.

Pinkerton, Janet Elizabeth (née Lant) FCO since April 1988; born 23.2.59; FCO 1978; Canberra 1980; Budapest 1981; Tortola 1983; FCO 1986; SUPL 1987; Grade S2; m 1985 John Pinkerton.

Pinnock, Stuart Graham; FCO since January 1989; (Second Secretary 1992); born 19.5.63; FCO 1981; Paris 1984; Lagos 1986.

Piper, Geoffrey Hubert; Second Secretary (Management) Dar es Salaam since October 1991; born 7.7.37; FO 1962; Mbabane 1967; Rome 1970; Castries 1973; FCO 1977; Panama City 1980; Lagos 1983; FCO 1985; Atlanta 1989; m 1959 Marie Ann Marsh (2s 1965, 1969).

Piper, Rebecca Louise; Sofia since March 1991; born 24.9.68; Inland Revenue 1987; FCO 1989; Grade 10.

Pirie, Gordon Andrew; First Secretary (Commercial) and Deputy Head of Mission Rabat since March 1992; born 26.10.36; FO 1957; POMEF Cyprus 1957; Brussels 1959; Moscow 1962; Tehran 1964; FCO 1968; Kinshasa 1971; Second Secretary FCO 1974; Second Secretary (Inf) Tehran 1977; Second Secretary (Comm) Beirut 1980; Consul (Inf) Milan 1982; First Secretary (Inf) Rome 1984; FCO 1987; Chargé d'Affaires, a.i. later First Secretary (Comm) Tehran 1988; First Secretary (Deputy Head of Mission) Luanda 1989; m 1961 Maria Vaccaro (1d 1961; 1s 1965).

Pirnie, Graham John Campbell; First Secretary Head of Chancery/Consul Quito since August 1989; born 9.8.41; FO 1966; Phnom Penh 1968; Paris 1970; Second Secretary (Comm) The Hague 1974; Second later First Secretary FCO 1977; HM Consul Geneva 1982; FCO 1986; m 1967 Kathleen Gunstone (2s 1968, 1971; 1d 1983).

Pitman, John Richard; Moscow since May 1992; born 31.3.48; Grade SO; m 1992 Alison Jane Kesby.

Pitts, Barbara Anne, MVO (1989); FCO since August 1990; born 26.1.54; FCO 1975; Lagos 1975; Moscow 1977; FCO 1979; Nairobi 1981; FCO 1984; Kuala Lumpur 1987; Grade S1.

Plant, Michael Geoffrey; Second Secretary (Comm/Cons) Al Khobar since December 1990; born 12.10.46; Post Office 1964; FO 1966; Moscow 1969; Rabat 1970; Peking 1973; Brussels (JAO) 1975; FCO 1978; Banjul 1980; Los Angeles 1984; Second Secretary FCO 1987; m 1971 Hayfa Theodora Massouh (2d 1972, 1975).

Plastow, Caroline Mary; Third Secretary (Aid) Harare since August 1992; born 15.9.66; FCO

1990; on loan to the ODA 1990; Grade 9.

Plater, Stephen James; First Secretary (Comm) Tokyo since February 1990; born 23.1.54; FCO 1976; Second Secretary Tokyo 1978; Second later First Secretary FCO 1982; First Secretary and Head of Chancery UKDEL MBFR Vienna 1987; First Secretary UKDEL CACN Vienna 1989; m 1980 Keiko Kurata(1d 1990).

Platt, David Watson; Third Secretary (Immig) Bridgetown since November 1988; born 9.4.54; Inland Revenue 1972; FCO 1973; Beirut 1977; Brasilia 1980; Sofia 1981; FCO 1983; Dhaka 1985; Grade 9.

Platt, Janet Elizabeth (née Howells); UKREP Brussels since February 1992; born 26.3.61, Brussels (NATO) 1982, Washington 1985; FCO 1987; Anguilla 1988; FCO 1991; Grade S2A; m 1988 Philip Charles Platt (2s 1987, 1990).

Pleasant, Helen Ann (née Campbell); Valletta since September 1992; born 20.6.67; FCO 1986; Cairo 1989; FCO 1991; Grade S2; m 1991 Charles Roy Pleasant.

Plowman, Carol; SUPL since February 1991; born 4.4.64; FCO 1985; Vienna 1987; Grade 10; m 1991 Robin John Shackell.

Plumb, Michael Barry George; First Secretary (Comm) Jakarta since February 1990; born 16.5.45; DSAO 1965; Kampala 1968; Lahore 1971; FCO 1975; Washington 1977; Canberra 1979; Baghdad 1982; First Secretary FCO 1986; m 1968 Linda Wills Gledhill (1s 1972; 1d 1975).

Plumbly, Derek John, CMG (1991); Counsellor and Head of Chancery UKMIS New York since May 1992 ; born 15.5.48; FCO 1972; Reporting Officer New York 1972; FCO 1973; MECAS 1973; Second later First Secretary Jedda 1975; First Secretary Cairo 1977; FCO 1980; First Secretary (Comm) Washington 1984; Counsellor and Head of Chancery Riyadh 1988; m 1979 Nadia Youssef Gohar (1d 1983; 2s 1985, 1987).

Pocock, Andrew John; First Secretary FCO since June 1992; born 23.8.55; FCO 1981; Second later First Secretary (Comm) Lagos 1983; First Secretary FCO 1986; First Secretary (Chancery) Washington 1988; m 1976 Dayalini Pathmanathan.

Polatajko, Mark Alexander; FCO since July 1991; born 16.10.70; Grade 10.

Poll, Gillian Ann (née Smith); FCO since April 1991; born 30.4.58; HCS 1976; FCO 1985; Brussels 1987; UKREP Brussels 1990; Grade S2A; m 1988 Christopher John Poll.

Pollard, Colin Cecil; FCO since June 1984; born 6.12.35; GPO 1952; HM Forces 1954-56; GPO 1956; FO 1964; Paris 1964; Saigon 1966; FO

1967; Rawalpindi 1968; FCO 1970; Rome 1974; FCO 1977; Hong Kong 1978; FCO 1980; Prague 1981; Grade 8; m 1964 Marian Cook.

Pook, Brian Arthur; Lilongwe since April 1991; born 2.7.38; Army 1957-77; Moscow 1984; Montevideo 1985; Nicosia 1986; Helsinki 1989; Havana 1990; Grade SO; m 1973 Greta.

Poole, Christopher George Robert; Antananarivo since June 1991; born 19.4.52; FCO 1970; Algiers 1973; Brasilia 1974; Rio de Janeiro 1976; Freetown 1978; Paris 1981; Kinshasa 1984; FCO 1988; Grade 9; m 1977 Maria Madalena Gomes Ferreira.

Poole, Christopher James, MBE (1987); Management Officer ECMIS Zagreb since June 1992; born 24.12.46; CRO 1964; FCO 1968; Georgetown 1969; Africa Floater 1969; St Lucia 1971; Bridgetown 1973; FCO 1976; Munich 1979; FCO 1982; Beirut 1985; Second Secretary Luxembourg 1987; m (1) 1973 Lillian Hodgson (2d 1979, 1980); (2) 1987 Marilyn Kathleen Povey.

Pooley, Nigel Arthur; FCO since September 1991; born 12.11.61; Grade 9; m 1985 Helena Falle (2s 1986, 1991; 1d 1988).

Porter, Elizabeth Judith; SUPL since August 1988; born 18.1.63; FCO 1985; Pretoria 1987; Grade S2.

Porter, Gillian Sarah; Moscow since January 1991; born 7.4.1966; FCO 1988; Grade S2.

Porter, Neil David; FCO since June 1992; born 14.4.63; FCO 1982; Riyadh 1985; Budapest 1989; Grade 9; m 1986 Gajetana Dominica Maria de Wit.

Poston, James; Counsellor FCO since September 1992; born 19.6.45; Third Secretary FCO 1970; concurrently Third Secretary and Vice-Consul HM Embassy to Chad; Second Secretary and Private Secretary to Head of UKDEL EC Brussels 1971; First Secretary Tel Aviv 1973; FCO 1978; First Secretary (Comm) Lagos 1982; FCO 1985; Counsellor and Head of Chancery Pretoria 1988; m. 1976 Anna Caroline Bos.

Pothecary, William Sidney; FCO since October 1987; (First Secretary 1991); born 31.7.35; GPO 1952; HM Forces 1954-56; GPO 1956; FO 1960; Moscow 1961; FO 1962; Tokyo 1963; Prague 1966; FCO 1968; Bridgetown 1972; Copenhagen 1975; FCO 1978; Second Secretary Pretoria 1985; m 1959 Barbara Elizabeth Bissitt (3s 1963, 1965, 1969).

Potter, Richard William; First Secretary (Information) Nicosia since April 1990; born 22.5.60; FCO 1983; Third later Second Secretary Riyadh 1985; Second Secretary FCO 1988.

Potter, Terence George; Rome since July 1990; born 5.9.41; HM Forces (Army) 1959-83; Prague 1983; Stockholm 1986; Peking 1989; Grade SO; m 1987 Valerie Amelia Levine.

Poundes, Michael Dudley; Third Secretary Lagos since February 1989; born 9.8.39; FO 1966; Singapore 1967; FCO 1969; Kinshasa 1971; FCO 1972; Tokyo 1974; FCO 1977; Islamabad 1978; FCO 1981; Third Secretary Athens 1984; FCO 1987; Grade 8; m 1960 Joan Butler (3s 1961, 1964, 1968).

Pover, Alan John, CMG (1990); High Commissioner Banjul since October 1990; born 16.12.33; HM Forces 1953-54; MPNI 1954; CRO 1961; Second Secretary (Admin) Lagos 1962; Second Secretary (Admin) Tel Aviv 1966; Second Secretary (Comm) Karachi 1970; First Secretary (Admin1/Cons) Islamabad 1971; FCO 1973; Consul (Comm) Cape Town 1976; First Secretary FCO 1980; Counsellor Overseas Inspectorate FCO 1983; Counsellor (Admin) and Consul-General Washington 1986; m 1964 Doreen Elizabeth Dawson (2d 1965, 1971; 1s 1966).

Powell, David Herbert; First Secretary Tokyo since October 1988; born 29.4.52 MOD 1974; FCO 1984 Gillian Mary.

Powell, Eric; FCO since May 1992; born 12.2.49; FCO 1978; Peking 1983; FCO 1986; Helsinki 1989; Grade 9; m 1976 Jennifer Keene.

Powell, Gillian Ann; FCO since May 1989; born 15.6.58; FCO 1977; Warsaw 1980; FCO 1982; Brussels 1986; Grade 9.

Powell, Hugh Eric; FCO since October 1991; born 6.2.67; Grade 8.

Powell, Ian Francis; First Secretary (Admin/Cons) Kingston since September 1989; born 30.12.47; Commonwealth Office (later FCO) 1966; Freetown 1970; Havana 1973; FCO 1975; Stockholm 1978; Dublin 1981; (Second Secretary 1983); Second Secretary FCO 1986; m 1969 Priscilla Ann Fenton (2d 1974, 1980).

Powell, Jonathan Nicholas; First Secretary (Chancery) Washington since July 1991; born 14.8.56; FCO 1979; Third later Second Secretary Lisbon 1981; Second later First Secretary FCO 1984; UKDEL CDE Stockholm 1986; UKDEL CSCE Vienna 1986; First Secretary FCO 1989; m 1980 Karen Elizabeth Drayne (2s 1982, 1985).

Powell, Martin; Second Secretary Singapore since January 1988; born 21.10.46; FCO 1969; Warsaw 1973; FCO 1974; Brussels 1982; FCO 1985; m (1) 1972 Susan Kay Bower (diss); (2) 1982 Patricia Helen Scruby (1s 1987).

Powell, Richard Stephen; First Secretary (Science) Tokyo since April 1992; born

19.10.59; FCO 1981; Third later Second
Secretary Helsinki 1983; First Secretary FCO
1988.

Power, Anne Maria; UKDEL Strasburg since
February 1992; born 14.8.65; FCO 1989; Grade
9.

Power, Carmel Angela; FCO since September
1990; born 30.10.63; Grade 9.

Powles, Michael Walter; Consul (Commercial)
Johannesburg since July 1992; born 27.9.41; FO
1964; Yaoundé 1965; FO 1967; Geneva 1968;
FCO 1971; Prague 1972; UKDEL NATO
Brussels 1977; Second Secretary FCO 1978; HM
Consul Rio de Janeiro 1982; First Secretary
(Comm) Brasilia 1983; FCO 1985; First
Secretary Kingston 1986; First Secretary FCO
1990; m 1965 Cherrell Elaine Nunn (2s 1968,
1972).

Pratt, David Ernest; FCO since December 1988;
born 23.11.51; FO 1968; Warsaw 1986; Grade 9;
m 1970 Rosemary Catherine Eburne (2s 1971,
1973).

Precious, Mark; SUPL since October 1990; born
29.8.56; FCO 1983; First Secretary BIS Buenos
Aires 1986; First Secretary FCO 1989; m 1985
Amanda Lucille Hamilton Brookfield (1s 1990).

Preece, Peter Boswell; Counsellor (Political)
Jakarta since May 1990; born 8.10.44; Second
Secretary FCO 1971; Language student Sheffield
University 1973; Language student Tokyo 1974;
First Secretary Tokyo 1975; FCO 1979; First
Secretary Islamabad 1982; On loan to Cabinet
Office 1985; m 1967 Jennifer Elizabeth Palmer
(1d 1970; 2s 1972, 1977).

Prendergast, Sir (Walter) Kieran, KCVO (1991),
CMG (1990); British High Commissioner Nairobi
since October 1992; born 2.7.42; FO 1962;
Istanbul 1964; Ankara 1965; FO 1967; Second
Secretary Nicosia 1969; Civil Service College
1972; First Secretary FCO 1972; First Secretary
(Inf later Econ) The Hague 1973; Assistant
Private Secretary to the Secretary of State 1976;
UKMIS New York 1979; Counsellor, Head of
Chancery and Consul-General, Tel Aviv 1982;
Counsellor FCO 1986; High Commissioner
Harare 1989; m 1967 Joan Reynolds (2s 1968,
1976; 2d 1971, 1973).

Prentice, Christopher Norman Russell; First
Secretary FCO since September 1989; born
5.9.54; FCO 1977; Language Student MECAS
1978; Third later Second Secretary Kuwait 1980;
First Secretary on loan to Cabinet Office 1983;
First Secretary Washington 1985; m 1978 Marie-
Josephine (Nina) King (2s 1981, 1988; 1d 1982).

Preston, Joseph Raymond; Nicosia since August
1989; born 1.6.61; FCO 1980; Dhaka 1983;
Kathmandu 1985; Grade 10; m 1984 Gemma

Margaret Josephine Wynn.

Preston, Linda Jane; Nairobi since April 1992;
born 9.10.58; FCO 1981; Caracas 1982; Grand
Turk 1986; FCO 1989; Warsaw 1990; Grade S2.

Preston, Thomas Hugo; Counsellor Wellington
since December 1988; born 1.6.38; FO 1962;
Third Secretary Tokyo 1963; Second later First
Secretary FO (later FCO) 1966; Hong Kong
1970; Peking 1972; FCO 1974; First Secretary
later Counsellor UKMIS New York 1979; FCO
1984; m 1966 Junko Monica Atsumi (1s 1967;
1d 1969).

Preston, William Edward Johnston; First
Secretary (Comm) Bucharest since November
1992; born 7.7.47; FCO 1965; Ankara 1969;
Kinshasa 1972; FCO 1974; Rabat 1976; Oslo
1979; Second Secretary (Admin) Moscow 1983;
Second Secretary FCO 1985; Second Secretary
(Comm) Port of Spain 1988; m 1969 Anne
Kathleen Smith (1s 1974).

Price, Donald Stanley, MBE (1988); Second
Secretary FCO since July 1988; born 9.12.35;
GPO 1951; HM Forces 1955-57; GPO 1957;
FO 1963; Tel Aviv 1965; Singapore 1968;
FCO 1970; Geneva 1971; Cairo 1972; FCO
1974; Madrid 1977; FCO 1979; Bucharest
1980; FCO 1981; Warsaw 1984; m 1957 Ann
Shirley King (1s 1962; 3d 1958, 1960, 1964).

Price, Kenneth George; FCO since November
1991; born 12.4.65; FCO 1983; Bonn 1985;
Accra 1988; Grade 9; m 1987 Carol Margaret
Lowe.

Price, Michael Anthony, LVO (1991); First
Secretary (Press and Public Affairs) Washington
since October 1988; born 13.8.44; Board of
Trade 1964; DSAO 1966; Commonwealth Office
1967; New Delhi 1969; Second Secretary
(Chancery) Freetown 1972; FCO 1973; Second
later First Secretary (Aviation and Defence)
Paris 1974; Consul (Comm) Montreal 1979;
JSDC Greenwich 1983; First Secretary FCO
1984; m 1968 Elizabeth Anne Cook (1d 1972;
1s 1974).

Price, Sarah Helena; FCO since September 1990;
Second Secretary 1992; born 4.6.66; Grade 9.

Priest, Janet Susan Christine (née Huish); First
Secretary (Disarmanent) UKMIS New York since
January 1991; born 24.12.45; FCO 1973;
Islamabad 1976; SUPL 1978; FCO 1980; Second
Secretary (Comm) Peking 1986; First Secretary
FCO 1988; m Derek Stanley Priest.

Priest, Timothy Ian; First Secretary (Chancery/
Info) Athens since April 1989; born 27.10.47;
FCO 1972; Vienna 1975; First Secretary FCO
1980; First Secretary (Chancery) Helsinki 1981;
FCO 1985; m Teresa Jean Bagnall (2d 1975,
1980; 2s 1978, 1987).

Priestley, Carol Ann (née Edwards); Auckland since July 1989; born 11.11.53; FCO 1974; Paris 1976; Düsseldorf 1979; Kathmandu 1980; FCO 1982; Dhaka 1985; Grade 9; m 1976 Lawrence Minton Priestley.

Priestley, Philip John; HM Consul-General Geneva since August 1992; born 29.8.46; FCO 1969; Third Secretary Sofia 1971; Third later Second Secretary Kinshasa 1973; First Secretary FCO 1976; Head of Chancery Wellington 1979; First Secretary FCO 1984; Counsellor (Comm) Manila 1987; HM Ambassador Libreville 1990; CDA Harvard University 1991; m 1972 Christine Rainforth (1d 1976; 1s 1978).

Prime, Ashley Walter John; FCO since February 1989; born 6.8.59; FCO 1978; Bonn 1980; Kingston 1983; Peking 1986; Grade 9; m 1985 Tina Thackstone.

Prime, Tina (née Thackstone); FCO since February 1989; born 5.2.61; HM Treasury 1980; FCO 1982; Port Stanley 1983; Kingston 1984; Peking 1986; Grade S1; m 1985 Ashley Walter John Prime.

Prince, Graham James; Second Secretary (Economic) Tokyo since November 1991; born 8.11.63; FCO 1987; Langauge Training 1989; Full-Time Language Training Kamakura 1990; m 1991 Elaine Heather MacCormack.

Pring, Alison June; Second Secretary FCO since August 1991; born 18.6.61; FCO 1983; SUPL 1983; FCO 1984; Third Secretary Brussels 1986; Third later Second Secretary Caracas 1989.

Pring, Mary; FCO since August 1991; born 29.6.60; Grade 9.

Pringle, Anne Fyfe; on secondment to the European Political Cooperation Secretariat since June 1991; born 13.1.55; FCO 1977; Moscow 1980; San Francisco 1983; Second Secretary UKREP Brussels 1986; Second later First Secretary FCO 1987; m 1987 Bleddyn Glynne Leyshon Phillips.

Pringle, Julia Margaret Georgina; FCO since October 1991; born 28.3.48; FCO 1966-1971; Metropolitan Police 1971; Grade 10; m 1971 Raymond Elliott Pringle (1d 1981).

Pringle, Raymond Elliott; Second later First Secretary FCO since October 1989; born 28.11.51; Department of Employment 1968-69; FCO 1970; UKREP Brussels 1972; Quito 1975; FCO 1978; Bilbao 1981; Barcelona 1983; Second Secretary (Chancery/Inf) Lilongwe 1986; m 1971 Julia Margaret Georgina Wright (1d 1981).

Pritchard, Grant; FCO since September 1990; born 2.6.70; Grade 10.

Pritchard-Davies, William Noel Devon

Drummond; FCO since August 1990; Police 1962-71; New Delhi 1971; Moscow 1973; Bonn 1974; Helsinki 1976; FCO 1978; Brussels 1979; UKDEL NATO Brussels 1984; Bonn 1987; Grade 9; m 1964 Diane Margaret Johnston (dec'd 1983) (2s 1966, 1971; 1d 1968).

Procter, Barbara Ann; Second Secretary (Chancery) Wellington since March 1992; born 8.5.60; FCO 1982; Latin America Floater 1984; Third Secretary (Trade Policy) Washington 1986; Second Secretary FCO 1990.

Proctor, Matthew Joel; FCO since September 1991; born 16.7.71; Grade 10.

Prouten, Matthew David; Tokyo since November 1992; born 10.3.69; FCO 1988; Grade 10.

Pryce, Andrew William; Washington since March 1991; born 9.2.70; FCO 1988; Grade 10.

Publicover, Ralph Martin; First Secretary FCO since July 1992; born 2.5.52; FCO 1976; Language Student MECAS 1977; Second later First Secretary Dubai 1979; First Secretary (Econ) Ottawa 1981; First Secretary on loan to Cabinet Office 1985; FCO 1987; First Secretary (Chancery) Washington 1989; m 1973 Rosemary Sheward (1d 1979; 1s 1983).

Pugh, David Evan; Tokyo since August 1992; born 26.4.51; FCO 1982; Pretoria 1983; Cairo 1988; Grade 8; m 1976 Bethan Jones (4d 1980, 1982, 1984, 1986).

Pugh, Helen Natalie; Third later Second Secretary Bonn since June 1990; born 17.7.66; FCO 1988; on secondment to the Auswartiges Amt 1989.

Pullen, Brian Peter; First Secretary, FCO since June 1988; born 2.5.41; GPO 1960; FO 1961; Jedda 1963; Brussels 1965; Belgrade 1967; Freetown 1970; FCO 1974; Second Secretary (Admin/Cons) Algiers 1977; Consul Bordeaux 1980; Second (later First) Secretary (Econ) Paris 1982; m 1965 Annie Bernes (2s 1967, 1969).

Pullen, Roderick Allen; Counsellor (Technology) Paris since November 1990; born 11.4.49; MOD 1975; Second Secretary UKDEL NATO Brussels 1978; MOD 1980; First Secretary UKDEL CSCE Madrid 1981; FCO 1982; DHC Suva 1984; First Secretary 1988; m 1971 Karen Lesley Sketchley (1d 1975; 1s 1978).

Pullen, Russell Lewis; First Secretary FCO since April 1986; born 10.1.54; Second Secretary FCO 1975; m 1979 Gillian May Wright (1s 1985; 1d 1988).

Purves, Michael; Third later Second Secretary (Econ/Aid) Kuala Lumpur since April 1989; born 3.11.57; FCO 1975; New Delhi 1978; ME Floater 1982; Mogadishu 1983; FCO 1986;

Grade 9; m 1985 Ruth Joan Goodwin (1d 1986).

Puryer, Stuart John; Copenhagen since October 1990; born 3.6.67; FCO 1987; Grade 9.

Pyle, Nicholas John; FCO since July 1992; born 9.12.60; FCO 1981; UKMIS Geneva 1984; Prague 1984; Kabul 1986; Jedda 1990; Grade 9.

Q

Quantrill, William Ernest; HM Ambassador and Consul-General Youndé since April 1991; additionally HM Ambassador and Consul-General (non resident) to the Repulic of Chad, to Equatorial Guinea and to the Central African Republic; born 4.5.39; FO 1962; Third later Second Secretary (Comm) Brussels 1964; Second Secretary (Comm) Havana 1966; First Secretary FCO 1969; Head of Chancery Manila 1973; FCO 1977; Counsellor (Comm) Lagos 1980; Head of Training Dept FCO 1980; Deputy Head of POD FCO 1981; Counsellor, Head of Chancery Caracas 1984; Deputy Governor Gibraltar 1988; m 1964 Rowena Mary Collins (3s 1965, 1966, 1970; 1d 1968).

Quayle, Quinton Mark; First Secretary FCO since January 1991; born 5.6.55; FCO 1977; Language Training 1978; Third Secretary (Chancery) Bangkok 1979 (Second Secretary 1981); FCO 1983 (First Secretary 1984); ENA Paris 1986; First Secretary Paris 1987; m 1979 Alison Marshall (2s 1982, 1985).

Quinn, Jean Margaret (née Leiper); SUPL since April 1990; born 21.3.53; FCO 1975; Abidjan 1978; Brasilia 1982; Second Secretary FCO 1984; m 1985 Peter Nugent Quinn (1d 1987; 1s 1989).

Quinn, Lorraine; FCO since May 1991; born 25.6.66; Grade S2; m 1986 Martin Quinn (1s 1988).

R

Radcliffe, Adam; UKMIS Geneva since September 1990; born 10.6.67; FCO 1988; Grade 10.

Radcliffe, James Crossley, mvo (1980); On Secondment to the Inter-Parliamentary Union since January 1992; born 17.3.40; Ministry of Labour 1961; MECAS 1965; Kuwait 1967; Frankfurt 1970; Polytechnic of Central London 1973; FCO 1974; Second Secretary (Comm) Algiers 1977; Consul (Comm) Stuttgart 1981; First Secretary (Chancery) Dublin 1984; First Secretary FCO 1989; m 1966 Angela Goldie (2s

1967, 1969).

Rae, William Innes, obe (1992), mbe (1980); Deputy Head of European Council Unit (in Edinburgh) since March 1992; born 17.4.40; FO 1958; Hargeisa 1961; Mogadishu 1962; Dubai 1963; DSAO 1968; MECAS 1969; Baghdad 1971; Jedda 1973, later Second Secretary (Comm) FCO 1979; First Secretary (Comm) Paris 1983; First Secretary and Head of Chancery Bahrain 1986; m 1964 Helen Elizabeth McGuffog (dec'd 1973) (1d 1965; 1s 1970).

Raine, John Andrew; First Secretary FCO since January 1991; born 12.7.62; FCO 1984; Language Training 1986; Second Secretary (Inf) Kuwait 1988.

Rajguru, Harish L; Sofia since August 1992; born 23.4.61; HCS cadre of the FCO 1989; FCO 1990; Grade 10.

Rakestraw, Mark Andrew; Athens since September 1990; born 30.11.67; FCO 1988; Grade 10.

Ralph, Richard Peter, cvo (1991); Counsellor Washington since February 1989; born 27.4.46; Third Secretary FCO 1969; Third later Second Secretary Vientiane 1970; Second later First Secretary (Inf) Lisbon 1974; First Secretary FCO 1977; First Secretary and Head of Chancery Harare 1981; First Secretary later Counsellor FCO 1985; m 1970 Margaret Elisabeth Coulthurst (1s 1970; 1d 1974).

Ramsay, Sir Allan (John), kbe (1992), cmg (1989); HM Ambassador Khartoum since June 1990; born 19.10.37; HM Forces 1958-71; FCO 1971; First Secretary (Comm) Cairo 1973; First Secretary Head of Chancery and Consul Kabul 1976; FCO 1978; Counsellor Baghdad 1980; Head of Chancery Mexico City 1983; Counsellor FCO 1985; HM Ambassador Beirut 1988; m 1966 Pauline Therése Lescher (1s 1967; 1d 1969).

Ramsay, Paul Andrew, mbe (1988); Assistant Management Officer Madrid since Aprll 1992; born 10.10.55; FCO 1975; East Berlin 1977; Istanbul 1979; UKDEL NATO Brussels 1981; Tehran 1984; FCO 1987 (Second Secretary 1990); m 1980 Carey-Jane Lambert (1d 1987, 1s 1989).

Ramscar, Michael Charles; First Secretary FCO since October 1991; born 26.2.48; Second Secretary FCO 1975; Second Secretary (Econ) Lagos 1977; First Secretary (Econ) Brasilia 1979; First Secretary FCO 1982; Madrid 1986; San José 1989; m 1970 Janis Lemon (2s 1976, 1981).

Ramsden, Sir John (Charles Josslyn), Bt; Counsellor and Deputy Head of Mission East Berlin later British Embassy Berlin Office, since

May 1990; born 19.8.50; FCO 1975; Third later Second Secretary Dakar 1976; First Secretary UKDEL MBFR Vienna 1979; First Secretary Head of Chancery and Consul Hanoi 1980; First Secretary FCO 1982; on loan to HM Treasury 1988; First Secretary FCO 1988; m 1985 Jane Bevan (2d 1987, 1989).

Ramsey, Mary Colette Josephine; Buenos Aires since January 1990; born 1.5.58: FCO 1984; Rome 1987; Grade S2.

Ramsey, Patricia Anne; SUPL since February 1991; born 9.1.48; FO 1967; UKDEL EEC Brussels 1969; Rio de Janeiro 1972; FCO 1974; Athens 1980; UKMIS Geneva 1983; FCO 1986; Paris 1987; Grade 9; m 1990 Paul Lever.

Rankin, Elaine Jean; SUPL since December 1988; born 10.2.57; FCO 1982; Second Secretary UKREP Brussels 1984; FCO 1985.

Rankin, John James; Legal Adviser UKMIS and UKDIS Geneva since August 1991; born 12.3.57; FCO 1989; Senior Assistant Legal Adviser; m 1987; Lesley Marshall (1d 1989).

Ranson, Catherine Fraser (née Armstrong); Athens since February 1989; born 16.7.53; FCO 1971; Paris 1974; Gaborone 1977; FCO 1980; Manila 1985; Grade 9; m 1981 Clive Paul Ranson.

Rapp, Stephen Robert; Hanoi since June 1992; born 9.3.52; HO 1986; FCO 1986; Accra 1988; Grade 10; m 1978 Judy Elizabeth Flewett.

Ratcliffe, Deborah; FCO since September 1991; born 6.4.62; FCO 1980; UKMIS Geneva 1982; Harare 1985; Manila 1988; Grade 9.

Ratcliffe, Yvonne; Peking since August 1992; born 18.6.62; FCO 1988; Athens 1989; Grade S2.

Ratford, David John Edward, CMG (1984), CVO (1979); HM Ambassador Oslo since May 1990; born 22.4.34; HM Forces 1953-55; FO 1955; Prague 1959; Second Secretary Mogadishu 1961; FO 1963; (First Secretary 1965); First Secretary (Comm) Moscow 1968; FCO 1971; Counsellor (Agric1/Econ) Paris 1974; Counsellor and Head of Chancery Copenhagen 1978; Minister Moscow 1983; AUSS (Europe) FCO 1986; m 1960 Ulla Monica Jerneck (2d 1961, 1966).

Raven, Martin Clark; First Secretary (Chancery) UKMIS New York since April 1988; born 10.3.54; FCO 1976; Third Secretary Lagos 1978; FCO 1979; Third, later Second Secretary New Delhi 1979; Second later First Secretary FCO 1983; m 1978 Philippa Michele Morrice Ruddick (2s 1982, 1984).

Rawbone, Jane Lynn; Madrid since March 1991; born 21.3.53; FCO 1976; UKDEL MBFR Vienna 1977; Helsinki 1980; FCO 1982; Mexico City 1984; UKMIS New York 1988; Grade S1.

Rawlins, Helen Catherine; Manila since May 1991; born 31.7.64; FCO 1986; Bonn 1988; Grade 9.

Rawlinson, Colin James; First Secretary FCO since June 1984; born 21.2.46; DSAO 1967; Reykjavik 1968; Nicosia 1971; Hamburg 1973; Second Secretary FCO 1976; Copenhagen 1979; Second Secretary (Comm) New Delhi 1981; m 1966 The Hon Catharine Julia Trend (2d 1967, 1969).

Rawlinson, Ivor Jon, OBE (1988); First Secretary FCO since October 1988; later Counsellor; born 24.1.42; FO 1964; Warsaw 1966; Bridgetown 1969; Second Secretary FCO 1971; Assistant Private Secretary to Minister of State, FCO 1973; Second Secretary (Econ) Paris 1974; First Secretary FCO 1978; First Secretary (Comm) Mexico City 1980; Consul Florence 1984; m 1976 Catherine Paule Caudal (1s 1980; 2d 1977, 1983).

Rawlinson, Timothy Simeon; Second later First Secretary (Inf) Lagos since March 1991; born 12.1.62; Second Secretary FCO 1988.

Ray, Peter Warwick; Consul (Commercial) Atlanta since July 1991; born 8.8.41; CO 1958-59; CRO 1961; Lahore 1963; Paris 1965; Tel Aviv 1968; FCO 1971; Nairobi 1974; Ankara 1977; (Second Secretary 1980); Vice-Consul Munich 1981; on loan to the DTI 1985; Second Secretary (Comm) Peking 1989; m 1962 Aileen (2s 1966, 1969).

Rayner, Barbara Heulyn (née Dunlop); First Secretary FCO since March 1970; born 20.5.39; FO 1962.

Rayner, Robert Alan; Consul (Comm) Osaka since June 1989; born 14.12.50; FCO 1968; Islamabad 1972; Language Student 1974; Tokyo 1975; DOT 1979; FCO 1982; Second Secretary (Chancery/Inf) and Vice-Consul Lima 1984; FCO 1987; m (1) 1972 Jeannette Denise Oddy (diss 1984); (2) 1984 Dawn Carol Ashton.

Rea, Elizabeth Rose; UKREP Brussels since January 1992; born 31.10.54; FCO 1976; Luxembourg 1978; Lima 1981; Washington 1984; FCO 1987; Grade S1.

Read, Rachel Frances; Cairo since March 1991; born 23.10.65; FCO 1989; Grade S2.

Read-Ward, Melanie; Warsaw since November 1991; born 16.5.68; FCO 1989; Grade 9.

Readdie, Catherine Alison Jane; Third Secretary (Chancery/Visits) Warsaw since September 1992; born 17.6.66; FCO 1990; Grade 9.

Reade, Brian Anthony; Counsellor FCO since April 1986; born 5.2.40; Second Secretary FO (later FCO) 1965; First Secretary Bangkok 1970; FCO 1974; Consul (Econ) Düsseldorf 1977; FCO 1981; First Secretary later Counsellor Bangkok 1982; m 1964 Averille van Eugen (1s 1969; 1d 1970).

Reader, David George; First Secretary (Management) and Consul Belgrade since July 1992; born 1.10.47; CRO, DSAO and FCO 1964; Warsaw 1969; Paris 1972; Bucharest 1974; FCO 1976; Kinshasa 1979; Kathmandu 1982; Second Secretary FCO 1984; Vice-Consul (Comm) Brisbane 1987; m 1969 Elaine McKnight (1s 1975; 1d 1980).

Rebecchi, Silvano Marco Raffaele; Paris since January 1990; born 14.8.52; Department of Education and Science 1972; FCO 1975; Baghdad 1977; Valletta 1981; Dhaka 1984; FCO 1986; Grade 9; m 1984 Eileen Zammit (2s 1985, 1987).

Reddaway, David Norman, MBE (1980); Chargé d'A ffaires a.i. Tehran since October 1990; (Counsellor 1991); born 26.4.53; FCO 1975; Language Student SOAS 1976 and Iran 1977; Third later Second Secretary (Commercial) Tehran 1977; Second later First Secretary (Chancery) Tehran 1978; First Secretary (Chancery) Madrid 1980; First Secretary FCO 1985; Private Secretary to Minister of State 1986; First Secretary, British Interests Section, Tehran 1988; First Secretary (Chancery) New Delhi 1988; m 1981 Roshan Taliyeh Firouz (1s 1983, 1d 1987).

Redden, Michael James; FCO since July 1990; born 22.2.70; DHSS 1987; Grade 10.

Reddicliffe, Paul, FCO since September 1989; born 17.3.45; FCO 1977; Principal Research Officer (DS Grade 5); First Secretary Canberra 1985; m 1974 Wee Siok Boi (2s 1977, 1979).

Redmond, Caroline Anne; FCO since September 1990; born 10.9.68; Grade 8.

Redshaw, Peter Robert Gransden; Counsellor FCO since February 1992; born 16.4.42; Third later Second Secretary FCO 1968; Second later First Secretary Kampala 1970; FCO 1973; First Secretary later Counsellor Lagos 1982; FCO 1985; Counsellor Kuala Lumpur 1988; m 1970 Margaret Shaun Mizon (1s 1978; 2d 1980; 1985).

Rees, Anwen Eluned; FCO since Febraury 1991; born 22.7.64; Grade S2..

Rees, William Lyndon; Second Secretary (Management) New Delhi since October 1989; born 7.8.33; FO 1964; Beirut 1966; Ottawa 1969; UKDEL Brussels 1972; FCO 1975; Karachi 1978; Cairo 1982 (Second Secretary 1983); Second Secretary FCO 1985; m 1965 Angela Rhodes (2s 1967, 1970; 1d 1968).

Reeve, Sir Anthony, KCMG (1992), CMG (1986); HM Ambassador Pretoria/Cape Town since July 1991; born 20.10.38; Second Secretary CRO 1965; MECAS 1966; Second later First Secretary and Assistant Political Agent Abu Dhabi 1968; First Secretary FCO 1970; First Secretary Washington 1973; Counsellor 1978; Study Visit to Chatham House 1978; Head of Arms Control and Disarmament Dept FCO 1979; Counsellor Cairo 1981; Head of Southern African Department FCO 1984; AUSS (Africa) FCO 1986; HM Ambassador Amman 1988; m 1964 Pamela Margaret Angus (diss. 1988) (1s 1968; 2d 1972, 1977).

Reeve, Richard Robert; First Secretary FCO since February 1987; born 28.7.48; FCO 1971; Third later Second Secretary Singapore 1973; Language student Cambridge University 1975 and Hong Kong 1976; Trade Commissioner Hong Kong 1977; First Secretary FCO 1981; First Secretary Hong Kong 1983; m 1971 Monique Marie-Louise Moggio (2s 1974, 1977).

Reeve, Roy Stephen; Consul-General Sydney since May 1991; born 20.8.41; Customs and Excise 1961-62; FO 1966; Moscow 1968; First Secretary FCO 1973; First Secretary (Comm) Moscow 1978; FCO 1980; Counsellor on loan to HCS 1983; Deputy Consul-General Johannesburg 1985; Counsellor FCO 1989; m 1964 Geraldine Lee (2d 1969, 1971).

Reeves, Ceinwen Mary; FCO since September 1989; born 9.6.57; FCO 1976; SUPL 1976; FCO 1979; Bonn 1982; Lilongwe 1984; Paris 1987; Grade 9.

Reeves, John Alan, LVO (1989); First Secretary (Admin) Singapore since May 1988; born 26.1.39; CRO 1962; Port of Spain 1964; Georgetown 1966; Bangkok 1967; Brunei 1970; FCO 1973; Muscat 1976; Tripoli 1980; Second Secretary FCO 1981; Second Secretary (Admin) and Consul Sana'a 1984; m (1) 1964 Angela Marcia Bird (1s 1965; 1d 1967); (2) 1973 Christine Eva Barrett (2d 1975, 1977).

Regan, Michael John; First Secretary FCO since November 1991; born 17.8.55; FCO 1983; Second later First Secretary Kabul 1986; FCO 1988; First Secretary (Chancery/Econ) Dubai 1989; m 1986 Carolyn Gaye Black (2s 1987, 1989).

Rehal, Opinder Kumar; Canberra since April 1992; born 15.9.48; FCO 1979; Bonn 1982; FCO 1985; Islamabad 1989; FCO 1990; Grade 8; m 1974 Jagdeep Nandra (1s 1975 (dec'd 1990); 1d 1978).

Reid, Andrea Lynn; FCO since June 1989; born 6.2.70; Grade 10..

Reid, Gordon Bryden; First Secretary (Chancery) Islamabad since August 1990; born 9.5.56; FCO

1980; Second Secretary Budapest 1982; First Secretary FCO 1985; First Secretary (Chancery) Santiago 1988; m 1979 Marinella Ferro (2s 1982, 1988; 1d 1984).

Reid, Janet Catherine; Paris since March 1990; born 13.8.66; FCO 1988; Grade S2A.

Reid, Norma Fraser; FCO since December 1988; born 19.8.43; Saigon 1968; Rome 1970; Bucharest 1971; FCO 1973; HCS 1975; Latin America Floater 1977; Peking 1979; FCO 1980; Moscow 1983; FCO 1984; Rome 1986; Grade 9.

Reilly, J C (Sean); Moscow since October 1991; born 17.2.38; Royal Navy 1953-77; Islamabad 1977; Budapest 1979; Kingston 1980; Paris 1984; Moscow 1986; Lusaka 1988; Grade CSO; m 1959 Jennifer Longley (1s 1963; 1d 1964).

Reilly, Dr Michael David; First Secretary (Political) and Consul Seoul since October 1991; born 1.3.55; FCO 1978; Language Training Seoul 1979; First Secretary FCO 1984; First Secretary UKDEL OECD Paris 1988; m 1981 Won-Kyong Kang (1d 1987; 1s 1992).

Reilly, Michael Patrick; FCO since April 1991; born 30.7.66; FCO 1984; Bonn 1987; Bombay 1990; Grade 9; m 1991 Andrea Louise Bradley.

Reilly, Peter James; FCO since December 1991; born 4.10.71; Grade 10.

Remmington, Gillian Elizabeth; Berne since December 1988; born 26.2.56; FCO 1984; Quito 1985; Grade S2.

Renfrew, Laura; FCO since October 1992; born 16.3.62; FCO 1984; Moscow 1986; FCO 1988; Damascus 1989; Grade 9.

Rennie, Brian William; FCO since December 1989; born 6.2.40; FO 1964; Bangkok 1965; FO (later FCO) 1967; St Helena 1969; FCO 1971; Tehran 1972; FCO 1975; Darwin 1976; FCO 1978; Warsaw 1979; FCO 1981; Attaché Havana 1982; FCO 1985; Rangoon 1986; Grade 8; m 1963 Annie Daurge (2s 1964, 1971; 1d 1967).

Renwick, Sir Robin (William), KCMG (1989); CMG (1980); HM Ambassador Washington since August 1991; born 13.12.37; FO 1962; Dakar 1963; FO 1964; Second later First Secretary New Delhi 1966; Private Secretary to the Minister of State, FCO 1970; Paris 1972; Counsellor on loan to the Cabinet Office 1976; Head of Rhodesia Department FCO 1978; Sabbatical at Harvard University 1980; Counsellor (Pol/Mil) Washington 1981; Head of Chancery 1982; AUSS (European Community) 1984; HM Ambassador Pretoria/Cape Town 1987; m 1965 Anne Colette Giudicelli (1s 1966; 1d 1977).

Reuter, Alan; Third Secretary (Comm) Kuala Lumpur since November 1988; born 5.7.51; FCO 1970; Bucharest 1972; Kaduna 1974; Frankfurt 1978; Gaborone 1980; FCO 1982; Tel Aviv 1986; Grade 9; m (1) 1973 Christine Caton; (2) 1982 Brenda Yvonne Mary Neumann (1s 1983, 1d 1985).

Rey, Rosemary; Caracas since September 1990; born 14.3.55; FCO 1974; Cayman Islands 1976; FCO 1978; Gibraltar 1979; Bogota 1981; FCO 1986; Bogota 1988; Grade S2; m 1983 Alvaro Rey Romero (1s 1991).

Reynolds, Gillian Marjorie; Peking since May 1991; born 16.10.50; FCO 1976; New Delhi 1977; Budapest 1979; Mbabane 1981; Singapore 1987; Grade S1.

Reynolds, Colin; Nicosia since October 1992; born 3.7.71; FCO 1990; Grade 10.

Reynolds, Heather (née Turnbull); FCO since December 1991; born 30.5.54; FCO 1973; Moscow 1975; FCO 1976; Brasilia 1977; Bridgetown 1980; SUPL 1983; Kuala Lumpur 1984; FCO 1986; Prague 1988; SUPL 1990; Grade 9; m 1982 Keith James Reynolds.

Reynolds, Keith James; FCO since November 1990; born 2.8.44; FCO 1969; Bridgetown 1980; Kuala Lumpur 1982; FCO 1986; Second Secretary Prague 1988; m 1982 Heather Turnbull.

Reynolds, Leon; FCO since April 1980; born 24.4.35; RN 1953-80; Grade 9; m 1961 Frances Margaret Highman (2d 1963, 1965).

Reynolds, Leslie Roy; Islamabad since November 1988; born 22.9.59; DTI 1978; Passport Office 1979; HO 1984; FCO 1984; Wellington 1986; Grade 9; m 1982 Tracey Sapsford.

Reynolds, Michael John; Counsellor Berlin since October 1990; born 30.5.45; Third Secretary FO 1967; Vice-Consul Düsseldorf 1969; Second Secretary FCO 1973; First Secretary Budapest 1974; On loan to HCS 1977; FCO 1979; Paris 1981; First Secretary later Counsellor FCO 1986; m 1969 Jessamy Rachel Smith (2s 1970, 1971; 1d 1974).

Reynolds, Victoria Caroline; Lagos later Abuja since May 1992; born 7.6.69; FCO 1988; Grade S2.

Rhodes, Keith; Second later First Secretary FCO since April 1987; born 11.12.35; GPO 1951; HM Forces 1954-56; GPO 1956; FO 1963; Moscow 1965; Rawalpindi 1966; Rome 1968; FCO 1971; Hong Kong 1975; FCO 1978; Hong Kong 1986; m 1963 Anne Dwyer.

Rice, Douglas; Second later First Secretary FCO

since September 1986; born 28.1.46; FO 1964;
Jedda 1968; Paris 1970; Sana'a 1972; Sofia
1973; FCO 1974; Doha 1978; Dusseldorf 1982;
Second Secretary (Cons/Passports) Singapore
1983; m 1969 Christine Elizabeth Chisholm (1d
1973; 1s 1977).

Rice, John Gordon; Deputy High Commissioner
Windhock since April 1992; born 6.1.46; Home
Office 1962; Commonwealth Office DSAO and
FCO 1967; Ankara 1969; Paris 1972; FCO 1976;
Seoul 1978; Assistant Trade Commissioner
(Second Secretary) Hong Kong 1980; Second
later First Secretary (Parliamentary Clerk) FCO
1985; Second later First Secretary (Comm) and
Head of Chancery Doha 1988; m 1972 Gail
Marjorie Pearce (2s 1975, 1979; 1d 1976).

Richards, Barbara (née Espey); Nicosia since
November 1989; born 28.2.45; DSAO 1967;
Accra 1967; Peking 1969; Beirut 1970; FCO
1973; UKREP Brussels 1976; Lusaka 1982; FCO
1985; Grade 9; m 1974 Conway Brian Richards.

Richards, Francis Neville, cvo (1991); Minister
Moscow since July 1992; born 18.11.45; Army
1967-69; Third Secretary FCO 1969; Moscow
1971; Second later First Secretary UKDEL
MBFR Vienna 1973; First Secretary FCO 1976;
Counsellor (Comm/Econ) New Delhi 1985;
Counsellor FCO 1988; High Commissioner
Windhoek 1990; m 1971 Gillian Bruce Nevill
(1s 1975; 1d 1977).

Richards, Geoffrey; Second Secretary FCO since
March 1991; born 24.11.42; CRO 1961; Accra
1964; Mexico City 1968; Dubai 1970; FCO
1973; Madras 1975; Stockholm 1979; FCO 1982;
Second Secretary (Comm) Port of Spain 1985;
Second Secretary and Consul Warsaw 1988; m
1967 Joy Patricia Marshall (3d 1968, 1971,
1972).

Richards, James William Bruce; Counsellor
Brussels since November 1990; born 30.7.47;
Third Secretary FCO 1969; Language Student
Hong Kong 1971; Second later First Secretary
FCQ 1973; First Secretary (Consul) Peking 1977;
First Secretary (UN/PRESS) UKMIS Geneva
1980; First Secretary FCO 1984; m 1970
Jacqueline Nassif (2s 1977, 1985).

Richards, Owen Jeremy; Bombay since April
1991; FCQ 1988; Grade 9.

Richards, Rodney Elizabeth, mbe (1986); FCO
since April 1991; born 27.8.48; FO 1967;
Geneva 1970; Phnom Penh 1972; Islamabad
1973; Saigon 1975; FCO 1975; Jakarta 1976;
FCO 1978; Nairobi 1983; Kampala 1986; Grade
S2.

Richards, Steven Thomas; Vice-Consul Moscow
since September 1990; born 29.1.58; FCO 1978;
New Delhi 1980; Beirut 1982; Europe Floater
1985; FCO 1987; Warsaw 1988; FCO 1988;

Grade 9; m 1989 Tracey Lee Barnett.

Richardson, Christine Lynn; Floater Duties
Africa/Middle East since August 1992; UKREP
Brussels 1989; born 4.10.67; FCO 1987; Grade
10.

Richardson, Lesley Gwen; SUPL since May
1991; born 1.2.66; FCO 1986; Vienna 1988;
Grade S2.

Richardson, Michael John; FCO since
November 1991; born 16.5.66; FCO 1985;
Warsaw 1988; Grade 10; m 1989 Audrey Zena
Fairall.

Richardson, Peter James; Management Officer/
Consul Damascus since July 1991; born 26.7.46;
FO (later FCO) 1963; Stockholm 1969;
Wellington 1972; FCO 1975; LA Floater 1978;
Second Secretary Bangkok 1981; Second
Secretary FCO 1983; Second Secretary (Aid/Inf)
La Paz 1986; Second Secretary FCO 1988; m
1983 Ratana Thawornporn.

Richardson, Thomas Legh, cmg (1991); Deputy
Permanent Representative (with personal rank of
Ambassador) UKMIS New York since August
1989; born 6.2.41; Seconded Institute of African
Studies University of Ghana 1962; Third
Secretary FO 1963; Dar es Salaam 1965; Second
Secretary 1966; Vice-Consul (Comm) Milan
1967; Seconded to N M Rothschild and Sons
1970; First Secretary FCO 1971; First Secretary
UKMIS New York 1974; FCO 1978; Counsellor
on loan to Cabinet Office (CPRS) 1980; Head of
Chancery Rome 1982; Counsellor FCO 1986; m
1979 Alexandra Wasiqullah (née Ratcliff).

Richman, Menna Frances; Third Secretary
(Institutions) UKREP Brussels since September
1991; born 16.9.67; FCO 1989; m 1990 Stephen
Charles Richman.

Richmond, Alan Thomas; FCO since October
1991; born 22.4.55; Department of Education
and Science 1973; FCO 1975; Maputo 1977;
Lima 1981; FCO 1983; Islamabad 1985;
Singapore 1988; Grade 9, m 1976 Iscabal
MacLean Graham (1d 1986).

Richmond, David Frank; First Secretary FCO
since September 1991; born 9.7.54; FCO 1976;
Language Student MECAS 1977; Third later
Second Secretary Baghdad 1979; Second later
First Secretary FCO 1982; First Secretary
(External Trade) UKREP Brussels 1987; m 1990
· Caroline Florence Pascale Gilberte.

Rickerd, Martin John Kilburn, mvo (1985); First
Secretary FCO since July 1991; born 17.8.54;
FCO 1972; UKDEL NATO Brussels 1975;
Wellington 1978; Assistant PS to Parliamentary
Under Secretary of State 1980; Bridgetown 1982;
Consul (Inf) Milan 1986; ; m 1976 Charmain
Gwendoline Napier (2s 1986, 1988).

Ricketts, Peter Forbes; First Secretary (later Counsellor) FCO since November 1989; born 30.9.52; FCO 1974; New York 1974; FCO 1975; Third Secretary Singapore 1975; Second Secretary UKDEL NATO Brussels 1978; First Secretary FCO 1982; APS to Secretary of State 1983; First Secretary (Chancery) Washington 1986; m 1980 Suzanne Julia Horlington (1s 1982; 1d 1987).

Rickitt, Clare Louise; FCO since October 1991; born 20.9.64; Grade 7.

Ridge, Ann Elizabeth; New Delhi since April 1992; born 23.10.62; FCO 1990; Grade S2.

Ridge, Christopher Edward; FCO since July 1990; born 9.5.71; Grade 10.

Ridgway, David Frederick Charles, OBE (1988) First Secretary FCO since February 1988; born 9.6.41; FO 1960; Vice-Consul La Paz 1963; DSAO later FCO 1966 (Second Secretary 1968); Second Secretary (Econ) Colombo 1971; Vice-Consul (Poll/Inf) Durban 1975; Second later First Secretary FCO 1977; First Secretary (Comm) Buenos Aires 1980; FCO 1982; Resident Chargé d'A ffaires a.i. San Salvador 1984; m 1966 Dora Beatriz Siles (1d 1972; 1s 1981).

Ridgway, Jack; Second Secretary Brussels since April 1984; born 18.5.27; GPO 1943; HM Forces 1947-49; GPO 1949; New Delhi (seconded to CRO) 1951; FO 1955; Paris 1956; Prague 1956; FO 1957; Tokyo 1958; FO 1960; Sofia 1961; Pretoria1/Cape Town 1962; FO 1965; Bangkok 1966; FO (later FCO) 1967; Bonn 1970; FCO 1973; Second Secretary Singapore 1978; FCO 1981; m Theresa Joan Smith (1s 1964; 1d 1962).

Ridley, Michelle; Kaduna since July 1990; born 22.1.63; DHSS 1986-87; FCO 1987; Grade S2A.

Ridout, Richard William; Moscow since January 1990; born 19.11.67; FCO 1986; Grade 10; m 1992 Sarah Beth Evans..

Ridout, William Anthony Frederick; Consul Milan since May 1990; born 27.4.50; MOD 1970; FCO 1974; Islamabad 1976; Stuttgart 1979; Bridgetown 1982; FCO 1982; Bombay 1984; Second Secretary (Comm) East Berlin 1988; m (1) 1971 Muriel Jessica Stewart Benigan; (2) 1980 Frances Mary Bond.

Riemer, Jacqueline Anne (née Elms); Geneva since September 1991; born 11.9.63; FCO 1983; Vienna 1986; SUPL 1988; Bonn 1989; Grade S2; m 1990 Bernard Riemer.

Riley, John Lawrence; Hanoi since June 1991; born 13.8.61; FCO 1982; Cairo 1984; FCO 1986; Ankara 1986; Grade 10; m (1) 1982 Caroline Peacock (diss.) m (2) 1990 Ayce Birergin.

Ringrose, Alison; FCO since February 1990; born 1.7.57; FCO 1980; Bangkok 1982; FCO 1984; Addis Ababa 1985; FCO 1987; Damascus 1988; Grade S2.

Riordan, Shaun Christopher; First Secretary FCO since August 1991; born 11.2.61; FCO 1984; Language Training Taiwan 1986; Second later First Secretary (Chancery) Peking 1988.

Ripard, Elizabeth Anne (née Auld); Third Secretary (Cultural/Inf) Valletta since March 1991; born 27.6.57; FCO 1976; Madrid 1979; SEA Floater 1982; San José 1984; FCO 1988; Grade 9; m 1992 Nicholas Charles Ripard.

Ripley, Charles Edward Arthur; First Secretary (Inward Investment) Tokyo since July 1992; born 3.10.36; HM Forces 1955-57; Baghdad 1957; Tokyo 1958; Vice-Consul Yokohama 1963; DSAO (later FCO) 1967; Vice Consul Los Angeles 1970; Vice Consul San Francisco 1971; FCO 1973; Vice-Consul Antwerp 1974; Second Secretary (Comm) Tokyo 1977; Second Secretary (Inf) Tokyo 1980; on loan to DOT 1982; Consul Tokyo 1985; on loan to DTI 1988; m 1961 Ann Morgan (2d 1962, 1964; 1s 1966).

Ritchie, Paul John; First Secretary UKMIS New York since June 1991; born 26.3.62; FCO 1983; Second Secretary (Chancery) Nicosia 1986; Second later First Secretary FCO 1988; m 1991 Jane Risley.

Rixon, Margaret Carol; FCO since December 1991; born 16.2.57; FCO 1976; Castries 1978; Washington 1980; Peking 1982; FCO 1983; UKMIS Vienna 1984; East Berlin 1987; Kingston 1988; Grade S1.

Roach, Janet Elizabeth; FCO since June 1989; born 9.11.64; Grade S3C.

Road-night, Susan Catherine; Kiev since September 1992; born 13.3.67; FCO 1991; Grade S2.

Robb, Lee; FCO since March 1992; born 4.4.72; Grade 10.

Robbins, Christopher William; On loan to the DTI since December 1991; born 16.6.46; First Secretary FCO 1984; First Secretary (Chancery) New Delhi 1987; First Secretary FCO 1990; m 1978 Susan Mary Reynolds.

Roberts, Anne Catherine; Floater duties since July 1991; born 7.5.63; FCO 1985; Bucharest 1988; FCO 1990; Grade S2.

Roberts, Colin; Second Secretary (Econ) Tokyo since November 1990; born 31.7.59; FCO 1989; Called to the Bar 1986.

Roberts, David Eric; Helsinki since June 1989; born 15.8.54; Customs and Excise 1971; FCO

1973; Lagos 1977; Doha 1979; FCO 1983; Washington 1986; Grade 9; m 1979 Kim Louise Fyleman (2d 1990, 1992).

Roberts, David George; First Secretary (Financial) Paris since January 1991; born 11.4.55; FCO 1976; Second Secretary Jakarta 1977; Second Secretary (Chancery) Havana 1981; First Secretary FCO 1984; First Secretary (Econ) Madrid 1988; m 1985 Rosmarie Rita Kunz (1d 1990).

Roberts, Graeme; First Secretary and Consul Rome since June 1990; born 16.11.39; National Assistance Board 1960; WO 1962; FO 1962; Washington 1963; Madrid 1966; La Paz 1969; FCO 1972; Zagreb 1975; Second Secretary San José 1978; Second Secretary FCO 1983; First Secretary and Resident Representative Grenada 1986; m 1963 Gillian Mary Price (1s 1964; 1d 1967).

Roberts, Ian; Buenos Aires since August 1991; born 26.10.66; FCO 1987; Grade 10.

Roberts, Ivor Anthony; Minister Madrid since March 1989; born 24.9.46; Third Secretary FCO 1968; MECAS 1969; FCO 1970; Paris 1970; Second Secretary 1971; Second later First Secretary FCO 1973; First Secretary (Chancery) later First Secretary (Econ/Comm/Agric) Canberra 1978; First Secretary FCO 1982; Counsellor FCO 1986; m 1974 Elizabeth Bray Bernard Smith (2s 1976, 1979; 1d 1982).

Roberts, Jeffrey; First Secretary FCO since May 1988; born 26.4.33; HM Forces 1951-53; United Kingdom Atomic Energy Authority 1953; MSS 1958; FO (later FCO) 1967; Rawalpindi/Islamabad 1969; Johannesburg 1972; Vice-Consul (Comm) 1973; on loan to DOT 1977; Second Secretary and Vice-Consul Paris 1981; First Secretary (Comm) Singapore 1984; m 1966 Pamela Hudson Waude (1s 1973; 1d 1975).

Roberts, Michael John Wyn; First Secretary FCO since September 1991; born 4.7.60; Second Secretary FCO 1984; Second later First Secretary (Chancery) Athens 1987; m 1985 Margaret Anne Ozanne.

Roberts, Philip John Barclay; First Secretary (Chancery) Lisbon since April 1991; born 4.12.49; FCO 1973; Third later Second Secretary Islamabad 1977; First Secretary FCO 1980; Head of Chancery and Consul Hanoi 1982; First Secretary Tokyo 1984; First Secretary FCO 1987; m 1987 Magdalena Henri Adrienne Lammens.

Roberts, Roy Leonard; UKDEL Brussels since August 1990; born 20.9.39; RAF 1955-1977; Moscow 1980; Lagos 1982; Washington 1983; The Hague 1985; Belgrade 1988; Grade SO; m 1970 Marilyn Lesley Warner (2d 1972, 1977).

Roberts, Trevor Martin; FCO since December

1986; born 12.7.55; FCO 1974; UKMIS Geneva 1978; Floater duties 1982; Kuwait 1984; Grade 9.

Roberts, William Herbert; Athens since April 1990; born 23.9.31; Army 1950-52; Washington 1976; Budapest 1977; Ankara 1979; Oslo 1980; Sofia 1984; Lagos 1986; Prague 1988; Grade SO; m 1974 Constance Hodgson (2d 1958, 1960).

Robertson, Brian; First Secretary (Management/Consular) Copenhagen since May 1991; born 24.7.45; FO 1963; Cairo 1967; Washington 1968; Castries 1969; Warsaw 1974; FCO 1976; Gaborone 1979; Second Secretary Maseru 1982; Second Secretary and Head of Chancery Asunción 1985; FCO 1989; m 1967 Ellen Roberts.

Robertson, Craig Douglas; FCO since December 1984; born 4.10.66; Grade 10.

Robertson, Ewan; Nicosia since July 1987; born 16.2.28; RAF 1946-74; Budapest 1974; Rome 1976; Baghdad 1979; UKMIS Geneva 1980; Warsaw 1982; Pretoria 1983; Lusaka 1985; Grade SO; m 1950 Evelyn Mary Jennings.

Robertson, Henry Macloskie; Second Secretary FCO since January 1987; born 10.10.41; ECGD 1960; CRO 1961; Zomba 1964; DSAO (later FCO) 1968; Freetown 1970; Tripoli 1972; Vientiane 1974; Kuala Lumpur 1975; FCO 1979; Sana'a 1981; Second Secretary Bridgetown 1985; m 1966 Audrey Lucy Duté (2s 1967, 1970).

Robertson, William Smellie; Riyadh since April 1989; born 5.3.66; FCO 1984; Dublin 1986; Grade 9; m 1986 Catherine Elizabeth McGregor Brown.

Robins, Nicole Jane; Accra since February 1992; born 12.1.63; FCO 1981; Paris 1983; Mbabane 1986; FCO 1990; Grade 9.

Robins, Terence Frederick; Vice-Consul Algiers since November 1991; born 15.10.66; FCO 1989; Grade 9.

Robinson, David; Havana since November 1991; born 26.3.39; RAF 1960-83; Warsaw 1983; New York 1984; BM Berlin 1987; Moscow 1990; Grade SO; m 1960 Judith Mary Horner.

Robinson, David John; FCO since January 1988; born 27.2.45; Army 1962-85; Moscow 1985; Baghdad 1986; Grade 9; m 1976 Pauline Reed.

Robinson, Deborah; Maputo since November 1990; born 20.4.58; FCO 1989; Grade S2.

Robinson, Diane; Lusaka since April 1990; born 15.7.60; FCO 1981; Bogotá 1982; Jakarta 1985; FCO 1988; Grade S1.

Robinson, Julie Anne (née Whitehead); Bahrain since June 1988; born 2.8.63; FCO 1984; Washington 1985; Grade S2; m 1985 Philip Robinson.

Robinson, Louise Ann; Warsaw since May 1991; born 18.3.66; FCO 1984; Ottawa 1987; Budapest 1989; Grade 10.

Robinson, Michael John; Deputy Head of Mission and Consul-General Belgrade since November 1990; born 19.12.46; Third Secretary FCO 1968; Language Student 1969; Third later Second Secretary Moscow 1970; Second later First Secretary (Inf) Madrid 1972; First Secretary FCO 1977; CSCE Madrid 1980; First Secretary and Head of Chancery Madrid 1981; SUPL with OECD Paris 1982; Deputy Head of Delegation, UKDEL UNESCO, Paris 1985; First Secretary FCO 1986 (Counsellor 1990); m 1971 Anne Jamieson Scott (2d 1974, 1987; 2s 1977, 1983).

Robinson, Philip Andrew; Second Ssecretary FCO since July 1991; born 18.9.51; FCO 1970; Warsaw 1973; Jedda 1974; FCO 1977; Wellington 1978; Islamabad 1980; FCO 1982; Johannesburg 1985; Moscow 1987; (Second Secretary 1988); m 1972 Elizabeth Andrina Mathieson Riding (2d 1976, 1980).

Robinson, Susan Patricia; FCO since August 1989; born 6.11.47; FCO 1979; Paris 1980; Helsinki 1982; Bridgetown 1986; Grade S1

Robinson, William; Pretoria since July 1992; born 26.11.44; RAF Regiment 1962; Islamabad 1987; Moscow 1991; Grade SO; m 1966 Cynthia Margaret Pugh, (2s 1966, 1969)

Robson, Elizabeth Carol; Second later First Secretary (Chancery) UKMIS Geneva since February 1988; born 14.1.55; FCO 1977; Latin America Floater 1981; FCO 1982; Moscow 1984; Second Secretary FCO 1985.

Roche, Claire Louise; FCO since September 1991; born 17.3.72; Grade 10.

Rock, Gail Denise (née Purvis); Tokyo since March 1990; born 26.6.56; FCO 1978; Mexico 1979; Rome 1981; FCO 1984; Islamabad 1987; FCO 1988; Grade S1; m Dereck Anthony Rock.

Rocque, Stefany Elizabeth; Floater Duties since July 1992; born 28.7.66; FCO 1989; Grade 10.

Rodemark, Janet Mary; Islamabad since July 1992; born 28.5.65; FCO 1988; Grade 9.

Rodgers, Catherine Mary; FCO since November 1990; born 18.4.46; FCO 1965; Resigned 1968; Grade 10; m 1968 James Patrick Rodgers (2d 1970, 1972 1s 1975)

Rodgers, James Patrick; First Secretary FCO since April 1991; born 17.3.42; FO 1966; Bathurst 1968; Paris 1971; Belgrade 1974; FCO 1976; Bridgetown 1979; Istanbul 1982; Port Stanley 1984; Second Secretary Algiers 1986; m 1968 Catherine Mary Anderson (2d 1970, 1972; 1s 1975).

Rodney, David William; FCO since November 1988; born 25.1.41; FO (later FCO) 1967; St Helena 1969; FCO 1970; Accra 1972; FCO 1974; Tehran 1976; FCO 1979; Cairo 1980; FCO 1984; Gaborone 1985; Grade 8; m 1967 Wilhelmina Parsons (2s 1970, 1971).

Rodwell, David William; Second Secretary FCO since February 1992; born 9.5.39; GPO 1955; FO (later FCO) 1966; Singapore 1969; FCO 1971; Athens 1972; FCO 1975; Bahrain 1977; FCO 1980; New Delhi 1980; FCO 1983 (Second Secretary 1987); Second Secretary Washington 1989; m (1) 1962 Pearl Davies (dec'd) (1s 1967; 2d 1963, 1966); (2) 1969 Daphne Margaret Stroud (1d 1970) (3) 1988 Erica Florence Tibbetts.

Roe, Kirsty Gordon; Bucharest since June 1988; born 25.8.46; WRNS 1965-73; FCO 1974; New Delhi 1976; Hanover 1979; Bonn 1980; FCO 1982; Colombo 1985; Grade 9.

Roebuck, William John; First Secretary (Chancery) Caracas since August 1990; born 20.7.49; FCO 1971; BMG Berlin 1975; FCO 1978 (First Secretary 1979); Harare 1983; First Secretary FCO 1987; m 1984 Winifred Leigh Murphree (2d 1980, 1984).

Roff, Derek Michael, OBE (1972); First Secretary later Counsellor FCO since May 1977; born 1.8.32; First Secretary FO 1967; Consul Frankfurt 1968; First Secretary UKDEL Brussels (EC) 1970; FCO 1972; Consul (Econ) Düsseldorf 1973; m 1957 Diana Susette Barrow (3s 1959, 1961, 1963).

Rogan, Janet Elizabeth; Second later First Secretary (Chancery) Peking since January 1991; born 19.12.62; FCO 1986; Language Training 1988; Language Training Hong Kong 1989.

Rogan, Peter; First Secretary (Comm) Wellington since February 1990; born 17.7.34; Board of Trade 1954; Port of Spain 1963; Dacca 1967; FCO 1970; Lagos 1973; Ibadan 1974; First Secretary (Comm) Baghdad 1977; Vancouver 1978; First Secretary FCO 1983; First Secretary (Immig) Islamabad 1985; m 1962 Jane Finn-Kelcey (3d 1963, 1968, 1973; 1s 1965).

Rogers, David Alan; First Secretary FCO since July 1991; born 16.5.49; FCO 1971; Copenhagen 1974; Second Secretary 1975; Second later First Secretary FCO 1978; Jakarta 1981; First Secretary Brunei 1983; First Secretary FCO 1985; First Secretary (Chancery) Islamabad 1988; m (1) 1981 Elaine Patricia Hunt (diss 1988) (2) 1989 Julie Anne Gardiner (1d 1990).

Rogers, Martyn Graham; FCO since August 1980 (Second Secretary 1991); born 10.9.52; FCO 1974; Beirut 1978.

Rogers, Michael Roy; Second Secretary FCO since February 1990; born 14.12.48; FCO 1967; Pretoria/Cape Town 1976; Tunis 1973; Bridgetown 1975; FCO 1978; Bahrain 1981; Wellington 1984; Resigned 1989; Reinstated 1990; m 1970 Elaine Anne Stewart (2s 1980, 1986).

Rogers, Sue; Language Training since October 1990; born 28.10.65; FCO 1989; Grade 9.

Roissetter, Frederick Charles; Third later Second Secretary Tel Aviv since March 1989; born 9.10.50; Army 1966-77; FCO 1978; Cabinet Office 1979; FCO 1984; m 1979 Kay Jacqueline (2d 1981, 1984; 1s 1986).

Roland, Peter Stephen; Principal Research Officer FCO since October 1978; born 7.9.36; FO (later FCO) 1961; PRO (DS Grade 5); m 1964 Hilary Margaret Silver (2d 1965, 1970; 1s 1967).

Roll, Maurice Arnold; Third Secretary Tel Aviv since August 1986; born 21.7.37; Royal Navy 1952-64; FO (later FCO) 1965; St Helena 1969; FCO 1970; Peking 1972; FCO 1973; Delhi 1974; FCO 1976; Belgrade 1977; FCO 1978; Jakarta 1979; FCO 1981; Attaché Lilongwe 1982; Grade 8; m 1961 Patricia Mary Williams.

Rolland, Frieda King; UKREP Brussels since January 1990; born 17.10.63; FCO 1988; Grade S2A.

Rolleston, George Lancelot St Leger, MBE (Mil) (1969); Counsellor Algiers since May 1991; born 8.5.39; Army 1958-69; Second Secretary FCO 1969; First Secretary Baghdad 1971; FCO 1971; First Secretary Sana'a 1972; FCO 1976; Sana'a 1978; First Secretary later Counsellor Jedda (later Riyadh) 1981; Counsellor FCO 1986; m 1976 Claude-Annie Cointet (1d 1980; 1s 1982).

Rollitt, Philip Vivian; Counsellor (Management) Bonn since October 1989; born 29.12.38; FO 1957; HM Forces 1958-60; Moscow 1961; Latin America Floater 1964; Vice-Consul San Juan 1965; Second Secretary 1966; Second Secretary (Comm) Copenhagen 1968; FCO 1972; First Secretary (Admin/Cons) Singapore 1976; First Secretary & Consul Islamabad 1981; First Secretary later Counsellor FCO 1985; m 1969 Corry Ruth Berthel Baer (née Iversen) (2s 1970, 1973, 1 step s 1963).

Ronchetti, Paul Anthony; FCO since September 1982; born 7.4.51; FCO 1969; Washington 1972; Africa Floater 1975; Port of Spain 1977; Baghdad 1979; Grade 9.

Rooney, Sean Michael; FCO since July 1991; born 17.2.72; Grade 10.

Rooney, Terence; Vice-Consul (Comm) Karachi since December 1985; born 15.6.44; GPO 1961; Commonwealth Office 1966; Budapest 1968; FCO 1970; Jedda 1974; FCO 1977; Ottawa 1978; FCO 1980; On attachment to DTI 1984; Grade 7; m (1) 1967 Clarice Howard Watson (diss 1978) (1s 1972); (2) 1978 Patricia Maureen Whiteside (diss 1983); (3) 1983 Frances Mary Rivers.

Roper, Martyn Keith; Third Secretarty (Pol/Aid) Karachi since June 1991; born 8.6.65; FCO 1984; Tehran 1986; Maputo 1988; Kuwait 1990; Grade 9; m 1989 Elisabeth Melanie Harman Watson.

Roscoe, Helen Margaret; Lagos since May 1992; born 25.7.67; FCO 1987; Oslo 1989; Grade 9.

Rose, Barbara Claire; FCO since July 1991; born 15.1.51; FCO 1973; Washington 1973; Dacca 1976; Hanoi 1976; FCO 1977; Valletta 1982; FCO 1984; Lagos 1986; Istanbul 1987; FCO 1988; Floater Duties 1989; Grade 9.

Rose, Emily Anne, MBE (1986); Second Secretary and Consul Brussels since March 1992; born 13.2.36; Ministry of Labour 1953; Dakar 1962; Nairobi 1964; Aden 1967; Lomé 1968; Middle East and North Africa Floater 1970; Moscow 1974; Nairobi 1976; FCO 1977; Vice-Consul Budapest 1980; Second Secretary Admin Officer and Consul Helsinki 1983; Second Secretary (Admin/Cons) Maputo 1987;Second Secretary FCO 1990.

Rose, Kay; on Floater duties since February 1991; born 11.11.63; FCO 1984; Budapest 1985; Paris 1987; Grade S2.

Roseblade, Stephen George; Third Secretary Pretoria since July 1992; born 25.1.52; FCO 1969; Moscow 1979; FCO 1980; Singapore 1983; FCO 1984; Canberra 1984; FCO 1987; Grade 8; m 1984 Linda Duncan.

Rose, Philip Edmond; Second Secretary (Commercial) Peking since June 1991; born 12.12.63; FCO 1987; Language Training 1988; Language Training Hong Kong 1989.

Roskilly, Karen Elizabeth; Amsterdam since November 1991; born 18.10.65; FCO 1990; Grade 9.

Ross, Adele Elizabeth; Paris since February 1992; born 4.7.71; FCO 1990; Grade S2A.

Ross, Allison Marie (née Johns); Washington since January 1991; born 20.11.66; FCO 1988; Grade S2A; m 1989 Anthony Ross.

Ross, Barry Thomas; SUPL since October 1991;

born 22.8.65; FCO 1985; Tokyo 1987; FCO 1990; Grade 10.

Ross, Carne William; Third Secretary (Pol) Bonn since July 1992; born 24.8.66; FCO 1989; Grade 8.

Ross, Iain Caithness; First Secretary later Counsellor FCO since November 1990; born 11.11.37; FCO 1973; First Secretary (Inf) Lusaka 1975; First Secretary Pretoria 1978; FCO 1981; First Secretary Kuala Lumpur 1982; First Secretary Khartoum 1985; First Secretary Singapore 1987.

Ross, William Lawson; FCO since December 1991; born 13.9.53; FCO 1973; UKMIS New York 1975; CG New York 1977; Tunis 1978; Kinshasa 1981; FCO 1984; Nassau 1985; Warsaw 1988; Grade 9; m 1978 Mary Margaret Delaney (1d 1980; 1s 1982).

Ross McDowell, Amanda; (née Ross); Zurich since November 1991; born 25.11.62; FCO 1981; 10 Downing St. 1985; Cape Town 1988; Grade 9; m 1987 Christopher McDowell.

Rossiter, Lynne; Tel Aviv since August 1992; born 10.8.50; FCO 1990; Grade S2A.

Rothery, James Peter; FCO since September 1985; born 15.4.51; FCO 1975; Masirah 1977; Washington 1982; Grade 8.

Rothwell, Margaret Irene, CMG (1992); HM Ambassador and Consul-General Abidjan since December 1990 and, additionally, HM Ambassador (non-resident) to Niger and HM Ambassador and Consul-General (non-resident) to Burkina; born 25.8.38; FO 1961; Third later Second Secretary UKDEL to the Council of Europe Strasbourg 1964; FO 1966; Second Secretary (Private Secretary to the Special Representative in Africa) Nairobi 1967; Second later First Secretary Washington 1968; FCO 1972; First Secretary and Head of Chancery Helsinki 1976; FCO 1980; Counsellor and Head of Training Department FCO 1981; Counsellor and Head of Chancery Jakarta 1984; Counsellor FCO 1987.

Rous, Matthew James; FCO since September 1991; born 29.6.64; Grade 7; m 1989 Beryl Scott.

Rouse, Philip Terence, MBE (1976); First Secretary, Resident Representative Castries since March 1990; born 13.10.43; Ministry of Aviation 1960; MOD 1966; FO (later FCO) 1967; Bogotá 1969; Singapore 1973; Saigon 1973; FCO 1975; Bahrain 1979; Asunción 1981; Second Secretary FCO 1985; m 1968 Janice Eileen Williamson (3s 1971, 1974, 1978).

Rousseau, Jenifer Lesley (née Hill); Paris since December 1986; born 9.7.60; FCO 1983; Kabul 1984; FCO 1986; Grade S2; m 1988 Frank Stephane Frederick Rousseau.

Routh, Diana Florence Elizabeth (née Cardell Oliver); Second Secretary FCO since January 1991; FCO 1963; Lima 1963; Belgrade 1966; Tam Sui 1967; Pretoria/Capetown 1969; FCO 1971; SEA Floater 1977; UKDEL NATO 1978; Barcelona 1979; FCO 1983; Second Secretary La Paz 1988; m 1991 Francis John Routh.

Rowe, David Ian; Bucharest since May 1991; born 16.6.66; FCO 1985; Addis Ababa 1987; Grade 10.

Rowe, Kenneth Herbert, MBE; FCO since December 1984 (Second Secretary 1985); born 11.3.39; GPO 1955; FO 1963; Singapore 1965; FO 1967; Washington 1968; Lagos 1971; FCO 1972; Moscow 1973; FCO 1974; Nairobi 1977; FCO 1979; Bonn 1982; m 1972 Glenis Christine Northrop (2s 1963, 1965; 1d 1971).

Rowell, Anthony Aylett, CMG (1992); Counsellor Pretoria since July 1990; born 10.1.37; Second Secretary FO 1966; Lusaka 1968; First Secretary FCO 1969; Bucharest 1970; FCO 1973; Nicosia 1979; FCO 1980; Counsellor Nairobi 1985; m (1) 1963 Bridget Jane Reekie (diss 1985) (1d 1969; 1s 1970); (2) 1985 Caroline Jane Edgecumbe.

Rowett, Caroline Sarah; Jakarta since November 1992; FCO 1990; born 16.9.58; Grade 9; m 1992 Joseph Spurgeon.

Rowland, Bethany Louise; Mexico City since April 1991; born 11.12.68; FCO 1988; Grade S2.

Rowland, Keith Irving; Moscow since February 1992; born 9.11.46; Royal Navy 1963-88; Islamabad 1988; Grade SO; m 1971 Helena Sloan.

Rowland Jones, Sarah Caroline; First Secretary (Political) Budapest since September 1992; born 8.9.59; FCO 1981; Language Training 1982; Third later Second Secretary (Chancery) Amman 1984; First Secretary FCO 1987.

Rowlands, Jane Ellen; Mexico City since December 1989; born 16.3.67; FCO 1987; Grade 10.

Rowlandson, Peter Roderick Saxby; FCO since November 1991; born 22.9.49; FCO 1970; Georgetown 1972; FCO 1976; Brussels 1978; Moscow 1981; FCO 1982; Brussels 1984; Madrid 1985; New Delhi 1988; Grade 9; m (1) 1973 Nancy Lee Townend (1d 1974); (2) 1989 Jillian Roberts (1d 1992).

Rowney, Michael Ernest, MBE (1991); Lisbon since January 1991; born 23.6.53; FCO 1972; Warsaw 1975; Kinshasa 1976; Hamilton 1979; Bahrain 1982; FCO 1985; Vice-Consul Monrovia 1988; Grade 9; m 1981 Margaret Elaine Cullern (2d 1983, 1984).

Rowswell, Claire; FCO since October 1988; born 13.1.55; FCO 1979; Quito 1979; UKREP Brussels 1981; Moscow 1984; FCO 1985; Mexico City 1986; Grade S1.

Rowton, Alastair Clifford; FCO since August 1986; born 28.11.46; FCO 1979; Gaborone 1981; FCO 1982; BGWRS Darwin 1984; Grade 8; m 1976 Jean Margaret Cowie (2d 1982, 1986).

Royal, Caroline Patricia; Lisbon since October 1992; born 22.1.57; MOD 1973; FCO 1990; Grade S2A.

Royle, Catherine Jane; First Secretary FCO since November 1991; born 17.8.63; FCO 1986; Third later Second Secretary (Chancery) Santiago 1988; m 1991 Marcelo Enrique Camprubi Valledor.

Rumiel, Jacqueline Denise; Yaoundé since May 1989; born 24.3.66; FCO 1987; Grade 10; m 1990 Robert Rumiel.

Runacres, Mark Alastair; First Secretary (Chancery) Paris since March 1991; born 19.5.59; FCO 1981; Third later Second Secretary New Delhi 1983; Second later First Secretary FCO 1986; m 1989 Shawn Reid.

Rundall, John Charles Anthony; First Secretary (Chancery) Bahrain since January 1989; born 29.10.42; Third later Second Secretary FCO 1967; First Secretary (Scientific) Tokyo 1971; ' First Secretary FCO 1974; First Secretary Jakarta 1975; FCO 1979; Dar es Salaam 1982; FCO 1985; m (1) 1971 Dorienne Perry (diss 1980); (2d 1974, 1976); (2) 1981 Janet Summerson (1d 1982).

Rundle, Christopher John Spencer, OBE (1983); FCO since 1985; born 17.8.38; Army 1957-59; FO 1963; Tehran 1967; Second Secretary (Oriental) Kabul 1968; FCO 1970; On loan to Cabinet Office 1975; FCO 1977; First Secretary Tehran 1981 (Head of Chancery and Press Officer 1983); Research Counsellor; m 1970 Qamar Said (1d 1982).

Russell, Andrew John; Second Secretary later First Secretary FCO since April 1987; born 12.8.48; FO (later FCO) 1967; Bonn 1972; Berlin 1973; FCO 1975; Second Secretary Vienna 1982; m 1972 Marilyn Elizabeth Turp (2d 1974, 1984; 1s 1982).

Russell, Joan; Lima since March 1992; born 4.5.43; FCO 1986; UKMIS Vienna 1988; Grade S2.

Russell, Malcolm Arthur; FCO since July 1992; born 27.2.54; FCO 1973; Kuala Lumpur 1976; FCO 1980; Frankfurt 1983; Tehran 1985; Third Secretary Nuku'alofa 1988; Peking 1989; Grade 9; m 1982 Jean Frances Matthews (1d 1987; 1s 1992).

Russell, Neil; Abu Dhabi since March 1992; born 18.2.69; FCO 1989; Grade 10.

Russell, Roger; Canberra since November 1989; born 14.5.54; FCO 1970; Brussels 1983; FCO 1986; Grade 8; m 1983 Teresa Mary McGeough.

Rutherford, John; FCO since June 1987; (Second Secretary 1988); born 2.1.59; FCO 1978; Nairobi 1980; Jedda (later Riyadh) 1983; m 1989 Karen Chapman.

Rutherford, Karen (née Chapman); Warsaw since October 1990; born 19.2.59; FCO 1977; Rome 1979; Floater duties 1982; FCO 1986; Grade 9; m 1989 John Rutherford.

Rutter, Amanda Jayne; UKREP Brussels since September 1989; born 20.3.64; HM Land Registry 1984; FCO 1988; Grade S2A.

Ryan, Arthur John; Third later Second Secretary FCO since August 1986; born 9.7.44; GPO 1965; FCO 1969; Nairobi 1970; Tehran 1973; FCO 1976; Brussels 1980; Bucharest 1983; m (1) 1967 Pamela Elizabeth Winstanley (1s 1970; 1d 1972); (2) 1979 Gillian Jean Wright (2 step d 1970, 1972).

Ryan, Gerald Anthony; Second Secretary (Admin/Cons) Sana'a since December 1988; born 19.10.46; Royal Navy 1963-73; FCO 1974; Baghdad 1976; Paris 1979; FCO 1982; Paris 1984; FCO 1988; m 1972 Daniele Louise Marie.

Ryan, Pamela Jane; FCO since June 1990; born 26.4.67; Grade S3C.

Rycroft, Matthew John; Third Secretary (Chancery) Paris since May 1991; born 16.6.68; FCO 1989; Grade 8.

Ryde, John; First Secretary FCO since August 1987; born 26.10.50; Third later Second Secretary FCO 1973; Language Student 1976; MECAS 1977; Second Secretary (Comm) Sana'a 1978; First Secretary Tripoli 1980; FCO 1983; First Secretary (UN/Press) UKMIS Geneva 1986; m 1974 Christine May Rydzewska (1s 1979).

Ryder, Martin Frederick John; First Secretary (Management) Bangkok since January 1992; born 29.5.41; Army 1959-68; Ministry of Defence 1968; FCO 1969; Ankara 1972; Nuku;alofa 1975; UKDEL NATO Brussels 1976; Second Secretary FCO 1979; Language Student 1980; Second Secretary and Consul Ankara 1981; Assistant Trade Commissioner, later Trade Commissioner Hong Kong 1985; First Secretary FCO 1989; m 1973 Susan Mary Longhurst (1s 1978; 1d 1990).

Ryder, Michael; First Secretary FCO since July 1988; born 13.11.53; FCO 1984; Second later First Secretary BMG Berlin 1986.

S

Sadler, Henry Edwin; Consul Los Angeles since May 1990; born 27.12.36; FO 1966; Bonn 1968; Tamsui 1971; Bridgetown 1972; FCO 1975; Lagos 1978; Chicago 1981; Second Secretary FCO 1984; Second Secretary (Cons) New Delhi 1987; m 1967 Nancy Cathleen Crocker (1s 1982).

Sadler, Stuart Roger; FCO since December 1990; born 22.12.70; Grade 10.

Sage, Kelly Jane; The Hague since March 1992; born 29.1.68; FCO 1989; Grade 10.

Sainty, Christopher James; Third Secretary (Chancery) New Delhi since June 1992; born 29.3.67; FCO 1989; Language Training FCO 1991; Grade 8.

Salkeld, Peter Charles; Second Secretary New Delhi since September 1989; born 31.8.53; FCO 1969; Bonn 1980; FCO 1983; m 1978 Carol Elizabeth Ann Dent (2s 1985, 1988).

Salmons, Jane; Vienna since February 1991; born 5.1.65; FCO 1988; Grade S2.

Salt, Richard André; FCO since January 1990; born 30.7.62; FCO 1980; UKREP Brussels 1983; Algiers 1985; Banjul 1988; Grade 9; m 1992 Karen Baden Davies.

Salter, Gaynor (née Cawley); FCO since March 1987; born 7.9.60; Inland Revenue 1977; FCO 1982; Dublin 1984; Grade 9; m 1988 Robert Charles Salter.

Salter, Leigh Audra; Wellington since April 1991; born 13.3.69; FCO 1988; Grade S2.

Salvesen, Charles Hugh; First Secretary FCO since August 1988; born 10.9.55; Second Secretary FCO 1982; BMG Berlin 1984; First Secretary (Internal) Bonn 1985; m 1983 Emilie Maria Ingenhousz (twin s 1987).

Sams, Estelle Mary; FCO since February 1984; born 8.5.49; FCO 1975; Amman 1976; Tripoli 1978; Jakarta 1980; Grade S2.

Samuel, Hugh Lennon; Deputy High Commissioner Port Louis since May1991; born 9.3.36; Air Ministry 1957; CO 1957; CRO 1961; Madras 1961; CRO 1963; Lusaka 1964; Lagos 1967; Antigua 1971; Second Secretary FCO 1974; Second Secretary (Comm) Brussels 1977; Second Secretary (Aid/Inf/Comm) Maseru 1980; First Secretary (Admin/Consular) Harare 1982; First Secretary FCO 1987; m 1968 Maria Callinicos (1d 1969).

Samuel, Richard Christopher, CMG (1983), CVO (1983)1; HM Ambassador Riga since October 1991; born 8.8.33; Royal Navy 1952-54; FO 1957; Third Secretary Warsaw 1958; Rome

1960; FO 1963 (Second Secretary 1963, First Secretary 1966); Private Secretary to the Parliamentary Under-Secretary of State, FO 1965; Hong Kong 1968; First Secretary and Head of Chancery Singapore 1969 and Peking 1971; Counsellor Washington 1973; Head of Far Eastern Department FCO 1976; Counsellor (Comm) Moscow 1980; Minister and DHC New Delhi 1982; AUSS (Europe) FCO 1985; on loan to ODA 1986; SUPL 1988; m 1986 Frances Margaret Draper (1d 1987; 1s 1991).

Samuels, Lisa Elaine; FCO since August 1992; born 31.10.72; Grade S2.

Sanda, Lorraine (née Rose); FCO since June 1990; born 18.10.63; FCO 1982; Warsaw 1984; Caracas 1986; Grade 9; m 1987 Manuel Sanda Casal.

Sanderson, Michael John; Second Secretary FCO since March 1988; born 21.1.48; FO 1967; Cairo 1972; FCO 1976; UKMIS New York 1979; Second Secretary (Chancery) Oslo 1984; m 1976 Pauline Elizabeth Tippett (1d 1979; 1s 1982).

Sandover, William Geoffrey; First Secretary (Chancery) Buenos Aires since August 1992; born 7.4.55; FCO 1979; Third later Second Secretary UKMIS Vienna 1981; First Secretary FCO 1984; First Secretary (Chancery) Dublin 1986; First Secretary FCO 1987; m (1) 1981 Sharman Winsome Knight (diss 1985) (2) 1992 Beatrice Martin..

Sands, Richard Martin; First Secretary FCO since May 1992; born 25.8.37; FO 1955; HM Forces 1956-58; FO 1958; Warsaw 1963; DSA 1966; Second Secretary (Inf) Dakar 1968; Canberra 1972; Second later First Secretary (Econ) BMG Berlin 1976; First Secretary FCO 1980; First Secretary (Civil Aviation) Bonn 1985; First Secretary and Head of Chancery Berlin 1989; m 1964 Janet Ridgeway (dec'd 1983) (2d 1966, 1968).

Santonocito, Johnny Franco; FCO since January 1991; born 28.2.72; Grade 10.

Sargeant, Ian Charles; Vice-Consul (Commercial) Düsseldorf since March 1991; born 24.4.52; FCO 1971; Language Student SOAS 1974; Bangkok 1975; LA Floater 1979; FCO 1982; Manila 1986; Deputy Economic Adviser Berlin 1990; m 1988 Mari Grace Santa Cruz Eddun (1d 1989).

Sargon, Derrick Stanley; Islamabad since July 1988; born 8.7.31; FCO 1974; Bonn 1974; East Berlin 1975; Lusaka 1976; Kuala Lumpur 1977; Kinshasa 1979; Harare 1980; Nicosia 1984; Moscow 1987; Grade SO; m 1954 Marie Rita Dibble.

Sattaur, Christopher; FCO since November

1991; born 25.1.71; Grade 10.

Saunders, Caroline Ann; Third Secretary (Chancery) Kuala Lumpur since May 1991; FCO 1983; New Delhi 1986; FCO 1988; Grade 9; m 1989 Rhodri Christopher Kevin Meredith.

Saunders, Julia Edwina (née Golding); Warsaw since August 1992; born 16.3.69; FCO 1990; Language Training 1991; Grade 8; m 1992 Jonathon Sterling Saunders.

Saunders, Katharine Angela Margaret; First Secretary FCO since September 1974; born 16.10.38; FO (later FCO) 1963; Second Secretary Peking 1971; First Secretary Hong Kong 1972; Principal Research Officer (DS Grade 5); m 1976 Leonard Michael Peter Kaye.

Saunders, Martina Henrietta (née Farren); Tel Aviv since August 1989; born 15.12.60; FCO 1980; Canberra 1982; Maputo 1985; Grade 9; m 1987 Christian Saunders.

Saunders, Robert Wayne; Deputy High Commissioner Banjul since November 1989; born 22.3.45; MOD (Army) 1965; FCO 1968; UKMIS Geneva 1970; FCO 1973; Paris 1974; FCO 1977; Tarawa 1979; Second Secretary (Pol/Inf) Rabat 1982; Second Secretary FCO 1987; m (1) 1968 Susan Ann Hunter (diss); (2) 1973 Valerie Ann Lutz (1d 1976).

Saunderson, Lesley Margaret; FCO since August 1991; born 18.11.69; Grade 9.

Savage, Francis Joseph, OBE (1989), LVO (1986); First Secretary FCO since November 1990; born 8.2.43; Passport Office 1961; FO 1966; Cairo 1967; Washington 1971; Aden 1973; Second Secretary FCO 1975; Vice-Consul (Comm) later Consul (Comm) Düsseldorf 1978; First Secretary (Admin) and HM Consul Peking 1982; First Secretary (Immig/Consul) Lagos 1987; m 1966 Veronica Mary McAleenan (2s 1969, 1971).

Savage, Thomas William, Counsellor FCO since April 1984; born 21.11.37; FCO 1968; Second Secretary Dar es Salaam 1970; First Secretary FCO 1973; Counsellor on loan to Cabinet Office 1981; m 1966 Gloria Jean Matthews (3d 1967, 1969, 1972).

Savill, Margaret Ann; Second Secretary FCO since July 1989; born 6.4.46; FCO 1968; Third Secretary Georgetown 1972; Geneva 1975; Second Secretary Rio de Janeiro 1975; FCO 1980; FCO Second Secretary (Inf) Berne 1984.

Saville, John Donald William; First Secretary FCO since July 1991; born 29.6.60; FCO 1981; Third later Second Secretary Jakarta 1983; FCO 1985; Second later First Secretary (Inf) Warsaw 1988.

Sawers, Robert John; First Secretary FCO since September 1991; born 26.7.55; FCO 1977; Sana'a 1980; SUPL 1980; Language Training 1981; Second Secretary Damascus 1982; First Secretary FCO 1984 (PS to Minister of State 1986); First Secretary Pretoria/Cape Town 1988; m 1981 Avril Helen Shelley Lamb (2s 1983, 1985; 1d 1987).

Sawyer, Jeffrey David; First Secretary (Political) The Hague since June 1992; born 8.12.44; CRO 1961; Treasury 1964; CO (later FCO) 1966; Karachi 1969; Helsinki 1973; Second Secretary FCO 1975; Manila 1978; Vice Consul (Comm) Chicago 1982; First Secretary FCO 1985; m 1969 Carmel Rosemary Tucker (2d 1970, 1984; 2s 1971, 1977).

Say, Sarah Gillian; Washington since January 1991; born 2.4.59; FCO 1986; Paris 1988; Grade S2.

Sayer, Jack; Paris since March 1988; born 4.12.32; RAF 1951-74; Havana 1974; Pretoria 1975; Havana 1977; BMG Berlin 1979; Stockholm 1981; East Berlin 1982; Washington 1984; Havana 1987; Grade SO.

Sayle, Lorraine Mary; FCO since November 1990; born 22.9.72; Grade 10.

Scaddan, Simon Mansfield; First Secretary FCO since March 1992; born 22.1.44; FO 1962; Sofia 1966; Zomba 1967; Karachi 1970; Lahore 1971; Karachi 1972; FCO 1974; Durban 1977; Second Secretary Kuala Lumpur 1979; FCO 1982; Aden 1985; First Secretary (Aid) Nairobi 1986; First Secretary Islamabad 1988; m 1970 Frances Anne Barker (1s 1972; 1d 1973).

Scanlon, Michelle; FCO since July 1992; born 2.3.69; FCO 1989; Tokyo 1991; Grade S2.

Scantlebury, Ian Patrick; FCO since February 1991; born 12.9.60; FCO 1978; Georgetown 1981; S.E.A. Floater 1985; Calcutta 1987; Grade 9; m 1989 Rahat Uppal.

Scarborough, Bryan David; Third Secretary (Commercial) Jakarta since November 1991; born 19.1.45; FCO 1973; Warsaw 1975; Douala 1976; Delhi 1979; Freetown 1983; FCO 1985; Lilongwe 1988; Grade 9; m 1969 Kathleen Mary Johnston (1s 1980).

Scarborough, Vernon Marcus; Consul (Commercial) Auckland since October 1990; born 11.2.40; Passport Office 1958; CRO 1961; Dacca 1962; CRO 1964; Karachi 1965; Vice-Consul Brussels 1969; Banjul 1971; Second Secretary FCO 1977; Second Secretary (Comm) Muscat 1980; First Secretary (Admin) Kuala Lumpur 1984; First Secretary FCO 1987; m 1966 Jennifer Bernadette Keane (3d 1970, 1972, 1980).

Scarlett, John McLeod, OBE (1987); First Secretary later Counsellor Moscow since October 1991; born 18.8.48; FCO 1971; Third Secretary Nairobi 1973; (Second Secretary 1974); Language Student 1974; Second later First Secretary Moscow 1976; First Secretary FCO 1977; First Secretary Paris 1984; First Secretary FCO 1989; m 1970 Gwenda Mary Rachel Stilliard (3d 1971, 1976, 1979; 1s 1986).

Scarlett, Robert David Campbell; First Secretary later Counsellor FCO since November 1985; born 15.11.39; First Secretary FCO 1972; Lagos 1975; First Secretary FCO 1977; On loan to MOD 1979; Canberra 1981; m 1965 Sally Bruce (2s 1967, 1969).

Schofield, Nigel; FCO since May 1990; born 17.4.70; Grade 10.

Scholes, Elizabeth Marian; Third later Second Secretary (Chancery) Buenos Aires since June 1990; born 28.4.66; FCO 1987.

Schroeder, Dominic Sebastian; Second Secretary FCO since January 1992; born 13.11.65; FCO 1988; Third later Second Secretary Kinshasa 1989.

Schumann, Carol Ann (née Hill); Bonn since July 1991; born 18.7.46; FCO 1976; Paris 1977; FCO 1980; Washington 1981; FCO 1987; The Hague 1988; Grade S1; m 1980 Jürgen Klaus Dieter Schumann (2s 1981, 1983).

Scobie, William Robert; Ankara since December 1989; born 27.11.41; FCO 1968; St Helena 1970; FCO 1972; Jedda 1973; FCO 1975; Kingston 1976; FCO 1980; Darwin 1982; FCO 1984; Grade 8; m 1967 Maureen Elizabeth Fisher (2d 1972, 1976).

Scott, Gavin David; Third Secretary (Commercial) Bogotá since August 1991; born 26.6.60; FCO 1978; Paris 1981; Beirut 1983; Washington 1985; FCO 1988; Grade 9.

Scott, George; FCO since November 1991; born 11.10.56; FCO 1981; E Berlin 1982; Luxembourg 1984; Lagos 1986; Grade 9.

Scott, Keith John; FCO since October 1991; born 12.2.69; Grade 8.

Scott, William Cockburn Garden; Second Secretary FCO since November 1990; born 17.6.41; MOD 1961; DSAO (later FCO) 1965; Karachi 1969; Islamabad 1971; Lagos 1973; Second Secretary on loan to DOT 1977; Kuala Lumpur 1981; Second Secretary (Comm) Consul and Admin Office Monrovia 1984; Second Secretary FCO 1985; T/D Milan 1989; m 1969 Jean Elizabeth Anne Critchley (2d 1971, 1972; 1s 1982).

Scott, William Norman; FCO since May 1983; (Second Secretary 1985); born 27.12.38; Inland

Revenue 1961; FO 1962; Moscow 1963; La Paz 1965; Zagreb 1968; Madras 1969; FCO 1973; Nicosia 1976; Bangkok 1979; m 1963 Marjorie Ann Brown (2s 1967, 1972).

Scrafton, Douglas; First Secretary and Head of Chancery Ottawa since January 1989; born 14.7.49; FCO 1967; UKDEL Brussels 1970; Kampala 1973; Mbabane 1975; FCO 1977; Jedda 1980; Second Secretary Riyadh 1982; Cairo 1984; Second later First Secretary FCO 1985; on loan to Cabinet Office 1987; m 1975 Caroline Patricia Collison (1s 1976; 1d 1977).

Scroby, Gary Vance; Floater duties since March 1992; born 15.7.69; FCO 1988; UKREP Brussels 1989; Grade 10.

Sculthorpe, Elizabeth; Full-Time Language Training Seoul since January 1992; born 1.5.66; FCO 1990; Grade 8.

Seaby, Paul Robert; Third Secretary (Commercial) Muscat since March 1991; born 24.5.56; FCO 1975; Warsaw 1978; Masirah 1978; Ottawa 1979; Floater duties 1982; Port Moresby 1984; FCO 1987; Grade 9; m 1984 Lynette Margaret Heffernan.

Sealy, Amanda Sarah (née Franklin) Windhoek since June 1991; born 3.1.59; FCO 1980; Pretoria 1983; Cape Town/Pregoria 1984; Warsaw 1986; FCO 1988; Grade 9; m 1989 Dominic John Sealy (1s 1992).

Seaman, Michael William; Second Secretary FCO since August 1992; born 1.11.55; FCO 1975; Jakarta 1977; Bombay 1981; FCO 1984; Second Secretary (Chancery) The Hague 1988; m 1978 Jane Lesley Stockwell (2d 1984, 1987).

Seaman, Stephen James; Second Secretary (Commercial) Lilongwe since June 1991; born 4.12.55; DOT 1975; Copenhagen 1979; Salisbury 1980; DOT 1980; FCO 1982; Bucharest 1983; FCO 1986; Second Secretary Monrovia 1988; m 1980 Katherine Ann Barker.

Seamer, Helen Maria; SUPL since October 1989; born 25.11.60; FCO 1981; Cairo 1985; SUPL 1988; Amsterdam 1989; Grade 9; m (1) 1984 Timothy John Unsworth (diss.); m (2) Raymond Clive Seamer.

Searight, Pauline Mabel; Banjul since February 1990; born 27.6.55; FCO 1988; Grade S2; m 1991 Graham Kenneth Denham.

Seaton, Andrew James; First Secretary FCO since January 1987; born 20.4.54; FCO 1977; Third later Second Secretary Dakar 1979; Trade Commissioner (China) BTC Hong Kong 1981; m 1983 Helen Elizabeth Pott (1s 1989).

Seddon, Barry Charles; First Secretary (Chancery) Kuwait since December 1991; born

30.4.40; FO 1957; Peking 1961; Bonn 1962;
Kuwait 1965; Nicosia 1966; FCO 1970; MECAS
1971; Baghdad 1973; FCO 1975; Second
Secretary 1976; Consul Jerusalem 1978; First
Secretary (Comm) Bucharest 1983; First
Secretary (Aid) and Head of Chancery Sana'a
1986; First Secretary FCO 1990; m 1963 June
Anne Clifford (2s 1964, 1969).

Seddon, David William; FCO since November
1991; born 30.5.48; FO (later FCO) 1966; Bonn
1970; FCO 1971; Port of Spain 1973; Vila
1977; FCO 1981; Milan 1983; Grade 7; Vice-
Consul (Comm/Admin/Cons) Douala 1987; m
1972 Monica Elizabeth Josefina van Loon (1s
1976).

Sedwill, Mark Philip; Second Secretary
(Political/External) Cairo since August 1992;
born 21.10.64; FCO 1989; Language Training
1990; Second Secretary Language Training Cairo
1991.

Seear, Roger William; First Secretary FCO since
September 1984; born 1.2.38; Board of Trade
1956; RAF 1956-58; BOT 1958; Lahore 1964;
Attaché and Vice-Consul Manila 1968; FCO
1972; Second Secretary 1974; Second Secretary
(Comm) Bombay 1977; First Secretary (Admin)
and Consul Jakarta 1981; m 1963 Wendy
Beverley Levy (2s 1967; 1969).

Seeley, Louis Christopher Robin; Counsellor
Tokyo since October 1989; born 28.8.37; Third
Secretary FO 1965; Second Secretary Tehran
1967; First Secretary FCO 1970; Kampala 1973;
Ankara 1974; FCO 1978; Counsellor Rome
1981; FCO 1985; m 1973 Teruko Mary
Winterton (née Kawano).

Seery, Elaine, FCO since September 1990; born
25.10.66; Grade 9.

Seery, Michael Joseph; Second Secretary
(Immig) Lagos since March 1992; born 7.12.38;
RAF 1957-62; FO 1963; Conakry 1964; Lahore
1966; Karachi 1967; FCO 1969; Sofia 1972;
Blantyre 1974; FCO 1977; Second Secretary
(Comm) Kingston 1981 Second Secretary
(Admin) Tel Aviv 1983; Second Secretary FCO
1988; m (1) 1964 Marjory Rosa Curtis (2s 1966,
1970; 1d 1965); (2) 1987 Cilla Stähli.

Segar, Christopher Michael John; on loan to the
MOD since March 1991; born 25.11.50; FCO
1973; Language Student MECAS 1974; Third
later Second Secretary (Comm) Dubai 1976;
First Secretary FCO 1979; First Secretary
(Comm) and Head of Chancery Luanda 1984;
First Secretary UKDEL Paris 1987; Counsellor
Consul-General and Deputy Head of Mission
Baghdad 1990.

Self, Andrew Paul; Third Secretary (Inf) Sana'a
since January 1992; FCO 1988; m 1987 Michele
Carmichael Crouch.

Setterfield, (James) Robert; First Secretary FCO
since February 1992; born 6.5.47; DSAO (later
FCO) 1967; Bombay 1969; New Delhi 1970;
MECAS 1972; FCO 1973; Second Secretary
(Aid/Inf) Rangoon 1976; Vice-Consul (Cons/
Admin) Stuttgart 1980; Vice-Consul Düsseldorf
1982; First Secretary FCO 1985; First Secretary
(Pol/Inf) Wellington 1987; m 1980 Margaret
Jean McMahon (1s 1983).

Sexton, Karen Louise; FCO since October 1988;
born 8.4.67; Grade S2A.

Seymour, Irene Frances; FCO since January
1990; born 2.12.64; FCO 1984; San José 1987;
Grade S2; m 1991 Peter James Seymour.

Seymour, Peter James; FCO since September
1991; born 10.2.62; FCO 1984; Second Secretary
(Chancery and Inf) and Vice-Consul San José
1987; Second Secretary FCO 1989; SUPL 1990;
m 1991 Irene Frances McDonagh.

Shackell, Robin John; Management Officer/Vice
Consul La Paz since January 1991; born 4.2.63;
HCS 1983; FCO 1985; UKDEL MBFR Vienna
1987; T/D Munich 1989; Grade 9; m 1991 Carol
Plowman.

Shackleton, Richard David; Third Secretary
(Political) UKMIS New York since June 1992;
born 26.5.68; FCO 1990; Grade 9.

Shaikh, Farida; FCO since September 1990;
born 16.10.65; Grade 9.

Shaill, Brenda Anne Phyllis; FCO since May
1969; born 2.12.47; Grade S2.

Shakespeare, Karen Marie; FCO since July
1992; born 25.10.70; Grade S2.

Shand, Ian; FCO since October 1991; born
17.1.54; FCO 1973; Accra 1975; Munich 1979;
FCO 1982; Bonn 1985; Islamabad 1988; Grade
9; m 1975 Lyndsey Elizabeth Hall (2d 1983,
1985).

Shannon, Keith; Third Secretary (Chancery/Aid)
Maputo since June 1991; born 17.9.66; FCO
1988; Grade 9.

Shapcott, William James; Second Secretary
(Chancery/Information) Bonn since September
1990; born 25.7.61; HM Forces 1980-88; Second
Secretary FCO 1988; m 1986 Shelley Mary
Harrison.

Shapland, Anthony Gregory; FCO since July
1992; born 17.12.49; PRO (DS Grade 5); FCO
1979; on loan to the Cabinet Office 1990; m (1)
1973 Margaret Elizabeth Moriarty (diss); m (2)
1982 Leonora Alexandra Hebden (1s 1983).

Sharkey, Anne Margaret; Hanoi since January
1991; born 21.11.61; FCO 1986; UKMIS Vienna

1988; Grade S2.

Sharland, Edward John; High Commissioner
Victoria since January 1992; born 25.12.37; FO
1961; Third later Second Secretary (Comm)
Bangkok 1962; Second later First Secretary FO
(later FCO) 1967; First Secretary Vienna 1969;
First Secretary and Head of Chancery Bangkok
1972; First Secretary (Comm) and Consul
Montevideo 1976; FCO 1979; HM Consul-
General Perth 1982; Consul-General Cleveland
1987; High Commissioner Port Moresby 1989; m
1970 Susan Mary Rodway Millard (4d 1971,
1972, 1974, 1975).

Sharp, David Stewart; UKMIS New York since
July 1992; born 19.1.71; FCO 1989; Grade 10.

Sharp, James Lyall; Second Secretary Cairo
since June 1989; born 12.4.60; Second Secretary
FCO 1987; Language Training Cairo 1988; m
1992 Sara Eggam El-Gammal.

Sharp, Jonathan Dinsdale; Paris since August
1991; born 31.3.67; FCO 1988; Karachi 1990;
Grade 10.

Sharp, Paul John Gibson; Second Secretary
Pretoria since May 1990; born 24.9.48; FCO
1967; New Delhi 1975; FCO 1976; Rome 1978;
FCO 1981; Attaché Ankara 1981; FCO 1985;
Attaché Moscow 1987; Second Secretary FCO
1989; m 1969 Anita Tsang (2s 1972, 1976).

Sharp, Raymond Sidney; FCO since May 1984;
born 2.11.29; HM Forces 1950-52; FO 1954;
Rome 1955; Prague 1956; Bangkok 1957;
Budapest 1959; FO 1960; Singapore1/Rangoon
1961; Delhi 1962; FO 1964; Saigon 1965; FCO
1966; Buenos Aires 1971; FCO 1976; Warsaw
1980 m (1) 1954 Pamela Yvonne Collins (1s
1956); (2) 1965 Sandra Marion Chambers (1
step d 1962; 1d 1966); (3) 1980 Jean Stella
White.

Sharp, Richard; Second Secretary FCO since
October 1990; born 8.3.49; FO (later FCO 1967);
Karachi 1971; Canberra 1972; Port Moresby
1974; Santiago 1975; Jakarta 1977; FCO 1980;
Cairo 1984; Second Secretary (Admin) Moscow
1987; m 1974 Patricia Anne Whitby (1s 1979;
1d 1983).

Sharp, Sara Jane; FCO since September 1991;
born 24.12.67; Grade 9.

Sharpe, Jean Cynthia; First Secretary and Consul
Bangkok since December 1991; born 18.10.47;
CO 1964; DSAO 1965; The Hague 1970;
Kingston 1973; FCO 1974; Dubai 1974; FCO
1975; Freetown 1978; JAO Brussels 1981;
Second Secretary FCO 1984; on loan to DTI
1986; Second Secretary (Comm) Nairobi 1988.

Sharpe, Rosemary Helen; First Secretary
(Economic) Berlin since July 1991; born 11.3.56;

Second Secretary FCO 1982; First Secretary
UKREP Brussels 1987; Second Secretary (Inf)
New Delhi 1985; First Secretary FCO 1988.

Sharpless, Kristian; Kathmandu since May 1992;
born 17.6.67; Dept of Employment 1985; FCO
1987; Brussels 1989; Grade 10; m 1990 Fiona
Ure McGowan.

Shaughnessy, Kevin John; Bonn since July
1991; born 10.11.64; FCO 1983; Tehran 1986;
Kingston 1988; Grade 9.

Shave, Alan William, OBE (1991); Governor
Anguilla since August 1992; born 3.11.36; HM
Forces 1957-59; COI 1960; Salisbury 1961; Dar
es Salaam 1962; Second Secretary (Inf) Sydney
1964 and La Paz 1966; FCO 1970; Second
Secretary (Comm) Santiago 1972; Consul
(Comm) Barcelona 1977; Consul (Comm) Milan
1981; First Secretary FCO 1984; First Secretary,
Consul, and Deputy Head of Mission La Paz
1988; m 1961 Lidia Donoso Bertolotto (1d 1966;
1s 1967).

Shaw, Alan John; Washington since August
1989; born 9.6.66; FCO 1987; Grade 10; m 1989
Claire Louise Morgan.

Shaw, Andrew John; Bonn since August 1991;
born 3.3.70; FCO 1989; Grade 10.

Shaw, Claire Louise (née Morgan); FCO since
March 1992; born 18.6.68; FCO 1987;
Washington 1989; Grade 10; m 1989 Alan John
Shaw.

Shaw, David Robert; First Secretary FCO since
October 1991; born 7.5.43; Ministry of Housing
and Local Government 1961; Commonwealth
Office (later FCO) 1965; Monrovia1/Kinshasa
1968; Mogadishu 1969; Tokyo 1969; Warsaw
1972; FCO 1973; Bombay 1975; Mbabane 1980;
Second Secretary FCO 1982; Second Secretary
later First (Comm) Singapore 1988.

Shaw, John Stuart; Second Secretary FCO since
September 1988; born 10.10.48; FCO 1967;
Kuala Lumpur 1970; East Berlin 1974; Lilongwe
1975; FCO 1977; Mogadishu 1979; FCO 1981;
New York 1983; Nairobi 1986; m 1973 Ann
Picton (1d 1975; 1s 1977).

Shaw, Lyn(da) Jane (née Tovey); FCO since
September 1991; born 5.2.57; FCO 1976; Paris
1978; Tokyo 1981; Middle East/African Floater
1983; FCO 1986; Bangkok 1988; Grade 9; m
1986 Graham Patrick Shaw.

Shaw, Redmond; First Secretary FCO since May
1992; born 13.4.38; Crown Agents 1954-62; HM
Forces 1956-58; CRO 1962; Singapore 1963;
DSAO 1965; Accra 1968; Lusaka 1971; Dar es
Salaam 1972; Second Secretary 1974; on loan to
DOT 1977; Nicosia 1980; First Secretary
(Comm) Washington 1984; First Secretary

(Comm) Algiers 1988; m 1963 Dorothy Janet
Alderson (1s 1966; 1d 1969).

Shaw, Sandra Heather; FCO since March 1992;
born 7.9.43; Grade S2.

Shaw, Warren Anthony; FCO since April 1991;
born 14.7.71; Grade 10.

Shead, Robert John; Second Secretary Manila
since April 1992; born 14.4.50; FCO 1969; Bonn
1973; Seoul 1976; FCO 1977; Paris 1978;
Damascus 1982; FCO 1985; Damascus 1986;
FCO 1987; Nairobi 1988; m (1) 1981 Carol Ann
Bostock (diss 1987); (2) 1987 Fayha Sultan (1s
1987).

Shearing, Sally Louise; Sofia since February
1992; born 20.4.66; FCO 1985; Budapest 1988;
FCO 1990; Grade S2.

Shearman, Martin James; Full-Time Language
Training Tokyo since August 1992; born 7.2.65;
Third later Second Secretary FCO 1989;
Language Training 1991.

Sheinwald, Nigel Elton; First Secretary later
Counsellor FCO since September 1987; born
26.6.53; FCO 1976; Moscow 1978; Second later
First Secretary FCO 1979; First Secretary
(Chancery) Washington 1983; m 1980 Julia
Dunne (1s 1984).

Sheldon, Anita Morag Moir; First Secretary/
Counsul Cairo since July 1991; born 12.5.38;
Department of Social Security 1959-65; DSAO
1966; Cairo 1968; Rawalpindi (later Islamabad)
1969; Brussels 1971; FCO 1974; Kuala Lumpur
1977; Jakarta 1979 (Second Secretary 1981);
Vice-Consul (Comm) Brisbane 1983; Second
later First Secretary FCO 1987.

Sheldon, John Barry; FCO since March 1992;
born 11.2.71; Grade 10.

Shelly, Simon Richard; FCO since May 1991;
Second Secretary 1992; born 5.7.60; HM
Customs and Excise 1981-83; FCO 1983; Kabul
1986; Paris 1988; m 1991 Monique Marie Renée
Le Roux.

Shelton, Craig Stuart Michael; FCO since May
1992; born 16.11.44; FCO 1969; MECAS 1971;
Amman 1973; Sana'a 1974; FCO 1977; Second
later First Secretary (Comm) Jedda 1979; First
Secretary (Aid) Khartoum 1983; FCO 1987;
Head of British Interests Section Tripoli 1988;
Deputy Head of Mission Rangoon 1990.

Shepherd, John Alan, CMG (1989); Minister Bonn
since October 1991; born 27.4.43; Third
Secretary CRO 1965; MECAS 1966; Second
Secretary Amman 1968; Rome 1970; First
Secretary FCO 1973; First Secretary (Econ) later
Head of Chancery The Hague 1976; First
Secretary later Counsellor and Head of Chancery

UKREP EC Brussels 1980; Counsellor FCO
1985; HM Ambassador and Consul-General
Bahrain 1988; m 1969 Jessica Mary Nichols (1d
1975).

Shepherd, Victoria Ann; UKMIS New York
since April 1992; born 25.9.70; FCO 1990;
Grade S2.

Sheppard, David Anthony; FCO since April
1989; later Second Secretary 1992; born 6.7.51;
HCS 1968; Hong Kong 1977; FCO 1980;
Baghdad 1983; Tel Aviv 1986; m 1988 Bonita
Dorsman.

Sheppard, Nicholas Ugo; Second Secretary
(Commercial) New Delhi since May 1992; born
2.6.56; DTI 1973; FCO 1974; UKDEL OECD
Paris 1977; Islamabad 1980; FCO 1982; Aden
1983; Canberra 1986; Second Secretary FCO
1989; m 1977 Susan Mary Gill (1d 1986; 1s
1988).

Sherar, Paul Desmond; Second Secretary
(Commercial/Aid) Luanda since November 1991;
born 24.2.53; FCO 1970; Brussels 1973; Africa
Floater 1976; Georgetown 1978; FCO 1981;
Vice-Consul (Comm) BTDO New York 1986.

Sherman, Penelope Anne; Harare since July
1990; born 29.8.43; Tokyo 1971; Calcutta 1973;
Jakarta 1975; Hanoi 1977; Rio de Janeiro 1978;
FCO 1980; Algiers 1983; Nicosia 1987; FCO
1989; Grade S1.

Sherrin, Barrie Robert; Lisbon since August
1992; born 20.7.44; Royal Marines 1961-84;
Baghdad 1989; Mowscow 1991; Grade SO; m
1967 Kathleen Mary.

Sherrington, Simon Richard; Second Secretary
FCO since September 1989; born 27.5.55; FCO
1980; Language Training Kamakura 1982;
Tokyo 1983; Second Secretary FCO 1987;
Second Secretary (Chancery/Admin)
Johannesburg 1987.

Sherry, Patricia Angela; FCO since August
1992; born 23.8.64; FCO 1985; Madrid 1989;
Grade S2.

Sherwood, David Andrew; Havana since
December 1988; born 2.11.55; FCO 1975; Accra
1978; The Hague 1982; FCO 1985; Bridgetown
1985; Grade 10; m 1978 Susan Jean Hannay (1s
1985; 1d 1988).

Shingler, Michael John; Consul (Management)
Istanbul since October 1991; born 31.1.47; Post
Office 1963; DSAO 1965; Manila 1969; Prague
1973; Dacca 1975; FCO 1979; Dar es Salaam
1981; FCO 1984; Consul (Comm) Casablanca
1984; FCO 1988; m 1969 Katina Janet Wall (1d
1972; 1s 1975).

Shipman, John Gervase Trafford; Counsellor

FCO since March 1991; born 7.7.39; HMOCS Eastern Aden Protectorate 1963-67; Assistant Adviser; Second later First Secretary FCO 1968; Muscat 1970; FCO 1973; Jedda 1977; FCO 1981; First Secretary later Counsellor Abu Dhabi 1984; FCO 1987; on loan to Cabinet Office 1988.

Shipster, Michael David, OBE (1990); Consul Johannesburg since February 1991; born 17.3.51; Second later First Secretary FCO 1977; First Secretary (Chancery) Moscow 1981; First Secretary FCO 1983; New Delhi 1986; First Secretary (Chancery) Lusaka 1990; m 1974 Jacquelynne Mann (2d 1981, 1982; 1s 1987).

Short, George Andrew, MBE (1980); Kingston since Novermber 1990; born 11.9.34; Bucharest 1982; Santiago 1984; Bonn 1986; Tokyo 1988; Grade SO; m 1988 Victoria Elena Crowther Concha.

Short, James Walter; Shanghai since September 1991; born 19.10.66; FCO 1986; Calcutta 1989; Grade 10; m 1990 Stephanie Sansukta Ghosh.

Short, Roger Guy, MVO (1971); Counsellor FCO since October 1990; born 9.12.44; Third Secretary Commonwealth Office (later FCO) 1967; Third later Second Secretary Ankara 1969; First Secretary FCO 1974; Consul (Comm) Rio de Janeiro 1978; Head of Chancery Ankara 1981; Counsellor and Deputy Head of Permanent Under-Secretary;s Department FCO 1984; Counsellor, Head of Chancery and Consul-General Oslo 1986; m 1971 Sally Victoria Taylor (2d 1978, 1982; 1s 1988).

Shorter, Hugo Benedict; Second Secretary on attachment to ENA Paris since September 1992; born 11.8.66; FCO 1990.

Shortridge, Charlotte Irene Elizabeth; BM Berlin since April 1990; born 27.10.51; HM Forces 1972-80; Bucharest 1988; Grade SO.

Shott, Philip Nicholas; First Secretary FCO since April 1991; born 27.11.54; FCO 1980 (Second Secretary 1980); First Secretary Lagos 1983; First Secretary FCO 1986; First Secretary (Chancery) Nicosia 1987; m 1981 Lesley Ann Marsh (1s 1986, 1d 1987).

Shute, Christopher David; Second Secretary FCO since November 1990; born 8.10.49; HMIT 1968; FCO 1969; Middle East Floater 1972; Lagos 1974; Cairo 1975; FCO 1979; Rome 1983; Second Secretary FCO 1986; Second Secretary (Comm) Warsaw 1987; m 1975 Peta Ann Dewhurst (1s 1987).

Sidnell, Gail Marilyn; Nairobi since October 1989; born 9.4.53; FCO 1974; Addis Ababa 1975; Monrovia 1977; Gibraltar 1981; FCO 1982; Prague 1983; FCO 1985; Grade 9.

Silva, Ginny Anne (née Kesterton); Seoul since June 1989; born 9.7.64; Immig Service Heathrow 1985; FCO 1987; Grade 9; m 1989 Ronie Silva.

Silvester, Olive; FCO since August 1986; born 11.3.33; FCO 1966; Bonn 1967; FCO 1969; The Hague 1971; UKDEL NATO Brussels 1971; FCO 1973; Transferred to MAFF 1976; Rejoined FCO 1977; Belgrade 1977; FCO 1978; Bonn 1984; Grade S1.

Silverwood, Jane Mary; FCO since September 1991; born 6.8.60; FCO 1985; Mexico City 1987; Grade S2.

Sime, Charles; First Secretary FCO since January 1992; born 11.3.46; CO 1963; FCO 1965; Pretoria1/Cape Town 1969; Warsaw 1972; Muscat 1974; FCO 1975; Kinshasa 1978; Perth 1981; FCO 1983; Second Secretary (Management) Dar es Salaam 1986; m 1968 Edith Gregg.

Simm, Michael James; Second later First Secretary FCO since April 1980; born 5.10.46; FCO 1971; Amman 1977.

Simmonds, Julie Laura; FCO since December 1982; born 31.12.64; Grade 9.

Simmonds, Steven John; FCO since April 1992; Vienna 1989; born 30.12.68; FCO 1987; Grade 10.

Simmons, Belinda Jayne; Buenos Aires since November 1990; born 12.9.65; FCO 1988; Grade S2A.

Simmons, Christine Susan; Tokyo since February 1992; born 16.9.59; FCO 1980; Dar es Salaam 1982; Bonn 1985; Grade S2; Nairobi 1988; FCO 1991; m 1981 David Arthur Simmons (1s 1988; 1d 1991).

Simmons, Ian Paul; First Secretary (Political) Hanoi since November 1992; born 5.9.55; FCO 1983; Second Secretary (Inf) New Delhi 1987; First Secretary FCO 1989; Full-Time Language Training Point Cook, Melbourne 1992.

Simmons, Timothy Michael John; Second later First Secretary FCO since February 1988; born 8.4.60; FCO 1982; Warsaw 1985; m 1989 Caroline Mary Radcliffe (1s 1990).

Simms, Stephen Nathaniel; First Secretary FCO since November 1990; born 16.7.40; CRO 1959; Lagos 1960; CRO 1963; Calcutta 1965; Delhi 1966; New York 1969; Vice-Consul (Comm) San Francisco 1971; FCO 1972; Second Secretary 1974; Seconded to DOT 1974; Second Secretary (Comm) Santiago 1976; Havana 1981; First Secretary on MCDC 1984; First Secretary FCO 1984; First Secretary (Comm) Bogotá 1988; m 1968 Jean Ogilvie Duxbury.

Simon, Susannah Kate; Third later Second

Secretary (Chancery) Bonn since June 1989; born 7.6.64; FCO 1988.

Simpson, Beverley Jayne; Floater Training since December 1991; born 11.6.70; FCO 1989; Grade 10.

Simpson, Brian; Lagos since February 1991; born 8.5.67; FCO 1986; Warsaw 1988; Grade 10.

Simpson, Dominic Mark; Second Secretary (Political) Sana'a since September 1991; born 22.12.63; FCO 1985; Language Training 1987; Language Training Cairo 1988; Second Secretary (Pol) Riyadh 1989; m 1991 Georgina Felicity Little.

Simpson, Georgina Felicity (née Little); Second Secretary (Comm/Econ/Political) Sana'a since December 1991; born 23.2.64; FCO 1986; Language Training 1987; Second Secretary Amman 1989; SUPL 1991; m 1991 Dominic Mark Simpson.

Simpson, Gordon Grant; Second Secretary (Immigration) Islamabad since May 1990; born 25.8.46; FO 1964; Peking 1968; Lisbon 1970; Ibadan 1972; FCO 1975; Bucharest 1978; Nairobi 1979; Lisbon 1982; Second Secretary FCO 1985; Second Secretary (Comm) Luanda 1987; m 1970 Jenny Frances Parker (1d 1974; 2s 1975, 1982).

Simpson, Karen Frances (née Thomas); Lagos since April 1987; born 25.8.54; FCO 1975; Islamabad 1976; FCO 1978; UKREP Brussels 1979; Cairo 1982; FCO 1985; Grade S2; m 1981 Kenneth Simpson.

Simpson, Kay; Tokyo since September 1990; born 29.1.62; FCO 1988; Grade S2.

Simpson, Louise Jane; FCO since February 1992; born 24.6.66; FCO 1986; Lima 1988; SUPL 1990; Grade S2.

Simpson, Scott; FCO since September 1991; born 28.3.70; Grade 10.

Simpson, Timothy John; FCO since February 1988; born 14.9.60; Grade 9; m 1985 Lisé Margaret Finlay (1d 1986).

Sims, Lynda; FCO since September 1977; born 10.11.50; MOD 1968; FCO 1970; Kuala Lumpur 1973; Bucharest 1976; Grade 9; m 1981 Richard Ian Taylor.

Sinclair, Rachel Elizabeth; Harare since March 1992; born 7.2.65; FCO 1984; Grade S2; m 1991 Alexander Field Douse.

Sinclair, Robert Nelson Gurney; FCO since October 1991; born 10.12.52; FCO 1972; Dacca 1975; Algiers 1978; E Berlin 1980; CG Berlin 1981; FCO 1984; Third later Second Secretary Jakarta 1987; m 1975 Diana Sawyer (1s 1986).

Sindall, Adrian John; High Commissioner Bandar Seri Begawan since April 1991; born 5.10.37; FO 1956; MECAS 1958; Baghdad 1960; Rabat 1962 (Second Secretary 1965); Second later First Secretary FCO 1967; Beirut 1970; First Secretary and Head of Chancery Lima 1972; FCO 1976; Counsellor Head of Chancery and Consul-General Amman 1979; Head of South America Department FCO 1982; Consul-General Sydney 1985; on secondment to MOD 1988; m (1) 1958 Barbara Endersby (1d 1961; 1s 1963); (2) 1978 Jill Margaret Cowley.

Sindon, Alison Jane; FCO since March 1991; born 16.11.63; FCO 1983; Mexico City 1985; Ascuncion 1988; Grade 9.

Sindon, Ronald William; First Secretary (Comm) Nairobi since November 1988; born 5.3.38; CRO 1961; Accra 1962; Nairobi 1965; La Paz 1967; FCO 1970; Third later Second Secretary San José 1974; Vice-Consul (Comm) Karachi 1979; Second later First Secretary FCO 1981; Assistant to Deputy Governor Gibraltar 1984; m 1959 Jane Bezzina (2d 1963, 1964).

Singleton, Jean Patricia; SUPL since January 1990; born 10.3.49; FCO 1987; Grade S2A.

Sinkinson, Philip Andrew; Second Secretary (Commercial) Sao Paulo since December 1991; born 7.10.50; Inland Revenue 1967; FCO 1970; Warsaw 1973; FCO 1974; East Berlin 1974; Rome 1975; FCO 1976; Rio de Janeiro 1978; Quito 1978; Prague 1979; FCO 1981; Blantyre 1982; Lilongwe 1985; FCO 1986; m 1971 Clare Maria Catherine Jarvis (1s 1974).

Sinton, William Baldie; First Secretary FCO since December 1985; born 17.6.46; Third Secretary FCO 1968; Third later Second Secretary (Comm) Prague 1970; Second later First Secretary UKDEL NATO Brussels 1973; First Secretary FCO 1977; First Secretary (Comm) Prague 1978; FCO 1979; First Secretary (Comm) Algiers 1981.

Sizeland, Paul Raymond; First Secretary (Chancery) Lagos since April 1988; born 19.2.52; FCO 1980; UKDEL NATO Brussels 1981; Doha 1985; Second Secretary FCO 1986; m 1976 Vasantha Jesudasan (2d 1981, 1982).

Skeate, Christopher Thomas William; Counsellor FCO since October 1989; born 16.9.38; FO 1962; Third Secretary Rio de Janeiro 1964; FO 1965; Second Secretary Lisbon 1966; Second Secretary (Inf) Havana 1968; First Secretary FCO 1970; First Secretary Madrid 1977; FCO 1981; First Secretary later Counsellor Canberra 1985; m 1966 Daphne Graeme Stannard (née Verel) (2s 1968, 1971).

Skingle, Diana; First Secretary (Info) UKDEL NATO Brussels since December 1988; born 3.5.47; Commonwealth Office (later FCO) 1966;

Kampala 1970; FCO 1972; Abidjan 1974; Vila 1975; Prague 1977; Casablanca 1979; Second Secretary FCO 1982; Second Secretary (Aid/Comm) Georgetown 1985; Second Secretary (Dev) Bridgetown 1986.

Skinner, Dawn Emma; Angiulla since November 1991; born 18.5.65; FCO 1985; Prague 1987; UKREP Brussels 1989; Grade S2.

Skinner, Kathleen; FCO since June 1984; born 3.12.55; FCO 1975; Accra 1978; FCO 1980; Mexico City 1981; Grade S2.

Slade, David Henry Edward; Peking since April 1988; born 28.6.39; RAF 1955-79; Kuala Lumpur 1980; Havana 1981; Amman 1982; Moscow 1984; Paris 1985; Grade SO; m 1960 Valerie (2s 1962, 1963).

Slater, Duncan, CMG (1982);High Commissioner Kuala Lumpur since February 1992; born 15.7.34; MECAS 1958; FO 1959; Assistant Political Agent Abu Dhabi 1962; First Secretary Rawalpindi 1966; New Delhi 1966; First Secretary and Head of Chancery Aden 1968; FCO 1969; Special Assistant to Sir William Luce 1970-71; First Secretary UKREP Brussels 1973; Counsellor 1975; UK Permanent Representative to IAEA/UNIDO Vienna 1975; Counsellor and Head of Chancery Lagos and Consul-General (non-resident) Benin 1979; HM Ambassador Muscat 1981; AUSS (Energy/UN) FCO 1986; m 1972 Candida Coralie Anne Wheatley (1s 1975; 2d 1977, 1979).

Slater, David John; Accra since July 1991; born 2.3.68; FCO 1987; Abu Dhabi 1989; Grade 9.

Slater, Gina Michelle (née Lambert); Harare since August 1992; born 29.7.54; FCO 1974; Port Stanley 1976; SUPL 1978; Lisbon 1982; FCO 1986; Dhaka 1988; Grade 9; m 1976 Gordon Slater (diss) (1d 1981).

Slater, Judith Mary; Third later Second Secretary (Econ) Canberra since April 1989; born 26.6.64; FCO 1988.

Slater, Karen Elizabeth Sunley; Lagos since November 1991; born 3.7.70; FCO 1988; Grade 9.

Slater, Shannon Elizabeth (née Dent); SUPL since September 1988; born 29.3.58; FCO 1979; Lusaka 1979; Peking 1981; Athens 1982; Dubai 1985; Bahrain 1987; Grade S2.

Sleet, Peter; Attaché Helsinki since April 1992; born 3.7.43; British Telecom 1969; FCO 1982; Moscow 1985; Washington 1986; FCO 1986; Grade 8; m 1962 Ann Florence Turner (3d 1962, 1963, 1966).

Slinn, David Arthur; Second Secretary (Info/Aid) Pretoria/Capetown since February 1990; born

16.4.59; FCO 1981; UKDIS Geneva 1983; Language Training 1986; Second Secretary and Head of Chancery Ulan Bator 1987; m 1982 Melody Sarah Hesford.

Sloan, Frederick David; Peking since November 1992; born 1.5.49; Athens 1990; Grade SO; m 1974 Wendy Davis (1s 1977; 1d 1979).

Sloan, Kevin Joseph Carnegie; First Secretary Phnom Penh since July 1992; born 31.8.58; FCO 1984; Second later First Secretary (Chancery) Islamabad 1987; First Secretary FCO 1990; m 1991 Christine Ruth Lowson.

Sloane, Ian Christopher; Counsellor (Management) New York since April 1990; born 28.1.38; FO 1956; HM Forces 1957-59; FO 1959; MECAS 1960; Vice-Consul Khartoum 1961; Algiers 1964 (Second Secretary 1965); Vice-Consul Saigon 1967; Second Secretary (Comm1/Aid) Dacca 1967; Second Secretary (Econ) Lahore 1967; Academic year for Management Studies at the Polytechnic of Central London 1970; FCO 1971; Second Secretary UKDIS Geneva 1973; Head of Chancery and Consul Seoul 1974; First Secretary (Econ) Bonn 1978; First Secretary FCO 1983; First Secretary (Cultural) Moscow 1985; First Secretary (Econ/Comm) Ankara 1986; FCO 1989; m 1968 Phyllis June Barton (2s 1971, 1974).

Slough, Christopher George James; FCO since July 1986; born 28.11.67; Grade 10.

Small, Susan Jane Rosemary; UKMIS New York since April 1992; born 23.1.49; FCO 1985; Banjul 1986; UKDEL NATO Brussels 1989; Grade S2.

Smallcorn, Philip Julian; FCO since November 1991; born 11.4.72; Grade 10.

Smallman, David Leslie, LVO (1990); Deputy High Commissioner Port of Spain since August 1990; born 29.4.40; National Assistance Board 1961; Commonwealth Office 1966; Rawalpindi (later Islamabad) 1967; Second Secretary (Immig) Nicosia 1971; Second Secretary (Comm) Singapore 1973; Second later First Secretary FCO 1977; Consul and later Head of Chancery Aden 1981; First Secretary and Head of Chancery Rangoon 1983; FCO 1987; m (1) 1967 (diss 1979) (1s 1969); (2) 1979 Sandra Jill Furlong (née Browne) (1 step s 1970, 1 step d 1972).

Smart, Christopher David Russell; Kingston since April 1991; born 22.5.52; FCO 1971; UKDEL OECD Paris 1974; Bridgetown 1977; Lilongwe 1980; FCO 1983; Port Moresby 1987; Grade 9; m 1980 Patricia Margaret King.

Smart, Patricia Margaret (née King); Kingston since May 1991; born 3.3.53; FCO 1972; Geneva 1974; Peking 1975; FCO 1976; Addis Ababa 1977; Bridgetown 1979; SUPL 1980; FCO 1983; SUPL 1987; Port Moresby 1989; Grade S1; m 1980 Christopher David Russell Smart.

Smart, Stephen Brian; Cairo since June 1991; born 21.3.58; FCO 1975; UKREP Brussels 1978; Seoul 1980; Karachi 1983; FCO 1985; Warsaw 1988; FCO 1990; Grade 9; m 1980 Catherine Jane Beard (1s 1986).

Smith, Alan John; First Secretary (Management Paris since July 1991; born 2.10.41; FO 1959; Cairo 1962; Havana 1965; Africa Floater 1966; UK Mission Geneva 1967; Vice-Consul Hanoi 1970; FCO 1971; Casablanca 1975; Second Secretary (Admin) Jedda 1977; Melbourne 1979; First Secretary FCO 1984; First Secretary (Admin) Mexico City 1988; m 1975 Susan Melanie Jane Bennett (1d 1980).

Smith, Alan Peter; Accommodation Manager Brussels since January 1992; born 29.10.39; FCO 1969; Mbabane 1972; Stockholm 1974; Mexico 1975; FCO 1980; Doha 1983; FCO 1983; New Delhi 1985; FCO 1989 (Second Secretary November 1989); m Jillian Ann Whitnall (1d 1962; 1s 1968).

Smith, Alexander Duff; Second Secretary FCO since April 1981; born 17.1.41; FO 1958; Elizabethville 1962; Tehran 1965; Kampala 1967; FCO 1971; New Delhi 1974; on loan to DOT 1978; m 1962 Gillian Holmes (1s 1964; 1d 1966).

Smith, Andrea Carey; Second Secretary on secondment to Hong Kong Government; born 8.10.62; FCO 1985; Language Training 1986.

Smith, Andrew Dominic Charles; FCO since September 1990; born 1.6.67; Grade 9.

Smith, Anne; Reykjavik since March 1991; born 16.5.60; FCO 1989; Grade S2.

Smith, Anthony Donald Raymond; First Secretary FCO since June 1991; born 8.11.58; FCO 1986; Second (later First) Secretary Madrid 1988.

Smith, Antony Francis; Counsellor (Management) and Consul-General Washington since June 1990; born 6.5.42; FO 1959; Phnom Penh 1963; Vice-Consul Luanda 1964; Warsaw 1968; FCO 1970; Tehran 1971; FCO 1974; Second later First Secretary Accra 1976; UKDEL OECD Paris 1979; Lisbon 1983; First Secretary later Counsellor FCO 1985; m 1963 Marion Frances Hickman (2d 1971, 1975).

Smith, Brian, OBE (1975); High Commissioner Port of Spain since November 1991; born 15.9.35; FO 1952; HM Forces 1954-57; Bahrain 1957; Doha 1959; Vice-Consul Luxembourg 1960 and Casablanca 1962; Tehran 1964; Second Secretary (Comm) 1966 and Berne 1967; FCO 1969; First Secretary 1970; Kampala 1973; First Secretary (Comm) Tehran 1975; FCO 1977; Director and Deputy Consul-General BTDO New York 1979; Counsellor (Comm) Bonn 1982;

FCO 1986; High Commissioner Gaborone 1989; m 1955 Joan Patricia Rivers (1s 1956; 2d 1959, 1964).

Smith, Carol Ann; Budapest since June 1992; born 11.11.63; FCO 1987; Cape Town 1989; Grade S2.

Smith, Carol Susan (née Woods); New Delhi since March 1990; born 27.4.47; FCO 1970; Warsaw 1971; FCO 1971; Cairo 1972; FCO 1975; Karachi 1977; Kampala 1980; Bahrain 1983; FCO 1987; Grade S1; m 1976 Raymond Peter Smith.

Smith, Claire Helen (née Stubbs); SUPL since May 1990; born 23.12.56; FCO 1979; Language Training Hong Kong 1981; Second Secretary Peking 1983; First Secretary FCO 1985; m 1986 Michael Forbes Smith (1d 1989).

Smith, Cyril Leslie; FCO since October 1990; born 28.10.38; GPO 1955; HM Forces 1957-59; GPO 1959; FO 1962; Moscow 1964; Kuala Lumpur 1965; FO 1967; Tel Aviv 1968; FCO 1970; Sofia 1971; FCO 1973; Bucharest 1976; Hong Kong 1980; FCO 1983; Second Secretary Brussels 1988; m 1962 Barbara Mary Beck (1d 1966).

Smith, David Joseph; Second Secretary (Assistant Trade Commissioner) BTC Hong Kong since April 1989; born 12.1.51; FCO 1969; Tokyo 1972; Kuwait 1977; Warsaw 1979; FCO 1981; Osaka 1984; m 1975 Hitomi Takahashi (2d 1978, 1982).

Smith, David Leslie Darwin; FCO since December 1976; born 20.4.42; Grade 9.

Smith, Derek Moir; Riyadh since April 1989; born 12.9.67; Dept of Employment 1986; FCO 1987; Grade 10.

Smith, (George) Neil, CMG (1987); HM Ambassador Helsinki since November 1989; born 12.7.36; FO 1953; RAF 1954-56; FO 1957; Rangoon 1958; Berne 1961; Second Secretary (Comm) Berne 1964; DSAO 1965; Second later First Secretary Commonwealth Office 1966; Berlin 1969; FCO 1973; Counsellor (Comm) Helsinki 1977; Consul-General Zurich 1980; Counsellor FCO 1985; RCDS 1988; m 1956 Elvi Vappu Hamalainen (1d 1957; 1s 1959).

Smith, Gerald Dominic; Islamabad since April 1992; born 4.4.70; FCO 1988; Grade 10; m 1992 Penny Jane Clifford.

Smith, Gerald Thomas Harry, RVM (1979); Pretoria since June 1991; born 29.8.33; Royal Navy 1951-63; GPO 1963; Tel Aviv 1973; Sofia 1974; Nicosia 1976; Gaborone 1979; Salisbury 1980; Moscow 1982; Nicosia 1983; Port of Spain 1986; Baghdad 1988; Grade SO; m 1955 Elizabeth Joan Hemming (1s 1956).

Smith, Guy William; Rio de Janeiro since July 1991; born 20.4.66; FCO 1985; UKREP Brussels 1987; Sofia 1989; Grade 10.

Smith, Hugh Maxwell; New York since January 1992; born 4.4.59; FCO 1981; Brussels 1985; FCO 1988; Grade 9.

Smith, James; Bonn since April 1990; born 23.2.42; RAF 1962-67; Post Office 1967; FCO 1970; Amman 1972; SE Asia Floater 1977; Tehran 1979; FCO 1980; Kampala 1981; FCO 1982; Hanoi 1983; Atlanta 1984; FCO 1986; Grade 9.

Smith, Jason R; Sofia since December 1991; born 20.11.70; FCO 1989; Grade 10.

Smith, John Lawrence; Vice-Consul Chicago since September 1990; born 15.10.65; FCO 1988; Grade 9.

Smith, John Stephen; Second Secretary (Chancery) UKMIS New York since January 1987; born 28.3.57; Third Secretary FCO 1979; Third later Second Secretary (Comm) Seoul 1980; Second Secretary FCO 1985; m 1984 Wanda Won Min Kim.

Smith, Joy Diana; Muscat since September 1992; born 1.7.71; FCO 1990; Grade S2.

Smith, Katherine Jane; FCO since August 1990; born 21.5.67; Grade 9.

Smith, Katherine Lucy; Second Secretary (Chancery/Inf) Athens since January 1991; born 10.1.64; FCO 1987; Full-time Language Training 1990.

Smith, Lloyd Barnaby; Counsellor FCO since May 1990; born 21.7.45; Third Secretary FCO 1968; Third later Second Secretary (Chancery) Bangkok 1970; First Secretary FCO 1974; First Secretary (Chancery/Information) Paris 1977; Head of Chancery Dublin 1978; ENA Paris 1981; First Secretary later Counsellor (Press) UKREP Brussels 1982; Counsellor and Consul-General Bangkok 1987; m (1) 1972 Nicola Mary Whitefield (diss); (2) 1983 Mary Sumner (1d 1983; 1s 1985).

Smith, Lynne Marie; FCO since June 1990; born 17.2.63; FCO 1982; Peking 1984; Ankara 1987; Grade 9; m 1989 Ahmet KalaycioFglu.

Smith, Michael Forbes; Consul (Commercial) Zurich since June 1990; born 4.6.48; Board of Trade 1966-68; Army 1971-78; FCO 1978; Second, later First Secretary and Head of Chancery Addis Ababa 1979; Deputy to the Civil Commissioner and Political Adviser Port Stanley 1983; First Secretary FCO 1985; m (1) 1974 Christian Joanna Kersley (Annulled 1983) (1d 1975); (2) 1986 Claire Helen Stubbs (1d 1989; 1s 1992).

Smith, Nicolette Jane; Kuala Lumpur since March 1992; born 30.4.70; FCO 1989; Grade 10.

Smith, Paul Anthony; Kuwait since July 1991; born 18.9.38; RAF 1956; Warsaw 1988; Cape Town 1989; Grade SO; m 1961 Doreen May (2d 1962, 1966; 1s 1963).

Smith, Paula Louise; UKMIS New York since January 1990; born 13.10.68; FCO 1987; Grade 10.

Smith, Peter; FCO since August 1991; born 6.8.51; FCO 1971; Canberra 1974; East Berlin 1976; Khartoum 1978; FCO 1982; Dhaka 1983; Manila 1988; Washington 1989; Grade 9; m 1974 Cynthia Angela Shearn (1d 1975).

Smith, Peter John; Royal College of Defence Studies since January 1992; born 15.5.42; FO 1962; Saigon 1964; Paris 1968; Second Secretary 1969; Commercial Publicity Officer, BIS New York 1970; FCO 1973; Second later First Secretary (Comm) Mexico City 1976; DHC and Head of Chancery Port Louis 1981; First Secretary FCO 1984; Deputy Consul-General Montreal 1987; Deputy Consul-General Toronto 1988; m 1964 Suzanne Pauline Duffin (1s 1965; 1d 1967).

Smith, Raymond Peter; First Secretary (Management) New Delhi since March 1990; born 27.6.33; Inland Revenue 1960; FO 1962; Singapore 1962; Bonn 1963; Ankara 1966; FCO 1968; Warsaw 1971; Cairo 1972; FCO 1975; Karachi 1977; Second Secretary Kampala 1980; Second Secretary (Admin/Consular) Bahrain 1983; Second Secretary FCO 1987; m (1) 1959 Maureen Ann Caffery (diss) (1d 1963); (2) 1976 Carol Susan Woods.

Smith, Robert Nicholas Eyre; First Secretary (Chancery) Kampala since July 1989; born 12.9.47; Third Secretary FCO 1969; Jakarta 1970; Third later Second Secretary FCO 1973; Nicosia 1975; First Secretary FCO 1977; Caracas 1980; FCO 1983; m 1981 Mary Alice Walker (1d 1982).

Smith, Roland Berkeley; FCO since March 1992; born 6.7.55; FCO 1973; Bonn 1975; Karachi 1979; FCO 1981; Nicosia 1985; Manila 1987; Grade 9; m 1978 Shirley Kathleen Sandford (1s 1988).

Smith, Roland Hedley; Minister and Deputy Permanent Representative UKDEL NATO Brussels since April 1992; born 11.4.43; Third Secretary FO 1967; Second Secretary Moscow 1969; Second later First Secretary UKDEL NATO Brussels 1971; First Secretary FCO 1974; First Secretary (Cultural) Moscow 1978; FCO 1980; Counsellor CDA at IISS 1983; Head of Chancery BMG Berlin 1984; Counsellor FCO 1988; m 1971 Katherine Jane Lawrence (2d 1972, 1975).

Smith, Shirley Kathleen (née Sandford); Second Secretary FCO since July 1991; born 5.1.56; FCO 1974; Bonn 1977; Karachi 1979; FCO 1981; Nicosia 1985; Manila 1987; m 1978 Roland Berkeley Smith (1s 1988).

Smith, Simon John Meredith; First Secretary FCO since June 1992; born 14.1.58; Dept of Employment 1981; Second Secretary FCO 1986; language training FCO 1987; Language Training Kamakura 1988; Second later First Secretary Tokyo 1989; m 1984 Sian Stickings.

Smith, Simon Richard; FCO since July 1988; born 3.10.57; FCO 1974; Peking 1982; FCO 1983; Third Secretary Bucharest 1986; Grade 9.

Smith, Stephen Jeremy; Second Secretary (Commercial) Dar es Salaam since April 1991; born 25.10.44; FO later DSAO 1964; Baghdad 1968; Sofia 1973; FCO 1974; Vice-Consul Sydney 1977; FCO (Assistant Parliamentary Clerk) 1982; Second Secretary (Admin) and Consul Algiers 1983; FCO 1986; on secondment to the Birmingham Chamber of Industry & Commerce 1989; m 1969 Delyth Morris (2d 1973, 1977; 2s 1975, 1978).

Smith, Stephanie Clare; Lisbon since August 1991; born 20.2.70; FCO 1988; Grade 10.

Smith, Stuart Harris; Belgrade since October 1991; born 24.4.48; Nicosia 1989; Grade SO; m 1969 Carol Ann (1s 1971; 1d 1974).

Smith, Stuart Vaughan; FCO since June 1991; born 5.7.72; Grade 10.

Smith, William John; Bonn since March 1988; born 20.2.48; Royal Marines 1964-88; Grade SO; m 1971 Doreen (1s 1973; 2d 1971, 1976).

Smith-Laittan, James; Deputy Senior Trade Commissioner Hong Kong since February 1991; born 13.5.39; HM Forces 1958-60; Admiralty 1960; CRO 1963; Dacca 1964; FO, Commonwealth Office 1966; Brussels 1967; FCO 1968; Rabat 1969, Second Secretary 1970; Second Secretary (Admin) Accra 1972; Second Secretary (Comm) Rome 1975; First Secretary FCO 1979; Trade Commissioner Hong Kong 1982; First Secretary FCO 1986; m 1969 Mary Susan Messer (3d 1973, 1976, 1978).

Smithson, David; New York (UKMIS) since July 1991; born 16.4.70; FCO 1988; Grade 10.

Smyth, Caroline Ann; FCO since November 1989; born 2.6.61; FCO 1980; Moscow 1982; Strasbourg 1983; Peking 1987; Grade 9.

Smyth, Darren Owen; FCO since July 1992; born 13.7.66; FCO 1984; Harare 1988; Santiago 1990; Grade 10.

Smyth, James Patrick, MBE (1973); First Secretary FCO since August 1990; FCO since August 1990; born 14.6.41; Inland Revenue 1959; CO 1965; Commonwealth Office 1966; Asunción 1968; Port of Spain 1969; Islamabad 1970; Nicosia 1973; FCO 1976; Second Secretary (Admin) Kuwait 1978; Second Secretary FCO 1984; Consul (Comm) Vancouver 1986; First Secretary (Admin) Athens 1989; m 1967 Daphne Dawson (2s 1968, 1974; 2d 1969, 1979).

Smyth, Nicola Anne; Quito since March 1992; born 11.8.65; FCO 1988; Bucharest 1989; Grade S2.

Smyth, Thomas Henry; The Hague since December 1990; born 9.11.32; Belgrade 1979; Helsinki 1980; Pretoria/Cape Town 1983; Moscow 1985; UKMIS Geneva 1986; Peking 1989; Grade SO; m 1956 June Turner.

Sneddon, Deborah Phillips; FCO since September 1992; born 20.12.63; FCO 1985; UKMIS Geneva 1987; Valletta 1990; Grade S2.

Snell, Michael George, MVO (1980); Second Secretary Washington since November 1988; born 9.6.47; FCO 1972; Darwin 1973; FCO 1975; Rome 1978; Banjul 1981; FCO 1982; Sofia 1983; Second Secretary FCO 1985; m 1973 Diana Mary Powell-Williams (2d 1977, 1979; 1s 1982).

Snook, Andrew John; FCO since March 1992; born 18.7.72; Grade 10.

Snowdon, Susan Carol; Manila since October 1989; born 12.7.65; MOD 1983; FCO 1985; Brussels 1987; Grade 10.

Snoxell, David Raymond; First Secretary FCO since April 1991; born 18.11.44; FCO 1969; Islamabad 1972; UKMIS Geneva 1976; Second later First Secretary FCO 1984; Executive Director and Consul (Inf) BIS New York 1986; m 1971 Anne Carter (2s 1972, 1977; 1d 1973).

Somerset, William Francis; First Secretary Kiev since August 1992; born 18.1.46; POSB 1964; DSAO 1965; Africa Floater 1967; Ulan Bator 1969; Detroit 1971; FCO 1974; Victoria (Seychelles) 1977; Second Secretary FCO 1980; Second Secretary (Consul) Moscow 1983; Second Secretary (Comm) Lusaka 1987; m 1968 Susan Elizabeth Dixon Bostock (1s 1971; 1d 1974).

Soper, Andrew Keith; First Secretary FCO since December 1990; born 6.7.60; FCO 1985; Second later First Secretary (Chancery) Mexico City 1987; m 1987 Kathryn Garrett Stevens.

Soutar, Samuel Ian; Counsellor FCO since November 1991; born 2.6.45; Third Secretary FCO 1968; Third later Second Secretary UKDEL Brussels (EC) 1970; Saigon 1972; First Secretary

FCO 1974; Private Secretary to the
Parliamentary Under-Secretary of State for
Foreign and Commonwealth Affairs 1976; First
Secretary Washington 1977; First Secretary FCO
1981; DHC and Head of Chancery Wellington
1986; On loan to the RCDS 1991; m 1968 Mary
Isabella Boyle (1s 1971; 1d 1973).

Southcombe, Julie Ann; SUPL since December
1988; born 13.10.57; FCO 1982; Moscow 1983;
UKREP Brussels 1984; FCO 1987; Grade S2.

Sowerby, Karen Dorothy Howell; FCO since
May 1991; born 14.6.46; Grade S2.

Sowerby, Lynne; East Berlin since May 1990;
born 17.9.67; FCO 1988; Grade 10.

Spalding, Thomas James; FCO since November
1990; born 10.11.46; FCO 1970; Lusaka 1971;
FCO 1973; New Delhi 1977; FCO 1980; Darwin
1981; FCO 1983; Darwin 1988; Grade 9; m
1969 Jenifer Blackburn (1d 1976).

Sparkes, Andrew James; FCO since January
1988; born 4.7.59; FCO 1982; Second Secretary
(Chancery) Ankara 1985; m 1985 Jean Mary
Meakin.

Sparrow, Bryan, CMG (1992); HM Ambassador
Zagreb since July 1992; born 8.6.33; FO 1951;
HM Forces 1951-53; FO 1953; SUPL to attend
University 1954; FO 1957; Belgrade 1958;
Second Secretary FO 1961; Second Secretary
(Comm) Moscow 1964 and Tunis 1967; First
Secretary (Comm) and Consul Casablanca 1968;
First Secretary FCO 1970; First Secretary1/Head
of Chancery, Kinshasa 1972; First Secretary
(Comm) Prague 1976; Counsellor (Comm)
Belgrade 1978; HM Ambassador and Consul-
General Yaoundé 1981; also HMA (non-resident)
to Equatorial Guinea 1981 and to Central
African Republic 1982; Canadian National
Defence College 1984; Consul-General Toronto
1985; HM Consul-General Lyons 1989; m 1958
Fiona Mary Mylechreest (1d 1960; 1s 1962).

Spearman, Richard David; Consul Istanbul since
August 1992; born 30.8.60; FCO 1989; m 1987
Caroline Jill Scoones (1s 1992).

Spedding, David Rolland; OBE (1980), CVO
(1984); Counsellor FCO since January 1992;
born 7.3.43; Third Secretary FO 1967; Second
Secretary 1969; MECAS 1968; Beirut 1970;
Second Secretary Santiago 1972; First Secretary
FCO 1974; Abu Dhabi 1978; FCO 1981;
Counsellor Amman 1983; Counsellor on loan to
Cabinet Office 1987; m 1970 Gillian Leslie
Kinnear (2s 1971, 1975).

Speller, Paul Anthony; First Secretary FCO since
April 1989; (Private Secretary to the
Parliamentary Under Secretary of State
1991);born 21.1.54; FCO 1983; Second later
First Secretary Bonn 1986; m 1989 Sabine Anne

Sparwasser.

Speller, Susan Barbara (née Arnold); FCO since
November 1990; born 22.10.56; FCO 1984;
Hamburg 1986; Munich 1987; Düsseldorf 1988;
Grade 9.

Spellman, Antoinette Marie (née Mills); UKDEL
NATO Brussels since February 1991; born
24.5.65; FCO 1988; Grade S2A; m 1990 Garry
James Spellman.

Spencer, David Paul, MBE (1988); First Secretary
(Political) Stockholm since January 1992; born
4.4.59; FCO 1978; Kuala Lumpur 1981; FCO
1983; Aden 1985; First Secretary FCO 1988; m
1988 Patricia Anne McCullock (1s 1990).

Spencer, Elaine Joan; FCO since March 1976;
born 24.3.49; FO 1966; DSAO 1966; FO (later
FCO) 1967; Bonn 1972; Khartoum 1975; Grade
S2.

Spencer, Rosemary Jane, CMG (1991); AUSS
(Public Departments) FCO since June 1989; born
1.4.41; FO 1962; Third later Second Secretary
Nairobi 1965; FO (later FCO) 1967; Second later
First Secretary and Private Secretary to the Hon
Sir Con O;Neill, EC Negotiating Team 1970;
Brussels UKDEL (EC) 1972; Lagos 1974; First
Secretary FCO 1977; RCDS 1980; Counsellor
(Agric/Econ) Paris 1980; Counsellor (Eernal
Relations) UKREP Brussels 1984; Counsellor
FCO 1987.

Spencer, Sarah; Kathmandu since May 1990;
born 31.5.68; FCO 1988; Grade 10.

Spiceley, Peter Joseph, MBE (1977); First
Secretary FCO since January 1991; born 5.3.42;
FO 1961; Bogotá 1964; DSAO 1967; Lima
1969; Second Secretary (Comm) Yaoundé 1972;
Vice-Consul (Comm) Douala 1974; Second later
First Secretary Quito 1976; FCO 1982; Consul
Miami 1986; m 1965 Cecilia Orozco (2d 1967,
1970).

Spicer, Haden Richard; Moscow since October
1992; Abu Dhabi since January 1989; born
18.6.62; FCO 1985; Abu Dhabi 1989; Grade 10;
m 1988 Carole E. Pymble.

Spindler, Guy David St. John Kelso; Second
Secretary (Comm) Moscow since August 1989;
born 9.6.62; Second Secretary FCO 1987.

Spinks, Derek Donald; Lagos since January
1991; born 20.1.34; RAMC 1951-74; MOD
1975-78; Dublin 1978; Moscow 1979; Cairo
1980; Nairobi 1981; UKMIS Geneva 1984;
Peking 1987; Helsinki 1988; Grade SO; m 1956
Winifred (3s 1956, 1962, 1969).

Spires, David Mark, MVO (1992); Paris since
June 1991; born 18.11.61; FCO 1980; Lima
1985; FCO 1986; Islamabad 1987; Grade 9; (1s

1986).

Spittles, Cheryl Jean; Islamabad since September 1990; born 14.1.50; FCO 1978; Paris 1980; Tunis 1983; Wellington 1985; FCO 1988; Grade S1.

Spivey, Donald; Tokyo since June 1992; born 12.4.68; FCO 1989; Grade 10.

Sprague, David Keith, MVO (1972); High Commissioner Freetown since May 1991; born 20.2.35; FO 1953; HM Forces 1953-55; Addis Ababa 1955; UKDEL Paris 1957; Belgrade 1960; FO 1963; Second Secretary (Inf) Budapest 1966; Second Secretary Kuala Lumpur 1969; Second Secretary (Comm) Abidjan 1972; First Secretary FCO 1974; First Secretary (Comm) Sofia 1979; FCO 1982; DHC Madras 1986; HM Ambassador Ulan Bator 1989; m 1958 Audrey Mary Mellon (2s 1959, 1960; 1d 1969).

Sprake, Anthony Douglas; Counsellor (Commercial) The Hague since April 1989; born 16.7.44; DEmp 1968; First Secretary (Labour) Brussels 1977; FCO 1980; DHC Freetown 1982; First Secretary later Counsellor FCO 1986; Counsellor UKDEL CACN Vienna 1989; m 1977 Jane McNiel (2s 1980, 1982).

Springfield, Major Patrick Maurice Osborn; Queen;s Messenger since 1985; born 20.1.42; Army 1961-79.

Sprunt, Patrick William; First Secretary (ECOSOC) UKMIS New York since June 1992; born 13.4.52; Third Secretary FCO 1975; Language Student SOAS 1976; Second later First Secretary Tokyo 1978; FCO 1982; UKREP Brussels 1982; First Secretary Bonn 1983; First Secretary FCO 1986; First Secretary Tokyo 1987; m 1979 Haang Ai-Yuan Wong (1s 1985; 1d 1989).

Squibb, Keith Norman; Tel Aviv since April 1991; born 2.9.49; Prague 1989; Grade SO; m 1974 Brigitte Promei (3s 1974, 1978, 1984).

Squires, George Thomas; First Secretary (Comm/Dev) Bangkok since July 1990; born 20.10.48; FCO 1968; Dacca 1971; Antigua 1973; Warsaw 1975; Jakarta 1976; FCO 1979 (Second Secretary 1983); Vice-Consul later Consul and Administration Officer Sydney 1985; m 1979 Helen Mary Thomas (2s 1983, 1985).

Stacey, Christopher Robin; Nicosia since May 1992; born 9.12.47; RAF 1965-74; FCO 1974; Islamabad 1976; Budapest 1980; Singapore 1983; FCO 1984; Manila 1988; Grade 9; m 1977 Coral Jane Charge (2s 1981, 1987).

Stafford, Andrew Jeremy; First Secretary (Chancery) Brussels since June 1991; born 1.2.53; Third Secretary FCO 1975; Stockholm 1977; FCO 1979; Second Secretary Accra 1979;

Second later First Secretary FCO 1981; First Secretary and Consul Prague 1984; First Secretary FCO 1987; m (1) 1977 Felicity Joanna Maria Kelly; (2) 1983 Elizabeth Rosemary Kempston (1d 1985).

Stagg, Allan James; FCO since January 1990; born 7.10.53; DHSS 1975; FCO 1979; Paris 1981; East Berlin 1984; Kuwait 1986; Grade 9; m 1984 Julie Sandra Marshall.

Stagg, Julie Sandra (née Marshall); SUPL since May 1991; born 13.2.58; FCO 1984; East Berlin 1984; Kuwait 1986; FCO 1990; Grade S2; m 1984 Allan James Stagg.

Stagg, Charles Richard Vernon; First Secretary (Info) UKREP Brussels since July 1991; born 27.9.55; FCO 1977; Third later Second Secretary Sofia 1979; The Hague 1982; First Secretary FCO 1985; UKREP Brussels 1987; First Secretary FCO 1988; m 1982 Arabella Clare Faber (2s 1984, 1985).

Stallworthy, Brian Arthur; FCO since August 1971; born 27.1.35; GPO 1951; HM Forces 1954-56; GPO 1956; FO 1963; Washington 1966; FCO 1968; Sofia 1969; Grade 6; m 1961 Anna Rose Drew.

Standbrook, Timothy William; Full time Language Training since February 1990; born 8.6.63; FCO 1988; Grade 9.

Stanton, Karen Jane; Third Secretary (Chancery) Rome since February 1991; born 25.1.62; FCO 1984; Language Training Kamakura 1986; Vice-Consul Tokyo 1987; Grade 9; m 1990 Anthony Graham Stanton.

Stanton, Louise Jane; Language Training Tokyo since September 1992; born 14.8.68; FCO 1990; Language Training 1991; Grade 9.

Stanyer, Julie Grace (née Robins); FCO since February 1992; born 15.3.48; FCO 1984; Bridgetown 1985; UKDEL NATO Brussels 1989; Grade S1; m 1988 Patrick Julian Scrville.

Staples, Graham Raymond; Dublin since October 1989; born 24.1.69; FCO 1988; Grade 10.

Stapley, Angela; SUPL since September 1991; born 6.4.63; FCO 1982; Paris 1984; Dakar 1987; Grade 9.

Starkey, Nicholas Andrew; Second Secretary FCO since July 1992; born 20.12.52; FCO 1972; SE Asia Floater 1975; Warsaw 1977; Bridgetown 1979; FCO 1981; Kuwait 1985; Second Secretary (Cons) Lagos 1989; m 1981 Rhodora Corrales Maroto (1s 1983, 1d 1985).

Staunton, Andrew James; Third Secretary (Chancery/Management) Strasbourg since April 1991; born 7.8.67; FCO 1987; Peking 1989;

Grade 9; m 1990 Rebecca Anne Nixon (1s 1991).

Stead, Alexander Ernest; First Secretary and Consul Warsaw since April 1991; born 1.12.36; CRO 1963; Karachi 1964; Amman 1966; Tehran 1968; Kinshasa 1971; FCO 1975; Beirut 1977; Belgrade 1980; FCO 1984; (Second Secretary 1984); Second Secretary and Vice-Consul Cairo 1987; m 1960 Grace Lynham (2s 1961, 1963; 1d 1967).

Stead, Michael; FCO since August 1991; born 19.1.58; British Library 1976; FCO 1979; Jedda 1981; Riyadh 1982; LA Floater 1985; Rio de Janeiro 1988; Grade 9.

Stearns, Vivienne Elizabeth; Warsaw since May 1992; born 2.10.61; FCO 1991; Grade S2.

Steele, Christopher David; Second Secretary (Chancery) Moscow since March 1990; born 24.6.64; FCO 1987; m 1990 Laura Kathleen Hunt.

Steel, Diane Elizabeth; St Petersberg since September 1992; born 2.8.60; FCO 1978; UKREP Brussels 1982; Dar es Salaam 1985; Doha 1989; Grade S2.

Steeples, John Charles; Vienna since August 1992; born 14.2.45; Army 1966-70; 1972-73; FCO 1973; Dacca 1976; UKDEL NATO Brussels 1978; Prague 1981; FCO 1981; Paris 1985; FCO 1987; Brussels 1988; Grade 9; m 1975 Jennifer Maureen Davis (2s 1980, 1983; 1d 1977).

Steers, Reginald; Athens since May 1990; born 21.6.38; Army 1954-78; Tehran 1978; Budapest 1980; Bangkok 1983; Singapore 1984; Santiago 1985; Warsaw 1987; Vienna 1989; Grade CSO; m 1962 Mary Tam Geok Hua (1s 1962; 1d 1963).

Stein, Gordon; UKMIS Geneva since October 1991; born 20.2.69; FCO 1989; Grade 10.

Stephen, Ann (née Barbour); Paris since November 1990; born 2.4.66; FCO 1988; Grade S2A; m 1992 Robert Stephen.

Stephens, Adrian Charles; First Secretary FCO since December 1990; born 19.3.46; DSAO (later FCO) 1964; Karachi 1968; Colombo 1970; Budapest 1972; FCO 1974; Islamabad 1976; FCO 1978, (Second Secretary 1979); Bangkok 1982; Consul Berlin 1986; m (1) 1968 Susan Jane Everitt (1d 1971; 1s 1973).

Stephenson, John Edmund; First Secretary FCO since June 1992; born 19.12.60; FCO 1986; Second later First Secretary (Inf) Santiago 1989; m 1986 Jacqueline Denise Clayton (1s 1990).

Stephenson, Lawrence; First Secretary FCO

since April 1990; born 12.3.45; FO 1964; Cairo 1966; Khartoum 1967; Tel Aviv 1967; Seoul 1969; Moscow 1972; FCO 1973; Hanoi 1976; Rome 1977; Second Secretary Lusaka 1979; Second later First Secretary FCO 1982; First Secretary (Comm/Dev) Bangkok 1985.

Steven, John Young; Washington since May 1992; born 21.5.68; FCO 1988; Moscow 1989; Grade 10.

Stevens, Ian James; New Delhi since May 1992; born 15.5.66; FCO 1985; UKDEL NATO Brussels 1989; Grade 9; m 1987 Adele Oliver (1d 1989).

Stevens, Jill Frances; Moscow since September 1990; born 10.3.57; FCO 1977; Damascus 1979; Bridgetown 1982; FCO 1984; Dar es Salaam 1987; FCO 1989; Grade S2.

Stevens, John Anthony; First Secretary FCO since April 1992; born 27.6.39; FO 1963; Beirut 1965; Dacca 1968; FCO 1971; Second Secretary (Aid1/Inf) Rangoon 1973; Kingston 1977; Second later First Secretary FCO 1981; First Secretary (Cons/Immig) Lagos 1985; First Secretary (Admin) Accra 1988; m 1966 Anne Rosalind Beck (diss 1974).

Stevens, Mark; Second Secretary (Management/Vice-Consul) Tunis since June 1992; born 5.7.49; DSAO 1966; FCO 1968; Georgetown 1970; Madrid 1973; East Berlin 1976; FCO 1978; Kingston 1982; New Delhi 1985; Second Secretary FCO 1988; m 1970 Pauline Elaine Graber (2d 1973, 1976).

Stevens, Paul David; FCO since July 1991; born 8.9.59; MOD 1977; FCO 1981; UKMIS Geneva 1983; Kampala 1985; Washington 1988; Grade 9.

Stevenson, Peter Stuart; Third Secretary Copenhagen since September 1989; born 18.11.53; FCO 1970; New Delhi 1978; FCO 1979; Washington 1982; FCO 1985; Grade 9; m 1974 Margaret Joan Ramagni (2d 1978, 1980; 1s 1984).

Stevenson, William Michael; Khartoum since August 1988; born 4.9.51; FCO 1971; UKDEL NATO Brussels 1973; Luxembourg 1977; Addis Ababa 1979; Moscow 1983; FCO 1985; Grade 9; m 1982 Laura Birse Stirton (1s 1986).

Stew, Timothy David; Third Secretary (Chancery) Riyadh since August 1991; born 8.10.66; FCO 1988; language training 1989; language training Cairo 1990; Grade 9.

Steward, Timothy, MBE (1991); Jakarta since October 1992; born 12.12.43; RAF 1962; Havana 1988; Amman 1989; Grade SO; m 1964; Jean Macfarlane; (2d 1965, 1968).

Stewart, Brian Edward; First Secretary FCO

since March 1989; born 4.2.50; Third Secretary FCO 1972; MECAS 1973; Third later Second Secretary Amman 1975; on loan to Cabinet Office 1978; (First Secretary 1979); FCO 1980; First Secretary and Head of Chancery Singapore 1982; Head of Chancery Tunis 1986; m 1975 Anne Elizabeth Cockerill.

Stickland, Victoria Louise; Second Secretary FCO since April 1992; born 12.3.66; FCO 1987; Language Training FCO 1988; Language Training Bangkok 1989.

Still, Anthony Gerald; Second Secretary FCO since November 1989; born 21.6.36; GPO 1952; HM Forces 1954-56; GPO 1956; FO 1963; Bonn 1963; Moscow 1966; FO 1967; Bahrain 1968; FCO 1969; Budapest 1971; FCO 1972; Nicosia 1973; FCO 1976; Brasilia 1979; FCO 1983; Second Secretary New Delhi 1986; m (1) 1956 Margaret Leslie Wolsey (diss 1977) (1d 1957; 2s 1960, 1965); (2) 1978 Jean Margaret Wilton.

Still, Jean Margaret (née Wilton); Second later First Secretary FCO since January 1990; born 16.12.46; FO (later FCO) 1965; Prague 1969; Rio de Janeiro 1971; Nicosia 1974; FCO 1975; Brasilia 1979; Second Secretary FCO 1983; Second Secretary on loan to CAD Hanslope Park 1982; Second Secretary New Delhi 1986; m 1978 Anthony Gerald Still.

Stitt, (Thomas) Clive Somerville; Counsellor UKMIS New York since August 1992; born 1.1.48; Third Secretary FCO 1970; Language Student Tehran 1972; Kabul 1972; Third later Second Secretary New Delhi 1974; First Secretary FCO 1977; UKMIS Geneva 1982; First Secretary later Counsellor FCO 1986; m 1977 Margaret Ann Milward (2d 1982, 1984).

Stiven, George Roy, OBE (1987); First Secretary FCO since July 1987; born 25.1.32; GPO 1948; HM Forces 1950-52; GPO 1952; FO 1960; Cairo 1962, FO 1964; Washington 1965; FO 1967; Buenos Aires 1968; FCO 1969; on loan to MOD 1972; FCO 1975; Warsaw 1979; Second Secretary FCO since August 1980; First Secretary Moscow 1983; m (1) Greta Keith Mathers (3d 1956, 1960, 1963; 1s 1964); (2) 1982 Marjorie Chapman.

St. Johnston, Rosemary; FCO since February 1985; born 28.10.34; Bonn 1962; Bamako 1965; Addis Ababa 1966; FO 1967; Lagos 1968; Paris 1970; Brussels 1972; Colombo 1976; FCO 1979; Dhaka 1982; Grade 9.

Stock, Suzanne Victoria; FCO since August 1991; born 1.12.65; Home Office 1988-91; Grade 9.

Stoddart, Anne Elizabeth; Deputy Permanent Representative (Economic Affairs) UKMIS Geneva since January 1991; born 29.3.37; FO 1960; Third Secretary Berlin 1963 (Second

Secretary 1964); Second later First Secretary FO (later FCO) 1967; Ankara 1970; First Secretary and Head of Chancery Colombo 1974; First Secretary FCO 1977; Counsellor 1981; Deputy Permanent Representative UKDEL Strasbourg 1981; on loan to DTI 1987.

Stokes, Paul Terence; Bonn since October 1988; born 9.10.63; FCO 1984; Grade 10.

Stokoe, Kay; FCO since June 1989; born 23.6.69; Grade 10.

Stokey, Tracy Joanne Tudor; Bonn since April 1990; born 10.3.65; FCO 1988; Grade S2; m 1988 Brendan Stokey.

Stollery, Mark Thomas; Second Secretary (EC Affairs) Brussels since April 1990; born 8.10.60; Royal Navy 1978-88; Second Secretary FCO 1988; m 1990 Denise Jekyll.

Stone, David Lawrence; Bucharest since June 1992; born 11.7.36; HM Forces 1954-58; HO 1958-79; Sofia 1979; Islamabad 1980; Tokyo 1982; Peking 1985; Ankara 1986; Accra 1988; Grade SO; m 1955 Christine Pickering (2d 1955, 1959).

Stone, Jemma Catherine; FCO since September 1991; born 8.1.70; Grade S2.

Stones, Adrian; First Secretary (Chancery) Washington since September 1992; born 16.10.60; FCO 1986; Second later First Secretary (Inf) New Delhi 1989; First Secretary FCO 1991; m 1990 Gillian Ruth Millman (1s 1992).

Storey, Ian George, MBE (1980); FCO since November 1991; born 24.10.42; Army 1961-83; Bucharest 1986; Cairo 1988; Grade CSO; m 1963 Valerie Piggott (1d 1963; 1s 1964).

Storey, Nicola; FCO since November 1990; born 8.12.70; Grade S2.

Storey, Patricia Angela (née Goodfellow); SUPL since January 1991; born 24.10.54; FCO 1978; UKDEL Brussels 1979; Sana'a 1981; Lilongwe 1987; Grade S2; m 1980 Paul Storey (1d 1985, 1s 1988).

Storm-Turner, Susannah, MBE (1982); FCO since February 1983; born 23.11.35; FO 1961; Ankara 1962; FO 1964; Tripoli 1967; FCO 1969; Islamabad 1971; Athens 1973; Bangkok 1976; FCO 1978; New Delhi 1981; Grade S1.

Stoves, Margaret; Lisbon since February 1990; born 3.7.45; FCO 1987; Grade S2.

Stowell, Gerald; Hanoi since October 1992; born 9.1.38; RAF 1958-82; Lagos 1982; Budapest 1985; BMG Berlin 1987; Helsinki 1990; Grade SO; m 1969 Patricia Jean (diss. 1985) (1s 1973; 1d 1975).

Strain, Scott Robert; Pretoria since November 1991; born 4.10.70; FCO 1989; Grade 10.

Strange, Peter Leonard; Second Secretary FCO since August 1984; born 28.2.43; GPO 1963; FCO 1969; Delhi 1971; Pretoria 1973; FCO 1975; Attaché Nicosia 1978; FCO 1981; Belgrade 1981; m 1963 Susan Barnett (1s 1963; 1d 1966).

Streams, Peter John, CMG (1986); HM Ambassador Khartoum since November 1991; born 8.3.35; Board of Trade 1953; Trade Commission Service Bombay 1960 and Calcutta 1962; Second Secretary (Comm) Oslo 1966; FCO 1970; First Secretary and Head of Chancery Mexico City 1973; First Secretary later Counsellor FCO 1977; HM Consul-General Karachi 1982; Counsellor (Comm) Stockholm 1985; HM Ambassador and Consul-General Tegucigalpa and HMA (non-resident) to El Salvador 1989; m 1956 Margareta Decker (2s 1959, 1964; 1d 1961).

Street, Michael Edward; Mexico City since April 1992; born 28.2.34; Royal Navy 1951-76; Prison Dept 1976; Cairo 1982; Moscow 1983; Madrid 1984; Warsaw 1987; Colombo 1988; Grade CSO; m 1954 Alice Caroline Brooks (1d 1958; 1s 1960).

Streeton, Matthew Charles; Third Secretary (Aid) Harare since May 1989; born 30.1.63; FCO 1982; Floater duties 1984; Singapore 1986; Grade 9.

Stringer, Bryan; Lisbon since November 1989; born 25.2.36; RAF 1954-82; MOD 1983; East Berlin 1983; Oslo 1985; Peking 1988; Grade SO; m 1956 Doreen (1d 1964).

Stringer, David James; Second Secretary FCO since September 1988; born 6.9.39; GPO 1956; HM Forces 1960-62; GPO 1962; FO 1964; Nairobi 1965; Bucharest 1968; FCO 1970; Singapore 1973; New York 1977; FCO 1980; Munchen Gladbach 1986; m 1962 Jean Kathleen Hawkins (1s 1966; 1d 1969).

Strong, Stuart Stanger; First Secretary (Comm) Accra since May 1989; born 13.6.43; HO 1961; FO 1964; Havana 1966; Nicosia 1967; New Delhi 1970; FCO 1973; Canberra 1976; Belgrade 1979; FCO 1980; Vice-Consul later Consul (Comm) Düsseldorf 1984; m 1972 Katherine Margaret Beaton.

Stuart, Edward Paterson; Tokyo since September 1990; born 12.1.39; Army 1961-83; Moscow 1983; Lusaka 1984; Washington 1988; Grade SO; m 1959 Alice Robertson (2d 1960, 1962).

Stuart, Julia Mary; FCO since January 1992; born 24.8.65; FCO 1988; Luanda 1990; Grade S2.

Stuart-Black, Lois Margaret; SUPL since March 1991; born 4.7.53; FCO 1977; Oslo 1977; FCO 1980; Copenhagen 1984; FCO 1987; Grade 9.

Stubbings, Christopher; BEM (1983); Sofia since November 1990; born 26.4.44; Royal Marines 1959; Bonn 1987; Grade SO.

Stubbings, Graham James; New Delhi since February 1989; born 17.9.57; DHSS 1974; FCO 1976; UKMIS New York 1979; Kingston 1982; FCO 1986; Grade 10; m 1989 Kirsty Alexander (1s 1987).

Stubbins, Caroline Mary; FCO since April 1991; born 26.2.52; FCO 1972; Prague 1974; FCO 1976; New York 1978; FCO 1981; Canberra 1984; FCO 1987; Washington 1988; Grade S2.

Stucley-Houghton, Nicholas John Knight; Johannesburg since September 1992; born 3.10.54; Inland Revenue 1974; Santiago 1976; Mbabane 1979; Warsaw 1982; FCO 1983; Kathmandu 1986; FCO 1988; Copenhagen 1989; Grade 9; m 1976 Beatriz Elvira Sierra-Galindo (1s 1978; 1d 1980).

Studham, Clare Nicola; FCO since July 1988; born 29.6.58; FCO 1977; Washington 1979; FCO 1982; Floater duties 1983; Brasilia 1984; Grade 9.

Stump, William Douglas, MBE (1968); First Secretary FCO since January 1991; born 15.10.43; FO 1962; Lubumbashi 1965; Geneva 1968; Jakarta 1971; Second Secretary FCO 1975; Honiara 1978; First Secretary (Aid) Nairobi 1981; First Secretary FCO 1984; First Secretary (Dev. and Comm.) Lusaka 1987; m (1) 1966 Susan Mary Hart (diss 1986); (1d 1967); (2) 1986 Barbara Lyne.

Sturgeon, Christopher Charles Alexander; Floater Duties since December 1990; born 15.3.68; FCO 1988; Grade 10.

Sturgeon, Mary Nicol; Nicosia since March 1991; born 27.5.48; FCO 1973; Bangkok 1974; Kuwait 1976; Suva 1978; Kartoum 1980; FCO 1982; Resigned 1985; Reinstated 1988; Grade S1.

Sturgess, Neil; Helsinki since November 1991; born 13.5.62; FCO 1980; Grade 9; m 1988 Wendy Alison

Styles, Graham Charles Trayton; FCO since February 1992; born 16.4.58; FCO 1977; SUPL 1978; FCO 1981; Port Louis 1985; Paris 1989; Grade 9; m 1984 Rachael Jane Hopkins (1d 1989).

Styles, Rachael Jane (née Hopkins); SUPL 1988; born 14.5.62; FCO 1980; Port Louis 1985; Grade 9; m 1984 Graham Charles Trayton Styles (1d 1989).

Sullivan, Janet Ann; Floater Duties since June 1992; born 15.2.58; FCO 1977; Kuala Lumpur 1980; Montevideo 1984; Tel Aviv 1988; Grade S2.

Sullivan, Michael Frederick, MBE (1980); Counsellor FCO since October 1990; born 22.6.40; CRO 1962; Moscow 1967; Ulan Bator 1967; FCO 1970; Second Secretary Sydney 1970; Second later First Secretary FCO 1975; BTDO New York 1979; First Secretary (Cultural Attaché) Moscow 1981; First Secretary FCO 1985; Counsellor (Cultural Affairs) Moscow 1988; on loan to DTI 1989; m 1967 Jennie E. Saunders.

Sullivan, Peter Joseph; Head of Chancery The Hague since October 1987; born 23.10.41; Department of Employment 1966-78 and 1982-83; Labour Attaché Rome 1978; First Secretary FCO 1983; m 1968 Brenda Patricia Sealey (1d 1973; 1s 1980).

Summers, Alexander; Second Secretary (Consular) Nairobi since October 1989; born 7.11.36; FCO 1965; Karachi 1965; Paris 1969; Ankara 1972; FCO 1974; Nicosia 1977; Kathmandu 1980; Second Secretary FCO 1984; Second Secretary (Admin) and Consul Bucharest 1986; m 1967 Cynthia Isaac (1s 1970; 1d 1974).

Summers, David; FCO since June 1991; born 13.11.64; FCO 1983; Islamabad 1985; Lisbon 1988; Grade 9; m 1987 Anita Cecilia Marsh.

Surman, Derek Malcolm; Canberra since March 1990; born 20.6.47; Commonwealth Office1/ DSAO 1967; Kinshasa 1969; FCO 1970; Madrid 1971; Dacca 1974; Stuttgart 1976; Beirut 1977; Durban 1978; Salisbury 1978; Khartoum 1982; FCO 1985; Grade 9; m (1) 1970 Julia Mary Newns; (2) 1982 Frances Louise Stapelberg.

Surtees, Carol Ann; FCO since November 1991; born 30.10.56; FCO 1979; Islamabad 1981; Tehran 1983; Hanoi 1985; FCO 1987; Cairo 1988; Grade S2.

Sutcliffe, Claire Penelope; FCO since August 1991; born 16.9.68; Grade 9.

Sutcliffe, Nicholas Derek; Second Secretary (Economic) Brasilia since March 1990; born 9.12.57; FCO 1985; m 1985 Carole Ann Hunter (2s 1990, 1992).

Suter, Neil Ronald Ivor; First Secretary (Management Officer) Tehran since September 1991; born 22.3.39; Royal Navy 1956-66; DWS 1968; FCO 1970; Durban 1972; Tokyo 1975; FCO 1977; Baghdad 1980; FCO 1984; Second Secretary (Admin) Kuwait 1985; Language Training 1989; Second Secretary (Admin) JAO Brussels 1989; m 1979 Margaret Ann Winn.

Sutherland, Elizabeth Victoria (née Myles) FCO

since June 1987; (Second Secretary 1988); born 27.4.49; FCO 1971; Havana 1972; Sana'a 1974; FCO 1975; Paris 1984; m 1988 Neil Sutherland.

Sutherland, Veronica Evelyn (née Beckett), CMG (1988); AUSS (Deputy Chief Clerk) since August 1990; born 25.4.39; Third later Second Secretary FO 1965; Second later First Secretary Copenhagen 1967; FCO 1970; Counsellor (Dev) New Delhi 1975; FCO 1978; Counsellor and Permanent UK Delegate UNESCO Paris 1981; Counsellor FCO 1984; HM Ambassador and Consul-General Abidjan 1987; also HMA (non-resident) to Niger 1987; and HM Ambassador (non-resident) to Burkina 1988; m 1981 Alex James Sutherland.

Sutter, Kimm; FCO since December 1991; born 12.10.73; Grade 10.

Sutton, Alan Edward; Consul Berlin since May 1991; born 21.3.43; FO (later FCO) 1967; Düsseldorf 1970; Istanbul 1972; FCO 1975; Islamabad 1978; FCO 1980; Georgetown 1981; FCO 1985; Second Secretary and Consul Riyadh 1987; m 1965 Jacqueline Anderson (1d 1966; 1s 1969).

Sutton, Janet (née Christie); FCO since May 1991; born 25.3.64; Dept of Employment 1983; FCO 1984; Abidjan 1987; Paris 1990; Grade 9; m 1986 Andrew Richard Sutton (1s 1987).

Sutton, Larissa Elizabeth; FCO since November 1991; born 18.4.71; Grade 10.

Swain, Debra Jayne (née Folkard); FCO since June 1992; born 26.5.60; Grade S2; FCO 1980; Brussels 1989; m 1989 Gregory Michael Swain.

Swain, Gregory Michael; FCO since June 1992; born 11.2.55; FCO 1978; Brussels 1989; Grade 10; m 1989 Debra Jayne Folkard.

Swain, Sarah Elizabeth; FCO since July 1991; born 6.12.68; Grade S2.

Sweeney, Carole Mary (née Crofts); Second later First Secretary FCO since May 1991; born 24.6.59; MOD 1985; FCO 1987; SUPL 1988; Second Secretary Bonn 1989; Second Secretary East Berlin 1990; m 1988 Paul Martin Sweeney (1d 1990; 1s 1992).

Sweet, Linda Michelle; Ankara since October 1992; born 14.3.56; FCO 1979; Rome 1980; Tokyo 1982; Manila 1985; Floater Duties 1986; FCO 1989; Belgrade 1992; Grade S1.

Sweid, Janice Ann Townsend (née Oldfield); Second Secretary (Admin) Tel Aviv since May 1987; born 13.6.50; FCO 1970; on loan to Cabinet Office 1973; FCO 1974; Accra 1977; FCO 1979; Washington 1984; m 1980 Youda Yomtob Sweid.

Swift, Hans Eric; First Secretary FCO since April 1991; born 14.5.58; FCO 1980; New Delhi 1982; Second Secretary FCO 1986; Second later First Secretary (Chancery) Stockholm 1988; m 1981 Susan Mary Brown (1d 1988, 1s 1991).

Swift, Susan Mary (née Brown); SUPL since July 1988; born 26.4.60; FCO 1979; New Delhi 1983; FCO 1986; Grade 9; m 1981 Hans Eric Swift (1d 1988, 1s 1991).

Sykes, Elizabeth Anne; Grand Cayman since January 1989; born 4.6.64; FCO 1984; Oslo 1986; Grade S2.

Sykes, Graham Leslie; New Delhi since January 1992; born 20.9.60; FCO 1987; Grade 10.

Sykes, Roger Michael Spencer; Second Secretary FCO since February 1990; born 22.10.48; HM Customs and Excise 1967; FCO 1968; Caracas 1971; Freetown 1972; Karachi 1976; Valletta 1978; FCO 1981; Lagos 1982; Vila 1986; m 1976 Anne Lesley Groves Gidney (3s 1977, 1980, 1988).

Syme, Avril; Addis Ababa since May 1992; born 13.4.65; FCO 1987; Dublin 1989; Grade S2.

Symes, Dorothy Margaret, OBE (1990); First Secretary FCO since July 1989; born 21.8.38; FO 1957; Athens 1961; Latin America Floater 1965; Second Secretary DSAO (later FCO) 1966; Nicosia 1969; Vice-Consul (Cons/Admin) Düsseldorf 1974; Consul (Cons/Admin) Düsseldorf 1977; First Secretary FCO 1979; First Secretary (Comm) Vienna 1985.

Symons, Norman Henry; FCO since December 1983; born 19.1.29; HM Forces 1947-49; Ministry of Aviation 1958; FO 1961; New Delhi 1963; FO 1964; Singapore 1965; FO 1967; Sofia 1968; FCO 1970; Sana'a 1971; FCO 1972; Bangkok 1974; Dacca 1976; FCO 1978; Third Secretary Moscow 1979; FCO 1980; Muscat 1982; Grade 8; m 1955 Monica O;Shea (3s 1957, 1958, 1959).

Synnott, Hilary Nicholas Hugh; Counsellor FCO since April 1989; born 20.3.45; Royal Navy 1962-73; Second Secretary FCO 1973; First Secretary UKDEL OECD Paris 1975; First Secretary Bonn 1978; FCO 1981; Counsellor, Consul-General and Head of Chancery Amman 1985; m 1973 Anne Penelope Clarke.

Syrett, Nicholas Simon; FCO since September 1989; born 7.12.60; Grade 7.

T

Taffs, Suzanne Patricia; UKDEL Strasbourg since July 1991; born 7.2.68; FCO 1987; Washington 1988; Grade S2.

Tagg, Neil Kevin; Third later Second Secretary Abu Dhabi since February 1988; born 29.12.55; FCO 1973; resigned 1974; reinstated 1977; Valletta 1978; Sofia 1981; FCO 1984; m 1977 Patricia Anne Lodge.

Tait, Donald George; Full-Time Language Training Cairo since May 1992; born 18.5.67; FCO 1990; Language Training 1991; Grade 8.

Tait, Michael Logan, CMG (1987), LVO (1972); HM Ambassador Tunis since June 1992; born 27.9.36; FO and MECAS 1961; Bahrain 1963; Assistant Political Agent Dubai 1963; Second later First Secretary FO 1966; Private Secretary to Minister of State, FO (later FCO) 1968; First Secretary and Head of Chancery Belgrade 1970; First Secretary (Pol), Head of Chancery and Consul Amman 1972; FCO 1975; Counsellor and Head of Chancery Baghdad 1977; Counsellor FCO 1978; CSCE Madrid 1980; Counsellor (Econ/Finance) UKDEL OECD Paris 1982; Counsellor, Head of Economic Relations Department FCO 1984; HM Ambassador Abu Dhabi 1986; AUSS (Eastern Europe) 1990; m 1968 Margaret Kirsteen Stewart (1d 1970; 2s 1973, 1975).

Talbot, Peter John, MBE; Second later First Secretary FCO since June 1978; born 28.6.29; GPO 1945; HM Forces 1947-49; GPO 1949; FO 1959; Ankara 1960; Budapest 1962; FO 1963; Nairobi 1964; Peking 1967; FCO 1968; Warsaw 1970; FCO 1972; East Berlin 1976; m 1952 Joan Mary Turner (1s 1955; 2d 1957, 1968).

Talmadge, Graham John; Second later First Secretary on loan to HCS since October 1986; born 26.11.48; FCO 1971; Hong Kong 1974; FCO 1977; Second Secretary (Chancery) Lagos 1980; Second Secretary FCO 1985; m 1973 Linda Margaret Giles.

Tandy, Arthur David; Second Secretary FCO since May 1989; born 16.8.49; HO 1974-85; FCO 1985; Second Secretary Riyadh 1987; m 1973 Hilary Denise Watson (1s 1978; 1d 1982).

Tansley, Anthony James Nicholas; First Secretary FCO since April 1991; born 19.7.62; FCO 1984; Language Training 1986; Second Secretary (Chancery) Riyadh 1988; Second Secretary (Chancery) Baghdad 1989.

Tantum, Geoffrey Alan, OBE (1981); Counsellor FCO since September 1988; born 12.11.40; HM Forces 1959-66; Second Secretary FCO 1969; Kuwait 1970; First Secretary and Head of Chancery Aden 1972; FCO 1973; Amman 1977; First Secretary FCO 1980; Counsellor Rome 1985; m 1977 Caroline Anne Kent (3d 1979, 1981, 1983).

Tarling, Derek Edwin; First Secretary FCO since June 1988; born 26.3.36; CO 1952-61; RAF 1954-56; CRO 1961; Delhi 1962; High Commission Singapore 1964; FCO 1969; Vice-Consul Benghazi 1969; FCO 1972; Second

Secretary 1975; Lisbon 1977; New Delhi 1980; First Secretary Washington 1983; m 1961 Frances Ann Ryan (2d 1962, 1964).

Tarran, Anthony William; FCO since August 1986; born 15.6.38; FCO 1968; Benghazi 1971; FCO 1972; OECD Paris 1974; Tokyo 1977; Algiers 1978; FCO 1981; Dubai 1984; Grade 9.

Tarry, Stephen Norman; Warsaw since March 1991; 'born 21.1.54; FCO 1971; Washington 1974; Damascus 1977; Brussels 1981; FCO 1983; Islamabad 1983; FCO 1988; Grade 9; m 1981 Julie Christine Lawrence (dec'd 1985) (1d (adopted) 1984).

Tasker, Alastair Robin; FCO since July 1984; born 6.4.41; FO (later FCO) 1957; Bonn 1972; FCO 1974; Second Secretary Peking 1976; FCO 1979; Bonn 1982; m 1966 Lesley Mitchell (1d 1975; 1s 1977).

Tasker, Vaughan Owen; Peking since August 1992; born 1.6.36; Army 1953-57; Cairo 1978; Peking 1980; Brussels 1981; Nicosia 1983; Islamabad 1984; Bonn 1986; Harare 1988; Brussels 1990; Grade CSO; m 1957 Molly Shawer (2d 1958, 1960; 1s 1964).

Tassell, Ernest Joseph; FCO since August 1990; born 25.1.34; Royal Navy 1949-58; FO 1959; Singapore 1960; Delhi 1962; FO 1964; Jedda 1965; Lagos 1966; FO (later FCO) 1967; Tokyo 1969; FCO 1972; Lusaka 1975; FCO 1976; Helsinki 1978; Bucharest 1979; FCO 1982; Aden 1983; FCO 1985; Kuwait 1987; Grade 8; m 1953 Marion Joyce Matthews (1s 1961).

Tatham, David Everard, CMG (1991); Governor Falkland Islands, also Commissioner South Georgia and the South Sandwich Islands since August 1992; born 28.6.39; FO 1960; Third Secretary New York 1962; FO 1963; Vice-Consul Milan 1963; (Second Secretary 1966); MECAS 1967; Second later First Secretary Jedda 1969; FCO 1971; First Secretary and Head of Chancery Muscat 1974; First Secretary FCO 1977; (NATO Defence College) Rome 1980; Counsellor Dublin 1981; HM Ambassador and Consul-General Sana'a 1984; later additionally HMA (non-resident) to Djibouti 1984; Counsellor FCO 1987; HM Ambassador Beirut 1990; m 1963 Valerie Ann Mylechreest (3s 1964, 1965, 1972).

Tatham, Michael Harry; Third Secretary (Chancery) Prague since January 1990; FCO since September 1987; born 2.7.65; Grade 8.

Tattum, Alison Clare (née Hunt); Windhoek since May 1991; born 8.7.65; FCO 1984; Washington 1986; SUPL 1989; Grade S2; m 1988 Steven John Tattum.

Tauwhare, Richard David, MVO (1983); First Secretary FCO since October 1989; Paris since

June 1986; born 1.11.59; FCO 1980; Third later Second Secretary (Chancery/Inf) Nairobi 1982; Second later First Secretary UKDEL OECD Paris 1986; m 1985 Amanda Jane Grey.

Taylor, Alexander; FCO since April 1991; born 31.7.72; Grade 10.

Taylor, David Edward; Berlin since March 1992; born 20.1.36; RAF 1954-81; Budapest 1983; UKMIS Geneva 1984; Bucharest 1987; FCO 1988; Grade CSO; m 1957 Noreen Anne (1d 1958; 1s 1963).

Taylor, David Reeves; First Secretary (Regional Affairs) Hong Kong since June 1992; born 11.6.51; FCO 1980; Aden 1982; First Secretary FCO 1982; Damascus 1984; First Secretary FCO 1986; m 1986 Louise Mary Carter (1d 1990).

Taylor, Colonel David Walter Frederick; Queen;s Messenger since 1984; born 8.10.35; HM Forces 1952-1984.

Taylor, Duncan John Rushworth; First Secretary (Commercial) Budapest since July 1992; born 17.10.58; FCO 1982; Third later Second Secretary Havana 1983; First Secretary FCO 1987; Language Training 1991; m 1981 Marie-Beatrice (Bébé) Terpougoff (3 step d 1972 (2), 1973; 2s 1984, 1986).

Taylor, Edward; Second Secretary (Cons/Comm) Windhoek since September 1992; born 30.5.49; FCO 1968; Antigua 1970; Sofia 1973; Algiers 1976; Beirut 1976; FCO 1978; Gaborone 1982; on loan to DTI 1985; Vice Consul (Comm) BTDO New York 1988.

Taylor, Francis; Nairobi since June 1983; born 26.7.56; FCO 1980; Grade 9.

Taylor, Helen de Chaville; First Secretary FCO since April 1991; born 15.2.48; FCO 1970; Santiago 1973; Singapore 1974; Second Secretary (Comm) Paris 1978; FCO 1981; First Secretary FCO 1984; First Secretary UKMIS New York 1986; m 1987 Adrian George Ferguson Porter.

Taylor, Hugh Mackay; Second Secretary (Chancery/Info) Lisbon since September 1988; born 15.5.54; FCO 1972; UKREP Brussels 1975; Brunei 1977; FCO 1981; Munich 1985; m 1977 Christine Caggie.

Taylor, Jeffrey; Second Secretary (Commercial) Helsinki since June 1992; born 15.8.57; FCO 1976; BMG Berlin 1979; Lusaka 1982; Moscow 1984; FCO 1985; Melbourne 1988; Canberra 1990; m 1981 Janette Anne Hunt (1s 1987).

Taylor, Jennifer Margaret; First Secretary (Cons/Management) Nicosia since September 1989; born 23.11.40; FO 1958; Belgrade 1962; FO 1964; Warsaw 1967; Canberra 1968; Nicosia

1971; FCO 1974; Second Secretary 1975; Second Secretary (Immig) Nairobi 1977; Salisbury 1980; Second Secretary (Comm/Econ) Accra 1982; First Secretary FCO 1986.

Taylor, John Lawrence; Counsellor New Delhi since September 1991; born 27.5.46; FCO 1971; Second Secretary (UN) UKMIS Geneva 1973; Language Student 1976; First Secretary Moscow 1977; FCO 1980; First Secretary Stockholm 1982; First Secretary FCO 1986; m 1975 Amanda Jane Bright (2d 1976, 1978).

Taylor, John Stannard; Second later First Secretary FCO since August 1990; born 30.11.41; FO 1959; Abu Dhabi 1963; Mexico City 1965; Tokyo 1968; FCO 1970; Rabat 1974; Amman 1977; FCO 1978; HM Vice-Consul (Comm/Aid) Karachi 1981; Second Secretary (Comm/Aid) Lima 1986; m (1) 1965 Marta Zlotowska (2s 1970, 1973); (2) 1984 Joan Warrender (née Hinde).

Taylor, Joanna May; FCO since July 1992; born 4.12.61; Grade S2.

Taylor, Julie Ann; Peking since September 1990; born 15.2.67; FCO 1988; Grade S2.

Taylor, Karen Ruth (néeNelms); Port Louis since November 1992; born 23.6.57; FCO 1987; New Delhi 1978; Peking 1982; Washington 1983; FCO 1985; Grade 9; m 1991 Nigel David Muir Taylor.

Taylor, Kathryn Anne; Ottawa since April 1992; born 21.7.70; FCO 1989; Grade 10.

Taylor, Keith Arnold, OBE (1989); First Secretary (Management) Kuala Lumpur since November 1990; born 13.6.35; FCO 1971; Budapest 1974; Cairo 1975; FCO 1979; Second Secretary (Comm) Manila 1981; Second Secretary FCO 1985; First Secretary (Admin/Cons) Kampala 1987; m 1965 Sandra Kay de St Jean (2s 1966, 1969).

Taylor, Kim Irene; Wellington since January 1992; born 14.3.60; FCO 1979; Pretoria 1983; FCO 1985; Copenhagen 1987; FCO 1990; Grade S2.

Taylor, Melvyn Ernest; Moscow since November 1991; born 30.9.43; Army 1961-83; Police 1983-91; Grade SO.

Taylor, Nigel David Muir; Port Louis since October 1992; born 21.4.61; FCO 1981; Kaduna 1982; Africa M/E Floater 1986; FCO 1989; Grade 9; m 1991 Karen Ruth Nelms.

Taylor, Robert James; FCO since March 1989; born 7.4.57; HCS 1987; Grade 10.

Taylor, Ronald Frederick; First Secretary (Management) Jakarta since December 1991;

born 15.7.35; Board of Trade 1953; Delhi 1961; Paris 1965; Vientiane 1967; FCO 1970; Tehran 1974; Second Secretary (Aid) Dacca 1977; Second Secretary FCO 1980; First Secretary (Admin) New Delhi 1986; m 1964 Davina Ruth Anne Heath (2s 1966, 1967).

Teale, Ian Robert McKinnon; FCO since July 1991; born 28.2.71; Grade 10.

Tebbit, Kevin Reginald; Counsellor FCO since January 1992; born 18.10.46; MOD 1969-1979; UKDEL NATO 1979; First Secretary FCO 1982; First Secretary and Head of Chancery Ankara 1984; On secondment as Directeur du Cabinet, Cabinet of the Secretary-General of NATO Brussels 1987; Counsellor (Pol/Mil) Washington 1988; m 1966 Alison Tinley (1d 1972; 1s 1975).

Telfer, Corin; Stockholm since July 1990; born 26.5.66; FCO 1985; Amman 1987; Grade 10.

Telford, Lorraine; Jakarta since February 1992; born 3.4.65; FCO 1989; Grade S2.

Tennison, Lesley; FCO since July 1985; born 5.9.57; FCO 1980; Moscow 1983; Grade 9.

Terry, Anthony Jonathan; FCO since August 1990; born 24.4.46; Third Secretary FCO 1969; Third Secretary Nairobi 1970; FCO 1972; Second Secretary (Comm) Havana 1973; FCO 1976; First Secretary (Comm) Belgrade 1979; FCO 1983; First Secretary (Chancery) Santiago 1986; m 1968 Paule Michèle Antoinette Homère (3d 1972, 1979, 1981).

Terry, Brian Richard; UKDEL Brussels since July 1991; born 12.6.35; RAF 1953-75; Singapore 1982; Peking 1983; Islamabad 1984; East Berlin 1985; Cape Town 1987; Budapest 1989; Grade SO; m (1) 1956 (1s 1959; 1d 1961); (2) 1979.

Terry, Raymond Frederick; Second Secretary (Comm) Jakarta since March 1988; born 18.10.44; MAFF 1961; DSAO (later FCO) 1966; Addis Ababa 1968; Peking 1971; FCO 1974; Islamabad 1976; Second Secretary (Admin) Amman 1980; Second Secretary FCO 1983; Second Secretary (Admin) and Vice-Consul Maputo 1984; m 1968 Lois Mary Jones Evans (2d 1970, 1973).

Tesoriere, Harcourt Andrew Pretorius; First Secretary FCO since July 1991; born 2.11.50; Royal Navy 1969-73; FCO 1974; Language Student SOAS and Iran 1975; Oriental Secretary Kabul 1976; Nairobi 1979; Second Secretary and Vice-Consul Abidjan 1981; FCO 1985; First Secretary and Head of Chancery Damascus 1987; m 1987 Alma Gloria Vasquez.

Thain, Robert; Vice-Consul Helsinki since January 1992; born 9.9.52; FCO 1975; Warsaw 1977; Rabat 1979; Zagreb 1982; FCO 1984;

Canberra 1986; FCO 1990; Grade 9; m 1977 Susan Mary Nice.

Thake, Richard Louis; FCO since September 1990; born 13.1.44; GPO 1960; FO (later FCO) 1965; Bonn 1972; FCO 1975; Accra 1977; FCO 1980; Second Secretary Nairobi 1987; m (1) 1971 Angela Rosa Butcher (2d 1971, 1973); (2) 1977 Carmel Frances McCourt.

Thickett, Michael Godfrey; Counsellor FCO since September 1990; born 22.10.40; Second Secretary FCO 1969; Lusaka 1971; First Secretary FCO 1975; Consul (Inf) Hamburg 1978; First Secretary (Chancery) Bonn 1980; FCO 1983; Counsellor Pretoria/Cape Town 1986; m 1970 Heather Caroline Fraser (1d 1972; 2s 1978, 1980).

Thiel, Ann Bernadette; FCO since June 1988 (Second Secretary 1991); born 2.8.52; FCO 1971; Moscow 1973; Kuwait 1975; Düsseldorf 1978; FCO 1981; Floater duties 1984; Moscow 1986.

Thom, Dr Gordon; First Secretary (Comm) New Delhi since September 1989; born 18.5.53; DOE 1978; FCO 1979; Second later First Secretary Tokyo 1981; FCO 1985; m 1977 Margaret Pringle (1s 1982; 1d 1986).

Thomas, Amanda Joyce; Algiers since March 1992; born 21.12.67; DHSS 1986; FCO 1987; Pretoria 1989; Grade 10.

Thomas, Anthony Richard; Counsellor FCO since January 1989; born 11.7.39; Third Secretary Caracas 1963; FO 1965; Second Secretary Budapest 1966; Centre for Administrative Studies 1968; First Secretary Washington 1968; FCO 1972; First Secretary and Head of Chancery Madrid 1975; First Secretary FCO 1979; Deputy Consul-General Johannesburg 1981; Counsellor and HM Consul-General Brasilia 1985; m 1976 Henrietta Parks (1d 1980; 1s 1982).

Thomas, Dr Catherine Clare Mitchell; FCO since July 1987; born 3.2.58; Senior Research Officer (DS Grade 7); m 1989 Martin Brian Howe.

Thomas, Christopher John; Second Secretary Lagos since December 1988; born 14.11.40; FCO 1970; Darwin 1977; FCO 1979; Masirah 1979; FCO 1980; Masirah 1981; FCO 1983; Cyprus 1983; FCO 1986; m 1975 Margaret Gladys MacDonald.

Thomas, Colin Ronald; FCO since October 1987; born 27.3.49; Board of Trade 1967; FCO 1969; Dacca 1971; Havana 1974; Maputo 1975; FCO 1979; Geneva 1984; Rio de Janeiro 1987; Grade 9; m 1972 Jill Marion Perfect.

Thomas, David Roger; Consul-General Stuttgart

since April 1990; born 1.1.45; FCO 1968; Third Secretary Cairo 1971; Attaché later Second Secretary UKREP Brussels 1974; Ankara 1978; Second later First Secretary FCO 1982; Consul (Comm) Frankfurt 1986; m (1) diss 1977 (2d 1968, 1970); (2) 1978 Fiona Lindsey Tyndall.

Thomas, Elspeth; FCO since October 1990; born 8.1.62; FCO 1983; Tokyo 1985; Bonn 1988; Grade TS1.

Thomas, Gareth Frederic; Nairobi since January 1991; born 5.8.39; CRO 1962; Bombay 1963; Bathurst 1965; FCO 1968; Moscow 1972; Manila 1972; FCO 1975; JAO Brussels 1978; FCO 1981; Washington 1982; FCO 1985; Grade 9; m 1965 Maureen Elizabeth Wiseman (1s 1968; 1d 1969).

Thomas, Graeme Gordon; Second Secretary (Commercial) Riyadh since September 1992; born 26.9.48; FCO 1968; Africa Floater 1971; FCO 1972; Africa Floater 1973; Sana'a 1975; Jedda 1976; Far East Floater 1977; South East Asia Floater 1978; FCO 1980; Victoria 1982; FCO 1986; Second Secretary and Consul Warsaw 1987; Second Secretary FCO 1988; m 1981 Penelope Ann Richmond.

Thomas, Jeffrey; Consul Oporto since June 1991; born 13.7.47; CO 1964; FO (later FCO) 1966; Manila 1969; Berlin 1973; FCO 1975; Ibadan 1978; Kaduna 1980; Second Secretary FCO 1984; Second Secretary (Admin/Cons) Muscat 1987; m 1969 Lesley Anne Wishart (3s 1973, twins 1975).

Thomas, Jenkin; Deputy Permanent Representative UKDEL Paris since August 1990; born 2.1.38; FO 1960; Third later Second Secretary and Private Secretary to HM Ambassador Pretoria1/Cape Town 1963; Second Secretary Saigon 1966; Centre for Administrative Studies 1968; First Secretary FCO 1968; First Secretary (Comm) Washington 1973; First Secretary FCO 1977; On loan to Cabinet Office 1978; Counsellor (Econ) Tokyo 1980; Counsellor (Comm) Athens 1983; Counsellor FCO 1987.

Thomas, Joanna Lynne; FCO since February 1979; born 25.4.49; FO 1967; Nicosia 1970; FCO 1973; Jakarta 1973; FCO 1975; Rome 1976; Grade S2.

Thomas, Mark Hilliard; FCO since October 1992; born 29.4.64; FCO 1986; Riyadh 1989; Grade 9.

Thomas, Martin Hugh Stevenson; First Secretary (Comm) Belgrade since October 1991; born 2.7.42; FO 1965; Moscow 1967; Kabul 1969; Ottawa 1971; FCO 1974; Nairobi 1977; Rio de Janeiro 1980; Second Secretary Brasilia 1982; Second Secretary FCO 1983; First Secretary (Comm) Amman 1988; m 1966 Patricia Saward (2d 1971, 1973).

Thomas, Penelope Ann (née Richmond); FCO since January 1989; born 17.2.50; FCO 1973; UKREP Brussels 1974; Caracas 1977; FCO 1979; Victoria 1982; SUPL 1987; Grade S1; m 1981 Graeme Gordon Thomas.

Thomas, Philip Lloyd; Counsellor (Pol/Mil) Washington since November 1991; born 10.6.48; FCO 1972; Second Secretary Belgrade 1974; Second later First Secretary FCO 1977; First Secretary (Comm) Madrid 1981; FCO 1984; First Secretary (Press) UKREP Brussels 1987; Counsellor on loan to the Cabinet Office 1989.

Thomas, Richard, cmg (1990); HM Ambassador Sofia since May 1989; born 18.2.38; HM Forces 1959-61; CRO 1961; Private Secretary to Parliamentary Under-Secretary 1962; Second Secretary Accra 1963; Lomé 1965; Second later First Secretary UKDEL NATO 1966; FCO 1969; First Secretary (Econ) Delhi 1972; First Secretary FCO 1976; Sabbatical at Chatham House 1978; Counsellor and Head of Chancery Prague 1979; HM Ambassador and Consul-General Reykjavik 1983; Counsellor FCO 1986; m 1966 Catherine Jane Hayes (2d 1967, 1971, 1s 1969).

Thompson, Carol; Floater duties since September 1984; born 15.12.58; FCO 1981; Grade 9.

Thompson, Charles Henry; Second later First Secretary FCO since January 1986; born 5.8.42; FO 1959; Geneva (UKMIS) 1963; Colombo 1966; Rawalpindi 1967; Vice-Consul (Comm) Casablanca 1970; FCO 1973; Second Secretary Buenos Aires 1976; Consul Manila 1980; Second Secretary (Aid and Comm) Port Louis 1982; m 1963 Vivien Joyce Kenyon (1d 1966; twin s and d 1968).

Thompson, Christopher Colin; FCO since July 1989; born 18.5.69; Grade 10.

Thompson, Clive Vincent; Consul (Commercial) later First Secretary Munich since December 1990; born 3.4.47; FCO 1973; MECAS 1975; Islamabad 1976; Tunis 1978; Stuttgart 1981; Second Secretary FCO 1983; Second Secretary (Consul) Moscow 1987; Second Secretary FCO 1990; m 1969 Carol Knight (2d 1973, 1974).

Thompson, Gillian Hazel; Berlin since February 1991; born 8.6.53; FCO 1979; Rio de Janeiro 1980; FCO 1981; Belgrade 1982; FCO 1984; Lisbon 1986; FCO 1989; Grade S2.

Thompson, Heather; Language Training Kamakura since August 1991; born 1.2.68; FCO 1989; Language Training 1990; Grade 9.

Thompson, Jack Francis; First Secretary (Commercial) Mexico City since March 1991; born 10.11.41; HM Customs and Excise 1959; HO 1968; New Delhi 1974; Second Secretary FCO 1979; Vice-Consul Zagreb 1981; Second

Secretary (Comm) Santiago 1985; First Secretary FCO 1989; m 1964 Isabel Requena Matallana (2s 1965, 1970; 1d 1967).

Thompson, Jan; Second Secretary Bonn since November 1991; born 25.8.65; FCO 1990 (Second Secretary 1991).

Thompson, John, mbe (1975); Counsellor and Director of Trade Promotion BTIO New York since September 1992; born 28.5.45; FO 1964; DSA 1965; Vice-Consul Düsseldorf 1966; Abu Dhabi 1969; Phnom Penh 1972; Management Studies Polytechnic of Central London 1974; Second Secretary on loan to DOT 1975; FCO 1977; First Secretary and Head of Chancery Luanda 1979; Consul (Comm) São Paulo 1981; First Secretary FCO 1985; High Commissioner Vila 1988; m 1966 Barbara Hopper (1d 1967).

Thompson, Lynne Diana; FCO since September 1988; born 20.8.59; FCO 1981; Warsaw 1982; Bandar Seri Begawan 1983; FCO 1986; Vienna 1987; Grade S1.

Thompson, Mary Stephanie; FCO since August 1988; born 26.12.40; FCO 1978; Aden 1978; FCO 1979; Bucharest 1981; UKMIS New York 1983; Oslo 1986; Grade S1.

Thompson, Michael Jacques, cmg (1989), obe (1977); Counsellor FCO since March 1985; born 31.1.36; HM Forces 1954-56; HMOCS 1960; FO 1964; Second Secretary Kuala Lumpur 1965; First Secretary FO (later FCO) 1967; Saigon 1970; Lusaka 1973; First Secretary FCO 1976; Counsellor Kuala Lumpur 1979; HQBF Hong Kong 1982; m 1967 Mary Susan Everard (1s 1968; 1d 1970).

Thompson, Pauline; FCO since August 1992; born 11.10.63; Bridgetown 1989; FCO 1987; Grade S2.

Thompson, Richard Paul Reynier; Second later First Secretary Stockholm since March 1991; born 17.8.60; FCO 1989; m 1991 Louisa Halliday-Yates.

Thompson, Sarah Jane; FCO since April 1982; born 1.4.58; FCO 1979; Pretoria/Cape Town 1980; Grade S2.

Thomson, Adam McClure; First Secretary (Chancery) Washington since July 1991; born 1.7.55; FCO 1978; Third later Second Secretary Moscow 1981; Second later First Secretary UKDEL Brussels 1983; FCO 1986; on loan to Cabinet Office 1989; m 1984 Fariba Shirazi.

Thomson, Dick; First Secretary (Chancery/Inf) Copenhagen since April 1988; born 18.12.42; Ministry of Transport 1961; DSAO (later FCO) 1966; Havana 1969; Athens 1970; Warsaw 1972; FCO 1973; San Francisco 1976; Second Secretary 1978; Algiers 1980; First Secretary

FCO 1984; m 1972 Jacqueline Margaret Dunn (1d 1976; 1s 1979).

Thomson, Fergus Russell Cullen; First Secretary FCO since December 1987; born 16.5.44; DWS 1964; DSAO 1967; Peking 1969; Lagos 1972; Second Secretary FCO 1976; BTDO New York 1978; First Secretary (Comm) Addis Ababa April 1984; m 1970 Jeanette Patricia Louis Mutton.

Thomson, Jennifer Alexandria; FCO since June 1992; born 19.11.68; FCO 1988; Peking 1990; Grade 10.

Thomson, Margaret Sarah; Islamabad since November 1990; born 8.7.66; FCO 1987; Grade 9.

Thomson, Peter Alexander Bremner, cvo (1986); Counsellor FCO since November 1991; born 16.1.38; Royal Navy 1955-74; First Secretary FCO 1975; First Secretary (Econ/Tech Co-operation) Lagos 1977; BTC Hong Kong 1979; FCO 1982; Counsellor and Head of Chancery Peking 1984; High Commissioner Belmopan 1987; m 1965 Lucinda Sellar (2s 1970, 1972).

Thomson, Ruth Elizabeth; Ankara since October 1991; born 12.11.63; FCO 1985; Moscow 1988; FCO 1989; Grade S2.

Thorne, Barry Edward; Deputy Consul-General Istanbul since October 1988; born 17.10.35; HM Forces 1952-59; Malawi Police 1961-68; FCO 1968; Dacca 1969; FCO 1971; Durban 1972; Second Secretary 1974; on loan to DOT 1974; Colombo 1978; FCO 1979; Second later First Secretary Addis Ababa 1980; Consul (Comm) Milan 1984; First Secretary FCO 1986; m (1) 1965 (1d 1966; 1s 1969); (2) 1980 Jacqueline Mary Wright (1s 1981; 1d 1982).

Thorne, Frederick Michael Frank, MBE (1992); FCO since May 1992; born 7.2.38; HM Forces 1954-65; FO 1965; St Helena 1967; FCO 1969; Islamabad 1970; FCO 1972; Darwin 1974; FCO 1975; Addis Ababa 1976; FCO 1979; Singapore 1980; FCO 1984; Third Secretary Lagos 1985; Third Secretary Tel Aviv 1989; Grade 8; m 1963 Patricia Ann Edmonds (3s 1964, 1971, 1980).

Thorne, Karen Ann (née Higgins); FCO since March 1984; born 9.3.57; FCO 1974; Lusaka 1978; Grand Turk 1983; Grade S2; m 1978 Richard J. Thorne (1d 1981).

Thorne, Nicholas Alan; Counsellor (Commercial) and Deputy Head of Mission Helsinki since July 1991; born 31.3.48; FO (later FCO) 1965; Yaoundé 1971; UKREP Brussels 1974; Second Secretary FCO 1977; Central London Polytechnic 1977; FCO 1978; Second later First Secretary UKMIS New York 1980; First Secretary Head of Chancery Manila 1983; First Secretary FCO 1987; on secondment to Thorn EMI 1989; m 1974 Ann Margaret Boorman (1s 1978; 1d

1980).

Thornton, Daniel Vernon; FCO since September 1991; born 6.8.69; Grade 8.

Thornton, John Norris; Third Secretary Geneva since June 1991; born 6.7.59; FCO 1978; BGWRS Darwin 1980; FCO 1982; Beirut 1983; FCO 1984; Third Secretary Tehran 1986; FCO 1987; Grade 8; m 1980 Angela Dawn Clarke.

Thornton, James Sebastian; Second Secretary (Commercial/Information) Algiers since April 1992; born 2.11.64; UKAEA 1986-1989; FCO 1989.

Thornton, Patricia Ann; Consul Johannesburg since December 1991; born 11.1.52; FCO 1971; Tehran 1973; Lima 1976; New Delhi 1979; FCO 1982; Guatemala City 1984; FCO 1987; Second Secretary (Comm) Santiago 1988.

Thornton, Sarah; FCO since March 1992;born 5.6.72; Grade 10.

Thorp, Jeremy Walter; Head of Chancery Dublin since March 1988; born 12.12.41; HM Treasury 1963-81; Washington 1971-73; On loan to FCO 1978; Transferred to FCO 1981; Lima 1982; First Secretary later Counsellor FCO 1986; m 1973 Estela Lessa.

Thorpe, Adrian Charles; Minister Tokyo since December 1991; born 29.7.42; FO 1965; Language Student Tokyo 1965; Third later Second Secretary (Inf) Tokyo 1968; FCO 1970; Seconded to HCS 1971; FCO 1972; First Secretary Beirut 1973; First Secretary and Head of Chancery Beirut 1975; FCO 1976; First Secretary (Econ) Tokyo 1976; First Secretary FCO 1981; Counsellor Head of Information Technology Dept 1982; Counsellor (Econ) Bonn 1985; Deputy High Commissioner Kuala Lumpur 1989; m 1968 Miyoko Kosugi.

Thorpe, Nigel James, cvo (1991); Counsellor FCO since July 1992; born 3.10.45; Third Secretary FCO 1969; Third later Second Secretary Warsaw 1970; Second later First Secretary Dacca 1973; FCO 1975; First Secretary (Econ) Ottawa 1979; on loan to DOE 1981; FCO 1982; Counsellor and Head of Chancery Warsaw 1985; Deputy High Commissioner Harare 1989; m (1) 1969 Felicity Thompson (diss 1976) (2s 1971, 1972); (2) 1978 Susan Diane Bamforth (twin d 1985, 1d 1991).

Thurlow, John Robert; Bridgetown since August 1992; born 28.8.67; FCO 1984; Algiers 1990; Grade 10.

Thursfield, Martin Robert; Full-time Language Training since September 1991; born 8.6.67; FCO 1989; Grade 8.

Thurston, Brenda Pauline; Karachi since July

1990; born 9.11.49; DHSS 1980; FCO 1984; Damascus 1986; Port Louis 1987; Grade S2; m 1974 John Anthony Thurston.

Tibber, Peter Harris; PS to the Minister of State since September 1990; born 7.9.56; Second Secretary FCO 1984; Second later First Secretary Paris 1986; First Secretary FCO 1989; m 1983 Eve Levy-Huet (3s 1986, 1988, 1992).

Tiffin, Sarah Anne; Third later Second Secretary Paris since December 1990; born 5.11.65; FCO 1988; ENA Paris 1989.

Tillyard, Barbara Ann (née Levett); Abu Dhabi since October 1992; born 27.1.46; FCO 1974; UKREP Brussels 1975; FCO 1979; SUPL 1979; FCO 1983; Washington 1985; FCO 1989; Grade S1; m 1977 Brian William Tillyard.

Timewell, John Michael; Ankara since November 1989; born 14.3.38; Army 1956-87; Moscow 1988; Grade SO; m 1966 Iris May Gummer (2s 1967, 1971).

Timmins, Jacqueline Margaret; Hong Kong (China Trade) since May 1984; born 28.7.61; FCO 1982; Grade S2; m 1985 Richard John Wickerson.

Tindale, David Charles; Singapore since March 1988; born 16.7.36; GPO 1966; St Helena 1967; FCO 1969; Darwin 1974; FCO 1975; Delhi 1975; FCO 1977; Athens 1979; FCO 1981; Tokyo 1983; FCO 1986; Grade 8; m 1962 June Mitton Watson (2s 1964, 1973).

Tisdell, Sara Helen; Dubai since June 1989; born 11.1.65; FCO 1984; Peking 1987; Grade 9.

Tissot, Philip Marius Arthur; Second Secretary (Chancery) UKMIS New York since May 1990; born 10.2.60; FCO 1978; Africa Floater 1981; Lagos 1983; FCO 1986; Vice-Consul Toronto 1988 (Second Secretary 1989); m 1985 Julie Anne Grant (1s 1989, 1d 1990).

Tobin, Michael John Henry; First Secretary FCO since January 1992; born 27.12.38; RAF 1958-63; CO 1964; FO 1966; Wellington 1967; Bonn 1970; East Berlin 1973; FCO 1975; Vice-Consul Cairo 1978 (Second Secretary 1980); Vice-Consul (Comm) Houston 1982; First Secretary on loan to British National Space Centre 1987; First Secretary (Admin/Cons) Amman 1988; m 1961 Elizabeth Hughes (2s 1962, 1964; 1d 1965).

Todd, Damian Roderic; First Secretary (Econ) Bonn since August 1991; born 29.8.59; FCO 1980; Third later Second Secretary Capetown/ Pretoria 1981; Second Secretary FCO 1984; First Secretary and Consul Prague 1987; First Secretary FCO 1989; m 1987 Alison Mary Digby (1s 1989).

Todd, Sylvia Mary; FCO since March 1988; born

2.10.33; CENTO Secretariat Ankara 1958; La Paz 1960; Geneva (UKDEL) 1962; Bucharest 1964; FCO 1965; Ottawa 1971; FCO 1974; Moscow 1975; FCO 1976; Madrid 1985; Grade S1.

Tolfree, Alison (née Oxenford); Belgrade since March 1992; born 17.2.66; Grade S2; m 1991 Mark Tolfree.

Tomkins, Michael Paul; UKMIS Geneva since December 1989; born 23.12.50; FCO 1970; Honiara 1972; Aden 1976; Kingston 1977; Wellington 1980; Warsaw 1982; FCO 1983; Dhaka 1986; Grade 9; m 1979 Eleanor Michelle Ritch (1d 1986; 1s 1989).

Tomkins, Roger James; Islamabad since January 1992; born 30.6.48; Royal Navy 1966-88; Prison Service 1988-90; Budapest 1990; FCO 1990; Grade SO; m 1971 Pauline Bennett (1s 1974, 1d 1976).

Tomlinson, Deborah Jane; FCO since May 1990; born 16.2.63; FCO 1981; Islamabad 1984; Jakarta 1986; Grade 9.

Tomlinson, Jean Lesley; Rabat since June 1991; born 14.7.62; FCO 1989; Grade S2.

Tomlinson, Margaret; FCO since March 1986; born 21.1.31; Karachi 1960; Kingston 1962; FO 1966; Washington 1968; FCO 1970; Kampala 1972; FCO 1973; Nicosia 1974; Belgrade 1979; FCO 1982; Pretoria 1984; Grade 9.

Tomlinson, Richard John Charles; FCO since September 1991; born 13.1.63; Grade 7; m 1988 Betty Cordi (2d 1987, 1990).

Tomnay, Charles; Second Secretary FCO since May 1985; born 12.12.33; Post Office 1949; CRO 1962; Nairobi 1963; Hong Kong 1965; Beirut 1967; FCO 1970; Dacca 1973; Maseru 1976; East Berlin 1983; m 1953 Anne Farrell Houston (3s 1955, 1958, 1960; 1d 1966).

Tongs, John Edward; Havana since June 1991; born 10.12.35; Royal Navy 1951-75; Ankara 1976; Sofia 1978; Georgetown 1979; Moscow 1981; Caracas 1982; Nairobi 1984; Brussels 1986; Budapest 1989; Grade CSO; m 1972 Maureen Carter.

Tonkin, Ramsey Harris; First Secretary (Management) Oslo since October 1989; born 17.4.44; FO 1964; Ankara 1966; Bonn 1969; FCO 1972; Tehran 1975; Second Secretary (Comm) Port of Spain 1978; Second Secretary FCO 1982; Second later First Secretary (Admin/ Consul) Bombay 1987; m 1966 Valerie Anne Duff (2d 1967, 1969).

Tonner, Janice Wight (née Taylor) Lilongwe since August 1990; born 6.11.64; FCO 1985; Rome 1987; Grade S2; m 1987 Gary Campbell Tonner.

Toothe, Adrian Gerald; Second later First
Secretary FCO since August 1989; born 7.1.52;
FCO 1972; Jedda 1976; Second Secretary FCO
1980; UKMIS Geneva 1985; m 1976 Diane
Whitehead (2s 1982, 1985).

Topping, Pamela Anne (née Beavis), MBE (1968);
East Berlin since April 1990; born 23.11.34;
Tehran 1962; Khorramshahr 1964; Kinshasa
1965; Bonn 1968; Vienna 1970; FCO 1976;
Budapest 1981; Ankara 1983; Havana 1985;
FCO 1988; Grade S1; m 1984 Thomas Redpath
Topping.

Topping, Patrick Gilmer; First Secretary FCO
since Dember 1991; born 5.9.59; FCO 1986;
Second later First Secretary (Chancery) Kuala
Lumpur 1990; m 1985 Indira Annick
Coomaraswamy.

Topping, Thomas Redpath; East Berlin since
April 1990; born 25.7.36; Army 1953-76; Ankara
1983; Havana 1985; Floater duties 1988; Grade
SO; m 1984 Pamela Anne Beavis.

Torlot, Timothy Achille; Second Secretary FCO
since May 1992; born 17.9.57; FCO 1981;
Muscat 1984; Second Secretary (Chancery)
Wellington m 1986 Bridie Morton (1d 1990).

Torrance, David John Baillie; Third Secretary
and Vice Consul San Salvador since August
1990; born 29.2.56; FCO 1975; Bangkok 1978;
LA Floater 1982; Doha 1984; FCO 1987;
Grade 9.

Torry, Peter James; Counsellor Washington
since July 1989; born 2.8.48; FCO 1970; Third
Secretary Havana 1971; Second Secretary
(Econ1/Comm) Jakarta 1974; First Secretary
FCO 1977; First Secretary (Chancery) Bonn
1981; First Secretary later Counsellor FCO 1985;
m 1979 Angela Wakeling Wood (3d 1980, 1982,
1985).

Toseland, Brian Ernest; Second later First
Secretary FCO since September 1987; born
6.9.38; FO 1956; RAF 1957-59; Warsaw 1960;
Port au Prince 1962; FO 1963; DSAO 1965;
Brussels 1968; FCO 1971; Warsaw 1971;
Islamabad 1973; Second Secretary FCO 1976;
Quito 1980; Second Secretary (Admin/Aid) San
José 1983; Second Secretary (Admin) Mexico
City 1984; m (1) 1966 Diane Dodd (diss) (2s
1968, 1970; 1d 1973); m (2) 1983 Marthe Ines
Coray.

Totty, Alastair Walton; Abu Dhabi since June
1991; born 24.7.69; FCO 1988; Grade 10.

Tough, Mary Hampton; First Secretary
(Management) Harare since November 1991;
born 15.4.38; FO 1962; Vienna 1963; Peking
1966; Nicosia 1967; FCO 1970; South East Asia
Floater 1973; Zurich 1975; Moscow 1975; Lagos
1976; Second Secretary Panama City 1979; FCO

1983; Second Secretary (Aid/Comm) Maseru
1988.

Towe, Sheila; On loan to the DTI since January
1992; born 26.7.62; FCO 1981; East Berlin
1983; FCO 1985; Baghdad 1987; FCO 1990;
Grade 10.

Townend, Warren Dennis; Consul (Commercial)
Düsseldorf since August 1991; born 15.11.45;
FO 1964; DSAO 1965; FO (later FCO) 1967;
Hanoi 1969; Hamburg 1970; Second Secretary
(Comm) Dacca 1973; FCO 1976; Second later
First Secretary Bonn 1979; First Secretary
(Comm) Bangkok 1984; First Secretary FCO
1987; m Ann Mary Riddle (1d 1977; twin s
1979; 1s 1980).

Towner, John Arthur; First Secretary (Econ)
Rome since April 1989; born 19.3.39; HMOCS
1961-71; FCO 1972; Second later First Secretary
Tokyo 1974; FCO 1979; First Secretary
(Chancery) Vienna 1981; FCO 1985; m 1979
Kumiko Takahashi (2d 1980, 1983).

Townsend, David John; Vienna since September
1991; born 31.5.57; ECGD 1984-89; FCO 1989;
Grade 9.

Townsend, Stephen Thomas; FCO since January
1990; born 10.7.61; FCO 1980; Caracas 1982;
Kinshasa 1986; Grade 9.

Townson, Jennifer Caroline; Third Secretary
(Chancery) Paris since June 1992; born 22.2.68;
FCO 1989; On loan to the ODA 1991; Grade 9.

Towsey, Malcolm John; First Secretary
(Management) Lagos since March 1991; born
6.5.47; Ministry of Defence 1963; FO (later
FCO) 1965; Baghdad 1969; Warsaw 1972; Rabat
1973; Dacca 1976; FCO 1979; Maseru 1982;
Second Secretary FCO 1984; Second Secretary
(Comm) Dublin 1986; Second Secretary FCO
1990; m 1976 Erica Pamela Filder (1s 1979; 1d
1981).

Toynton, Edward James; UKDEL Brussels since
Aprll 1990; born 23.11.39; FCO 1988; Moscow
1989; Grade SO; m 1961 Janet Lillian Waye.

Traina, Fiona; FCO since April 1992; born
14.1.73; Grade 10.

Trainer, Norman Stanley; Helsinki since
September 1987; born 17.7.35; RAF 1956-69;
Brussels (EC) 1970; Sofia 1972; Pretoria 1973;
Tokyo 1976; Santiago 1979; Warsaw 1982;
UKMIS Geneva 1984; Grade SSO; m 1956
Sheila O;Brien (1s 1958; 1d 1961).

Traylor, Owen John; First Secretary (Chancery)
Berlin since November 1990; born 26.9.55; FCO
1977; Language Student Tokyo 1980; Second
Secretary (Econ) Tokyo 1981; First Secretary
FCO 1985; m (1) 1981 Angela Carmel Webb

(diss 1989) (1d 1985); (2) 1991 Carola Wangerin.

Treadell, Alan; FCO since April 1990; born 8.11.51; FCO 1971; Stockholm 1973; Sana'a 1976; FCO 1977; Islamabad 1979; FCO 1983; Kuala Lumpur 1985; Grade 7; m 1985 Victoria Marguerite Jansz.

Treadell, Victoria Marguerite (née Jansz), MVO (1989); FCO since April 1990; born 4.11.59; FCO 1978; Islamabad 1981; FCO 1983; Kuala Lumpur 1985; Grade 9; m 1985 Alan Treadell.

Treleven, Philip, MVO (1991); FCO since November 1991; born 21.1.64; FCO 1984; Dhaka 1986; Canberra 1988; Grade 9.

Tremayne, Jennifer Jane; Floater Duties since July 1989; born 20.2.60; FCO 1979; Gaborone 1981; Islamabad 1984; FCO 1987; Grade S2.

Trevelyan, Sarah Frances; Kampala since March 1990; born 6.2.65; FCO 1983; Lisbon 1987; Grade S2.

Tricks, William Tobias Foster; Second Secretary Nairobi since January 1992; born 16.10.62; Second Secretary FCO 1989; m 1991 Fiona Macdonald.

Triunfo, Amanda Lesley (née Webb); Mexico City since November 1992; born 11.5.62; FCO 1985; Montevideo 1987; FCO 1989; Grade S2; m 1989 Juan Carlos Triunfo.

Trott, Christopher John; FCO since September 1991; (Second Secretary 1992); born 14.2.66; m 1992 Sunna Park.

Trowbridge, Frank Maynard; Athens since November 1992; born 18.4.36; Brussels 1976; Peking 1977; Athens 1980; Helsinki 1983; Cairo 1986; Grade CSO; Sofia 1987; Nairobi 1989; m 1955 Valerie June Banks (2s 1956, 1970; 1d 1957).

Truman, Gary Douglas; FCO since November 1990; born 15.10.63; (FCO Home Civil Service February 1981); Grade 10.

Tubman, Richard; Islamabad since September 1987; born 6.3.35; Army 1956-78; Prague 1978; UKDEL NATO Brussels 1980; Jedda 1983; Sofia 1985; Grade SO; m 1969 Pamela Jane Taylor (1d 1971).

Tucker, Ernest; Warsaw since December 1991; born 16.3.45; Army 1963-1991; Grade SO; m 1965 Ute Elli Wilkelmine (1s 1978).

Tucker, Andrew Victor Gunn; First Secretary FCO since January 1991; born 20.12.55; Joint Technical Language Service 1978-81; FCO 1981; Second Secretary Dar Es Salaam 1982; First Secretary on loan to the Cabinet Office 1985; First Secretary and Press Attaché Moscow 1987;

m 1986 Judith Anne Gibson.

Tucker, James Philip; FCO since September 1990; born 10.1.66; Grade 8; m 1991 Susie Elizabeth Betts.

Tuckey, Jillian; Pretoria since October 1990; born 13.11.58; FCO 1979; Moscow 1981; FCO 1983; Bahrain 1984; FCO 1986; Grade S2.

Tucknott, John Anthony, MBE (1990); Second Secretary (Admin) Beirut since November 1988; born 2.1.58; DEmp 1975; FCO 1977; Rome 1980; Cairo 1982; FCO 1985; m 1980 Susan Jayne Elliott.

Tucknott, Susan Jayne; (née Elliott), MBE (1991); Beirut since November 1988; born 13.6.61; FCO 1978; SUPL 1980; Rome 1982; SUPL 1982; Cairo 1984; FCO 1985; Grade 9; m 1980 John Anthony Tucknott.

Tudor, Andrea Jayne; FCO since July 1989; born 22.1.68; Grade 10; m 1990 Duncan Nicholas Fife.

Tufnall, Lindsay Susan; FCO since May 1989; born 30.7.70; Grade 9.

Tuhey, Claire Elizabeth; FCO since November 1988; born 7.2.57; FCO 1976; SUPL 1976; FCO 1979; Paris 1982; Africa/Middle East Floater 1985; Vice-Consul New York 1987; Grade 9.

Tuke, John; BDSMO Hong Kong since March 1989; born 22.6.33; FCO 1972; Washington 1974; UKREP Brussels 1977; Salisbury 1980; FCO 1980; Rome 1982; Bonn 1983; Islamabad 1987; Grade 10; m 1961 Diane Brace (1d 1964; 1s 1968).

Tuke, Sarah Frances; Floating Duties since November 1990; born 8.3.63; FCO 1982; Capetown/Pretoria 1984; Jakarta 1987; Grade S2.

Tully, Colin Nigel; New Delhi since February 1987; born 15.7.58; FCO 1980; Amman 1982; FCO 1985; Grade 9; m 1983 Wendy Joyce Ogden (1s 1985; 1d 1989).

Tunn, Douglas Charles; UKMIS New York since September 1989; born 18.2.68; FCO 1987; Grade 10.

Tunn, Rachel Elizabeth; Bucharest since April 1991; born 28.5.68; FCO 1989; Grade S2.

Tunnell, Hugh James Oliver Redvers; HM Ambassador and Consul-General Bahrain since February 1992; born 31.12.35; HM Forces 1954-56; FO 1956; Amman 1959; MECAS 1962; FO 1964; Second Secretary Aden 1964; CRO 1965; Damascus 1966; FO 1967; UKDEL EC Brussels 1968; Second Secretary FCO 1970; First Secretary (Comm) Kuwait 1972; FCO 1976; Head of Chancery Muscat 1979; Consul-General

Brisbane 1983; Consul-General Jedda 1989; m
(1) 1958 Helen Miller (diss) (3d 1959, 1960,
1962); (2) 1979 Margaret Louise Seelaf (2d
1984, 1988).

Tunnicliffe, Christopher John Robin; Prague
since December 1991; born 11.11.69; FCO 1989;
Grade 10; m 1991 Veronica Mary Walters.

Tunstall, David George, MBE (1985); First
Secretary FCO since September 1990; born
23.9.41; FO 1961; Baghdad 1962; Montevideo
1965; Moscow 1968; FCO 1969; MECAS 1971;
Khartoum 1975; FCO 1979; HM Consul Jedda
(later Riyadh) 1982; First Secretary (Cons)
Harare 1986; m (1) 1966 Mary Lillian Jones (2d
1968, 1971); m (2) 1982 Maureen Kathleen
Murkin (née Brown) (1 step s 1970; 1 step d
1974).

Turkington, Victoria Dolores; Vice-Consul
Stockholm since February 1991; born 24.5.35;
FCO 1971; Berne 1971; Tunis 1974; FCO 1976;
Tokyo 1978; FCO 1982; Warsaw 1985; FCO
1987; Berlin 1988; Grade 9.

Turnbull, David Robert; FCO since September
1991; born 25.8.55; MOD 1976; Ankara 1980;
FCO 1983; Maputo 1984; The Hague 1988;
Grade 9; m 1987 Eva Marianne Persson.

Turner, Alan Roger; Caracus since June 1992;
born 9.4.48; Royal Air Force 1965-1968; Grade
9; m 1974 Caroline Grace.

Turner, Andrew William; Third Secretary
(Chancery) Muscat since June 1989; born
8.12.63; FCO 1986; Language Training 1987;
Grade 8.

Turner, David Harvey; First Secretary (Comm)
Lisbon since July 1989; born 17.2.45; FO 1966;
Bonn 1968; Lagos 1970; Brasilia 1973; FCO
1975; Maputo 1978; Vice-Consul São Paulo
1981; Second later First Secretary FCO 1985; m
1966 Janet Mary Field (1s; 1d 1975).

Turner, Lesley; FCO since March 1991; born
29.10.61; FCO 1982; Harare 1983; Rangoon
1986; Grand Turk 1988; Grade S1.

Turner, Mark Robin; Second Secretary FCO
since June 1991; born 23.8.55; FCO 1975;
Budapest 1977; Maseru 1979; Islamabad 1982;
FCO 1984; Los Angeles 1988; m 1981 Patricia
Louise Brown (2d 1984, 1987).

Turner, Richard Patrick; FCO since June 1991;
born 19.1.63; FCO 1981; UKREP Brussels 1984;
Dar es Salaam 1986; Third Secretary (Admin)
UKDEL Strasbourg 1988; Grade 9.

Turner, Robert Leigh; First Secretary (Economic)
Moscow since November 1992; born 13.3.58;
Department of Transport 1979; PSA 1980; DOE
1981; HM Treasury 1982; FCO 1983; Second

Secretary (Chancery) Vienna 1984; First Secretary
FCO 1987; Language Training 1991.

Turner, Stephen Edward; Consul (Commercial)
Seattle since October 1990; born 25.3.46; CRO
1963; DSAO 1965; Jakarta 1968; DTI 1972;
Kuala Lumpur 1972; Second Secretary FCO
1976; Valletta 1978; Second Secretary (Comm)
Jakarta 1983; First Secretary Jakarta 1986; First
Secretary FCO 1988; m 1966 Maureen Ann Dick
(2s 1969, 1971; 2d 1973, 1982).

Turney, Nicholas; FCO since September 1984;
born 31.3.53; FCO 1971; Washington 1981;
Grade 8.

Turpin, Nicola Sarah; FCO since March 1991;
born 27.10.71; ODA 1989; Grade S3A.

Turquet, Andrew William; First Secretary FCO
since August 1989; born 11.7.42; Third later
Second Secretary FO (later FCO) 1967; Second
Secretary Lagos 1969; FCO 1971; Consul (Inf)
Karachi 1973; FCO 1975; Bridgetown 1979;
First Secretary FCO 1981; Kampala 1986; m
1968 Susan Jane Masterton (2d 1970, 1977; 2s
1972, 1974).

Turtell, Melvyn Edward Geoffrey; Second
Secretary FCO since October 1988; born 7.1.43;
FO 1966; Helsinki 1968; San Salvador 1972;
Washington 1973; FCO 1976; Quito 1979; on
loan to PSA 1982; Second Secretary (Admin)
Havana 1986; m 1965 Janet George (1s 1966; 2d
1969, 1970).

Turunc, Susan Kay (née Powell); Istanbul since
May 1990; born 27.3.49; FCO 1968; Peking
1970; FCO 1971; resigned 1972; Home Civil
Service 1975-79; reinstated FCO 1989; Grade
S2; m 1991 Gokkan Turunc.

Turvill, Stuart Graham; FCO since October
1991; born 18.2.71; Grade 10.

Tutt, Roger Clive, MBE (1967); Counsellor FCO
since February 1989; born 22.3.39; FO 1966;
Second Secretary Copenhagen 1967; Lusaka
1969; FCO 1971; First Secretary (Inf)
Bridgetown and RIO Eastern Caribbean 1974;
First Secretary FCO 1979; Counsellor UKMIS
New York 1987; m 1963 Gwendoline Leeke (2s
1967, 1969; 1d 1973).

Tutton, Anthony Colin; First Secretary FCO
since April 1989; born 22.10.39; FCO 1963;
Georgetown 1967; FCO 1968; Rome 1971; FCO
1976; Resigned 1977; Reinstated 1979; First
Secretary (Chancery) Rome 1986; m 1972
Doreen Rosaria Willis (2d 1974, 1991; 1s 1975).

Twells, Francis Joseph; East Berlin since August
1988; born 6.1.29; Army 1946-74; UKMIS New
York 1974; Moscow 1975; Georgetown 1976;
Bonn 1977; Lagos 1980; Warsaw 1981; Nairobi
1982; Kampala 1983; Tehran 1984; Stockholm

1985; Grade SSO; m 1949 Mary Kathleen Cruikshank (2s 1956, 1957).

Twigg, Mark Paul; FCO since April 1989; born 1.3.56; FCO 1975; Beirut 1979; FCO 1980; Düsseldorf 1981; Harare 1981; Tripoli 1987; Grade 9.

Twigg, Monique Antoinette; Third Secretary (Chancery) UKDIS Geneva since June 1992; born 22.7.64; DTI 1985; FCO 1987; Kinshasa 1989; Grade 9.

Twyman, Robin Edward; Harare since August 1989; born 27.8.68; FCO 1987; Grade 10.

Tylor, Patrick Roy; Tel Aviv since May 1991; born 21.7.35; RAF 1953-77; Islamabad 1977; Prague 1979; Buenos Aires 1980; Montevideo 1982; Washington 1982; Bonn 1985; Moscow 1988; Valletta 1989; East Berlin 1990; Grade CSO; m 1958 Eileen Ward Dewar (4s 1959, 1961, 1964, 1967).

U

Uden, Martin David; FCO 1990; born 28.2.55; FCO 1977; Seoul 1978; Second later First Secretary FCO 1982; First Secretary (Econ) Bonn 1986; m 1982 Fiona Jane Smith (1s 1986).

Unutulmaz; Caroline Frances (née Grigg); FCO since January 1990; born 14.10.64; FCO 1983; Düsseldorf 1986; Third Secretary (Aid) Khartoum 1988; Grade 9; m 1985 Vahit Hakan Unutulmaz.

Upton, Grant; Bangkok since August 1987; born 17.3.59; FCO 1980; Bonn 1982; Kampala 1985; Grade 10; m 1990 Wanpen Songsang.

Upton, Michael John; First Secretary FCO since July 1992; born 28.10.51; RAF 1970-76; FCO 1976; Havana 1978; Aden 1982; FCO 1982; Bogota 1984; Second Secretary UKMIS New York 1986; Vice-Consul (Inward Investment) Los Angeles 1990; m 1978 Susan Marshall (1s 1981; 1d 1983).

Usher, Janet Clare; Floater Duties since June 1991; born 23.4.65; FCO 1983; Washington 1986; Prague 1989; Grade 9.

Usher, Judith; Peking since February 1991; born 14.10.69; FCO 1988; Grade 10.

Usher, Stephen; New Delhi since January 1991; born 27.6.69; FCO 1987; UKMIS Vienna 1989; Grade 10.

V

Van Der Plank, Ian Derek; Third Secretary Lagos since September 1990; born 21.8.56. Royal Navy 1972-77; FCO 1981; Paris 1987; Grade 9.

Van Drie, Katherine Stephanie (née Fawdry); SUPL since July 1991; born 20.9.63; FCO 1982; The Hague 1985; LA/Caribbean Floater 1988; Moscow 1989; Grade 9; m 1989 Jeffrey Van Drie.

Vargas, Emlyn Barry; Caracas since February 1989; born 2.2.46; HM Forces 1964-86; FCO 1986; Grade 8; m 1991 Carmen Rafaela Velazquez.

Varney, Carol June; UKMIS Geneva since July 1992; born 24.11.43; FCO 1969; Budapest 1972; Dacca 1973; Frankfurt 1976; FCO 1978; Stockholm 1981; New Delhi 1984; FCO 1987; UKDEL Brussels 1991; Grade 9.

Vaughan, Denise Ann; Washington since August 1988; born 15.10.64; FCO 1983; Bonn 1985; UKDEL CSCE Vienna 1988; Grade S2.

Vaygelt, Robin (née Maitland); FCO since August 1988; born 14.6.61; FCO 1984; Rio de Janeiro 1986; Grade S2; m 1992 Marek Stephen Fernyhough Vaygelt.

Venning, John Ralph; First Secretary FCO since September 1991; born 14.8.41; Second Secretary FCO 1970; First Secretary Islamabad 1972; Consul (Inf/Pol) Karachi 1972; First Secretary FCO 1974; First Secretary (Inf) Nicosia 1978; First Secretary FCO 1982; First Secretary (Chancery) Oslo 1987; m 1964 Sybil Mary Whinney (2d 1967, 1970; 1s 1977).

Vereker, Peter William Medlicott; Counsellor FCO since April 1991; born 13.10.39; FO 1963; Third later Second Secretary Bangkok 1964; Chiang Mai 1967; Centre for Administrative Studies 1968; FCO 1968 (First Secretary 1970); Canberra 1971; First Secretary and Head of Chancery Athens 1975; FCO 1978; Counsellor on loan to MOD (RCDS) 1982; Counsellor Bangkok 1983; Counsellor (GATT) later Deputy Permanent Representative (Economic Affairs) UKMIS Geneva 1987; m 1967 Susan Elizabeth Dyball (3s 1971, 1973, 1981).

Verma, Neeras; FCO since March 1992; born 21.11.62; FCO 1982; UKDEL NATO Brussels 1984; Luanda 1988; Grade 9; m 1985 Sarah-Jane Dodman.

Verma, Sarah-Jane (née Dodman) FCO since May 1992; born 31.12.63; FCO 1983; UKREP Brussels 1985; Luanda 1988; Grade 9; m 1985 Neeras Verma.

Vernon, Joanna Elizabeth; SUPL since March 1992; FCO 1990; born 26.9.65; Grade 7.

Vickers, David Victor Edwin; FCO since May 1992; born 1.5.53; FCO 1973; Lusaka 1975; Kathmandu 1979; Sofia 1983; FCO 1984; Islamabad 1985; Ankara 1989; Grade 9; m (1) 1979 Anne Elizabeth Murphy (diss) (2) 1983 Pamela Barron (née Scott).

Vidal, Ruben Joel; FCO since September 1989; born 7.3.41; Royal Marines 1967-72; FCO 1979; Damascus 1981; FCO 1985; Harare 1988; Grade 9; m 1975 Delores Annett (1d 1983).

Virgo, John; FCO since September 1991; born 1.9.69; Grade 8.

Vivian, Bryan; Havana since July 1989; born 3.12.32; Army 1953-76; Geneva 1976; Bucharest 1977; Singapore 1979; Buenos Aires 1983; East Berlin 1983; Islamabad 1985; Pretoria 1986; Grade SO; m May Joan (2s 1953, 1963).

Vlasto, Richard; Second Secretary (Chancery) Nairobi since April 1992; born 11.11.51; FCO 1975; Prague 1977; FCO 1979; Third Secretary UKMIS Geneva 1981; FCO 1985; m (1) 1981 Amanda Gabrielle Lewis (diss. 1991) (2s 1985, 1987) (2) Gillian Felicity Turnbull (3 stepd 1978, 1980, 1983).

Vosper, Alistair John; Islamabad since March 1992; born 9.4.70; FCO 1989; Grade 10.

Vowles, John Philip, Tehran since September 1991; born 13.8.47; Royal Marines 1962-87; Moscow 1987; Pretoria 1989; Grade SO; m 1968 Maureen Cann.

Voyce, Robert Stephen; Vice-Consul later Third Secretary (Political) Berlin since October 1990; born 25.2.67; FCO 1988; Grade 9.

W

Wadvani, Sanjay Mark; ECO/Vice-Consul Damascus since June 1991; born 6.12.66; FCO 1987; Peking 1989; Grade 9.

Wain, Geoffrey William; FCO since May 1992; born 10.5.65; FCO 1983; Islamabad 1986; Istanbul 1989; Grade 9; m 1985 Kathleen Anne Lowe (1d 1992).

Wain, Kathleen Anne (née Lowe); FCO since July 1992; born 11.2.63; FCO 1982; Addis Ababa 1984; FCO 1985; Islamabad 1986; Istanbul 1989; Grade 9; m 1985 Geoffrey William Wain (1d 1992).

Wainwright, Charles Williams; Counsellor FCO since September 1992; born 5.9.41; HM Forces 1960-67; Second Secretary FO (later FCO) 1968; Accra 1969; FCO 1971; First Secretary (Inf) Athens 1972; First Secretary FCO 1976; Dacca 1979; First Secretary FCO 1982; Counsellor

Berne 1988; m 1973 Patricia Ann Evans (2s 1975, 1977).

Waite, Timothy Matthew; FCO since October 1991; born 21.7.62; PSA 1988-91; Grade 9.

Walawalkar, Margaret Ann; on CDA at SOAS since January 1991; born 1.4.48; FCO 1975; PRO; m 1974 Govind Anant Walawalkar.

Walder, Alan Charles; First Secretary FCO since January 1990; born 26.1.36; Ministry of Housing and Local Government 1953; FO 1959; Warsaw 1959; Vice-Consul Seoul 1960; FO 1962; DSAO 1965; Bahrain 1965; Copenhagen 1969; Singapore 1969; Second later First Secretary FCO 1973; First Secretary (Comm) Jakarta 1977; Budapest 1981; on loan to MOD 1983; First Secretary (Comm) New Delhi 1986; m 1964 Patricia Mary Swingler (2d 1965, 1967).

Walder, Jacqueline Ann; Vice-Consul and Attaché to the African Development Bank Abidjan since March 1992; born 30.8.67; FCO 1989; Grade 9.

Walford, Thomas Alexander; Second Secretary FCO since January 1991; born 2.3.49; FCO 1968; Malta 1971; Belmopan 1974; Tunis 1975; FCO 1978; Canberra 1981; The Hague 1983; FCO 1986; Deputy Head of Mission, Panama City 1989; m 1974 Mary Theresa Heafield (1s 1977; 1d 1979).

Walker, Alisdair James; Third Secretary (Chancery) Islamabad since September 1991; born 14.9.65; FCO 1989; Grade 9.

Walker, Angela Ruth; Second Secretary FCO since August 1989; born 7.5.54; FCO 1980; The Hague 1983; Vice-Consul Rio de Janeiro 1986.

Walker, David Critchlow, LVO (1976); CVO (1988); High Commissioner Accra and HM Ambassador (non-resident) Togo since June 1992; born 9.1.40; CRO 1963; Third later Second Secretary Mexico City 1965; Second Secretary (Comm) Brussels 1968; First Secretary FCO 1971; First Secretary Washington 1973; First Secretary (later Counsellor) FCO 1979; (Home Inspector September 1980); Consul-General São Paulo 1983; Minister Madrid 1986; Counsellor FCO 1989; m 1965 Tineke Van der Leek (3s 1966, 1967, 1970).

Walker, Delia-Jane; First Secretary (Management/Consular) Accra since October 1991; born 15.3.49; MAFF 1967; FCO 1969; Islamabad 1972; Floater duties 1975; FCO 1978; Second Secretary (Technical Cooperation) Quito 1981; First Secretary (UN) UKMIS Geneva 1985; First Secretary FCO 1990.

Walker, Derek Leonard; FCO since June 1992; born 28.11.44; FCO 1971; Tripoli 1974; Bucharest 1976; Ottawa 1978; FCO 1980; JAO

Brussels 1984; Lagos 1988; Grade 9; m 1965
Janice Ann Gamble-Beresford (2d 1968, 1970).

Walker, Elizabeth Doreen; Peking since
December 1991; born 8.8.36; FCO 1987; Jakarta
1988; Grade S2; (1d 1960).

Walker, Frances Mary; Vice Consul Dusseldorf
since November 1989; born 8.9.47; FCO 1967;
UKDEL NATO Brussels 1970; New Hebrides
1972; FCO 1974; Blantyre 1976; Port Louis
1978; FCO 1979; Stockholm 1983; Quito 1986;
FCO 1986; Grade 9.

Walker, Gary; Helsinki since February 1991;
born 30.11.47; Royal Marines 1967-1990; FCO
1990; T/D Helsinki 1990; Grade S0; m 1971
Pauline Jane Clifford.

Walker, Helen Mary; FCO since September
1991; born 23.7.69; Grade 8.

Walker, Jane Lesley; FCO since September
1989; born 15.2.71; Grade S2.

Walker, Janice Lesley; FCO since May 1984;
born 24.8.60; FCO 1981; Oslo 1982; Grade S2;
m 1985 Stephan Raymond Walker.

Walker, Jason Robert; Khartoum since
September 1990; born 4.6.70; FCO 1988; Grade
10.

Walker, John Frank; Buenos Aires since
September 1991; born 10.2.64; Royal Engineers
1980-85; FCO 1987; Grade 9; m 1990 Caroline
Jane Masters (2s 1985, 1991).

Walker, John Ronald; FCO since March 1985;
born 4.5.60; Senior Research Officer (DS5).

Walker, John Stanley; Doha since February
1991; born 20.10.66; FCO 1984; Bucharest 1989;
Grade 10.

Walker, Lawrence Edward, LVO (1979), OBE
(1984), MBE (1973); Consul-General Jedda since
August 1992; born 21.7.42; FO 1960; MECAS
1963; Kuwait 1965; FO 1967; Frankfurt 1968;
Second Secretary Tripoli 1970; On loan to DHSS
1974; First Secretary, Head of Chancery and
Consul Bahrain 1976; First Secretary (Comm)
Baghdad 1980; FCO 1984; First Secretary
(Comm) Ankara 1988; Deputy Head of Mission
Kuwait 1991; m (1) 1963 Jill Catherine Mackey
(2s 1968, 1970) (diss. 1983); (2) 1991 Olive
Harmer.

Walker, Mary Elizabeth; SUPL since October
1991; born 24.6.68;FCO 1990; Grade 9.

Walker, Olivia Rosalyn; FCO since May 1983;
born 28.8.54; FCO 1975; Caracas 1980; m 1983
Dr Paul Stewart Henley (1d 1987).

Walker, Patricia Arlow; Berlin since November

1990; born 29.9.63; FCO 1988; Grade S2.

Walker, Sandra Patricia (née Wright); FCO
since January 1992; born 3.3.65; Brussels 1986;
FCO 1984; Dhaka 1989; Grade S2; m 1989
Robert Freeman Walker.

Wall, Eric Simon Charles; First Secretary FCO
since March 1991; born 4.9.57; Royal Navy
1976-86; Second Secretary FCO 1986; Second
later First Secretary UKMIS Geneva 1988; m
1983 Elizabeth Anne Gibson (1s 1990).

Wall, (John) Stephen, CMG (1991), LVO (1983);
On loan to the Cabinet Office (at No. 10 as
Foreign Affairs PS to the Prime Minister) since
March 1991; born 10.1.47; Third Secretary FCO
1968; Third later Second Secretary Addis Ababa
1969; Private Secretary to HM Ambassador Paris
1972; Second later First Secretary FCO 1974; on
loan to No 10 Downing Street 1976; Assistant
Private Secretary to the SOS 1977; First
Secretary (Chancery) Washington 1979; First
Secretary FCO 1983; Counsellor FCO 1985; PPS
to the Secretary of State 1988; m 1975 Catharine
Jane Reddaway (1s 1979).

Wall, Stuart Ian; Kuala Lumpur since May 1991;
born 19.7.45; FCO 1976; Islamabad 1976; FCO
1978; Darwin 1979; FCO 1982; Moscow 1984;
FCO 1985; Pretoria 1986; FCO 1989; Grade 9;
m 1968 Susan Edgar (1d 1970).

Wallace, Euan; FCO since June 1990; born
15.6.63; FCO 1981; Paris 1984; Moscow 1986;
Resigned 1988; Reinstated 1990; Grade 9; m
1987 Gillian Whittaker.

Wallace, Gillian (née Whittaker); FCO since
May 1988; born 14.11.63; FCO 1983; Paris
1985; Moscow 1987; Grade S1; m 1987 Euan
Wallace.

Wallace, Lindsay Ann; FCO since September
1991; born 6.2.72; Grade 10.

Wallace, Neil Douglas; FCO since February
1990; born 5.11.69; Grade 10.

Waller, Clare Helen; FCO since October 1991;
born 11.9.72; Grade 10.

Waller, John Alfred James; Dublin since
October 1989; born 5.5.36; RAF 1955-78; Prague
1981; Amman 1982; BMG Berlin 1984; Warsaw
1987; Grade SO; m 1962 Dorothy Ruth Pearson
(1s 1964; 2d 1965, 1970).

Waller, Mark; Kingston since July 1989; born
29.9.67; FCO 1987; Grade 10.

Walley, Martin; Third Secretary (Commercial)
Manila since May 1992; born 11.6.58; HMIT 1977;
FCO 1978; Ankara 1980; Mexico City 1984; FCO
1985; Budapest 1985; Dhaka 1987; FCO 1990;
Grade 9; m 1981 Dilek Sule (1s 1991).

Wallis, Sir Peter (Gordon), KCVO (1992), CMG (1990); High Commissioner Valletta since October 1991; born 2.8.35; Ministry of Labour and National Service 1958; Assistant Principal HM Customs and Excise 1959 (Private Secretary 1961-64); Principal 1964-68 (seconded to Diplomatic Service as First Secretary UKMIS Geneva 1965-67); FCO 1968; Tel Aviv 1970; Nairobi 1974; Counsellor Ankara 1977; RCDS 1981; Seconded to Cabinet Office 1982; Counsellor FCO 1983; Minister Pretoria/Cape Town 1987; Head of British Liaison Ofice, later Acting High Commissioner, Windhoek 1989; Counsellor FCO 1990; m 1965 Delysia Elizabeth Leonard (3s 1967, 1975, 1977; 1d 1968).

Wallis, Peter Vaughan; First Secretary (Chancery) Kuwait since March 1991; born 25.12.46; Second Secretary FCO 1973; Language Student MECAS 1975; FCO 1976; First Secretary (Comm) Sana'a 1977; First Secretary (Econ) Damascus 1978; FCO 1980; Lagos 1983; First Secretary FCO 1986; First Secretary (Chancery) Khartoum 1990; m 1975 Alison Beech (2s 1976, 1979; 1d 1978).

Wallis, Robin John; Vice-Consul (Inf/Aid) Johannesburg since November 1992; born 9.7.61; FCO 1986; Second Secretary (Chancery) Buenos Aires 1988; Second Secretary FCO 1990; m 1989 Janette Staubus (1s 1989; 1d 1992).

Wallis, Victor Charles; Second Secretary FCO since September 1989; born 6.2.47; CO 1963; Commonwealth Office (later FCO) 1966; Bermuda 1969; Accra 1972; FCO 1975; Second Secretary Helsinki 1979; Vice Consul (Comm) Sydney 1985; m 1971 Jacqueline Wadhams (1s 1979).

Walmsley, Alan; FCO since February 1988; born 6.9.61; FCO 1981; Abu Dhabi 1984; Grade 9.

Walmsley, Andrea Elizabeth (née Walker);Bombay since May 1990; born 17.6.63; FCO 1981; UKDEL Brussels 1983; FCO 1986; Nicosia 1987; Grade 9; m 1986 Mark Ronan Walmsley.

Walmsley, Mark Ronan; Bombay since May 1990 (Second Secretary (Consular) 1991); born 17.6.58; FCO (HCS) 1978; FCO 1980; Bucharest 1981; African/ME Floater 1983; FCO 1984; Nicosia 1987; m 1986 Andrea Elizabeth Walker.

Walpole, The Hon Alice (Louise); Second Secretry (Chancery) Dar es Salaam since June 1991; born 1.9.63; FCO 1985; Third later Second Secretary (External Relations and Internal Market) UKREP Brussels 1987; language training 1990; m 1990 Angel Csar Carro Castrillo (Twin d 1990).

Walsh, Nicola Jane; FCO since August 1990; born 24.1.61; FCO 1980; Bahrain 1982; Bridgetown 1985; Kingstown 1986; LA/

Caribbean Floater 1988; Grade 9.

Walsh, Paul Richard; Islamabad since February 1991; born 15.3.69; DHSS 1987; FCO 1988; Berlin 1990; Grade 9.

Walsh, Penelope Ruth; Third Secretary (UN) UKMIS Geneva since April 1991; born 19.12.66; FCO 1990; Grade 9.

Walters, Alison Jane (née Lund); SUPL since October 1991; born 28.8.57; FCO 1976; Yaoundé 1978; FCO 1982; Sofia 1985; Paris 1987; SUPL 1988; Third Secretary (Inf/Chancery) Islamabad 1989; Grade 9; m 1978 Robert Leslie Walters.

Walters, David Anthony, MVO (1985); Vice-Consul Atlanta since August 1991; born 3.1.57; NSB 1975; FCO 1977, Tehran 1979; Bonn 1980; Port of Spain 1982; FCO 1986; Dhaka 1988; Grade 9; m 1980 Janis Anne McPhail (2s 1982, 1984).

Walters, Jonathan Mark; FCO since September 1990; born 28.7.67; Grade 9.

Walters, Robert Leslie; Third Secretary (Comm) Islamabad since June 1989; born 23.1.50; FCO 1970; Havana 1972; Kaduna 1973; Valletta 1976; Masirah 1977; FCO 1977; Yaoundé 1978; FCO 1982; Sofia 1985; Paris 1987; Grade 9; m (1) 1973 Mary Elaine Lee (diss 1978); (2) 1978 Alison Jane Lund.

Walters, Stephen Brett; FCO since January 1985; born 23.8.60; FCO 1981; Peking 1982; Kingston 1983; Grade 9.

Walton, Gillian Mary (née Booth); First Secretary Oslo since April 1992; born 16.8.54; FCO 1975; Second Secretary Moscow 1987; Second Secretary FCO 1989; m 1979 (diss 1986).

Walwyn, David Scott; First Secretary FCO since July 1990; born 14.4.59; FCO 1985; Second later First Secretary (Chancery) Bangkok 1987; m 1988 Fiona Cassels-Brown.

Ward, Anthony John; Moscow since October 1991; born 8.5.47; Royal Marines 1964-88; UKREP Brussels 1988; Grade SO; m 1987 Sheila Anne Beddoes; (3s 1974, 1975, 1977).

Ward, Beryl Olive; Manila since April 1992; born 13.11.39; Tel Aviv 1966; Peking 1968; Caracas 1969; FCO 1972; Copenhagen 1981; FCO 1984; Istanbul 1990; Grade 9.

Ward, Christine (née Gray) Paris since April 1988; born 25.12.59; FCO 1978; Budapest 1980; Istanbul 1982; SUPL 1986; Grade 9; m 1986 Michael John Ward.

Ward, David Gordon; First Secretary (Aid) Harare since November 1990; born 25.7.42; CRO

1961; DSA 1965; Montevideo 1967; Dakar 1970; FCO 1974; Second Secretary (Aid) Victoria (Seychelles) 1977; Second Secretary Luxembourg 1981; First Secretary 1982; Consul Oporto, 1983; First Secretary FCO 1988; m (1) 1966 Rosemary Anne Silvester (2s 1968, 1974; 1d 1972); (diss 1980); (2) 1980 Margaret Martin (1s 1982; 1d 1984).

Ward, Michael David; FCO since June 1989; born 1.6.63; FCO March 1983; New Delhi 1986; Grade 9.

Ward, Michael John; Third later Second Secretary (Science and Technology) Paris since May 1988; born 25.12.58; FCO 1982; Istanbul 1985; m 1986 Christine Gray.

Wardale, Sharon, Tokyo since February 1991; born 2.2.66; FCO 1985; Islamabad 1988; FCO 1989; Grade S2.

Wardle, Sharon Anne; Vice-Consul Beirut since September 1991; born 2.3.65; FCO 1985; Moscow 1987; FCO 1989; Ex-Floater Duties 1990; Grade 9.

Ware, Jillian Angela; FCO since May 1990; born 17.12.62; FCO 1982; UKMIS New York 1984; Africa/ME Floater 1988; Grade 9; m 1990 David Edward Ware (1d 1991).

Warmington, Thomas George; Peking since April 1992; born 3.12.38; RAF 1960-82; Budapest 1984; Cairo 1985; BMG Berlin 1987; Sofia 1990; Grade SO; m 1958 Doreen Rosa (3d 1959, 1961, 1965).

Warr, Martyn John; FCO since April 1988 (Second Secretary 1989); born 1.5.59; FCO 1981; Language Training 1983; Jedda 1984.

Warren, David Alexander; On loan to Cabinet Office since November 1991; born 11.8.52; Third Secretary FCO 1975; Language Training SOAS 1976; Language Student Kamakura 1977; Second Secretary and Private Secretary to HM Ambassador Tokyo 1978; Second later First Secretary (Econ) Tokyo 1979; First Secretary FCO 1981; Head of Chancery Nairobi 1987; FCO 1990.

Warren, Gillian Rose; FCO since June 1991; born 20.7.37; Grade S2A; m 1958 Ronald William (2s 1961, 1968).

Warren, Susan Jennifer; FCO since June 1990; born 16.12.70; Grade 10.

Warren-Gash, Haydon Boyd; Deputy High Commissioner Nairobi since February 1991; born 8.8.49; FCO 1971; Language Student, London University 1972; Third Secretary Ankara 1973; Second later First Secretary (Chancery) Madrid 1977; First Secretary FCO 1981; PS to Minister of State 1982; First Secretary (Comm) Paris

1985; First Secretary FCO 1989; m 1973 Caroline Emma Bowring Leather (1s 1975; 1d 1977).

Warrington, Guy Murray; Second Secretary UKMIS New York since June 1992; Third later Second Secretary (Science/Tech) Singapore 1988; born 23.9.63; FCO 1986; Grade 8.

Warrington, Kirsty Julia Shade; FCO since December 1990; born 17.7.73; Grade S2.

Warwick, Sharon Joy; FCO since August 1983; born 31.1.57; FCO 1979; Rangoon 1980; Kuala Lumpur 1982; Grade S2; m 1983 Aiden Eustace Warwick.

Watchorn, Kenneth Graham; FCO since July 1992; born 20.9.54; FCO 1971; Washington 1979; FCO 1982; Vienna 1984; FCO 1987; Riyadh 1987; Grade 8; m 1980 Rossalyn Keen (2s 1983, 1985).

Watchorn, Mark; Africa/Middle East Floater since January 1990; born 28.7.65; FCO 1984; Cape Town/Pretoria 1987; Grade 10.

Waterhouse, Christine; Nairobi since September 1991; born 15.9.67; FCO 1987; Grade 10.

Waterhouse, Peter Laurance; Nicosia since June 1991; born 3.2.58; FCO 1975; Bonn 1987; FCO 1990; Grade 8; m 1985; Clare Rachel Dewar.

Waters, Alan Victor; First Secretary FCO since December 1991; born 10.4.42; CO 1958; CRO 1961; Freetown 1963; UKDEL ECSC Luxembourg 1967; Prague 1968; Anguilla 1970; Peking 1971; FCO 1973; Kinshasa 1976; Second Secretary (Comm) Bombay 1980; FCO 1984; First Secretary 1986; First Secretary (Econ) Copenhagen 1987; m 1977 Elizabeth Ann Newman (1s 1982; 1d 1984).

Waterton, James; Consul later First Secretary Durban since January 1991; born 25.4.49; FCO 1968; Havana 1970; Valletta 1972; Bonn 1974; FCO 1977; Wellington 1981; Second Secretary (Chancery/Comm) Montevideo 1984; Second Secretary FCO 1987; m 1981 Gaenor Whitfield.

Waterworth, Peter Andrew; FCO since October 1987; born 15.4.57; Assistant Legal Adviser (DS Grade 5); m 1981 Hilary Young.

Watkins, Brian; High Commissioner Mbabane since May 1990; born 26.7.33; RAF 1954-58; HMOCS Sierra Leone 1959-63; retired as District Commissioner Administrator Tristan da Cunha 1966-69; Solicitor 1970; First Secretary FCO 1971; Consul (Inf) New York (BIS) 1973; on loan to HCS 1976; FCO 1978; Deputy Governor Bermuda 1981; Counsellor (Comm) Islamabad 1983; Consul-General Vancouver 1986; m (1) 1957 Thelma Waite (diss) (1s 1958); (2) 1982 Elisabeth Arfon-Jones (1d 1985).

Watkins, Graeme Arthur; FCO since February 1991; born 13.6.61; FCO 1979; UKREP Brussels 1982; Singapore 1984; Managua 1988; Grade 9.

Watkinson, Anthony; Cape Town since January 1991; born 5.5.37; RAF 1955-77; Prague 1979; Lagos 1981; Budapest 1982; Montevideo 1984; Belgrade 1986; Bonn 1987; Berlin 1990; Grade SO; m 1958 Margaret Ayre.

Watkinson, Barry; FCO since December 1991; born 22.8.44; FCO 1984; Brussels 1988; Grade 9; m 1988 Patricia Rose.

Watmough, Sally Joanne; FCO since September 1992; born 22.5.64; FCO 1984; Belgrade 1987; FCO 1989; Buenos Aires 1990; Grade S2.

Watson, David James; First Secretary FCO since February 1992; born 4.3.57; FCO 1988; Second later First Secretary Harare 1989; m 1989 Sheelah McKeown (2d 1989, 1991).

Watson, Derrick Stuart; First Secretary later Counsellor FCO since December 1989; born 12.6.39; FO 1964; Third later Second Secretary Nairobi 1966; FCO 1969; First Secretary East Berlin 1973; First Secretary FCO 1975; Accra 1980; First Secretary FCO 1983; First Secretary Muscat 1986; m 1971 Elspeth Jean Sturrock (1d 1972; 1s 1973).

Watson, Joanne Louise; SUPL since March 1992; born 30.4.68; FCO since 1986, Wellington 1988; Grade 10.

Watson, Joel Aaron; Belmopan since July 1991; born 14.9.69; FCO 1989; Grade 10.

Watson, James Spencer Kennedy; Second Secretary (Chancery/Information) Kuwait since December 1991; born 30.11.64; FCO 1988.

Watson, John Philip; Counsellor British Trade Commission Hong Kong since April 1992; born 11.6.44; First Secretary FCO 1975; First Secretary Kuala Lumpur 1978; First Secretary (Consul) Peking 1980; First Secretary FCO 1983; Counsellor Rome 1988; Counsellor FCO 1991; m 1969 Patricia Katerina Tylecote (dec'd 1988) (1d 1973; 1s 1978).

Watson, Karen; FCO since November 1990; born 31.3.67; FCO 1987; Cairo 1989; Grade 10.

Watson, Pauline Ann; Bangkok since April 1988; born 3.8.65; FCO 1984; Peking 1987; Grade S2.

Watson, Stephen; FCO since September 1988; born 18.6.57; HO 1975; FCO 1976; Jedda 1979; Hong Kong 1982; Brasilia 1986; Grade 9.

Watt, James Wilfrid; Deputy Head of Mission Amman since August 1992; born 5.11.51; FCO 1977; MECAS 1978; Second later First Secretary

Abu Dhabi 1980; First Secretary FCO 1983; First Secretary (Chancery) UKMIS New York 1985; First Secretary FCO 1989; m 1980 Elizabeth Ghislaine Villeneuve (1s 1981; 1d 1986).

Wattam, John; FCO since September 1991; born 11.5.63; FCO 1982; Bonn 1984; Karachi 1987; Grade 9; m 1991 Anne Michelle Watson.

Watters, Brian Campbell; First Secretary (Chancery) Colombo since February 1992; born 9.4.42; First Secretary FCO 1973; First Secretary Singapore 1977; FCO 1980; Dar es Salaam 1985; First Secretary FCO 1988; m 1979 Debra Josephine de Souza (1d 1983).

Watts, Julie Yvonne; Budapest since May 1991; born 22.12.67; FCO 1987; UKMIS New York 1988; Grade S2.

Waugh, Margaret Pauline, MBE (1991); Second Secretary FCO since December 1990; born 21.3.36; Paris 1960; Rio de Janeiro 1963; Vientiane 1965; DSAO 1967; FCO 1968; Tokyo 1972; Athens 1975; FCO 1978; Valletta 1981; FCO 1983; Stockholm 1984; FCO 1985; Second Secretary (Cons) Baghdad 1987.

Way, Lawrence Sidney; Third later Second Secretary FCO since October 1984; born 1.12.49; FO (later FCO) 1967; Washington 1974; FCO 1977; Amman 1978; FCO 1981; Madrid 1982; m 1970 Patricia Margaret Allcock (1s 1975; 1d 1977).

Weale, William Anthony Peter; Second Secretary FCO since December 1985; born 26.1.45; HM Forces 1964-70; FCO 1970; Dacca 1971; Jedda 1973; Lagos 1974; FCO 1976; Moscow 1977; FCO 1979; Hanoi 1980; Beirut 1983; m 1977 Sheila Ellen Anderson (1d 1985).

Weaver, Roy Edward; First Secretary FCO since March 1990; born 28.11.38; First Secretary FCO 1972; BMG Berlin 1974; FCO 1977; Nairobi 1979; First Secretary FCO 1983; First Secretary Bonn 1987; m 1974 Joan Waud.

Webb, Andrea Lynne; FCO since January 1990; born 27.3.66; FCO 1985; The Hague 1987; Grade 9.

Webb, Elizabeth Jane; Washington since October 1988; born 4.8.61; FCO 1984; Moscow 1986; Grade 9.

Webb, Michael Ian Peter; on Secondment to EEC Brussels as Counsellor (National Expert) since March 1989; born 2.11.48; Third Secretary FCO 1970; Second Secretary Warsaw 1972; Second later First Secretary Santiago 1974; on loan to Cabinet Office 1978; First Secretary FCO 1980; First Secretary (Eernal Relations) UKREP Brussels 1982; FCO 1987; m 1978 Jennifer Ferguson Bastin (1s 1979).

Webb, Richard; Vice-Consul (Comm) Melbourne since June 1988; born 20.11.43; Inland Revenue 1962; FO 1965; Peking 1967; Rio de Janeiro 1968; Lagos 1972; FCO 1974; Far East Floater 1978; FCO 1980; Jedda 1981; Second Secretary FCO 1984; m (1) 1966 Hilary Anne John (diss 1977) (1d 1970; 1s 1971); (2) 1983 Sandra May Williams (1d 1985).

Webb, Robert; Second Secretary FCO since August 1989; born 6.6.50; DSAO (later FCO) 1966; Singapore 1971; Guatemala City 1974; FCO 1978; Floater duties 1982; Hanoi 1984; Second Secretary and Consul Mexico City 1985; m 1989 Maria Del Carmen Colín Irieta.

Webb, Sarah Jane; FCO since January 1992; born 2.12.66; FCO 1987; Budapest 1990; Grade S2.

Webb, Sophie Victoria; New Delhi since July 1991; born 14.4.69; FCO 1990; Grade S2.

Webb-Bowen, Martin Edward; First Secretary FCO since January 1992; born 14.6.58; HM Forces 1978-1985; Second Secretary FCO 1986; Second later First Secretary (Chancery) Nairobi 1989; m 1988 Susan Mary Hibbert (1s 1992).

Webber, Martin George; UKMIS Geneva since April 1990; born 19.10.60; HO 1979-81; FCO 1989; Grade 10.

Webster, John Auld; FCO since September 1992; born 6.9.68; FCO 1988; Nicosia 1990; Grade 9.

Webster, Vanessa Iris; FCO since September 1991; born 16.5.66; Grade 8.

Weekes, Victor Charles, BEM (1975); Floater Duties since April 1992; born 27.6.40; Belgrade 1983; Washington 1985; UKREP Brussels 1988; Karachi 1990; Grade SO; m 1961 Gwendolen Mabel Faulkner, (3s 1961, 1963, 1964).

Weeks, Alan Richard; First Secretary FCO since March 1991; born 29.7.48; FCO 1965; Tripoli 1970; Sofia 1972; Beirut 1974; Innsbruck 1976; FCO 1979; Second Secretary (Dev) New Delhi 1984; Second Secretary (Admin) and Consul East Berlin 1987; m 1971 Penelope Dibb (2s 1974, 1976).

Weeks, Sarah Marguerite; Abidjan since March 1990; born 15.10.68; FCO 1987; Grade 9.

Weild, Melanie Jane; FCO since March 1991; born 5.3.71; Grade S2.

Weinrabe, Stephen Michael; Second Secretary FCO since May 1991; born 13.6.50; FO (later FCO) 1967; Bucharest 1971; Paris 1972; Dublin 1973; Tehran 1975; FCO 1977; Nicosia 1981; Bangkok 1984; Second Secretary (Admin) Lagos 1988; m 1973 Eugenia Del Transito Poppescov Lazo.

Welborn, (Robert) Victor; First Secretary (Management) Ottawa since November 1989; born 14.7.38; HM Forces 1956-59; WO 1960; POSD 1961; FO 1962; Budapest 1962; Doha 1964; Sofia 1968; FCO 1969; Islamabad 1973; Second Secretary Kampala 1977; Bangkok 1977; FCO 1981; First Secretary (Admin) and Consul Tehran 1984; FCO 1988; Tehran 1988; Baghdad 1989; m 1962 Jean Newbould (2s 1964, 1966).

Weldin, Jonathan Michael; First Secretary (Chancery) Tunis since September 1990; born 23.2.59; FCO 1982; Second later First Secretary (Chancery) Sana'a 1986; First Secretary FCO 1988; m 1984 Fiona Jean Nesbitt (1s 1987, 1d 1989).

Weldon, Carole; Stockholm since April 1988; born 2.12.54; DOE 1973; FCO 1979; Jakarta 1980; Washington 1982; FCO 1985; Grade S1.

Weldon, Lawrence John, MVO (1980); Second Secretary (Comm) Caracas since March 1989; born 6.3.50; FCO 1972; Attaché (Dev) Bangkok 1975; Attaché (Comm) Tunis 1978; FCO 1981; Johannesburg 1983; Second Secretary FCO 1986; m (1) 1972 Pauline Whyatt (dec'd 1974); (2) 1984 Sarah Helen Burn (1d 1989).

Weldon, Paul; FCO since November 1989; born 3.4.59; FCO 1975; Pretoria 1987; Grade 8; m 1986 Karen Louise Ritchie (1s 1988).

Wellfare, Ian Bradshaw; Consul (Comm) Shanghai since June 1990; born 13.9.46; FO (later FCO) 1964; Kinshasa 1969; Guatemala City 1972; FCO 1975; Peking 1978; Hong Kong 1980; Second Secretary (Comm) Peking 1981; Vice-Consul (Comm) Cleveland 1983; Second Secretary FCO 1986 (First Secretary 1989); m 1968 Ann Palmer (1d 1972).

Wells, Andrew Justin; Floater Duties since July 1991; born 8.3.68; FCO 1988; Grade 10.

Wells, Daniel; FCO since April 1989; born 21.7.70; Grade 10.

Wells, David John; Bucharest since June 1992; born 29.6.63; FCO 1982; New Delhi 1988; FCO 1991; Grade 9.

Welsh, Jolyon Rimmer; Second Secretary (Chancery/Inf) Colombo since October 1992; born 22.12.67; FCO 1990; Grade 8.

Welsh, Margaret Mary; Dublin since March 1992; born 3.10.66; FCO 1988; Cairo 1990; FCO 1991; Grade S2.

Welsh, Paul Anthony; Floater Training since March 1992; born 12.10.67; FCO 1986; Harare 1988; Grade 10; m 1988 Anne McCoy.

Welsted, David Curtis; Washington since January 1992; born 17.10.52; FCO 1969; Attaché

Warsaw 1975; FCO 1976; Tehran 1978; FCO 1978; Nairobi 1980; FCO 1983; Attaché Amman 1984; Grade 7; FCO 1987; m 1974 Gillian Mary Harris (1s 1978; 1d 1982).

Wenban-Smith, (William) Nigel, CMG (1991), High Commissioner Lilongwe since November 1990; born 1.9.36; Royal Navy 1955-57; CRO 1961; Private Secretary to Parliamentary Under-Secretary 1963-64; Second Secretary Kinshasa 1965; First Secretary Kampala 1967 and Head of Chancery 1968; First Secretary FCO 1970; Dublin 1974; Brussels (Comm) 1976; Counsellor (Comm) Brussels 1978; on loan to Cabinet Office 1980; Head of EAD, FCO 1982; CDA Canadian National Defence College 1985; DHC Ottawa 1986; m (1) 1961 Charlotte Chapman-Andrews (diss 1975); (2s 1963, 1966; 2d 1967, 1969); (2) 1976 Charlotte Susanna Rycroft (dec'd 1990) (2s 1979, 1981).

West, Brian William; Second Secretary (Commercial) Paris since August 1991; born 4.1.48; FCO 1968; Moscow 1971; Kampala 1972; Strasbourg 1975; FCO 1977; Port Louis 1980; Second Secretary (Comm) Abidjan 1984; Second Secretary FCO 1988; m 1976 Marie-Odille Mariette Marthe Gilbert (2s 1977, 1980).

West, Peter Bernard; First Secretary (Pol/Inf) Copenhagen since September 1992; born 29.6.58; FCO 1977; Ankara 1978; Buenos Aires 1980; Auckland 1984; Second later First Secretary FCO 1986; m 1980 Julia Anne Chandler.

West, Veronica' Frances Bailey; Sofia since January 1991; born 16.6.46; FCO 1977; Amman 1978; FCO 1981; Colombo 1983; FCO 1986; Kuwait 1987; Grade S1.

Westbrook, Roger, CMG (1990); High Commissioner Dar-es-Salaam since September 1992; born 26.5.41; FO 1964; APS to the Chancellor of the Duchy of Lancaster and Minister of State, FO 1965; Yaoundé 1967; Second Secretary 1970; Second later First Secretary Rio de Janeiro 1971; Brasilia 1972; FCO 1974; Private Secretary to Minister of State, FCO 1975; Head of Chancery Lisbon 1977; FCO 1980; Counsellor and Deputy Head Falkland Islands Dept FCO 1982; Counsellor, Overseas Inspector FCO 1984; High Commissioner Bandar Seri Begawan 1986; HM Ambassador Kinshasa and concurrently HM Ambassador (non-resident) to Rwanda and to Burundi 1991.

Westcott, Nicholas James; First Secretary FCO since September 1989; born 20.7.56; Second Secretary FCO 1982; Seconded to European Commission, Brussels 1984; First Secretary (Agric/Finance) UKREP Brussels 1985; m 1989 Miriam Pearson.

Westgarth, Nicholas Philip; First Secretary (Chancery) Nicosia since April 1991; born

25.11.56; FCO 1980; Third Secretary (Econ) Athens 1981; Second Secretary FCO 1984; Language Training 1985; First Secretary Hong Kong 1986; First Secretary FCO 1989; m 1988 Kate Judith Sykes (1s 1992).

Westmacott, Peter John; Counsellor FCO on secondment to Buckingham Palace as Assistant Private Secretary to TRH The Prince and The Princess of Wales since February 1990; born 23.12.50; FCO 1972; Third later Second Secretary Tehran 1974; FCO 1978; Seconded to EC Commission Brussels 1978; First Secretary Paris 1980; FCO 1984; PS to Minister of State 1984; Head of Chancery Ankara 1987; m 1972 Angela Margaret Lugg (2s 1975, 1979; 1d 1977).

Weston, Sir Michael (Charles Swift) KCMG (1991), CVO (1979); Head of Delegation UKDIS Geneva since April 1992 (holds personal rank of Ambassador); born 4.8.37; MECAS 1961; Third Secretary Kuwait 1962; Second Secretary FO 1965; First Secretary Tehran 1968; UKMIS New York 1970; FCO 1974; Counsellor Jedda 1977; RCDS 1980; Counsellor (Inf) Paris 1981; Counsellor Cairo 1984; Counsellor FCO 1987; HM Ambassador Kuwait 1990m (1) 1959 Anne Tickner (2s 1963, 1965; 1d 1970); (diss 1990); (2) 1990 Christine Julia Ferguson.

Weston, Sir (Philip) John, KCMG (1992), CMG (1985); UK Permanent Representative on the North Atlantic Council Brussels (with personal rank of Ambassador) since October 1991; DUSS (Defence) FCO 1989; born 13.4.38; Royal Marines 1956-58; FO 1962; Hong Kong 1964; Second Secretary 1965; Peking 1967; First Secretary FCO 1969; UKREP Brussels 1971; APS to the Secretary of State 1974; Counsellor and Head of Presidency Secretariat 1976; Visiting Fellow at All Soul;s College Oxford 1977; Counsellor Washington 1978; Head of Defence Dept FCO 1981; AUSS (Defence) FCO 1984; Minister Paris 1985; on loan to Cabinet Office as Deputy Secretary 1988; Political Director and DUSS (Europe) FCO 1990; m 1967 Margaret Sally Ehlers (2s 1969, 1975; 1d 1970).

Westwood, Mary; FCO since November 1985; born 3.7.37; CA 1955; DTC (ODA) 1965; MEDD Beirut 1968; MEOD Amman 1975; ODA 1981; FCO 1982; Oslo 1983; Grade S2.

Wetherell, Gordon Geoffrey; Counsellor (Political/Military) Bonn since July 1992; born 11.11.48; FCO (concurrently Third Secretary Vice-Consul to British Embassy Chad) 1973; Third later Second Secretary East Berlin 1974; First Secretary FCO (concurrently First Secretary UKDEL CTB at Geneva) 1977; First Secretary UKDEL CTB Geneva 1979; New Delhi 1980; First Secretary FCO 1983; on loan to HM Treasury 1986; FCO 1987; Counsellor and Head of Chancery Warsaw 1988; m 1981 Rosemary Anne Myles (4d 1982, 1985, 1987, 1989).

Wetton, Philip Henry Davan; Director-General for British Trade Development in Italy and Consul-General Milan since May 1990; born 21.9.37; Second Secretary FO 1965; First Secretary Tokyo 1968; Consul (Comm) Osaka 1970; FCO 1973; Special leave to join EEC Brussels 1973; Counsellor (Comm) Seoul 1983; m (1) 1968 Prudence Mary Garwood; Counsellor FCO 1987; m (2) 1983 Roswitha Hilde Kortner.

Whale, Geoffrey; Peking since April 1988; born 3.7.52; FCO 1983; Grade 8; m 1985 Ingrid Moore (1s 1987).

Whalley, Marion; Paris since April 1990; born 4.3.69; FCO 1988; Grade 10.

Whatley, Malcolm George; Management Officer and Vice-Consul Rio de Janeiro since April 1992; born 5.9.52; FCO 1973; Washington 1975; Kuwait 1978; Budapest 1982; Dhaka 1984; FCO 1985; Muscat 1986; FCO 1989; Grade 9; m 1975 Mary Elizabeth Niven (1s 1979; 1d 1983).

Wheater, Emma Kate; Kampala since May 1992; born 12.5.69; FCO 1989; Grade 10.

Wheatley, Karen (née Wilkinson); Third later Second Secretary (Internal Affairs) Amman since June 1991; born 1.12.65; FCO 1988; language training Cairo 1990; m 1989 Giles Wheatley (1s 1992).

Wheeler, Bernadette; Lisbon since November 1989; born 13.2.68; MOD 1986; FCO 1988; Grade 10.

Wheeler, Brenda May; Canberra since July 1991; born 12.5.42; Vienna 1964; Lusaka 1968; Phnom Penh 1970; FCO 1972; Lima 1974; FCO 1977; Islamabad 1979; FCO 1985; Jakarta 1987; Grade S1.

Wheeler, Frank Basil, cmg, 1990; HM Ambassador Quito since August 1989; born 24.4.37; HM Forces 1956-58; FO 1958; Moscow 1961; APS to Minister of State FO 1963; Second Secretary (Comm) Berne 1965; First Secretary FO (later FCO) 1968; First Secretary and Head of Chancery Wellington 1972; FCO 1975; Counsellor and Head of Chancery Prague 1977; Home Inspector 1979; Head of Home Inspectorate 1980; Head of Personnel Policy Dept FCO 1982; Counsellor and Head of Chancery UKDEL NATO Brussels 1984; Counsellor FCO 1986; on loan to DTI 1986; m (1) 1959 Catherine Saunders Campbell (dec'd 1979) (1s 1962); (2) 1984 Alyson Ruth Lund (née Powell) (diss 1989); (3) Susana Plaza Larrea.

Wheeler, Fraser William; Second Secretary (Commercial) Moscow since October 1991; born 23.3.57; FCO 1980; Accra 1982; FCO 1984; UKMIS Geneva 1985; FCO 1988; Language Training 1990 (Second Secretary 1991); m 1988 Sarah Humphreys.

Whipp, Kathryn Sarah; Kiev since October 1992; born 1.3.67 FCO 1988; Grade 10.

Whitaker, Giles David Humphrey; Second Secretary (Chancery) UKDEL Brussels since October 1989; born 5.3.62; HM Forces 1980-88; Second Secretary FCO 1988; m 1990 Lucy Phyllida Whately Anderson (1s 1992).

Whitbread, David Harry, mbe (1977); First Secretary FCO since October 1989; born 18.4.38; Kuwait 1962; Baghdad 1964; FO 1968; Beirut 1970; FCO 1976; Second Secretary Jedda 1980; First Secretary FCO 1983; First Secretary (Inf) Amman 1986; m 1964 Caroline Elizabeth Aron (2d 1966, 1967; 1s 1971).

Whitby, John Benjamin; Language Training since September 1992; born 21.2.67; FCO 1990; Grade 8.

White, Alan; Deputy Consul-General Boston since September 1988; born 2.12.37; Official Receivers Service 1956; Royal Navy 1956-58; Board of Trade 1958; Madras 1961; Second Secretary (Comm) Nairobi 1964; Consul and Second Secretary (Admin) Prague 1969; First Secretary 1972; Consul (Comm) Sydney 1972; FCO 1977; Head of Chancery Quito 1979; FCO 1983; DHC Freetown 1985; m 1961 Jean Cook (1d 1965, 1s 1969).

White, Anthony William; FCO since November 1988; born 29.12.54; FCO 1973; Peking 1980; FCO 1982; Lilongwe 1985; Grade 8.

White, Bernard James; Lagos since April 1991; born 23.11.41; Army 1958-82; Peking 1983; Baghdad 1984; East Berlin 1986; Oslo 1988; Grade SO.

White, David James; First Secretary FCO since October 1988; born 29.7.37; FO 1964; Third later Second Secretary Kampala and Vice-Consul Rwanda 1969; Second Secretary (Chancery) Lusaka 1971; FCO 1972; Second Secretary Banjul 1974; FCO 1974; First Secretary Pretoria 1985; Principal Research Officer; Senior Principal Research Officer in 1990.

White, Derek Leslie; High Commissioner Tarawa since January 1990; additionally HM Ambassador (non-resident) to the Federated States of Micronesia and the Marshall Islands since July 1992; born 18.4.33; Royal Air Force 1950-63; FO 1963; Helsinki 1964; Sofia 1967; Algiers 1968; Tripoli 1970; FCO 1972; Baghdad 1975; Second Secretary 1977; Port Louis 1979; Antananarivo 1982; Second later First Secretary FCO 1984; Consul Marseilles and Monaco 1986; First Secretary FCO 1989; m 1989 Elizabeth Pilling (1d 1966 from previous m).

White, Jacqueline Denise (née Hill) Dar-es-

Salaam since May 1989; born 24.5.64; FCO 1987; Grade S2; m 1990 Jerry Lee White.

White, Penelope Jane; Kingston since October 1992; born 13.7.71; FCO 1989; Grade 10.

White, Richard Michael, MBE (1983); Deputy High Commissioner Valletta since October 1992; born 12.7.50; FCO 1969; UKDEL (later UKREP) EC Brussels 1971; Language Student 1974; Tehran 1975; Second Secretary 1978; APS to the Minister of State 1978; APS to the Lord Privy Seal 1979; FCO 1979; Second Secretary (Comm/Admin) and Consul Dakar 1980; First Secretary (Tech) Paris 1984; First Secretary FCO 1988; m 1979 Deborah Anne Lewis; (1s 1984; 1d 1986).

White, Susan Maia Grant; First Secretary (Cons) Nairobi since April 1990; born 24.5.33; FO 1952; Paris 1954; Athens 1957; FO 1958; Vienna 1961; Conakry 1964; Moscow 1965; FO 1966; DSAO (later FCO) 1967; Paris 1971; Algiers 1974; FCO 1976; Second Secretary 1977; Antananarivo 1979; Second Secretary Luxembourg 1983; First Secretary FCO 1987.

Whitecross, Andrew Ronald; Second Secretary FCO since January 1989; born 14.4.49; Army 1964-76; FCO 1976; Sana'a 1981; Baghdad 1985; m 1980 Nancy-Jane Evans.

Whitecross, Nancy-Jane (née Evans); FCO since January 1989; born 26.6.57; FCO 1977; Sana'a 1981; Baghdad 1985; Grade S2; m 1980 Andrew Ronald Whitecross.

Whitehead, Ian Richard; Deputy High Commissioner Dar es Salaam since January 1991; born 21.7.43; FO 1960; Addis Ababa 1965; Brussels (NATO) 1969; Dubai 1971; Casablanca 1972; FCO 1975; Second Secretary (Comm) Bridgetown 1978; First Secretary (COCOM) Paris 1983; First Secretary FCO 1988; m 1970 Linda Nunn (diss 1988) (1d 1975).

Whitehead, Laurence Jeremy; Second later First Secretary FCO since January 1990; born 17.4.61; FCO 1984; Second Secretary Jakarta 1987.

Whitehead, Peter John; Second Secretary (Chancery/Information) Abidjan since February 1992; born 1.4.52; FCO 1978; Rangoon 1980; Manila 1982; Montreal 1985; on loan to ODA 1988; Second Secretary FCO 1990; m 1984 Jesusa Valdez Bueno.

Whitehead, Roger; Third Secretary (Cons) Toronto since August 1991; born 22.5.54; FCO 1976; Lagos 1979; Kathmandu 1982; FCO 1984; Rangoon 1988; Grade 9; m 1979 Diane Mann (1d 1989).

Whitehorn, Caroline Mary; FCO since September 1990; born 4.10.67; Grade 9.

Whiten, Peter Frank, MBE (1991); Second

Secretary (Commercial) Madras since August 1991; born 5.12.51; FCO 1974; South East Asia Floater 1976; UKDEL NATO Brussels 1978; Port of Spain 1981; Second Secretary FCO 1986; m 1987 Antonia Ramsaroop (2s 1989, 1991).

Whiteside, Andrew John; FCO since September 1991; born 21.9.68; Grade 8.

Whiteside, Bernard Gerrard; Second Secretary (Chancery/Aid) Bogota since January 1992; born 3.10.54; FCO 1979; Moscow 1983; UKDIS Geneva 1986; (Second Secretary 1988); Second Secretary FCO 1989.

Whiteside, Derek Robert William; FCO since June 1992; born 24.11.38; RAF 1958-60; FO 1960; Darwin 1971; FCO 1973; Jedda 1975; FCO 1977; Addis Ababa 1979; FCO 1981; Attaché Peking 1982; FCO 1985; Ankara 1986; FCO 1990; Third Secretary Nairobi 1991; Grade 8; m (1) 1965 diss; (2) 1977 Clarice Howard (3d 1966, 1971, 1977).

Whiteway, Paul Robin; DHC Kampala since April 1990; born 1.12.54; FCO 1977; Third later Second Secretary (Dublin) 1980; First Secretary FCO 1984; First Secretary Port Stanley 1986; First Secretary FCO 1987; Seconded to MODUK (Navy) 1988.

Whitfield, Merle Olene; FCO since August 1992; born 6.8.41; FO 1967; Rawalpindi 1968; Lusaka 1969; Luanda 1971; Kuwait 1974; FCO 1976; Dar es Salaam 1978; Kuala Lumpur 1981; Jedda 1984; Riyadh 1985; FCO 1987; Colombo 1989; Grade S1.

Whitmore, Alan Shepherd; Second Secretary (Admin/Cons) Santiago since January 1989; born 3.8.39; RAF 1957-69; FCO 1969; Paris 1972; Lisbon 1974; Guatemala City 1977; Montevideo 1979; FCO 1982; Third later Second Secretary (Comm) Edmonton 1984; m (1) 1959 Joyce Mavis (2d 1960, 1961; 1s 1963); (2) 1982 Doreen Elena Rotherham.

Whitting, Ian Robert; First Secretary (Chancery) Dublin since November 1990; born 2.4.53; FCO 1972; Moscow 1975; Tunis 1976; Athens 1980 (Second Secretary 1981); FCO 1983; Second Secretary (Comm) Moscow 1985; Second Secretary FCO 1988; m 1986 Tracy Anne Gallagher (1d 1990).

Whittingham, Stephen Arthur; FCO since September 1990; born 29.1.56; FCO 1972; Brussels 1981; FCO 1983; Hong Kong 1988; Grade 7; m 1977 Christine Mary Ruth Hodgson (1d 1978).

Whittle, Lesley Elizabeth; Paris since November 1990; born 4.7.58; FCO 1980; Amman 1981; Cairo 1984; FCO 1987; Grade 9; m 1986 Simon F D Mallett.

Whitton, William; First Secretary (Political/EC) Copenhagen since March 1992; born 2.4.46; FO 1963; DSAO (later FCO) 1965; Jedda 1969; Vienna 1972; FCO 1975; (Second Secretary 1976); Second Secretary (Comm) Bonn 1977; Second Secretary and Consul Mexico City 1979; Second later First Secretary FCO 1984; Deputy High Commissioner Bandar Seri Begawan 1988; m 1969 Jane Cynthia Anderson (1d 1972; 1s 1974).

Whomersley, Christopher Adrian; FCO since September 1977; born 18.4.53; Legal Counsellor; m 1977 Jeanette Diana Szostak.

Whomsley, Deborah Jane; FCO since March 1991; born 25.4.67; Grade S2.

Whyte, Evelyn Russell; FCO since February 1992; born 13.7.54; FCO 1985; Reykjavik 1986; The Hague 1989; FCO 1991; Grade S2A.

Whyte, Michael James; Bucharest since January 1992; born 24.3.42; Royal Havy 1958-89; Grade SO; m 1979 Karen Nina Renée Walters.

Wickens, Rachel Christine; UKMIS New York since March 1991; born 5.11.68; FCO 1988; Grade S2.

Wicks, Graham; FCO since February 1992; born 2.7.55; FCO 1974; Luxembourg 1976; Islamabad 1976; Peking 1979; Karachi 1981; FCO 1983; Victoria 1986; Vice-Consul Sofia 1990; Grade 9; m 1978 Genevieve Harriot-Jane McCrossan (2s 1988, 1989).

Wicks, Joanna Ruth (née Collett); SUPL since October 1989; born 9.5.56; FCO 1978; Warsaw 1981; FCO 1982; SUPL 1984; Second Secretary FCO 1986; m 1984 Nigel Earl Wicks (1d 1989).

Wicks, Nigel Earl; FCO since June 1992; born 21.3.56; HM Forces 1973-76; FCO 1980; Attaché Damascus 1984; FCO 1986; Lisbon 1989; Grade 9; m 1984 Joanna Ruth Collett (1d 1989).

Wigginton, Christopher James; FCO since March 1991; (Second Secretary 1992); born 23.5.60; FCO 1982; Language Training 1984; Tehran 1984; Stockholm 1988.

Wightman, Andrew Norman Scott; First Secretary (FCO) since December 1991; born 17.7.61; FCO 1983; Second Secretary Peking 1986; First Secretary FCO 1989; On loan to the Cabinet Office 1989; m 1988 Anne Margaret Roberts.

Wigzell, Jacqueline Margaret; Third Secretary (Comm) East Berlin since January 1990; born 12.5.65; FCO 1987; Grade 9.

Wilbourn, Lillian; Brasilia since September 1990; born 27.7.47; FCO 1985; Madrid 1987; Grade S2.

Wildash, Elizabeth Jane (née Walmsley); FCO since September 1992; born 17.10.58; FCO 1978; E Berlin 1980; FCO 1981; Abidjan 1983; FCO 1984; SUPL 1987; FCO 1988; Harare 1989; Grade 9; m 1981 Richard James Wildash (1d 1987).

Wildash, Richard James; First Secretary FCO since September 1992; born 24.12.55; FCO 1977; E Berlin 1979; Abidjan 1981; Second Secretary FCO 1984; Language Training 1986; FCO 1986; First Secretary (Chancery/Inf) Harare 1984; m 1981 Elizabeth Jane Walmsley (1d 1987).

Wilde, John; First Secretary FCO since July 1991; born 6.10.41; FO 1959; Conakry 1962; Pretoria 1964; Kuwait 1965; Tripoli 1968; FCO 1969; Consul Zagreb 1972; Second Secretary (Comm) Singapore 1976; FCO 1979; Assistant to Deputy Governor Gibraltar 1982; Joint Service Defence College 1985; First Secretary FCO 1985; DHC/Head of Chancery Lilongwe 1987; m 1965 Jeanette Grace Reed (1s 1969; 1d 1974).

Wildman, Richard Hugh; Bridgetown since July 1989; born 18.8.54; FCO 1983; Grade 8; m 1989 Fay Dawn Reid (1d 1983).

Wiles, Ann; Warsaw since December 1991; born 12.3.41; Melbourne 1972; The Hague 1974; UKREP Brussels 1977; FCO 1980; UKDEL MBFR Vienna 1981; Tokyo 1982; FCO 1984; Sofia 1986; Brasilia 1987; FCO 1990; Grade S1.

Wiles, Celia Imogen; Language Training Kamakura since September 1988; born 23.4.63; FCO 1986; Grade 9.

Wiles, Harry; Consul (Comm) Barcelona since March 1990; born 17.6.44; FO 1964; Ankara 1966; Paris 1969; Algiers 1972; FCO 1975; Bilbao 1978; Jedda 1981; Second Secretary (Admin) Riyadh 1983; Second Secretary (Comm) Abu Dhabi 1984; Second later First Secretary on loan to ECGD 1988; m 1966 Margaret Bloom (2d 1967, 1970).

Wilkie, Paula Jane; FCO since June 1991; born 14.8.72; Grade 10.

Wilkie, Peter Finlayson; Second Secretary FCO since December 1991; born 30.10.42; FO 1960; Bahrain 1964; Moscow 1966; Athens 1967; FCO 1970; India Floater (Cons1/Imm) 1973; Düsseldorf 1975; Second Secretary (Chancery) Addis Ababa 1978; FCO 1980; Second Secretary The Hague 1984; Second Secretary (Management) Paris 1986.

Wilkie, Robert Andrew; FCO since January 1989; born 9.12.59; FCO 1979; Nairobi 1980; FCO 1983; Darwin 1987; Grade 9; m 1986 Sarah Jane Abraham (1d 1987).

Wilkin, Richard Cecil, MBE (Mil) (1976), LVO (1979); First Secretary FCO since January 1992;

born 17.9.44; Army 1962-75; First Secretary
FCO 1975; First Secretary (Inf) Lusaka 1978;
FCO 1980; First Secretary (Chancery)
Bridgetown 1988; m Jane Susan Elliot (diss
1989).

Wilkins, John Leslie; Second Secretary FCO
since October 1990; born 14.5.45; MPBW 1962;
CO 1964; Maseru 1966; FCO 1969; Düsseldorf
1972; New Delhi 1975; FCO 1978; Jakarta 1982;
Second Secretary Islamabad 1985; m 1967
Margaret Stuchbury (1d 1973).

Wilkins, Robert Smith; BEM (1980); Sofia since
August 1992; born 8.7.36; Royal Navy 1951-79;
Nairobi 1980; Moscow 1981; Paris 1983;
Bangkok 1985; The Hague 1988; Havana 1991;
Grade CSO; m 1958 Jean Elizabeth Grist (2d
1959, 1963).

Wilkinson, Arnold Graham; Counsellor FCO
since November 1984; born 9.6.44; Third
Secretary FO 1966; Kampala 1968; Second
Secretary FCO 1970; Language Student SOAS
1973 and Isfahan 1974; First Secretary Tehran
1974; FCO 1978; First Secretary (Chancery)
Madrid 1981; m 1966 Wendy Christine
Humphreys (2d 1967, 1970).

Wilkinson, Richard Denys, LVO (1992);
Counsellor (Info) Paris since December 1988;
born 11.5.46; FCO 1972; Second later First
Secretary Madrid 1973; FCO 1977; First
Secretary (Econ/Comm) Ankara 1983; Counsellor
and Head of Chancery Mexico City 1985; m
1982 Maria Angela Morris (2s 1983, 1986, 1d
1991).

Wilks, Jonathan Paul; Full-Time Language
Training Cairo since May 1992; born 30.9.67;
FCO 1989; Grade 8.

Willan, Lucina Jane; Second Secretary FCO
since July 1978; born 15.11.43; FCO 1968-71;
FCO 1973; Second Secretary 1976; Second
Secretary (Inf1/Tech Asst) Yaoundé 1976.

Willasey-Wilsey, Timothy Andrew; First
Secretary FCO since October 1989; born 12.9.53;
Second Secretary FCO 1981; First Secretary
(Chancery) Luanda 1983; First Secretary Head of
Chancery (later DHM) and Consul San José
1986; m 1983 Alison Middleton Mackie (3s
1986, 1988, 1989).

Willcocks, Alison Jane (née Westlake); SUPL
since August 1990; born 30.9.52; FCO 1971;
Moscow 1976; FCO 1977; Pretoria 1978;
UKMIS New York 1981; FCO 1984; Singapore
1986; FCO 1986; Grade S2; m 1989 David Peter
Tooley Willcocks.

Willcocks, Richard; First Secretary FCO since
February 1976; born 4.12.38; MECAS 1960;
Bahrain 1962; Deputy Director (Admin) MECAS
1964; FCO 1968; Second Secretary 1969; Vice-

Consul Jerusalem 1971; m 1961 Janet Elizabeth
Round (2s 1966, 1968).

Willey, Clive, MBE (1988); Second Secretary FCO
since November 1988; born 7.3.49; FCO 1972;
Hong Kong 1977; FCO 1981; Second Secretary
Nairobi 1984; m 1975 Heather Joyce Bird (2s
1976, 1977).

Williams, Catrin Ceiros; FCO since January
1976; born 22.11.51; FCO 1972; Valletta 1974;
Grade 10.

Williams, David; Madrid since October 1978;
born 23.4.47; FO (later FCO) 1964; New Delhi
1969; Wellington 1973; FCO 1975; Grade 9; m
1970 Mavourneen Faye Joan Beaumont (1s
1974).

Williams, David John; Bombay since November
1990; born 6.6.67; FCO 1986; UKMIS Geneva
1988; Grade 9; m 1989 Denise Nowak (1d
1991).

Williams, David Llewellyn; Kampala since
August 1991; born 13.12.42; Royal Marines
1961-83; Baghdad 1984; Islamabad 1986; Paris
1987; Peking 1990; Grade SO; m 1969 Gillian
Myra (3d 1961, 1963, 1971; 1s 1966).

Williams, Deborah Mary; Buenos Aires since
April 1990; born 30.10.64; FCO 1985; Tokyo
1987; Grade 10.

Williams, Derek; BMG Berlin since January
1990; born 13.1.33; Prison Dept 1959-81;
Moscow 1981; Pretoria 1983; New Delhi 1984;
Havana 1986; Kampala 1987; Grade SO; m 1955
Gladys Florence Hunt (1s 1960).

Williams, Douglas James; FCO since January
1991; born 9.2.55; FCO 1978; Suva 1981;
UKREP Brussels 1984; New Delhi 1987; Grade
9; m 1981 Susan Anwen Jones (1s 1984; 1d
1986).

Williams, George, BEM (1975); Dhaka since
February 1991; born 6.2.43; HM Forces 1962-84;
Prague 1984; Singapore 1985; Moscow 1987,
Washington 1988; Grade SO; m 1965 Eileen (2s
1965, 1968).

Williams, Gordon John Brereton; HM Consul-
General Osaka since February 1990; born
15.9.38; HM Forces 1957-59; Board of Trade
1959-60; FO 1963; Helsinki 1964; Tokyo 1965;
(Second Secretary 1969); Warsaw 1971; FCO
1974; First Secretary Oslo 1977; First Secretary
(Comm) Tokyo 1979; First Secretary FCO 1984;
On loan to DTI 1985; First Secretary (Comm)
Tokyo 1988; Counsellor 1990; m 1965 Elizabeth
Lee (1s 1976).

Williams, John; Vice-Consul Johannesburg since
January 1992; born 17.6.59; FCO 1978; Moscow
1981; Rabat 1982; FCO 1985; Masirah 1985; LA

Floater 1986; FCO 1988; Grade 9; m 1981 Jacqueline Peplow (diss 1987).

Williams, Judith Frances; Rome since March 1990; born 9.12.68; FCO 1987; Grade S2.

Williams, Karen Jane; FCO since May 1991; born 28.4.70; Grade 10.

Williams, Karen-Lane; Second Secretary (Chancery) The Hague since July 1992; born 9.4.63; FCO 1989.

Williams, Karen Lesley; UKMIS New York since January 1991; born 28.6.63; FCO 1987; Riyadh 1988; Grade S2.

Williams, Kenneth Mark; Counsellor FCO since March 1992; born 31.12.44; Royal Navy 1963-74; Second later First Secretary FCO 1974; First Secretary (Inf) later (Econ) Kuala Lumpur 1976; FCO 1979; First Secretary Bridgetown 1981; First Secretary FCO 1985; Counsellor Harare 1988; m 1969 Josephine Mary Lang (1d 1972; 1s 1975).

Williams, Martin John; cvo (1983)1, obe (1979); Counsellor FCO since April 1990; born 3.11.41; CRO 1963; Private Secretary to Permanent Under-Secretary of State CRO 1964; Third later Second Secretary Manila 1966; Vice-Consul (Comm) Milan 1970; On loan to CSD, 1972; FCO 1973; First Secretary (Comm) Tehran 1977; First Secretary FCO 1980; Counsellor and Head of Chancery New Delhi 1982; Head of Chancery Rome 1986; m 1964 Susan Dent (2s 1966, 1967).

Williams, Nigel Christopher Ransome, CMG (1985); HM Ambassador Copenhagen since January 1989; born 29.4.37; Third later Second Secretary Tokyo 1961; FO 1966; First Secretary 1968; Private Secretary to the Minister of State 1968; PS to the Chancellor of the Duchy of Lancaster 1969; UKMIS New York 1970; FCO 1973; Counsellor (Econ) Tokyo 1976; on loan to Cabinet Office 1980; Head of United Nations Department FCO 1980; Minister Bonn 1985.

Williams, Paul; Second Secretary FCO since December 1990; born 25.11.48; Immigration Service 1969; m 1969 Barbara Jane Briggs; (2s 1975, 1979).

Williams, Paul Henry; First Secretary (Economic) Athens since April 1991; born 28.10.43; DSAO 1967; FCO 1967; Kinshasa 1968; Belgrade 1972; FCO 1975; Second Secretary (Comm) Brussels 1979; Second later First Secretary (EC/Econ) Madrid 1983; First Secretary FCO 1988; Full-time Language Training 1990; m 1970 Andrée Eileen Anna Goossens.

Williams, Paula Jean; Algiers since March 1990; born 22.10.54; Islamabad 1976; UKDEL NATO

Brussels 1976; BMG Berlin 1979; Dakar 1980; Pretoria/Cape Town 1981; FCO 1984; Grade 9.

Williams, Peter Keegan, CMG (1992); HM Ambassador Hanoi since October 1990; born 3.4.38; MECAS 1962; Second Secretary Beirut 1963-67 (Jedda 1964); Commonwealth Office 1967; First Secretary FCO 1969; BIS New York 1970; First Secretary FCO 1973; First Secretary, Head of Chancery and Consul Rabat 1976; Counsellor UKMIS Geneva 1979; HM Ambassador Aden 1983; Counsellor FCO 1986; CDA at the RCDS 1989; m 1969 Rosamund Mary de Worms (2d 1970, 1971).

Williams, Philip George; FCO since July 1988; born 26.7.54; FCO 1972; Nairobi 1985; Grade 7; m 1987 Susann Traise McAlden.

Williams, Rebecca Louise; UKMIS Geneva since October 1991; born 17.8.71; FCO 1989; Grade S2.

Williams, Dr Rhodri Huw; First Secretary (Econ) Vienna since July 1992; born 14.5.59; FCO 1990; m 1986 Hilary Clair Wakeham (1s, 1d twins 1991).

Williams, Roger Gordon; Washington since January 1991; born 28.7.48; Army 1963-89; Prague 1989; Grade SO; m 1974 Anne Elizabeth (1d 1974; 2s 1978, 1980).

Williams, Simon John; FCO since February 1992; born 22.8.60; FCO 1979; Manila 1981; Mbabane 1984; Kaduna 1986; Grade 9; m 1987 Rosemarie Coguntas Diaz.

Williams, Stephen Michael;First Secretary (Commercial/Economic) Oslo since October 1991; born 20.7.59; FCO 1981; Third later Second Secretary Sofia 1984; Second later First Secretary FCO 1987; m 1983 Fiona Michèle Hume (2d 1986; 1989; 1s 1991).

Williams, Tony Scott; FCO since July 1989; born 12.9.62; FCO 1981; UKDEL NATO Brussels 1984; Prague 1986; Dhaka 1988; Grade 9; m 1985 Denise Tilbrook (1s 1992).

Williamson, Morven Jane; FCO since July 1991; born 16.4.71; Grade 10.

Williamson, Peter Roger; Counsellor on loan to the Cabinet Office since February 1992; born 20.4.42; Third later Second Secretary FO (later FCO) 1966; Kuala Lumpur 1970; Second later First Secretary FCO 1973; First Secretary Hong Kong 1975; First Secretary FCO 1979; Counsellor Kuala Lumpur 1985; Counsellor FCO 1989; m 1977 Greta Helen Clare Richards (1s 1980; 1d 1983).

Willis, Iain Edward; FCO since October 1991; born 25.5.71; Grade 10.

Willis, Peter; First Secretary FCO since September 1989; born 27.2.44; FO 1963; Amman 1965; Benghazi 1969; MECAS 1972; Third Secretary (Aid) Amman 1974; FCO 1977; Consul (Comm) Casablanca 1980; First Secretary (ECOSOC) UKMIS New York 1985; m 1965 Margaret Simpson Allan (2d 1967, 1968; twin d 1971).

Willis, Stephen David; FCO since September 1991; born 29.8.67; FCO 1986; Brussels 1989; Grade 10.

Willmer, Nigel Stuart; Madrid since July 1990; born 3.7.65; FCO 1983; Grade 9; m 1985 Jackie Mann (1d 1986).

Willock, Oriel; Amman since June 1990; born 23.4.68; FCO 1988; Grade 10.

Wills, Jane Stirling; Second Secretary FCO since December 1989; born 12.12.46; Commonwealth Office (later FCO) 1964; Prague; 1969; Copenhagen 1971; UKDEL MBFR Vienna 1973; Bombay 1976; FCO 1980; Prague 1983; Ankara 1986.

Wills, Ruth Margaret; Second Secretary FCO since December 1991; born 7.11.54; FCO 1977; Rio de Janeiro 1980; Paris 1984; Second Secretary (Press/Info) Bonn 1989.

Willsher, Ian Robert; Second Secretary Nairobi since September 1990; born 14.4.47; FCO 1970 Washington 1974; Vienna 1977; FCO 1979; Accra 1982; Geneva 1985; FCO 1988; Grade 8; m 1976 Amanda Jane Labram (2s 1978, 1979; 1d 1985).

Wilmshurst, Elizabeth Susan; FCO since April 1991; born 28.8.48; Solicitor 1972; FCO 1974; First Secretary later Counsellor on loan to Law Officers Department 1986; Legal Counsellor.

Wilson, Anthony James Denis Alexander; Language Training Bangkok since May 1992; born 26.6.66; FCO 1989; Language Training FCO 1991, Grade 8.

Wilson, Christine Anne, MVO; Washington since July 1990; born 5.1.66; FCO 1988; Grade 9.

Wilson, Fiona-Margaret Sievewright (née Riddoch); Istanbul since August 1989; born 23.3.68; FCO 1986; Grade 10; m 1988 Robert Lennox Wilson.

Wilson, Fraser Andrew; MBE (1980); First Secretary FCO since May 1990; born 6.5.49; Commonwealth Office (later FCO) 1967; Havana 1970; South-East Asia Floater 1971; Seoul 1973; Salisbury 1977; Second Secretary FCO 1980; Language Training 1983; Second Secretary (Comm) Moscow 1984; Second Secretary (Comm) and Vice-Consul (later First Secretary (Comm) Rangoon 1986; m 1981 Janet Phillips (2s 1982, 1985).

Wilson, Gillian Grace; Accra since November 1991; born 19.4.65; ODA 1981; FCO 1989; Temporary Duty Dhaka 1991; Grade 9.

Wilson, Gillian Maeve; FCO since February 1988; born 1.1.28; Delhi 1967; Prague 1969; Anguilla 1970; Bridgetown 1971; FCO 1972; Nairobi 1974; FCO 1976; Istanbul 1977; Washington 1980; Freetown 1983; Tokyo 1986; Grade S2.

Wilson, Ian Laurence; Second Secretary (Management) Bucharest since March 1992; born 19.6.44; FO 1962; Moscow 1966; Colombo 1967; FCO 1971; UKDEL NATO Brussels 1974; Banjul 1977; FCO 1981; Canberra 1983; FCO 1987; Second Secretary (Cons/Admin) Calcutta 1987; m 1970 Deirdre L. de Krester (1d 1974; 1s 1976).

Wilson, Ian Stewart; Warsaw since August 1988; born 16.4.34; RAF 1953-81; Peking 1982; Madrid 1983; Baghdad 1986; Grade SO; m 1964 Barbara Davies Rae (1d 1965; 1s 1968).

Wilson, James Jeffrey; Canberra since January 1992; born 7.8.67; FCO 1988; Grade 10.

Wilson, Keith Edward; FCO since April 1990; born 18.6.46; CRO (later FCO) 1963; Islamabad 1970; Lagos 1974; Dacca 1977; FCO 1980; Tehran 1983; Johannesburg 1988; Grade 9; m 1984 Christine Maria Theresia del Negro (1d 1985; 1s 1988).

Wilson, Michael George; Dakar since November 1991; born 10.12.70; FCO 1989; Grade 10.

Wilson, Patrick John; First Secretary FCO since September 1989; First Secretary (IAEA) UKMIS Vienna since January 1985; born 16.3.44; FCO 1967; Turin 1968; FCO 1970; MECAS 1971; Jedda 1972; Abidjan 1975; FCO 1982; First Secretary (IAEA) UKMIS Vienna 1985; m 1969 Liliana Rossi (2s 1972, 1974).

Wilson, Paul; First Secretary (Chancery) Islamabad since May 1991; born 9.12.54; FCO 1986; m 1985 Elizabeth Linne

Wilson, Peter Russell; Second Secretary (Economic) Jakarta since May 1992; born 27.5.67; FCO 1988.

Wilson, Philip John; Sofia since January 1992; born 9.1.66; FCO 1985; The Hague 1988; FCO 1989; Grade 10.

Wilson, Robert Thomas Osborne; First Secretary and Head of Chancery Abu Dhabi since May 1989; born 28.1.52; FCO 1982; Senior Research Officer; m 1979 Susan Ann Watson (2d 1985, 1988).

Wilson, Roy Andrew; Bombay since September 1990; born 3.12.59; HCS 1978; FCO 1979; Karachi 1982; Seoul 1985; FCO 1987; Grade 9.

Wilson, Simon Charles Hartley; Second
Secretary (Chancery/Info) Lisbon since December
1992; born 9.8.57; FCO 1975; Johannesburg
1978; Helsinki 1981; FCO 1984; Tehran 1987;
Riyadh 1987; m 1984 Heather Graine Richardson
(1s 1990).

Wilson, Simon Jules; Third later Second
Secretary (Economic) Athens since January 1991;
born 13.3.66; FCO 1988.

Wilson, Susan Jean; FCO since July 1989; born
1.2.70; Grade 10.

Wilson, Susan Mary (née Slade); SUPL since 1987;
born 21.1.48; FCO 1973; Canberra 1973; Bucharest
1976; Damascus 1978; FCO 1981; Latin America
Floater 1982; FCO 1984; Grade S1; m 1984 John
Henry Bainbridge Wilson (1s 1987).

Wilson, Suzanne; FCO since July 1985; born
3.7.67; Grade 10.

Wilson, Vikki Ann; FCO since February 1992;
born 9.6.66; FCO 1988; Berne 1989; Grade S2.

Wilson, William Watson; Second Secretary
(Management) Riyadh since August 1991; born
30.5.39; FO 1957; HM Forces 1959-61;
Khartoum 1962; Baghdad 1963; Düsseldorf 1965;
Kuala Lumpur 1967; Lahore 1969; FCO 1971;
Mbabane 1975; Paris 1979; Second Secretary
FCO 1983; Second Secretary (Accounts)
Washington 1986; m 1960 Patricia Evelyn Daniel
(1s 1963; 1d 1966).

Wilson Webb, Louise Patricia; Rome since
December 1991; born 13.5.37; FCO 1987;
Ottawa 1989; Grade S2.

Wilton, Christopher Edward John; Counsellor
(Commercial) Riyadh since September 1990;
born 16.12.51; FCO 1977; MECAS 1978;
Second later First Secretary Bahrain 1979; FCO
1981; First Secretary (Chancery) Tokyo 1984; on
loan to Cabinet Office 1988; m 1975 Dianne
Hodgkinson (1d 1981; 1s 1984).

Wiltshire, Terence Keith; FCO since January
1987; born 24.12.57; FCO 1981; New Delhi
1983; Grade 9.

Wincott, Ian Albert; Amman since August 1991;
born 12.11.40; Royal Marines 1958-80; UKDEL
New York 1982; Havana 1984; Helsinki 1985;
Bonn 1988; Grade SO; m 1978 Maxine Elizabeth
Pearson (1d 1980; 1s 1982).

Windham, Ashe Adrian; Consul (Man/Con)
Düsseldorf since April 1991; born 28.11.41; HM
Forces 1960-70; FCO 1970; UKDEL NATO
Brussels 1973; FCO 1975; Hamburg 1976; Vice-
Consul (Inf) Johannesburg 1979; Second
Secretary FCO 1983; First Secretary (Cons)
Kuala Lumpur 1987; m 1969 Daphne Anne
Thomas (1d 1977).

Windle, Ian Peter; FCO since April 1986; born
29.11.58; FCO 1978; Hong Kong 1980; FCO
1983; European Floater 1984; Grade 9; m 1988
Jacqueline Ann Finch.

Windle, William James; First Secretary FCO
since September 1992; born 3.7.52; FCO 1972;
on loan to MOD 1975; FCO 1977; Second
Secretary (Comm) Muscat 1980; Second later
First Secretary FCO 1984; First Secretary
(Chancery) Washington 1989; m 1974 June
Constance Grimmond (3s 1980, 1982, 1985).

Wing, Owen Simon; FCO since May 1984; born
18.8.60; FCO 1980; Darwin 1982; Grade 9; m
1986 Susan Jane Marum (1d 1986).

Winnington-Ingram, Charles Pepys; Second
Secretary (Chancery/Inf) Oslo since March 1989;
born 6.10.55; Barrister 1977; Export Credits
Guarantees Department 1979; FCO 1980; Tokyo
1981; Second Secretary FCO 1985.

Winter, Colin Richard, MBE (1991); First
Secretary (Commercial) Kuwait since October
1991; born 3.3.41; Royal Navy 1957-68; FCO
1968; Singapore 1969; FCO 1971; Islamabad
1973; FCO 1975; San Francisco 1978; Abu
Dhabi 1981; Second Secretary (Cons) Dar es
Salaam 1984; Second later First Secretary FCO
1988; m 1961 Vivienne Cecilia Brighton (2d
1962; 1963; 2s 1964, 1971).

Winter, Douglas; Second Secretary
(Commercial) Abu Dhabi since September 1990;
born 21.1.51; FCO 1969; Mogadishu 1972;
Antigua 1974; FCO 1978; Bangkok 1981; Zagreb
1984; Warsaw 1985; Second Secretary FCO
1987; m 1972 Linda Margaret Harmer (1s 1975;
1d 1978).

Winterburn, Christine Catherine (née Lowrie);
Management Officer/Consular Kaduna/Abuja
since June 1992; born 20.4.67; FCO 1986;
Copenhagen 1987; FCO 1989; Grade 9; m 1989
John Paul Winterburn.

Wintour, Alexandra Mary; Vienna since March
1991; born 25.3.66; Office of Fair Trading 1985;
FCO 1987; UKMIS New York 1988; Grade S2.

Wise, Graeme Michael; Lagos since August
1988; born 17.6.64; FCO 1984; Addis Ababa
1985; Grade 10.

Wise, Patricia (née Donnelly); Cape Town/
Pretoria since August 1990; born 24.2.58; FCO
1982; Port Stanley 1983; Lusaka 1983; Rome
1987; Grade S1; m 1985 Edward Meredith
Leighton (diss 1991); m 1992 David Wise.

Wiseman, Julian Paul Geoffrey; Counsellor
Islamabad since October 1990; born 3.10.44; HM
Forces 1963-76; First Secretary FCO 1976; UKMIS
Geneva 1978; FCO 1982; First Secretary (Chancery)
Dhaka 1984; First Secretary FCO 1987; m 1973

Diana Christine Spooner (2d 1977, 1980).

Wisker, Rita; UKDEL Brussels since January 1992; born 15.9.51; FCO 1972; Tokyo 1973; FCO 1975; Washington 1977; UKREP Brussels 1980; BMG Berlin 1983; UKMIS New York 1984; FCO 1985; Grade S1.

Witchell, Emma Jane (née Tuxill); FCO since September 1990; born 6.5.66; FCO 1984; Canberra 1987; East Berlin 1989; Grade 10; m 1991 Stuart Witchell.

Witchell, Stuart; FCO since September 1990; born 23.11.64; FCO 1985; East Berlin 1989; Grade 10; m 1991 Emma Jane Tuxill.

Withers, John Walter Charles; Third Secretary Bucharest since July 1991; born 24.11.47; FCO 1975; Moscow 1979; FCO 1982; Lagos 1982; FCO 1985; Ottawa 1986; New York 1987; FCO 1989; Grade 8; m 1970 Vivienne Chater (1d 1976; 1s 1986).

Withers, Matthew Robert; Kathmandu since June 1992; born 14.10.67; FCO 1987; Kuala Lumpur 1988; Grade 10.

Witting, Lisa Marie; Dublin since December 1989; born 22.2.69; FCO 1988; Grade S2A.

Wogan, Patrick Francis Michael, cmg (1991); HM Ambassador and Consul-General Reykjavik since September 1991; born 26.4.37; FO and Khartoum 1959; FO 1961; Tehran 1965; Vice-Consul 1966; Vice-Consul Khorramshahr 1968; Second Secretary (Inf) Political Agency Bahrain 1970; Second later First Secretary FCO 1972; Brussels 1976; FCO 1981; Counsellor Home Inspectorate FCO 1983; Counsellor Tehran 1984; RCDS 1987; Consul-General Karachi 1988; m (1) 1960 Rosmarie Diederich (2s 1961, 1967; 1d 1963). (2) 1988 Afsaneh Khalatbari.

Wolstenholme, Jonathan David; FCO since August 1990; born 15.1.60; FCO 1980; Baghdad 1982; Moscow 1984; Harare 1986; Grade 9; m 1986 Karen Suzanne Vivian (1d 1989).

Wolstenholme, Karen Suzanne (née Vivian); Second Secretary FCO since October 1990; born 16.10.62; FCO 1980; Language Training 1983; FCO 1984; Moscoow 1984; Harare 1986; m 1986 Jonathan David Wolstenholme (1d 1989; 1s 1992).

Wong, Lillian Paterson (née Walker); FCO since February 1976; born 16.2.44; FCO 1970; Second Secretary (Inf/Aid) Yaoundé 1973; Principal Research Officer; (DS Grade 5); m 1979 Robert Puck Keong Wong.

Wood, Andrew Marley, cmg (1986);DUSS (Chief Clerk) since April 1992; born 2.1.40; FO 1961; Third Secretary Moscow 1964; Second later First Secretary Washington 1967; FCO 1970; Seconded to Cabinet Office 1971; First Secretary

FCO 1973; First Secretary and Head of Chancery, later Counsellor Belgrade 1976; Head of Chancery Moscow 1979; Head of West European Department FCO 1982; Counsellor, Head of Personnel Operations Department FCO 1983; HM Ambassador Belgrade 1985; Minister Washington 1989; m (1) 1972 Melanie LeRoy Masset (dec'd 1977) (1s 1975); (2) 1978 Stephanie Lee Masset (1d 1981; 1s 1985).

Wood, Christopher Terence; On loan to the Department of Environment since January 1992; born 19.1.59; FCO 1981; SOAS 1982; Language Student Hong Kong 1983; On secondment to Hong Kong Government as Assistant Political Adviser 1984; First Secretary FCO 1987.

Wood, Colin Oliver; FCO since March 1990; born 12.5.38; FO 1955; HM Forces 1957-59; Khartoum 1959; Vientiane 1963; Vice-Consul Tokyo 1965; FO (later FCO) 1967; Vice-Consul later Second Secretary and Consul Jedda 1970; Second Secretary and Consul Tripoli 1973; Second later First Secretary FCO 1977; First Secretary Head of Chancery and Consul Mogadishu 1981; First Secretary FCO 1983; First Secretary (Admin) Dacca 1986; m (1) 1960 Odette Lucie George (diss) (1d 1962; 1s 1966); (2) 1985 Siham Ahmed (1 step s 1977; 1s 1986).

Wood, David Edward; FCO since July 1992; born 2.1.70; FCO 1989; Pretoria 1991; Grade 10.

Wood, James Sebastian Lamin; Full-Time Language Training Taiwan since July 1991; born 6.4.61; FCO 1982; Language Student 1984; Second Secretary Bangkok 1986; Second later First Secretary FCO 1989; m 1990 Sirihat Pengnuam (1d 1992).

Wood, Michael Charles; Counsellor (Legal Adviser) UKMIS New York since July 1991; born 5.2.47; called to the Bar, Gray;s Inn 1968; Assistant Legal Adviser FCO 1970; Legal Adviser Bonn 1981; Legal Adviser later Legal Counsellor FCO 1984.

Wood, Michael John Hemsley; First Secretary FCO since July 1987; born 16.9.48; FCO 1972; Third later Second Secretary Athens 1974; FCO 1976; First Secretary Harare 1980; Language Training 1983; First Secretary Head of Chancery and Consul Hanoi 1984; m (1) 1975 Susan Christine Langford; (2) 1983 Wendy Mary Smith.

Wood, Peter Gilruth; First Secretary FCO since December 1989; born 2.11.53; FCO 1982; Language training 1983 (Taiwan 1984); First Secretary (Econ) Peking 1986.

Wood, Richard John; FCO since October 1991; born 27.8.67; Grade 8.

Wood, Richard Lewis; Vice-Consul Riyadh since September 1992; born 7.6.61; FCO 1982; Sofia 1984; Bandar Seri Begawan 1986; FCO 1989;

Grade 9.

Wood, Terence Courtney, cmg (1989); HM
Ambassador Vienna since April 1992; later
additionally Head of Delegation UKDEL CFE/
CSBM Vienna; born 6.9.36; HM Forces 1955-57;
First Secretary FO (later FCO) 1968; Rome
1969; FCO 1973; SOWC Greenwich 1977;
Counsellor (Comm/Econ) New Delhi 1977; Head
of Chancery BMG Berlin 1981; Head of SAD
FCO 1984; CDA, Harvard Center for
International Affairs 1986; Minister Rome 1987;
m (1) 1962 Kathleen Jones (1s 1965; 1d 1969)
(diss); m (2) 1982 Diana Humphreys-Roberts.

Woodcock, Andrew; AMO/Vice-Consul Brasilia
since June 1991; born 18.9.65; FCO 1988; Vice-
Consul Baghdad 1990; Grade 9.

Woodfield, Colin Keith, obe (1982); Deputy High
Commissioner Kaduna since January 1989; born
5.4.36; HM Forces 1954-56; FO 1956; Rio de
Janeiro 1962; Vice-Consul Jakarta 1964; Second
Secretary (Inf) Madras 1965; FCO 1968; Berne
1971; First Secretary (Admin) Dacca 1974; FCO
1976; Permanent Secretary Eernal Affairs
Belmopan 1979; Consul (Comm) Zurich 1982;
FCO 1986; m 1960 Lorna Brown Sime (2s 1962,
1965; 1d 1968).

Woodland, Clive Howard, obe (1992); First
Secretary (Management) and Consul General
Riyadh since May 1990; born 27.10.38; Crown
Agents 1957-62; HM Forces 1958-60; CRO
1962; Karachi 1962; DSAO 1964; Canberra
1965; Addis Ababa 1968; Second Secretary FCO
1972; Second Secretary and Consul Lisbon 1975;
São Paulo 1980; First Secretary FCO 1983; First
Secretary and Resident Representative St Lucia
1987; m 1961 Margaret Ann Callow (1s 1962;
1d 1964).

Woodrow, John Peter Gayford; FCO since
January 1992; born 21.11.47; FCO 1972;
Barcelona 1975; Quito 1976; FCO 1979; La Paz
1983; Consul Istanbul 1988; Grade 7; m 1977
Yvonne Leffmann.

Woodruff, Helen; FCO since July 1992; born
3.8.1963; FCO 1985; Washington 1987; Harare
1989; Grade S2.

Woodruffe, John Michael; Amman since April
1992; born 26.6.57; FCO 1986; Dublin 1989;
Grade 10; m 1989 Marian Barrett.

Woods, Alison Louise; FCO since May 1988; born
28.10.62; FCO 1982; Kabul 1986; Grade S2.

Woods, David John; Counsellor Harare since
March 1992; born 4.8.51; Third later Second
Secretary FCO 1976; Second later First Secretary
(UNIDO & IAEA) Vienna 1978; FCO 1981;
First Secretary (Econ) Bucharest 1981; First
Secretary FCO 1985; m 1972 Rachel Haydon
White (1s 1977; 1d 1979).

Woods, Ian Alexander; First Secretary FCO since
February 1989; born 10.6.51; Third Secretary FCO
1976; Second Secretary UKMIS New York 1977;
First Secretary FCO 1980; BMG Berlin 1984; Bonn
1986; m 1978 Stephanie Flett (2s 1982, 1986).

Woodward, Amanda Jane; FCO since September
1991; born 7.3.66; FCO 1985; Dhaka 1987; FCO
1989; Montevideo 1990; Grade S2. ·

Woodward, Amanda Jane; FCO since November
1991; born 29.4.56; FCO 1978; Brasilia 1979;
New Delhi 1982; Moscow 1985; FCO 1988;
Lisbon 1989; Grade S1.

Woodward, Gillian Yvonne (née Aplin); Mexico
City since January 1990; born 20.12.46; DSAO
(later FCO) 1966; UKDEL OECD Paris 1969;
Yaoundé 1972; FCO 1974; Lagos 1979; SUPL
1981; Helsinki 1984; FCO 1987; Grade 9; m
1977 Roger Charles Woodward.

Woodward, Roger Charles; Second Secretary
(Commercial) Mexico City since January 1990;
born 15.3.48; Commonwealth Office (later FCO)
1967; Dacca 1970; Caribbean Floater 1972; Doha
1973; FCO 1976; Lagos 1979; Helsinki 1982
(Second Secretary 1984); FCO 1987; m 1977
Gillian Yvonne Aplin.

Wooff, Erica Mielle; Full-Time Language
Training Peking since May 1992; born 7.1.67;
FCO 1990; Language Training 1991; Grade 9.

Woolley, Lesley Ann; Islamabad since July
1986; born 27.4.64; FCO 1984; Grade 10; m
1984 Samuel Patrick David Woolley.

Wooten, David Andrew; Second Secretary FCO
since July 1992; born 19.6.41; FO 1964; Kuwait
1966; Madrid 1970; Budapest 1973; FCO 1974;
New Delhi 1977; Valletta 1981; FCO 1984
(Second Secretary 1986); Second Secretary
(Cons/Admin) Jedda m 1966 Carol Ann Aves
(2d 1968, 1970; 1s 1977).

Wooten, Sarah Elizabeth; Third Secretary
(Consular) Valletta since June 1992; FCO 1989;
born 4.2.68; Grade 9; m 1991 Carl Sun.

Wootton, Adam Nicholas; FCO since July 1988;
born 19.5.60; FCO 1983; Baghdad 1985;
Grade 8; m 1984 Adele Wright (2s 1991).

Wordsworth, Ellyse Nichole (née Mingins);
SUPL since July 1989; born 12.8.54; FCO 1975;
UKREP Brussels 1977; Moscow 1980; FCO
1981; Second Secretary (Comm) Lagos 1984;
FCO 1986; m 1981 Stephen John Wordsworth
(1s 1987).

Wordsworth, Stephen John; First Secretary FCO
since July 1988; born 17.5.55; FCO 1977; Third
later Second Secretary Moscow 1979; FCO 1981;
First Secretary (Econ/Comm) Lagos 1983; On
loan to Cabinet Office 1986; m 1981 Ellyse

Nichole Mingins (1s 1987).

Worster, Paul Anthony; Washington since December 1986; born 14.5.62; FCO 1983; Warsaw 1985; Grade 10.

Worthington, Ian Alan; Second Secretary (Chancery) Kingston since July 1992; born 9.8.58; FCO 1977; Language Training 1978; Moscow 1980; Lusaka 1982; Second Secretary FCO 1985; Second Secretary (Comm) Seoul 1988.

Wotton, Alan Leslie; First Secretary FCO since December 1991; born 14.6.40; Passport Office 1960; CRO 1961; Valletta 1964; Bahrain Residency 1967; Vice-Consul Saigon 1970; FCO 1973; Düsseldorf 1977; FCO 1980; Second Secretary (Comm) Algiers 1983; Second Secretary FCO 1987; First Secretary (Comm) Oslo 1989; m 1967 May Bonella (1d 1968).

Wragg, Ann Desson (née Traill); FCO since August 1992; born 20.3.65; FCO 1983; Paris 1985; FCO 1988; UKMIS New York 1989; Grade 9; m 1988 John Wragg.

Wright, Carol; Pretoria since January 1992; born 27.6.62; FCO 1988; Grade S2A.

Wright, Clive David; Vice-Consul (Pol/Admin) Johannesburg since July 1989; born 14.1.58; Royal Marines 1976; FCO 1977; Ankara 1980; Tripoli 1983; FCO 1984; Doha 1986; (Second Secretary 1989); m 1982 Christine Bernadette Caldwell (1d 1989).

Wright, Cynthia Munro; FCO since February 1991; born 17.8.39; FCO 1976; Brussels 1977; Lusaka 1979; FCO 1982; Stockholm 1983; Rome 1986; FCO 1987; UKDEL Paris 1988; Grade S2.

Wright, David Alan, OBE (1984); First Secretary later Counsellor FCO since August 1987; born 27.5.42; FO 1965; APS to Minister of State FO 1966; MECAS 1968; Baghdad 1971; Second Secretary (Comm) and Vice-Consul Doha 1973; on loan to DHSS 1976; Second later First Secretary FCO 1978; Consul and Head of Post Durban 1980; First Secretary (Comm) Baghdad 1984; m 1966 Gail Karol Mesling (4s 1966, 1968, 1971, 1983; 1d 1978).

Wright, David John, CMG (1992), LVO (1990) HM Ambassador Seoul since April 1990; born 16.6.44; Diplomatic Service 1966; Third later Second Secretary Tokyo 1966; Second later First Secretary FCO 1972; ENA Paris 1975; First Secretary Paris 1976; Private Secretary to Secretary of Cabinet 1980; Counsellor (Econ) Tokyo 1982; Counsellor FCO 1985; On secondment to Buckingham Palace as Deputy Private Secretary to HRH The Prince of Wales 1988; m 1968 Sally Ann Dodkin (1s 1970; 1d 1973).

Wright, David Stephen; Second Secretary

(Chancery) Mexico City since August 1991; born 4.2.63; FCO 1989.

Wright, Julia Helen; FCO since October 1991; born 6.2.65; Grade 9.

Wright, Matthew Alistair; FCO since July 1991; born 18.9.71; Grade 10.

Wright, Stephen John Leadbetter; Counsellor (External Relations) UKREP Brussels since September 1991; born 7.12.46; Third Secretary FCO 1968; Havana 1969; Second Secretary FCO 1972; (First Secretary 1975); Director of Policy and Reference Division and Consul (Inf) New York (BIS) 1975; UKREP Brussels 1980; First Secretary FCO 1984; Counsellor 1985; on loan to Cabinet Office 1985; Counsellor and Head of Chancery New Delhi 1988; m 1970 Georgina Susan Butler (1d 1977; 1s 1979).

Wyatt, Catherine Margaret; FCO since March 1990; born 7.5.60; Grade S2A.

Wyatt, David; First Secretary FCO since August 1988; born 18.4.46; DSAO 1965; Lusaka 1968; SOAS 1971; Bangkok 1972; Second Secretary Yaoundé 1976; FCO 1977; First Secretary 1979; National Defence Course Latimer 1980; Athens 1981; First Secretary and Head of Chancery Bangkok 1984; m 1969 Rosemary Elizabeth Clarke (1s 1972; 1d 1974).

Wyatt, Susanne; FCO since September 1991; born 20.6.46; Grade S2.

Wye, Roderick Francis; First Secretary FCO since October 1988; born 13.9.50; Research Officer FCO 1983; PRO 1983; Peking 1985; m 1989 Katelin Rebecca Teller.

Wyeth, Jean; On loan to the DTI since January 1991; born 13.1.43; Mbabane 1968; Moscow 1971; UKMIS New York 1973; Africa/ME Floater 1976; FCO 1980; Brussels 1983; FCO 1986; On loan to Privy Council Office 1989; FCO 1990; Grade S1.

Wyithe, Philip Leslie; Vice-Consul Sana'a since April 1992; born 30.12.64; FCO 1983; Moscow 1987; Floater Duties 1990; Gabarone 1991; Grade 9.

Wylde, Richard Norman Gordon; First Secretary FCO since July 1992; born 18.10.58; FCO 1985; Second (later First) Secretary (Chancery) and Deputy Permanent Representative ESCAP Bangkok 1989.

Wylie, James; UKMIS Geneva since January 1992; born 30.11.33; Bucharest 1981; Cairo 1983; Moscow 1984; Stockholm 1986; Bangkok 1988; Grade SO; m 1959 Catherine Allan (2s 1963, 1965).

Wynburne, Mark Barry; Second later First

Secretary FCO since June 1981; born 29.3.45; Army 1963-64; FO 1966; Prague 1967; FCO 1968; Islamabad 1974; FCO 1978; Second Secretary and Vice-Consul Hanoi 1980.

Y

Yaghmourian, Paul Barkef; First Secretary FCO since March 1989; born 14.2.58; FCO 1984; Second later First Secretary Lisbon 1986.

Yapp, John William; First Secretary (Inf/Pol) Wellington since November 1991; born 14.1.51; FCO 1971; Islamabad 1973; Kuala Lumpur 1975; FCO 1978; Dubai 1980 (Second Secretary 1983); Second Secretary (Comm) The Hague 1984; First Secretary FCO 1988; m (1) 1973 (1d 1975); (2) 1979 Helen Elizabeth Brooke (1s 1981; 2d 1983, 1987).

Yarnold, Patrick; Consul-General Hamburg since October 1990; born 21.3.37; HM Forces 1955-57; FO 1957; Addis Ababa 1960; Belgrade 1964 (Second Secretary 1965); FO (later FCO) 1966; First Secretary 1967; First Secretary and Head of Chancery Bucharest 1970; First Secretary (Comm) Bonn 1973; FCO 1976; Counsellor (Comm) Brussels 1980; Consul General Zagreb 1983; Counsellor, Head of Chancery and Consul-General Belgrade 1985; Counsellor FCO 1987; m 1961 Caroline Martin (2d 1962, 1964).

Yarrow, Jon William; FCO since August 1987; born 29.1.69; Grade 10.

Yates, Sharon Jane; FCO since November 1989; born 25.4.61; Grade S2.

Yeadon, Joanne Mary; FCO since May 1992; born 1.8.65; FCO 1983; Washington 1986; Gibraltar 1989; Grade S3.

Yeoman, Elizabeth; FCO since December 1989; born 20.1.64; FCO 1985; Accra 1988; Grade S2.

Yeoman, Ruth Margaret; Third Secretary (Chancery) Madrid since January 1991; born 22.9.64; FCO 1988; Grade 9.

Youde, Joanna Clare; Moscow since January 1992; born 17.2.69; FCO 1988; Grade S2.

Young, Andrew John; FCO since September 1990; born 2.4.60; Assistant Legal Adviser.

Young, Carol Piper; Bangkok since September 1990; born 5.9.61; FCO 1986; Pretoria 1988; Grade S2.

Young, David A; Cairo since September 1991; born 2.10.46; Royal Marines (CDO) 1963-86;

Belgrade 1987; Pretoria 1988; Grade SO; m 1986 Patricia-Anne (1s 1973; 1d 1987).

Young, (David) Junor; Deputy High Commissioner Karachi since February 1991; born 23.4.34; FO 1951-52; HM Forces 1952-54; Berlin 1955; Ankara 1958; Pretoria/Cape Town 1961; Second Secretary DSAO 1965; Second Secretary (Inf) Port Louis 1968; FCO 1972; First Secretary (Admin/Cons) Belgrade 1975; Consul (Comm) Stuttgart 1978; Head of Chancery Kampala 1981; Consul-General Hamburg 1984; Counsellor (Comm) Bonn 1986; High Commissioner Honiara 1988; m 1954 Kathleen Brooks (2d 1955, 1967; 2s 1958, 1964).

Young, (John) Rob(ertson), CMG (1991); Minister Paris since March 1991; born 21.2.45; Third Secretary FO 1967; MECAS 1968; Third later Second Secretary Cairo 1970; Second later First Secretary FCO 1973; Private Secretary to Parliamentary Under-Secretary later Minister of State FCO 1975; ENA Paris 1977; Paris 1977; FCO 1981; Acting Head of WED FCO 1983; Counsellor & Head of Chancery Damascus 1984; Counsellor FCO 1987; m 1967 Catherine Houssait (2d 1969, 1978; 1s 1971).

Young, Margaret Ann (née Pegg); Belgrade since April 1992; born 7.1.34; FCO 1970; Lagos 1970; Tortola 1972; Cayman Islands 1974; Ottawa 1976; Havana 1978; Valletta 1980; Budapest 1982; UKREP Brussels 1984; Warsaw 1987; Lusaka 1988; SUPL 1990; Grade S1; m 1979 Ernest Frank Edwin Young.

Young, Peter Michael Heppell; Counsellor (Management) Lagos since January 1990; born 23.4.39; HM Forces 1958-60; FO 1964; Sofia 1967; UKMIS Geneva 1970; Second Secretary (Econ) Pretoria1/Capetown 1971; FCO 1974; First Secretary (Inf) Lagos 1977; DHC Ibadan 1979; Consul (Comm) Lyons 1980; First Secretary FCO 1984 (Counsellor 1989); m 1969 Maria Laura Aragon.

Young, Sarah Louise (née Boxall) FCO since September 1989; born 16.9.63; FCO 1984; Lisbon 1987; Grade 10; m 1990 Alan Young (1d 1991).

Young, Thomas Nesbitt; Counsellor and Director of Trade Promotion Canberra since November 1990; born 24.7.43; FO (later FCO) 1966; Ankara 1969; Madrid 1973; Second Secretary FCO 1977; Ankara 1978; First Secretary and Head of Chancery Ankara 1979. Deputy Director BTDO, New York 1981; First Secretary Washington 1981; First Secretary FCO 1984; Deputy High Commissioner Accra 1987; m 1971 Elisabeth Hick (1d 1973; 1s 1975).

Younger, Alexander William; FCO since September 1991; born 4.7.63; Grade 7.

Printed in the United Kingdom for HMSO
Dd.294670 11/93 C32